20^{00}

November 1981

Ron LeValley

D1616063

THE CALIFORNIA ISLANDS:
PROCEEDINGS OF A MULTIDISCIPLINARY SYMPOSIUM

EDITED BY DENNIS M. POWER

SANTA BARBARA MUSEUM OF NATURAL HISTORY
SANTA BARBARA, CALIFORNIA

The California Islands:
Proceedings of a Multidisciplinary Symposium

*Printed in the United States of America
by Haagen Printing, Santa Barbara, California*

*Cover photograph by F. G. Hochberg
Cover design by Sarah Mollett*

Library of Congress Cataloging in Publication Data

Main entry under title:

The California Islands : Proceedings of a Multidisciplinary Symposium

Includes bibliographies and index.
1. Island ecology—California. 2. Islands—California.
3. Natural history—California. I. Power, Dennis M.

QH105.C2C35   574.9794'9   80-463
ISBN 0-936494-01-8

Preface

The idea that the Santa Barbara Museum of Natural History would organize and host a multidisciplinary symposium dealing with scientific research on the California Islands was formulated in 1972 when Charles Remington of Yale University and I were conducting field studies on San Clemente Island. As island researchers can attest, discussion can reach lofty heights when you are on one of these unique outposts in the Pacific Ocean. Away from the duties of the office, a major forum dealing with the California Islands seemed like a splendid idea. However, back on the mainland, other work took precedence so that it was not until 1975 that a preliminary announcement and questionnaire could be sent out. The response was highly favorable. A date for the meeting was set, a grant application was prepared, papers were invited to provide the foundation of a well-rounded program, contributed papers were solicited to insure an inclusive and encompassing symposium, and, finally, on February 27, 28, and March 1, 1978, the conference was underway. Over 400 scientists, students, government employees, and interested laymen registered for the symposium. The titles of 69 papers appeared on the final program.

This turned out to be a particularly important event for the Museum because it brought into sharper focus our own commitment to research on the islands. Founded in 1916, this non-profit, privately supported museum has developed research, collections, exhibits, and educational programs—all emphasizing central and southern California and the islands offshore.

Over the past decade there have been several small symposia on the California Islands at annual meetings of various scientific societies. However, the last gathering to make an important mark in island research was the "Symposium on the Biology of the California Islands." Held in 1965, this event was organized by the Santa Barbara Botanic Garden and led to a significant publication—the *Proceedings*, which was edited by Dr. Ralph N. Philbrick and appeared in print in 1967. That symposium had, in large part, stimulated much of the research that was reported on at our symposium in 1978. Looking back, it is interesting to observe that, because we are now working with new models and new data, much of what was discussed in 1978 could not have been presented 13 years earlier. In 1965, theories relating to plate tectonics and continental drift still had ardent critics, biochemical systematics was in its infancy, multivariate statistics was understood by only a few, and a dynamic equilibrium theory of island biogeography was still being bandied about the seminar rooms of Princeton and Harvard Universities. A review of the role these theories and methods have in more recent island research is given in the Summary of this book.

At scientific meetings—and in the pages of many journals—one often sees two factions that, unfortunately, do not get together often enough. On the one hand there are those interested in gathering data about a particular group of organisms or a specific geographic region, and on the other hand there are the theorists, the model builders, and those who gather data from the real world primarily in order to use modern hardware or new techniques. I think that the tendency today is not to put one above the other, but to realize that gathering data and building theoretical models must go on concurrently if science is to remain a reputable enterprise. Clearly, the foundation of any lasting theory must consist of reliable and abundant data from the real world, not a hypothetical one. There must be an unshakable foundation of hard data in order to build a scientific structure that will last. Certainly it can be argued from any practical standpoint that we also need all the basic facts we can get about an ecosystem in order to conserve or manage its natural resources. (The paucity of data dismayed us all when trying to assess the impact of the oil well blowout in the Santa Barbara Channel in 1969.) However, as long as basic facts must be gathered, should they not address problems that are intellectually challenging as well as useful?

Facing the limitations of time and finances, the data that seem most valuable to me are the kinds which apply directly to management problems or which support or refute patterns that have been spotted in other bodies of data—patterns that are worked into theories or models. This is not to argue that there is any permanence to the scientific concepts that may emerge. As philosopher/scientist Jacob Bronowski discusses in *The Origins of Knowledge and Imagination* (Yale University Press, New Haven, Conn., 1978), nature is not a gigantic formalizable system, because to formalize it we have to make some assumptions which cut away some of the parts. That part of the world which we can inspect and analyze is always finite, and no formal system can embrace all of the questions that can be asked.

What this is leading to is simply a statement of my goals in organizing the symposium on the California Islands and in editing this publication: that we might build intellectually challenging structures on the foundations that have been completed, and that we continue to provide new data where the foundations are now inadequate.

The California Islands Symposium offered a chance to acquire new ideas, share advances in research, re-establish old professional ties, and make new acquaintances who share an interest in the islands. Providing permanency to the information that had been brought forth at the meeting and insuring the dissemination of that knowledge meant that a publication was called for and established the rationale for the present volume.

In retrospect, there seems little question that the papers from this symposium will constitute important documentation of the state of natural science research on the California Islands in our time. This, I hope, is a fitting tribute to the scientists whose work is presented here, and to those researchers who have gone before and on whose work our present studies are based.

Acknowledgments
I am grateful to the entire staff of the Santa Barbara Museum of Natural History for their dedicated help in running the Multidisciplinary Symposium on the California Islands held at the Museum on February 27 through March 1, 1978. Special thanks are due Dr. Charles D. Woodhouse, Jr., Dr. F. G. Hochberg, Jr., Kenneth Saxton, Paula Marie Juelke, Paul Collins, Carey Smith, Joan Pursell, and Howard Cunningham.

The Systematic Biology Program of the National Science Foundation provided partial financial support for the Symposium. Publication of the proceedings was partially subsidized by the Atlantic Richfield Foundation, Mrs. George W. Hanscomb, and the Edwin and Evelyn Stanton Fund by Carey Stanton, a special fund of the Santa Barbara Museum of Natural History. I am most appreciative of this important assistance, without which this project could not have been completed.

I am especially grateful to the authors, who took time from already busy schedules to provide manuscripts and then revisions in response to my inquiries, which I hope were not too burdensome.

One person must be singled out for her dedication and skill. As editorial assistant, Paula Marie Juelke brought patience, accuracy, an eye for detail, and a thorough command of the English language to the production of this book. Her contribution is inestimable. Also, Sarah Mollett and the staffs of McAdams Type (especially Norma Horton) and Haagen Printing (especially Robert Bernstein) added their care and technical skill to the publication. Typing of some sections was ably provided by Evelyn Mulcahy.

Finally, I thank my wife, Kristine, for her support, understanding, and encouragement in the months preceding the symposium, and in the months of editing and writing that followed.

Dennis M. Power
February 1980

TABLE OF CONTENTS

VEGETATION CHANGES
AND THE IMPACT OF FERAL ANIMALS

EVOLUTION AND ECOLOGY
OF LAND PLANTS

BIOGEOGRAPHY, EVOLUTION,
AND ECOLOGY
OF MARINE ORGANISMS

BIOGEOGRAPHY, EVOLUTION,
AND ECOLOGY
OF LAND ANIMALS

Introduction

Dennis M. Power

Santa Barbara Museum of Natural History,
Santa Barbara, California 93105

The California Islands offer a fascinating set of natural laboratories that have caught the interest of researchers for many decades. To one degree or another, almost all of the museums and universities on the California coast, as well as governmental agencies concerned with natural resources, have been involved with research on the islands or in the Southern California Bight (see Loefer 1967 for a partial list). Among these, the Los Angeles County Museum of Natural History conducted a biological survey of the Channel Islands from 1938 to 1941 (Comstock 1939). They published the results of their studies in the period 1939 to 1964. In 1965, the Santa Barbara Botanic Garden, an institution with its own research interests on the islands, held a symposium on the biology of the California Islands, the published proceedings (Philbrick 1967) from which stimulated even more research in the years that followed. In addition, the fact that the continental borderland is important from economic and recreational perspectives has stimulated the gathering and analysis of new data. For example, the Outer Continental Shelf Office of the Bureau of Land Management (Department of the Interior) has recently conducted extensive investigations in the Southern California Bight, the National Park Service is involved in baseline and management studies on islands under its jurisdiction, and the Catalina Island Conservancy and Nature Conservancy (Santa Cruz Island) have gained research interests in the islands in the last few years.

This scientifically productive atmosphere gave rise to the Multidisciplinary Symposium on the California Islands held early in 1978 at the Santa Barbara Museum of Natural History. The purpose of the meeting was to bring together researchers from several disciplines and to provide a forum to summarize and advance our knowledge of the California Islands and the adjacent waters. The papers in this book stem from this symposium.

The Setting

The California Islands are situated along the west coast of North America, roughly between 38 and 27.5 degrees north latitude (Fig. 1). Because they are distributed along the edge of a continent, they are best classified as "fringing islands" (Carlquist 1974), rather than an "archipelago," which, in the strict sense, is defined as a sea containing many islands. All of the islands, except one, are on a topographically complex region called the continental borderland, a region made up of a diversity of submarine canyons and ridges (Shepard and Emery 1941). Guadalupe Island, the exception, is volcanic rock that rises some 15,000 ft (4,570 m) from the ocean floor (Hubbs 1967).

The islands vary considerably in size, topography, and distance from the mainland (Table 1). The largest is Cedros, with a land area of 134 mi^2 (348 km^2). The smallest is Año Nuevo, with an area of slightly less than 12 acres, or 0.02 mi^2 (0.05 km^2). There are a number of small islets associated with some of the islands (see Philbrick 1967, table 1). Guadalupe, the second-largest of the islands, reaches the greatest maximum elevation and is farthest from the mainland, facts which make its biota among the most interesting for study.

Climatologists classify this region as one with a "Mediterranean Dry-Summer Subtropical" climate (Kimura 1974). Temperature, precipitation, cloud cover, and wind are strongly influenced by proximity to the sea, wherein seasonal patterns in currents, temperature gradients, and other physical and biological properties are also variable. If one general theme can be derived

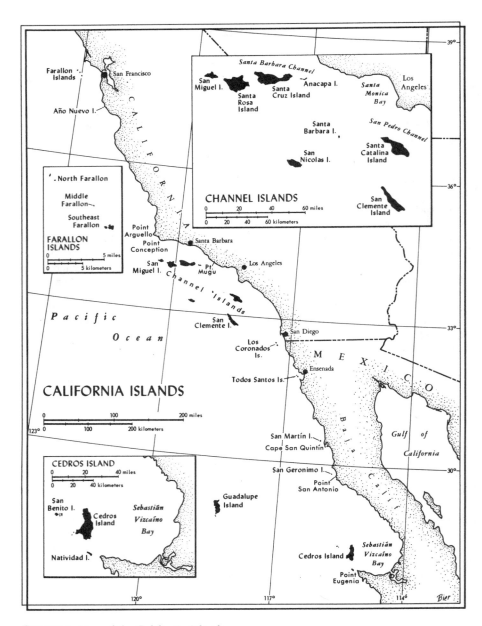

FIGURE 1. *Map of the California Islands.*

TABLE 1. Some physical attributes of the California Islands.*

Island	Area km²	Area mi²	Greatest elevation m	Greatest elevation ft	Distance to nearest mainland point km	Distance to nearest mainland point mi
Northern California Islands						
Farallon group†	0.9	0.3	109	358	33	20
SE Farallon†	0.5	0.2	109	358	33	20
Año Nuevo	0.05	0.02	18	60	0.5	0.3
Northern Channel Islands						
San Miguel	37	14	253	830	42	26
Santa Rosa	217	84	475	1560	44	27
Santa Cruz	249	96	753	2470	30	19
Anacapa†	2.9	1.1	283	930	20	13
Southern Channel Islands						
Santa Barbara	2.6	1.0	194	635	61	38
San Nicolas	58	22	277	910	98	61
Santa Catalina	194	75	648	2125	32	20
San Clemente	145	56	599	1965	79	49
Baja California Islands						
Los Coronados†	2.5	1.0	204	670	13	8
Todos Santos	1.2	0.5	96	315	6	4
San Martín	2.3	0.9	143	470	5	3
San Geronimo	0.4	0.2	40	130	9	6
Guadalupe	255	98	1402	4600	252	157
San Benito†	6.4	2.5	201	660	66	41
Cedros	348	134	1204	3950	23	14
Natividad	7.2	2.8	149	490	7	5

* Data on area and distance to the mainland are from Philbrick (1967, tables 1 and 2 of the Introduction). Data on elevation are from Johnson *et al.* (1968). Data on the total Farallon group are from National Wildlife Refuge information provided by Point Reyes Bird Observatory (pers. comm.).

† Area for these islands represents the total for various numbers of smaller islands, as follows: Farallon group, 7; Southeast Farallon, 2; Anacapa, 3; Los Coronados, 4; Todos Santos, 2; and San Benito, 3.

from the collection of research papers in this book, it is that the physical and biological components of both land and sea are interwoven in often complex, cause-and-effect relationships. For the California Islands, variation in size, shape, and degree of isolation, coupled with variance in oceanographic and climatic setting, prepare the stage for evolutionary changes and ecological interactions within the biota.

Organization of This Book

Forty-three papers are presented here, not including this introduction and a summary. The papers are organized by topic, not by formal, academic discipline. The judgment as to which papers belong to what topic is mine, not the authors'. (I apologize for disturbing any reader's expectations about organization.)

The first section treats general geological history and two specific topics in geology and paleontology. Next are two papers concerned with prehispanic Indians in California. These are followed by papers with a geographical flavor that deal with changes in the landscape and in the vegetation, including the impact of extinct mammoths, Indians, and feral goats and sheep. The next section concerns botany in the usual sense and deals with the evolution and ecology of land plants. Then, there are two large sections dealing with biogeography, evolution, and ecology—first, of marine organisms and, second, of land animals. The marine section begins with an oceanographic topic that sets the stage for several analyses of marine plants and invertebrates. The marine section also includes the results of research on kelp fish, sea birds, and pinnipeds. The section on land animals begins with a paper about vertebrate distribution in the absence of land bridges. This is followed by more specific works on amphibians, reptiles, birds, and mammals. In the summary, I have attempted to pull together some of the threads common to various works, even though the collection of topics may be too diverse to do this in a totally satisfying way.

REFERENCES

CARLQUIST, S. 1974. Island biology, Columbia University Press, New York, N.Y.

COMSTOCK, J. A. 1939. Contributions from the Los Angeles Museum—Channel Island biological survey. Bull. So. California Acad. Sci. 38:133-134.

HUBBS, C. L. 1967. A discussion of the geochronology and archaeology of the California Islands. Pp. 337-341 in R. N. Philbrick, ed., Proceedings of the symposium on the biology of the California Islands. Santa Barbara Botanic Garden, Santa Barbara, Calif.

JOHNSON, M. P., L. G. MASON, and P. H. RAVEN. 1968. Ecological parameters and plant species diversity. Amer. Natur. 102:297-306.

KIMURA, J. C. 1974. Climate, Pp. 2-1 to 2-70 in M.D. Dailey, B. Hill, and N. Lansing, eds., A summary of knowledge of the southern California coastal zone and offshore areas. So. California Ocean Studies Consort. (BLM Contract no. 08550-CT4-1).

LOEFER, J. 1967. Institutional scientific interests in the Southern California Islands. Pp. 9-12 in R. N. Philbrick, ed., Proceedings of the symposium on the biology of the California Islands. Santa Barbara Botanic Garden, Santa Barbara, Calif.

PHILBRICK, R. N., ed. 1967. Proceedings of the symposium on the biology of the California Islands. Santa Barbara Botanic Garden, Santa Barbara, Calif.

SHEPARD, F. P., and K. O. EMERY. 1941. Submarine topography off the California coast: canyons and tectonic interpretations. Geol. Soc. Amer. Spec. Paper 31.

GEOLOGIC HISTORY
AND PALEONTOLOGY

Topographic Evolution of the Southern California Borderland During Late Cenozoic Time

J. G. Vedder and D. G. Howell

*U.S. Geological Survey, 345 Middlefield Road,
Menlo Park, California 94025*

INTRODUCTION

Misconceptions about the topographic configuration and history of development of the seafloor surrounding the Southern California Islands have arisen as a result of erroneous inferences by both geologists and biologists. These mistaken opinions often are reiterated, not only in journalistic accounts, but also in scientific reports. The purpose of this paper is twofold: to help dispel misleading ideas that have been introduced in earlier literature and to describe in general terms the key events that created the present seafloor topography. Even though much conjecture remains, some of our interpretations may assist biologists who are investigating endemic evolutionary trends in the coastal and offshore region.

In recent years, a wealth of new geologic data has been gathered through shipboard and island studies on the California Continental Borderland north of 32° N latitude (Fig. 1). This work has demonstrated that the structure and stratigraphy are not as simple as previously supposed and that they rival their mainland counterparts in complexity. The history of some parts of the borderland now can be traced as far back as 100 m.y. (million years), and one isolated rock mass has been dated at 160 m.y. (Mattinson and Hill 1976).

That a large region seaward from southern California consists of extremely variable submarine topography was recognized early (Blake 1855). Few detailed descriptions of the water-covered terrain were published, however, until Shepard and Emery (1941) provided the framework upon which all later studies have been built. Two other fundamental contributions are those of Emery (1960), who described the interrelated aspects of the marine environments of the area, and Moore (1969), who demonstrated the importance of acoustic-reflection profiling in determining marine geologic processes in the same area.

Because of the fragmentary nature of the record before the beginning of late Miocene time (10 to 12 m.y. ago), the origin and development of features such as mainland shorelines, land bridges, insular platforms, and submergent ridges and basins is uncertain. The evidence that permits the reconstruction of sequential diastrophic events since the Miocene Epoch is relatively firm, even though chronologic dating of rocks older than Pleistocene seldom has a precision of better than ±1 m.y. In terms of the geologic scale, the Miocene Epoch ended a short time ago (*ca.* 5.2 m.y.); but the same span is much too great, perhaps by a factor of 10, for resolution of evolutionary and migratory patterns of the Quaternary insular biota. This disparity in the rates of natural processes is an inherent problem in integrating geologic and biologic phenomena.

A number of published paleogeographic maps of California involving different time intervals have portrayed a variety of land masses, seaways, and islands. Since Arnold's (1909) and Clark's (1921) early efforts, the most noteworthy regional paleogeographic reconstructions that include the borderland are those of Reed and Hollister (1936), Corey (1954), Clements (1955), Emery (1960), and Valentine and Lipps (1967). For the offshore area, all were based upon scant information and are highly interpretive.

The maps of Reed and Hollister (1936) and Corey (1954) are schematic representations that were compiled from mainland and island geology and sparse seafloor samples. Included are

7

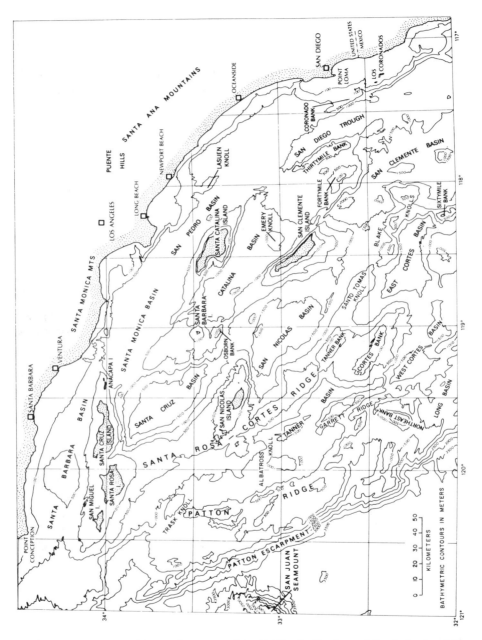

FIGURE 1. *Index map of the northern part of the California Continental Borderland and the adjoining mainland.*

land areas, outcrop distribution, sediment thickness, lithofacies, and faults for several episodes of Tertiary time. These workers, however, did not consider large lateral dislocations along faults and pre-uplift deposition and subsequent erosion of sediment. Emery's (1960) maps are simplified versions of Corey's (1954), supplemented by locations of offshore samples and profiles used for interpreting ancient shorelines, both emergent and submergent. Pliocene and Pleistocene shorelines depicted by Dunkle (1950) and Clements (1955) are misleading. Dunkle apparently did not apply available geologic and bathymetric criteria in his southern supplement to Reed's (1933) map. Clements used an early Pleistocene low sea-level stand of approximately minus 1,000 m, far lower than suggested by recently compiled Pleistocene sea-level curves (Curray 1965, Milliman and Emery 1968, Dillon and Oldale 1978, MacIntyre et al. 1978). The onshore parts of the two maps by Valentine and Lipps (1967), which also illustrate shoreline positions during parts of Pliocene and Pleistocene time, probably are nearly correct; but the offshore parts are generalized and imply high-standing areas for which there is little supporting evidence.

Axelrod's (1967) maps are simplified and slightly modified versions of Corey's (1954) for late Miocene and Pliocene time; consequently, they have the same deficiencies. The account by Weaver (1969) pertains to the northernmost part of the borderland, for which he discusses long-term Tertiary structural developments; his map of basins, uplifts, and sediment-transport directions is schematic and was not intended for use in studying Quaternary biogeography. A set of maps prepared by Fischer (1976) shows late Cenozoic shorelines, sedimentary facies, and depositional trends for the Santa Barbara Channel region as interpreted from acoustic-reflection profiles and core holes. This detailed work, however, covers only a small segment of the borderland.

GEOLOGIC SETTING
Geomorphology

The modern geomorphic provinces of coastal southern California (Reed 1933, Jenkins 1941, Jahns 1954) are characterized by aligned topographic entities that have two distinct directional trends (Fig. 2). The west-trending features of the long, narrow Transverse Ranges province transect the dominant northwest grain of the Coast Ranges and Peninsular Ranges provinces. As defined by Shepard and Emery (1941) and Moore (1969), the California Continental Borderland is bounded on the northwest by Point Arguello and Arguello Canyon, and on the southeast by Bahía Sebastián Vizcaíno and Isla de Cedros. Its western edge is marked by the base of the Patton Escarpment at the north and by the Cedros Deep at the south (Moore 1969, pl. 1). If the onshore provinces are extended offshore, the California Continental Borderland seems to include the submergent parts of both the Transverse Ranges and Peninsular Ranges with the result that all three provinces overlap. Although this apparent discrepancy has been a source of contention, discussion of the definitions is beyond the scope of this paper. Of greater importance is the fact that these geomorphic provinces generally reflect the underlying geologic structures and that two discrete orientations are discernible. Notwithstanding more than 50 years of study, geologists have just begun to decipher the origin and evolution of these intersecting structural domains.

North of latitude 31° N, the borderland is typified by elongate northwest- and west-trending seafloor basins and ridges, some of which protrude above sea level as islands. Offshore from southern California, the borderland differs from an ordinary continental shelf in that it encompasses large depressions as deep as 2,100 m below sea level and island peaks as high as 750 m above sea level. Topographic relief within a single ridge-basin pair is as much as 2,700 m (Santa Cruz Island-Santa Cruz Basin). Locally, the relief along the Patton Escarpment is more than 2,750 m; yet the term escarpment is a misnomer for the feature, which generally has a

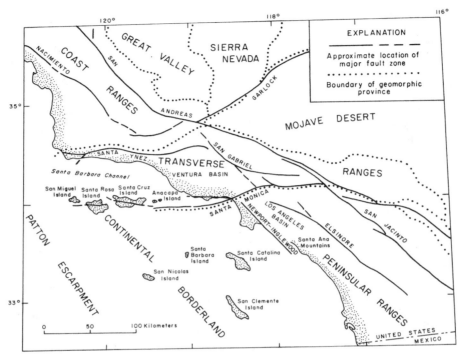

FIGURE 2. *Physiographic provinces and major faults of southern California. Modified from Yerkes* et al. *(1965).*

slope gradient of less than 15°. North of the Mexico-U.S. boundary, there are eight islands which range in area from 2.5 km² to nearly 250 km² (Fig. 1), and several isolated pinnacles (Richardson Rock, Wilson Rock, Begg Rock, and Bishop Rock), which range in size from 5,500 m² and 16 m above sea level to a submergent reef of about 0.2 km² and 4 to 10 m below sea level.

Major Geologic Events

As background for the discussion of late Cenozoic history that follows, several significant geologic events are summarized. During Oligocene time, about 30 m.y. ago, a fundamental change in crustal behavior occurred in western California and resulted in a shift from a convergent plate tectonic regime to one of right-lateral shear. The new stress field was instrumental in forming a basin-and-ridge topography that replaced the pre-existing broad shelf and regionally extensive depositional aprons (Blake *et al.* 1978). At the end of Oligocene time and early in Miocene time (24 to 20 m.y. ago), an episode of igneous activity began in coastal and offshore southern California; it culminated shortly thereafter (16 to 12 m.y. ago), then diminished rapidly (10 to 7 m.y. ago). At places, borderland relief was accentuated by the volcanism, which built composite volcanoes and superimposed lava flows; some basins apparently developed in conjunction with differential subsidence that was associated with waning volcanism. Recently reported paleomagnetic measurements suggest that 75° to 90° of clockwise tectonic rotation took place in the western Transverse Ranges after middle Miocene time (Kamerling and Luyendyk 1977) and must have affected topographic alignments. Table 1 summarizes these and other geologic events and their timing. The exact tectonic mechanisms that created the vertical and lateral earth movements and that generated the volcanism have not been completely resolved, and the measured crustal rotation involves complex kinematics that are not yet understood.

LATE MIOCENE TOPOGRAPHY

Interpretation of borderland topography before Miocene time is very uncertain because the older stratigraphic record is preserved at few places. Although early and middle Miocene events are relatively well documented, they are discussed only briefly inasmuch as they probably had a minimal influence on dispersal patterns of modern biota of the borderland region. In general, an episode of marine transgression and basin subsidence dominated in coastal southern California during late Miocene time.

Without some means of determining former water depths, inferences about pre-existing seafloor topography are unreliable. Ordinarily, bedding character, lithofacies relations, sediment composition, and fossil assemblages are used in combination to infer depth of deposition. Many of these criteria are inaccessible from shipboard, and our paleobathymetric reconstructions are based largely upon depth ranges of assemblages of fossil benthic foraminifers retrieved in cores of bedrock (Arnal 1976, Arnal and Vedder 1976). Although these assemblages may be partly time transgressive, the inferred paleobathymetry probably is valid for a tripartite division of Miocene time.

By the end of the Miocene (*ca.*6 to 5 m.y. ago), large parts of the Ventura and Los Angeles regions were deep marine basins; a total sub-sea relief of at least 2,000 m had developed on the borderland. A few islands of unknown dimensions survived from a subsiding middle Miocene volcanic archipelago, remnants of which are preserved at Santa Cruz, San Clemente, and Santa Catalina Islands (Nolf and Nolf 1969, Fisher and Charlton 1976, McLean *et al.* 1976, Vedder and Howell 1976, 1977). In addition to the volcanic archipelago, a shallow submarine ridge at the present site of the southern Santa Rosa-Cortes Ridge (Fig. 3) seems to have subsided 300 to 500 m near the end of Miocene time (Fig. 4). Abyssal depths (> 2,500 m), not evident in middle Miocene time, developed to the south and west of this area. Even though mid-bathyal depths apparently prevailed over most of the region between the subsiding ridge and the present shoreline, the water was shallower near the northern end of Coronado Bank, where depths were less than 500 m (Fig. 4). In the Los Angeles and Ventura areas, the basin troughs subsided to lower bathyal and abyssal depths (1,000 to > 2,500 m) (Natland 1957, Ingle 1973). In the late Miocene, Los Angeles basin seafloor gradients steepened and the margins shoaled abruptly northward and eastward (Yerkes *et al.* 1965).

At most places on the Channel Islands, late Miocene strata either have been removed completely by erosion or were never deposited, leaving an incomplete record of events. The assignment of volcaniclastic strata on Santa Rosa Island to the upper Miocene (Jennings 1959) is misleading, for microfossils from interlayered shale beds are no younger than middle Miocene (Avila and Weaver 1969, J. A. Barron *in litt.* 1976). The only known island exposures of late Miocene sediments occur as thin discontinuous beds on Santa Catalina and San Clemente Islands, where fossil assemblages indicate a range of depths from middle bathyal to littoral (Vedder and Howell 1976, 1977, Vedder and Moore 1976). On Santa Catalina Island, both mollusks and foraminifers in sediments deposited on an irregular volcanic flow surface imply a steep bottom slope from an inner sublittoral environment to one possibly as deep as 1,000 m. At San Clemente Island, only shallow-water mollusks are present in correlative beds, which form thin, depression-filling veneers on the older lava surface (Vedder and Moore 1976). All of these limited outcrops are insufficiently preserved to interpret the original distribution and thickness of the sedimentary unit that they represent. Moreover, paleogeographic infer-

TABLE 1. Chronology, major events, and geologic evidence for late Cenozoic changes in topography on the southern California borderland. Ages of the epoch boundaries are from Van Couvering (1978).

ERA	PERIOD	EPOCH Boundary ages in millions of years	MAJOR GEOLOGIC EVENTS	EFFECTS AND EVIDENCE
Cenozoic	Quaternary	Holocene ———— 0.011 ————	10 End of rapid sea-level rise *ca.* 6,000 years ago	Drowned and backfilled drainage channels along mainland coast and at Santa Cruz and Santa Catalina Islands.
		Pleistocene	9 Beginning of post-glacial sea-level rise *ca.* 17,000 years ago	Eolianites on outer islands. Submergent surf-cut platforms around islands and along mainland coast.
			8 Filling of onshore basins; fluctuating eustatic sea levels Continuing local uplift and subsidence	Emergent surf-cut platforms around the islands and along the mainland coast. Nonmarine sediments throughout large parts of onshore basins.
			7 Increase in tectonism with widespread intensive uplift and subsidence	Thick accumulations of marine and nonmarine sediments in onshore and near-shore basins. Deformed and deeply eroded basin margins on mainland. Faults throughout region.
		———— 1.6–2.0+ ————	6 Eustatic lowering of sea level with onset of polar glaciation	Shallow-marine deposits on Santa Rosa, Santa Cruz, and San Clemente Islands, and along basin margins at Santa Monica Mountains, Puente Hills, San Joaquin Hills, and San Diego.
		Pliocene ———— *ca.* 5.2 ————	5 Accelerating rate of deposition in near-shore basins accompanied by local subsidence	Deep-marine deposits in central Ventura and Los Angeles basins. Basin-edge unconformities throughout the borderland.

Cenozoic	Tertiary	Miocene	4	Encroaching seas and deepening near-shore basins. Diminishing volcanism *ca*. 10-7 m.y. ago	Widespread deep-marine deposits in Ventura and Los Angeles basins. Local igneous intrusions, flows, and ash falls at Santa Catalina Island, Santa Monica Mountains, Palos Verdes Hills, Puente Hills, and San Joaquin Hills.
			3	Formation of discrete basins and ridges and peak volcanic activity *ca*. 16-12 m.y. ago. Incipient rotation(?)	Shallow-marine deposits and tephra at Santa Cruz and Santa Catalina Islands. Marine-nonmarine breccias along southern mainland coast. Igneous intrusions, flows, and tephra in Santa Monica Mountains, margins of Los Angeles basin, and Santa Barbara, Santa Catalina, and San Clemente Islands. Volcanic rocks throughout inner borderland ridges.
			2	Commencing basin development and initial volcanism *ca*. 24-20 m.y. ago	Basin-margin breccia at Santa Cruz and Santa Catalina(?) Islands. Igneous flows at San Miguel Island and Tanner-Cortes Bank area.
		ca. 24			
		Oligocene	1	Plate-tectonic shift from convergent to transform regime *ca*. 30 m.y. ago. Global low-standing sea level	Disrupted magnetic-anomaly patterns. Transgressive shallow-marine deposits 30-23 m.y. old at Northern Channel Islands, Santa Monica Mountains. and northeast margins of Ventura and Los Angeles basins. Nonmarine deposits along margins of Ventura and Los Angeles basins and Santa Rosa and Santa Catalina Islands. Unconformities on San Miguel and Santa Cruz Islands. Marine deposits restricted to western Santa Ynez Mountains and southern Santa Rosa-Cortes Ridge.

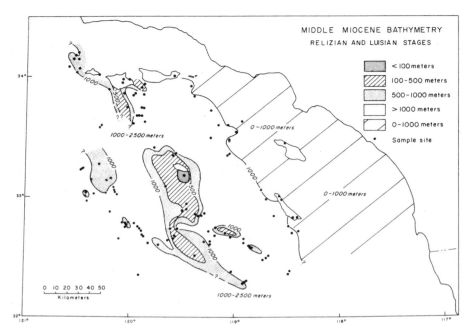

FIGURE 3. *Middle Miocene bathymetry inferred from selected benthic foraminiferal assemblages. Parts of the Santa Barbara Channel and the inner basins, banks, and shelf are generalized or omitted because of an insufficient number of available samples. Mainland basins are not included. Modified from Arnal (1976).*

ences based upon isolated or missing strata should be made with caution. For example, the local absence of late Miocene marine beds led Corey (1954, fig. 7) to depict several islands that otherwise are unsubstantiated. However, deep-water sediments of identical age (Vedder *et al.* 1974, 1976) have been cored on the seafloor adjoining the postulated large islands, suggesting that these strata may have completely draped the sites and subsequently were entirely eroded. Bottom samples from other places on the inner and outer ridge systems where Corey (1954) shows islands have yielded middle and lower bathyal foraminiferal assemblages (Arnal and Vedder 1976).

Beneath the seafloor, geologic structures ordinarily are interpreted from acoustic-reflection profiles, examples of which are shown in Figure 5. Growing structures that affected borderland topography and depositional patterns are manifested by unconformities that separate middle and upper Miocene strata along the Patton and Santa Rosa-Cortes Ridges (J. K. Crouch, Arne Junger *in litts.* 1977) and the flanks of the Santa Monica and San Pedro Basins (Junger and Wagner 1977). All of these discordant sequences may reflect the same episode or closely spaced phases of uplift and subsidence. Nearer to the former coast, similar discontinuities break the successions of marine rocks along the edges of the Ventura and Los Angeles basins. Identifications of the specific faults and folds that created the borderland uplift and subsidence and resulting unconformities are not certain. Pre-Pliocene faults that presumably contributed to these deformations are present along the margins and beneath many of the offshore basins (Vedder *et al.* 1974, Junger and Wagner 1977, Junger 1979). The estimated maximum rate of

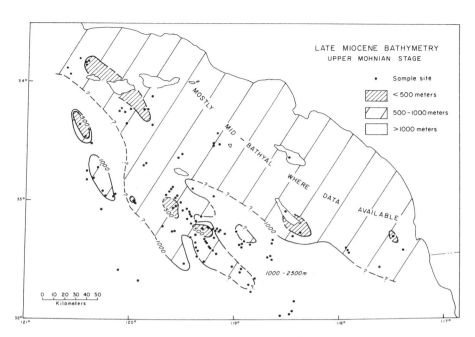

FIGURE 4. *Late Miocene bathymetry inferred from selected benthic foraminiferal assemblages. Mainland basins are not included. Modified from Arnal and Vedder (1976).*

late Miocene deformation in the offshore region is in the vicinity of Santa Catalina Island, where subsidence may have amounted to as much as 1.0 m per 1,000 years.

It is noteworthy that the greatest encroachment of seas and some of the deepest basins of late Cenozoic time in southern California developed near the end of Miocene time, perhaps in response to diminishing igneous activity and the concomitant subsidence that accompanied thermal cooling within the crust. This local deepening and advancing of the sea onto areas that now are far inland is well documented by the paleontologic record (Natland 1957, Ingle 1973). The shallow marine incursions combined with basin subsidence seem to be reflected in the vertical temperature gradients inferred by Addicott (1969) from coexisting marine invertebrates with different depth ranges. Shoreline configuration along the margins of these coastal basins is shown on Corey's (1954, fig. 7) map of late Miocene geography.

PLIOCENE TOPOGRAPHY

Until a few years ago, Pliocene deposits had been recognized only on Santa Cruz Island; all other islands were believed to have been above sea level, and published paleogeographic maps omitted marine Pliocene from all of the modern ridges, banks, and islands of the borderland. However, thin remnants of nearshore marine beds of probable late Pliocene age were mapped beneath Pleistocene terrace deposits on northeastern Santa Cruz Island by Rand (1933) and Weaver and Meyer (1969). Shallow-water Pliocene strata have since been reported from San Clemente Island (Vedder and Howell 1976, Vedder and Moore 1976, Stadum and Susuki 1976), and correlative lower bathyal strata are now known to occur on Santa Catalina Island. Recent fieldwork on Santa Rosa Island has revealed the presence of calcareous sandstone beds that

16 LATE CENOZOIC TOPOGRAPHIC EVOLUTION

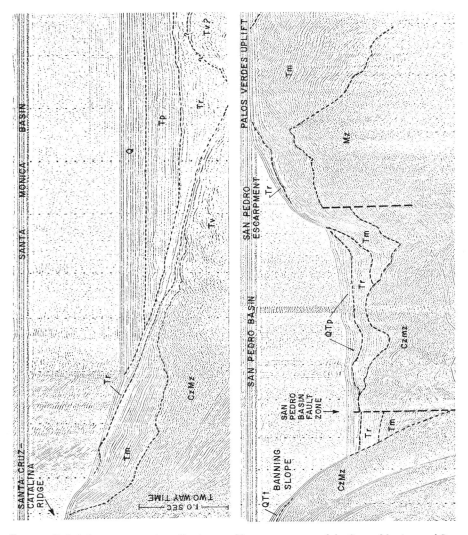

FIGURE 5. *Sub-bottom acoustic-reflection profiles across parts of the Santa Monica and San Pedro Basins showing interpreted rock units (letter symbols), structures, and unconformities (from Junger and Wagner 1977). Vertical exaggeration is approximately 6:1. The length of the profile across the Santa Monica Basin is about 35 km; across the San Pedro Basin, about 30 km.*

have yielded foraminifers which are assigned a late(?) Pliocene age by R. E. Arnal (*in litt.* 1977). In addition, shallow-water Pliocene mollusks embedded in volcanic detritus have been dredged from Northeast Bank (Hawkins *et al.* 1971). Outer sublittoral species of mollusks of possible Pliocene age are preserved in samples of fine-grained sandstone from southeastern Coronado Bank (Vedder *et al.* 1976). Each of these occurrences represents a stratigraphically incomplete and areally limited record that cannot be directly related to either the scattered

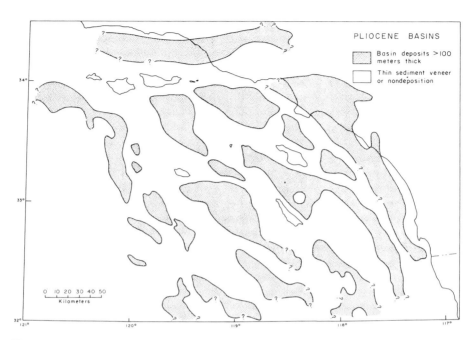

FIGURE 6. *Basins in which it is estimated that more than 100 m. of Pliocene and younger marine sediments were deposited. Intervening, unpatterned tracts indicate ridges and slopes where either thin veneers of sediment were laid down or where there was no marine deposition.*

outcrops on the mainland shelf or the nearly completely buried thick sequences in the deep basins. Pliocene insular platforms are difficult to identify on the borderland, because strata that might provide clues on their sites now are confined primarily to lower slopes and basins deeper than 500 m and are virtually inaccessible for study.

Along the mainland coast, very thick accumulations of marine sediments were deposited as turbidites in the now-filled parts of the Pliocene Los Angeles (4,200 m) and Ventura (3,800 m) basins, and deposition in these areas during the early part of the epoch was in water as deep as 1,500 m near Ventura and 2,500 m southeast of Los Angeles (Natland 1957, Ingle 1973). The thick, rapid sedimentation in these initially deep, down-bowing basins implies that the bordering highland areas to the north and east were being actively eroded, probably concurrently with continuing uplift and deformation (Conrey 1967, Yerkes *et al.* 1965, Crowell *et al.* 1966, Crowell 1976, Yeats 1965, 1976). In these basins, the influx of sediment seems to have kept pace with or surpassed the amount of subsidence with the result that seafloor relief may have become increasingly subdued.

Beneath the central Santa Barbara Basin, correlative strata are about 1,800 m thick; to the west and south, these beds thin and wedge out. In the Santa Monica and San Pedro Basins, maximum thicknesses of Pliocene rocks are 2,700 m and possibly 1,500 m, respectively (Junger and Wagner 1977). Equivalent sections are less than half as thick in the near-shore basins west of Oceanside and San Diego, and the basins seaward from the islands generally contain no more than 600 m of these sediments. Figure 6 shows the general outlines of Cenozoic basins in which more than 100 m of Pliocene sediment were deposited. The relatively thin sections in the outer basins suggest that adjacent submarine ridges and possibly islands impeded dispersal of terrigenous sediments and that pelagic debris and locally derived detritus from the barrier ridges was not voluminous. The geometry of these tracts of Pliocene basin deposits implies a seafloor topography that was much like that on the borderland today.

Unconformities within the basin-margin sections in the Santa Barbara, Santa Monica, and San Pedro Basins (Fischer 1976, Greene 1976, Junger and Wagner 1977) demonstrate that adjoining areas were being structurally deformed, particularly on the north and east. Pliocene unconformities have not been recognized in the outer basins where tectonism apparently did not effectively disrupt the comparatively slow accumulation of land-derived sediments.

Pliocene shorelines are preserved at few places in southern California. There is equivocal evidence for their presence on the north edges of Santa Rosa and Santa Cruz Islands, where dune deposits cap shallow marine beds on a surf-cut bench (Weaver and Meyer 1969), and on San Clemente Island, where deposition probably was in sublittoral environments not far from the surf zone (Vedder and Moore 1976). Along the mainland coast, embayed shorelines fringed the narrowing and filling Ventura and Los Angeles basins and the shoaling San Diego shelf during the latter part of the epoch, while the sea was retreating. Most of the paralic features, however, have been eradicated by subsequent erosion. Islands presumably occupied the present sites of the Santa Monica Mountains and San Joaquin Hills as delineated by Corey (1954, fig. 8), but evidence for strand lines in those places is obscure. Whether or not large islands were present on the outer borderland is conjectural. Even though the nearshore basins were receiving large amounts of sediment and the sea was withdrawing toward the end of Pliocene time, the axial parts of these basins remained as deep as 1,500 m in the vicinity of Ventura and Los Angeles, probably as a result of continuing subsidence and sediment compaction.

Late Pliocene marine strata now in water depths of 1,000 to 1,250 m near the northwest end of San Clemente Ridge contain foraminiferal assemblages that imply water depths of 2,500 m or more at the time of deposition, and early Pliocene beds on Santa Catalina Island contain species that now live in depths in excess of 2,000 m (R. E. Arnal *in litts.* 1977, 1978). These assemblages, therefore, suggest local uplifts on the borderland as much as 2,000 m since the early part of the epoch and 1,000 m since the late part; other areas, such as the San Diego shelf and perhaps the northern island platform, remained relatively stable. Maximum rates of uplift are estimated to have ranged between 0.5 and 0.7 m per 1,000 years.

Although it is possible that a Pliocene land bridge could have connected the northern island group with the mainland to the east (Greene 1976), it is unlikely that either the San Clemente or Santa Cruz-Catalina Ridges formed pathways for dispersal of the terrestrial biota because of the intervening deep water. Seafloor samples from these ridges rarely contain fossiliferous Pliocene strata, but where they do, the fossils usually indicate bathyal depths. Similarly, microfossil assemblages from discontinuous Pliocene deposits along the mainland shelf between San Pedro and La Jolla suggest water depths greater than 200 m. Because only Miocene and older rocks have been sampled from most of the Patton Ridge area, it is possible that parts of the ridge formed positive features from which Pliocene sediments subsequently were eroded.

PLEISTOCENE–HOLOCENE TOPOGRAPHY
Introduction

Crustal deformation and eustatic changes in sea level had a marked influence on mainland and borderland topography during the last two million years. Some of the features created by these changes were recognized as early as 1853 (Blake 1855, 1857), and they drew the attention of many early geologists. Fairbanks (1897) introduced one of his several studies on coastal and island landforms by stating, "Various interpretations of the records left by these movements have been given by different observers, but their results do not harmonize with each other, nor

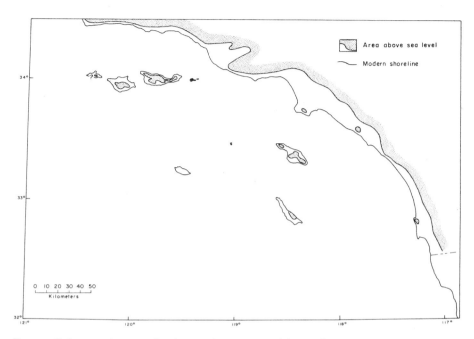

FIGURE 7. *Interpretive map showing maximum extent of the sea during the last 500,000 years. Patterned areas are those that presumably have been continuously above sea level. Because the geologic record is incomplete, neither a specific point in time nor a single ancient shoreline is implied.*

does any one of them appear to express the whole truth." This remark is as relevant now as it was then. In order to facilitate discussion, the effects of basin deposition, terrace development, tectonic deformation, possible land bridge sites, and submarine canyon cutting are treated under separate headings.

Basin Deposition

Marine and nonmarine sediments accumulated rapidly in the coastal basins during Pleistocene time, while farther offshore, deposition of marine beds generally decreased with increasing distance from the mainland. Holocene deposits mantle these basin sequences nearly everywhere except along the edges of the Ventura and Los Angeles basins, but the dense spacing of wells drilled for oil in these two basins has provided substantive information on their thickness and composition, which in turn, give evidence of topographic development.

Near Ventura, the subsurface Pleistocene sedimentary section may be as much as 4,000 m thick, and near Los Angeles, about 1,500 m. Nonpersistent unconformities along the margins of these thick sequences attest to nearly continuous tectonic deformation and changing depositional trends. Similar unconformities are recognizable on acoustic-reflection profiles in the Santa Barbara, Santa Monica, and San Pedro Basins, where the sections are thinner (Greene *et al.* 1975, Fischer 1976, Junger and Wagner 1977, Nardin and Henyey 1978). In basins farther offshore, interruptions in sedimentation are less distinct, suggesting that tectonism diminished seaward. Although marine embayments reached well inland during the last 500,000 years (Fig. 7), by the end of the epoch, the mainland basins were completely filled. The comparatively thin

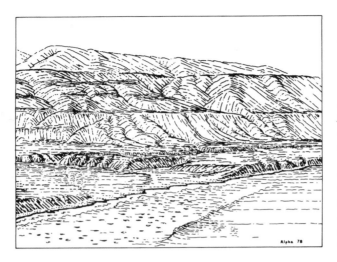

FIGURE 8. *Sketch of surf-cut platforms that reflect former sea-level stands at Pyramid Cove, San Clemente Island. View toward the northeast. The platform on the skyline has an altitude of about 300 m; the modern sea cliff in the foreground is 8 to 10 m high. Drawing by Tau Rho Alpha.*

sections in outer borderland basins indicate slow deposition far from source areas as well as differences in depositional mechanisms and agents. Late Pleistocene-Holocene rates of terrigenous sedimentation also diminished in the outer basins with the post-glacial rise in sea level, a change that is described by Emery (1960) and Gorsline, Drake, and Barnes (1968), although the rates vary from basin to basin. As a result of these slow sedimentation rates, the geometry of the outer basins probably has not changed significantly since the beginning of Pleistocene time.

Terraces

Oscillation of sea level resulting from repeated growing and melting of Pleistocene polar ice caps is manifested by well-preserved marine shorelines in coastal southern California (Fig. 8). Superimposed on these eustatic changes were both provincial and local diastrophic events that may have surpassed all earlier episodes of tectonism in their amount and rate of development. Despite the fact that ancient surf-cut platforms (terraces) and their sediment cover both above and below the modern strand line provide a superb record of still-stands of sea level during the latter part of the epoch, the exact ages and correlation of many remain in doubt.

As pointed out by Putnam (1954), Sharp (1954), Vedder and Norris (1963), Bradley and Griggs (1976), and many others, correlation of terraces is difficult because of the influence of two variables: eustatic oscillation of sea level and disharmonious tectonic deformation of individual crustal blocks. These variables were not considered in most early reports, in which terrace cutting was ascribed primarily to regional uplift, and correlation was assumed to be simply a matter of matching altitudes. Figure 9 illustrates the differences between the numbers of recognized emergent terraces together with their maximum preserved altitude at selected places on the borderland and mainland coast. Other differences, not shown in the figure, are the inconsistent vertical spacing and width of platforms. Published maps and tables indicating terrace correlation must be used with caution because most of them do not specify the criteria used either for age control or for the identification of shoreline position, except in general terms.

As many as five well-defined submergent terraces between the depths of 10 and 130 m were recorded by Emery (1960), who believed that they dated from Wisconsin time and that they

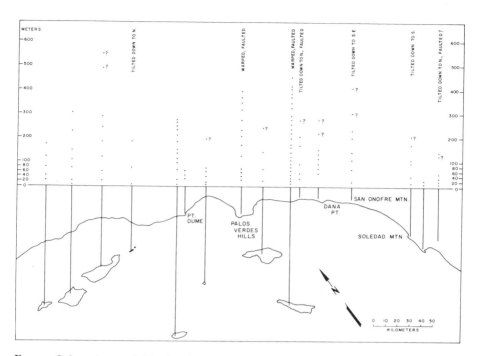

FIGURE 9. *Locations and altitudes of emergent terraces at selected places on the mainland and islands. The type of deformation is noted where all or part of a sequence is known to have been structurally modified. Sources of measurements are: San Miguel Island, Emery (1960); Santa Rosa Island, Orr (1960, 1967); Santa Cruz Island, Rand (1933); Anacapa Island, Valentine and Lipps (1963); San Nicolas Island, Vedder and Norris (1963); Point Dume, south side, Birkeland (1972); Santa Barbara Island, Lipps et al. (1968); Palos Verdes Hills, Woodring et al. (1946); Santa Catalina Island, Smith (1897, 1933); San Clemente Island, Lawson (1893), Smith (1898); Newport Beach, Vedder (1970); South Laguna-Dana Point, Vedder (unpubl.); San Onofre Mountain, McCrory and Lajoie (in litt. 1978); Soledad Mountain, McCrory and Lajoie (in litt. 1978); Point Loma, Kern (1977); San Diego Mesa, Hertlein and Grant (1954).*

since have been regionally tilted seaward. Later work indicates that some of these sub-sea platforms are likely to be local features and consequently are difficult to correlate and possibly can be attributed to other causes such as submarine slumping. It is noteworthy that the submergent terraces are both erosional and constructional in origin (Ridlon 1972, Fischer 1976, Junger 1978). M. E. Field (*in litt.* 1978) suggests that depositional terraces on the island platforms were built during regressive phases, effectively enlarging the shelves, but most of these terraces probably were destroyed during transgressive phases when erosional terraces were cut. Terraces deeper than 120 m along the Santa Rosa-Cortes and Santa Cruz-Catalina Ridges (Uchupi 1961, Junger and Wagner 1977) and elsewhere (Emery 1960) probably are older than late Pleistocene, and some may be as old as late Pliocene.

According to Curray (1965) and Milliman and Emery (1968), the sea last began to return to its present level about 17,000 to 18,000 years ago. During this low stand (Fig. 10) and subsequent

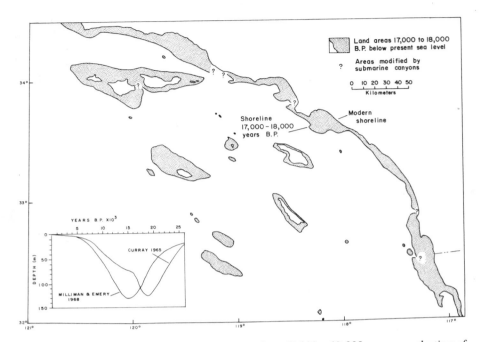

FIGURE 10. *Approximate position of the shoreline about 17,000 to 18,000 years ago, the time of probable maximum sea-level lowering to ±120 m. Sea-level curves adapted from Curray (1965) and Milliman and Emery (1968).*

transgression, the unusual eolianites (cemented dunes) and caliche deposits on the upper surfaces of the outer islands may have begun to form (Vedder and Norris 1963, Johnson 1967, Olmsted 1958).

Even though the Pleistocene Epoch represents a short period of time (1.5 to 2.0 m.y.), the lack of precise dating techniques, particularly for the older part, hinders accurate chronologic identification of the ancient shorelines. Recent application of radiometric and amino acid stereochemistry dating methods have been helpful (Veeh and Valentine 1967, Ku and Kern 1974, Szabo and Rosholt 1969, Szabo and Vedder 1971, Wehmiller *et al.* 1977). At present the areal coverage by these dates is spotty, and unbroken stratigraphic sequences have not been thoroughly sampled either within individual terrace deposits or through entire terrace flights.

Deformation

Rates of tectonic deformation differed from place to place on the borderland and along the mainland coast throughout the last third of the Pleistocene Epoch. That the borderland consisted of independent structural blocks is evident from the lack of correlation between emergent surf-cut terraces on the islands and along the mainland coast (Fig. 8); these differentially moving blocks are further corroborated by seafloor faults and folds of Pleistocene and Holocene age (Vedder *et al.* 1974, Greene *et al.* 1975, Fischer 1976, Junger and Wagner 1977, Nardin and Henyey 1978). One of the most striking examples of deformation and erosion is evident in the vicinity of the Dos Cuadras and Carpinteria offshore oil fields southeast of Santa Barbara, where several thousand meters of Pliocene and early Pleistocene strata were removed from the crest of a growing anticline during late Pleistocene and Holocene time to form a nearly flat seafloor.

Amino acid age inferences for terrace flights at San Nicolas Island, Palos Verdes Hills, and San Joaquin Hills imply different rates of uplift for each of these structural blocks as well as rate changes during the last 500,000 years (Lajoie and Wehmiller 1978). The highest estimated rate among these sites is slightly less than 1.0 m per 1,000 years at Palos Verdes Hills. Recent work by K. R. Lajoie and others (*in litt.* 1977) indicates that local tectonic uplift rates on an anticline along the Ventura coast amounted to more than 10 m per 1,000 years during the last 100,000 years. Extraordinary short-term uplift and subsidence have been measured throughout the now-active "Palmdale bulge," the effects of which have reached the Ventura area (Castle *et al.* 1977).

Land Bridges

In the proceedings volume for the predecessor of this symposium, Valentine and Lipps (1967) reviewed the late Cenozoic history of the borderland and emphasized the implications of the Pleistocene marine fossil records on both the mainland coast and islands. Their well-documented discourse is still the commonly accepted interpretation of the Pleistocene physical geography of coastal southern California and for the occurrence of fossil land mammals on the Northern Channel Islands. They proposed that these animals migrated westward along a peninsula created by eustatically lower sea level during an interval or intervals of medial Pleistocene time, while coinciding uplift and erosion affected large parts of the mainland. Later, during the latter third of the epoch, eustatically rising sea level and local structural deformation severed the connection between the mainland and the west-trending peninsula to isolate the terrestrial organisms, which subsequently were subjected to endemic evolution. The authors concluded with the statement that sea level dropped more than 100 m below its present position with the last glaciation but not sufficiently to rejoin the northern island platform to the mainland.

Most geologists who have considered the locations of former land bridges to the southern California islands agree that the only plausible post-Pliocene link was one that projected westward from the Santa Monica Mountains through the Northern Channel Island platform. However, even this bridge has been questioned by Johnson (1973), and Junger and Johnson (1980) note that mammoth remains on San Miguel, Santa Rosa, and Santa Cruz Islands can be explained by the swimming capability of elephants and that acoustic-reflection profiles do not show evidence for a Quaternary subaerial ridge between Anacapa Island and the mainland. A bathymetric map of the area (Fig. 11) indicates a maximum water depth of about 250 m and a minimum distance of about 7 km between the 120 m isobaths in the narrows that separate the Anacapa Island shelf from the Oxnard shelf, a seaway that large mammals could have crossed (Sondaar 1977). In addition, the maps of Pleistocene sediments compiled by Fischer (1976) show that slope and basin deposits extended eastward as far as the site of Hueneme Canyon, a condition that would severely limit the bounding edge of a land bridge, if one existed.

Alternatively, Greene (1976) states that an emergent ridge connected the island platform to the Santa Monica Mountains during part of Pliocene or early Pleistocene time; however, this ridge probably pre-dated the arrival of mammoths in North America 1.3 m.y. ago (C. A. Repenning pers. comm. 1978). According to Edwards and Gorsline (1978) there is evidence of a west-directed late Pleistocene drainage network beneath the modern gap that possibly could indicate an exposed sill during lowest sea levels at the southeast end of the Santa Barbara Channel. Subsequent transgression then would have reopened the seaway. High-velocity tidal currents must have swept through the narrow passage during low sea-level stands; such currents certainly would have been a deterrent to the successful crossings of swimming animals. Slow subsidence of the southern shelf (Fischer 1976) possibly could account for the submergence of a

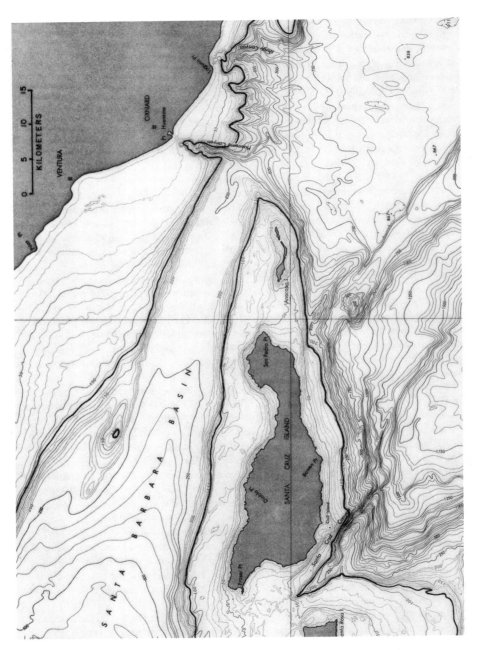

FIGURE 11. *Bathymetric map of the region between the Northern Channel Islands platform and the mainland. The 120-meter isobath is emphasized to indicate the probable configuration of the seaway and approximate shoreline position during the low stand of sea level about 17,000 to 18,000 years ago. Modified from National Ocean Survey Map NOS 1206N-16.*

late Pleistocene land bridge at the southeast end of the channel, a condition that might not be evinced from apparent structural and stratigraphic relations on acoustic-reflection profiles. In any case, if such a connection existed, it must have been a transitory feature.

Neither geological nor geophysical evidence substantiates any other Pleistocene links between the mainland and the islands or between the two island groups of the southern California borderland.

Submarine Canyons

Nearly a century ago, bathymetric surveys along the California coast detected submarine canyons; since then, these remarkable features have attracted the interest of geologists as well as oceanographers. Not only are the canyons of the borderland one of the most striking elements of sub-sea topography, but they also are believed to be primary contributors to seafloor destruction at their headward ends and construction beyond their basinward ends. Even though the major canyons have been intensively studied, the time of origin and the erosive agents that cut them are in dispute. To describe the details of morphology and the history of development of the canyons is beyond the scope of this paper; Shepard and Emery (1941), Emery (1960), and Shepard and Dill (1966) discuss them at length.

Large canyons along the mainland shelf of southern California, such as Redondo, La Jolla, and Coronado, have walls from 250 to 500 m high and incised channels as long as 16 km. With the exception of Santa Cruz and Catalina Canyons, there are none on the flanks of the offshore ridges and banks that rival the near-shore canyons in size. Forerunners of the modern canyons may have begun to dissect newly formed borderland slopes as long ago as the Pliocene, yet the headward ends of some on the mainland shelf are actively cutting into strata as young as Holocene. It seems likely, therefore, that the carving processes endured through much of Quaternary time. Sharp bends along the courses of some canyons possibly are attributable to erosion along cross faults and straight courses of others to channeling along longitudinal faults. However, the origin of most of the southern California canyons cannot be directly related to structural deformation.

CONCLUSIONS

Despite the obscurity of some episodes of the geologic history of coastal and offshore southern California, much more is now known about the evolution of borderland topography than was evident at the time of the 1965 symposium on the biology of the islands (Axelrod 1967, Orr 1967, Valentine and Lipps 1967). The mid-Cenozoic change in structural style that initiated basin and ridge development seems to be fairly well documented on the basis of both plate tectonic reconstructions and borderland geology. Even though we are unable to explain the kinematics of some tectonic relations, such as the inferred rotation of a large segment of the western Transverse Ranges, understanding of concurrent Miocene volcanic and sedimentary events now is fairly clear. Later phases of waning volcanism, subsidence, marine transgression, and sediment influx during Miocene and Pliocene time are recorded through interpretations of paleobathymetry based upon foraminiferal paleoecology and depositional trends. Eustatic sea-level changes and local intense structural deformation imposed a complex pattern of shoreline cutting and basin filling throughout the Quaternary. There is sufficient evidence, both geologic and geophysical, to demonstrate that land bridges were not primary features during the last half of the Pleistocene Epoch. The single possible link, which may have connected the Northern Channel Islands platform to the Santa Monica Mountains, presumably was ephemeral, if it existed at all.

Although we now have greater confidence in our reconstructions than we did a decade ago, much more work on seafloor geology is required before accurate paleogeographic maps can be compiled. Of particular significance is the need for refinement of dating techniques, which ultimately will provide a satisfactory resolution of events, especially in the Pleistocene. Exploratory drilling for petroleum, now under way, will yield valuable subsurface information as will proposed drilling solely for research purposes. Obviously, our comprehension of the geologic history of the borderland is limited, but the background furnished here may help guide future work.

SUMMARY

Fragmentary geologic evidence suggests that coastal and offshore southern California changed from a shelf-slope setting to one of basins and ridges during late Cenozoic time. Precursory events that contributed to post-middle Miocene development of borderland features included a fundamental change from a convergent plate tectonic regime to one of right-lateral shear about 30 m.y. ago and a subsequent episode of widespread volcanism that persisted from about 24 to 10 m.y. ago. The ridge-and-basin configuration that was created by the right-shear stress field was overprinted with island-building composite volcanoes and lava flows that accompanied flourishing igneous activity. Toward the end of Miocene time (*ca.* 7 to 5 m.y. ago), near-shore basins, now on land, deepened and began to receive large amounts of terrigenous sediment derived from rising mountains to the north and east, while offshore features began to resemble their modern counterparts in shape and size. During the same time span, local subsidence was associated with diminishing and sporadic volcanism. The Pliocene (*ca.* 5 to 2 m.y. ago) was a time of rapid sediment accumulation in the near-shore basins and the beginning of accelerated tectonism that seems to have peaked during the Pleistocene to form large areas of high relief. Sea-level oscillations resulting from the waxing and waning of Pleistocene polar ice caps, combined with the differential uplift of crustal blocks, carved the mainland and islands into flights of surf-cut platforms. Although these terraces provide a remarkable record of former sea levels, they are difficult to correlate because of localized tectonic deformation. Apparent maximum uplift rates along the mainland coast exceed those estimated for the offshore region, where the highest rates probably averaged less than 1.0 m per 1,000 years throughout the late Tertiary and Quaternary.

If a Pleistocene land bridge joined the Santa Monica Mountains with the Northern Channel Islands, it presumably was an ephemeral feature, as marine geophysical data do not confirm its existence. Available geologic evidence does not substantiate any other Pleistocene connecting links between the mainland and the islands or between the two island groups.

ACKNOWLEDGMENTS

Discussions with a number of colleagues have provided perspectives on the geologic evolution of the borderland that otherwise might have been overlooked. To them, our grateful thanks. We also are indebted to Arne Junger, who contributed information on acoustic-reflection profiles; K. R. Lajoie and P. A. McCrory, who provided measurements of terrace deformation and altitudes at several places; J. K. Crouch, who estimated sediment thicknesses in some of the offshore basins; and C. A. Repenning, who offered opinions on mammalian chronology. Particularly, we wish to acknowledge R. E. Arnal and M. E. Field who read a draft of the manuscript and made suggestions for its improvement.

REFERENCES

ADDICOTT, W. O. 1969. Tertiary climatic change in the marginal northeastern Pacific Ocean. Science 165:583-586.

ARNOLD, R. 1909. Environment of the Tertiary faunas of the Pacific Coast of the United States. J. Geology 17:509-553.

ARNAL, R. E. 1976. Miocene paleobathymetric changes of the Santa Rosa-Cortes Ridge area,

California Continental Borderland. Pp. 60-79 *in* D. G. Howell, ed., Aspects of the geologic history of the California Continental Borderland. Amer. Assoc. Petroleum Geologists, Pacific Sec., Misc. Publ. 24.

ARNAL, R. E., and J. G. VEDDER. 1976. Late Miocene paleobathymetry of the California Continental Borderland north of 32°. Pp. 1-12 *in* A. E. Fritsche, H. Ter Best, Jr., and W. W. Wornardt, eds., The Neogene symposium. Soc. Econ. Paleontologists and Mineralogists, Pacific Sec.

AVILA, F. A., and D. W. WEAVER. 1969. Mid Tertiary stratigraphy of Santa Rosa Island. Pp. 48-67 *in* D. W. Weaver *et al.*, Geology of the Northern Channel Islands. Amer. Assoc. Petroleum Geologists and Soc. Econ. Paleontologists and Mineralogists, Pacific Secs., Spec. Publ.

AXELROD, D. I. 1967. Geologic history of the Californian insular flora. Pp. 267-315 *in* R. N. Philbrick, ed., Proceedings of the symposium on the biology of the California Islands. Santa Barbara Botanic Garden, Santa Barbara, Calif.

BIRKELAND, P. W. 1972. Late Quaternary eustatic sea-level changes along Malibu Coast, Los Angeles County, California. J. Geology 80:432-448.

BLAKE, M. C., Jr., R. H. CAMPBELL, T. W. DIBBLEE, JR., D. G. HOWELL, T. H. NILSEN, W. R. NORMARK, J. G. VEDDER, and E. A. SILVER. 1978. Neogene basin formation in relation to plate-tectonic evolution of San Andreas fault system, California: Amer. Assoc. Petroleum Geologists Bull. 62:344-372.

BLAKE, W. P. 1855 [1856]. Observations on the physical geography and geology of the coast of California, from Bodega Bay to San Diego. U.S. Coast Survey [Annual Report], Appendix 65:376-398.

————. 1857. Geological report [Williamson's reconnaissance in California]. U.S. War Dept. Explor. and Surveys for Railroad, Mississippi to Pacific Ocean Reps., v. 5, pt. 2.

BRADLEY, W. C., and G. B. GRIGGS. 1976. Form, genesis, and deformation of central California wave-cut platforms. Geol. Soc. Amer. Bull. 87:433-449.

CASTLE, R. O., M. R. ELLIOTT, and S. H. WOOD. 1977. The southern California uplift. EOS, Trans. Amer. Geophysical Union 58:495.

CLARK, B. L. 1921. The marine Tertiary of the west coast of the United States: its sequence, paleogeography, and the problems of correlation. J. Geology 29:583-614.

CLEMENTS, T. 1955. The Pleistocene history of the Channel Islands region, southern California. Pp. 311-322 *in* Essays in the natural sciences in honor of Captain Allan Hancock. Allan Hancock Found. Sci. Research, Southern California University Press, Los Angeles, Calif.

CONREY, B. L. 1967. Early Pliocene sedimentary history of the Los Angeles basin, California. California Div. Mines and Geology, Spec. Rep. 93.

COREY, W. H. 1954. Tertiary basins of southern California. Pp. 73-83 *in* R. H. Jahns, ed., Geology of southern California. California Div. Mines Bull. 170(8).

CROWELL, J. C. 1976. Implications of crustal stretching and shortening of coastal Ventura basin, California. Pp. 365-382 *in* D. G. Howell, ed., Aspects of the geologic history of the California Continental Borderland. Amer. Assoc. Petroleum Geologists, Pacific Sec., Misc. Publ. 24.

CROWELL, J. C., R. A. HOPE, J. E. KAHLE, A. T. OVENSHINE, and R. H. SAMS. 1966. Deep-water sedimentary structures, Pliocene Pico Formation, Santa Paula Creek, Ventura basin, California. California Div. Mines and Geology, Spec. Rep. 89.

CURRAY, J. R. 1965. Late Quaternary history, continental shelves of the United States. Pp. 723-735 *in* H. E. Wright, Jr., and D. G. Frey, eds., The Quaternary of the United States. Princeton University Press, Princeton, N.J.

DILLON, W. P., and R. N. OLDALE. 1978. Late Quaternary sea-level curve: reinterpretation based on glaciotectonic influence. Geology 6:56-60.

DUNKLE, M. B. 1950. Plant ecology of the Channel Islands of California. Pp. 247-386 *in* Allan Hancock Pacific Expeditions, 13(3). Southern California University Press, Los Angeles, Calif.

EDWARDS, B. D., and D. S. GORSLINE. 1978. New evidence of current winnowing activity on Hueneme sill, California Continental Borderland [abs.]. Amer. Assoc. Petroleum Geologists Bull. 62:511.

EMERY, K. O. 1960. The sea off southern California, a modern habitat of petroleum. John Wiley & Sons, New York, N.Y.

FAIRBANKS, H. W. 1897. Oscillations of the coast of California during the Pliocene and Pleistocene. Amer. Geologist 20:213-245.

FISCHER, P. J. 1976. Late Neogene-Quaternary tectonics and depositional environments of the Santa Barbara Basin, California. Pp. 33-52 *in* A. E. Fritsche, H. Ter Best, Jr., and W. W. Wornardt, eds., The Neogene symposium. Soc. Econ. Paleontologists and Mineralogists, Pacific Sec.

FISHER, R. V., and D. W. CHARLTON. 1976. Mid-Miocene Blanca Formation, Santa Cruz Island, California. Pp. 228-240 *in* D. G. Howell, ed., Aspects of the geologic history of the California Continental Borderland. Amer. Assoc. Petroleum Geologists, Pacific Sec., Misc. Publ. 24.

GORSLINE, D. S., D. E. DRAKE, and P. W. BARNES. 1968. Holocene sedimentation in Tanner Basin, California Continental Borderland. Geol. Soc. Amer. Bull. 79:659-674.

GREENE, H. G. 1976. Late Cenozoic geology of the Ventura basin, California. Pp. 499-529 *in* D. G. Howell, ed., Aspects of the history of the California Continental Borderland. Amer. Assoc. Petroleum Geologists, Pacific Sec., Misc. Publ. 24.

GREENE, H. G., S. H. CLARKE, JR., M. E. FIELD, F. I. LINKER, and H. C. WAGNER. 1975. Preliminary report on the environmental geology of selected areas of the southern California Continental Borderland. U.S. Geol. Survey Open-file Rep. 75-596.

HAWKINS, J. W., JR., E. C. ALLISON, and D. MACDOUGALL. 1971. Volcanic petrology and geologic history of Northeast Bank, southern California borderland. Geol. Soc. Amer. Bull. 82:219-228.

HERTLEIN, L. G., and U. S. GRANT, IV. 1954. Geology of the Oceanside-San Diego coastal area, southern California. Pp. 53-63 *in* R. H. Jahns, ed., Geology of southern California. California Div. Mines Bull. 170(4).

INGLE, J. C., JR. 1973. Biostratigraphy and paleoecology of early Miocene through early Pleistocene benthonic and planktonic Foraminifera, San Joaquin Hills-Newport Bay-Dana Point area, Orange County, California. Pp. 18-38 *in* Miocene sedimentary environments and biofacies, southeastern Los Angeles basin, guidebook. Soc. Econ. Paleontologists and Mineralogists.

JAHNS, R. H. 1954. Investigations and problems of southern California geology. Pp. 5-29 *in* R. H. Jahns, ed., Geology of southern California. California Div. Mines Bull. 170(1).

JENKINS, O. P. 1941. Geomorphic provinces of California. Pp. 83-88 *in* O. P. Jenkins, ed., Geologic formations and economic development of the oil and gas fields of California. California Div. Mines Bull. 118(2).

JENNINGS, C. W. 1959. Santa Maria Sheet, geological map of California, scale 1:250,000. California Div. Mines and Geology.

JOHNSON, D. L. 1967. Caliche on the Channel Islands. California Div. Mines and Geology, Mineral Information Service 20:151-158.

————. 1973. On the origin and extinction of pygmy elephants, Northern Channel Islands,

California [abs.]. Geol. Soc. Amer., Abstracts with Programs 5(7):683.

JUNGER, A. 1979. Maps and seismic profiles showing geologic structure of the Northern Channel Islands platform, California Continental Borderland. U.S. Geol. Survey, Map MF-991.

JUNGER, A., and D. L. JOHNSON. 1980. Was there a Quaternary land bridge to the Northern Channel Islands? Pp. 33-39 *in* D. M. Power, ed., The California Islands: proceedings of a multidisciplinary symposium. Santa Barbara Museum of Natural History, Santa Barbara, Calif.

JUNGER, A., and H. C. WAGNER. 1977. Geology of the Santa Monica and San Pedro Basins, California Continental Borderland. U.S. Geol. Survey Misc. Field Studies Map MF-820.

KAMERLING, M. J., and B. P. LUYENDYK. 1977. Tectonic rotation of the Santa Monica Mountains in southern California. EOS, Trans. American Geophysical Union 58:1126.

KERN, J. P. 1977. Origin and history of upper Pleistocene marine terraces, San Diego, California. Geol. Soc. Amer. Bull. 88:1553-1566.

KU, T., and J. P. KERN. 1974. Uranium-series age of the upper Pleistocene Nestor Terrace, San Diego, California. Geol. Soc. Amer. Bull. 85:1713-1716.

LAJOIE, K. R., and J. F. WEHMILLER. 1978. Quaternary uplift rates, southern California borderland. Abstracts of papers, a multidisciplinary symposium on the California Islands. Santa Barbara Museum of Natural History, Santa Barbara, Calif.

LAWSON, A. C. 1893. The post-Pliocene diastrophism of the coast of southern California. California Univ. Publs. Geology 1:115-160.

LIPPS, J. H., J. W. VALENTINE, and E. MITCHELL. 1968. Pleistocene paleoecology and biostratigraphy, Santa Barbara Island, California. J. Paleontology 42:291-307.

MACINTYRE, I. G., O. H. PILKEY, and R. STUCKENRATH. 1978. Relict oysters on the United States Atlantic continental shelf: a reconsideration of their usefulness in understanding the late Quaternary sea-level history. Geol. Soc. Amer. Bull. 89:277-282.

MATTINSON, J. M., and D. J. HILL. 1976. Age of plutonic basement rocks, Santa Cruz Island, California. Pp. 53-58 *in* D. G. Howell, ed., Aspects of the geologic history of the California Continental Borderland. Amer. Assoc. Petroleum Geologists, Pacific Sec., Misc. Publ. 24.

MCLEAN, H., B. M. CROWE, and D. G. HOWELL. 1976. Source of the Blanca Formation volcaniclastic rocks and strike-slip faulting on Santa Cruz Island, California. Pp. 294-308 *in* D. G. Howell, ed., Aspects of the geologic history of the California Continental Borderland. Amer. Assoc. Petroleum Geologists, Pacific Sec., Misc. Publ. 24.

MILLIMAN, J. D., and K. O. EMERY. 1968. Sea levels during the past 35,000 years. Science 162:1121-1123.

MOORE, D. G. 1969. Reflection profiling studies of the California Continental Borderland— structure and Quaternary turbidite basins. Geol. Soc. Amer. Spec. Paper 107.

NARDIN, T. R., and T. L. HENYEY. 1978. Plio-Pleistocene diastrophism in the area of the Santa Monica and San Pedro shelves, California Continental Borderland. Amer. Assoc. Petroleum Geologists Bull. 62:247-272.

NATLAND, M. L. 1957. Paleoecology of West Coast Tertiary sediments. Pp. 543-571 *in* H. S. Ladd, ed., Treatise on marine ecology and paleoecology. Geol. Soc. Amer. Mem. 67.

NOLF, B., and P. NOLF. 1969. Santa Cruz Island volcanics. Pp. 91-94 *in* D. W. Weaver, ed., Geology of the Northern Channel Islands. Amer. Assoc. Petroleum Geologists and Soc. Econ. Paleontologists and Mineralogists, Pacific Secs., Spec. Publ.

OLMSTED, F. H. 1958. Geologic reconnaissance of San Clemente Island, California. U.S.

Geol. Survey Bull. 1071-B:55-68.

ORR, P. C. 1960. Late Pleistocene marine terraces on Santa Rosa Island, California. Geol. Soc. Amer. Bull. 71:1113-1119.

———. 1967. Geochronology of Santa Rosa Island, California. Pp. 317-325 *in* R. N. Philbrick, ed., Proceedings of the symposium on the biology of the California Islands. Santa Barbara Botanic Garden, Santa Barbara, Calif.

PUTNAM, W. C. 1954. Marine terraces of the Ventura region and the Santa Monica Mountains, California. Pp. 45-48 *in* R. H. Jahns, ed., Geology of southern California. California Div. Mines Bull. 170(1).

RAND, W. W. 1933. The geology of Santa Cruz Island, California. Ph.D. thesis, University of California, Berkeley, Calif.

REED, R. D. 1933. Geology of California. Amer. Assoc. Petroleum Geologists, Tulsa, Okla.

REED, R. D., and J. S. HOLLISTER. 1936. Structural evolution of southern California. Amer. Assoc. Petroleum Geologists, Tulsa, Okla.

RIDLON, J. B. 1972. Pleistocene-Holocene deformation of the San Clemente Island coastal block, California. Geol. Soc. Amer. Bull. 83:1831-1844.

SHARP, R. P. 1954. Some physiographic aspects of southern California. Pp. 5-20 *in* R. H. Jahns, ed., Geology of southern California. California Div. Mines Bull. 170(3).

SHEPARD, F. P., and R. F. DILL. 1966. Submarine canyons and other sea valleys. Rand McNally, Chicago, Ill.

SHEPARD, F. P., and K. O. EMERY. 1941. Submarine topography off the California coast—canyons and tectonic interpretation. Geol. Soc. Amer. Spec. Paper 31.

SMITH, W. S. T. 1897. The geology of Santa Catalina Island [California]. California Acad. Sci. Proc., 3rd ser., Geology 1:1-71.

———. 1898. A geological sketch of San Clemente Island [California]. U.S. Geol. Survey 18th Ann. Rep., pt. 2:465-496.

———. 1933. Marine terraces on Santa Catalina Island [California]. Amer. J. Sci. 25: 123-136.

SONDAAR, P. Y. 1977. Insularity and its effects on mammal evolution. Pp. 671-707 *in* M. K. Hecht, P. C. Goody, and B. M. Hecht, eds., Major patterns in vertebrate evolution. Plenum, New York, N.Y.

STADUM, C. J., and T. SUSUKI. 1976. The discovery of marine Pliocene strata on San Clemente Island, California [abs.]. Geol. Soc. Amer., Cordilleran Sec., Abstracts with Programs, 8(3):411.

SZABO, B. J., and J. N. ROSHOLT. 1969. Uranium-series dating of Pleistocene shells from southern California—an open system model. J. Geophys. Research 74:3253-3260.

SZABO, B. J., and J. G. VEDDER. 1971. Uranium-series dating of some Pleistocene marine deposits in southern California. Earth and Planetary Sci. Lett. 11:283-290.

UCHUPI, E. 1961. Submarine geology of the Santa Rosa-Cortes Ridge. J. Sed. Petrology 31:534-545.

VALENTINE, J. W., and J. H. LIPPS. 1963. Late Cenozoic rocky-shore assemblages from Anacapa Island, California. J. Paleontology 37:1292-1302.

———. 1967. Late Cenozoic history of the Southern California Islands. Pp. 21-35 *in* R. N. Philbrick, ed., Proceedings of the symposium on the biology of the California Islands. Santa Barbara Botanic Garden, Santa Barbara, Calif.

VAN COUVERING, J. A. 1978. Status of late Cenozoic boundaries. Geology 6:169.

VEDDER, J. G. 1970. Road log, Geomorphic features, Pp. 2-4 *in* L. A. Headlee, A. D. Warren, and J. L. Wildharber, eds., Geologic guidebook, southeastern rim of the Los Angeles basin, Orange County, California. Amer. Assoc. Petroleum Geologists, Soc. Econ. Paleontologists and Mineralogists, Soc. Exploration Geophysicists, Pacific Secs.

VEDDER, J. G., L. A. BEYER, A. JUNGER, G. W. MOORE, A. E. ROBERTS, J. C. TAYLOR, and H. C. WAGNER. 1974. Preliminary report on the geology of the continental borderland of southern California. U.S. Geol. Survey Misc. Field Studies Maps MF-624.

VEDDER, J. G., and D. G. HOWELL. 1976. Neogene strata of the southern group of Channel Islands, California. Pp. 80-106 in D. G. Howell, ed., Aspects of the geologic history of the California Continental Borderland. Amer. Assoc. Petroleum Geologists, Pacific Sec., Misc. Publ. 24.

———. 1977. Interrelations of Catalina Schist, Miocene igneous rocks, and post-Cretaceous(?) strata, Santa Catalina Island, California [abs.]. Geol. Soc. Amer. Abstracts with Programs 9:1210.

VEDDER, J. G., and E. J. MOORE. 1976. Paleoenvironmental implications of fossiliferous Miocene and Pliocene strata on San Clemente Island, California. Pp. 107-135 in D. G. Howell, ed., Aspects of the geologic history of the California Continental Borderland. Amer. Assoc. Petroleum Geologists, Pacific Sec., Misc. Publ. 24.

VEDDER, J. G., and R. M. NORRIS. 1963. Geology of San Nicolas Island, California. U.S. Geol. Survey Prof. Paper 369.

VEDDER, J. G., J. C. TAYLOR, R. E. ARNAL, and D. BUKRY. 1976. Map showing location of selected pre-Quaternary rock samples from California Continental Borderland. U.S. Geol. Survey Misc. Field Studies Map MF-737.

VEEH, H. H., and J. W. VALENTINE. 1967. Radiometric ages of Pleistocene fossils from Cayucos, California. Geol. Soc. Amer. Bull. 78:547-550.

WEAVER, D. W. 1969. Paleogeographic implications and geologic history. Pp. 115-124 in D. W. Weaver, et al., Geology of the Northern Channel Islands [California]. Amer. Assoc. Petroleum Geologists and Soc. Econ. Paleontologists and Mineralogists, Pacific Secs., Spec. Publ.

WEAVER, D. W., and G. L. MEYER. 1969. Stratigraphy of northeastern Santa Cruz Island. Pp. 95-104 in D. W. Weaver, et al., Geology of the Northern Channel Islands [California]. Amer. Assoc. Petroleum Geologists and Soc. Econ. Paleontologists and Mineralogists, Pacific Secs., Spec. Publ.

WEHMILLER, J. F., K. R. LAJOIE, K. A. KVENVOLDEN, E. PETERSON, D. F. BELKNAP, G. L. KENNEDY, W. O. ADDICOTT, J. G. VEDDER, and R. W. WRIGHT. 1977. Correlation and chronology of Pacific Coast marine terrace deposits of continental United States by fossil amino acid stereochemistry—technique, evaluation, relative ages, kinetic model ages, and geologic implications. U.S. Geol. Survey Open-file Rep. 77-680.

WOODRING, W. P., M. N. BRAMLETTE, and W. S. W. KEW. 1946. Geology and paleontology of Palos Verdes Hills, California. U.S. Geol. Survey Prof. Paper 207.

YEATS, R. S. 1965. Pliocene seaknoll at South Mountain, Ventura basin, California. Amer. Assoc. Petroleum Geologists Bull. 49:526-546.

———. 1976. Neogene tectonics of the central Ventura basin, California. Pp. 19-32 in A. E. Fritsche, H. Ter Best, Jr., and W. W. Wornardt, eds., The Neogene symposium. Soc. Econ. Paleontologists and Mineralogists, Pacific Sec.

YERKES, R. F., T. H. MCCULLOH, J. E. SCHOELLHAMER, and J. G. VEDDER. 1965. Geology of the Los Angeles basin, California—an introduction. U.S. Geol. Survey Prof. Paper 420-A.

Was There a Quaternary Land Bridge to the Northern Channel Islands?

Arne Junger[1] and Donald Lee Johnson[2]

[1]*Department of Geology, University of California, Santa Barbara, California 93106*

[2]*Department of Geography, University of Illinois, Urbana, Illinois 61801*

INTRODUCTION

It has long been assumed that a Pleistocene land bridge once connected the Northern Channel Islands to the mainland (Fig. 1). However, this assumption has been questioned in recent years (see Johnson 1972, 1973, 1978, and Wenner and Johnson 1980). Of the two principal lines of evidence cited in support of a land bridge, one is paleontologic and the other is geologic. The paleontologic evidence consists of island elephant remains coupled with the belief that elephants do not swim or could not swim to the islands. However, we now know that elephants swim well, and the short distances required for them to cross a narrowed Santa Barbara Channel during low sea-level periods were within their swimming capacities (Johnson 1972, 1978, and in prep.). But the fact that elephants could swim to the islands does not prove that they did, so the general geologic and glacio-eustatic evidence for a bridge was reviewed; this evidence, however, was found wanting (see geologic discussions in Wenner and Johnson 1980, and Johnson 1978). We, therefore, thought that geologic evidence for or against a bridge ought to be obtained from seismic reflection profiles in the eastern Santa Barbara Channel, the area where the bridge was presumed to have existed. Upon careful examination and re-examination of the sub-bottom stratigraphy and structure as revealed through the seismic profiles, our belief is that there was no Quaternary land bridge. The remainder of this paper shows why we reached this conclusion.

LOCATION OF PROPOSED BRIDGE

Emery (1960) and Howell (1976) provide two rather graphic bathymetry maps of the seafloor of the well-known California Continental Borderland, which includes all the California Channel Islands as well as various submarine banks and interlying basins out to the continental slope. There was little deformation of this entire area during the Quaternary so that, except for local areas of sedimentation, these maps also represent the general configuration of the seafloor during the Quaternary. A perusal shows the area between West Anacapa Island and the mainland as the only likely area for such a land bridge. It is also the area where all proponents of a land bridge have placed it (Fig. 1).

Figure 2 shows the bathymetry of the eastern Santa Barbara Channel. It is now the area of shallowest water (236 m) between the Northern Channel Islands platform and the mainland. One can readily visualize a tectonic ridge, now buried in sediments, connecting the islands with the mainland to the east.

SEISMIC PROFILES
Late Pliocene and Early Pleistocene

The black lines on Figure 2 are the locations of seismic profiles. Figure 3a is the most westerly profile and shows the existence of a tectonic structure, the Anacapa Ridge (unidentified sediments in Figure 3a are due to blockage by seismic signals). This ridge consists of

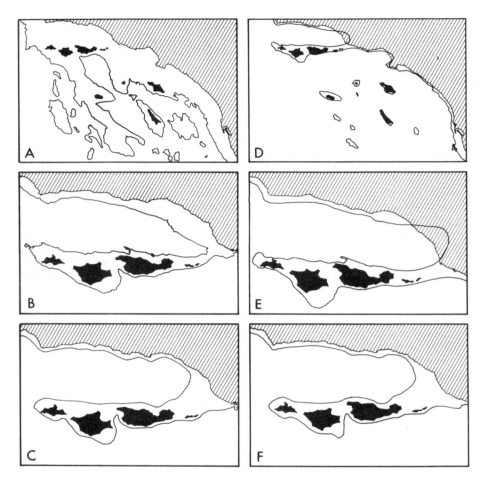

FIGURE 1. *Reconstruction of Channel Island land bridges by various authors. A—early Pleistocene (Clements 1955), B—early Pleistocene (Van Gelder 1965), C—Pleistocene (Chaney and Mason 1930), D—middle Pleistocene (Valentine and Lipps 1967), E—possibly middle to late Pleistocene (Remington 1971), F—late Pleistocene (Stock 1943).*

middle Miocene volcanics and Monterey Formation strata and was uplifted during late Miocene to early Pliocene time. On the north side of the ridge, upper Pliocene and Quaternary strata (the Pico, Santa Barbara, and San Pedro Formations) buttress against the flank of the ridge. Except for a slight north dip of the deepest horizons, the strata are horizontal, testifying to minimal tectonic deformation of the area in Pleistocene time. The contact between the horizontal strata of the Santa Barbara Formation and the crossbedded strata of the San Pedro Formation is a very prominent feature which can be recognized at depths close to 400 m on all profiles in the area. The age of the Santa Barbara Formation ranges from very late Pliocene to early Pleistocene. The contact with the San Pedro is of early Pleistocene age. Figure 3b again shows the Anacapa Ridge, but structurally lower than in Figure 3a, with sediments extending nearly to the crest. The contact between the Santa Barbara and San Pedro Formations is again apparent at an

FIGURE 2. *Bathymetric map of the eastern Santa Barbara Channel, California, showing seismic reflection profiles OC-1, P-14, and P-16 (see Figure 3; more profiles are shown in Figure 5). Contour interval is 300 ft (92 m; after Emery 1960).*

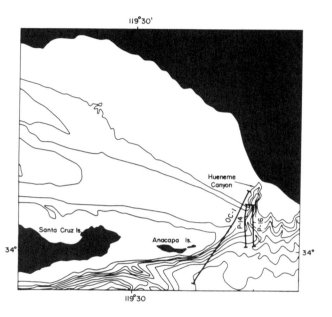

FIGURE 3. *Three seismic reflection profiles (a, b, and c) across the eastern end of the Santa Barbara Channel, California.*

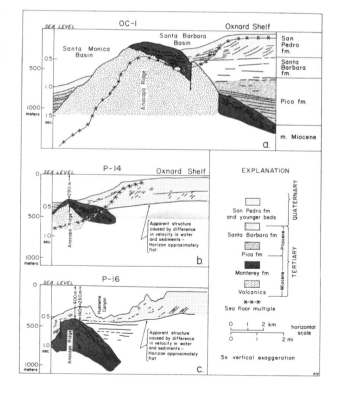

36

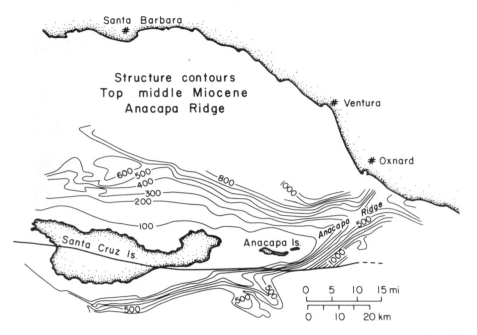

FIGURE 4. *Map of the contoured Miocene surface, eastern Santa Barbara Channel, California.*

approximate depth of 400 m. Figure 3c shows the most easterly seismic profile, with the crest of the ridge at a depth of 400 m, only slightly higher than the Santa Barbara-San Pedro contact and buried in sediments derived from the Oxnard shelf.

From the above profiles and other data, a map of the top of the Miocene was contoured (Fig. 4) which shows a saddle on the ridge at a depth of slightly greater than 400 m. It shows that there is a ridge connecting the Northern Channel Islands platform to the mainland, but the essential question is: did it ever act as a land bridge?

Figure 5 is a composite profile northeast of Santa Cruz Island. The northern part shows the Santa Barbara-San Pedro contact at approximately 400 m depth. The southern part shows three terraces, an upper one at 100 m depth, presumably of Wisconsin age, an intermediate terrace poorly developed here but better on other profiles in the area, and a lower one at a depth of 200 m. Note that the Santa Barbara-San Pedro contact buttresses into the slope of the lower terrace. The terrace material is, therefore, roughly the time equivalent of the upper part of the Santa Barbara Formation, that is, of very early Pleistocene age. The top of the terrace is at a depth of 200 m, indicating that sea level has risen 200 m since formation of the terrace. The saddle on the ridge to the mainland, now at a depth of 400 m, was thus at a depth of 200 m in early Pleistocene time. Not only was this far too deep for elephants to walk across, they probably had not yet arrived in North America in their journey from Siberia (and even if they had, *Mammuthus columbi,* the species which colonized the islands, did not evolve until much later; see Wenner and Johnson 1980).

Since inception of sedimentation of the San Pedro Formation, the central part of the ridge became blanketed by sediments and therefore could not have acted as a land bridge. Any

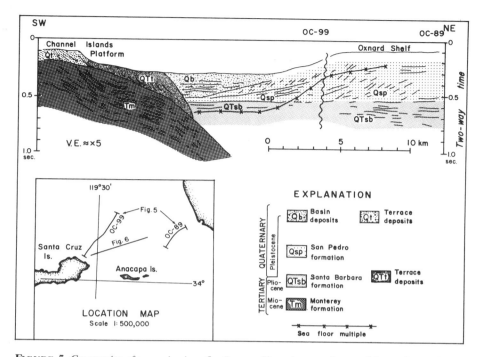

FIGURE 5. *Composite of two seismic reflection profiles taken northeast of Santa Cruz Island, California.*

subsequent mainland connection would have to have been across the sedimentary blanket of the Oxnard shelf and the present narrow channel where the seafloor appears nearly level with the top of the lower terrace. That such a land connection did not exist is demonstrated by Figure 6, which shows the lower terrace in more detail, though in a different location than Figure 5. Note that the top is an erosional surface, part of which cuts Monterey Shale. Visible on the extreme left of Figure 6 is the toe of the next higher (presumably intermediate) terrace. A thin layer of bottomset beds of this terrace extends across the wave-cut lower terrace, over its fore-edge, and down into the adjoining channel. From these relationships we can determine that the seafloor in the channel at the time the foreset beds were laid down was 137 m below the top of these beds and 120 m below the erosional surface on the terrace, and probably deeper when the terrace was cut. Again, elephants could not have walked to the island at that time.

Middle and Late Pleistocene

The preceding discussion has focused on water depths in the Santa Barbara Channel during early Pleistocene time. Since this is earlier than the time of arrival of mammoths in California, and considerably before the insular population *M. columbi* evolved as a species, channel conditions in the middle and late Pleistocene are equally, if not more, relevant to our investigation. In this regard, the two upper (intermediate and highest) terraces provided a measure of water depth over the channel during time of low sea-level stands subsequent to the formation of the deepest terrace. It is assumed that in a sequence of submarine terraces, the age of individual terraces becomes younger upward, since a terrace would be destroyed by wave action during

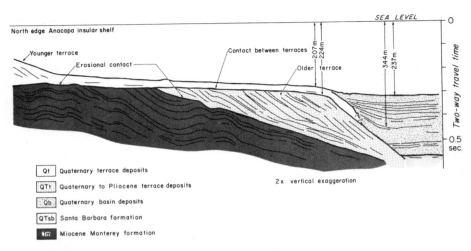

FIGURE 6. *Detail of lower terrace shown in Figure 5.*

subsequent lowering of sea level. Thus, sea level was never lower than the lowest terrace subsequent to erosion of its top. The level of the seafloor during formation of the higher terraces is unknown, but from Figure 5 it can be concluded that at no time during the Quaternary was the water depth in the channel less than 100 m. The best estimates of the lowest sea-level stand during Wisconsin stage is 130 m, giving a channel depth of 100 m if the seafloor was no lower than at present.

CONCLUSIONS

In light of the above information gleaned from sub-bottom seismic reflection profiles across the narrow eastern end of the Santa Barbara Channel, we conclude that at no time during the Quaternary was the water depth between the islands and the mainland less than 100 m, and that, therefore, no land bridge existed.

ACKNOWLEDGMENTS

We thank D. N. Johnson and A. Wenner for critically reviewing this manuscript, and the Geography Department at the University of California, Santa Barbara, for secretarial help in typing.

The geological interpretation is based on seismic profiles obtained by the U. S. Geological Survey during various cruises on the research vessels *Valero IV, Oil City,* and *Polaris* in the period 1966 to 1970.

REFERENCES

CHANEY, R. W., and H. L. MASON. 1930. A Pleistocene flora from Santa Cruz Island, California. Carnegie Inst. Washington Publ. 415:1-24.

CLEMENTS, T. 1955. The Pleistocene history of the Channel Islands region—southern California. Pp. 311-323 *in* Essays in the natural sciences in honor of Captain Allan Hancock. University of Southern California Press, Los Angeles, Calif.

EMERY, K. O. 1969. The sea off southern California. John Wiley & Sons, New York, N.Y.

HOWELL, D. G., ed. 1976. Aspects of the geologic history of the California Continental

Borderland. Assoc. Amer. Petroleum Geologists, Pacific Sec., Misc. Publ. 24.

JOHNSON, D. L. 1972. Landscape evolution on San Miguel Island, California. Ph.D. thesis, University of Kansas, Lawrence, Kan. (also "Dissertation Abstracts," University Microfilms, Inc., Ann Arbor, Mich., Order no. 73-11, 902).

——————. 1973. On the origin and extinction of pygmy elephants, Northern Channel Islands, California. Program and Abstracts, Geol. Soc. Amer.

——————. 1978. The origin of island mammoths and the Quaternary land bridge history of the Northern Channel Islands, California. Quaternary Research 10:204-225.

REMINGTON, C. L. 1971. Natural history and evolutionary genetics of the California Islands. Discovery 7:2-18.

STOCK, C. 1943. Foxes and elephants of the Channel Islands. Los Angeles Co. Mus. Quart. 3:6-9.

VALENTINE, J. W., and J. H. LIPPS. 1967. Late Cenozoic history of the Southern California Islands. Pp. 21-35 *in* R. N. Philbrick, ed., Proceedings of the symposium of the biology of the California Islands. Santa Barbara Botanic Garden, Santa Barbara, Calif.

VAN GELDER, R. G. 1965. Channel Islands skunk. Nat. Hist. 74:30-35.

WENNER, A. M., and D. L. JOHNSON. 1980. Land vertebrates on the California Channel Islands: sweepstakes or bridges? Pp. 497-530 *in* D.M. Power, ed., The California Islands: proceedings of a multidisciplinary symposium. Santa Barbara Museum of Natural History, Santa Barbara, Calif.

Invertebrate Megafossils of Pleistocene (Sangamon Interglacial) Age From Isla de Guadalupe, Baja California, Mexico

David R. Lindberg,[1] Barry Roth,[1] Michael G. Kellogg,[1]
and Carl L. Hubbs[2,3]

[1]California Academy of Sciences, Golden Gate Park,
San Francisco, California 94118.

[2]Scripps Institution of Oceanography, La Jolla,
California 92093.

INTRODUCTION

The presence of marine invertebrate fossils on the dominantly volcanic Isla de Guadalupe, Mexico (29° N, 118° 20′ W), approximately 275 km off the west central coast of Baja California, has been mentioned periodically in the literature (Johnson 1953, Chace 1958, Squires 1959, Hubbs 1960, 1967, Goldberg 1965, Hubbs and Jehl 1976). Johnson (1953: 235) reported an Isla de Guadalupe "upper Tertiary or Quaternary" marine faunule "from the Melpomene Cove seacliff, about 75 feet above sea level and interbedded within the pyroclastic series" (Fig. 1). Johnson considered the stratification and cross-bedding of the sequence to be suggestive of water deposition. Fossils reported from this deposit were an unidentified gastropod, echinoid spines, fish scales, and foraminifera, the latter apparently serving as the basis for the general age assignment. We have not reinvestigated this locality, but if the description is accurate, especially regarding elevation and interbedding, we suspect it to be of a different age and depositional history than the unit described herein.

In 1957 Carl L. Hubbs and Emery P. Chace discovered a fossiliferous sedimentary deposit near the island's present sea level. Collections were made then and on subsequent trips in 1960, 1963, 1965, 1966, and 1969. On the basis of part of these collections, Chace (1958) first reported the presence of a warm-water Pleistocene faunule on Isla de Guadalupe. A hermatypic coral and echinoid spines from this faunule were sent to J. W. Durham at Berkeley in 1958 and several times subsequently. A sample of the coral was sent by Chace to D. F. Squires, who noted (Squires 1959:339) that it was "a remarkable occurrence of *Pocillopora* . . . apparently closely related to *P. palmata* Palmer, and specimens of *P. robusta* Verrill," indicating "a northern shift of approximately 8 degrees of latitude from the most northerly occurrence of *Pocillopora* outside the Gulf of California at the present time." Goldberg (1965:R126) dated a sample of the Guadalupe *Pocillopora* obtained from Hubbs as "130,000 years [before present] by the uranium 234:thorium-230 technique and 110,000 years by the uranium-234:uranium-238 technique." Edward C. Wilson and Hubbs conducted further, unpublished, studies on fossils obtained from the deposit. In June of 1975, David R. Lindberg visited Isla de Guadalupe and collected invertebrate fossils from a previously unstudied locality belonging to the same unit. Specimens studied are deposited in the Department of Paleontology, San Diego Museum of Natural History (SDMNH), San Diego, California; Department of Geology, California Academy of Sciences (CASG), San Francisco, California; and the University of California Museum of Paleontology (UCMP), Berkeley, California. In the appendix to this paper, the *Pocillopora* species is described as new (Durham 1980).

---

[3]Deceased, 30 June 1979.

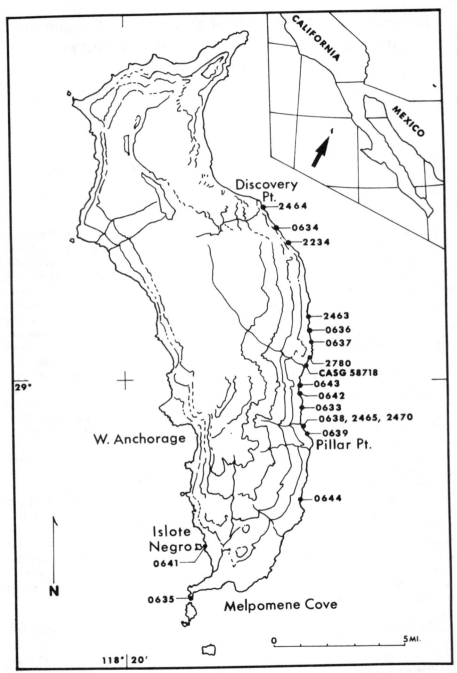

Figure 1. *Map of Isla de Guadalupe, Baja California, Mexico, showing features referred to in text and Pleistocene fossil localities.*

THE DISCOVERY POINT FORMATION

Isla de Guadalupe rises steeply over 4,500 m from the ocean bottom with its highest point approximately 1,524 m above sea level. It is one of few emergent volcanoes of the Baja California Seamount province (Menard 1955) and rests upon a basement of oceanic crust supposed, on paleomagnetic evidence, to be 12 million years of age or older (Doyle and Gorsline 1977). Batiza (1977) cites unpublished work by H. W. Menard indicating that Isla de Guadalupe is flanked symmetrically by magnetic anomaly 5B, 15.5 million years old, and is built on the axis of an extinct spreading center. Approximately 80 km of deep ocean separate Isla de Guadalupe from the continental crust of the margin of the Baja California borderland (Doyle and Gorsline 1977: fig. 1). The island consists of two partly overlapping shield volcanoes that are overlain by a thick series of flank and fissure eruptions. The northern shield volcano is the younger of the two (Batiza 1977); its oldest exposed rocks are subaerial flows of alkali olivine basalt that have been radiometrically dated at 7 ±2 million years before present (Engel and Engel 1971). This places the island in existence since at least the latest Miocene epoch (Berggren and Van Couvering 1974: fig. 1).

The fossiliferous rocks at low elevation consist of coarsely clastic sediments that grade laterally from conglomerate, locally with pebbles of volcanic origin, to a biostrome formed chiefly of hermatypic coral fragments and mollusk shells. It is partly concealed by younger shoreline talus deposits which occur at the base of the steep cliffs surrounding much of the island. At most localities there seems to be no Pleistocene wave-cut bench, terrace, or platform. Exposed subaerial lava flows are erosionally truncated at and near present sea level. The sediments are moderately to well indurated, usually with calcitic cement. There is no basal conglomerate like those which characterize many deposits of similar age on the mainland. In places one can see the irregular contact between the sediments and eroded surfaces of the lava. Interbedding as described by Johnson (1953) at the Melpomene Cove locality was nowhere observed.

The name "Discovery Point Formation" was proposed and the deposit described by Wilson and Hubbs, in manuscript, as follows:

> The type section of the formation is at Discovery Point [Fig. 1] on the east shore of the island. A description of this locality and the nature of the formation there is given in the locality register (SDMNH Locality 0634) [included below]. The Discovery Point Formation extends discontinuously along much of the eastern side of Isla Guadalupe, around the southern end, and up the western side at least as far as Islote Negro. The west side of the island was investigated only for about 1 km north of the south end at Islote Negro, at West Anchorage, and briefly at a few other spots. At some localities where [the deposit] lies between large blocks of talus close to sea level, it is thick enough for sea caves to have been formed in it. These caves may be highly fossiliferous, with fossils on the ceilings, walls, and floors. At other localities, the formation is only a few inches in thickness, coating the talus or ledges along the seashore. Some former exposures seem to have been covered by recent talus slides and many exposures must have been destroyed by wave action. The existing exposures extend from the present sea level to about 1 to 8 meters above the present high tide line. The uniform distribution of the formation suggests that the island has been tectonically stable since at least Pleistocene times. It has not been determined whether or not the formation extends into the submarine area or if there are submerged terraces. Divers operating around the island have not reported fossils.

Although the deposit is at and near present sea level, the fossils and lithology indicate that it was laid down subtidally, and this is consistent with higher former sea levels inferred for the Sangamon interglacial stage.

LITHOLOGY

The fossiliferous matrix from Locality CASG 58718 consists of a poorly indurated, tan, arenaceous, pebble conglomerate consisting predominantly of angular grains of volcanic rock, comminuted shell debris, and quartz and lava sand. A smaller number of rounded to sub-rounded grains are present. The rock is highly porous and the sand grains and pebbles are coated with clay. A hand specimen from Locality SDMNH 0634 is well indurated and contains a higher proportion of shell debris and a few pumiceous clasts in addition to angular to subangular volcanic pebbles. The pebbles are mostly scoriaceous. Angular quartz grains, some showing striations on unworn crystal faces, are present. The rock is cemented by tan to pinkish gray calcite, presumably redeposited from the detrital invertebrate remains.

In composition and fabric, both these rock samples suggest deposition in shallow subtidal depths, following minor mechanical sorting, with source rocks no great distance from the deposit. The angular lithic fragments and quartz grains appear to have undergone little transport or mechanical abrasion. A component interpreted as beach rubble is present. Rounded clasts in the sample from CASG 58718 are almost certainly wave-worn. They and some of the marine invertebrate remains may have been transported onshore initially by waves, as occurs at present. Lindberg, for example, at Isla de Guadalupe in June 1975, observed storm-generated waves tossing onshore living *Tegula regina* (Stearns 1892), a gastropod which lives at depths of 9 m and more (McLean 1969). Material deposited in the intertidal zone would have been removed by subsequent wave scouring before induration could occur. The clay component coating the pebbles and sand grains was probably distributed interstitially at a later time.

The topographic setting was similar to the island's present periphery, where steep cliffs shed landslide debris into the intertidal and supratidal zones. Additional terrestrial debris is introduced into these zones as sediments carried down the arroyos which transect the island. Some reworking of the sediments by wave action has been suggested (Hubbs and Jehl 1976), but the dominance of angular grains in the sample from CASG 58718 indicates that, for this site at least, reworking was minimal. Shells of minute, delicate gastropods and bivalves, which are present intact in several samples, and unworn foraminiferan tests, give no evidence of reworking.

REGISTER OF LOCALITIES

All localities refer to Isla de Guadalupe, Baja California, Mexico. (Abbreviations: SDMNH—San Diego Museum of Natural History, Department of Paleontology; CASG—California Academy of Sciences, Department of Geology; UCMP—University of California, Berkeley, Museum of Paleontology.)

SDMNH 0633. East side of island; north edge of large sea cave, approximately ½ inch south of 29° latitude line on U. S. Hydrographic Office map 1688 (1962). Coll. E. C. Wilson, 2 March 1965.

SDMNH 0634. East side of island; conglomerate from ceiling of Discovery Cave, approximately 2¼ inches north of 29° latitude line and opposite "50" fathom sign on U. S. Hydrographic Office map 1688 (1962). Coll. E. C. Wilson, 1 March 1965.

SDMNH 0635. East side of island; intertidal conglomerate at center of northernmost of two small islands due south of the weather station. At low tide the islands form a peninsula as shown on U. S. Hydrographic Office map 1688 (1962), north to Isla de Adentro and west of the "G" in "Good landing." Coll. E. C. Wilson, 3 March 1965.

SDMNH 0636. East side of island; estimate 6.4 km south of SDMNH 0634. Coll. E. C. Wilson, 1 March 1965.

SDMNH 0637. East side of island; approximately 0.16 km north of large sea cave and 0.8 km south of the Nursery, 4 to 6 m above sea level. Coll. C. L. Hubbs *et al.*, 1 March 1965.

SDMNH 0638. East side of island; coquina between two caves approximately halfway between Pillar Point and the point midway between Pillar and Red Cinder Cone Points, just south of a canyon. Coll. C. L. Hubbs *et al.*, 25 April 1963.

SDMNH 0639. East side of island; coquina, approximately 0.5 km north of Pillar Point. Coll. C. L. Hubbs *et al.*, 25 April 1963.

SDMNH 0640. Exact locality unknown. Coll. E. P. Chace and C. L. Hubbs, 17 December 1957.

SDMNH 0641. West side of the island; coquina, southern end, east side of Islote Negro, 3 to 6 m above sea level, formed in two rock slides. Coll. C. L. Hubbs, 19 April 1957.

SDMNH 0642. East side of island; 28° 59.6′ N, 118° 13.6′ W (Hydrographic Office map 1688 [1956]), cliff talus, 1 to 5 m above sea level. Coll. C. L. Hubbs *et al.*, 27 January 1957.

SDMNH 0643. East side of island; 28° 59′ 25″ N. Coll. C. L. Hubbs and E. P. Chace, 17 December 1957.

SDMNH 0644. East side of island; 28° 56′ 18″ N. Coll. C. L. Hubbs and E. P. Chace, 17 December 1957.

SDMNH 0645. East side of island; about midway on the island. In cliff, 1 to 5 m above high tide line. Coll. C. L. Hubbs, January 1960.

SDMNH 2233. East side of island; within 0.8 km of 29° 4.7′ N (Hydrographic Office map 1688 [1956]), between Discovery and Dyke Points, southerly of two exposures. Coll. C. L. Hubbs, 2 April 1966.

SDMNH 2234. As SDMNH 2233, but northerly of two exposures. Coll. C. L. Hubbs, 2 April 1966.

SDMNH 2463. East side of island; the Nursery, cave shelf approximately 3 to 4 m above sea level. Coll. C. Nelson and Lo-Chai Chen, 2 May 1967.

SDMNH 2464. East side of island; 29° 6′ N (Hydrographic Office map 1688 [1957]), Discovery Point, in small sea caves. Coll. C. Nelson, 2 May 1967.

SDMNH 2465. East side of island; approximately 28° 58.4′ N (Hydrographic Office map 1688 [1957]). Coll. C. Nelson and C. L. Hubbs, 3 May 1967.

SDMNH 2470. East side of island; approximately 28° 58.4′ N (Hydrographic Office map 1688 [1957]). Coll. C. L. Hubbs, 3 May 1967.

SDMNH 2780. East side of island; 29° 0.6′ N, 118° 13.3′ W (Hydrographic Office map 1688 [1956]), approximately 0.5 km southwest of Red Cinder Cone Point. Coll. C. L. Hubbs, 18 February 1969.

CASG 35020. Same as SDMNH 0643.

CASG 58718. East side of island; approximately 750 m north of Lobster Camp located at 29° 0′ 10″ N, 118° 13′ 40″ W (Defense Mapping Agency Hydrographic Center chart 21661 [1976]), approximately 3 m above sea level. Coll. D. R. Lindberg and J. E. Sutton, 5, 7, and 8 July 1975.

UCMP B-6554. Same as SDMNH 0643.

UCMP B-7336. Same as SDMNH 0642.

UCMP D-1547. Same as SDMNH 0633.

UCMP D-1548. Same as SDMNH 0634.

UCMP D-1549. Same as SDMNH 0637.

UCMP D-7297. Same as CASG 58718.

AGE AND CORRELATION

The radiometric age determinations obtained from the coral by Goldberg (1965), 110,000 and 130,000 years B.P. (before present), fall within the range of the Sangamon interglacial stage

TABLE 1. Invertebrate megafossils from Isla de Guadalupe, Mexico.

Taxa	CASG 58718	SDMNH 0633	SDMNH 0634	SDMNH 0635	SDMNH 0636	SDMNH 0637	SDMNH 0638	SDMNH 0639	SDMNH 0640	SDMNH 0641	SDMNH 0642	SDMNH 0643	SDMNH 0644	SDMNH 0645	SDMNH 2233	SDMNH 2234	SDMNH 2462	SDMNH 2463	SDMNH 2464	SDMNH 2465	SDMNH 2470	SDMNH 2780	Province	Tide level	Recent
CNIDARIA																									
Anthozoa																									
Pocillopora guadalupensis Durham, n. sp.	x	x	x	x		x	x	x				x	x		x	x			x	x	x		(1)		
ANNELIDA																									
Polychaeta																									
Dexiospira sp.												x													
Serpulidae	x		x													x			x						
Sabellidae			x																x						
ARTHROPODA																									
Crustacea																									
Tetraclita squamosa (Bruguière)	x	x	x							x					x	x			x	x	x		B	L	x
Paguridae										x															
Eriphia (?) sp.										x															
Hapalogaster sp.										x															
Majidae										x															
Cycloxanthops cf. C. novemdentatus (Lockington)	x										x	x											C	S	x
Xanthidae		x									x	cf								x	x				
Pinnixa sp.																					x				
Pachygrapsus sp.			x																			x			
Petrolisthes edwardsii (Saussure)			x																			x	P	L	

MOLLUSCA

Polyplacophora

Species	Province	Tide level	Recent
Callistochiton palmulatus Pilsbry	C	S	x
Nuttallina californica (Reeve)	C	L	x
Lepidozona, n. sp.	C	L	E
Gastropoda			
Haliotis fulgens guadalupensis Talmadge	C	S	E
Sinezona rimuloides (Carpenter)	B	S	x
Fissurella volcano Reeve	C	L	x
Collisella digitalis (Rathke)	C	L	x
Collisella limatula (Carpenter)	B	L	x
Collisella scabra (Gould)	C	L	x
Lottia gigantea Sowerby	C	L	x
Norrisia norrisi (Sowerby)	C	SL	x
Tegula eiseni Jordan	C	L	x
Tegula gallina (Forbes)	C	L	x
Homalopoma luridum (Dall)	C	L	x
Astraea undosa (Wood)	C	S	x
Tricolia sp.			
Littorina keenae Rosewater	C	L	x
Barleeia haliotiphila Carpenter	C	L	
Barleeia subtenuis Carpenter	C	L	
Alvinia purpurea (Dall)	C	S	x
Alvinia oldroydae (Bartsch)	B	S	x
Amphithalamus inclusus Carpenter	C	S	x
Rissoella excolpa Bartsch	P	?	
Rissoella tumens (Carpenter)	P	?	

Symbols: cf = tentative identification. Province column—B, biprovincial; C, Californian; I, Indo-Pacific; P, Panamic. Tide level column—L, littoral; S, sublittoral; SL, littoral and sublittoral. Recent column—x, present in Recent fauna of Isla de Guadalupe; E, endemic to Isla de Guadalupe.

TABLE 1. (Cont.)

Taxa (Localities)	CASG 58718	SDMNH 0633	SDMNH 0634	SDMNH 0635	SDMNH 0636	SDMNH 0637	SDMNH 0638	SDMNH 0639	SDMNH 0640	SDMNH 0641	SDMNH 0642	SDMNH 0643	SDMNH 0644	SDMNH 0645	SDMNH 2233	SDMNH 2234	SDMNH 2462	SDMNH 2463	SDMNH 2464	SDMNH 2465	SDMNH 2470	SDMNH 2780	Province	Tide level	Recent
Truncatella guadalupensis Pilsbry	x	x														x					x	x	C	L	E
Heliacus sp.																			x						
Petaloconchus cf. *P. montereyensis* Dall										x										x					
Petaloconchus sp.			x																						
Vermetus (Thylaeodus) cf. *V. compactus* (Carpenter)			x																	x					
Dendropoma lituella (Moerch)																						x			x
Bittium sp.																						x			
Hipponix cranioides Carpenter	cf	x	x				x	x			x	x		x				x				x	B	L	x
Cypraea cernica Sowerby	cf		x									cf		cf									I	S	x
Sinum sp.	x																							S	
Erato columbella Menke			x																				B	S	x
Trivia solandri (Sowerby)			x																				B	S	x
Bursa californica (Hinds)			x									x											B	S	x
Murexiella cf. *M. lappa* (Broderip)																				x			P	S	
Purpura pansa Gould		x	x																				P	L	
Thais biserialis (Blainville)								x															P	L	
Thais planospira (Lamarck)		x	x				x							x						x		x	P	L	x
Morula lugubris (C. B. Adams)		x	x				x					x											B	S	x
Columbella aureomexicana (Howard)			x																				P	L	
Columbella sp.																						x			

Taxon	Province	Tide level	Recent
Mitrella guttata (Sowerby)	P	L	
Latirus sp.			
Mitra rupicola Reeve	P	S	
Volvarina taeniolata Moerch	B	SL	x
Conus californicus Hinds	C	SL	x
Conus purpurascens Sowerby	P	L	
Conus princeps Linnaeus	P	L	
Conus fergusoni Sowerby	P	SL	
Odostomia navisa Dall & Bartsch	B	?	x
Odostomia aepynota Dall & Bartsch	B	?	x
Odotomia terebellum (C. B. Adams)	B	?	x
Odostomia sp.			
Turbonilla (*Chemnitzia*) sp.			
Pedipes liratus Binney	B	L	
Bivalvia			
Barbatia reeveana (Orbigny)	B	S	
Brachidontes adamsianus (Dunker)	B	L	x
Ostrea sp.			
Lasaea sp.			
Codakia distinguenda (Tryon)	P	S	
Ctena mexicana (Dall)	P	S	
Chama squamuligera Pilsbry & Lowe	P	SL	x
Chione squamosa (Carpenter)	P	S	

ECHINODERMATA
  Echinoidea

Taxon	Province	Tide level	Recent
Eucidaris thouarsii Valenciennes	P	S	x
non-cidaroid			

Symbols:cf=tentative identification. Province column—B, biprovincial; C, Californian; I, Indo-Pacific; P, Panamic. Tide level column—L, littoral; S, sublittoral; SL, littoral and sublittoral. Recent column—x, present in Recent fauna of Isla de Guadalupe; E, endemic to Isla de Guadalupe.

(Berggren and Van Couvering 1974). In harmony with this late Pleistocene age assignment, the fossil faunule, as far as determinable, except for the coral, consists entirely of extant species.

Coral and mollusk specimens from several late Pleistocene formations in southern California have also yielded radiometric age determinations within the range ascribed to the Sangamon interglacial. These deposits include: Palos Verdes sand, 115,000 ±20,000 years B.P. (Fanale and Schaeffer 1965; based on He/U ratios in bivalve and gastropod shells) and 130,000 to 140,000 years B.P. (Kaufman and Broecker in Fanale and Schaeffer 1965; based on Th^{230}/U^{238}); Cayucos terrace, 130,000 ±30,000 and 140,000 ±30,000 years B.P. (Veeh and J. W. Valentine 1967; based on Th^{230}/U^{238}); and San Nicolas Island lower terrace, 120,000 ±20,000 and ≥120,000 years B.P. (J. W. Valentine and Veeh 1969; by Th^{230}/Th^{232}). Amino acid age estimates agree with the radiometric determinations on the Cayucos and San Nicolas Island terraces (LaJoie et al. 1975).

Inferred paleotemperatures, discussed below, do not allow correlation at an equal level of precision, but are consistent with a late Pleistocene climatic model based on the Palos Verdes sand and other correlative deposits in southern California and northern Baja California (J. W. Valentine 1961, J. W. Valentine and Meade 1961, P. C. Valentine 1976).

Hopkins (1967), from little-deformed late Cenozoic marine sequences in Alaska, estimated a Sangamon interglacial sea level of +10 m. Lipps et al. (1968), working on Santa Barbara Island off southern California, identified a strandline at +9 m as possibly Sangamon. Land et al. (1967) in Bermuda, Oaks (1965) in Virginia, Butzer and Cuerda (1962) in southern Mallorca, and Lipps et al. (1968) in southern California recognized sea stands at between 30 and 40 m above present sea level which correlate with pre-Illinoian interglacials, either Yarmouth or Aftonian. Goldberg (1965) noted that radiometric determinations in the 130,000-year range seemed to define an interval just preceding the last major pre-Recent regression when sea level stood about 10 m higher than today. Flint (1971) summarized late Quaternary eustatic sea level fluctuations as follows: the maximum height of sea level during the Sangamon interglacial stage as questionably +20 m; the lowest position of sea level during the Wisconsin glacial maximum as questionably −100 m; and little or no fluctuation since the end of the Wisconsin stage. Milliman and Emery (1968) indicated a maximum lowering to about −130 m between 14,000 and 16,000 years B.P.; and Heusser (1960) suggested a post-Wisconsin rise of 1 to 2 m above present sea level.

Based on this historical model and assuming tectonic stability for Isla de Guadalupe during the late Quaternary, we interpret the fossil locality of Johnson (1953) at Melpomene Cove as pre-Sangamon and possibly associated with the +30 to +40 m pre-Illinoian transgression. The Discovery Point Formation, with upper limit 1 to 8 m above present sea level, was deposited in shallow subtidal water prior to the marine regression of the Wisconsin glacial stage. It stood higher (possibly considerably higher) above the lowered sea level of Wisconsin time than it does now. Post-Wisconsin transgressions, if any, may have removed lower portions of the formation by direct wave action and undercutting—a process continuing today.

Hubbs and Jehl (1976) by implication suggested that reworking had caused a temporal mixture of tropical and warm-temperate faunal elements in the formation, and at least superficial reworking may have accompanied recession of the post-Sangamon sea level to its Wisconsin low. Both tropical and warm-temperate elements occur, however, throughout the thickness of the formation. Neither group is noticeably more abraded than the other. The main effect of changing sea level was probably removal, not redeposition, of Discovery Point sediments.

PALEONTOLOGY

The megafauna obtained from the Discovery Point Formation (Table 1) consists of eighty-six species of marine invertebrates: one scleractinian coral, three polychaete worms, ten crusta-

TABLE 2. Taxa extraneous to the Surian province.

---

(1) Species not now ranging south of Isla Cedros
    Callistochiton palmulatus (P)
    Lepidozona n. sp. (P, E)
    Haliotis fulgens guadalupensis (P, E)
    Alvinia purpurea (P)
    Truncatella guadalupensis (P, E)
    Dendropoma lituella (at Cedros) (P)

(2) Species not now ranging north of Cabo San Lucas on the outer coast of Baja California.
    Rissoella tumens (at Cabo San Lucas)
    Rissoella excolpa (at Cabo San Lucas)
    Thais planospira (at Cabo San Lucas)
    Mitra rupicola
    Conus princeps
    Ctena mexicana
    Chione squamosa

P = present in Recent fauna of Isla de Guadalupe. E = endemic to Isla de Guadalupe.

ceans, fifty-nine gastropods, eight bivalves, three chitons, and two echinoids. The faunule contains species whose modern occurrence is principally in subtropical and tropical regions (Panamic) and others which characteristically inhabit warm-temperate waters (Californian). Most of the species (>80 per cent), whether mainly of Californian or Panamic distribution, occur at present along the western coast of Baja California between Isla Cedros (approximately 28° N) and Cabo San Lucas (approximately 23° N). Also noteworthy is the presence of a small element (one gastropod and the coral) with Indo-Pacific affinities.

The Panamic marine molluscan province coincides approximately with that portion of the west coasts of North and South America with marine hydroclimates dominated by the Pacific Equatorial Water Mass. The Californian province is influenced by the North Pacific Subarctic Water Mass (Sverdrup *et al.* 1942), the southward-flowing California Current and, characteristically, the presence of cold-water upwelling near shore during at least a part of the year. For exposed-coast faunal communities, the boundary between the Californian and Panamic provinces lies at approximately 23° N, near Cabo San Lucas; for embayment and protected-shore communities, it lies at about 28° N, near Isla Cedros and Bahía Sebastián Vizcaíno (J. W. Valentine 1961). The portion of the outer coast of Baja California between Isla Cedros and Cabo San Lucas is characterized by Californian molluscan species in exposed-coast biotopes and Panamic species in protected and embayed situations and has been named the Surian province (J. W. Valentine 1966). A similar set of provinces, based on the distribution of Holocene Ostracoda, has recently been recognized (P. C. Valentine 1976). The Surian province has a very small number of endemic, "index," mollusk species, of which none occur in the Discovery Point faunule. Moreover, Isla de Guadalupe lacks large embayments which, on the Baja California mainland, are reservoirs of typically Panamic species. Therefore, for the following analysis we recognize two zoogeographic groupings, designating as "Californian" those species which at present range north of Isla Cedros, and as "Panamic" those which range south of Cabo San Lucas (Table 1). Species whose modern ranges are entirely north of Isla Cedros or entirely south of Cabo San Lucas are listed in Table 2. Species which range both north and south of the Surian province are termed "biprovincial." The northern boundary of the Californian province lies near Point Conception, California, approximately 35° N. The southern boundary

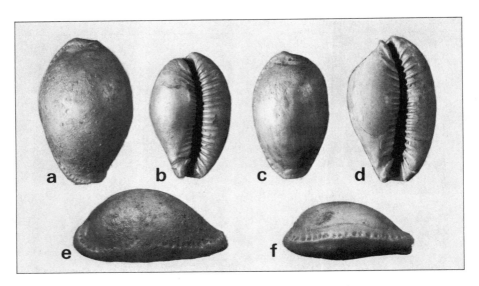

FIGURE 2. Cypraea cernica *Sowerby from Discovery Point Formation.*

of the Panamic province is stated by Keen (1971) to occur at Punta Aguja, Peru. In general, Panamic species are thermophilic, with their northward distribution limited by minimum temperatures. The southern distribution of Californian species is, conversely, presumed to be limited by maximum temperatures.

Several gastropod fragments and two entire specimens from six localities represent the only cowry known from the Discovery Point Formation and are referable to the Indo-Pacific *Cypraea (Erosaria) cernica* Sowerby 1870 (Fig. 2). The existence of *C. cernica* at Isla de Guadalupe during the Pleistocene represents an extension of over 3,200 km from its presently known distribution. The Recent range of *C. cernica* encompasses the entire Indo-Pacific region including Mauritius, Australia, New Caledonia, Okinawa, Japan, Hawaii, and the Tuamotu Archipelago (Burgess 1970). Despite the great distance involved this extension of range is not surprising considering the power of dispersal exhibited by *C. cernica* in attaining its present distribution. The Cypraeidae have a long pelagic larval stage and eleven Recent Indo-Pacific cypraeids (including two *Erosaria*) occur in the tropical eastern Pacific (Keen 1971). The currents available for transport of Recent Indo-Pacific species to the eastern Pacific have been discussed by Abbott (1966).

Indo-Pacific molluscan species (exclusive of opisthobranchs) known to occur in the Recent fauna of the tropical eastern Pacific have been summarized by Emerson (1978). Robertson (1976: 17) cautioned that "apparent novelties among eastern Pacific marine mollusks may be outliers from the Indo-West-Pacific that are already known." Conversely, it may be expected that some species described from the tropical eastern Pacific (especially the oceanic islands) will eventually be found in the Indo-Pacific region. The occurrence of *C. cernica* in the Pleistocene of Isla de Guadalupe emphasizes the necessity of considering the Indo-Pacific fauna when identifying fossil or Recent specimens from the eastern Pacific. (Kellogg [1976] reported *C. cernica* as the first Indo-Pacific mollusk recognized in the fossil record of the eastern Pacific. However, Bratcher and Burch [1971] synonymized *Hastula gnomon* Keen 1943, described from the Miocene of California, with *H. albula* [Menke 1843], an Indo-Pacific

FIGURE 3. *Exposure of Discovery Point Formation at Locality CASG 58718 containing large lava cobbles and detrital invertebrate remains.*

species also found in the Recent faunas of Isla Clarión and Isla Socorro, Mexico.)

The Discovery Point megafauna represents a mixture of intertidal and shallow subtidal, rocky shore communities. A rock substratum is indicated by the presence of species of *Haliotis, Collisella, Lottia, Chama,* and *Tetraclita.* An abundance of the hermatypic coral *Pocillopora guadalupensis* Durham, n. sp., indicates the proximity of substantial coral growth but not necessarily structural reef development. The genera *Codakia, Barbatia,* and *Ctena* were probably nestlers in pockets of sand. In aggregate, this faunal composition suggests a complex, outer coast environment with microhabitats ranging from protected to exposed. Comparable environments, with sand, coral, and rock substrata closely associated, are moderately widespread in the Recent Panamic province. Fossils from the Discovery Point Formation show no evidence of massive transport. The coral fragments are mostly abraded but in indentations on some specimens the calices are intact. Such wear and breakage as is apparent most likely resulted from local surf action rather than from transport over long distances. Faunal evidence indicates relatively little bathymetric displacement as well, since all taxa now live intertidally or at shallow subtidal depths. *Cypraea cernica* lives at depths of 12 to 183 m, but beach shells in excellent condition may be locally common (Cate 1960, 1962, Burgess 1970).

Part of the sample consists of beach rubble, perhaps displaced downslope through the effect of storm waves. Several unidentified polychaete tube casts, two specimens of the sessile gastropod *Hipponix cranioides,* and one *Chama squamuligera* are attached to a cobble which was probably dislodged from the intertidal zone. Specimens at Locality CASG 58718 were found embedded among lava cobbles (Fig. 3) such as compose many Recent beaches on Isla de Guadalupe.

In addition to the detrital megainvertebrate remains, a small microfauna occurs in the

Discovery Point Formation. Robert W. Crouch, who examined a sample from Locality SDMNH 2780, submits the following identifications:

Foraminiferida
  Cibicides fletcheri Galloway and Wissler
  Diocibicides biserialis Cushman and Valentine
  Gavelinopsis turbinata (Cushman and Valentine)
  Neoconorbina sp., cf. *N. terquemi* (Rzebak)
Coral fragments (much abraded)
Echinoid spines.

Concerning the foraminifera in the sample, Crouch comments (pers. comm. October, November 1977), "all have been recorded from this latitude (Recent) in water depths of 5 to 30 meters. The abraded corals are a different matter; they were no doubt buffeted by wave action and torn loose from the substrate and deposited in slightly deeper water below the wave influence. The forams, however, were preserved with no sign of abrasion." Absence of the foraminiferan genera *Bolivina* and *Uvigerina* indicates a maximum depth of deposition of less than 40 m. Deposition as shallow as 5 to 15 m is compatible with inferred Sangamon interglacial sea levels. The megafaunal evidence does not require deposition any deeper than this.

PALEOTEMPERATURES

An estimate of paleotemperatures during the depositional period of the Discovery Point Formation has been made from three lines of biological evidence: (1) the temperature range indicated by the extreme thermophilic and cryophilic mollusk species present in the faunule, (2) the thermophilic and cryophilic mollusk species taken in aggregate, and (3) the presence of the hermatypic coral, *Pocillopora guadalupensis* Durham, n. sp. (see Appendix). All proceed on the assumption that the thermal tolerances of these invertebrates were the same in the past as they are at present. The first method has been used for southern Californian Pleistocene faunas by J. W. Valentine and Meade (1961), who stated, "in a thermally mixed fossil assemblage the thermophilic species establish a lower limit to the maximum (effective) temperature. . . . That is, water temperatures must have been *at least* high enough during appropriate seasons to support the most warmth-loving species—the species least tolerant of low temperatures. Similarly, frigophilic [=cryophilic] species place an upper limit on the minimum temperature. Together the warm- and cool-water elements define the minimum temperature *range* represented by a fossil fauna."

In this case the method yields untenable results. *Mitra rupicola* appears to be the most critically thermophilic element in the Discovery Point faunule. Its Recent range extends from Panama to Ecuador (Keen 1971) and the lowest average annual minimum sea-surface temperature within this range is 20° C (Sverdrup *et al.* 1942). Cerohorsky (1976) synonymized *M. rupicola* with *Mitra muricata* (Broderip 1836). This extends the northern range of the *Mitra* from Panama (*M. rupicola*) to Cabo San Lucas (*M. muricata*) but does not affect our use of it as the most critically thermophilic element because the minimum sea-surface temperature experienced by the species occurs in the southern portion of its range. We interpret five species as the most critically cryophilic elements in the faunule: *Callistochiton palmulatus* and *Alvinia purpurea*, both with Recent ranges extending from Monterey, California, to Isla de Guadalupe (Smith 1963, as *C. palmulatus mirabilis*, a synonym of *C. palmulatus;* and Lindberg unpubl.), and three other species which are strictly Guadalupe endemics. The maximum sea-surface temperature within this range, to the nearest 1° C, is 20° C (Robinson 1973). Thus the minimum temperature suggested by the extreme thermophilic element is equal to the maximum temperature suggested by the extreme cryophilic elements. While this implies a single temperature at which the extreme elements could, hypothetically, coexist, we consider it unlikely that a

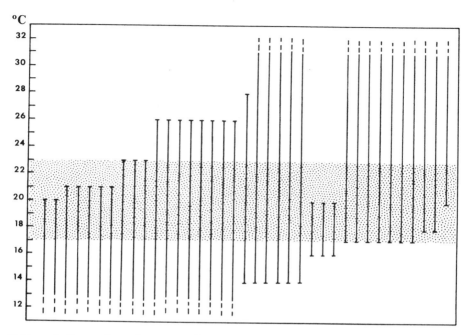

FIGURE 4. *Recent thermal ranges of 37 mollusk species in Discovery Point Formation and inferred annual paleotemperature range, to nearest 1° C (pattern). Temperature data from Robinson (1973) and Sverdrup et al. (1942); molluscan range data from various sources.*

thermal regime with no variation could have existed in the nearshore environment at Isla de Guadalupe.

If the extreme thermophilic and cryophilic elements are not separately considered, the thermophilic (Panamic) and cryophilic (Californian) mollusks taken in aggregate suggest a sea-surface temperature range of 17° to 23° C (Fig. 4). Only taxa identified to species are included in this analysis. Biprovincial species are excluded; their range end-points are not critical here. Ninety-two per cent of taxa considered have Recent ranges which include sea-surface temperatures of 17° to 20° C. Sixty-five per cent (81 per cent of thermophiles, 52 per cent of cryophiles) have Recent ranges spanning sea-surface temperatures of 17° to 23° C. Outside the latter limits, the number decreases sharply. Above 23° C only 38 per cent of the cryophilic species remain present; below 17° C only 44 per cent of the thermophilic species remain.

An important constraint on inferences drawn from this method is the observation (Hutchins 1947, P. C. Valentine 1976) that organisms are limited in distribution not only by survival temperatures but by a narrower temperature range within which repopulation (including reproduction and larval development) can occur. If the southward distribution of any of our cryophilic species is limited not by survival temperature but by winter repopulation temperature, it is possible that they could have existed on Isla de Guadalupe as nonreproducing waifs in a warmer environment than here inferred. Conversely, a cooler marine environment might support thermophilic waifs.

The proportion of Panamic and Californian species offers little help in choosing between the alternatives: Panamic and Californian forms are present in approximately equal numbers. Three of the Californian taxa are Guadalupe endemics, otherwise known only from the Recent fauna of the island. Unless they had a broader Pleistocene distribution which left no mainland fossil record, these could not be waifs from more northern regions. Yet, clearly, their limiting temperatures must be outside the range now reached at the island.

Squires (1959) states that, in tropical waters, active reef growth is largely confined to areas with a mean annual thermal range of 25° to 29° C (although component corals of the reefs may exist well outside these limits), and that 18° C is the minimum temperature at which a few hardy hermatypic corals may be present. Wells (1956) noted that a few hermatypic corals can live at temperatures as low as 15° C, but that most are found in waters above 18° C. Although the *Pocillopora* is abundant in the Discovery Point Formation samples, no reef structures were found, and there is no secondary evidence of true structural reef development (*e.g.*, more than one species of coral, or obligate reef-associated invertebrates). The coral growth may have been similar to, although less taxonomically diverse than, that currently present near El Pulmo, Baja California Sur, in the southern Gulf of California, where, according to Squires (1959), the coral community is locally concentrated on rock ledges and is dominant only in certain areas. Squires (*op. cit.*) cited an annual temperature range of 17° through 26° C for Bahía El Pulmo and suggested that for part of the year the water there is too cold for active reef growth.

In summary, the maximum sea-surface temperature suggested by 52 per cent of the cryophile Mollusca (23° C), the minimum temperature suggested by 81 per cent of the thermophile Mollusca (17° C) and the range of temperature suggested by the coral ($\geq$18° C, <25° C) lead us to infer an annual temperature range of 17° to 18° through 23° C for the nearshore waters of Isla de Guadalupe during the deposition of the Discovery Point Formation.

DISCUSSION

Comparison can be made with Recent thermal conditions, based on data from Robinson (1973). At Isla de Guadalupe, the late Sangamon annual minimum temperature was 1° to 2° C higher than the Recent annual minimum; the late Sangamon annual maximum temperature was 3° C higher than the Recent annual maximum. The late Sangamon annual temperature range was 5° to 6° C, slightly greater than the Recent annual range of 4° C. The Recent monthly temperature at Isla de Guadalupe averages 1.95° C higher than that along the Baja California mainland at the same latitude, and the annual range (4° C) is less than the mainland annual range (5° C). Similarly, the late Sangamon annual range (5° to 6° C) was the same or less than that inferred (J. W. Valentine 1961) for a comparable stretch of mainland coast in the late Pleistocene (6° C). The late Sangamon annual maximum temperature for Isla de Guadalupe was the same (23° C) indicated by J. W. Valentine (1961: fig. 13; "August" temperature) for this portion of the mainland coast in the late Pleistocene, and the late Sangamon annual minimum (17° to 18° C) was the same or one degree higher (J. W. Valentine *op. cit.*: fig. 11; "February" temperatures).

These comparisons suggest that the same general relationship between the marine thermal regime at Isla de Guadalupe and the mainland regime existed during Sangamon time as exists between the island and the peninsula today, except that temperatures averaged 2° to 3° C warmer. The insular regime during the late Sangamon was more equable than that along the mainland, as it is at present. Also as at present, this equability was expressed as a higher minimum annual temperature, such as occurs in the Recent during the spring months. The presence of seasonal upwelling near the mainland and its absence around Isla de Guadalupe (Dawson 1951, Emerson 1956) was probably the cause, then as now.

The discrepancy between insular and mainland temperatures today is most marked in May, when insular temperatures are 2.7° C higher, and is minimal in November, when temperatures are equal (data from Robinson 1973). The warmer Recent sea-surface temperatures in the vicinity of the island result from an offshore northward displacement of isotherms which begins in June and continues through October. The 18° C isotherm, which we theorize may not have moved south of Isla de Guadalupe (latitude 29° N) during the depositional period of the Discovery Point Formation, today stands north of the island from June through November. The most southerly Recent position of this isotherm is 25° N between the months of February and April. Thus a minimum northward shift of 4 degrees of latitude is necessary to accommodate Isla de Guadalupe south of the range of this isotherm throughout the year.

The partly Californian, partly Panamic, and dominantly Surian molluscan fauna of the Discovery Point Formation is unlike the faunas of other eastern Pacific islands or the mainland. Emerson (1967) summarized the provincial relationships of the Recent molluscan faunas of the tropical eastern Pacific oceanic islands. Cocos and the Galapagos Islands have molluscan faunas which belong to the Panamic molluscan province, as well as some endemic species and a few Indo-Pacific taxa. Clipperton Island mollusks are about half Panamic and half Indo-Pacific. The known fauna of the Islas Revillagigedos is largely Panamic with about 25 per cent Californian species.

The Recent marine molluscan fauna of Isla de Guadalupe belongs largely to the Californian province. According to the definitions employed above in the section on paleontology, 74.7 per cent of the Recent Mollusca are Californian, 19 per cent are biprovincial, and 6.3 per cent are Panamic (faunal list modified after Chace 1958; range data from several sources). Nine species, 5.6 per cent, are strictly endemic to the island and two others occur otherwise only in the Surian region of Baja California. One Indo-Pacific species, *Morula uva* (Röding 1798), is reported (Keen 1971). If present mainland distributions are considered indicative of source-areas for the Isla de Guadalupe marine fauna, approximately 80 per cent of the mollusk species could have colonized the island from southern California waters. Approximately 59 per cent could have had a Surian source.

Chace (1958: 322) considered 34 of 193 Recent mollusk species at Isla de Guadalupe to "belong to the Panamic Fauna, occurring on the mainland between San Diego and Panama." As noted earlier, for outer-coast mollusks the northern boundary of the Panamic province falls near Cabo San Lucas. By this criterion, only 17 of the Mollusca listed by Chace are exclusively Panamic. In addition, we question Chace's identification of "*Bursa calcipicta* Dall"; all specimens of *Bursa* which we have seen from Isla de Guadalupe are *Bursa californica* (Hinds 1843), which ranges from Monterey Bay, California, to the Gulf of California (McLean 1969). *Crenella megas* Dall, listed by Chace, is probably a synonym of *Megacrenella columbiana* (Dall 1897), which ranges north to the Aleutian Islands (Keen 1971) and was also included in Chace's faunal list. *Liotia heimi* Strong and Hertlein, said by Chace to be known only from Isla de Guadalupe and Panama, is a synonym of *Parviturbo stearnsii* (Dall 1918) (McLean *in* Keen 1971), which ranges north on the outer coast of Baja California to Isla Asunción. The occurrence of "*Cystiscus*" *minor* (Adams) at Isla de Guadalupe was not substantiated during later studies of Panamic Marginellidae (Coan and Roth 1966, Coan and Roth *in* Keen 1971). Some other identifications are questionable in light of later work (Keen 1971, Lindberg in prep.). This leaves only 10 species which do not otherwise range north of the Panamic province in the strict sense. None are reported to be common at Isla de Guadalupe. They do nevertheless establish the possibility of colonization of the island from Panamic sources. The rest of the taxa which have partly Panamic ranges also occur in the Surian region on the outer coast of Baja California. None of the extra-Surian Panamic species in the Recent fauna are present in the Discovery Point faunule.

Evolution of the molluscan fauna of Isla de Guadalupe from late Sangamon time to Recent has consisted of: (1) the local extinction of a number of major Panamic elements (species with part or all of their modern distribution south of the Surian region), and their replacement by

Californian elements; (2) the apparent extinction of at least one of the Californian species; and (3) the apparent introduction of many new Californian and a few Panamic province species. In addition, an unknown number of unrecorded introductions and extinctions must have occurred. At the same time the hermatypic coral biotope has disappeared. It is difficult to assess the effect of the coral's disappearance on the molluscan fauna because none of the mollusks in the Discovery Point faunule is known to be an obligate associate of coral. Thirty-two of the mollusk species known from the Recent fauna of the island have been recovered from the Discovery Point Formation (Table 1). All are either Californian or biprovincial. One conspicuous Californian province fossil mollusk, *Tegula eiseni* Jordan, is unknown in the Recent fauna of Isla de Guadalupe. Two others, *Barleeia haliotiphila* and *Barleeia subtenuis*, are unknown in the Recent fauna but may have been overlooked by collectors. None of the strictly Panamic species of the Discovery Point Formation occur in the island's Recent fauna. *Acanthina lugubris* (Sowerby) and *Haliotis cracherodii* Leach, two of the most conspicuous species in the Recent intertidal zone, are not known from the Discovery Point Formation. One Indo-Pacific species, *Cypraea cernica*, has become locally extinct; another, *Morula uva*, may have established itself.

Of particular interest among the mollusks which are present in both the Recent and fossil faunas are three taxa which are known only from Isla de Guadalupe: *Haliotis fulgens guadalupensis*, *Truncatella guadalupensis*, and *Lepidozona* n. sp. Because the chances are remote that these strictly insular endemics evolved, became locally extinct, and then were reintroduced to the island without leaving either surviving mainland populations or any trace in the rich mainland Pleistocene fossil record, they provide evidence for a core group of mollusks which were present on the island in Sangamon time and lasted through the Wisconsin glacial stage into the Holocene. The *Lepidozona* is morphologically most similar to the warm-temperate to boreal *Lepidozona mertensii* (Middendorff 1846) (A. J. Ferreira pers. comm.); and the *Haliotis* is a subspecies of the Californian *H. fulgens* Philippi 1845. *Truncatella guadalupensis* differs from *T. californica* Pfeiffer 1857, which ranges from southern California to the northern Gulf of California, in having a strong vertical rib or varix behind the outer lip and in details of suture and whorl proportion. It bears a striking resemblance to *T. succinea* C. B. Adams 1845 of the Caribbean area and *T. guerinii* Villa and Villa 1841, which is widespread in the Indo-Pacific region.

The Discovery Point faunule, therefore, may be thought of as having a "persistent" component—those taxa which survived on the island into Recent times—and a "transient" component—taxa now locally extinct. The "persistent" component, as already stated, consists entirely of Californian and biprovincial elements. These presumably were constitutionally better equipped to withstand the cooler marine conditions accompanying the Wisconsin glaciation, while the Panamic species and the coral, *Pocillopora*, were eliminated. During the Wisconsin glacial stage, temperatures probably dropped too low for survival of many thermophilic taxa. Also, with depression of the isotherms during this stage the mainland ranges of many thermophiles must have retreated southward; any taxa which had existed on Isla de Guadalupe only as nonreproducing waifs might no longer have received recruitment from their original sources.

The "transient" component consists mainly of thermophiles, but also includes *Tegula eiseni* and possibly *Barleeia haliotiphila* and *B. subtenuis*. Why these Californian species should have become locally extinct is not clear. Ten of the fourteen neogastropods in the Discovery Point faunule are "transient"; so are six of the eight bivalves. Any hypothesis which seeks to explain the extinction in ecological/trophic terms has to account for a similar response in these two ecologically and trophically dissimilar groups. By contrast only one of twelve archaeogastropod taxa became locally extinct. Some species may have been very short-term transients, like the southern spiny lobster *Panulirus gracilis* Streets 1871 observed by Hubbs (1967), and introduced during periodic local and temporary current changes. Zinsmeister (1974) gave criteria for recognizing such species in fossil assemblages. His criteria *2* and *3* are not met by any species in the Discovery Point faunule; his criterion *1* requires a larger sample than is now available.

Isla de Guadalupe has been capable of supporting a shallow-water marine fauna since at least the late Miocene. At that time the deterioration of widespread tropical thermal regimes which characterized the later Tertiary and Quaternary periods (Durham 1950, Addicott 1969) was not as far advanced as at present. Since its beginning as an island, Isla de Guadalupe has come under the influence of alternating tropical, temperate, and subarctic water masses (Ingle 1973: fig. 4). The southward flow of the California Current was the dominant oceanographic factor throughout this interval, as it has been since at least the Cretaceous period (Sliter 1972). Superimposed thereon are climatic oscillations with isotherms shifting north and south along the coast, their migrations detectable by the composition of the megafossil and microfossil records. For most of its history, Isla de Guadalupe has been within the zone of tropical-subtropical planktonic foraminiferal biofacies (Ingle *loc. cit.*), corresponding to waters 20° C and warmer. Under these conditions the shallow-water invertebrate fauna would have been predominantly "Panamic" (remembering that at these times the northern boundaries of the proto-Panamic province were well north of their present positions).

Subsequent cooling, the incursion of first temperate and finally subarctic waters, caused the local extinction of many Panamic forms and their replacement by cryophiles. This may have occurred gradually but more likely in a series of pulses, of which the transition from Sangamon to Recent faunas is only the latest and possibly the most dramatic. Each extinction altered the community composition of the fauna and hence the possibilities of establishment of new taxa. In between cold pulses, local warming may have allowed re-establishment of certain Panamic taxa (such as the 10 tropical species on the island today), their success or failure at colonization depending at least partly on the existing community makeup of the insular fauna.

SUMMARY

Marine invertebrate fossils, mainly mollusks, occur in a superficial deposit, the Discovery Point Formation, around the periphery of Isla de Guadalupe. The fossiliferous sediments grade laterally from conglomerate containing volcanic pebbles to a biostrome formed chiefly of hermatypic coral fragments and mollusk shells. Radiometric dating indicates a Sangamon interglacial age. The deposit apparently was laid down at shallow subtidal depths on irregular volcanic basement; a component interpreted as beach rubble is present.

More than 80 per cent of the taxa occur today on the Baja California mainland between Isla Cedros (28° N) and Cabo San Lucas (23° N); others are extralimital, either north or south. One gastropod species and a hermatypic coral, both now extinct on Isla de Guadalupe, have Indo-Pacific affinities. The faunule suggests a complex, outer-coast environment. Modern thermal tolerances of the invertebrates suggest late Sangamon marine temperatures 1° to 3° C higher than Recent, with an annual range of 5° to 6° C (compared to 4° C Recent range): more equable than the climate inferred for the adjacent mainland, probably because of the absence of upwelling.

The Recent marine molluscan fauna of Isla de Guadalupe is largely Californian. Evolution of the island's molluscan fauna from late Sangamon to Recent time has consisted of the local extinction of major tropical elements and their replacement by Californian forms, the apparent extinction of at least one conspicuous Californian species, and the apparent introduction of many new Californian and a few Panamic province species.

ACKNOWLEDGMENTS

We are grateful to Arnold Ross (formerly of San Diego Museum of Natural History) who made available the SDMNH fossil material and supplied valued procedural advice; E. C. Wilson (Los Angeles County Museum of Natural History) who worked on an earlier version of the manuscript and offered many helpful suggestions; W. K. Emerson (American Museum of Natural History) for encouragement and constructive criticism; J. W. Durham (University of California Museum of Paleontology) for consultation and critique of the text; and R. W. Crouch (Los Osos, Calif.) who kindly contributed identifications and interpretation of microfossils. We gratefully acknowledge the aid of the following individuals who loaned material, identified specimens, or otherwise advised us concerning their various specialties: R. Batiza, C. N. Cate, E. P. Chace, D. D. Chivers, A. J. Ferreira, A. M. Keen, P. I. LaFollette, J. H. McLean, P. U. Rodda, the late G. E. Radwin, G. G. Sphon, R. R. Talmadge, and D. W. Taylor.

REFERENCES

ABBOTT, D. P. 1966. Factors influencing the zoogeographic affinities of the Galapagos inshore marine fauna. Pp. 108-122 *in* R. L. Bowman, ed., The Galapagos. University of California Press, Berkeley and Los Angeles, Calif.

ADDICOTT, W. O. 1969. Tertiary climatic change in the marginal northeastern Pacific Ocean. Science 165:583-586.

BATIZA, R. 1977. Petrology and chemistry of Guadalupe Island: An alkalic seamount on a fossil ridge crest. Geology 5:760-764.

BERGGREN, W. A., and J. A. VAN COUVERING. 1974. The late Neogene, biostratigraphy, geochronology and paleoclimatology of the last 15 million years in marine and continental sequences. Elsevier Sci. Publ. Co., Amsterdam.

BRATCHER, T., and R. D. BURCH. 1971. The Terebridae (Gastropoda) of Clarion, Socorro, Cocos, and Galapagos Islands. Proc. California Acad. Sci., ser. 4, 37:537-566.

BURGESS, C. M. 1970. The living cowries. A. S. Barnes and Co., New York, N.Y.

BUTZER, K. W., and J. CUERDA. 1962. Coastal stratigraphy of southern Mallorca and its implications for the Pleistocene chronology of the Mediterranean Sea. J. Geol. 70:398-416.

CATE, C. N. 1960. A new Hawaiian subspecies of *Cypraea cernica* Sowerby. Veliger 3:3-7.

———. 1962. A new Dampierian *Cypraea*. Veliger 4:175-177.

CERNOHORSKY, W. O. 1976. The Mitridae of the world. Part I. The subfamily Mitrinae. Indo-Pacific Mollusca 3:273-528.

CHACE, E. P. 1958. The marine molluscan fauna of Guadalupe Island, Mexico. Trans. San Diego Soc. Nat. Hist. 12:319-332.

COAN, E. V., and B. ROTH. 1966. The west American Marginellidae. Veliger 8:276-299.

DAWSON, E. Y. 1951. A further study of upwelling and associated vegetation along Pacific Baja California, Mexico. J. Marine Res. 10:39-58.

DOYLE, L. J., and D. S. GORSLINE. 1977. Marine geology of Baja California Continental Borderland, Mexico. Amer. Assoc. Petrol. Geol. Bull. 61:903-917.

DURHAM, J. W. 1950. Cenozoic marine climates of the Pacific Coast. Geol. Soc. Amer. Bull. 61:1243-1264.

———. 1980. A new fossil *Pocillopora* (Coral) from Guadalupe Island, Mexico. Pp. 63-70 *in* D.M. Power, ed., The California Islands: proceedings of a multidisciplinary symposium. Santa Barbara Museum of Natural History, Santa Barbara, Calif.

EMERSON, W. K. 1956. Upwelling and associated marine life along Pacific Baja California, Mexico. J. Paleontol. 30:393-397.

————. 1967. Indo-Pacific faunal elements in the tropical eastern Pacific, with special reference to the mollusks. Venus 25:85-93.

————. 1978. Mollusks with Indo-Pacific faunal affinities in the eastern Pacific Ocean. Nautilus 92:91-96.

ENGEL, A. E. J., and C. G. ENGEL. 1971. Mafic and ultramafic rocks. In The sea, v.3. Wiley-Interscience, New York, N.Y.

FANALE, F. P., and O. A. SCHAEFFER. 1965. Helium-uranium ratios for Pleistocene and Tertiary fossil aragonites. Science 149:312-317.

FLINT, R. F. 1971. Glacial and Quaternary geology. John Wiley & Sons, New York, N.Y.

GOLDBERG, E. D. 1965. An observation on marine sedimentation rates during the Pleistocene. Limnol. and Oceanogr. 10, suppl:R125-R128.

HEUSSER, C. J. 1960. Late-Pleistocene environment of North Pacific North America. Amer. Geog. Soc. Spec. Pub. 35:1-308.

HOPKINS, D. M. 1967. Quaternary marine transgressions in Alaska. Pp. 47-90 in D. M. Hopkins, ed., The Bering land bridge. Stanford University Press, Stanford, Calif.

HUBBS, C. L. 1960. Quaternary paleoclimatology of the Pacific coast of North America. Calif. Coop. Ocean. Fish. Inv. Rep. 7:105-112.

————. 1967. A discussion of the geochronology and archeology of the California Islands. Pp. 337-341 in R. N. Philbrick, ed., Proceedings of the symposium on the biology of the California Islands. Santa Barbara Botanic Garden, Santa Barbara, Calif.

HUBBS, C. L., and J. R. JEHL, JR. 1976. Remains of Pleistocene birds from Isla de Guadalupe, Mexico. Condor 78:421-422.

HUTCHINS, L. W. 1947. The bases for temperature zonation in geographical distribution. Ecol. Monogrs. 17:325-335.

INGLE, J. C. 1973. Summary comments on Neogene biostratigraphy, physical stratigraphy, and paleo-oceanography in the marginal northeastern Pacific Ocean. Init. Rep. Deep Sea Drill. Proj. 18:949-960.

JOHNSON, C. W. 1953. Notes on the geology of Guadalupe Island, Mexico. Amer. J. Sci. 251:231-236.

KEEN, A. M. 1971. Sea shells of tropical west America. Marine mollusks from Baja California to Peru. Stanford University Press, Stanford, Calif.

KELLOGG, M. G. 1976. A cowrie from the late Pleistocene of Isla Guadalupe, Mexico. West. Soc. Malacol. Ann. Rep. 9:43-44.

LAJOIE, K. R., J. F. WEHMILLER, K. A. KVENVOLDEN, E. PETERSON, and R. H. WRIGHT. 1975. Correlation of California marine terraces by amino-acid stereochemistry. Geol. Soc. Amer. Abstr. with Prog. 7:338-339.

LAND, L. S., F. T. MACKENZIE, and S. J. GOULD. 1967. Pleistocene history of Bermuda. Geol. Soc. Amer. Bull. 78:993-1006.

LIPPS, J. H., J. W. VALENTINE, and E. MITCHELL. 1968. Pleistocene paleoecology and biostratigraphy, Santa Barbara Island, California. J. Paleontol. 42:291-307.

McLEAN, J. H. 1969. Marine shells of southern California. Los Angeles Co. Mus. Nat. Hist. Sci. Ser. 24, Zool. 11:1-104.

MENARD, H. W. 1955. Deformation of the northeastern Pacific basin and the west coast of North America. Geol. Soc. Amer. Bull. 66:1149-1198.

MILLIMAN, J. D., and K. O. EMERY. 1968. Sea levels during the past 35,000 years. Science 162:1121-1123.

OAKS, R. Q., JR. 1965. Post-Miocene stratigraphy and morphology, outer coastal plain, southeastern Virginia. Ph.D. thesis, Yale University, New Haven, Conn.

ROBERTSON, R. 1976. *Heliacus trochoides*: An Indo-West-Pacific architectonicid newly found in the eastern Pacific (mainland Ecuador). Veliger 19:13-18.

ROBINSON, M. K. 1973. Atlas of monthly mean seasurface and subsurface temperatures in the Gulf of California, Mexico. San Diego Soc. Nat. Hist. Mem. 5:1-97.

SLITER, W. V. 1972. Upper Cretaceous planktonic forminiferal zoogeography and ecology— eastern Pacific margin. Paleogeogr. Paleoclim. Paleoecol. 12:15-31.

SMITH, A. G. 1963. A revised list of chitons from Guadelupe Island, Mexico (Mollusca: Polyplacophora). Veliger 5:147-149.

SQUIRES, D. F. 1959. Corals and coral reefs in the Gulf of California. Bull. Amer. Mus. Nat. Hist. 118:367-432.

SVERDRUP, H. U., M. W. JOHNSON, and R. H. FLEMING. 1942. The oceans, their physics, chemistry, and general biology. Prentice-Hall, New York, N.Y.

VALENTINE, J. W. 1961. Paleoecologic molluscan geography of the Californian Pleistocene. Univ. California Pub. Geol. Sci. 34:309-442.

————. 1966. Numerical analysis of marine molluscan ranges on the extratropical northeastern Pacific shelf. Limnol. and Oceanogr. 11:198-211.

VALENTINE, J. W., and R. F. MEADE. 1961. Californian Pleistocene paleotemperatures. Univ. California Pub. Geol. Sci. 40:1-46.

VALENTINE, J. W., and H. H. VEEH. 1969. Radiometric ages of Pleistocene terraces from San Nicolas Island, California. Geol. Soc. Amer. Bull. 80:1415-1418.

VALENTINE, P. C. 1976. Zoogeography of Holocene Ostracoda off western North America and paleoclimatic implications. U. S. Geol. Surv. Prof. Pap. 916:1-47.

VEEH, H. H., and J. W. VALENTINE. 1967. Radiometric ages of Pleistocene fossils from Cayucos, California. Geol. Soc. Amer. Bull. 78:547-550.

WELLS, J. W. 1956. Scleractinia. Pp. F328-F444 *in* R. C. Moore, ed., Treatise on invertebrate paleontology, Part F. Geological Society of America and University of Kansas Press, Lawrence, Kan.

ZINSMEISTER, W. J. 1974. A new interpretation of thermally anomalous molluscan assemblages of the California Pleistocene. J. Paleontol. 48:84-94.

APPENDIX
A New Fossil *Pocillopora* (Coral) from Guadalupe Island, Mexico

J. Wyatt Durham

Department of Paleontology, University of California,
Berkeley, California 94720

In late 1957, Carl L. Hubbs of the Scripps Institution of Oceanography, in company with Emery P. Chace, discovered a fossiliferous deposit on Guadalupe Island and collected numerous fossils. Among the fossils was a hermatypic coral which was forwarded to me by Hubbs. The coral was identified as belonging to the genus *Pocillopora* at that time and later mentioned as "reef coral" by Hubbs (1967). Other small collections subsequently made by Hubbs and various associates as well as by David R. Lindberg have also been deposited in the collections of the Museum of Paleontology at the University of California, Berkeley (UCMP). Coral material was also deposited at various times in the Natural History Museum of the San Diego Society of Natural History. Chace independently forwarded a specimen of the coral to Donald F. Squires who subsequently (Squires 1959) also identified it as a *Pocillopora*. About a decade ago the coral was identified as a new species by E. C. Wilson, now at the Los Angeles County Museum of Natural History. He has generously made all his data available to me in preparing the present description. The coral is particularly important because it represents the northernmost extent of the range of hermatypic corals known for the outer coast of North America during the Pleistocene and because it is more closely related to central and western Pacific species of *Pocillopora* than to the more southeastern Pacific species of the genus.

SYSTEMATIC DESCRIPTION
Order SCLERACTINIA Bourne
Family POCILLOPORIDAE Gray
Genus *Pocillopora* Lamarck
Pocillopora guadalupensis n. sp.
Plates 1, 2

Pocillopora [sp.] Squires, 1959, p. 309; Hubbs and Jehl, 1976, p. 421; "reef coral," Hubbs, 1967, p. 340.

Corallum usually ramose, rarely massive; in ramose forms branches usually heavy, varying from flattened to terete, terminations irregular; verrucae usually absent but a few broken branches have scattered heavy verrucae near the ends; calices deep, varying from about 0.5 mm to 1 mm in diameter; spacing of calices variable, in flattened areas usually distant about one-fourth to one-half a diameter but sometimes on ends of branches with only a common wall between them; on massive branches occasional calices distant more than a diameter from one another; 12 prominent septa present, usually extending nearly halfway to columella; very rarely a calice with 24 septa; columella prominent, usually styliform but sometimes slightly flattened, situated on well-developed directive septum, extending nearly halfway to surface; intercalicular surface with numerous prominent, usually pointed but sometimes flattened spinules; adcalicular spinules usually forming a slightly raised rim around calice.

Dimensions. —Holotype (UCMP-14544, pl. 1, fig. 7) a broken branch with terete branchlets (most typical morphology), height 98 mm, basal diameter about 26 mm; paratype (UCMP-14545, pl. 1, fig. 5), end of branch with flattened, heavy branchlets, height about 69 mm, diameter of basal broken surface, about 21 mm; paratype (UCMP-14551, pl. 1, fig. 1), a fragmentary branch with nodose verrucae (not typical of most specimens), height 54 mm, basal diameter 14 by 17 mm; paratype (UCMP-14553, pl. 2, fig. 2) a massive corallum, somewhat meandroid on top, height about 88 mm, about 80 by 87 mm at base; paratype (UCMP-14549,

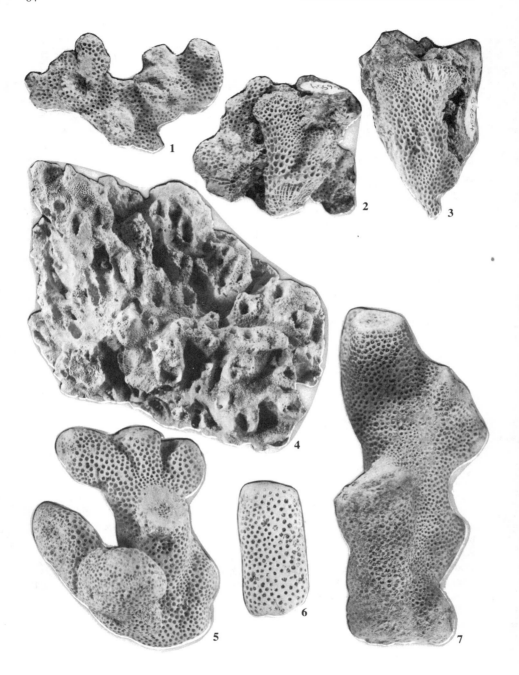

pl. 1, fig. 6), a fragment of an elongate terete branch, height 37.5 mm, maximum diameter 12.7 mm; paratype (UCMP-14558, pl. 2, fig. 5), a fragmentary atypical specimen with numerous small broken branchlets, calices and surface detail very well preserved, height 82.5 mm; paratype (UCMP-14554) with abraded flattened base, worn, massive, maximum diameter about 295 mm, height about 210 mm (second largest available specimen); paratype (San Diego Society of Natural History no. 19042, pl. 1, fig. 4), a worn, massive corallum, originally with tall meandroid branches, height about 335 mm, maximum diameter about 315 mm.

Materials.—Very numerous fragments and incomplete specimens (all representing the same species) in the collections of the Museum of Paleontology, University of California, Berkeley (UCMP localities B-6554, B-7336, D-1547, D-1548, D-1549, D-7297) and the Natural History Museum of San Diego Society of Natural History (locs. 0633 to 0635, 0637 to 0639, 0642 to 0644, 2233, 2234, 2464, 2465, 2470).

Types.—All designated types, except one paratype, are in the University of California Museum of Paleontology (UCMP) invertebrate collections: Holotype UCMP-14544, loc. B-6554; paratypes UCMP-14545, 14547, 14550, 14551, and 14554, all from loc. B-6554; paratype UCMP-14548, loc. B-7336; paratype UCMP-14646, 14549, 14552, 14553, all from loc. D-7297; paratype in San Diego Soc. Nat. Hist. Mus. no. 19042, their loc. 0633.

Comparisons.—The calicular characters of this species are very suggestive of *Pocillopora ligulata* Dana and its allies (*P. eydouxi* Milne-Edwards and Haime, *P. modumanensis* Vaughan, and *P. woodjonesi* Vaughan) but it is distinguished from them by the abundant verrucae of those species and their common absence on the Guadalupe Island specimens. On the available specimens of *P. ligulata* from the Hawaiian Islands the septa are usually slightly shorter than on the new species.

Taxonomy and nomenclature of the species of *Pocillopora* known from the eastern Pacific have varied considerably in the last three decades (see: Durham 1947, 1966; Durham and Barnard 1952; Glynn 1974; Glynn and Stewart 1973; Glynn, Stewart, and McCosker 1972; Porter 1972) and are still in a state of flux. In my earlier papers (Durham 1947; Durham and Barnard 1952) I employed a regional nomenclature largely based on the work of Verrill. Subsequently Squires (1959), using a more conservative taxonomy, considered the eastern Pacific taxa to be conspecific with central and western Pacific species and used their names (which had priority) for the species described by Verrill. For a few years (see Durham 1966) I used the nomenclature adopted by Squires but further studies caused me to largely revert to the earlier nomenclature (see identifications in Glynn, Stewart, and McCosker 1972 and Porter 1972). As a consequence the following names (some of which may be synonyms) have been employed for species and subspecies of *Pocillopora* from the eastern Pacific: *bulbosa* Ehrenberg 1834; *capitata* Verrill 1864; *cespitosa* Dana 1846; *damicornis* (Linnaeus) 1758; *elegans*

PLATE 1. *Pocillopora guadalupensis Durham, n. sp. Figures 1-3, 5-7, x1.0; Figure 4, x0.34.* FIGURE 1, *paratype UCMP 14551, loc. B-6554, atypical branch with nodose verrucae (tips broken).* FIGURE 2, *paratype UCMP 14547, loc. B-6554, three near-terminal fragments in matrix, central one flattened, with complete apex.* FIGURE 3, *paratype UCMP 14550, loc. B-6554, flattened termination of branch in matrix.* FIGURE 4, *paratype San Diego Soc. Nat. Hist. no. 19042, loc. 0633, a large, massive, eroded corallum, tops of branches removed.* FIGURE 5, *paratype UCMP 14545, loc. B-6554, branch with heavy, somewhat flattened branchlets—detail of Plate 2, Figure 1 from near center of basal frontal area.* FIGURE 6, *paratype UCMP 14549, loc. D-7297, fragment of terete branch.* FIGURE 7, *holotype UCMP 14544, loc. B-6554, part of a typical heavy branch, many Dexiospira tubes in calices (only a few calices well preserved).*

66

GUADALUPE INVERTEBRATE FOSSILS

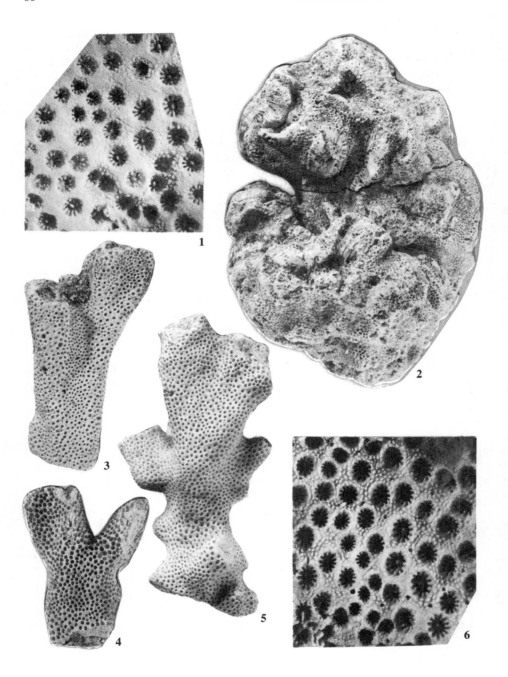

Dana 1846; *lacera* Verrill 1869; *meandrina* Dana 1846; *nobilis* Verrill 1864; *palmata* Palmer 1928; *porosa* Verrill 1869; *pumila* Verrill 1870; *robusta* Verrill 1870; *verrucosa* (Ellis and Solander) 1786.

The Museum of Paleontology coral collections contain representatives of nearly all the nominal taxa listed above and include material (in part fossil) from Nasca Ridge, Galapagos Islands, Panama, Cocos Island, western Mexico, Gulf of California, Clipperton Atoll, and Guadalupe Island. The Guadalupe Island *Pocillopora* has been compared with specimens from all these areas and is clearly distinct from all of them, being characterized by the usual absence of verrucae and the consistent presence of 12 well-developed septa and a prominent columella. The nominal species listed above consistently have well-developed verrucae and most specimens have the septa and columella poorly developed and sometimes absent. The Guadalupe Island species is more closely related to *P. ligulata* and its allies from the central and western Pacific than to the eastern Pacific species. This relationship seems strange, but is perhaps to be explained by the isolated geographic position of Guadalupe Island. The island is of volcanic origin, about 275 km offshore from Baja California and 1,100 km northwest of the nearest known eastern Pacific outer coast (exclusive of Gulf of California) occurrence of *Pocillopora* (both Pleistocene and Recent). Hubbs (1967) reports a radiometric date of about 7 million years from the volcanic rocks of which the island is formed, indicating that it has been in existence since the late Miocene, thus affording ample time for chance colonization from a central or western Pacific source and subsequent local evolution.

Glynn and Stewart (1973) in a study (largely based on *Pocillopora damicornis*) on the distribution of coral reefs in the Pearl Islands (Gulf of Panama) concluded that minimum temperatures of 20° to 21° C had a debilitating effect on the growth of coral. Inasmuch as coral reefs have not been recognized in the Guadalupe Island deposits, it seems probable that the mean surface water temperatures at the time the *Pocillopora* existed were slightly above 20° to 21° C. Glynn, Stewart, and McCosker (1972: fig. 8) observed that the various species of *Pocillopora* in the Panama area occurred to a depth of about 33 m, but were most abundant in "shallow depths." This suggests that the Guadalupe Island species probably lived at quite shallow depths inasmuch as the locality was apparently at the extreme northern margin of the habitable area for the genus *Pocillopora*.

Glynn (1974), working in the Gulf of Panama, described unattached mobile colonies of the hermatypic coral genera *Pavona*, *Porites*, and *Agariciella*, characterized by a high sphericity and proposed the term "corallith" for them. He presented evidence suggesting that most of the movement of the colonies was caused by browsing fish. He observed that colonies with this characteristic morphology are found in various other scleractinian genera as well as the Paleozoic tabulate coral *Favosites*. He also noted (p. 196) that "unattached colonies of

---

PLATE 2. Pocillopora guadalupensis *Durham, n. sp. Figures 1 and 6, approximately x10; Figure 2, approximately x0.83; Figures 3-5, x1.0.* FIGURE 1, *paratype UCMP 14545, loc. B-6554, enlargement of slightly eroded area, displaying septal pattern, near base of same specimen as Plate 1, Figure 5—contrast with uneroded surface detail in Figure 6.* FIGURE 2, *paratype UCMP 14553, loc. D-7297, a corallith sensu Glynn (1974).* FIGURE 3, *paratype UCMP 14546, loc. D-7297, fragment of branch, dividing at top.* FIGURE 4, *paratype UCMP 14548, loc. B-7336, part of branch with flattened cross-section.* FIGURE 5, *paratype UCMP 14558, loc. D-1549, branch with many more branchlets than usual, only rare suggestions of verrucae, surface detail mostly very well preserved.* FIGURE 6, *paratype UCMP 14552, loc. D-7297, uneroded surface showing spinules—compare with slightly eroded surface in Figure 1 where septal pattern is well displayed.*

Pocillopora move in a tumbling fashion with relative ease." One of the larger paratypes (UCMP-14553, pl. 2, fig. 2) of the Guadalupe Island species appears to fall within the corallith concept. No attachment area can be recognized and calices are present on all surfaces except where post-mortem abrasion has occurred, indicating that the colony had rotated considerably during life so that polyps had been able to maintain themselves. The gross shape is a somewhat elongated hemisphere, with the apparent lower surface much less convex than the upper. Incipient stubby meandrine branches are present on the "upper" surface, indicating that it was uppermost for longer intervals than the "lower" surface. In the Gulf of Panama the coralliths usually occur in depths of 5 to 9 m, below mean lower low water, just below the zone of coral reefs. Thus there is a suggestion that the Guadalupe Island specimen lived in a similar shallow depth.

The genus *Pocillopora* is now living only in the Pacific and Indian Oceans although during the mid-Cenozoic it had a pantropical distribution. Recently Geister (1977) has shown that a species of *Pocillopora* was widely distributed in late Pleistocene deposits of the Caribbean and that the genus was seemingly absent during the earlier Pleistocene and much of the Pliocene. A significant number of radiometric dates is available from the deposits in which the genus occurs and show that no occurrences are older than about 120,000 years B.P. Ages as young as 26,020 ±675 and 39,550 to 31,500 years B.P. have been reported for two low terrace occurrences, but other data suggest that these may be minimum ages only. At least some of these Caribbean occurrences are thus synchronous with the occurrence of *Pocillopora* on Guadalupe Island. Geister previously (1975) had designated the Pleistocene *Pocillopora* from San Andrés Island (Caribbean) as *P.* cf. *palmata* Palmer but in his 1977 discussion he avoids using a specific name and merely notes that the Caribbean form "closely resembles" *P. palmata*. Squires (1959) concluded that the Guadalupe Island species was closely related to *P. palmata* Palmer which he felt should not be included within the concept of *P. robusta* Verrill (a synonym of *P. elegans* Dana according to Squires) as I (Durham 1947) had done. Geister (1977) likewise concluded that *P. palmata* Palmer was a part of the *P. robusta-P. elegans* complex but left the specific nomenclature of the Caribbean Pleistocene species open until a better understanding of the taxonomy of the genus is available. One "cotype" of *P. palmata* Palmer (original of his pl. 11, fig. 2) is in the Museum of Paleontology collections (UCMP no. 30326). Although Palmer (1928) described his species as having six septa, the calices, where not weathered, on this "syntype" consistently show a prominent columella and 12 septa, substantiating Squires' suggestion that *P. palmata* should be compared with *P. eydouxi* and *P. woodjonesi*. To avoid future confusion, the specimen in the Museum of Paleontology (no. 30326) is here designated the lectotype of *P. palmata* Palmer (1928). At this time the relationship to the Caribbean species is uncertain but in contrast to Geister's description (1977) of his species as having one to two calices per verruca, the lectotype of *P. palmata* has from three to six calices per verruca.

Geister (1977) notes that I had informed him that *Pocillopora* was a member of the eastern Pacific fauna during the Pliocene. This conclusion is based on the occurrence of *Pocillopora* in late Pliocene-early Pleistocene terrace deposits in the Galapagos Islands, and on its occurrence as fossil on an unnamed guyot on Nasca Ridge about 1,540 km west of the coast of Chile. The Nasca Ridge occurrence (long. 85° 25' W, lat. 25° 44' S) is from a dredge haul from depths between 210 and 227 m (over twice the depth at which hermatypic corals can live). It was reported by Allison, Durham, and Mintz (1967) where the occurrence was given a probable Miocene age on the basis of a shipboard coral identification (*Plesiastrea*) from a nearby locality by J. W. Wells. Unfortunately the specimen on which Wells' determination was made was subsequently lost in the mail. The fossil material reported in Allison, Durham, and Mintz is now given UCMP loc. D-7298 rather than B-6555 (now reserved for Recent organisms only) as cited in that publication. The fossil corals include

Pocillopora sp., UCMP hypotype no. 14555

Porites sp., UCMP hypotype no. 14560-a, b, c

Leptoseris (?) sp., UCMP hypotype no. 14577, frondose, unifacial.

A fourth coral, "*Stylophora* (?fossil)," was included in the 1967 list. Numerous incipient colonies of this coral are growing on the *Porites* but are of obviously younger age (Recent?). J. W. Wells (pers. comm., 12-3-74) informs me that this coral is referrable to *Madracis* [*Madracis* sp. cf. *M. pharensis* (Heller)] (UCMP hypotype no. 14559). Plate tectonics suggest that the age of the fossils could equally well be either Pliocene or Miocene.

The fossil *Pocillopora* from the Galapagos Islands is from locality UCMP B-3595 on Baltra Island. It (hypotype UCMP no. 14556) is an external mold, clearly assignable to *Pocillopora*, collected from a bed unconformably beneath a lava flow which Cox and Dalrymple (1966: table 2, sample G 30) assigned to the Matuyama reversed magnetic polarity epoch. The Matuyama epoch had a duration of about 700,000 to nearly 2,500,000 years, so it is obvious that this *Pocillopora* occurrence is either of early Pleistocene or Pliocene age. Although the evidence is scanty, it demonstrates the existence of *Pocillopora* in the eastern Pacific prior to the late Pleistocene (Sangamon) occurrence on Guadalupe Island and together with the Nasca Ridge occurrence indicates that the genus has been a continuous member of the eastern Pacific biota since at least the middle Cenozoic.

Notwithstanding this history, the characteristics of the Guadalupe Island *Pocillopora* suggest that it represents an invasion of the eastern Pacific by a different stock of the genus than that present in the more southern parts of the eastern Pacific. The lectotype of *P. palmata* Palmer designated above is described as coming from Pleistocene terrace deposits (Palmer 1928: 22 and legend to pl. 2, fig. 2) along the Mexican coast near Escondido Bay, Oaxaca. Although *P. palmata* is a distinct species, its septal characteristics show that it is also related to the *P. ligulata* group of species and it is suggested that it might represent a local colonization at the same time as the Guadalupe Island invasion. Thus it is tempting to suggest that the Puerto Escondido terrace is of the same age (Pleistocene: Sangamon) as the 2,500 km-distant Guadalupe Island deposits.

REFERENCES

ALLISON, E. C., J. W. DURHAM, and L. W. MINTZ. 1967. New southeast Pacific echinoids. Occas. Pap. California Acad. Sci. 62:1-23.

COX, A., and G. B. DALRYMPLE. 1966. Paleomagnetism and potassium-argon ages of some volcanic rocks from the Galapagos Islands. Nature 209:776-777.

DURHAM, J. W. 1947. Corals from the Gulf of California and the north Pacific coast of America. Geol. Soc. Amer. Mem. 20:1-68.

——————. 1966. Coelenterates, especially stony corals, from the Galapagos and Cocos Islands. Pp. 123-135 *in* R. L. Bowman, ed., The Galapagos. University of California Press, Berkeley and Los Angeles, Calif.

DURHAM, J. W., and J. L. BARNARD. 1952. Stony corals of the eastern Pacific collected by the *Velero III* and *Velero IV*. Allan Hancock Pac. Exped. 16:1-110.

GEISTER, J. 1975. Riffbau und geologische Entwickelungs-geschichte der Insel San Andres (westliches Karibisches meer, Kolumbien). Stuttgart Beitr. Naturk., Ser. B, 15:1-203.

——————. 1977. Occurrence of *Pocillopora* in late Pleistocene Caribbean coral reefs. Pp. 378-388 *in* Second Symposium international sur les coraux et récifs coralliens fossils. Paris, Sept. 1975. B. R. G. M. (Paris) Mem. 89.

GLYNN, P. W. 1974. Rolling stones among the Scleractinia: mobile coralliths in the Gulf of Panama. Proc. Second Internat. Coral Reef Symp. 2:183-198.

GLYNN, P. W., and R. H. STEWART. 1973. Distribution of coral reefs in the Pearl Islands (Gulf of Panama) in relation to thermal conditions. Limnol. and Oceanogr. 18:367-379.

GLYNN, P. W., R. H. STEWART, and J. C. MCCOSKER. 1972. Pacific coral reefs of Panama: structure, distribution and predators. Geol. Rundschau 61:483-519.

HUBBS, C. L. 1967. A discussion of the geochronology and archeology of the California Islands. Pp. 337-341 *in* R. N. Philbrick, ed., Proceedings of the symposium on the biology of the California Islands. Santa Barbara Botanic Garden, Santa Barbara, Calif.

HUBBS, C. L., and J. R. JEHL, JR. 1976. Remains of Pleistocene birds from Isla de Guadalupe, Mexico. Condor 78:421-422.

PALMER, R. H. 1928. Fossil and Recent corals and coral reefs of western Mexico. Three new species. Proc. Amer. Philosoph. Soc. 67:21-31.

PORTER, J. W. 1972. Ecology and species diversity of coral reefs on opposite sides of the Isthmus of Panama. Bull. Biol. Soc. Washington 2:89-116.

SQUIRES, D. F. 1959. Corals and coral reefs in the Gulf of California. Bull. Amer. Mus. Nat. Hist. 118:371-431.

PREHISPANIC
MAN

Early Man on Santa Rosa Island

Rainer Berger

*Departments of Anthropology and Geography and Institute of Geophysics,
University of California, Los Angeles, California 90024*

EARLY MAN IN NORTH AMERICA

American anthropology began about a century ago with a decided orientation toward ethnography inasmuch as many Indian tribes were still in existence and could be readily studied. Compared with the Old World there was no literary record to be found in the Americas, save for the only partially-understood glyphs of Mesoamerica. As a consequence, many aspects of American prehistory were shrouded in uncertainty. The question of the origin of early man in America could be answered on the basis of the racially-distinguishing features of the Indian population. They possess the Mongoloid appearance of the people of northeastern Asia. On the other hand, the time of entry of man from Asia into the New World was much more enigmatic. About 50 years ago the influential Smithsonian anthropologist Aleš Hrdlička (1928:491) declared: "The beginning of the migration into America did not take place before the time of the European late Palaeolithic or, more probably, the early Neolithic Period which reduced to years would be somewhere between possibly ten or at most fifteen thousands of years ago."

This picture of the American past gained notable quantitative support with the discovery and application of radiocarbon dating by W. F. Libby (1951) in the late 1940s. After it had been proven that radiocarbon measurements produce reliable dates by comparison of radiometric and known historical ages for the same samples, a committee of prominent archaeologists assisted in the selection of a number of important samples for Libby to date. As a result, the earliest clearly man-related dates in the Americas were found to be not older than about 10,000 years. In fact, it appeared that the end of the Pleistocene and the arrival of man in the New World were synchronous.

In California, over the course of the years, the Santa Barbara Channel Islands had become increasingly important in archaeological research. Santa Rosa Island in particular had gained a reputation for being rich in aboriginal sites and, moreover, in the occurrence of dwarf mammoth remains (Orr 1968). Interestingly enough, peculiar deep, red-baked circular fire areas had been found on the island, often in close proximity to the characteristically abundant dwarf mammoth remains. The suspicion thus arose very early that man and mammoth were somehow connected. Arguing against such a relationship was the notion that man had arrived in the Americas only at the very end of the Pleistocene, around 11,000 to 12,000 years ago. Indeed the oldest finds of human bone on Santa Rosa Island, at Arlington Springs, are dated at near that age (Olson and Broecker 1961, Berger in press). However, many fire areas were radiocarbon dated as much older (Orr and Berger 1966, Berger and Orr 1966), and it was suggested that these fires were actually pit barbecues, since so great a thickness of red-baked soil was inferred to be produced by digging a pit, filling it with burning embers, placing wrapped meat on top, covering that with more embers, and ultimately sealing the barbecue with soil.

A much greater antiquity of man was suspected when, for example, a fire pit containing apparently burned mammoth bones was found and dated as 29,700 ± 3,000 years old (Broecker and Kulp 1957). Yet the question arose whether these bones actually had been burned or perhaps discolored by a deposit of manganese from ground water. In short, missing was conclusive evidence such as directly-associated human bones or artifacts. Over a period of some 15 years, during which I was privileged to explore Santa Rosa Island, many fire areas were investigated

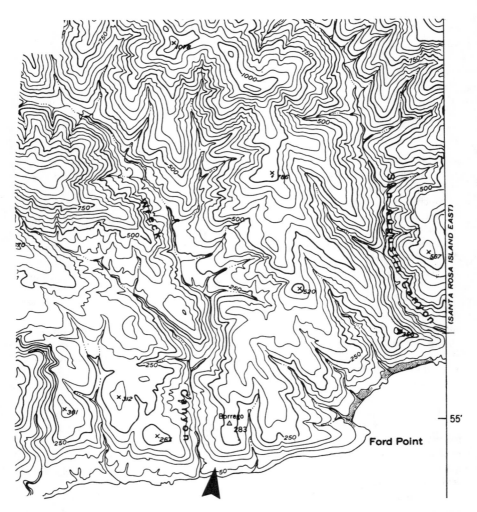

FIGURE 1. *Location of Woolley site near the mouth of Wreck Canyon, southern tip of Santa Rosa Island, marked by arrow.*

and dated, but any concrete connection between man and mammoth remained elusive. Many of these fire areas are exposed in the face of sea cliffs or canyon walls, often at levels as high as 30 m, that sometimes prove difficult to excavate. Erosion, however, exposes more of these red-baked areas every year and permits their inspection. In addition, some mammoth remains are found on the horizontal surface of the sea cliffs in close association with stone tools; but the question remains whether these surface finds are truly related or merely accidental.

THE WOOLLEY SITE

In 1975 geologist John Woolley of Vail and Vickers Co., owners of Santa Rosa Island, probed a badlands area near the mouth of Wreck Canyon and found, under a thick overburden, a

THE WOOLLEY SITE
Santa Rosa Island, California

THE WOOLLEY SITE
Santa Rosa Island, California

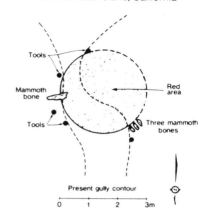

FIGURE 2. *Schematic cross section of gully in which hearth surrounded by mammoth bones and stone tools was discovered.*

FIGURE 3. *Top section of hearth.*

large fire area exposed by a naturally cut narrow trench or gully. This feature comprises a circular hearth 3 m in diameter which contains mammoth bones and stone tools made of metamorphically altered rock *in situ* around its exposed perimeter. In April of 1976 this site was partially excavated (Berger 1976; and see Figs. 1, 2, and 3).

This particular fire area is located in buff-colored, fine-grained alluvial sediments at the mouth of Wreck Canyon. These horizontally well-stratified deposits occasionally include horizons of small-sized pebbles 1 to 2 cm in diameter. Substantially-sized rocks are absent. The original fire burned a layer up to 80 cm thick which contains abundant charcoal, some of which was collected for radiocarbon dating.

The first sample (UCLA-2100A) came from the uppermost levels of the hearth, the second (UCLA-2100B) from a location directly above burned bones in the west bank at the same level as some of the stone tools. The third sample (UCLA-2100C) was taken from the east bank near mammoth bones, and the fourth (UCLA-2100D) came from the bottom layer underneath the consolidated red-burned alluvium. All samples were inspected microscopically in the laboratory. Inasmuch as the Santa Barbara Channel contains natural oil seeps, it was necessary to ascertain the origin of the material by observing the cellular structure of the charcoal; asphalt is characterized by a brightly reflecting amorphous mass containing gas bubbles. Indeed, the samples were found to be composed entirely of biological material.

All the charcoal samples were treated in the laboratory with hydrochloric acid and subsequently with dilute sodium hydroxide to remove both inorganic carbonates and humic acid contamination. After drying, the samples were converted to carbon dioxide and counted in a 7.5 l proportional counter. None of the four samples indicated any measurable radiocarbon activity and were therefore dated as older than 40,000 years, the upper limit for that particular dating method.

The great antiquity of the Woolley site prompted a careful macroscopic and microscopic analysis of the stone tools and mammoth remains. Most of these core tools are made of substantially-sized pieces of black metamorphic rock not belonging in the fine-grained al-

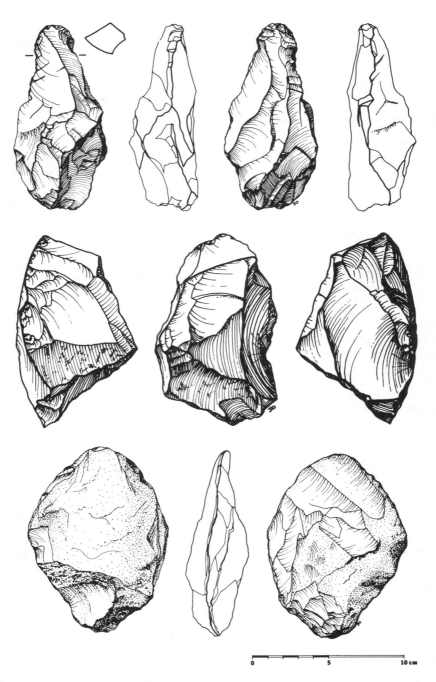

FIGURE 4. *Drawings of three representative stone tools consisting of metamorphically altered rock.*

FIGURE 5. *Photographs of two of the tools in Figure 4 to show actual appearance and greater detail of flaking. Lower photographs are close-ups of objects in upper photographs.*

luvium beds. The parent rock material, often found on the beach, is due to Miocene volcanism in the Santa Barbara Channel area which modified shales and sandstones. The tools at this site were apparently made very coarsely in an *ad hoc* fashion. The modifications effected on the cutting edges are clearly visible (Figs. 4 and 5). Closer examination also reveals tool wear at the cutting edges or points.

The mammoth bones themselves are being studied at present for wear marks and are being subjected to independent dating by amino acid racemization and radiocarbon analysis. It may also be possible to directly apply a particular uranium-series method of dating.

The remainder of the hearth is scheduled for excavation and a complete site report will be published after the conclusion of all excavation and analytical work. Hopefully, radiocarbon dating by accelerators may soon become possible (Berger 1978) so that a finite age for the site can be calculated. Otherwise, an enrichment date will be measured.

In the meantime, I suggest that the Woolley site presents itself as possibly one of the oldest mammoth kills in the Americas. From a paleoenvironmental point of view it is located near the wide, ocean-side mouth of a relatively shallow canyon in which, even today, a seasonal small stream runs. I believe that the picture may be true of a band of aboriginals chasing a dwarf mammoth into a muddy stream, killing and barbecueing it. But who these hunters were and what they looked like still remains a mystery today, for their skeletal remains have not yet been discovered. Moreover, the precise date of their first arrival on Santa Rosa Island is also not fixed, except that if the present evidence is accepted it must have been prior to 40,000 years ago. Once a more definite date is known it should be possible to suggest plausible means of how they entered the Channel Island complex from the mainland.

ACKNOWLEDGMENTS

This work would not have been possible without the excellent cooperation of Vail and Vickers Co., the Santa Barbara Museum of Natural History, and the assistance of the National Science Foundation and the United States Navy.

REFERENCES

BERGER, R. 1976. The earliest dates and sites in America. Proceedings IX Congrès Union Internationale des Sciences Préhistoriques et Protohistoriques, Nice, Sec. 4.

_____. 1978. Radiocarbon dating with accelerators. J. Archaeol. Sci. 6:1-3.

_____. UCLA radiocarbon datelist X. Radiocarbon v. 22 (in press).

BERGER, R., and P. C. ORR. 1966. The fire areas of Santa Rosa Island, California II. Proc. Natl. Acad. Sci. (US) 56:1678-1682.

BROECKER, W. S., and J. L. KULP. 1957. Lamont radiocarbon measurements IV. Science 126:1324-1334.

HRDLIČKA, A. 1928. The origin and antiquity of the American Indian. Smithsonian Report for 1923, U. S. Govt. Printing Office, Washington.

LIBBY, W. F. 1951. Radiocarbon dating. University of Chicago Press, Chicago, Ill.

OLSON, E. A., and W. S. BROECKER. 1961. Lamont natural radiocarbon measurements VII. Radiocarbon 3:141-175.

ORR, P. C. 1968. Prehistory of Santa Rosa Island. Santa Barbara Museum of Natural History, Santa Barbara, Calif.

ORR, P. C., and R. BERGER. 1966. The fire areas of Santa Rosa Island, California I. Proc. Natl. Acad. Sci. (US) 56:1409-1416.

Recent Developments in the Archaeology of the Channel Islands

Michael A. Glassow

Department of Anthropology, University of California,
Santa Barbara, California 93106

INTRODUCTION

The Channel Islands of southern California provide archaeology with some of its best laboratories in the world for investigating the development of human adaptive systems. Perhaps the most important reason why this is so is that the islands are discrete geographic units on which the diversity and abundance of many of the resources available to human populations may be accurately measured. In addition, the islands vary significantly in a number of environmental characteristics that affect human adaptations, and, as every scientist knows, effective tests of hypotheses require variability in the empirical world. No less important in efforts to develop and test hypotheses concerning human adaptation is the fact that the islands' ecosystems are relatively simpler and potentially easier to understand. Finally, all of the islands contain relatively intact sites in which the exploitation of marine resources is represented. Indeed, the degree of preservation of archaeological resources is especially high on some of the islands, in stark contrast with the coastal strip on the mainland where a large proportion of the sites representing a maritime cultural development has been destroyed. Mention might also be made of the fact that burrowing animals are absent from some of the Channel Islands, especially in the northern group, resulting in greater stratigraphic integrity than is normally found in mainland sites, which often serve as veritable havens for gophers and their kin.

There was comparatively little realization of these distinct advantages in the earlier research beginning in the 1870s, which was primarily concerned with obtaining collections of different kinds of artifacts, almost exclusively from aboriginal cemeteries, that would represent the archaeology of the Channel Islands in museum collections (*e.g.*, Schumacher 1877). Partly because of this early collecting, the archaeological potential of the Channel Islands became widely known, and in the 1920s there was a flourishing of activity by both relatively untrained amateurs and fully professional archaeologists being turned out by the emergent academic discipline of anthropology. Much of the work done at this time, especially that under the auspices of museums, carried on the tradition of the first explorers of Channel Island archaeology (*e.g.*, Heye 1921, Rogers 1929, Bryan 1970; see also Heizer 1969, Heizer and Elsasser 1956, Decker 1970), although somewhat more attention was given to recording provenience of artifacts according to site. Some of the professionals, however, began attempting to define the temporal and spatial variations in the archaeological records of the islands so that their culture histories could be reconstructed, primarily through stratigraphic excavation and simple chronological seriation of collections obtained from cemeteries (*e.g.*, Olson 1930).

After the considerable activity of the 1920s only sporadic archaeological research was carried out on the islands until after the Second World War. The work of Phil Orr on Santa Rosa Island, beginning just after the war and lasting about 20 years, serves as a link between the temporally-oriented workers of the 1920s and the work begun in the early 1950s (Orr 1951, 1968). It was Orr, in fact, who first made extensive use of radiocarbon dating on the Channel Islands.

Beginning in 1953, Clement Meighan and his students at the University of California at Los Angeles (UCLA) began a research program on the Channel Islands. With the founding of the

Archaeological Survey at UCLA in 1958 this program was intensified, involving extensive reconnaissance and some excavation on all of the Channel Islands except Santa Cruz, Santa Rosa, and San Miguel (Meighan and Eberhart 1953, McKusick 1959a, 1959b, McKusick and Warren 1959, Meighan 1959, Reinman and Townsend 1960, Swartz 1960a, 1960b, Reinman 1962, 1964).

The program begun by UCLA merged with that of Charles Rozaire, who not only participated in UCLA and Southwest Museum field projects on the Channel Islands in the late 1950s (Rozaire 1959a, 1959b), but maintained an active field program on many of the islands through the middle 1960s (Rozaire 1965, 1967, Rozaire *in* Bryan 1970). Although much of Rozaire's results is still in preparation, he produced some of the best data we have from his intensive surveys (many carried out by G. Kritzman) and careful excavations.

The major objectives of the research on the Channel Islands during the 1950s and early 1960s were to systematically inventory the archaeological resources of each of the Channel Islands investigated, identify the major periods of prehistoric development on each of the islands, and trace the evolution of maritime ecological adaptation. This latter objective is best characterized by Meighan's well-known study at Little Harbor on Santa Catalina Island (Meighan 1959) and Reinman's investigations on San Nicolas Island (see esp. Reinman 1964). In order to document the characteristics of maritime adaptations, the various workers abandoned the focus on cemetery excavations and began to use the techniques of midden analysis that had developed in California archaeology out of investigations of San Francisco Bay shellmounds. The ecological studies of this era laid the foundation for much of the current research.

Recent environmental legislation gave impetus to a major aspect of Channel Islands archaeological research beginning in the early 1970s. The federal government became committed to a much more active role in managing the cultural resources, which include archaeological sites, on the five Channel Islands it owns. The first steps in the evolving management programs are to inventory the archaeological resources and to assess the current state of archaeological knowledge so that the significance of the resources may be determined. An overview of Northern Channel Island archaeology was recently undertaken in light of the latter objective (Glassow 1977). Rozaire's surveys on Santa Barbara, Anacapa, and San Miguel Islands in the early 1960s anticipated the current inventory programs which are now being carried out on San Clemente Island by Michael Axford, and by Rozaire and his colleagues on San Nicolas Island. In addition, Roberta Greenwood is currently assessing the existing inventories and site conditions on Santa Barbara, Anacapa, and San Miguel Islands.

As part of the current emphasis on the conservation of archaeological resources, archaeologists are also finding themselves in the position of having to salvage information from sites before they are destroyed by some sort of land-modifying development. A crew from the UCLA Archaeological Survey, for instance, undertook salvage excavation at an important site near Avalon on Santa Catalina Island (Finnerty *et al.* 1970), and we can expect to see similar projects on many of the islands in the future.

Beyond the research related in one way or another to cultural resource management, there has been a recent increase in basic research on the Channel Islands. UCLA Archaeological Survey crews undertook extensive surveys on Santa Catalina Island during the early 1970s in order to identify the determinants of site distributions, and they have also expanded the sample of excavated material from the Little Harbor site investigated by Meighan in the 1950s (Nelson Leonard, III, pers. comm., Tartaglia 1976). Excavations were also undertaken at other sites on Santa Catalina Island by Leonard for the purpose of elucidating the nature of the steatite container manufacturing industry that is so obvious at sites on this island.

A similar program was initiated by Albert Spaulding and me on Santa Cruz Island for the purpose of studying the evolution of maritime adaptations. Not only have we surveyed about 10 per cent of the land area of this island, but we have also obtained a number of stratigraphic column samples from a series of coastal sites, most of which have been radiocarbon dated. In addition, we undertook major excavations at a large midden site at Prisoners Harbor.

Summarizing this discussion of the history of archaeological research on the Channel Islands, I would like to point out that in spite of the considerable amount of effort that has been devoted to collecting archaeological data, our knowledge of the prehistories of individual islands is still very sketchy. The type of research that is relevant to modern problem orientations only began in the 1950s and was devoted, for the most part, to surveys and comparatively small-scale excavation programs. Much of the research undertaken since the middle 1960s is still unpublished, although the results will be available within the next few years. But in spite of the fact that scientific archaeological research on the Channel Islands is just beginning, enough data are available to propose some tentative outlines of their prehistories and to compare their cultural developments.

THE DEVELOPMENT OF CHANNEL ISLAND CHRONOLOGIES

The degree to which the archaeologist is able to elucidate the nature of prehistoric develop-ment depends, to a large extent, upon the precision of a chronological framework, so it is appropriate to begin my review with a survey of the chronological information currently available for the Channel Islands. Initially, I should point out that there are still very real questions regarding when each of the Channel Islands was first inhabited. Phil Orr has contended that human occupation on Santa Rosa Island began on a more or less continuous basis during the late Pleistocene, perhaps as early as 37,000 B.P. (Orr and Berger 1966, Berger and Orr 1966, Orr 1968). Orr's evidence for Pleistocene occupation is rather circumstantial, however, and not enough of the data have been reported to allow a convincing argument to be made. The same must be said regarding a series of early post-Pleistocene dates from San Miguel Island obtained by Johnson (1977). These are purported to be associated with midden strata, but the contents of these strata, especially with regard to items definitely associated with human occupation, have not been reported. Consequently, the question of Pleistocene occupa-tion on Santa Rosa and San Miguel Islands cannot be answered until more adequate data are presented to the archaeological community.

The earliest clear evidence of extensive occupation of the Channel Islands comes from the northern group, in particular Santa Cruz and Santa Rosa Islands. The earliest radiocarbon dates unquestionably associated with human occupation on Santa Rosa Island come from samples collected from cemeteries located on the northwest coast dating between 7,500 and 6,800 B.P. On Santa Cruz Island, the basal levels of two sites, one near the northwestern extreme of the island and one at Punta Arena on the south coast, date about 6,700 and 7,100 B.P., respectively (Table 1). Three dates from purported middens on San Miguel Island also fall within this general range of time (Johnson 1977). Until very recently, the earliest dates so far available for any of the islands in the southern group did not extend beyond 5,000 B.P., and only one reported date, from recent excavations at the Little Harbor site, extended beyond about 4,000 B.P. (Tartaglia 1976, Nelson Leonard, III, pers. comm.). However, information from Michael Axford (pers. comm.) regarding two radiocarbon dates from a site on San Clemente Island indicates a period of occupation around 8,000 B.P. In addition, two other dates fall between 5,000 and 6,000 B.P. (Axford 1978); they appear to indicate that the Southern Channel Islands were occupied as early as, if not somewhat earlier than, the Northern Channel Islands. Three sites on San Nicolas Island, investigated in the 1960s, have yielded dates in the 3,000 to 4,000 B.P. range.

The difference between the earliest dates for the Northern and Southern Channel Islands should not necessarily be taken as representing a difference between time of earliest occupa-tion. The radiocarbon-dating programs have been relatively minimal on the Southern Channel

TABLE 1. Radiocarbon dates and column sample results from Santa Cruz Island.

Site number	Vicinity	Column number	Depth of radiocarbon-dated sample (cm)	Radiocarbon years B.P.
277	Near West Point	1	14-23	3210±150
		1	122-132	5920±150
		1	152-163	6730±230
195	East of Forneys	1		
	Cove	1	100-109	280±150
		1	380-388	2310±150
		1	406-410	1605±100
191	Christi Beach	2	55-67	1870±100
		2	103-115	2010±140
		4	73-80	1660±100
236	"	1	100-121	630±100
		1	185-195	1685±100
		1	238-248	4435±100
		2	205-220	1535±150
145	Mouth of Cañada	1	36-41	1630±150
	de los Sauces	1	36-41	1710±150
		1	50-55	2545±150
146	"	1	3-10	5290±150
192	Morse Point	1	17-25	740±150
		1	69-77	650±130
292	"	1	38-44*	3550±170
		1	50-57*	4360±180
109	Punta Arena	1	100-108	4600±150
		2	100-104	4790±150
		2	210-232	7140±210
127	"	1	11-20	1130±140
		1	120-130	1955±100
1	Mouth of Coches	1	7-23	<150
	Prietos drainage	1	123-131	2470±130
363	Lower Twin Harbors	1	0-16	4380±180
	drainages	1	20-29	4265±180
369	"	1	12-27	2650±140
		1	100-116	4800±120

* Not including 100-cm sterile dune-sand overburden.
† From tables in Damon *et al.* 1974.

Islands, whereas the number of dates for Santa Cruz Island and Santa Rosa Island for periods beginning around 7,500 B.P. has been much greater.

Beyond the problem of dating the earliest occupations of the various Channel Islands, chronologies covering the period from the first known occupations of the islands to the time of European contact are still poorly developed. Orr has proposed a chronology for Santa Rosa Island which has four period divisions. His sample of dated site components is so small, however, that his periods may only be said to be a convenient way to order the available data chronologically. The same may be said of Hoover's chronological scheme for Santa Cruz Island, which is based on an analysis of collections, primarily from cemeteries, obtained by Ronald Olson in the 1920s (Hoover 1971). Because of similarities in artifact forms to those from

Approximate solar years B.P.†	UCR‡ sample number	Depth of column sample (cm)	Shell density (g/1000 cm³)	Shell (%)	Fish (%)	Mammal (%)
3395	205	0-20	453.9	99.9	T	T
6580	203	120-130	736.0	99.5	0.1	0.4
7350	387	152-163	586.2	99.9	T	0.1
		20-40	258.0	96.2	3.3	0.5
unavailable	206	100-120	160.8	95.9	3.7	0.4
2305	207					
1540	386	387-406	810.1	98.9	0.8	0.3
1815	399	55-67	171.3	99.2	0.8	0.0
1965	398	103-115	42.0	98.8	0.8	0.4
1595	400	73-80	552.0	99.6	0.2	0.2
630	391	100-121	172.1	98.6	1.2	0.2
1625	130	183-195	316.0	97.0	2.7	0.3
4940	131	235-250	133.3	99.9	T	T
1470	132					
1565	208	27-40	196.4	97.7	2.0	0.3
1650	200					
2605	388	50-55	223.0	90.2	1.7	8.1
5930	202	0-19	181.9	99.9	T	T
725	396	0-17	342.0	97.4	2.4	0.2
650	397	77-83	118.7	86.2	13.3	0.5
3825	204	38-50*	554.7	99.7	0.1	0.2
4850	389	50-57*	437.7	99.6	0.3	0.1
5140	209	121-132	443.6	95.7	T	4.3
5480	201	104-119	362.3	97.4	T	2.6
unavailable	390	210-232	178.3	99.9	T	T
1080	403	11-20	415.7	94.7	1.5	3.8
1910	404	120-130	72.6	96.2	0.9	2.9
unavailable	395	7-23	446.5	95.4	2.3	2.3
2490	394	123-131	198.9	98.4	1.3	0.3
4875	401	0-16	337.5	99.9	T	0.0
4730	402	20-29	440.7	99.9	T	0.0
2580	392	12-22	394.4	99.9	0.1	T
5375	393	100-116	252.8	99.9	T	T

‡ University of California, Riverside, Radiocarbon Laboratory.
T = trace.

radiocarbon-dated sites on Santa Rosa Island, Hoover believes that the four phases in his sequence span roughly the same length of time as Orr's Santa Rosa Island sequence, beginning around 7,500 B.P.

Established sequences of this sort do not exist for the other Channel Islands, although there has been some recognition that chronological differences do exist. The three sites on San Miguel Island that Rozaire tested in the 1960s have not been radiocarbon dated, but the styles of shell beads, which serve as relatively sensitive time markers, indicate occupation between 5,200 B.P. (possibly somewhat earlier) and 1,000 B.P. For Anacapa Island, shell beads from Rozaire's excavations at two sites on the western islet indicate an occupation perhaps pre-dating 2,000 B.P. and extending into the historic period (Walker n.d.). The collections from Santa

Barbara Island do not contain sensitive time markers, although the presence of shell fishhooks and the relatively shallow deposits (between 45 and 60 cm in depth) appear to indicate relatively late and intermittent occupation, perhaps dating after 1,000 B.P.

On Santa Catalina Island, there has at least been recognition that there was considerable late prehistoric occupation, along with the earlier occupation first identified at Little Harbor (Finnerty *et al.* 1970, Nelson Leonard, III, pers. comm.). A similar differentiation has been made for San Nicolas Island; Reinman (1964) reports that the earlier sites contain only bone fishing gorges, while the later sites contain crescentic shell fishhooks, in addition. Moreover, mortars and pestles are rare in earlier sites but abundant in later ones (see also Reinman and Townsend 1960). On San Clemente Island, McKusick (1959a, 1959b) recognized three complexes, one of which contained historic material dating within the mission era. The other two complexes have no stratigraphic relationship to each other, and both contain shanked fishhooks that may indicate a date after 1,000 B.P.

It should be apparent from this brief summary of chronological information for the Channel Islands that the data are simply too meager to arrive at any clear understanding of the sequences of cultural development on any of the islands. The formal sequences on Santa Rosa and Santa Cruz Islands are probably premature and will undoubtedly require extensive revision once additional representative samples of occupational components have been clearly defined and dated. It is my impression, moreover, that discrete named periods or phases are really not necessary for understanding the cultural developments on the islands. The following discussions will simply make use of what chronological information is available.

DIVERSITY IN PREHISTORIC SUBSISTENCE

A reasonable place to begin developing an understanding of Channel Islands prehistory is with the study of subsistence systems, since these have so much to do with many other aspects of cultural adaptations. It will be profitable initially to compare some of the general differences between island and coastal mainland archaeological records; these differences will give some idea of how the habitats of the islands exerted considerable influence on prehistoric cultural systems.

Population Density

One of the most obvious clues to subsistence differences between the Channel Islands and the adjacent mainland is the relative density of sites. Generally speaking, densities are much higher on the Channel Islands than on the mainland. Quite a number of scholars have interpreted these higher site densities as indications of high population densities (see Meighan and Eberhart 1953) and have inferred that island population densities were much higher than on the coastal mainland, but there is every reason to believe that the high site densities are really only the result of high population *mobility*. That is, whereas mainland population aggregates may have seasonally occupied, perhaps, only five sites through the course of an annual cycle, the population aggregates on the islands may very well have occupied a far greater number, largely because of a much greater dependence by the islanders upon intertidal resources such as various species of shellfish. That shellfish were of much greater importance on the islands is indicated by a comparison of densities of shell in island and coastal mainland middens (Tables 1 and 2). Although available data are sparse for mainland sites, it appears that densities are usually below 100 g per 1,000 cm³; it is not unusual to find sites on the islands with densities over 400 g per 1,000 cm³. Furthermore, many of the exceptions on the islands are obviously the result of dune-sand accumulation during midden deposition.

Returning for the moment to the question of how dense the populations really were on the Channel Islands, population density is partially dependent upon the abundance and types of food resources in the environment. There are, of course, no good archaeological measures of

TABLE 2. Densities of shell in southern California midden sites.

Site number and location	Periods represented*	References	Maximum shellfish density in g/1000 cm³
SBa-142, Glen Annie Canyon, Goleta	Early	Owen, Curtis, and Miller 1964	11.5
LAn-267, Sweetwater Mesa, Malibu	Early	King 1967	121.0
LA-215, Parker Mesa, Malibu	Early	King 1962	18.0
Ven-3, *Shisholop*, Ventura	Late	Greenwood and Browne 1969	42.4
SMI-1, San Miguel Island	Early to Middle ?	Rozaire 1965	89.1
Surface samples from Anacapa Island sites	probably Middle to Late	McKusick 1959a	247.3
AnI-8, Anacapa Island	Middle to Late ?	McKusick 1959a	131.0
AnI-6, Anacapa Island	Late ?	McKusick 1959a	59.2
AnI-5, Anacapa Island	Late ?	McKusick 1959a	119.1
SNI-16, San Nicolas Island	Late	Reinman 1964	83.0
Little Harbor site, Santa Catalina Island	Middle	Meighan 1959	370.7†

* Early: 7500-3200 B.P., Middle: 3200-1000 B.P., Late: 1000-165 B.P.
† Only average density available

island population sizes, so it is necessary to depend upon ethnohistorical data of population sizes during the early mission period. In this paper I shall confine my investigation of this problem to the Northern Channel Islands and the adjacent coastal mainland which were occupied at the time of contact by Chumash-speaking peoples. Three sets of estimates of Chumash village sizes have been published (Brown 1967, King 1971, Whitehead and Hoover 1975); I have selected King's because it appears to be based on a greater variety of ethnohistoric and ethnographic information. Using the midpoints of each of King's range estimates, Santa Cruz Island, with eleven villages and a total population of 1,187, had a density of 4.76 people per km²; Santa Rosa Island, with eight villages and a population of 637, had a density of 2.94 people per km²; and San Miguel Island, with two villages and a total population of 107, had a density of 2.89 people per km². Anacapa Island had no historically recorded villages. In contrast, the coastal mainland strip from Rincon Point on the east to Gaviota on the west to the crest of the Santa Ynez Range on the north had a population of 4,908, using the mid-range estimates for the 17 villages in this region. The density along this mainland strip was 8.09 people per km², which is nearly twice that on Santa Cruz Island, the most densely occupied of the group.

The much lower population densities on the Northern Channel Islands—and probably on the Southern Channel Islands also—is undoubtedly the result of the much lower terrestrial resource diversity on the islands in comparison to the mainland. In fact, those portions of the coastal mainland with the greatest resource diversity, such as in the vicinity of well-developed sloughs, had much higher population densities than adjacent coastal mainland areas. The vicinity of the Goleta Slough, for instance, had a density of 11.00 persons per km². The greater population density on the mainland also reflects another significant aspect of island subsistence: the relatively greater abundance of marine resources around the peripheries of the islands did not offset the mainland advantage of having bountiful supplies of different kinds of terrestrial food resources.

Turning now to the variation in the density of sites between the different Channel Islands, we note considerable differences among the islands where adequate data are available. San Miguel Island, which has been completely surveyed, contains 542 sites (Charles Rozaire, pers. comm.) and has a density of 14.65 sites per km². Our survey of 15 drainage areas on Santa Cruz Island yielded a sample of 297 sites. If the sample is representative, the total number of sites on the island would be somewhat over 2,700, and the density would be 11.05 sites per km². The Anacapa islets contain 21 recorded sites, which appears to be the total number; the site density is 7.24 per km². Orr's survey data from Santa Rosa Island are not comparable because of the manner in which he grouped sites into "localities," and perhaps also because of the island's much better grass cover which may obscure sites. Forty to forty-five per cent of Santa Catalina Island's area that has been systematically surveyed has yielded about 900 sites (Nelson Leonard, III, pers. comm.), so the island total is probably on the order of 2,100, and the density would be approximately 10.81 sites per km². The intensive survey of San Clemente Island has so far covered about 30 per cent of the island and has yielded a total of 1,164 sites (Michael Axford, pers. comm.). The total for San Clemente Island may therefore be around 3,900, and the density would be 26.75 per km². Santa Barbara Island, with 19 sites, has a density of 7.34 sites per km². Meighan and Eberhart (1953) report only 68 sites on San Nicolas Island, an unusually low number compared to the other islands that appears to be the result of combining several discrete deposits under one site designation (e.g., SNI-16; see Reinman 1964, map 2). Rozaire (pers. comm.) suspects that the density of sites on San Nicolas Island is comparable to that on San Miguel Island.

Although some of the variation in site densities on the Channel Islands may be attributed to differences in technique among even the recent surveys, which are presumed to be generally more intensive and discriminating than earlier surveys, there appear to be some expectable patterns. First, the two smallest islands, Anacapa and Santa Barbara, are very similar in having the lowest site densities of all the Channel Islands. This was probably the result of very sporadic occupation of a few favored localities during periods when fresh water was available. On the other extreme are San Miguel Island and San Clemente Island; San Clemente Island's estimate seems especially high. It is possible that their high densities in comparison with the larger islands may be related to comparatively higher degrees of population mobility caused by greater dependence on marine resources. However, Michael Axford (pers. comm.) expects the unsurveyed portions of San Clemente Island to have lower densities; consequently, the overall density may actually be in line with that on San Miguel Island. This leaves Santa Cruz Island and Santa Catalina Island, which have quite similar densities that appear to be related to roughly comparable diversities of terrestrial resources (Raven 1967). It will be interesting to see how these explanations of differences among the Channel Island population densities hold up when we become more confident of comparability between the survey data from one island to the next.

Shellfish Exploitation

There is another factor that should be mentioned which might have something to do with the variation in densities of sites. This is the fact that there are some differences in the repertoires of exploited shellfish species between the different islands. Within the northern group, mussel (*Mytilus californianus*) nearly always comprises over 90 per cent by weight of the total shell in the midden deposits of any time period (*e.g.*, Rozaire 1965), and black abalone (*Haliotis cracherodii*) is usually next in abundance. There is a possibility that red abalone (*H. rufescens*) is predominant, perhaps even over mussel, in some of the earliest sites on the Northern Channel Islands, although this observation is based primarily on shells found in cemeteries rather than occupation middens (Orr 1968). By comparison, the proportions of different species of shellfish in sites on the Southern Channel Islands are quite variable. The Little Harbor site on Santa Catalina Island revealed a shift from a predominance of black abalone in the lower levels to a predominance of mussel in the upper levels (Meighan 1959). Just the opposite is true at the Eel Cove Canyon Shelter on San Clemente Island, and this site also contained significant amounts of black top (*Tegula funebralis*) shells throughout its depth (McKusick and Warren 1959). We see similar variability on San Nicolas Island, where mussel is even less important in comparison to other species, and the proportions of mussel, abalone, black top, and sea urchin (*Strongylocentrotus* sp.) vary considerably within and between sites (Reinman 1964).

The difference in the importance of mussel between the Northern and Southern Channel Islands appears to be related to its much greater productivity around the Northern Channel Islands. Prehistoric populations on the southern islands compensated for the lower abundance of mussel by using other species. The greater variety of shellfish in the middens on San Clemente Island, and especially on San Nicolas Island, may additionally be related to relatively higher levels of predation on the shellfish populations.

The shift through time in the emphasis on different species of shellfish, which has been noted on all of the Southern Channel Islands for which data are available, has been proposed to be the result of either local depletion of a particular species (Meighan 1959, Tartaglia 1976) or change in human preferences (Reinman 1964). The latter proposal should, it seems, be discarded since food preferences are determined to a large extent by the availability and costs of obtaining resources. The former proposal, however, is also less than satisfying since it implies that a period of hundreds or perhaps thousands of years—the duration of time represented in many of these sites—would be required for a population aggregate to deplete local shellfish resources. While resource depletion may very well be involved, it would probably have been a much more complex phenomenon related to human population growth and decline on each of the islands and perhaps also to minor climatic fluctuations. There is obviously much work that must be done before these processes of change in shellfish species exploitation will be better understood.

Fishing

Although shellfish remains are the most visible constituent in many of the sites on the Channel Islands, their dietary importance was moderate compared with fishing and sea mammal hunting (Meighan 1959, Tartaglia 1976). Of these two subsistence activities, the issues surrounding the importance and strategies of fishing have attracted the most attention. Direct evidence of fishing extends through all of the known prehistory of Santa Cruz Island, and the available evidence appears to indicate the same for all of the other islands. Nonetheless, the emphasis on fishing changed significantly through time. Orr (1968) notes the importance of

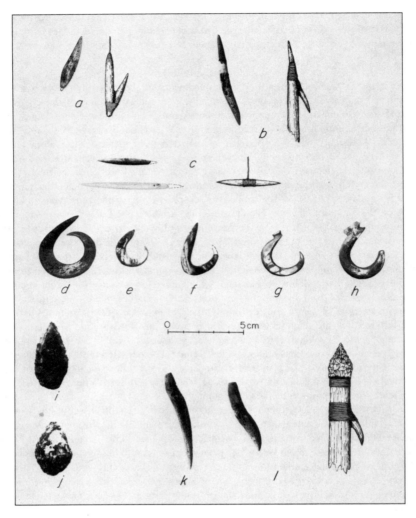

FIGURE 1. a: *Probable bone barb of a compound fishhook from Prisoners Harbor, Santa Cruz Island; drawing shows form of a complete hook.* **b:** *Bone point from Prisoners Harbor, Santa Cruz Island (note asphaltum deposits reflecting technique of hafting); drawing shows hafting technique.* **c:** *Bone fish gorges from Prisoners Harbor, Santa Cruz Island, and Tecolote Point, Santa Rosa Island; drawing shows technique of line attachment.* **d-f:** *Unshanked fishhooks of bone (d) and mussel shell (e, f) (note asphaltum deposits with line impressions on d and e); from Christi Beach (d, e) and Platts Harbor (f), Santa Cruz Island.* **g-h:** *Shanked fishhooks of abalone shell from San Nicolas Island.* **i-j:** *Chert projectile points which may have served as harpoon or spear points (asphaltum adhering to base of i reflects hafting technique); from Prisoners Harbor, Santa Cruz Island.* **k-l:** *Bone barbs that would have been attached to harpoon or spear shafts below the point (both have asphaltum deposits reflecting hafting technique); from Prisoners Harbor, Santa Cruz Island; drawing shows probable hafting arrangement of point and barb.*

fishing on Santa Rosa Island beginning with the Canaliño period, or roughly 2,500 B.P., and our data from Santa Cruz Island indicate a similar date for its increased importance (Tables 1 and 2). In addition, an increase in fishing, not yet dated, was recognized by Reinman (1964) in his analysis of material from San Nicolas Island. Data are not available from the other Channel Islands, but it is expected that the same general pattern will be consistent throughout, although the dates for the increase may vary.

Fishing is also indicated by the presence of fishhooks, which have been found on all of the Channel Islands (Fig. 1). There are a number of different types of fishhooks, and some of them are chronologically significant. More importantly, each type is undoubtedly associated with different fishing techniques or strategies. Recently, Tartaglia (1976) has attempted to identify the functional significance of many of the major fishhook forms; his inferences form the basis of the following discussion.

The earliest type is the bone gorge, which is prevalent in the Little Harbor site between about 5,000 and 4,000 B.P. It is also the earliest type on San Nicolas Island, dating around 4,000 B.P. In addition, fish gorges are the predominant type at a site that appears to date from about 3,200 B.P. on San Miguel Island (Rozaire 1965) and may also be the earliest type at the Prisoners Harbor site on Santa Cruz Island.

Tartaglia (1976) believes that gorges were used to catch shallow-water fish that, upon striking the bait, swallow the attached hook. These shallow-water fish could have been caught either from shore or from boats operating on the landward side of kelp. Significantly, seaworthy watercraft capable of crossing the channel would not have been necessary for this type of fishing.

Circular or "J"-shaped fishhooks of shell and sometimes bone or stone appear to have become important relatively late in prehistory, perhaps after A.D. 1. Circular hooks are especially abundant on San Nicolas Island and appear to indicate a much stronger emphasis on fishing compared with all the rest of the Channel Islands. Tartaglia (1976), citing experiments undertaken by Robinson (1942), believes that the circular hooks were used to obtain near-shore bottom-feeders occupying either sandy or rocky-bottom habitats; these hooks appear to be most effectively used from a boat, although not necessarily one capable of crossing the channel. The "J"-shaped hooks, on the other hand, would be used for trolling in the open waters beyond the kelp (Tartaglia 1976), necessitating the use of seaworthy craft.

Implicit in the literature treating the development of fishing on the Channel Islands and adjacent mainland is the assumption that the elaboration of fishing technology reflects an increasingly successful or improved cultural adaptation. Such an assumption neglects the fact that this development represents increasing investments in the manufacture and maintenance of the various tools and facilities associated with the fishing technology. Because of these investments, it is doubtful that the development of fishing technology was simply the result of discovering better ways to obtain food. The determinants of this development may be directly related to a broadly based population growth throughout the Channel Islands and adjacent mainland, and indirectly to the development of trade networks. The increasing importance of fishing, in other words, may have resulted from increasing population pressure on terrestrial and intertidal resources.

Before leaving the subject of fishing, some of the information that is available on variation in species of fish caught by the prehistoric fishermen of the Channel Islands should be noted. Identified collections of fish remains are still very few; in fact, it has only been within the last four or five years that there has been any systematic effort to identify fish remains from Channel Island sites, and most of the results are still unpublished. First, there are striking differences in the sizes and, to a lesser degree, the species of fish remains from a site excavated by Rozaire near Point Bennett on San Miguel Island compared with the remains in the column sample collections obtained from Santa Cruz Island. The most abundant remains from the San Miguel Island site are of lingcod, various rockfishes, sculpins, pile perch, and sheephead, all of which inhabit near-shore zones with rocky substrates. Most of these remains are several times larger than those of the rockfishes, surfperches, and sheephead that predominate in the Santa Cruz Island samples. The San Miguel Island collection also contains mackerel and tuna remains in small quantities, indicating exploitation of offshore waters to a limited extent. So far, no remains of these schooling fish have been found in the Santa Cruz Island column samples. The differences in the fish remains from San Miguel Island and Santa Cruz Island are due, at least in part, to the differences in water temperatures between the islands (Hubbs 1967) and to the considerably more extensive, shallow, rocky-bottom habitat around the perimeter of San Miguel Island, especially off the west end. San Miguel Island is obviously the best endowed of the Northern Channel Islands so far as nearshore fishing is concerned.

Two collections from West Anacapa Island have also been analyzed. The earlier of the two, perhaps dating around 2,000 B.P., contains primarily remains of rockfish and sheephead, which are especially abundant in the lower portions of the deposit. Elasmobranchs are better represented in the upper part of the deposit. The second site, probably dating after 350 B.P., contains an abundance of remains representing mackerel, bonito, and herring. All of these are schooling fish that would have been obtained from the open waters of the channel, the latter almost certainly with some sort of net or seine. This seems to indicate that Landberg's (1975) recent thesis that schooling fish were not important during the late prehistoric period may have to be re-evaluated.

There have yet to be made available analyses of fish remains from any of the Southern Channel Islands. Tartaglia (1976) does note that the lowest levels of the Little Harbor site contain predominantly skipjack, albacore, and some sheephead, whereas these species are absent in the upper levels. Since skipjack and albacore prefer warm waters and do not presently pass close to Santa Catalina Island, Tartaglia suspects their presence indicates that ocean temperatures were relatively warmer near the island than they are today.

While the analyses of fish remains are still too few to recognize more than tentative spatial and temporal patterns of fish exploitation, it has at least been possible to indicate that there is quite a bit of variability both between islands and between sites representing different periods of prehistory. It is likely that species living in near-shore zones with rocky substrates were not only among the first to be exploited, but also were always relatively important. The exploitation of schooling fish in the open channel and perhaps beyond probably began at the time when seaworthy watercraft were developed. This may have occurred as early as 5,000 to 4,000 B.P., if the data from the Little Harbor site are indeed representative. The Anacapa Island data seem to indicate that netting was added to fishing technology relatively late in prehistory. In general, the trend appears to have involved the expansion of the number of ocean habitats exploited and the concomitant elaboration of fishing technology to obtain a broader range of species.

Sea Mammal Hunting

Exploitation of sea mammals, including dolphins, porpoises, and several species of pinnipeds, appears relatively early in the prehistory of the Channel Islands. Meighan (1959) was the first archaeologist in southern California to clearly recognize that sea mammals, along with fish, became important much earlier than the late prehistoric period which began between 2,000 and 1,000 B.P. In his excavations of the Little Harbor site he found that an intensive exploitation of sea mammals had begun by 4,000 B.P., and recent radiocarbon dating at this site indicates that it may have begun a millennium earlier. On San Nicolas Island, sea mammals were equally important during the earliest occupation, and both sea mammals and fish were extremely important in the later occupation of that island (Reinman 1964). Interestingly, the use of sea

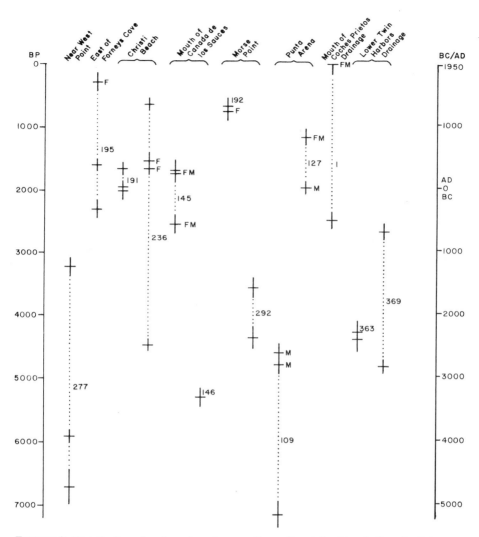

FIGURE 2. *Distribution of radiocarbon dates on Santa Cruz Island (excluding the Prisoners Harbor series).*

mammals—and sharks—on San Nicolas Island is reflected in a unique occurrence of rock art on this island (Reinman and Townsend 1960, Bryan 1970).

As expected, the sites on San Miguel Island, where extensive rookeries currently exist, contain abundant remains of pinnipeds. These animals were a major food resource on this island from the time of the earliest occupation. Phillip Walker (pers. comm.), who has analyzed the faunal remains not only from Rozaire's excavations, but also from a number of other Santa Barbara Channel Island and mainland sites, believes that sea mammal meat may have been extensively traded from the source on San Miguel Island. For Santa Cruz Island, the available

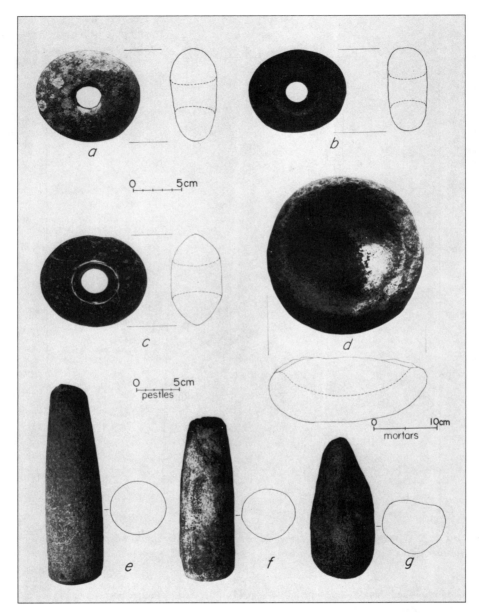

FIGURE 3. a-c: *Digging-stick weights of basalt (**a, b**) and serpentine (**c**); from Punta Arena (**a,** b*) *and Christi Beach (**c**), Santa Cruz Island.* **d:** *Sandstone mortar from Twin Harbors, Santa Cruz Island.* **e-g:** *Pestles of sandstone (**e**), shale (**f**), and basalt (**g**); from Prisoners Harbor (**e,** f*) *and Punta Arena (**g**), Santa Cruz Island.*

data indicate that sea mammals were a dietary constituent from the time of the earliest occupation and that they became very important, along with fish, by about 3,000 B.P. There is some evidence that they may have been intensively exploited by about 4,500 B.P., at least at some localities on the island (Table 1 and Fig. 2).

Walker (pers. comm.) has pointed out that the importance of sea mammals in the aboriginal diets of southern California maritime peoples has been greatly underestimated, seemingly because their exploitation is not emphasized in the ethnohistoric or ethnographic literature. Certainly the archaeological record indicates that sea mammals were dietarily very important on all of the Channel Islands by the late prehistoric period; sea mammals probably contributed protein to the aboriginal diet in an amount equal to or greater than that supplied by fish (Meighan 1959).

The means by which sea mammals were obtained has yet to be fully worked out. Pinnipeds are most easily obtained at their rookeries with a tool no more elaborate than a club, which is probably the principal reason why their remains are so prevalent in San Miguel Island middens. It is doubtful that pinnipeds were obtained from watercraft, given the difficulty of approaching the animals. Nevertheless, pinnipeds could have been stalked when they hauled out, although a harpoon or spear may have been necessary to ensure the catch. Dolphins and porpoises, of course, would have been obtained from watercraft by taking advantage of their natural curiosity; undoubtedly they were also salvaged when they washed ashore. Meighan (1959) suspects that the inhabitants of the Little Harbor site used spears to hunt these animals since he found no evidence of harpoons. This interpretation may be incorrect, however, since there are aboriginal harpoons in Santa Barbara Channel sites that were made by hafting a chert point onto a wood foreshaft and insetting a bone barb into the side of the shaft. Suitable chert points are present in the Little Harbor collection, and some of the bone items classified as fish gorges resemble harpoon barbs (Fig. 1). Whether or not such devices were true harpoons—that is, with lines attached—has not yet been verified.

Terrestrial Resources

Regarding terrestrial resources utilized by Channel Island aboriginal populations, comparatively little can be said because of the paucity of data. We can be sure that the few land mammals on the Channel Islands never constituted a major resource, although they probably were exploited to some extent. On the other hand, each of the Channel Islands does contain a variety of plant resources that could have been harvested. Santa Cruz and Santa Catalina Islands appear to have the greatest variety and abundance of food plants. Oaks and island cherry, both providing pulpy seeds, stand out as potentially highly-productive resources on these islands. In addition, a number of chaparral species on these and other islands could have provided significant amounts of seeds. Grasslands were extensive on all of the Channel Islands; these would also have provided various seeds, as well as roots, bulbs, and tubers (e.g., the blue dick, *Dichelostemma pulchellum*). Various seeds can be preserved in midden sites in a carbonized state; however, there are only casual reports that these have been found in late prehistoric sites (Meighan 1959).

Other more direct evidence of plant resource exploitation is the occurrence of various stone milling implements and digging-stick weights (Fig. 3). Mortars and pestles have been reported for all the Channel Islands; if they were used for the same purposes as mainland examples, they indicate the use of various seeds, especially pulpy ones such as acorns. There is some evidence that mortars and pestles were multipurpose. Their abundance on San Nicolas Island (Meighan and Eberhart 1953, Bryan 1970) does not seem to be easily accounted for, considering the small size of the island and the scarcity and low diversity of food plants that must have characterized the island even before overgrazing in the last century. Significantly, one of the accounts of the famous "lone woman" of San Nicolas Island mentions that the mortar and pestle was used to pound dried abalone meat (Meighan and Eberhart 1953, Heizer and Elsasser 1961), so it is possible that the mortar's major use on the Channel Islands was in preparing dried meat of all sorts (Hudson 1976). If this is so, the prevalence of mortars and pestles in the later periods of Channel Island prehistory may reflect the importance of meat storage, in contrast with earlier times when only fresh meat was eaten.

Digging-stick weights, or "doughnut stones," are much more abundant in all of the Channel Island sites than in mainland sites. These tools were used in procuring roots, bulbs, and tubers, which were presumably of relatively more importance on the Channel Islands. The greater emphasis on these resources on the islands compared with the mainland may reflect a dependence on more marginal plant foods, especially during seasons when fish and sea mammals were difficult to obtain.

In ending this discussion of subsistence, it should be pointed out that data from aboriginal sites on the Channel Islands have great potential for studies of aboriginal diet. The remains of marine resources are especially well preserved in the sites, and even the meager amount of information currently available is enough to demonstrate that there were considerable differences through time. The data also indicate that there were significant differences between the Channel Islands as a group and the adjacent mainland, so it should eventually be possible to discern in some detail the various ways that islands restrict cultural adaptations.

TRADE

It has been well known for many years that Santa Catalina Island was a source of exported manufactured steatite vessels which were distributed throughout much of coastal southern California (Schumacher 1878, Meighan and Rootenberg 1957, Finnerty et al. 1970). Steatite vessels and effigy art forms are also found abundantly on San Clemente Island (McKusick and Warren 1959) and San Nicolas Island (Bryan 1970). They are less abundant in the Santa Barbara Channel region, apparently because another form of talc schist, a serpentine found in the San Rafael Mountains behind Santa Barbara, was extensively exploited instead.

Interestingly, the Northern Channel Islands were also involved in manufacturing specialization. King (1971) has carefully compiled a variety of ethnohistoric and ethnographic accounts indicating that the Chumash on the Northern Channel Islands manufactured nearly all of the shell beads—and perhaps ornaments, as well—that are found in mainland sites throughout much of southern California, including interior regions. The archaeological record of the Northern Channel Islands bears witness to this specialization. Nearly every late prehistoric site on Santa Cruz Island contains abundant olivella shell detritus resulting from bead manufacture, along with small chert bladelets with narrowed chipped tips that were used to drill holes in the beads (Fig. 4). In addition, many of the sites on the eastern third of Santa Cruz Island, where the outcrops of high-quality chert occur, contain abundant chert refuse resulting from the manufacture of the bladelets. Heizer and Kelley (1961, 1962) have referred to the cores from which the bladelets were struck as "burins," but there is no evidence that these cores were used in the manner implied by the popular usage of the term "burin."

The dates of the beginnings of these manufacturing emphases on Santa Catalina and Santa Cruz Islands have not yet been firmly established. Shell beads and steatite objects generally do not occur in any abundance in southern California archaeological sites until relatively late in prehistory, presumably after A.D. 1000. This date is consistent with the analysis of radiocarbon-dated material from the Prisoners Harbor site, but would not mean that manufacturing specialization did not occur earlier on a lower level of intensity.

The question of what determined these manufacturing specializations on the Northern Channel Islands and Santa Catalina Island presents us with one of the most intriguing problems

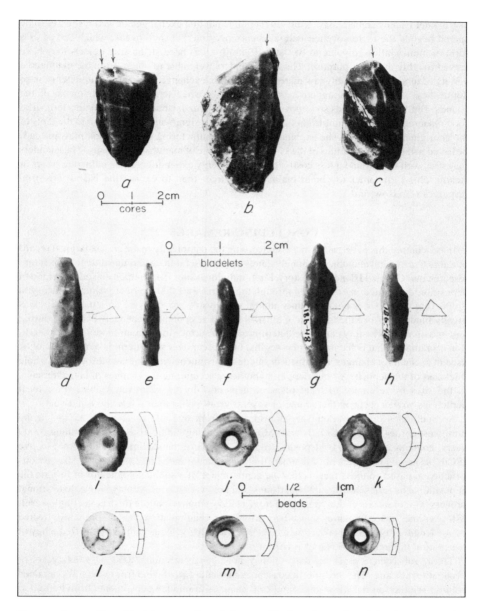

FIGURE 4. a-c: *Chert bladelet cores from Prisoners Harbor, Santa Cruz Island (arrows point to scars resulting from removal of bladelets).* **d-e:** *Unmodified chert bladelets from Christi Beach, Santa Cruz Island.* **f-h:** *Chert bladelets with prepared tips apparently broken from use; from Christi Beach, Santa Cruz Island.* **i:** *Shell bead blank made from callus of olivella with partially-drilled hole; from Christi Beach, Santa Cruz Island.* **j-k:** *Olivella callus beads with unprepared margins (**j** with dorsal grinding); from Christi Beach, Santa Cruz Island.* **l-n:** *Finished olivella wall beads from Christi Beach, Santa Cruz Island.*

of Channel Islands archaeology. King (1971) points out that exchange allowed resources to be spread beyond the region of their natural occurrence and that shell beads, which served as a form of money, allowed value to be "stored" until it was needed. Steatite objects may have served roughly the same purpose. Thus the islanders were able to obtain from the mainland a variety of foods, and probably raw materials as well, in exchange for manufactured items; in so doing they were able to compensate for the impoverished terrestrial environments of the islands. But were the islands so impoverished? Santa Cruz Island, at least, contains terrestrial food resources seemingly ample enough to have made a significant contribution to the diets of the aboriginal inhabitants. The explanation of the manufacturing specialization may, instead, be found to lie in the economics of the system of exchange of manufactured items. The islanders may very well have found it less costly in terms of energy expenditure to manufacture beads or steatite objects in order to obtain mainland resources than to exploit the island terrestrial resources (Glassow, n.d.).

CONCLUDING REMARKS

In concluding this paper, a few notes concerning the complexity in the archaeological record of Santa Cruz Island and other Channel Islands may be useful in designing strategies for future research into Channel Islands prehistory. First, individual sites may contain episodes of midden deposition distributed intermittently through the course of 3,000 years of island prehistory; a 2,000-year time span is not at all uncommon. As a result, the study of settlement patterns is greatly hindered, since the location of all sites that were contemporaneously occupied during any one time in prehistory cannot be determined from surface indications alone. This observation also implies that behavioral processes that only occur over short periods of time cannot be used to account for changes in artifacts or midden constituents that continue through the whole thickness of the deposit. As an example, hypotheses accounting for changes in faunal remains in the sites by reference to local resource depletion do not seem too viable, since local depletions would occur in the course of several years rather than a few thousand years.

Second, rates of deposition vary considerably from one site to another. A site on the northwest corner of Santa Cruz Island (SCrI-277), having radiocarbon dates spanning 3,000 years, contains only 1.6 m of deposits. Conversely, one of the shellmounds at Forneys Cove (SCrI-195) contains over 4 m of deposits that were accumulated in 2,000 years. The obvious conclusion based on these facts is that the depth or size of a site is no indicator of its age; the depositional histories of Channel Island sites probably varied considerably. Some depositional processes—for instance, those resulting from a heavy emphasis on shellfish collecting—result in higher rates of accumulation than others. Moreover, accumulation rates are probably affected by the length of time a site is occupied through an annual cycle, as well as by the frequency of occupation through the course of prehistory.

Third, subsistence practices may or may not change through 2,000 or 3,000 years of occupation at a site. The three north coast sites on Santa Cruz Island from which we obtained column samples do not show any significant changes in midden constituents from bottom to top, yet some of the south coast sites do show significant shifts. This implies that certain microhabitats on the island appear to restrict variety in subsistence practices much more than do others. Consequently, we cannot very easily generalize about subsistence changes based on data from just one site.

The most important conclusion that can be derived from these three observations is that a research program with the objective of developing an outline of the prehistory of any one of the Channel Islands must consider the archaeological resources of the island as a whole, or, to put it in modern archaeological parlance, the research must be regionally oriented.

ACKNOWLEDGMENTS

The research on Santa Cruz Island was supported by National Science Foundation grant no. GS-36573 awarded to Albert Spaulding and the author. In addition, portions of the background research for this paper were supported by two purchase orders from the National Park Service. I gratefully acknowledge these sources of financial support.

REFERENCES

AXFORD, M. 1978. Current archaeological investigations on San Clemente Island, California. Abstracts of papers, Multidisciplinary symposium on the California Islands, Santa Barbara Museum of Natural History, Santa Barbara, Calif.

BERGER, R., and P. C. ORR. 1966. The fire areas on Santa Rosa Island, California, II. Proc. Natl. Acad. Sci. 56:1678-1682.

BROWN, A. K. 1967. The aboriginal population of the Santa Barbara Channel. Univ. Calif. Archaeol. Surv. Reports, 69.

BRYAN, B. 1970. Archaeological explorations on San Nicolas Island. Southwest Mus. Papers 22.

DAMON, P. E., C. W. FERGUSON, A. LONG, and E. I. WALLICK. 1974. Dendrochronologic calibration of the radiocarbon time scale. Amer. Antiquity 39:350-366.

DECKER, D. A. 1970. Early archaeology on the Channel Islands: potential and problems. Unpubl. ms., Univ. California Archaeol. Surv. files.

FINNERTY, P., D. DECKER, N. LEONARD, III, T. KING, C. KING, and L. KING. 1970. Community structure and trade at Isthmus Cove: a salvage excavation on Catalina Island. Pacific Coast Archaeol. Soc. Occas. Paper 1.

GLASSOW, M. A. 1977. Archaeological overview of the Northern Channel Islands, including Santa Barbara Island. Western Archaeological Center, National Park Service, Tucson, Ariz.

————. n.d. The concept of carrying capacity in the study of culture process. In M. B. Schiffer, ed., Advances in Archaeological Method and Theory, v. 1. Academic Press, New York, N.Y. (in prep.).

GREENWOOD, R. S., and R. O. BROWNE. 1969. A coastal Chumash village: excavation of Shisholop, Ventura County, California. So. California Acad. Sci. Memoir 8.

HEIZER, R. F., ed. 1969. San Nicolas Island archaeology in 1901, by Philip Mills Jones. Masterkey 43:84-98.

HEIZER, R. F., and A. B. ELSASSER, eds. 1956. Archaeological investigations on Santa Rosa Island in 1901, by Philip Mills Jones. Univ. California Anthropol. Records 17(2).

————, eds. 1961. Original accounts of the lone woman of San Nicolas Island. Univ. California Archaeol. Surv. Reports, 55.

HEIZER, R. F., and H. KELLEY. 1961. Scraper plane burins. Masterkey 35:146-150.

————. 1962. Burins and bladelets in the Cessac collection from Santa Cruz Island, California. Amer. Philosophical Soc. Proc. 106:94-105.

HEYE, G. C. 1921. Certain artifacts from San Miguel Island. Indian Notes and Monogrs. 7(4). Museum of the American Indian, Heye Foundation, New York, N.Y.

HOOVER, R. L. 1971. Some aspects of Santa Barbara Channel prehistory. Ph.D. thesis, University of California, Berkeley, Calif.

HUBBS, C. L. 1967. A discussion of the geochronology and archaeology of the California Islands. Pp. 337-341 in R. N. Philbrick, ed., Proceedings of the symposium on the biology of the California Islands. Santa Barbara Botanic Garden, Santa Barbara, Calif.

HUDSON, D. T. 1976. Marine archaeology along the southern California coast. San Diego Mus. Papers, 9.

JOHNSON, D. L. 1977. The late Quaternary climate of coastal California: evidence for an ice age refugium. Quaternary Res. 8:154-179.

KING, C. 1962. Excavations at Parker Mesa (LAn-215). Univ. California Los Angeles Archaeol. Surv., Ann. Rep. 1961-62:91-157.

————. 1967. The Sweetwater Mesa site (LAn-267) and its place in southern California. Univ. California Los Angeles Archaeol. Surv., Ann. Rep. 1966-67:25-76.

————. 1971. Chumash inter-village economic exchange. Indian Historian 4:31-43.

LANDBERG, L. C. W. 1965. The Chumash Indians of southern California. Southwest Mus. Papers, 19.

McKUSICK, M. B. 1959a. Introduction to Anacapa Island archaeology. Univ. California Los Angeles Archaeol. Surv., Ann. Rep. 1958-1959:71-104.

————. 1959b. Three cultural complexes on San Clemente Island, California. Masterkey 33:22-25.

McKUSICK, M. B., and C. N. WARREN. 1959. Introduction to San Clemente Island archaeology. Univ. California Los Angeles Archaeol. Surv., Ann. Rep., 1958-1959:107-186.

MEIGHAN, C. W. 1959. The Little Harbor site, Catalina Island: an example of ecological interpretation in archaeology. Amer. Antiquity 24:383-405.

MEIGHAN, C. W., and H. EBERHART. 1953. Archaeological resources of San Nicolas Island, California. Amer. Antiquity 19:109-125.

MEIGHAN, C. W., and S. ROOTENBERG. 1957. A prehistoric miner's camp on Catalina Island. Masterkey 31:176-184.

OLSON, R. L. 1930. Chumash prehistory. Univ. California Publ. Amer. Archaeol. Ethnol. 28:1-21.

ORR, P. C. 1951. Ancient population centers of Santa Rosa Island. Amer. Antiquity 16:221-226.

————. 1968. Prehistory of Santa Rosa Island. Santa Barbara Museum of Natural History, Santa Barbara, Calif.

ORR, P. C., and R. BERGER. 1966. The fire areas on Santa Rosa Island, California. Proc. Natl. Acad. Sci. 56:1409-1416.

OWEN, R. C., F. CURTIS, and D. S. MILLER. 1964. The Glen Annie Canyon site, SBa 142: an early horizon coastal site of Santa Barbara County. Univ. California Los Angeles Archaeol. Surv., Ann. Rep. 1963-64:431-517.

RAVEN, P. H. 1967. The floristics of the California Islands. Pp. 57-67 in R. N. Philbrick, ed., Proceedings of the symposium on the biology of the California Islands. Santa Barbara Botanic Garden, Santa Barbara, Calif.

REINMAN, F. M. 1962. New sites on San Nicolas Island, California. Univ. California Los Angeles Archaeol. Surv., Ann. Rep. 1961-1962:11-21.

————. 1964. Maritime adaptation on San Nicolas Island, California: a preliminary and speculative evaluation. Univ. California Los Angeles Archaeol. Surv., Ann. Rep. 1963-1964:50-84.

REINMAN, F. M., and S. TOWNSEND. 1960. Six burial sites on San Nicolas Island. Univ. California Los Angeles Archaeol. Surv., Ann. Rep. 1959-1960:1-134.

ROBINSON, E. 1942. Shell fishhooks of the California coast. Bishop Mus. Occas. Papers 17:57-65.

ROGERS, D. B. 1929. Prehistoric man of the Santa Barbara coast. Santa Barbara Museum of Natural History, Santa Barbara, Calif.

ROZAIRE, C. E. 1959a. Archaeological investigations at two sites on San Nicolas Island, California. Masterkey 33:129-152.

————. 1959b. Excavations at site AnI-8, Le Dreau Cove. Univ. California Los Angeles Archaeol. Surv., Ann. Rep. 1958-1959:91-93 and *passim*.

————. 1965. Archaeological investigations on San Miguel Island. Unpubl. report submitted to National Park Service.

————. 1967. Archaeological considerations regarding the Southern California Islands. Pp. 327-336 *in* R. N. Philbrick, ed., Proceedings of the symposium on the biology of the California Islands. Santa Barbara Botanic Garden, Santa Barbara, Calif.

SCHUMACHER, P. 1877. Researches in the kjokkenmoddings and graves of a former population of the Santa Barbara Islands and the adjacent mainland. Bull. U.S. Geol. Geogr. Surv. of the Territories 3:37-61.

————. 1878. Ancient olla manufactory on Santa Catalina Island. Amer. Natur. 12:629.

SWARTZ, B. K. 1960a. Blade manufacture in southern California. Amer. Antiquity 25:405-407.

————. 1960b. Evidence for the Indian occupation of Santa Barbara Island. Kiva 26:7-9.

TARTAGLIA, L. J. 1976. Prehistoric maritime adaptations in southern California. Ph.D. thesis, University of California, Los Angeles, Calif.

WALKER, P. L. n.d. An ethnozoological analysis of faunal remains from four Santa Barbara Channel Island archaeological sites. Unpubl. ms., University of California, Santa Barbara, Calif.

WHITEHEAD, R. S., and R. L. HOOVER. 1975. Ethnohistoric Chumash placenames (map). *In* Papers on the Chumash. San Luis Obispo Co. Archaeol. Soc. Occas. Paper 9. San Luis Obispo, Calif.

VEGETATION CHANGES AND THE IMPACT OF FERAL ANIMALS

Episodic Vegetation Stripping, Soil Erosion, and Landscape Modification in Prehistoric and Recent Historic Time, San Miguel Island, California

Donald Lee Johnson

*Department of Geography, University of Illinois,
Urbana, Illinois 61801*

INTRODUCTION

San Miguel Island is the westernmost of the Northern Channel Islands of California. Nearly two thirds of its 10,000 acres (4,050 ha) are covered by loose or partially-indurated white sand dunes called eolianites, dating from Recent and Pleistocene times. The eolianites are multiple layercake deposits, separated from one another by buried fossil soils that outcrop as brown soil bands along sea cliffs.

The island lies exposed to the full force of northwest winds and the cool California Current which sweep south of Point Conception, making San Miguel Island one of the windiest, foggiest, most maritime, and wave-pounded areas on the west coast of North America. Like the rest of coastal California, it has a Mediterranean type of climate, with cool, wet winters and warm, droughty, fire-prone summers. The winter rainfall record is marked by wet and dry trends of variable duration during which individual wet or dry years frequently occur (Figs. 1 and 2). Temperatures are mild year-round and marked by a lack of extremes. Various lines of evidence from San Miguel Island and other coastal California sites indicate that the climate became slightly cooler and moister during glacial periods while retaining its basic Mediterranean character throughout the late Quaternary (Johnson 1977b).

Elephants roamed the island during the later Pleistocene, as indicated by their abundant remains scattered through deposits covering that time span. Elephants were replaced as faunal dominants by early Indians who arrived on the island at some as yet undetermined time prior to 8,000 years ago (Johnson 1972); Indians lived more or less continuously on the island until the 1800s when Europeans arrived.

Within this environmental context, covering later Pleistocene to recent historic time, recurrent episodes of vegetation stripping and soil erosion have left profound and indelible landscape changes on San Miguel Island; large areas, both on the island and offshore, have undergone significant modifications. The purpose of this paper is to examine the evidence and extent of the stripping episodes, the attendant landscape changes, and the factors which produced them. Specifically, it will be shown that the stripping episodes reflect the integrated effects of several factors operating on a wind-swept island that is periodically affected by droughts and fires; these factors are overgrazing and cultivation in historic time, and elephant and Indian activity in prehistoric time.

HISTORIC STRIPPING EPISODES
Droughts and Overgrazing

George Nidever, a long-time 19th-century resident of Santa Barbara, purchased San Miguel Island in 1863 from a man named Samuel C. Bruce, who raised sheep on it (Santa Barbara County Recorders Office, Miscellaneous Book A, pages 313-314). At that time, there were some 6,000 sheep, 125 head of cattle, and 25 horses, a collective number (about 6,200 animals)

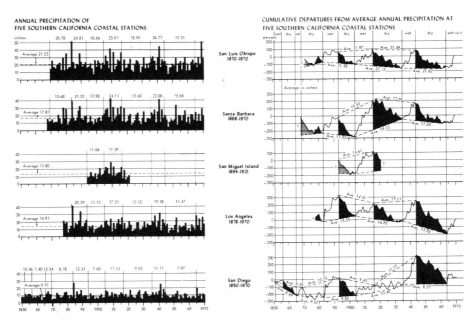

FIGURE 1. (left) *Precipitation records of various California coastal stations (after Johnson 1972).* **(right)** *Cumulative departures from average annual precipitation of stations on left, in percentages (after Johnson 1972). Note close correlation of wet-dry trends between stations.*

considerably beyond the island's carrying capacity, in light of the area's variable precipitation pattern. Severe drought hit that year in 1863 and lasted nearly three years, during which Nidever lost 5,000 sheep, 180 cattle, and 30 horses to starvation — over 80 per cent of his stock (Ellison 1937, and Fig. 3). In the process, most of the available vegetation was consumed, leading to the first of several stripping episodes which have swept the island in recent historic time.

Nidever's misfortune possibly may be the origin of a description given by unidentified sources in Rogers (1929) who recalled lush vegetation that once covered the island. It was described how this pasturage encouraged sheep grazing, which thrived for a while, but then several drought seasons were experienced which reduced the growth. This forced the sheep to strip the shrubs and trees of their lower branches, then the bark, and finally "the poor beasts even pawed into the earth and consumed the roots." Afterwards, the entire island was said to be devoid of trees and shrubs. An almost identical account in reference to the subsequent drought of 1870 was given by Mrs. Jane Kimberly, wife of an early resident of San Nicolas Island (Phillips 1927). After Kimberly arrived on San Nicolas (*ca.* 1857-58), he stocked the island:

> . . . with sheep which increased so rapidly that soon he had a flock of 15,000, and his income was $10,000 a year. Wool was very high, and he rode the top wave until the dry year of 1864 when many sheep died.
>
> Another dry season—'69 or '70—turned San Nicolas into a desert and drove Captain Kimberly out of the sheep business with a heavy loss. In those days, the island was covered with wild carrot and other vegetation. In their frantic efforts to get moisture [and food] the sheep dug two and three feet into the soil after the roots. Strong winds blew the sand completely over the island, burying the seeds so deeply, as well as the remaining

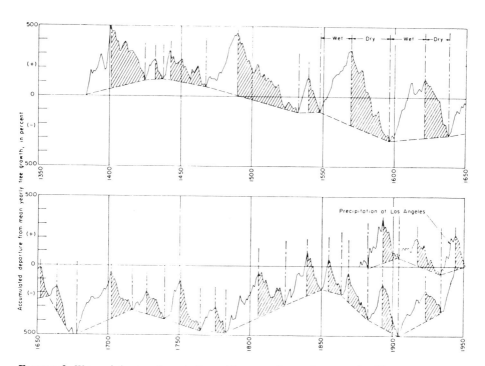

FIGURE 2. *Wet and dry trends as indicated by annual tree-ring growth of bigcone spruce in southern California. Records begins A.D. 1385 and ends 1944. Los Angeles climate precipitation record (from Figure 1), beginning 1878, overlaps 68 years of the tree-ring record, and shows very close correlation (Troxell and Hofmann 1954, Troxell et al. 1954).*

roots, that everything was killed. And a waste of blowing sand it remains today.

Both San Miguel and San Nicolas Islands during this time apparently experienced essentially parallel histories of drought, overgrazing, and consequent profound vegetation and soil stripping. During the dry trend of 1869-83 (Figs. 1 and 2), several droughts again struck California, once in 1870-72, and again in 1877. Although we lack historic record of precise conditions on San Miguel Island at this time, the effect of the 1877 drought on other nearby islands is suggested by the following statement:

About 25 thousand sheep will be slaughtered today on Santa Cruz Island. The hides and tallow will be preserved, but the mutton will be a loss. Scarcity of food induced by the want of rain, compels the sacrifice (*Santa Barbara Index,* March 22, 1877).

Another dry trend during 1893-1904 contained a drought which, according to one writer, was:
. . . one of the longest droughts in the history of southern California. It covered the years 1897-1900 (Lloyd 1948).

In 1924, during the dry trend of 1917-35, Robert L. Brooks, lessee of the island for many years, had to remove all his sheep due to lack of food during the low rainfall years of 1923-24 (R. Brooks, pers. comm. 1965).

The last dry trend, 1944-64, was the longest since precipitation records have been kept. During 15 years of this 20-year span, San Nicolas Island had an average annual rainfall of only 3.99 inches (101 mm), the lowest of its 110-year record (Johnson 1972).

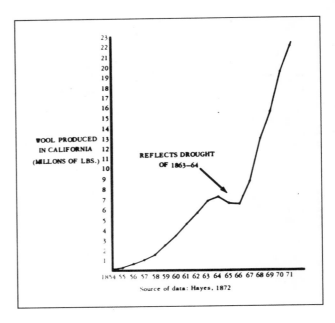

FIGURE 3. *Wool produced in California 1854-71 (after Johnson 1972).*

Cultivation

In the last quarter of the 19th century, cultivation was practiced, which proved disastrous in that it accelerated wind and water erosion. An insight to the matter was gained while searching ownership records of San Miguel Island. A sale statement, dated December 20, 1890 (Santa Barbara County Recorders Office, Deeds Book 29, pages 187-190), revealed that at that time there were about 3,000 sheep, 150 cattle, 10 horses and mules, hogs, poultry, goats, and farming and agricultural implements, including wagons, a cart, plows, harrows, and mowing machines. Other sale statements, dated December 19, 1889 and March 4, 1897 (Santa Barbara County Recorders Office, Deeds Book 26, pages 203-204; and Deeds Book 59, pages 233-234, respectively), list "hay farming implements." The documents show that farming was carried out on the island in the 1880s and 1890s at least. Farming activities are further documented by a map in an unpublished manuscript dated *ca.* 1893 which identified farmland as the "Cultivated Field" (Voy *ca.* 1893, and Fig. 4). Robert L. Brooks, lessee of the island during the 1920s and 1930s, offered the opinion that cultivation, not sheep grazing, was the principal cause of most 19th- and early 20th-century vegetation stripping and soil erosion, the wind removing all that the plow turned up (R. Brooks, pers. comm. 1965). Brooks, however, apparently was not aware of Nidever's graphic account of the results of the 1863-64 drought. Overgrazing *and* cultivation in a droughty, windswept environment combined to cause the demise of significant portions of the insular vegetation and soil.

LANDSCAPE MODIFICATIONS

Prior to the stripping episode beginning 1863, San Miguel Island apparently had a somewhat more luxuriant ground cover. Before this date there is a notable absence of pessimistic statements about blowing sand and barrenness so frequently alluded to by subsequent writers. Alden (1852), for example, in a terse but optimistic description of Cuyler Harbor, made no

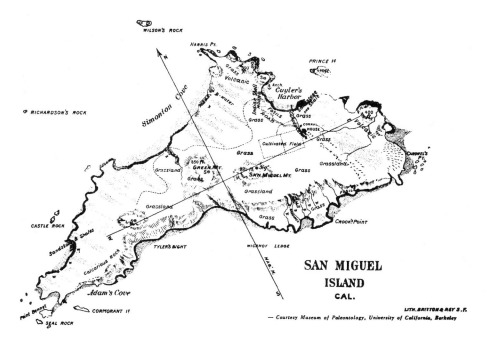

FIGURE 4. *Map of San Miguel Island from unpublished manuscript in University of California's Bancroft Library, Berkeley (Voy ca. 1893).*

mention of erosion, blowing sand, or lack of vegetation. Six years later, Davidson (1858) described San Miguel as being covered with grass and bushes; that same year Greenwell made a prolonged visit to the island as surveyor for the Coast Survey and made no mention of extensive erosion, widespread sand dunes, or lack of vegetation in reports to his superintendent, although he did mention several times that the island was entirely destitute of wood (Greenwell 1858a, 1858b, 1858c). (The use of the word "wood" in the context of the 19th century probably meant timber or trees usable for firewood. In this sense, whether types like *Rhus* and *Heteromeles* were considered "wood" is not known.) Greenwell's original field notes (1858d, courtesy National Archives) contain only four passages alluding to the character of ground cover at specific localities on San Miguel Island. San Miguel Hill (Fig. 5) he described as being "covered with low sage bushes and cactus," whereas now it is characterized primarily by bare, wind-stripped ground, patchy grass, and a few shrubs. At Black Point he found "dark looking bushes"; none are in evidence today. Devil's Knoll on Harris Point he described as being "covered with low black sage bushes and cactus," where presently no bushes or cactus exist. (Cactus may be present sparingly on the precipitous, inaccessible north face of Devil's Knoll beyond the reach of sheep, but the main part of the Knoll has no vegetation like that described by Greenwell.) His only reference to uncovered ground was at Big Dune (Brockway) on Caliche Flats, which he described as "a strip of white sand drift," as it essentially is today, although now partly stabilized by some herbaceous plants. Besides the brief descriptions of Alden (1852) and Davidson (1858), to my knowledge, those by Greenwell are the only pre-1863 vegetation descriptions of San Miguel available.

FIGURE 5. *Place-name map of San Miguel Island (modified from Map 1 and Lithomap A in Johnson 1972; aerial photograph taken April 1, 1960). Sand spit at east end of island had disappeared by 1979.*

Dune Encroachments and Wind Erosion

In the ensuing decades after the great droughts of 1863-64 and 1870, some two thirds of San Miguel Island periodically became a barren waste of drifting sand and blowing soil. Only two areas escaped catastrophic stripping: the area from Green Mountain west to the playa lake (Jackass Flats), and an area east of San Miguel Hill (The Gangplank). Descriptions of the surface character of the island after 1870, while principally disparaging in tone, were nevertheless inconsistent, ranging from the island being covered with grass to its being a barren waste of blowing sand (reasons for these inconsistent observations are explored later). In 1871, for example, Stehman Forney of the Coast Survey stated that San Miguel "is entirely destitute of wood, not a tree upon it . . . [and] is covered with coarse grasses . . . being destitute of under brush of any kind" (letter of October 31, 1871, courtesy National Archives). Forney arrived on San Miguel Island on April 12 and had seven months during spring, summer, and fall to gain his impressions. Three years later, Dall (1874) commented with disdain on the barren wastes, drifting, blowing sand, and the blighted condition of the vegetation:

> Near the shell heaps is a small grove of malva-trees, whose green leaves and penciled blossoms refresh the eyes. There are no young trees, however, as the omnipresent sheep crop every green thing within their reach close to the ground.

Dall did not indicate the season or year of his visit, but it was after the onset of the dry cycle of 1870-83, probably in 1873. During May of 1875, Schumacher (1875) visited San Miguel Island and disparagingly referred to it as a "barren lump of sand" and described the sheep as being in a starved condition. While writing about the same trip in a later publication (Schumacher 1877), he recalled the vegetation as consisting of "low bushes, cactus and grass, but no trees." In 1878, George Nidever stated that "I have not been to the Island for several years, but I am told that it is almost covered with sand" (Ellison 1937:77). His statement indicates a changed condition over that which prevailed in prior years. In 1879, the island was pictured by Wheeler

FIGURE 6. *Photograph of Cuyler Harbor taken sometime prior to 1893 by C. D. Voy (ca. 1893) and published by Yates (1902).*

(1879) as being barren and extremely desolate as a result of drifting sand. Seven years later, during a visit of 25 days in a wet-cycle year (late June-July, 1886), Streator (1887) gave his impressions of the surface character of the island:

> On approaching the Island the view is not very inviting, the cliffs rising two or three hundred feet, between which descend ever shifting banks of sand. By following a steep trail to the mesa we observe a fine pasture almost as far as the eye extends [The Gangplank], but on reaching other parts of the island I found it barren, and half of the area drifting sand.

During August and September of 1887, the resident occupants of the island informed the botanist Greene (1887) that the sand was fast encroaching upon and burying each year more and more of the fertile grassy acres of the eastern portion. Impressed with the extent and richness of the grassland at the time, but apparently ignorant of the 1863-64 disaster experienced by Nidever, Greene concluded:

> I judge that remarkably good and truly perennial pasturage [covers] the eastern third of the island [The Gangplank]. . . . These many acres of such pasturage have been the pride of the owner of San Miguel, whose horses, cows and sheep fare better on this cold bleak and desolate marine table-land and are much better secured against the perils of starvation than are the flocks and herds of any of the larger and more fertile members of the archipelago where, as on the mainland, the grass species are annual and the crop yearly good or poor according to the winter rain fall.

Sometime before 1893, probably within the 1883-93 wet cycle, Voy (*ca.* 1893) had this to say about the vegetation of San Miguel Island:

> The greatest portion of this island, appears to be good soil, and is good grazing land, the year round, and is abundantly supplied with nutritious native grasses. . . .
> At the present time the island is entirely destitute of timber, but from the general

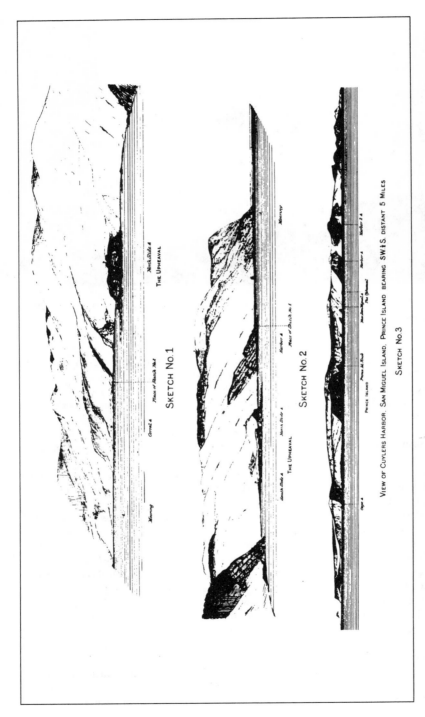

FIGURE 7. *Three sketches of Cuyler Harbor made by Coast Survey personnel in November 1895. These sketches were greatly photo-reduced from large bromex originals and some detail has been lost. Even so, the extensive dune blankets which cover the island are apparent, especially in Sketch No. 3. All areas in white are dunes (courtesy National Archives, and from Johnson 1972).*

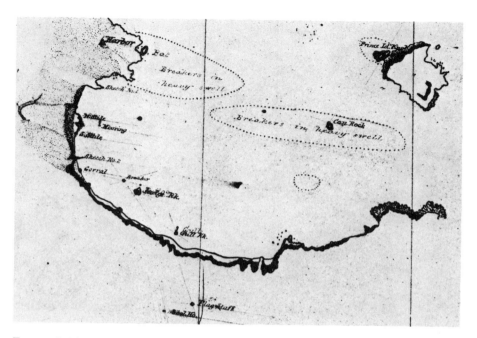

FIGURE 8. *Plan layout of Cuyler Harbor constructed and drawn by Coast Survey personnel in November 1895 (courtesy National Archives, and from Johnson 1972).*

appearance it has not always been so. In some of the isolated canyons and hills, in sheltered spots, are a great many varieties and species of handsome shrubs and bushes. . . .

One of Voy's photographs published later (Yates 1902) shows the huge dunes mentioned by Streator (1887) that were spilling into Cuyler Harbor during the 1880s and 1890s (Fig. 6). Coast Survey sketches made in November 1895 also show these massive dunes spilling into the harbor (Fig. 7; sketches 1 and 2) and into the open ocean off the north side of Harris Point (Fig. 7; sketch 3). A note which accompanied the large original sketches stated:

The areas of drifting sand are sketched in approximately. The dotted lines shown in the harbor [Fig. 8] enclose areas over which the sea was observed to break in heavy swell and could only be approximately delineated. Sketches Nos. 1 and 2 [Fig. 7] were made to exhibit the present appearance of the changes in the shore-line; and the extended sketch of San Miguel Island was made from the vessel, underway when leaving the island, to illustrate the fact of the great amount of drifting sand which is being constantly deposited in Cuyler's Harbor. . . . The kelpfield shown on topog. tracing of Cuyler's Harbor no longer exists except in small scattered bunches.

The topographic tracing referred to in the excerpt above is that executed by Forney in 1871 (Fig. 9). It is noteworthy that, whereas the terrestrial vegetation was directly destroyed by sheep, the marine vegetation (kelp) of Cuyler Harbor, and perhaps other areas, was essentially destroyed by submarine sedimentation of sand blown into the ocean. Thus, significant portions of both the subaerial and the submarine vegetation were destroyed by the direct and indirect effects of sheep and cultivation.

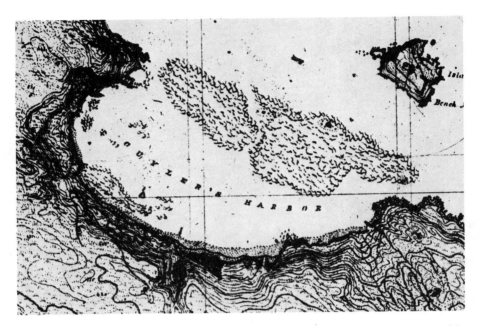

FIGURE 9. *Original topographic map of San Miguel Island executed in 1871 by S. Forney of the Coast Survey (courtesy National Archives, and from Johnson 1972).*

Willet (1910), visiting the island in June 1910, commented that:

[San Miguel Island] is mostly composed of rocks and sand hills, altho there is considerable grass on the most elevated portions. This, however, is being gradually covered up by sand which is drifting slowly but surely across the island, carried by the prevailing northwesterly winds. There are several varieties of shrubs on San Miguel but no trees worthy of names.

Holder (1910), Wright and Snyder (1913), and Heye (1921), among others, gave similar descriptions of the plant cover on San Miguel Island. Wright and Snyder, for example, concluded that the island "is nothing but a vast pile of continually drifting sand." During a late September 1927 visit to San Miguel Island, two mammalogists, C. C. Lamb and J. E. Green, observed that bushes were practically nonexistent. Most of the island was said to be sandy and "free of trees or even of bushy vegetation" (Grinnell *et al.* 1937).

Photographs taken since 1929 allow us to see what the character of the vegetation has been like for the past 50 years. Photographs taken near the ranch house during the early 1930s show little vegetation at that site (Lester 1974; see also Noticias 23, Fall 1977). Photographs in Bremner (1933:12,20) show extensive dune blankets on Crook Flats and The Wind Tunnel in the early 1930s. Aerial photographs taken in 1929, 1940, 1954, 1960, and 1972 give a general impression of the extent and cover of vegetation during that time span (Fig. 10) and show that vegetation has been gradually expanding at the expense of dune terrains since 1929, especially during the past two decades (most of the sheep were removed in 1950).

The impressions of the island landscape gained by visitors in the period 1871-1927, while mainly negative as indicated earlier, are nevertheless sufficiently varied to require explanation. What factors might account for such mixed assessments? One possibility is that assessment of

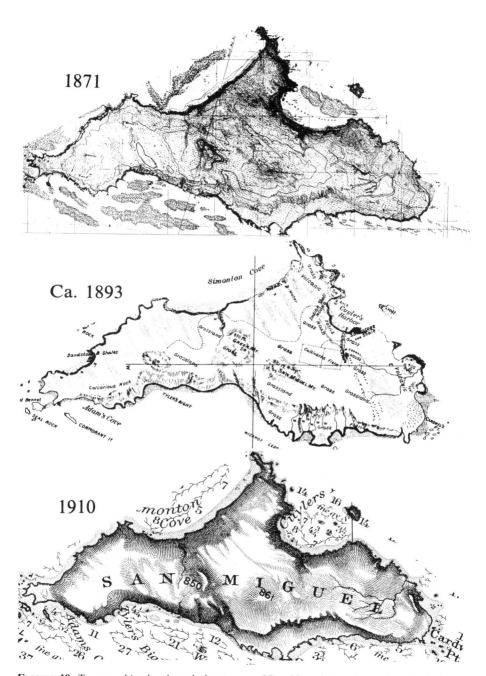

FIGURE 10. *Topographic sketch and photomaps of San Miguel Island covering the 101-year period 1871-1972. Note changing coastline and surface cover through time (adapted and modified from Johnson 1972).*   *(Figure continued on pp. 114-115.)*

1929

1940

1954

landscapes, like beauty, lies in the eye of the beholder, and some beholders apparently have far more (or less) critical eyes than others. Dunkle (1950) concluded as much about the observational integrity of early visitors to the islands. Another consideration is the specific location where the observations were made, for some areas, such as The Gangplank and Jackass Flats, have obviously experienced less stripping and more stability than have others. A third explanation, and the one I favor, is that the inconsistent observations indicate temporarily changing landscape conditions that are reflective of the total number of stock animals present and the season and/or year of visit. For example, a visitor to San Miguel Island during a summer that followed a relatively rainless winter would probably observe an overgrazed, stripped, and bleak landscape, the severity of which would depend on the number of stock animals present.

Change from Rocky to Sandy Shorelines

Nineteeenth- and early twentieth-century stripping of vegetation and soils resulted in marked shoreline changes about San Miguel Island. Reference again to Figure 10 shows, in stages, how the perimeter of the island has been modified through time. In 1871, the shoreline of the island was primarily rocky; sandy beaches occurred only on the windstruck northwest coast, eastern

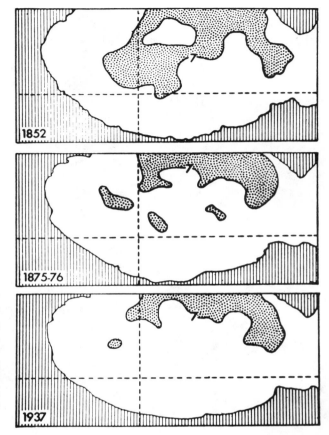

FIGURE 11. *Three stages of shallowing in Cuyler Harbor, based on bottom bathymetry obtained in 1852 (Chart 607), 1875-76 (issued 1883), and 1937 (Chart 5116). The stippled pattern shows depths greater than 7 fathoms (42 ft; 12.8 m).*

Cuyler Harbor, and a small area immediately north of Cardwell Point. The spit at Cardwell Point had not yet formed, nor had the bedrock-escalloped southern coast been filled with sand. The year 1870 was one of severe drought and was only six years removed from the ecological disaster of 1863-64. At this time, the stripping episode had apparently not yet manifested itself as modifications in the shoreline. By *ca.* 1893, however, enormous volumes of sand had encroached on many of the beaches, and Cuyler Harbor was being invaded by huge sand dunes cascading from Harris Point into the bay (Figs. 6 to 8 and 10). A comparison of bathymetric data collected in 1852, 1875-76, and again in 1937 shows marked shallowing of the bay (Fig. 11). Most of the shallowing and the greatest wind erosion occurred in the 12 years from 1863-64 to 1875-76. By the early 1900s, significant changes had occurred and extensive sand beaches were present all about the island (Fig. 10). The first aerial photos, taken in 1929, document the by then well-developed sand spit at Cardwell Point and show the smoothed, sandy shoreline perimeter which so contrasts with its escalloped bedrock character in 1871. Aerial photographs taken since show that the sand spit at Cardwell Point has diminished in size from its maximum development in 1940. Since then, the spit has been gradually reduced in size through marine erosion; by 1979, it had disappeared almost entirely.

Since the cessation of agricultural activity on the island in the 1940s and the removal of most

FIGURE 12. *Photos taken by author in 1964 showing extremely eroded parts of "Cultivated Field" identified in Figures 4 and 5. Note people for scale.*

of the sheep in 1950 (and all of them by the late 1960s), erosion has been markedly reduced and many plant species have actively re-established their numbers, probably to a greater degree than at any time during the past 115 years.

Water Erosion

While wind erosion appears dominant on San Miguel Island, water erosion has been locally severe and catastrophic. The "Cultivated Field" (Fig. 4) is, today, one of the most severely eroded tracts on the island, being actively dissected by huge ravines (Figs. 5 and 12). The topsoil in this area has been largely stripped away, leaving behind an essentially sterile surface. The periphery of the entire island is gullied and eroded by water action following overgrazing by sheep.

PREHISTORIC STRIPPING EPISODES

Fire and elephants operating in concert with the seasonality of the Mediterranean climate formed a natural erosional triumvirate long before man appeared on San Miguel Island. Upon arrival, however, prehistoric man replaced the elephant as the principal landscape modifier and increased the fire frequency.

Fire

Fire has long been an ecological force on San Miguel Island, as abundant charcoal in all the paleosols on the island testifies. These paleosols are of widely varying radiocarbon ages and, because many of them pre-date the first humans, the charcoal they contain indicates natural, lightning-caused fires (Johnson 1972). This is not unexpected in an environment that has been basically Mediterranean in character throughout late Quaternary time (Johnson 1977b).

Strong evidence exists that fire has long played an important stripping role on San Miguel Island. For example, in the Yardang Canyon area of Simonton Cove (Fig. 5), the Simonton

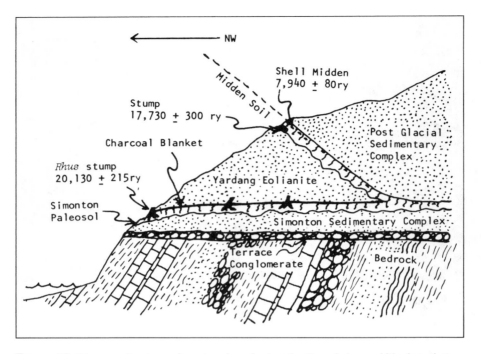

FIGURE 13. *Diagram showing sediment, paleosol, plant fossil, and charcoal blanket relation-ships as exposed in Yardang Canyon, Simonton Cove.*

Paleosol has outcrops in several places in which carbonized trunks of a subarboreal vegetation, in growth position, can be seen; one of the trunks has yielded a date of 20,130 ±250 radiocarbon years (Fig. 13). The fire which swept the vegetation growing on the old soil left a 1 mm-thick veneer of charcoal which blanketed the surface (locality 178 in Charcoal Canyon, Johnson 1972). The charcoal veneer defines an abrupt interface between the Simonton Paleosol and the overlying Yardang Eolianite. The Yardang sands apparently trapped the charcoal before it could be blown away, suggesting very rapid eolian deposition. The fire which swept the vegetation of the Simonton Paleosol apparently caused the reactivation of dune sands located upwind (northwest)—sands which subsequently migrated downwind and rapidly buried the soil, preserving the charcoal blanket. The absence of soil staining, incipient soils, or zones of caliche enrichment within the Yardang sands indicates extremely rapid emplacement. A carbonized root at the base of the soil which later developed upon the Yardang Eolianite gave a date of 17,730 ±300 radiocarbon years, which is chronologically consistent with the above interpretation of rapid sand emplacement. Here, then, is an example of an eolian sand emplacement event resulting from fire stripping of soil cover some 20,000 years ago. How many times this may have happened in the Pleistocene obviously cannot be determined, but the event just described probably was not unique.

Elephants
Elephants are second only to man in their propensity to modify their environment.
(G. B. Schaller, Science 190:263 [1975])

Elephants arrived on the Northern Channel Islands sometime during the later Pleistocene, becoming extinct towards its end, presumably by the hand of man shortly after he first arrived (Johnson 1972, 1973, and 1977a). If elephants are present on an island characterized by high winds and periodic droughts and fires, what resulting landscape modifications might be expected to occur? Fire or drought (or both) must have periodically reduced forage and water supplies then, as they do now, so that fluctuating numbers of elephants probably had profound effects on the insular landscape. While we have no direct information on the effect of too many elephants on the Channel Islands, we know what happened on San Miguel Island when the carrying capacity for domestic livestock was surpassed in the 19th century. The result was massive landscape stripping, excessive erosion, and wholesale deaths of sheep and other stock. Sheep are voracious eaters, but no land animal comes close to matching elephants in the amount of food consumed daily. They are vegetation consumers, modifiers, and destroyers of the first order, and when their numbers surpass the carrying capacity of an area, drastic vegetation destruction occurs (Napier Bax and Sheldrick 1963, Sheldrick 1972, Buechner and Dawkins 1961, Schaff 1972, Glover 1963, Giardino 1974, Laws et al. 1975). Several of the African national parks, which effectively function as "islands," have suffered catastrophic vegetation destruction due to the combined effects of too many elephants, drought conditions, and fire (Frame and Goddard 1972, Laws et al. 1975). Full-grown African elephants eat from 300 to 600+ lbs (136 to 27w kg) of plant food daily, and they normally damage more vegetation than they eat (Glover 1963, Laws et al. 1975).

In recent years, for example, the number of elephants at Tsavo National Park in Kenya has exceeded the carrying capacity of the park. The result is that, during droughts, wholesale deaths of elephants and great destruction of vegetation occur. Over the years:

[The water holes became] surrounded by nearly treeless, desert-like wastes up to 10 to 20 miles in radius. Every day the elephants were compelled to trek across these barrens in order to obtain water before returning to the ever more distant feeding grounds (Frame and Goddard 1972).

On this matter, W. Leuthold, Research Zoologist, Tsavo National Park (East), Kenya, states (in litt. 1972):

The last two years have been exceptionally dry here and the resultant dearth of green vegetation has caused the death of probably several thousand elephants within the Tsavo Park. All available evidence points to malnutrition as being the actual cause of death.

Before the creation of the Tsavo Park in 1948, whenever droughts occurred elephants migrated out of the area. This permitted the vegetation to recover before the elephants returned. Now, however, due to the creation of artificial water holes and frustration of their migratory habit by fences and farming activities, as well as by poaching outside the park, elephants no longer migrate but stay permanently at Tsavo. When droughts occur, the elephants simply begin dying after their food is depleted. Thus, with respect to the elephants, the park now functions as an island in a semiarid climate characterized by periodic droughts (rainfall at Tsavo is 10 to 20 inches [254 to 508 mm] per year, with drought years as low as 2.5 inches [63.5 mm]). The Tsavo elephants are at the mercy of their "insular" environment just as the Tsavo environment is at the mercy of the elephants.

We are now witnessing at Tsavo what may well have occurred repeatedly on San Miguel and the other northern islands (i.e., "Santarosae") during late Quaternary time; that is, wholesale destruction of insular vegetation and attendant landscape stripping. While we have no window on the past, it takes little imagination to trace what must have been a recurrent history on the Northern Channel Islands: too many elephants, too little food due to periodic drought and fires, and subsequent landscape stripping. Although we will never be able to document their full effects, elephants must have been a most important factor in Quaternary landscape modification. How those modifications are expressed in the present landscape is unknown, but probably elephants, along with fire, were major factors in the stripping and dune unstabilization-reemplacement episodes that occurred repeatedly in prehuman time on the island.

Aboriginal Man

For thousands of years following the extinction of the Pygmy Mammoth, man lived on the island and left evidence of his early tenure in the form of ancient kitchen middens, occasional abalone shells in paleosols, and abundant charcoal. If we assume that human occupation of the island has been at least intermittent for the last 8,000 years, then man must have had a noticeable, if not at times profound, effect on the environment. Kitchen middens, almost all of them fire-darkened with charcoal, cover extensive portions of San Miguel Island's northeastern and northwestern coasts.

Annual or frequent burning of the landscape by Indians has been documented for much of coastal and interior California (Lewis 1973). The arrival of fire-using humans on windswept San Miguel Island must have opened a new chapter in episodic landscape stripping. We can only speculate on the full range of ecological effects that aboriginal man may have had on the island ecology. It is, I believe, safe to assume that at times it must have been profound.

CONCLUSION

The episodic vegetational stripping and soil erosional history of San Miguel Island is an outstanding example of how intimate interrelationships of vegetation, climate (drought and wind), fire, animals, landforms, soil, and geomorphic process can be "upset" by human mismanagement, or by nature operating alone.

REFERENCES

ALDEN, J. 1852. Pp. 105-106 *in* U.S. Coast Survey. Report of the Superintendent, 1852, Appendix 18.

BREMNER, C. ST. J. 1933. Geology of San Miguel Island, Santa Barbara County, California. Santa Barbara Mus. Nat. Hist. Occas. Papers, 2.

BUECHNER, H. K., and H. C. DAWKINS. 1961. Vegetation change induced by elephants and fire in Murchison Falls National Park, Uganda. Ecology 42:752-766.

DALL, W. H. 1874. The lords of the isles. Overland Monthly 12:522-526.

DAVIDSON, G. 1858. San Miguel Island. Pp. 23-24 *in* Directory for the Pacific coast. Washington, D.C.

DUNKLE, M. B. 1950. Plant ecology of the Channel Islands of California. Reports on the collections obtained by the Allan Hancock expeditions, Univ. Southern California, B:247-386.

ELLISON, W. H. 1937. The life and adventures of George Nidever. University of California Press, Berkeley, Calif.

FRAME, G. W., and J. GODDARD. 1972. Too many elephants. Science Digest 71:33-38.

GIARDINO, J. R. 1974. When elephants destroy a valley. Geographical Mag. 47:174-181.

GLOVER, J. 1963. The elephant problem at Tsavo. East African Wildl. J. 1:30-39.

GREENE, E. L. 1887. A botanical excursion to the island of San Miguel. Pittonia 1:74-93.

GREENWELL, W. E. 1858a. U.S. Coast Survey. Report of the Superintendent, 1857, Appendix 44.

_____. 1858b. Senate documents, 1st Session, 35th Congress, 1857-1858, 15:394.

_____. 1858c. Superintendent's report (ms.), 22:449 (The National Archives, Record Group No. 23).

————. 1858d. Section 10, Description of signals (description of stations). Field notes, in Record Group No. 23, National Archives.

GRINNELL, J., J. S. DIXON, and J. M. LINSDALE. 1937. Fur-bearing mammals of California. University of California Press, Berkeley, Calif.

HEYE, G. G. 1921. Certain artifacts from San Miguel Island, California. In F. W. Hodge, ed., Indian notes and monographs. Museum of the American Indian, Heye Foundation 7:211.

HOLDER, C. F. 1910. The Channel Islands of California. A. C. McClurg & Co., Chicago, Ill.

JOHNSON, D. L. 1972. Landscape evolution on San Miguel Island, California. Ph.D. thesis, University of Kansas, Lawrence, Kan.

————. 1973. On the origin and extinction of pygmy elephants, Northern Channel Islands, California. Program and abstracts, Geol. Soc. Amer.

————. 1977a. The California ice-age refugium and the Rancholabrean extinction problem. Quaternary Res. 8:149-153.

————. 1977b. The late Quaternary climate of coastal California: evidence for an ice age refugium. Quaternary Res. 8:154-179.

LAWS, R. M., I. S. C. PARKER, and R. C. B. JOHNSTONE. 1975. Elephants and their habitats. Clarendon Press, Oxford.

LESTER, E. L. 1974. The legendary king of San Miguel: the Lesters at Rancho Rambouillet. W. T. Genns, Santa Barbara, Calif.

LEWIS, H. T. 1973. Patterns of Indian burning in California: ecology and ethnohistory. Ballena Press Anthropol. Papers, 1, Ramona, Calif.

LLOYD, R. B. 1948. Los Angeles Times, Mar. 7.

NAPIER BAX, P., and D. L. W. SHELDRICK. 1963. Some preliminary observations on the food of elephants in the Tsavo Royal National Park (East) of Kenya. East African Wildl. J. 1:40-53.

PHILLIPS, M. J. 1927. History of Santa Barbara County, California 1:103-114.

ROGERS, D. B. 1929. Prehistoric man of the Santa Barbara coast. Santa Barbara Museum of Natural History, Santa Barbara, Calif.

SCHAAF, D. 1972. Elephants, fire, and the environment. Animal Kingdom 75:8-15.

SCHUMACHER, P. 1875. Some remains of a former people. Overland Monthly 15:374-379.

————. 1877. Researches in the kjokkenmoddings and graves of a former population of the Santa Barbara Islands and the adjacent mainland. Bull. U.S. Geol. and Geogr. Surv. Territories 3(1):37-56.

SHELDRICK, D. 1972. Death of the Tsavo elephants. Saturday Review (Sept.), pp. 28-36.

STREATOR, C. P. 1887. The water birds of San Miguel Island. Santa Barbara Soc. Nat. Hist. Bull. 1:21-23.

TROXELL, H.C., and W. HOFMANN. 1954. Hydrology of the Los Angeles region. Geol. So. California, Bull. 170, 1:5-12.

TROXELL, H. C. et al. 1954. Hydrology of the San Bernardino and eastern San Gabriel Mountains, California. Dept. Interior, U.S. Geol. Surv. Hydrologic Investigations Atlas HA-I.

VOY, C. D. ca. 1893. San Miguel Island, California. Unpubl. ms., Bancroft Library, University of California, Berkeley, Calif.

WHEELER, G. M. 1879. Report upon U.S. geographical surveys west of the one hundredth meridian, v. 7, archaeology. U.S. Gov't. Printing Office, Washington, D.C.

WILLETT, G. 1910. A summer trip to the northern Santa Barbara Islands. Condor 12:170-174.

WRIGHT, H., and G. K. SNYDER. 1913. Birds observed in the summer of 1912 among the Santa Barbara Islands. Condor 15:86-92.

YATES, L. 1902. Prehistoric California. Bull. So. California Acad. Sci. 1:97-100.

Vegetation of Santa Cruz and Santa Catalina Islands

Richard A. Minnich

*Department of Geography, California State University,
Northridge, California 91330*

INTRODUCTION

Most research on the plant geography of the Southern California Channel Islands has focused on the flora, perhaps inspired most by the large number of endemic species found there. The question of insular geographic isolation has led to evaluation of the island flora from several standpoints, including: interisland and island-mainland species affinities; island size, habitat diversity, and species richness; and the general question of island endemism, autochthonous evolution, and the islands as refugia for species having former widespread distributions on the continent (Philbrick 1967).

However, overall, the vegetation of the Channel Islands is not well known. No vegetation maps have ever been produced, as these areas have escaped previous statewide vegetation surveys, including the Vegetation Type Map Survey and the State Cooperative Soil-Vegetation Survey (Colwell 1977). Small-scale renditions shown as part of larger maps are lacking in detail and contain significant errors (U.S. Dept. Agric. 1945, Kuchler 1977). Broad plant communities are generally recognized, but actual distributions have been only informally discussed (Raven 1963, Thorne 1967, Philbrick and Haller 1977). As an initial attempt at describing the plant cover of the Channel Islands, this study presents vegetation maps of Santa Cruz and Santa Catalina Islands as interpreted from color infrared aerial photography. The maps are drafted in color on eight 1:24,000 scale (7½ minute) U.S. Geological Survey topographic quadrangles (four for each island), and reduced to the format of this volume. The vegetation maps offer just one "snapshot" of a "motion picture" which shows plants in constant change. The vegetation is dynamic; changes are especially rapid in areas where feral herbivores are being controlled. The discussion to follow describes plant community distributions, physiognomic characteristics, and species dominance.

THE PHYSICAL ENVIRONMENT

Santa Cruz and Santa Catalina Islands are among the largest and most diverse of the Channel Island group, having respective areas of 249 and 194 km^2. Approximately 30 km in length, both islands are roughly east-west in orientation and consist of moderately dissected parallel ridges reaching 400 to 700 m elevation. Except in valley bottoms and ridgelines, most slopes are steeper than 20 degrees, but less than 30 degrees.

The climate is Mediterranean with mild temperatures, rainy winters, and dry summers. Winter precipitation results chiefly from frontal disturbances guided into southern California from the north Pacific Ocean by troughs (waves) in upper-level westerly circulation between November and April. The annual precipitation on Santa Catalina ranges from 200 mm at Little Harbor on the southwest to 350 mm on the channel slope in the vicinity of Avalon. Because of Santa Cruz Island's greater size and orographic influences of the Santa Ynez Mountains to the north, the annual precipitation is much greater. The Stanton Ranch in the interior central valley of Santa Cruz averages nearly 500 mm (data on file at the Stanton Ranch) with higher slopes to the west receiving perhaps as much as 600 mm. The predominance of large-scale air masses associated with the polar front jet stream minimizes island-mainland climatic differences during this season.

During summer, dynamic subsidence, associated with the surface Pacific high pressure system and weak anticyclonic circulation aloft, is dominant as cyclonic storms travel far to the north of southern California. Although the regional air mass is warm and dry, surface weather on the Channel Islands is strongly influenced by a shallow, coastal marine layer (a cool, moist, low-level air mass 300 to 800 m in vertical depth) which advects slowly south and eastward toward interior California from the cold, upwelling Pacific Ocean waters along the coast. It is the day-to-day persistence of the marine layer that ameliorates and differentiates island climate from that of the mainland during the summer drought season. Because Santa Cruz Island is located in exposed outer channel waters, annual temperatures there, especially in coastal areas facing west and north, are probably a few degrees colder than at Santa Catalina, which is sheltered in the southern California embayment. Diabatic heating and turbulent mixing of the marine layer with warmer air above rough terrain still produce noticeably warmer temperatures in the interior portions of both islands, particularly in the central valley of Santa Cruz Island (Hochberg 1980) where daytime temperatures are not unlike those in mainland coastal mountains and valleys as far inland as 20 km.

The islands have been overgrazed by feral goats, sheep, pigs, and other introduced domestic animals for more than a century. Historical records indicate that grazing, mostly by sheep, became important soon after statehood (1850) at a time when these activities were widespread in the coastal plains and mountains of southern California (Brumbaugh 1980, Coblentz 1980, Minnich 1978). The goat may have been introduced to Santa Catalina during the late Mexican period (Coblentz 1980). These animals gradually became feral and multiplied at will in the absence of indigenous predatory animals. Herds increased rapidly to tens of thousands and had so much impact on the vegetation that Santa Cruz Island was "ravaged" by the time of the 100th meridian survey of 1875 (Rothrock, in Wheeler 1876); ground photographs of Santa Catalina taken in the 1880s show strong evidence of vegetation stripping at present-day Avalon, the isthmus, and other sites (Huntington Library Photo Collection). Some measures have been taken to control these animals in the present century. Under the ownership of the Stanton family, portions of Santa Cruz Island—notably on the isthmus, in Central Valley, in several western drainages, and more recently in the southern drainages—have been fenced to keep sheep out. On Santa Catalina, commercial sheep and cattle grazing continued until the early 1950s when domestic stock were successfully removed (A. Douglas Probst, pers. comm.). Goats were also recently exclosed from interior drainages east of the Middle Ranch on Santa Catalina. Although goats are free to roam over major portions of the Island, the intensity of grazing pressure seems to be partly determined by behavior and territoriality of the animals (Coblentz 1976). Severest grazing appears to occur in Silver Canyon, Grand Canyon, the channel slope in the vicinity of Twin Rocks, and west of the isthmus. Herds on both islands are intermittently reduced by hunting.

METHODS

The vegetation maps were interpreted from 1:22,000 scale color infrared (CIR) photography (type 2443) done in July, 1970 (Santa Cruz Island) and February, 1976 (Santa Catalina Island). The film was reproduced on nine-inch square positive transparencies and properly exposed, except for some vignetting. (Color imbalance of the Santa Catalina photography was compensated for by excellent resolution.)

The photography was interpreted over a light table with a Bausch and Lomb rollfilm stereoscope with 3.3x and 8.8x magnification. There was no field mapping; rather, the primary role of fieldwork was the characterization of photographic data. The physiognomic vegetation classes were easily identified on the basis of crown structure, height, spread, and other morphological characteristics. In taxonomic identification from aerial photographs, on the other hand, the imagery appearance of a species had to be as familiar as its field appearance.

This involved conventional taxonomic identification in the field and determination of gross physical features which made plant species recognizable at a distance and ultimately from above. The process was one of cross-checking information from the field and from photographs. In the field, individual plants were located and plotted on topographic quadrangles and checked against photographs of the same area. In the laboratory, plant signatures on photography were extrapolated to other areas and checked in the field in order to develop consistent species identification. Species were identified singly or narrowed down into species "sets," often to the genus level (e.g., Arctostaphylos) or physiognomic class (e.g., coastal sage scrub, grassland). Instead of using an a priori typing system, the plant classification is based on information which could be interpreted from the photography.

The vegetation maps are both floristic and physiognomic constructs for which the data are shown by linework and color, respectively. Linework delimits polygons of individual species or species sets defined by a minimum cover threshold of 20 per cent. Polygons may overlap where species are found together. In areas of chaparral, color and linework may operate independently; here, colorwork denotes the dominant physiognomic layer defined in terms of equal abundance of individual physiognomic classes as observed from above in aerial photographs. Thus, a polygon delimiting an open stand of scrub oak (Quercus dumosa) underlain by contiguous grass is ascribed the color for grassland vegetation. Conversely, a contiguous cover of Quercus dumosa underlain by open grass is given the color for chaparral. Similarly, if the point of equal abundance of Quercus dumosa and grass falls within the polygon, a color boundary dividing both physiognomic classes may transect the polygon. For other vegetation types, the species mapped and colorwork for physiognomy are conformal. Areal data for the vegetation types were computed by areagram overlay on the maps (3 per cent error) and are shown in Tables 1 to 4. The author concedes that there may be errors in the maps because the detail of information gained from the air cannot match that which can be seen on the ground. The aerial view, on the other hand, allows for more efficient mapping of large areas by providing greater overall perspective of the spatial relations among plants, and will be useful until detailed field-mapping is done.

PRESENT VEGETATION

At the physiognomic level, the prevailing plant communities of Santa Cruz and Santa Catalina Islands are comparable to those found on mainland coast ranges. They include annual grassland, coastal sage scrub, chaparral, oak woodland, riparian woodland, and closed-cone pine forest. Cursory examination of the vegetation maps (Figs. 1 and 2) shows that the distribution of shrub and woodland vegetation is highly fragmented, covering mostly canyons and north-facing slopes, except at the east end of Santa Catalina where cover is continuous. Herbaceous vegetation prevails elsewhere. For the most part, the same species form the bulk of vegetal cover of both islands; some differences in the geographic patterning are evident, however, which seem to reflect important contrasts in their respective climates and grazing histories.

Grassland

Annual grasses form the major portion of the total vegetal cover of both islands. Field reconnaissance indicates that the dominant species are introduced European grasses, such as Avena fatua, A. barbata, Bromus rigidus, and B. rubens, although local depauperate populations of native perennial grasses, e.g., Stipa pulchra, may be found. Annual grassland seems to thrive best in deep loamy soils on alluvium or marine terraces, particularly in Central Valley, at the isthmus ridge, and on the west side of Santa Cruz Island. However, grassland may even prevail on steep rocky slopes, though usually admixed with woody vegetation. Herbaceous cover is completely absent only in relatively undisturbed coastal sage scrub and chaparral, such

TABLE 1. Vegetation summary of Santa Catalina and Santa Cruz Islands: physiognomic types (hundreds of hectares).

Physiognomic type[1]	S. Catalina	S. Cruz
n	194.0	249.0
Grassland	59.0	114.6
Coastal sage scrub	25.3	14.1
Prickly pear (*Opuntia*)	13.0	7.7
Chaparral	81.1	76.2
Oak woodland	2.6	17.5
Conifer forest	0.0	5.3
Riparian	0.3	2.6
Cultivated	3.1	0.6
Urban	1.4	0.0
Bare	8.2	10.4

[1]Area defined by dominant vegetal layer.

TABLE 2. Vegetation summary of Santa Catalina and Santa Cruz Islands: woodland, riparian, and sage species (hundreds of hectares).

Woodland, riparian, and sage species[1]	S. Catalina	S. Cruz
Lyonothamnus floribundus	0.3	3.0
Prunus lyonii	2.0	2.6
Quercus agrifolia	0.0	11.4
Q. chrysolepis	0.1	0.4
Q. tomentella	0.2	0.1
Pinus muricata	0.0	5.3
Baccharis glutinosa	—[2]	1.4
B. pilularis	0.2	4.0
Populus fremontii	0.2	0.4
Salix spp.	0.1	0.8
Artemisia, Salvia, spp.	38.8	15.3
Opuntia littoralis	15.0	9.1
Annual grasses	100.4	160.0

[1]Includes stands sympatric with chaparral.
[2]Present, but in insignificant amounts.

TABLE 3. Vegetation summary of Santa Catalina Island: chaparral (hundreds of hectares).[1]

Vegetation type	Contiguous stands	Sympatry with:			Total	Per cent contiguous
		Sage	Grass	Opuntia		
Adenostoma fasciculatum	0.6	0.4	0.9	—[2]	1.9	32
Arctostaphylos catalinae	—[2]	0.0	0.0	0.0	—[2]	—[2]
Heteromeles arbutifolia	14.0	0.8	17.0	0.2	32.0	44
Malosma (Rhus) laurina	1.1	1.3	2.4	1.2	6.0	18
Mixed (*Ceanothus megacarpus, C. arboreus, Cercocarpus betuloides*)	3.8	0.3	0.4	0.0	4.5	84
Quercus dumosa	24.0	1.2	23.4	0.2	48.8	49
Rhus integrifolia	3.3	10.8	14.7	0.6	29.4	11

[1]Area defined by 20 per cent cover and will overlap other types (values are not additive).   [2]Present, but in insignificant amounts.

TABLE 4. Vegetation summary of Santa Cruz Island: chaparral (hundreds of hectares).[1]

Vegetation type	Contiguous stands	Sympatry with:			Total	Per cent contiguous
		Sage	Grass	Opuntia		
Adenostoma fasciculatum	0.6	0.3	1.7	0.0	2.6	23
Arctostaphylos spp.	6.2	—[2]	2.3	—[2]	8.5	73
Mixed (*Ceanothus megacarpus, C arboreus, Cercocarpus betuloides*)	0.1	0.4	3.8	—[2]	4.3	2
Quercus dumosa (Heteromeles arbutifolia)	16.3	2.2	33.8	1.0	54.3	30
Rhus integrifolia	—[2]	2.3	3.8	0.4	6.5	—[2]
Totals	23.2	5.2	45.4	1.4	76.2	30

[1]Area defined by dominance.   [2]Present, but in insignificant amounts.

as at the Avalon end of Santa Catalina.

The density and cover of annual grassland varies significantly depending on grazing history. On Santa Cruz Island, grass quality is closely related to fencing history and sheep grazing (Orme and Minnich 1970). Grass is tall (*ca.* 1.0 m) and contiguous in areas free of sheep. Moderate grass cover occurs along the southern drainages where sheep have been managed since the 1950s. Cover is sparse in areas of heaviest sheep concentration, particularly the Devils Peak ridge north of Central Valley and "No Man's Land" southeast of Chinese Harbor. Grass quality on Santa Catalina Island also ranges from excellent to very poor, but occurs in a gradient having little correlation with fencing, perhaps owing to the territorial behavior of goats (Coblentz 1976). Poorest grass cover occurs where goat populations are highest (Silver Canyon, the channel slope near Twin Rocks, and west of the isthmus). Grass cover is best along the channel slope between Mt. Black Jack and Swains Canyon, and within the Wrigley and Middle Ranches.

Grass cover also varies seasonally. Germination and early growth occurs during winter and spring throughout the islands except in the most severely eroded areas. Normally, grasses keep up with grazing pressure until drought desiccation begins in late spring or early summer. By autumn, most herbaceous cover accessible to feral animals is stripped, except for toxic species such as *Eremocarpus setigerus* and *Mimulus longiflorus*.

Coastal Sage Scrub

Coastal sage scrub occurs primarily on south-facing slopes on over 20 per cent of Santa Catalina Island and over only 6 per cent of Santa Cruz Island. On Santa Cruz, coastal sage scrub is restricted to areas free of sheep. Largest stands occur where prevailing grass quality is best: on the south face of the isthmus, in Central Valley, and on the southwest end from Cañada Posa to Morse Point (also near Bowen Point). On Santa Catalina, the vitality of coastal sage scrub is inversely related to the intensity of goat grazing. Contiguous stands reminiscent of coastal sage scrub on nearby mainland mountain ranges (0.5 to 1.0 m tall; greater than 70 per cent cover) are widespread at the east end in the vicinity of Avalon. These contiguous stands grade into fragmented, degraded stands infested with prickly pear (*Opuntia*) toward the west into the interior drainages of the Wrigley and Middle Ranches and into the isthmus area. Field observations indicate the dominant species are *Artemisia californica, Salvia apiana*, and a procumbant *S. mellifera*.

Two evergreen sclerophyll shrubs, *Rhus integrifolia* and *Malosma (Rhus) laurina*, are also sympatric with coastal sage scrub over extensive areas of Santa Catalina and locally on Santa Cruz Island. *Baccharis pilularis* ssp. *consanguinea* appears to be invading annual grassland on protected southern and western portions of Santa Cruz Island. In areas where goats are most concentrated on Santa Catalina, *Opuntia* is dominant, although isolated individuals of coastal sage species may be found amidst dense *Opuntia* thickets. *Opuntia* on Santa Cruz Island is in poor condition, due to the introduction of the cochineal bug in the 1930s, and normally does not harbor browse-sensitive plants.

Endemic species of *Eriogonum* appear to be less resilient to grazing than the dominant shrubs. *Eriogonum grande* and *E. arborescens* occur only in local populations in the best protected areas on Santa Cruz. *E. giganteum* on Santa Catalina is most conspicuous around Avalon and the Wrigley Ranch. *Artemesia californica* is also subject to browsing, and it, too, is most abundant near Avalon and the Wrigley Ranch.

Chaparral

In large part, island chaparral is dominated by species familiar on the mainland. Yet the physiognomy of this association differs in terms of stand maturity, openness of cover, and diversity of growth form, ranging from tall "elfin forests" (sometimes grading into woodlands) to prostrate mats in wind-exposed locations on the north- and west-facing coasts. Chaparral rarely forms extensive cover except on north-facing slopes and canyons. The largest continuous stands on Santa Catalina Island occur on the channel slope between Swains Canyon and Avalon. On Santa Cruz Island the largest stands are along the north slope of Central Valley. Only one third of the stands have continuous cover. The remainder exist in parklands of primarily tall shrubs with sharp browse lines, underlain by annual grassland, coastal sage scrub, or prickly pear.

Broad floristic trends are common to both islands. The sumacs—*Rhus integrifolia* and *Malosma (Rhus) laurina* (Santa Catalina only)—tend to form open stands on south-facing slopes with an understory matrix of coastal sage scrub in protected areas, and grassland or prickly pear in overgrazed areas. *Malosma laurina* is most abundant in warmer interior portions of Santa Catalina. *Rhus integrifolia* is also almost ubiquitous over the island. On Santa Cruz, *R. integrifolia* is generally restricted to coastal localities.

On north-facing slopes, chaparral is dominated primarily by *Quercus dumosa*. *Rhus integrifolia* often forms an understory to the oak, especially on Santa Catalina. *Heteromeles arbutifolia* is locally dominant at coastal locations and in many mesic canyon sites elsewhere. *Cercocarpus betuloides* and *Ceanothus arboreus* are sparingly present in heaviest stands but normally absent from chaparral savannas. *Arctostaphylos* chaparral (*A. subcordata, A. insularis, A. tomentosa*) covers several areas of Santa Cruz Island, mostly gentle slopes and ridgelines south of the rift valley and along the crest of the isthmus. *Arctostaphylos* chaparral on Santa Catalina (*A. catalinae*) consists of only five unmappable populations amounting to a few hectares (Thorne 1967). Surprisingly, chamise chaparral (*Adenostoma fasciculatum*), widespread in southern California coastal mountains, is scarce on both islands. *Adenostoma* normally appears as a minor element of *Quercus dumosa* or *Arctostaphylos* chaparral. It is locally dominant, however, on mostly southern exposures; the most extensive stand (approximately 50 hectares) occurs just west of the Santa Catalina isthmus (a northern exposure). Open stands, widely admixed with *Ceanothus megacarpus* var. *insularis, Cercocarpus betuloides,* and *Quercus dumosa,* cover xeric slopes immediately north of the central rift valley of Santa Cruz Island. These also contain rare populations of *Rhus ovata* and *Rhamnus crocea* var. *pirifolia*. A prostrate ecotype of *Adenostoma fasciculatum* is also found at several locations on the island (*e.g.*, the isthmus and the ridgeline south of Cañada Cervada; Philbrick and Haller 1977).

Examination of the vegetation map shows that the floristic composition of Santa Cruz Island chaparral appears to be quite responsive to large climatic contrasts between the coast and the warmer, interior Central Valley. *Quercus dumosa, Heteromeles arbutifolia,* and *Rhus integrifolia* appear to be the only shrubs tolerant of the cold summers at the west end. In contrast, *Arctostaphylos, Adenostoma, Ceanothus megacarpus,* and *Cercocarpus* chaparral tend to be concentrated on interior sites.

The species richness of Santa Catalina Island chaparral appears to be inversely related to grazing pressure. In least disturbed areas around Avalon and the Middle and Wrigley Ranches, *Quercus dumosa* and *Heteromeles arbutifolia* are admixed with *Cercocarpus betuloides, Ceanothus arboreus,* and *C. megacarpus,* with embedded patches or understory of *Adenostoma fasciculatum* and coastal sage scrub on drier sites. Stands are mostly contiguous, have minimal browse damage, contain abundant fuels and, in the vicinity of Avalon, provide enough of a fire hazard to induce the Los Angeles County Fire Department to construct fuel breaks along ridgelines. In areas of heavier grazing, chaparral is dominated by the most durable robust shrubs, notably *Quercus dumosa* and *Heteromeles arbutifolia*. Stands are open, exhibit browse lines, and contain more herbaceous understory. *Malosma laurina* and *Rhus integrifolia,* however, seem to persist in the most goat-infested parts of Santa Catalina Island. In fact, the absence of browse lines on *Malosma laurina* in Grand Canyon suggests this species is somewhat protected by being unpalatable. On Santa Cruz, browse sensitive *Adenostoma* and *Ceanothus* species are also most abundant within areas protected from sheep, especially in Central Valley. A large stand of huge *Cercocarpus betuloides* (>6 m tall) occurs on south-facing slopes of the heavily grazed east end of Devils Peak ridge.

Many other chaparral species occur on the islands but are not abundant enough to be mapped. These include *Xylococcus bicolor, Garrya* spp., *Toxicodendron diversilobum, Comarostaphylis diversifolia, Rhamnus crocea* var. *pirifolia,* and the island endemic, *Crossosoma californicum*.

Oak Woodland

Mesic north-facing slopes, canyons, and bottomland support medium- to large-spreading trees, mostly of the genus *Quercus*, grouped in contiguous woodlands. The areal extent of this physiognomic type is more localized than chaparral, with the majority of populations occurring on Santa Cruz Island. On Santa Catalina, woodlands are narrowly confined to watercourse environments. The distribution of woodlands appears to be independent of grazing pressures because many of the best stands occur in areas heavily populated with sheep and goats.

Most woodlands on Santa Cruz consist of *Quercus agrifolia,* which is distributed along watercourses throughout the island. The most impressive stands occur in upper Cañada Cervada, in the interior Central Valley, and in the gorge draining Central Valley to Prisoners Harbor. Along the western channel slope of the heavily grazed Devils Peak ridge, *Quercus agrifolia* forms an extensive open parkland savanna covering ridges as well as canyons. Strangely, *Quercus agrifolia* is absent from Santa Catalina Island. Instead, the dominant woodland species here is *Prunus ilicifolia lyonii,* which occurs mostly along dry canyon bottoms. The finest populations are found at Cherry Cove west of the isthmus. On wetter Santa Cruz, *Prunus ilicifolia lyonii* mimics *Quercus agrifolia* by straying away from watercourses to cover rocky slopes and ridges, but rarely forms continuous cover as on Santa Catalina.

The islands share three additional oaks with localized distributions. Two species, *Q. chrysolepis* and *Q. tomentella,* form a hybrid complex in which expressions of each are found in divergent habitats. Small *Q. chrysolepis* patches cover the highest ridges of both islands (Santa Cruz: north slope of Devils Peak ridge; Santa Catalina: Mt. Orizaba, lower Cape Canyon). *Q. tomentella* occurs in cool, coastal localities, but often as solitary trees. The most impressive stands are found on Santa Catalina in Gallagher Canyon (Thorne 1967). Another hybrid, *Q. macdonaldii* (*Q. dumosa* x *Q. lobata*), a winter deciduous species, occurs as solitary trees or as hybrid swarm populations grading with *Q. dumosa* in many areas of both islands, particularly in wetter sites. All stands, however, are too small to be mapped.

The endemic *Lyonothamnus floribundus* forms small, compact groves, mostly in dry portions of canyons. It is widespread on Santa Cruz Island; 412 known groves, covering 300 hectares, occur throughout the island, except at the isthmus and on the warm, eastern half of the interior central valley. On Santa Catalina, 40 groves, covering only 30 hectares, are concentrated along the wettest portions of the channel slope from Avalon west to Long Point.

A few madrone (*Arbutus menziesii*) are reported along a watercourse on the channel slope of northwest Santa Cruz Island.

Riparian Woodland

In spite of the presence of some perennial streams, riparian vegetation on these islands is remarkably impoverished. The only taxa abundant enough to be mapped are *Salix* spp., *Populus fremontii,* and *Baccharis glutinosa,* all characterized by wind-borne seed. Heavy-seeded mainland riparian trees are quite rare or absent. *Platanus racemosa* was introduced to both islands in the early 20th century. *Alnus rhombifolia* and *Acer macrophyllum* are conspicuously absent. One *A. macrophyllum* occurring in a gully west of Prisoners Harbor was probably planted.

The geographic extent of riparian vegetation reflects the climatic differences between the islands. On Santa Catalina, this association is highly localized and consists largely of *Salix* thickets. One *P. fremontii* population occurs in lower Middle Canyon. Santa Cruz supports about 20 *P. fremontii* groves, several of which are long gallery forests along streams. *Salix* spp. often forms impenetrable stands where there is permanent water, while *Baccharis glutinosa* occurs along dry washes, especially those draining severely eroded portions of the island (notably the interior central valley, Laguna Canyon, and an unnamed drainage leading to Willows Anchorage on the south coast).

Closed-cone Pine Forest

Pinus muricata forests cover mostly north-facing slopes in three areas of Santa Cruz Island: the east half of the isthmus ridge, the channel slope just west of Prisoners Harbor, and several drainages leading to the Christi Ranch on the west end. The latter stand also extends southward along a sharp ridge to Sierra Blanca. Most populations are small and discrete. An impressive stand, however, covers more than 100 hectares in the upper headwaters of Cañada Cervada. The floristic composition and physiognomy of *Pinus muricata* forests varies considerably depending on grazing pressure (Hobbs 1980). Along the isthmus ridge and the west end, protected forests are contiguous, contain abundant pine reproduction and ground litter, and are admixed with a broken cover of a number of shrubs, including *Heteromeles arbutifolia, Arctostaphylos confertifolia, A. tomentosa, Vaccinium ovatum, Comarostaphylis diversifolia,* and prostrate *Quercus wislizenii*. Grazed forests on Sierra Blanca and west of Prisoners Harbor are open, contain few shrubs, and are lacking in reproduction except for toxic herbs such as *Eremocarpus setigerus*. The overall distribution of *P. muricata* is limited to sites exposed to maritime influences to the north and west, and to elevations where the marine layer is most frequently condensed as stratus during the summer (300 to 500 m), suggesting that this species may depend on summer stratus and fog drip to ameliorate drought stress.

ISLAND-MAINLAND VEGETATION AFFINITIES

In spite of their proximity to the southern California mainland, the vegetation of Santa Catalina and Santa Cruz Islands is strikingly different from the vegetation on nearby coastal mountain ranges, such as the Santa Ynez and the Santa Monica Mountains. This is surprising if one expects that similar environments near one another should have similar vegetation. This generalization holds true only to the level of species dominance. The vegetation data presented here reveal that species contributing most to island plant cover are also important mainland dominants. Present grasslands consist of exotic European annuals that also cover most of coastal California. The dominant species of coastal sage scrub are the familiar *Artemesia californica, Salvia apiana,* and *S. mellifera*. Among the chaparral, a few dominants endemic to the Channel Islands, or having limited distributions along the California coast, include *Arctostaphylos insularis, A. subcordata,* and *A. tomentosa*. Other species are not only significant mainland shrubs, but their distributional relations in the complex terrain of the Islands are much the same as those described for the coastal mountains of southern California (Hanes 1971). Oak woodlands contain two species endemic to the Channel Islands, *Quercus tomentella* and *Q. macdonaldii,* but most stands are dominated by *Q. agrifolia,* widespread from coastal central California to northern Baja California. Finally, the closed-cone pine, *Pinus muricata,* is found intermittently along a large stretch of the west coast from northern California to northern Baja California. The most notable endemic is *Lyonothamnus floribundus,* but it has a very localized distribution on the islands.

Major differences between island and mainland vegetation become apparent when one examines the physiognomy and geographic extent of the dominant plant communities. The strangest aspect of island vegetation is the generally oversized, arborescent appearance of chaparral shrubs and the open configuration of stands. An additional, related anomaly is the relative unimportance of woody vegetation and the widespread extent of grasslands. Grasses cover not only the heavier loams but also shallow rocky soils; these savannas, together with the shrub and woodland species, are reminiscent of the coast ranges of central California, rather than the solid brushfields covering southern California mountains.

Although many researchers have attributed these trends to the ameliorating influences of a cool, equable climate (Philbrick 1967), a more tenable explanation for these differences is believed to be long-term overgrazing by feral animals, particularly sheep and goats, which annually denude or damage the vegetation and disrupt normal plant life cycle processes. Grazing has also indirectly modified the natural fire regime due to the continual "harvest" of flammable brushland fuels. Although the Channel Islands are more exposed to maritime influences than are most mainland areas, they are still subject to summer drought, desiccation of vegetation, and the potential of fire. Historical accounts from before the turn of the present century, when fire suppression was begun, leave no doubt that fire was once widespread throughout coastal southern California (Minnich 1978). Fires ignited by lightning, Indians, and early European settlers apparently spread at will for long periods of time, perhaps weeks or months, until extinguished by fog or the first autumn rain. The fire regime on the islands could be considered in the context of natural and man-caused ignitions. However, fire is more a product of the physical environment, characterized by a tremendous imbalance between plant productivity and decomposition rates, and the accumulation of highly flammable fuels (Specht 1969, DeBano et al. 1977). How fires began in the past, and how extensively and frequently they spread, will probably never be known. Instead, it is important to recognize that fire is a natural part of the life cycle of this type of vegetation. The presence of numerous shrub species with survival strategies linked to fires gives strong evidence for the long-term role of fire on the islands.

The persistence, geography, and gigantism of present brush and woodland communities can be partly explained in terms of the relative tolerance of different species to browsing, and their ability to persist in the absence of fire. The resilience of a species to grazing is clearly a function of its size and height; feral animals browse almost all available vegetation within their reach. By late summer, annual grasses have been eaten, but these regenerate the following spring from seeds lying in the soil. Coastal sage scrub species are not so fortunate. Their limited size also virtually guarantees their destruction. The fact that coastal sage scrub is limited to areas protected from feral animals suggests that grazing may inhibit regeneration over large portions of both islands. Indeed, some areas of coastal sage scrub recently closed to goats or sheep have recovered, but very slowly. It is interesting to note that on south Santa Cruz Island most recovered areas are *Artemisia californica,* which are capable of long-distance wind dispersal. Interior portions of eastern Santa Catalina Island protected from goats in the 1950s are being rapidly invaded by *Artemisia californica, Salvia apiana,* and *S. mellifera* (Fig. 3). The survival of *Salvia,* which relies on seed storage, local dispersal, and disturbance for reproduction, was probably enhanced by widespread protective *Opuntia* thickets. Survival of *Salvia* and other locally dispersed species might also have occurred on Santa Cruz Island, were it not for the introduction of the cochineal insect to eradicate *Opuntia.*

Feral grazing is probably the primary factor for the gigantism and openness of the chaparral (Fig. 3). Shrubs experience so few fires that they are not forced to regenerate by sprouting or by seeds, as they do frequently on the mainland. Moreover, the shrubs are annually "pruned" by grazing, forcing crowns to grow taller than if left undisturbed. Stands thin out due to the combination of adult attrition and lack of reproduction. Most shrubs in heavily grazed areas are probably relicts of the pregrazing period.

Species selection due to long-term overgrazing may also explain some of the present floristic composition of the chaparral. The largest species, *Quercus dumosa, Heteromeles arbutifolia, Arctostaphylos* spp., and *Malosma laurina,* should survive best, particularly on mesic, north-facing slopes where, as a result of greater moisture availability and plant growth, these species send leaves beyond the browse line more quickly than do plants on drier slopes. Conversely, the possibility that frail *Adenostoma fasciculatum* and *Ceanothus megacarpus* would be more rapidly eliminated than other shrubs may account for their absence on the islands. As a current demonstration, the best stands of *Adenostoma fasciculatum* in goat- and pig-infested areas west of the Santa Catalina isthmus have rapidly thinned out in the last three years, during which time *Heteromeles arbutifolia, Quercus dumosa,* and *Rhus integrifolia* have held their own.

By virtue of their size, woodland species and *Pinus muricata* have probably suffered the least mechanical damage from feral animals, as is suggested by their distribution even in the most heavily grazed areas.

The elimination of fire would also be deleterious to chaparral species with fire-related survival strategies. Chaparral may be loosely divided into two classes whose strategies are highly divergent (Wells 1969). One group is characterized by long-lived species which have fleshy fruits that are consumed by animals, and seeds that may be dispersed over great distances. Such plants exhibit continuous reproduction between fire disturbances and recover from fire primarily by sprouting, an ancient trait common to angiosperms whether in flammable or nonflammable habitats. Examples include *Quercus dumosa, Heteromeles arbutifolia, Malosma laurina,* and *Rhus integrifolia.* The other group, which consists of *Adenostoma fasciculatum, Ceanothus* spp. and *Arctostaphylos* spp., exhibits seed dormancy and repro-duces *en masse* after fires by seed scarification; the abundance of species in this group is stimulated by burning (Horton and Kraebel 1955, Patric and Hanes 1964, Hanes 1971). In the absence of fire, chaparral succession develops by an ascendancy of long-lived shrubs over short-lived ones (Hanes 1971). Santa Cruz and Santa Catalina Islands seem to be an extreme case of this condition; *Ceanothus* spp. and, to a lesser extent, *Adenostoma fasciculatum* have a short life span and poor reproduction due to both the lack of fire disturbance and to grazing. It is curious that the island chaparral most closely resembles petran chaparral found on the desert margins of the southern California coast ranges (Hanes 1971). Both plant communities are dominated by the same long-lived genera, including *Quercus, Cercocarpus,* and *Arcto-staphylos,* in stands of tall, widely-spaced shrubs. Both experience fire frequencies too low to select for species with fire strategies, in one case due to a dry climate (low productivity), and in the other due to feral animal grazing.

Ironically, fire would be a death knell to woody vegetation under the present grazing regime. Shrubs will still not be able to reproduce and sprouts will be destroyed because they must regenerate within browse range. Only thick-barked pine and woodland species could survive, either by directly escaping combustion or by sprouting above the browse line.

Given the indiscriminate burning practices of 19th-century European livestock grazers in southern California (Minnich 1978), it is not at all improbable that much chaparral was removed by fire and grazing during the past hundred years. This is suggested by early ground photo-graphs which show heavy brush vegetation on presently denuded slopes on both Santa Cruz (see Brumbaugh 1980) and Santa Catalina (Fig. 3). Moreover, these photographs reveal chaparral physiognomy reminiscent of mainland stands, *i.e.,* contiguous cover and a low homogeneous height profile indicative of earlier burns. Browse lines and arborescence are absent. The similarity of the vegetation as recorded by vertical aerial photography both in 1929 and at present indicates, however, that the bulk of vegetation damage due to grazing and fire

FIGURE 3. *Views of Mt. Black Jack from the present airport site in central Santa Catalina Island taken in the 1880s (left) and the present (right).* **Left:** *Continuous low shrub matrix evident in the mid-ground and on the north slope of Mt. Black Jack is primarily* Adenostoma fasciculatum *interlaced with numerous goat trails. Larger shrubs embedded with* Adenostoma fasciculatum *and with grassland to the left and in the foreground are mostly* Quercus dumosa *and* Malosma (Rhus) laurina. *Note the browse lines on several individuals in the center left. Huntington Library Photo Collection, Pierce 4195.* **Right:** Adenostoma fasciculatum *has*

occurred before the turn of the century.

In contrast, cursory analysis of numerous ground photographs of Avalon Bay in eastern Santa Catalina Island (Huntington Library Photo Collection) shows dramatic increases in woody vegetation due to urbanization, attendant declines in browsing pressure, and fire protection. An overgrazed landscape of sparse grass, *Opuntia,* and open, pruned chaparral in the 1880s developed rapidly into coastal sage scrub by 1900 after the resort town was established. Thereafter, chaparral dominated by faunal-dispersed species, notably *Heteromeles arbutifolia* and *Rhus integrifolia,* have invaded at a slower pace, becoming conspicuous on photographs after about 1940. Such recovery would be expected over much of these islands if feral animals were removed. Present fire protection, on the other hand, is resulting in a serious wildland fire problem at Avalon.

CONCLUSION

Because most woody plant communities have not been able to reproduce over large areas of Santa Cruz and Santa Catalina Islands over a long period of time, one cannot assume that the

nearly disappeared and is replaced by grassland and an open stand of Quercus dumosa *and* Malosma (Rhus) laurina, *of much larger size than in the earlier photograph. These shrubs have also increased in abundance. Subshrubs in the center left are coastal sage scrub dominated by* Artemesia californica *and* Salvia apiana, *which invaded the area after goats were removed in the 1950s. According to A. Douglas Probst, thousands of dead* Adenostoma fasciculatum *burls were picked up by Avalon citizens throughout the island for use in barbecues until the practice was stopped by the Santa Catalina Island Conservancy about 20 years ago. Photo by A. Douglas Probst.*

present vegetation described here represents prehistoric conditions. On a global scale, forests and shrublands in many areas have been converted into savannas or grasslands due to excessive disturbance, mostly as the result of human activities. Among these vegetation transformations, evergreen sclerophyll scrub has been degraded by centuries of overgrazing and burning in several Mediterranean ecosystems (Naveh 1977, Susmel 1977, LeHouerou 1977). Similarly, Santa Catalina and Santa Cruz Islands probably supported widespread brushland vegetation before the introduction of domestic animals. For reasons given above, the plant communities which probably declined the most include coastal sage scrub and chaparral dominated by *Adenostoma fasciculatum* and *Ceanothus*. If one imagines the addition of large areas of these plant communities to areas with existing (and probably aboriginal) woody cover and, in particular, the replacement of grasslands on poor rocky sites, the removal of feral animals, and the burning of vegetation with some regularity, the resulting picture of prehistoric vegetation on these islands should be much like that now observed in any mountain range in coastal southern California.

REFERENCES

BRUMBAUGH, R. W. 1980. Recent geomorphic and vegetal dynamics on Santa Cruz Island, California. Pp. 139-158 *in* D.M. Power, ed., The California Islands: proceedings of a multidisciplinary symposium. Santa Barbara Museum of Natural History, Santa Barbara, Calif.

COBLENTZ, B. E. 1976. Wild goats of Santa Catalina. Natural History 85:70-77.

————. 1980. Effects of feral goats on the Santa Catalina Island ecosystem. Pp. 167-170 *in* D.M. Power, ed., The California Islands: proceedings of a multidisciplinary symposium. Santa Barbara Museum of Natural History, Santa Barbara, Calif.

COLWELL, W. L. 1977. The status of vegetation mapping in California today. Pp. 195-220 *in* M. G. Barbour and J. Major, eds., Terrestrial vegetation of California. John Wiley & Sons, New York, N.Y.

DEBANO, L. F., P. M. DUNN, and C. E. CONRAD. 1977. Fire's effect on the physical and chemical properties of chaparral soils. Pp. 65-74 *in* H. A. Mooney and C. E. Conrad, tech. coords., Proceedings of the symposium on the ecological consequences of fire and fuel management in Mediterranean ecosystems. August 1977. Palo Alto, Calif. U.S. Dept. Agric. Forest Serv., Gen. Tech. Rep. WO-3.

HANES, T. L. 1971. Succession after fire in the chaparral of southern California. Ecol. Monogrs. 41:27-52.

HOBBS, E. 1980. Effects of grazing on the northern population of *Pinus muricata* on Santa Cruz Island, California. Pp. 159-165 *in* D.M. Power, ed., The California Islands: proceedings of a multidisciplinary symposium. Santa Barbara Museum of Natural History, Santa Barbara, Calif.

HOCHBERG, M. C. 1980. Factors affecting leaf size of chaparral shrubs on the California Islands. Pp. 189-206 *in* D.M. Power, ed., The California Islands: proceedings of a multidisciplinary symposium. Santa Barbara Museum of Natural History, Santa Barbara, Calif.

HORTON, J. S., and C. L. KRAEBEL. 1955. Development of vegetation after fire in the chamise chaparral of southern California. Ecol. 36:244-262.

KUCHLER, A. W. 1977. The map of natural vegetation of California. Pp. 909-939 *in* M. G. Barbour and J. Major, eds., Terrestrial vegetation of California. John Wiley & Sons, New York, N.Y.

LEHOUEROU, H. N. 1977. Fire and vegetation in North Africa. Pp. 334-341 *in* H. A. Mooney and C. E. Conrad, tech. coords., Proceedings of the symposium on the ecological consequences of fire and fuel management in Mediterranean ecosystems. August, 1977. Palo Alto, Calif. U.S. Dept. Agric. Forest Serv., Gen. Tech. Rep. WO-3.

MINNICH, R. A. 1978. The geography of fire and conifer forests in the eastern Transverse Ranges, California. Ph.D. thesis, University of California, Los Angeles, Calif.

NEVAH, Z. 1977. The role of fire in the Mediterranean landscape of Israel. Pp. 299-306 *in* H. A. Mooney and C. E. Conrad, tech. coords., Proceedings of the symposium on the ecological consequences of fire and fuel management in Mediterranean ecosystems. August, 1977. Palo Alto, Calif. U.S. Dept. Agric. Forest Serv., Gen. Tech. Rep. WO-3.

ORME, A. R., and R. A. MINNICH. 1970. Remote sensing of disturbed insular vegetation from color infrared photography. Pp. 1235-1243 *in* Proceedings of the seventh international symposium on remote sensing of the environment. University of Michigan, Ann Arbor, Mich.

PATRIC, J. H., and T. L. HANES. 1964. Chaparral succession in a San Gabriel Mountain area of California. Ecol. 45:353-360.

PHILBRICK, R. N., ed. 1967. Proceedings of the symposium on the biology of the California Islands. Santa Barbara Botanic Garden, Santa Barbara, Calif.

PHILBRICK, R. N., and J. R. HALLER. 1977. The Southern California Islands. Pp. 894-906 *in* M. G. Barbour and J. Major, eds., Terrestrial vegetation of California. John Wiley & Sons, New York, N.Y.

RAVEN, R. H. 1963. A flora of San Clemente Island, California. Aliso 5:289-347.

SPECHT, R. L. 1969. A comparison of the sclerophyllous vegetation characteristics of Mediterranean type climates in France, California and S. Australia: dry matter, energy and nutrient accumulation. Australia J. Bot. 17:293-308.

SUSMEL, L. 1977. Ecology of systems and fire management in the Italian Mediterranean region. Pp. 307-317 *in* H. A. Mooney and C. E. Conrad, tech. coords., Proceedings of the symposium on the ecological consequences of fire and fuel management in Mediterranean ecosystems. August, 1977. Palo Alto, Calif. U.S. Dept. Agric. Forest Serv., Gen. Tech. Rep. WO-3.

THORNE, R. F. 1967. A flora of Santa Catalina Island, California. Aliso 6:1-77.

U.S. DEPT. AGRICULTURE. 1945. Map: vegetation types of California. Forest Service. California Forest and Range Experiment Station, Berkeley, Calif.

WELLS, P. V. 1969. The relation between mode of reproduction and extent of speciation in woody genera of the California chaparral. Evolution 23:264-267.

WHEELER, G. M. 1976. Annual report upon the geographical surveys west of the one hundredth meridian in California, Nevada, Utah, Colorado, Wyoming, New Mexico, Arizona, and Montana. Appendix JJ. U.S. Gov't Printing Office, Washington, D.C.

Recent Geomorphic and Vegetal Dynamics on Santa Cruz Island, California

Robert W. Brumbaugh

Department of Geography, University of California,
Los Angeles, California 90024

INTRODUCTION

Santa Cruz Island landscape has undergone significant change over the past one hundred years, generally due to widespread sheep-grazing activities. The native plant communities of Santa Cruz Island have been substantially modified. Accelerated erosion phenomena, especially intense hillslope gully development, are common features on the denuded hillslopes. Historical accounts, old photographs, and field evidence indicate that prior to the onset of sheep grazing in the mid-nineteenth century some areas of the island, now nearly barren, supported more vegetation. However, recent sheep removal from portions of the island has accounted for vegetation recovery and reversal of the accelerated erosion processes. A map of Santa Cruz Island, with place names referred to in the text, is given in Figure 1.

Transcripts of the U.S. District Court Proceedings (1857) indicate that Dr. James B. Shaw introduced sheep, cattle, and horses in 1853. Lt. Comdr. James Alden of the U.S. Coast Survey indicated that Santa Cruz Island had a few cattle and no inhabitants in 1852 (Alden 1852). He made no mention of sheep on Santa Cruz, although the adjacent island of Santa Rosa was listed by Alden as having 10,000 sheep. However, a year later, Harris Newmark (Newmark 1930) mentions that "at the time of my arrival [in Los Angeles in 1853], most of the mutton then consumed in Los Angeles [came] from Santa Cruz Island . . . [which] had much larger herds, and steamers running to and from San Francisco often stopped there to take on sheep and sheep products." Newmark could have been referring to Santa Rosa Island, which was well stocked by then. In addition, Dunkle (1950) states that there were 200 sheep on Santa Cruz Island in 1852. Pigs, which, along with the sheep, are now wild on the island, may also have been introduced during this time (U.S. District Court Proc. 1857, Phillips 1927, Glassow 1977). By 1857, there were some 7,000 or 8,000 head of sheep on the island (Greenwell 1858), and by 1860 there were 15,000 sheep (U.S. Bureau of Census, Census of Agriculture 1860). In 1870, the sheep population had swelled to 45,000 (U.S. Census, Census of Agriculture 1870). Other estimates of the sheep population during the last half of the nineteenth century range between thirty and sixty thousand or more (Cromise 1868, Wheeler 1876, Carman *et al.* 1892, Towne and Wentworth 1945). In recent decades, sheep grazing has been curtailed over large areas of the island. Today, most of the feral sheep are confined by fences to the more rugged, less accessible northwest and northeast coastlands and mountain ranges. Fewer, fluctuating numbers of sheep remain on the hilly southern portion of the island.

NINETEENTH CENTURY LANDSCAPE CHANGES
Vegetation

As mentioned earlier, the vegetation of Santa Cruz Island changed significantly over the past century. Coastal sage scrub, island chaparral, valley and foothill grassland, and oak woodland communities have either been suppressed or modified. However, scientific literature yields little information regarding either the nature of these changes or the character of the vegetation before sheep were introduced. Some early scientific surveys make brief mentions of spreading *Opuntia,* disappearing grass, exposed barren ridges, and disappearing sagebrush (Wheeler

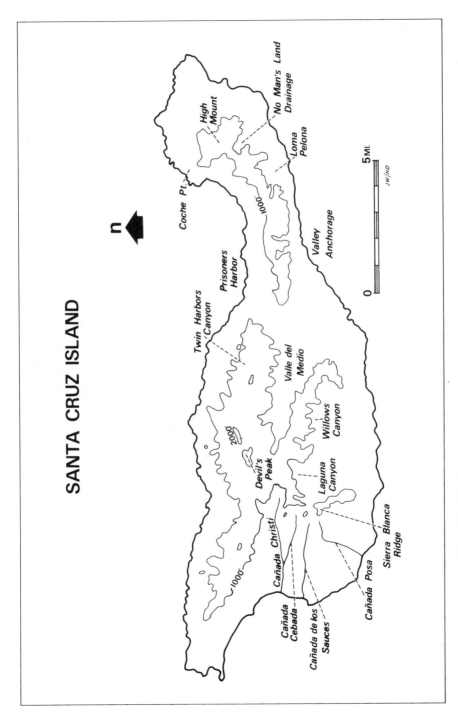

FIGURE 1. *Map of Santa Cruz Island, California.*

FIGURE 2. Top: *Sketch map of Coche Point in 1856 (Greenwell 1857). Courtesy of the National Archives.* **Bottom:** *1929 aerial photograph of Coche Point; arrow points to location of Coche Point Signal Station. Fairchild photo, courtesy of Whittier College Geology Dept.*

1876, Schumacher 1877), but the observations provide no accurate assessment of actual vegetation changes; some descriptions are obviously based on poor landscape interpretation. However, U.S. Coast Survey accounts detail several salient features of vegetation denudation on Santa Cruz Island during the mid-nineteenth century. Northeast portions may have undergone severe vegetal destruction. Greenwell (1857:62) describes Coche Point as follows: "The point is covered with a thick growth of dwarf oak, but the signal stands on a little knoll partly free of this." Aerial photographs (Fig. 2) show this knoll was clear of brush by 1929; it remains grassland today although the bluffs are partially covered with scrub oak. It is evident, however, that vegetal attrition has taken place on the bluffs at Coche Point since 1929; there was much more sage cover in 1929 than there is now. A year after Greenwell's observation, Davidson (1859) described portions of this northeastern part of the island as barren. Greenwell (1857:66) also described the ridge containing High Mount and El Montañon on the east part of the island isthmus: "Looking from Prisoner's Harbor to eastward is a high range of wooded mountains running apparently across the island." An accompanying sketch map of High Mount (Fig. 3) shows it to be very wooded on all sides. At present, many of these slopes are not wooded, and

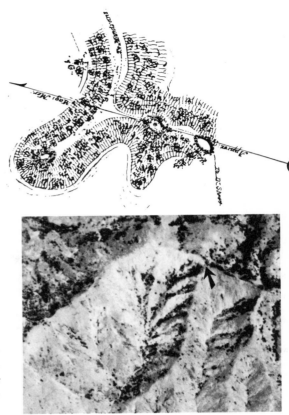

FIGURE 3. Top: *Sketch map of High Mount in 1856 (Greenwell 1857). Courtesy of the National Archives.* **Bottom:** *1929 aerial photography of High Mount; arrow points to summit.*

they were equally sparsely vegetated by 1929, as indicated by aerial photographs (Fig. 3). The slopes immediately west of Prisoners Harbor also have undergone severe destruction. A letter from U.S. Coast Survey Sub-Assistant W. M. Johnson to W. E. Greenwell (Johnson 1858) describes the area as:

> . . . so completely overgrown with high brush, that it will be impossible to get through it with the instrument; in putting up our signals the men were forced, in very many places, to move for considerable distances on their hands and knees, . . . [and] would find themselves at the end of that time, only about one-third of a mile from where they had started.

Today these slopes, covered with scattered chaparral patches, *Lyonothamnus* groves, and stands of *Pinus muricata,* have a much more open appearance than was described in 1858. The vegetal reduction may be due, in part, to fires on the slopes early in this century (Hobbs 1980). Sub-Assistant Johnson continues (in the same letter), "The country east of the harbor [has] little or no brush," a description which also applies to its present appearance. Government documents have been used elsewhere as a historical source of nineteenth-century landscape conditions (Buffington and Herbel 1965, Johnson 1972, Stoiber 1973, Cooke and Reeves 1976).

Early photographs of Santa Cruz Island yield the best information regarding vegetation denudation. Comparison of present-day vegetation with that shown in 1869 photographs indicates that coastal sage scrub on the south-facing slope north of the Valle del Medio has been greatly reduced (Figs. 4 and 5). Scattered *Quercus dumosa, Cercocarpus betuloides, Prunus lyonii, Rhus integrifolia, Heteromeles arbutifolia, Adenostoma fasciculatum,* and *Ceanothus* spp. presently are distributed on these xeric sheep-grazed slopes (Fig. 6). However, in 1869 these slopes were fully clad with coastal sage species (probably *Artemisia californica, Eriogonum* spp., *Salvia mellifera, Encelia californica*), providing a contiguous understory for the previously mentioned chaparral trees and shrubs (Figs. 4 and 5) that are now undergoing slow attrition. Today these coastal sage plants are either sparse or very limited in distribution. These photographs show little vegetational disturbance by sheep grazing by 1869 in the areas bordering the Valle del Medio, in contrast to possible earlier vegetation disturbances on the northeast portions of the island. However, these same chaparral plants lacked the arborescence and pruning in 1869 (Fig. 7) that is characteristic of much of the present-day chaparral and woodland. Indeed, the 1869 vegetation is not unlike that of the mainland chaparral, with respect to lack of arborescence. This similarity may suggest that fire played a more prominent role on the island prior to the advent of sheep grazing. The slopes bordering the Valle del Medio have not experienced fire during the twentieth century (recent fires on the island have been documented by Dr. Carey Stanton, pers. comm.). Thus, chaparral plants on the island have not experienced recurring wildfires recently. Most of the mainland chaparral experiences recurring wildfires with a frequency of every ten to forty years (Bauer 1936, Muller *et al.* 1968, Byrne *et al.* 1977, Vogl 1977). Perhaps at the time the 1869 photographs were taken the chaparral bordering the Valle del Medio had been recently burned (within the previous forty years). This would account for the lack of arborescence in 1869, an arborescence that is present today, although chaparral vegetation generally stagnates with little annual growth after sixty years (Hanes 1971, Mooney and Parsons 1973).

Certainly the possibility of prehistoric wildfire on the island cannot be discounted. There is abundant charcoal in late Holocene sediments over much of the island that may be the result of wildfires. University of California at Los Angeles (UCLA) radiocarbon dates of three charcoal samples from stream bank sediments are 400 ±80, 14,400 ±300, and 395 ±80 years B.P. (UCLA-2075, 2078, and 2089, respectively). In addition, charcoal is present in much older island sediments, for example, in mudstones of the Miocene San Onofre Breccia (upper Cañada de los Sauces). It does not matter, of course, whether the wildfires are natural or caused by man. Johnson (1972) has documented fire (Pleistocene to present) on nearby San Miguel Island and investigated the possibility of both lightning-caused fires and aboriginal burning on the Channel Islands. In addition, fire may purposely have been used to remove the low brush from portions of Santa Cruz Island in order to better facilitate sheep grazing during the middle and late nineteenth century (Minnich 1980). Stockmen often burned woody vegetation in California during the last half of the nineteenth century (Sampson 1944). The practice of brush burning is especially well-founded in the southern Mediterranean region of Europe (Traband 1977, LeHouerou 1974, Robertson 1977). The early ranch managers were European: Dr. Shaw was from England (U.S. Bureau of Census 1860, Ellison 1937), and Justinian Caire was from the Department of Hautes-Alpes in southern France (Towne and Wentworth 1945). Indeed, the Caire family extended many traditions of their homeland to their new domain (Hillinger 1958; Justinian Caire, II, 1978, "As I remember it," Oral History Research Office, Univ. California, Santa Barbara).

Other factors may also have been important in late nineteenth-century vegetation changes. Severe droughts plagued the Channel Islands during much of that time. Johnson (1972) has chronicled these droughts, especially those during the years of 1863-64, 1870-72, 1877, and 1893-1904. Johnson cites the following statement from the Santa Barbara *Index*, March 22, 1877: "twenty five thousand sheep [were] slaughtered on Santa Cruz Island . . . [because of]

FIGURE 4. *North slopes of Valle del Medio in 1869. Hillslopes in left background have dense cover of coastal sage scrub and chaparral. Photograph courtesy of Dr. Carey Stanton; reproduction by Ron Morgan.*

FIGURE 5. *North slopes of Valle del Medio in 1869 (Slightly west of Figure 4). Note lack of pruning of* Quercus dumosa *on footslopes. Photograph courtesy of Dr. Carey Stanton; reproduction by Ron Morgan.*

FIGURE 6. *North slopes of Valle del Medio at present. Slopes in left background are noticeably barren of low brush cover.*

FIGURE 7. *View westward along Valle del Medio in 1869. Note that the heavily vegetated north slopes lack the arborescent character evident today. Photograph courtesy of Dr. Carey Stanton; reproduction by Ron Morgan.*

FIGURE 8. *Exposed roots of prostrate* Quercus dumosa. *Gully is cut 4 m into San Onofre Breccia on a south-facing slope along Cañada Cebada.*

scarcity of food induced by want of rain."

Finally, man may have had a direct role in the vegetal destruction. There is a record that timber was taken off Santa Cruz Island for building in Santa Barbara on at least one occasion in 1817 (Spaulding 1964). In addition, woodcutting for use on the island ranch may have taken a significant toll on the wooded mountain slopes. Vegetal change on the island must be examined, then, in the light of these various dynamic forces; that is, the coincidence of extreme drought conditions with the introduction of sheep, along with additional direct modification by man in the form of possible brush burning and woodcutting.

Geomorphology

Nineteenth-century landscape change is evident in the intense hillslope gully development characteristic of many drainages on Santa Cruz Island. This accelerated erosion may be a recent expression of sheep-related geomorphic processes, rather than a continuing process pre-dating the introduction of sheep. Many of the hillslope gullies post-date the sometimes sparse vegetation growing on the slopes. Frequent root exposure on the entire individual gully span is characteristic of several incised hillslopes. On the west end of the island, exposed roots of

FIGURE 9. *Exposed roots of* Pinus muricata. *Gully is incised 1 m into Willows Diorite in northwestern portion of Laguna drainage, southwest Santa Cruz Island.*

prostrate *Quercus dumosa* often span gullies (Fig. 8), as do *Pinus muricata* roots (Fig. 9). In many cases the plant is still alive and the roots maintain their biological functions.

The response of valley bottoms to changes in the adjacent upland landscape can be distinguished in the simple stratigraphic sequence found in valley fills of several small watersheds. This sequence, consisting of fine alluvium underlying mostly coarser alluvium and colluvium, is evident in a drainage in the "No Man's Land" pasture. This drainage, located on the southeastern side of the isthmus, is still subject to extreme grazing by feral sheep. Much of the surface is completely barren, with only scattered shrubs (*e.g., Quercus dumosa*) at higher elevations in the watershed. This drainage is cut into diatomaceous Monterey Shale that dips to the west, orthogonally to the direction of drainage. Thus, the western canyon side is very steep and a large section of basal Monterey strata is exposed, while the eastern canyon side lies along the dip plane and, indeed, is marked by massive, deep-seated slope failure and severe contortion of the shale strata. The main channel bed of the drainage is characterized by incising

FIGURE 10. *Site of UCLA-2075, "No Man's Land." Recent rilling and mini-debris scars mark the slope. Bottom 50 cm is fine alluvium; arrow points to UCLA-2075 site.*

of alluvial and colluvial debris deposited along a very narrow canyon bottom (varying from 5 to 15 m wide). Large debris flow levees (up to 1.5 m in height) frequently lie on the channel bed. Sections of relatively coarse debris overlying finer alluvium are exposed along several long reaches where the valley fill is incised (up to 15 m of channel fill are exposed). Grain size, particle sorting, and the fabric of clastic sediments provide a measure of the energy of the depositing medium. Variation in the channel fill thus represents different geomorphic processes. The underlying alluvium (generally the bottom 50 cm of the exposed section) consists of moderately sorted clays and silts with occasional sand and pebble lenses. Generally, these characteristics are found in water-laid sediments or fluid mudflow deposits (Bull 1964). Coarser clasts overlie the fine alluvium. These deposits are poorly sorted and pebbles are irregularly arranged and are without preferred orientation—characteristics of viscous debris flow deposits (Bull 1964, 1972). Thus, the coarse debris probably represents either colluvial debris, debris-flow matrices, or, occasionally, coarse alluvium. This channel wall stratigraphy is shown in Figure 10. At no place are fine clays or silts deposited at the top of a section to any great extent. Charcoal taken from the top 10 cm of the fine alluvium in a channel bank (Fig. 10) was radiocarbon dated at 1,550 ±80 years B.P. (UCLA-2075). The fine alluvium was, therefore, probably deposited before the introduction of sheep to the island. A similar sequence is found in Cañada Cebada. Several long reaches expose charcoal-laden, fine-textured, floodplain deposits underlying coarser alluvium. The drainage, cut predominantly into dioritic and volcaniclastic rocks, has a fairly narrow floodplain (less than 70 m) along most of the canyon bottom. A radiocarbon date of 1,555 ±80 years B.P. (UCLA-2089) was obtained from charcoal from the top 2 cm of a dark clay-silt, organic-rich alluvium exposed on a channel bank. Above this fine alluvium (50 cm exposed above the channel bed) is a coarser unit of pebble and sand lens within a light-colored, fine-textured matrix (100 cm).

The coarser alluvium and colluvium may represent a byproduct of grazed hillslopes, rather than just lateral changes in stream channels that can result in varying types of clastic deposition. The slopes, overgrazed and made barren by sheep, may have become dominated by rilling and mass wasting processes as a result of the much reduced cover of both shrubby and herbaceous vegetation. The fine alluvium appears to represent a different geomorphic regime which may have existed at the time intensive sheep grazing commenced in the 1850s. This geomorphic regime is characteristic of a more vegetated landscape, where mass wasting processes would probably be inhibited to a greater extent, and a channel fill would represent either sheet wash, stream deposition, or very fluid mudflow deposits. Vegetated (especially brush covered) hillslopes would be likely to experience less debris avalanching and individual rockfall than hillslopes completely denuded of vegetation (Rice *et al.* 1969, Rice and Foggin 1971).

The presence of moderate amounts of charcoal in many of the channel banks of small drainages on Santa Cruz Island reinforces the possibility that the contact between silt-clay deposits and colluvium represents the time of arrival of sheep on the island. In each drainage I examined, the overlying coarse alluvium and/or colluvial matrix contained little or no charcoal. This absence is significant; wildfires have not been reported on the island in this century, except for a fire in the stands of *Pinus muricata* on the north side of the island near Pelican Bay (Hobbs 1980) and very localized fires, mostly grassfires (Dr. Carey Stanton, pers. comm.). Ubiquitous charcoal deposits in the underlying fine, and often indurated, alluvium thus provide reasonable evidence that the fine material represents at least pre-twentieth-century processes.

Similar valley-fill sequences have been reported elsewhere, although generally in broader basins than the "No Man's Land" drainage. In the broad cienegas of southeastern Arizona, Melton (1965) reported a sequence of coarse clasts burying pre-European settlement deposits of fine alluvium, following nineteenth-century grazing disturbance; the sequence was then incised because of steepened transverse gradients. Many instances of this "culturally" accelerated erosion in the southeast, central, and western United States are cited by Happ *et al.* (1940). In the cases cited, floodplain silts are often covered with mud and some boulders after disturbance of nearby slopes by either mining, agriculture, or urbanization. In some of the island drainages large enough to have small floodplains, the charcoal-laden fine deposits are indurated flood-plain deposits—stable for some period of time—that are now so rapidly aggrading as to prohibit development of an A_1 soil horizon on the floodplain surface (for example Cañada Cebada). Not all drainages on Santa Cruz Island are characterized by a "pre-sheep/post-sheep" stratigraphic sequence. For example, the Loma Pelona drainage adjacent to "No Man's Land" does not have fine alluvium lying beneath coarse alluvium and colluvium. Instead, the deeply incised (up to 6 m) terrace deposits along the narrow canyon bottoms consist of beds, each of different-sized clasts, ranging in size from small pebbles to large cobbles (Fig. 11). Some beds may represent sieve deposits (Bull 1972). The distinctly identifiable beds probably represent individual events and debris flow processes. The Loma Pelona drainage thus provides evidence that, indeed, some degree of catastrophic mass wasting was prevalent and dominant on some portions of the island before the introduction of sheep.

While slope failures are definitely part of the island geomorphic system under natural vegetation conditions, as they are on the mainland (Campbell 1975), it can be argued from the evidence present in the "No Man's Land" drainage, along with several other watersheds, that for *at least* the time immediately preceding sheep introduction on the island many drainages were not experiencing the kind of catastrophic debris avalanche and debris torrent events that disrupt the valley fills today. Rather, these drainages were characterized more or less by landscape "stability." It must be recognized, however, that historic landscape stability in

FIGURE 11. *Coarse deposits in Loma Pelona terraces.*

southern California is always suspect in view of the forces of wildfires, tectonic uplift and earthquakes, and erodability and instability of many coastal sediments. Processes on the hillslopes and adjacent valley bottoms are necessarily related to these forces and characteristics. I do not intend to imply complete, long-term geomorphic stability before sheep introduction, but rather a short-term, and perhaps localized, landscape stability, especially with respect to geomorphic processes.

PRESENT-DAY LANDSCAPE PROCESSES
Geomorphology

Sheep grazing has been progressively curtailed in large areas of Santa Cruz Island over recent years. Removal of the feral sheep has had a marked effect on hillslope gully processes in some areas. While some firmly established hillslope gullies continue to function as debris chutes, many of the gullies are aggrading, thus demonstrating the reversability of these accelerated erosion processes on steep watershed. Evidence of hillslope gully aggradation includes the

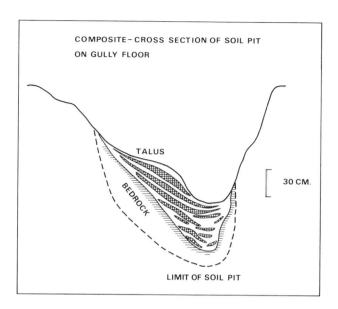

COMPOSITE-CROSS SECTION OF SOIL PIT
ON GULLY FLOOR

TALUS

BEDROCK

30 CM.

LIMIT OF SOIL PIT

FIGURE 12. *Representative cross sections of hillslope gully-fill; cross hatching represents organic lenses.*

recent burial of the root crowns of small shrubs on the gully floors, and gully-fill stratigraphy (Fig. 12). Many gully floors are now revegetated with grasses, at least; also, bank caving and scouring to bedrock by infrequent heavy storm runoff and debris flows are either greatly reduced or have ceased. Indeed, there has been no appreciable expansion of hillslope gully networks on Santa Cruz Island since 1929, as evidenced by aerial photographs taken in that year (1929 [Fairchild], 1954 [Mark Hurd], and 1970 [color infrared photos from Orme *et al.* 1971, on file at Geography Dept., Univ. California, Los Angeles]). This apparent cessation of hillslope gully enlargement may be partially explained by either the previously mentioned revegetation of some of the drainages and consequent gully healing, or by the fact that gully processes are presently weathering-limited. Indeed, many of the gullies incised into the steep drainages are cut to bedrock. The phenomenon of hillslope gully aggradation is documented in the South Carolina piedmont upland (Ireland *et al.* 1939) and in the loessial uplands of Iowa (Daniels and Jordan 1966). However, these researchers related gully stabilization not only to the revegetation process itself, but to expected stages of gully development.

Vegetation

Some portions of Santa Cruz Island are undergoing revegetation as a result of the reduction and restriction of sheep begun in the 1950s. Comparison of 1929, 1954, and 1970 aerial photographs indicates slow attrition of shrubs and trees in those areas still grazed by sheep. Hobbs (1980) has documented the lack of regeneration of *Pinus Muricata* on the heavily grazed slopes on the north side of the island near Pelican Bay, whereas the pine forests above Chinese Harbor and on the western portion of the island are undergoing regeneration in response to removal of sheep in those areas (Linhart *et al.* 1967, Hobbs 1980). Figure 13 shows present densities of *Pinus muricata* on Sierra Blanca ridge on the southwest portion of the island. The different densities of *Pinus muricata* on opposite sides of the fence line are probably, in part, a result of slope aspect and related fog drip. Aerial photographs of Sierra Blanca ridge can be compared for 1929 and 1970 (Fig. 14). Several of the slopes which, except

FIGURE 13. *Looking south along Sierra Blanca ridge. Fence line separates distinct* Pinus muricata *stands. Note youthful stature of* Pinus *to west (right) of fence line. Many dead stumps and fallen trees are found on the slope to east of fence line.*

for fallen trees, are now nearly barren supported small stands of *Pinus muricata* in 1929; slopes now experiencing pine regeneration were much more barren than at present. The slow attrition of *Pinus muricata* is aided by their relatively short life span of approximately 65 years (Linhart *et al.* 1967). In general, however, chaparral and woodland trees and shrubs (especially *Quercus dumosa*) show little change in extent or densities since 1929. Indeed, examination of the 1929 and 1970 aerial photographs reveals that, over most of Santa Cruz Island, shrubs and trees now present on the landscape were present in 1929. Likewise, little attrition has occurred since 1929, even on the slopes on the northern portion of the island which are still heavily grazed by sheep. There are exceptions, however, besides the previously mentioned *Pinus muricata*. For example, some shrubs on the heavily grazed upper east drainage of Twin Harbors on the north side of the island have been thinned (Minnich 1980). While *Quercus dumosa* has suffered no significant attrition since 1929, other shrubs (*e.g., Adenostoma fasciculatum*) have suffered up to 30 per cent localized decreases in cover in scattered stands. At present, I am undertaking a more complete evaluation of these changes over the period 1929 to 1970.

The capability of rapid vegetation recovery following removal of sheep is shown by examination of a small sheep exclosure located in the Valle del Medio (Fig. 15). At the time of construction (fall 1976), the 10 × 14 × 14-m exclosure contained one individual each of *Heteromeles arbutifolia, Quercus dumosa,* and *Opuntia littoralis*. No herbaceous cover was

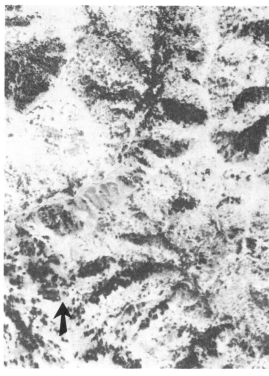

FIGURE 14. Left: *Aerial photograph of Sierra Blanca ridge in 1970; arrow points northward to fence line and ridge shown in Figure 13. Area to west of ridge crest is free of sheep; area to east has reduced, but fluctuating, numbers of sheep.* **Right:** *Aerial photograph of Sierra Blanca ridge in 1929; arrow points north. Several small clusters of* Pinus muricata *present in 1929 to east and northeast of arrow are absent by 1970 with no replacement.*

present at that time. Upon sheep exclusion, the *Heteromeles arbutifolia* and *Quercus dumosa* began sprouting vigorously from the base. The pre-exclosure pruned appearance is rapidly disappearing. In addition, *Artemisia californica,* a component of coastal sage scrub, is also now established within the exclosure; no *Artemisia californica* plants are present outside the exclosure where sheep can graze. The regeneration of coastal sage is evident on some portions of the island. Comparison of 1929 and 1970 aerial photographs shows a slight increase in sage density, especially on the steep southern slopes of the isthmus to the east of Valley Anchorage. The susceptibility of coastal sage to sheep grazing is also evident in the comparison of 1869 photographs with present-day photographs (Figs. 4, 5, and 6). Coastal sage, very prevalent in 1869 on the northern slopes of the Valle del Medio, is virtually absent today in areas heavily grazed by sheep.

   Exclusion of sheep for two winter and spring seasons (November 1976 to May 1978) also demonstrated some recovery of valley grassland-herbaceous vegetation. Herbaceous cover within and without the exclosure (examined May 1978) is dominated by introduced European grasses and forbs. *Avena barbata, Bromus mollis, Centaurea melitensis, Medicago polymorpha,* and *Silene gallica* are the most prevalent herbaceous species in the vicinity of and within the exclosure. Native *Hemizonia fasciculata* is also present. In May 1978, the native

FIGURE 15. *Sheep exclosure constructed on 22° south-facing slope in the Valle del Medio. Bedrock under shallow soil is volcanic.*

bunch grass *Stipa lepida* was present in 60 per cent of one-meter quadrats located along a belt transect within the exclosure. *Stipa lepida* was completely absent outside the exclosure. However, in the late spring of 1979, following a second consecutive wet winter, *Stipa lepida* was present outside the exclosure, probably due to the production of herbaceous vegetation in excess of consumption by feral sheep. In general, *Stipa* is present in the island grasslands, although it is not nearly as extensive or abundant as the introduced annual grasses (Philbrick and Haller 1977).

In addition to vegetal recovery following sheep exclusion, previously sheep-trampled soils (moderately fine-textured loams) within the exclosure have also demonstrated a regained resiliency. Penetration resistance, both within and without the exclosure, was measured in November 1976—at the time of exclosure construction—on a relatively dry soil; penetration resistance was measured again in February 1977 on a moist soil, and in December 1977 on a relatively dry soil (Table 1). Penetration resistance is a measure of near-surface soil compaction only, not of compaction of the entire soil column. A Student's *t*-test showed statistically significant differences in soil compaction (at the 0.05 probability level) inside and outside the exclosure in February 1977 and December 1977. Soils within the exclosure were substantially less compacted than soils still exposed to trampling by sheep. The soils within the exclosure exhibited a rapid recovery from the trampling effect of sheep. However, a sheep trail located within the exclosure did not show significant change in near-surface soil compaction. Penetration resistance measurements on these trampled soils showed no significant difference between November 1976 (4.09 kg/cm²) and December 1977 (3.87 kg/cm²). Intensive use of the trails by sheep evidently results in deeper compaction of soils than can be easily mitigated.

SUMMARY

Landscape change on Santa Cruz Island in the mid-nineteenth century can be related to the interaction of introduced animals, direct modification by man, and environmental constraints

TABLE 1. Changes in penetration resistance (compressive strength) for areas inside and outside sheep exclosure. Measured by a pocket penetrometer CL-700, in kg/cm² ±*s.e.*

	Inside exclosure	Outside exclosure	Probability level
Nov. 1976	4.62 ±0.46	3.37 ±0.87	0.20
	$n = 20$	$n = 20$	
Feb. 1977	1.95 ±0.30	3.91 ±0.81	0.01
	$n = 20$	$n = 20$	
Dec. 1977	2.14 ±0.37	3.81 =0.72	0.02
	$n = 20$	$n = 20$	

and phenomena. The introduction of sheep coincides with significant modification of the island vegetation. Coastal sage scrub appears to have been especially reduced in extent, while *Pinus* and chaparral woodlands have suffered slow attrition. Geomorphic phenomena also point to recent changes in the landscape. Changes in upland erosion and subsequent modifications of adjacent valley bottom deposits roughly concur with the vegetal changes. There is some evidence for reversal of accelerated erosion because of revegetation enhanced by sheep removal. Sheep exclosure evidence also indicates the possibility of rapid vegetal and soil recovery if soils are not completely eroded away to bedrock. Thus, direct and indirect modifications of the landscape by man are, in some cases, temporary.

ACKNOWLEDGMENTS

I thank C. Stanton, H. Duffield, L. Laughrin, R. Morgan, D. Johnson, W. Renwick, J. Leishman, M. Daily, R. Hornbeck, S. Gibbs, J. O'Leary, N. Diaz, R. Berger, A. Orme, J. Sauer, and M. D. Brumbaugh for their assistance in preparing this paper and in various parts of the continuing research.

REFERENCES

ALDEN, J., LT. COMDR. 1852. Report of the Superintendent, U.S. Coast Survey 1852, Appendix 18, pp. 104-1106.

BAUER, H. L. 1936. Moisture relations in the chaparral of the Santa Monica Mountains, California. Ecol. Monogrs. 6:409-454.

BUFFINGTON, L. C., and C. H. HERBEL. 1965. Vegetation changes on a semidesert grassland range from 1858 to 1963. Ecol. Monogrs. 35:135-164.

BULL, W. B. 1964. Alluvial fans and near surface subsidence in western Fresno County, California. U.S.Geol. Surv. Prof. Paper 437-A.

———. 1972. Recognition of alluvial-fan deposits in the stratigraphic record. Pp. 63-82 *in* J. K. Rigby and W. K. Hamblin, eds., Recognition of ancient sedimentary environments. Soc. Econ. Paleontol. Mineral. Spec. Publ. 16.

BYRNE, R., J. M. MICHAELSEN, and A. SOUTAR. 1977. Fossil charcoal as a measure of wildfire frequency in southern California: a preliminary analysis. Pp. 361-367 *in* H. A. Mooney and C. E. Conrad, tech. coords., Proceedings of the symposium on the environmental consequences of fire and fuel management in Mediterranean ecosystems. U.S. Dept. Agric. Forest Serv., Gen. Tech. Rep. WO-3. Washington, D.C.

CAMPBELL, R. H. 1975. Soil slips, debris flows, and rainstorms in the Santa Monica Mountains and vicinity, southern California. U.S. Geol. Surv. Prof. Paper 851.

CARMAN, E. A., H. A. HEATH, and J. MINTO. 1892. Special report on the history and present condition of the sheep industry of the U.S. U.S. Gov't. Printing Office, Washington, D.C.

COOKE, R. C., and R. W. REEVES. 1976. Arroyos and environmental change in the American Southwest. Clarendon Press, Oxford.

CROMISE, T. F. 1868. The natural wealth of California. H. H. Bancroft and Co., San Francisco, Calif.

DANIELS, R. B., and R. H. JORDAN. 1966. Physiographic history and the soils, entrenched stream systems, and gullies, Harrison County, Iowa. U.S. Dept. Agric. Tech. Bull. 1348.

DAVIDSON, G. 1859. Report of the Superintendent, U.S. Coast Survey 1858-59, Appendix 44, pp. 317-318.

DUNKLE, M. B. 1950. Plant ecology of the Channel Islands of California. Allan Hancock Pacific Expeditions Rep. 13: 247-386. University of Southern California Press, Los Angeles, Calif.

ELLISON, W. H. 1937. History of the Santa Cruz Island grant. Pacific Historical Review. 7:270-283.

GLASSOW, M. A. 1977. Archaeological overview of the Northern Channel Islands including Santa Barbara Island. National Park Service, Western Archaeological Center, Tucson, Ariz.

GREENWELL, W. E. 1857. Description of signals, Santa Cruz Island, Santa Barbara Channel, Section X, 1856-57. Field notes, in Record Group 23. National Archives.

_____. 1858. Report of the Superintendent, U.S. Coast Survey 1857, Appendix 44, pp. 392-395.

HANES, T. L. 1971. Succession after fire in the chaparral of southern California. Ecol. Monogrs. 41:27-52.

HAPP, S. C., G. RITTENHOUSE, and G. C. DOBSON. 1940. Some principles of accelerated stream and valley sedimentation. U.S. Dept. Agric. Tech. Bull. 695.

HILLINGER, C. 1958. The California Islands. Academy Publishers, Los Angeles, Calif.

HOBBS, E. 1980. Effects of grazing on the northern population of *Pinus muricata* on Santa Cruz Island, California. Pp. 159-165 *in* D.M. Power, ed., The California Islands: proceedings of a multidisciplinary symposium. Santa Barbara Museum of Natural History, Santa Barbara, Calif.

IRELAND, H. A., C. F. S. SHARPE, and D. H. EARGLE. 1939. Principles of gully erosion in the piedmont of South Carolina. U.S. Dept. Agric. Tech. Bull. 633.

JOHNSON, D. L. 1972. Landscape evolution on San Miguel Island, California. Ph.D. thesis, University of Kansas, Lawrence, Kan.

JOHNSON, W. M. 1858. Letter of 20 June 1858 to W.E. Greenwell. Bache Records (Entry 5), 1858, v. 16, pp. 281-283, in Record Group 23. National Archives.

LEHOUEROU, H. N. 1974. Fire and vegetation in the Mediterranean basin. Pp. 237-277 *in* H. A. Mooney and C. E. Conrad, tech. coords., Proceedings of the symposium on the environmental consequences of fire and fuel management in Mediterranean ecosystems. U.S. Dept. Agric. Forest Serv., Gen. Tech. Rep. WO-3. Washington, D.C.

LINHART, Y. B., B. BURR, and M. T. CONKLE. 1967. The closed-cone pines of the Northern Channel Islands. Pp. 151-177 *in* R. N. Philbrick, ed., Proceedings of the symposium on the biology of the California Islands. Santa Barbara Botanic Garden, Santa Barbara, Calif.

MELTON, M. A. 1965. The geomorphic and paleoclimatic significance of alluvial deposits in southern Arizona. J. Geol. 73:1-38.

MINNICH, R. 1980. Vegetation of Santa Cruz and Santa Catalina Islands. Pp. 123-137 *in* D.M. Power, ed., The California Islands: proceedings of a multidisciplinary symposium. Santa Barbara Museum of Natural History, Santa Barbara, Calif.

MOONEY, H. A., and D. J. PARSONS. 1973. Structure and function in the California chaparral—an example from San Dimas. Pp. 83-112 *in* F. di Castri and H. A. Mooney, eds., Mediterranean type ecosystems, origin and structure. Springer-Verlag, Heidelberg.

MULLER, C. H., and R. B. HANAWALT, and J. K. MCPHERSON. 1968. Allelopathic control of herb growth in the fire cycle of California chaparral. Bull. Torrey Bot. Club 95:225-231.

NEWMARK, M., and M. R. NEWMARK. 1930. Sixty years in southern California. Houghton Mifflin, New York, N.Y.

ORME, A. R., L. W. BOWDEN, and R. A. MINNICH. 1971. Remote sensing of disturbed insular vegetation from color infrared imagery. Pp. 1235-1243 *in* Proceedings of the seventh international symposium on remote sensing of the environment. University of Michigan, Ann Arbor, Mich.

PHILBRICK, R. N., and J. R. HALLER. 1977. The Southern California Islands. Pp. 893-906 *in* M. G. Barbour and J. Major, eds., Terrestrial vegetation of California. John Wiley & Sons, New York, N.Y.

PHILLIPS, M. J. 1927. History of Santa Barbara County. S. J. Clarke Publishers, Los Angeles, Calif.

RICE, R. M., E. S. CORBETT, and R. G. BAILEY. 1969. Soil slips related to vegetation, topography, and soil in southern California. Water Resources Res. 5:647-659.

RICE, R. M., and G. T. FOGGIN. 1971. Effect of high intensity storms on soil slippage on mountainous watersheds in southern California. Water Resources Res. 7:1485-1496.

ROBERTSON, J. S. 1977. Land use planning of the French Mediterranean region. Pp. 283-288 *in* H. A. Mooney and C. E. Conrad, tech. coords., Proceedings of the symposium on the environmental consequences of fire and fuel management in Mediterranean ecosystems. U.S. Dept. Agric. Forest Serv., Gen. Tech. Rep. WO-3. Washington, D.C.

SAMPSON, A. W. 1944. Plant succession on burned chaparral lands in northern California. California Agric. Expt. Sta. Bull. 685.

SCHUMACHER, P. 1877. Researches in the kjokkenmoddings and graves of a former population of the Santa Barbara Islands and the adjacent mainland. Bull. U.S. Geol. and Geogr. Survey of the Territories 3:37-61.

SPAULDING, E. S. 1964. A brief story of Santa Barbara. Santa Barbara Historical Society, Santa Barbara, Calif.

STOIBER, P. E. 1973. Use of the U.S. General Land Office Survey notes for investigating vegetation change in southern Arizona. M.A. thesis, University of Arizona, Tucson, Ariz.

TOWNE, C. W., and E. WENTWORTH. 1945. Shepherds empire. University of Oklahoma Press, Norman, Okla.

TRABAND, L. 1977. Comparison between the effect of prescribed fires and wildfires on the global quantitative evolution of Kermes scrub oak (*Quercus coccifera* L.) Garrigue. Pp. 271-282 *in* H. A. Mooney and C. E. Conrad, tech. coords., Proceedings of the symposium on the environmental consequences of fire and fuel management in Mediterranean ecosystems. U.S. Dept. Agric. Forest Serv., Gen. Tech. Rep. WO-3. Washington, D.C.

U.S. BUREAU OF CENSUS. 1860. Eighth census of U.S., v. 6, Santa Barbara County, Roll 65, California. National Archives Microfilm.

U.S. BUREAU OF CENSUS, CENSUS OF AGRICULTURE. 1860. Eighth census of U.S., v. 2, Schedule 4, Santa Barbara County (microfilm). California State Library, Sacramento, Calif.

————. 1870. Ninth census of U.S., v. 2, Schedule of agricultural recapitulation, Santa Barbara County (microfilm). California State Library, Sacramento, Calif.

U.S. DISTRICT COURT (San Francisco). 1857. Transcripts of the proceedings, case no. 176. Petition of Andres Castillero for the island of Santa Cruz, no. 340SD.

VOGL, R. J. 1977. Fire frequency and site degradation. Pp. 193-201 in H. A. Mooney and C. E. Conrad, tech. coords., Proceedings of the symposium on the environmental consequences of fire and fuel management in Mediterranean ecosystems. U.S. Dept. Agric. Forest Serv., Gen. Tech. Rep. WO-3. Washington, D.C.

WHEELER, G. M. 1876. Annual report upon the geographical surveys west of the one hundredth meridian in California, Nevada, Utah, Colorado, Wyoming, New Mexico, Arizona, and Montana, Appendix JJ, pp. 202-203, 215-216, and 225. U.S. Gov't. Printing Office, Washington, D.C.

Effects of Grazing on the Northern Population of *Pinus muricata* on Santa Cruz Island, California

Elizabeth Hobbs

Department of Geography, University of California,
Los Angeles, California 90024

INTRODUCTION

The effects of grazing on the vegetation of Santa Cruz Island have been apparent since 1875 (Wheeler 1876), only 22 years after the earliest documented introduction of sheep to the island (Shaw 1857). Although grazing damage has been mentioned in the literature since that time (Dunkle 1950, Linhart, Burr, and Conkle 1967), it is difficult to determine the extent or degree of damage from these descriptions.

Of the three main populations of *Pinus muricata* on Santa Cruz Island (Fig. 1), the western (Cañada Cervada) and eastern (Chinese Harbor) populations have been protected from grazing since about 1958 (C. Stanton, pers. comm.). The northern (Pelican Bay) population, however, has been subjected to continuous grazing pressure which, combined with the effects of an extensive fire that occurred sometime between 1929 and 1932 (C. Stanton and M. Daily, pers. comm.), has had a dramatic effect on the pines and associated species.

METHODS

Study areas were defined for each of the three pine populations on the island (Figs. 2 to 4). The sizes of the northern and western study areas were approximately equal (120 hectares) and each contained 14 systematically placed 25 m × 25 m sample sites. The eastern study area was much smaller (30 hectares) due to the much less extensive pine population in that area. Only four 25 m × 25 m sites were sampled in this study area. The proportion of the area sampled to the total study area was held constant for all three populations.

The vegetation of the sites was sampled by line transects to measure foliar cover of pines and other woody species; percentage cover for each site was estimated. Since overlapping individuals of different species were measured separately, it is possible to have greater than 100 per cent foliar cover. However, it should be noted that overlapping individuals of the same species were measured as one individual, so that some dominant species may be underestimated in relation to the rarer species.

Height was estimated visually; diameter at breast height (dbh) was measured for each pine intercepted by a line transect. Increment cores were taken from trees in several different size classes within each population. These data allowed estimation of the age structures of the three populations. In addition, seedling censuses were taken within the sample sites in each population to assess the regeneration potential of each population under present conditions. Seedlings were defined as any trees less than 3 m high.

RESULTS

Comparison of Populations

For the purposes of this study, it was assumed that the vegetation of the three closed-cone pine forests on the island was similar prior to disturbance and that gross differences could be attributed to disturbance, particularly grazing. However, the following environmental differences among the three populations should be noted as possibly sufficient to account for some differences in species composition and vegetation density.

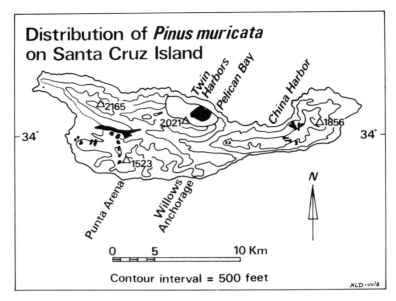

FIGURE 1. *Map of Santa Cruz Island showing distribution of Bishop Pines.*

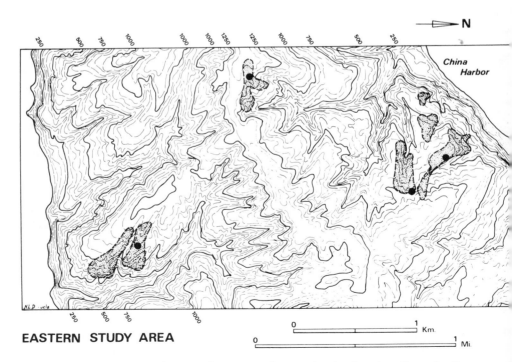

FIGURE 2. *Map of eastern study area showing location of sample sites.*

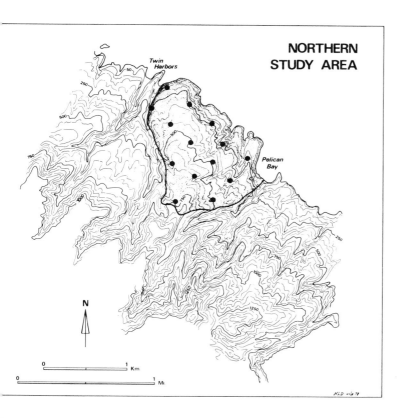

FIGURE 3. *Map of northern study area showing location of sample sites.*

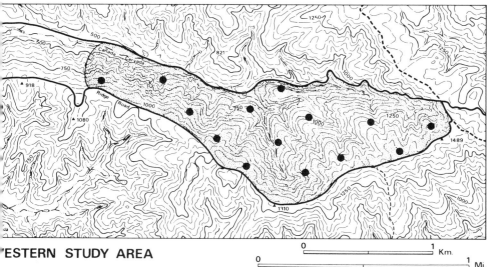

FIGURE 4. *Map of western study area showing location of sample sites.*

FIGURE 5. *View of Pelican Bay,* ca. *1929.*

Each of the three populations is on a different geologic substrate: the northern population is on soil derived from weathered basalt; the western population on soils derived from granitic parent materials; and the eastern population on sandy soils from a diatomaceous parent material (Linhart, Burr, and Conkle 1967). Although the soils of Santa Cruz Island have not been studied and no information is available, differences in water-holding capabilities of the soils could affect the density of the pines and the composition of associated vegetation as they do elsewhere (Cole 1974). Distance from the coast and exposure to wind could account for certain differences between the western (interior) population and the other two (coastal) populations. The northern population, which occurs primarily at elevations lower than the western and eastern populations, may also be unable to capture as much moisture from fog.

The presence, however, of a large number of dead pines and shrubs on the north side of the island attests to the potential of this area to support a greater living biomass than currently exists. Photographs taken in 1929 also give evidence of the formerly greater density of the northern population (Figs. 5 and 6). In contrast, the other two populations do not exhibit a reduction in density between 1929 and the present. Thus, it seems justifiable to assume that disturbance has been a major factor in causing or accentuating differences between the heavily grazed northern and the two protected populations.

Reduced Foliar Cover

Sheep grazing alone must not have been responsible for the degree of reduction in foliar cover observed on the north side of the island. Fire scars are still apparent over extensive areas as evidence of the Pelican Bay fire more than 45 years ago. Fire is capable of destroying more vegetation in a short amount of time than sheep could. However, the plant species affected should be fire-adapted and, in the absence of disturbance, full regeneration of the vegetation should have occurred in the time that has elapsed.

The northern population is presently well below both the western and eastern populations in both total foliar cover and foliar cover of each individual species (Table 1). Low values for foliar cover of shrub species were especially apparent in the northern population. The most abundant

FIGURE 6. *View of Pelican Bay, 1977.*

shrub species, *Heteromeles arbutifolia, Quercus dumosa,* and *Arctostaphylos tomentosa,* each covered only 1 per cent of the total area sampled there.

Even the most densely vegetated sites in the northern population were in the range of the sparsest sites of the other two populations. The greatest foliar cover measured for one 25 m × 25 m site in the northern population was 65 per cent. The most sparsely vegetated sites of the western and eastern populations were 60 per cent and 57 per cent, respectively. Foliar cover of sites in the western and eastern populations was estimated as high as 160 per cent and 138 per cent, respectively, for single sample sites.

Species Richness

The elimination of some species from portions of Santa Cruz and other California Islands has been referred to in the literature (Dunkle 1950, Thorne 1969). It appears that grazing has significantly reduced the species richness of the northern population. A total of 12 woody species was encountered on study sites within the northern population, as opposed to 28 in the western study area and 11 in the much smaller eastern study area (Table 1). The northern population had from 1 to 5 (average 2.4) species per sample site, while the western population had 7 to 14 (average 9.2) and the eastern population had 4 to 9 (average 7.0).

Many of the species missing from the northern population are subligneous shrubs typical of the coastal sage community. This raises the question of whether these plants might be more susceptible to grazing damage than the chaparral species. Wheeler (1876) describes sheep grazing on the "sagebrush." However, there is nothing in the description to indicate specifically to what plant or group of plants he was referring.

In addition to species that seem to be missing from the northern population due to disturbance, several species were observed in the northern study area which are absent or are found only in disturbed areas within the other two populations. These are *Opuntia littoralis, Pickerin-*

TABLE 1. Percentage of foliar cover of woody species by population.

	Northern	Western	Eastern
Adenostoma fasciculatum	0.1	0.5	0.1
Arctostaphylos insularis	-	0.5	-
Arctostaphylos tomentosa	1.0	4.7	14.9
Artemisia californica	-	0.3	-
Baccharis pilularis	-	0.3	-
Ceanothus arboreus	-	0.1	-
Ceanothus megacarpus	-	0.7	-
Comarostaphylis diversifolia	0.1	13.3	0.8
Coreopsis gigantea	-	0.1	-
Eriogonum arborescens	-	0.1	-
Eriogonum grande	-	2.3	-
Galium nuttallii	-	-	0.4
Haplopappus squarrosus	-	0.1	-
Haplopappus venetus	-	0.1	0.2
Heteromeles arbutifolia	1.2	11.6	-
Lotus scoparius	-	0.1	-
Lyonothamnus floribundus	2.7	-	-
Mimulus spp.	0.1	0.8	3.4
Opuntia littoralis	0.1	-	-
Pinus muricata	20.6	57.7	37.9
Quercus agrifolia	0.1	0.1	-
Quercus agrifolia x *wislizenii*	-	0.1	-
Quercus dumosa	1.2	12.1	23.6
Quercus tomentella	-	1.5	-
Quercus dumosa x *wislizenii*	-	-	1.6
Quercus wislizenii	0.7	2.8	4.8
Rhus diversiloba	-	0.1	-
Rhus integrifolia	0.1	0.9	0.1
Rhus ovata	-	0.1	-
Ribes menziesii	-	0.4	-
Salvia mellifera	-	0.9	-
Vaccinium ovatum	-	3.4	-
Total percentage foliar cover	30.5	114.6	85.0
Meters transected	700	700	200
Total number species	12	28	11

gia montana, and *Eremocarpus setigerus.* All of these seem to be favored within the northern pine population because of their spines or other defenses against grazing.

Regeneration

The most disturbing effect has been the creation of a senescent population of pines and possibly of associated shrubs due to the prevention of regeneration by the sheep. The western and eastern populations both had a wide range of tree sizes from small seedlings through trees of about 45 cm dbh. The western population had an average of 8.8 seedlings per site, with a maximum of 39. The eastern population had an average of 6.0 seedlings per site, with a maximum of 19. The northern population, on the other hand, had no seedlings on any of the study sites and no trees with a dbh smaller than 7.8 cm or a height less than 4 m. Increment cores taken from trees in each population showed that the majority of trees in the western population are less than 30 years of age. In the eastern population, most trees are about 20 to 40 years old. In the northern population, most trees are 40 to 70 years old. The youngest tree cored in the northern population was estimated to be about 30 years of age. This was not the smallest tree measured; a rough estimate of the age of the smallest tree encountered would be 15 to 25 years.

Trees in the northern population still produce abundant cones. Moreover, presence of viable seed and appropriate conditions for germination were attested to by two seedlings, each about 5 cm high. One of these was within the northern study area, near the coast west of Pelican Bay. The other was southeast of the study area, about halfway between Pelican Bay and Prisoners Harbor. These were the only seedlings observed on the northern side of the island, and it seemed that they would soon be eliminated when they became conspicuous enough to be noticed by the sheep. Moreover, the fact that abundant regeneration was recorded in the other two populations dismisses the question of whether fire is a necessary agent for opening the cones and distributing seeds.

CONCLUSION

The existing pines in the northern population continue to succumb to age and disease. The other woody species in the area show evidence of their relatively great age by their large sizes and arborescent forms. Most shrubs and pines on the north side of Santa Cruz Island show a distinct browse line. No significant regeneration of shrub species was observed. The foliar cover and species richness of the northern forest has already been greatly reduced. The lack of successful regeneration under present conditions of disturbance implies a limited future for this population of pines.

ACKNOWLEDGMENTS

The 1929 and 1977 photographs of Pelican Bay were made available by Bob Brumbaugh and Ron Morgan. Noel Diaz drew the maps.

REFERENCES

COLE, K. L. 1974. Edaphic restrictions in the La Purisima Hills with special references to *Pinus muricata* D. Don. M.S. thesis, California State University, Los Angeles, Calif.

DUNKLE, M. B. 1950. Plant ecology of the Channel Islands of California. Allan Hancock Pacific Exped. 13:247-386.

HOBBS, E. R. 1978. The effects of feral sheep grazing on *Pinus muricata* (Bishop Pine) forests, Santa Cruz Island, California. M.A. thesis, University of California, Los Angeles, Calif.

LINHART, Y. B., B. BURR, and M. T. CONKLE. 1967. The closed-cone pines of the Northern Channel Islands. Pp. 151-178 *in* R. N. Philbrick, ed., Proceedings of the symposium on the biology of the California Islands. Santa Barbara Botanic Garden, Santa Barbara, Calif.

SHAW, J. B. 1857. Testimony *in* Transcript of the proceedings in Case No. 176: Andres Castillero, claimant, vs. the United States, defendant, for "Island of Santa Cruz."

THORNE, R. F. 1969. The California Islands. Ann. Missouri Bot. Gard. 56:391-408.

WHEELER, G. M. 1876. Annual report upon the geographical surveys west of the one hundredth meridian. Appendix JJ. U.S. Gov't. Printing Office, Washington, D.C.

Effects of Feral Goats on the Santa Catalina Island Ecosystem

Bruce E. Coblentz

*Department of Fisheries and Wildlife, Oregon State University,
Corvallis, Oregon 97331*

INTRODUCTION

The goat (*Capra hircus*) has had a long history of association with man. Remains identified as belonging to this species have been found at the archaeological sites of the ancient cities of Jarma and Jericho and have been radiocarbon dated to 6,500 B.C. (Reed 1959). The goat may well have been the first domestic ruminant.

In spite of this long association, little about the goat is known. The purpose of the goat in many areas seems to have been that of a "poor man's cow" —an animal that excelled at nothing except survival on poor quality forage on lands that were marginal or unsuitable for more rewarding agricultural endeavor. In addition, the goat was small enough to be supported on the small plots of land that might be owned by poorer people (Devendra and Burns 1970).

A direct consequence of the goat's extreme adaptability is that little is known of its forage preferences. Goats are generally kept where little else can be expected to do well, and must simply make a living on whatever is available to them. At present, there remains considerable disagreement as to the forage preferences of goats (reviewed in Coblentz 1977).

In addition to the lack of ecological knowledge of the goat, the ancestral species has never been precisely defined. Taxonomically, the domestic goat is conspecific with the wild goat or bezoar; most authorities (Reed 1959, Harris 1962, Epstein 1971) consider the bezoar to be the true ancestor. However, there is evidence to suggest that certain breeds derived from hybridization between the bezoar and markhor (*Capra falconeri*) (Epstein 1971).

Bates (1956) summed up the scientific community's interest in goats when he wrote:

The goat . . . might well be called the ecological dominant over much of the Mediterranean region, the Venezuelan Andes, and many other parts of the world, including numerous oceanic islands. Yet, running through a series of ecology textbooks, I find no entry of "Goat" in the indexes.

I find it disheartening to report that my own examination of recent ecology textbooks revealed a similar lack of mention of goats.

HISTORY OF THE GOATS

The origin of the goats on Santa Catalina Island is uncertain. Until recently, goats were believed to have been liberated by either the early Spanish explorers or the English pirates that preyed upon the Spaniards (Coblentz 1976). It now appears (K. Johnson, pers. comm.) that goats were first brought to the island in the early 1800s by traders who avoided paying duties by leaving a portion of each cargo on Santa Catalina, and who then smuggled the contraband onto the mainland. At any rate, goats were well established by the mid-1800s (Curtis 1864).

It has never been clearly proven that goats caused the original defoliation of Santa Catalina, but it is clear that they have perpetuated it in all areas where they persist unchecked. Excessive grazing of sheep and cattle in the mid-1800s (22,000 sheep, Curtis 1864) and early 1900s (4,000 cattle, D. Propst, pers. comm.) certainly contributed to the deterioration of habitats on the island.

EFFECTS OF GOATS UPON VEGETATION

Unchecked populations of both tended and feral goats can have a severe impact upon the native flora of an area (reviewed by Coblentz 1977). There are several reasons, both physiological and behavioral, for the goat's ability to cause ecological damage.

The goat has a relatively large rumen, which facilitates greater efficiency in utilizing forage by allowing an increased passage time, resulting in more complete digestion of the forage. This means that the goat can survive and generally reproduce on amounts of forage that would not sustain many other large herbivores. Additionally, goats have a high threshold for bitter tastes (Bell 1959); this allows them to utilize bitter or oily shrubs that few other herbivores will eat.

The feeding activities of goats are considerably more destructive than most other herbivores. Because they can subsist on poor quality forage, they continue to eat what coarse vegetation remains in an area until there is little vegetative cover on the soil. In addition to direct destruction by foraging, goats also directly destroy vegetation by trampling and soil compaction due to their tendency to use regular trails. Trail formation by goats removes a considerable amount of land from production (1 to 2 per cent, Coblentz 1974) and can also initiate or contribute to gully erosion.

Goats exhibit remarkable behavioral plasticity, allowing them to utilize a greater proportion of the plant biomass in an area, which consequently results in increased environmental destruction. Goats not only feed within the zone of their easy reach but will often push over tall shrubs to get at the better quality forage, stripping most available leaves from the crown. Stems of brittle species, such as St. Catherine's lace (*Eriogonum giganteum*), a species endemic to Santa Catalina Island, are easily broken by this behavior.

Goats also assume the role of arboreal herbivores, climbing trees with low limbs or inclined trunks in order to browse on foliage and on various fruits and mast in certain seasons. The fruit and mast eating activities greatly reduce the number of new seedlings in goat-inhabited areas, and those few seedlings that do appear are soon eaten. Insular endemic plant species have been particularly sensitive to the foraging activities of goats.

The adaptability of the feral goat was exemplified, in part, by the seasonally changing food habits of Santa Catalina Island goats. During the period of study, they appeared to simply take the best forage available, regardless of the forage class (Table 1); grasses and forbs are consumed in May, when abundant, and browse is consumed during drier seasons, such as in December.

On Santa Catalina, the close proximity of areas with goat populations to areas from which goats had been extirpated some 15 years earlier made several comparisons meaningful. The vegetation in the two adjacent areas appeared different; several measurements were taken to ascertain if the apparent differences were real (see details in Coblentz 1977). Goat-inhabited areas on Santa Catalina Island had only about 60 per cent as much total vegetative cover as goat-free areas (Table 2). There was no sagebrush in the goat-inhabited area, compared with nearly 10 per cent in the goat-free zone. In addition, it was subjectively observed that the forage in the goat-free areas grew to greater height and was more vigorous. Annual grasses, which were nearly twice as abundant in the goat-free areas, were especially conspicuous by their larger size.

The impact of the goats on herbaceous vegetation was measured by establishing 0.0001-acre exclosures and matching plot pairs in both goat-free and goat-inhabited areas. These were clipped at the conclusion of the growing season and the forage weighed. Production was greater in the goat-free area in both years that samples were made, and the difference was greater in the drought year of the study (1971-72) than in the wet year (1972-73) (Table 3). In the goat area exclosures, production was about 2.5 times greater in the wet year than in the dry year, yet was only about 25 per cent higher in the exclosures in the goat-free area. Clearly, forage production

TABLE 1. Percentages of forage classes in the identified fraction of rumen contents samples from Santa Catalina Island goats.

	December 1974 (n = 29)	May 1975 (n = 28)
Grass	6	74
Forb	4	18
Browse	90	8

TABLE 2. Mean percentage of total vegetation cover, and associated 95 per cent confidence limits, in shrubland habitat of goat-inhabited (GI) and goat-free (GF) areas of Santa Catalina Island, California. Sampling by ten 100-point point transects in each area.

	November 1971	March 1972	November 1972	April 1973	All
GI	24 ±4	27 ±7	20 ±5	47 ±8	27 ±5
GF	42 ±7	37 ±7	31 ±7	57 ±7	42 ±5

TABLE 3. Estimates of herbaceous layer production in goat-inhabited (GI) and goat-free (GF) areas of Santa Catalina Island, California. Protected plots (p) and nonprotected plots (np) are presented to indicate utilization by goats. All figures are in kg/ha.

Growing season	GI-p	GI-np	GF-p	GF-np
1971-72	818	359	2202	1246
1972-73	2081	1540	2730	2612

was more stable in the goat-free area. Similarly, in the drought year, production was nearly three times greater in protected plots in the goat-free area than in the goat area, and only about 30 per cent greater in the wet year. Here again, these results illustrate the greater stability of the goat-free area and, in this instance, the high potential productivity of the goat-inhabited area.

DISCUSSION

The variability of production in the goat area was apparently due to the lack of any mulch layer on the soil surface, coupled with the lack of an organic layer in the upper horizons of the soil. The mulch layer is formed by dead herbaceous vegetation that remains after the grazing activities of herbivores and is especially important because it (1) retains soil moisture, (2) slows erosion, (3) prevents the soil surface from reaching excessive temperatures, and (4) provides nutrients. Wherever small amounts of mulch occur in the goat areas, primarily around the base of shrubs and in patches of *Opuntia*, greater herbaceous production occurs.

In addition to the quantitative measurements of vegetation taken from the goat-inhabited and goat-free areas, it was obvious that certain plant species had proliferated in the areas from which goats had been removed. It was also obvious that erosion had slowed considerably in the goat-free areas.

The great improvement of the vegetation observed in the goat-free areas occurred in spite of considerable grazing and browsing pressure from other animals. Bison (*Bison bison*), mule deer (*Odocoileus hemionus*), and feral pigs (*Sus scrofa*), all of which were exotic to the island, were present in fairly high numbers during the study. The goat, then, is implicated as being the major ecological disturbance on Santa Catalina Island.

The future of goat-affected habitats on Santa Catalina is not yet secure, in spite of significant efforts by the owners of the major portion of the island, the Santa Catalina Island Conservancy. Stabilization and recovery of some areas is progressing well; control of goats in other areas, however, would be exceedingly dangerous and costly. Poisoning, which would be effective (D. Propst, pers. comm.), is out of the question due to possible effects on non-target endemic wildlife. Furthermore, the goat is a potentially prolific animal. For any given geographical area (*e.g.*, herd home range, entire island), complete control is mandatory. Rudge and Smit (1970) have calculated that a goat population reduced by 80 per cent will attain 90 per cent of its former abundance within four years. Clearly, goats present a potentially continuing problem.

Considering the long periods of time required for biotic succession to occur in semi-arid environments, such as Santa Catalina Island, goat control or removal should proceed rapidly in all areas where it can readily be accomplished.

SUMMARY

Range relationships of feral goats (*Capra hircus*) were studied from June 1971 through April 1973, and again in December 1974, May 1975, and December 1975. Endemic vegetation was severely impacted by goats. The percentage of cover of shrubland vegetation was greater in areas where goats had been eliminated, as was production of the herbaceous layer. Overutilization of the vegetation in goat areas resulted in extensive gully and sheet erosion. Marked recovery of some plants has occurred since the total removal of goats from the central portion of Santa Catalina Island about 15 years prior to this study.

REFERENCES

BATES, M. 1956. Man as an agent in the spread of organisms. *In* W. L. Thomas, Jr., ed., Man's role in changing the face of the earth. University of Chicago Press, Chicago, Ill.

BELL, F. R. 1959. Preference thresholds for taste discrimination in goats. J. Agric. Sci. 52:125-158.

COBLENTZ, B. E. 1974. Ecology, behavior, and range relationships of the feral goat. Ph.D. thesis, University of Michigan, Ann Arbor, Mich.

_____. 1976. Wild goats of Santa Catalina. Natural History 85:70-77.

_____. 1977. Some range relationships of feral goats on Santa Catalina Island, California. J. Range Mgmt. 30:415-419.

CURTIS, J. F. 1864. Report to headquarters district of southern California. *In* War of the Rebellion: compilation of official records, Union and Confederate Armies. Series I, Vol. L, 1897. U.S. Gov't. Printing Office, Washington, D.C.

DEVENDRA, C., and M. BURNS. 1970. Goat production in the tropics. Commonwealth Agr. Bureaux, Farnham Royal, Bucks, England.

EPSTEIN, H. 1971. The origin of the domestic mammals of Africa, II. Africana Publ. Co., New York, N.Y.

HARRIS, D. R. 1962. The distribution and ancestry of the domestic goat. Proc. Linn. Soc. London. 173:79-91.

REED, C. A. 1959. Animal domestication in the prehistoric Near East. Science 130:1629-1640.

RUDGE, M. R., and T. J. SMIT. 1970. Expected rate of increase of hunted populations of feral goats (*Capra hircus* L.) in New Zealand. New Zealand J. Sci. 13:256-259.

EVOLUTION AND ECOLOGY
OF LAND PLANTS

Distribution and Evolution of Endemic Plants of the California Islands

Ralph Philbrick

Santa Barbara Botanic Garden,
Santa Barbara, California 93105

INTRODUCTION

How different are the plants of the California Islands from those of the mainland? In a plant found only on these islands, how much variation is there from island to island? To investigate these questions, I have gathered information on the endemic plants of the California Islands; pertinent information on a few nonendemic island plants is also included. This information is taken from the literature, from personal communication with other botanists, and from work in the field, in the herbarium, and with cultivated island plants by myself and others at the Santa Barbara Botanic Garden.

I have used such phrases as "island plant" to include any plant growing naturally on the California Islands. An "endemic plant" or "island endemic," on the other hand, denotes here a plant that does not occur naturally on the mainland and for which the entire known distribution is confined to one or more of these islands.

The organization of this paper is as follows: (1) plants with slight differences between island and mainland populations; (2) plants with slight differences from island to island; (3) subspecific taxa on different islands, with a special discussion of the Island Mallow, *Lavatera assurgentiflora;* (4) island endemics at the species level; (5) island endemics at the genus level; and (6) morphological and evolutionary tendencies and some of the processes resulting in hybridization, extinction, abundance, and widespread distribution among island plants.

Before proceeding, I wish to point out some distinctively different plants that were thought to be restricted to the islands and have been recently reported, or obscurely reported, from the mainland. These include the shrubby *Crossosoma californicum* from Palos Verdes in coastal Los Angeles County (J. Henrickson, pers. comm.); a Live-forever, *Dudleya virens,* from Palos Verdes (R. Moran, pers. comm.); a Buckwheat, *Eriogonum grande grande,* from Punta Banda, Baja California (M. Benedict, pers. comm.; T. Mulroy, pers. comm.); Island Wallflower, *Erysimum insulare,* from San Luis Obispo County (Cockerell 1937, Hoover 1970); a Tar Weed, *Hemizonia greeneana peninsularis* (Carlquist 1965, Moran 1969); *Orobanche parishii brachyloba* (Heckard 1973); Catalina Cherry, *Prunus ilicifolia lyonii* (Brandegee 1889); Island Black Sage, *Salvia brandegei* (Raven 1965); and *Senecio lyonii* (Munz 1935). Furthermore, Giant Coreopsis, *Coreopsis gigantea,* and Santa Cruz Island Pine, *Pinus remorata,* which are often thought of as island endemic plants, are well known from several scattered mainland locations along the California coast. Thus, none of the above are truly insular endemics, although their major concentrations are confined to the California Islands, and relatively minor environmental changes on the mainland could limit any of these to an island distribution.

A few insular endemics are known also from the fossil record of the mainland. Fossils of a Manzanita, *Arctostaphylos insularis,* are reported from La Brea Tar Pits in Los Angeles (J. Warter, pers. comm.). Fossils of Island Ironwood, *Lyonothamnus floribundus,* are known from various sites in California and Nevada. It is of special interest that the fossils of the Santa Catalina Island subspecies are found in coastal southern California while those of the equally insular subspecies *asplenifolius* occur in more interior locations (Raven and Axelrod 1978). Fossils of Island Oak, *Quercus tomentella,* are also known from the mainland of the western

United States. I am not aware of detailed morphological studies that contrast any present-day island plants with their mainland fossil counterparts. Presumably, the island and mainland populations once formed parts of widespread, more or less coherent taxa.

SLIGHT DIFFERENCES BETWEEN ISLAND AND MAINLAND POPULATIONS

Several species exhibit slight morphological differences between island and mainland populations. Within the widespread species *Arbutus menziesii,* the mainland plants usually have mature inflorescences of 9 to 14 cm. From the collections of Ralph Hoffmann (herbarium specimens at SBM)[1] and of Michael Benedict (SBBG), about five Madrone plants are known from Santa Cruz Island. Although other small samples of isolated individuals might show similar distinctions, it is interesting that the island Madrones, otherwise quite like those of the California mainland, are somewhat smaller and have consistently longer inflorescences of 17 to 24 cm.

In a similar way, the small population of the grass *Elymus condensatus* on Prince Island off San Miguel Island differs from those on the mainland and on other islands by its low habit of growth, conspicuously glaucous leaves, long glumes (20 mm), and long pubescence at the rachis nodes (1 mm for the island plants *vs.* a maximum of 0.7 for those from the mainland); these differences persist under cultivation on the mainland. Although the few *Elymus* plants on Prince Island are extreme for the morphological characters under discussion, individual clones at Gaviota on the mainland and at Cuyler Harbor on San Miguel do have glaucous leaves.

SLIGHT DIFFERENCES AMONG POPULATIONS FROM ISLAND TO ISLAND

Some plants, including four island endemics of the genera *Ceanothus, Eriophyllum, Lavatera,* and *Lotus,* differ slightly from island to island. The large shrub *Ceanothus arboreus* occurs only on Santa Rosa, Santa Cruz, and Santa Catalina Islands. The plants are quite similar, but those from the northern islands have small, dark, ellipsoidal seeds and small, relatively smooth fruit, while those on Santa Catalina have larger, olive-green, spherical seeds and large, warty fruit. Further study of the leaf pubescence and fruit surface will probably document slight differences between even the Santa Cruz and Santa Rosa populations.

The Silver-lace, *Eriophyllum nevinii,* is an island endemic of the floristically related Santa Barbara, Santa Catalina, and San Clemente Islands. The plants on each of these three islands have modally distinct leaf shapes.

The Santa Rosa Island *Lavatera assurgentiflora* is very similar to that on San Miguel, but when representatives of the two island populations are grown together under cultivation, the petals of the Santa Rosa plants are longer (5 mm or greater *vs.* less than 5 mm). In a similar manner, the sepals, floral bracts, and pedicels are also longer for the Santa Rosa material.

Three subspecies of low-growing *Lotus argophyllus* are restricted to the California Islands, and the subspecies *L. a. ornithopus* occurs on five islands (the four southern islands from Santa Barbara to San Clemente plus Guadalupe). The Santa Barbara Island populations differ from all others by having distinctly shorter peduncles.

SUBSPECIFIC DIFFERENCES

In contrast to these slight differences, about 30 subspecies (or varieties) are endemic to one or more of the California Islands and are thus different from all known mainland populations.

Eriogonum giganteum compactum is restricted to Santa Barbara Island (Philbrick 1972), *E.*

---

[1]Full names and addresses for standard herbarium abbreviations are given in Index Herbariorum (Regnum Vegetabile 92:303-354, 1974). Most of the specimens without herbarium citations are deposited at the Santa Barbara Botanic Garden (SBBG).

g. giganteum to Santa Catalina Island, and *E. g. formosum* to San Clemente Island. This level of taxonomic distinction among these Buckwheats is based on significant morphological differences including habit, leaf shape, and inflorescence.

Equally as distinct, but not yet recognized by a subspecific name, are the two taxa of Island Snapdragon, *Galvezia speciosa*. The well-known collections from Santa Catalina and San Clemente Islands contrast with those from Guadalupe Island, the latter being more subject to frost damage and having a different leaf shape, flower, and fruit, and a different habit of growth.

The wide-ranging subspecies *Lotus argophyllus ornithopus* is mentioned above as occurring on five islands. Two additional insular endemic subspecies are *L. a. nivus* on Santa Cruz and the strikingly beautiful *L. a. adsurgens* on San Clemente.

One of the best known examples of different subspecies occurring on different islands is offered by the two taxa of Island Ironwood, *Lyonothamnus floribundus*. The subspecies *L. f. asplenifolius*, with palmately divided leaves and incised leaflets, is found only on Santa Rosa, Santa Cruz, and San Clemente; the entire-leaved *L. f. floribundus* is only on Santa Catalina. Some confusion has persisted in the literature on this distribution pattern, perhaps in part because very young seedlings of both taxa have divided leaves and also because the shape of occasional leaves of either subspecies may approach those of the other [*Blakley 5401;* Brandegee 1890a, pl. 5, figs. 1-7; *Moran 652* (LAM, SBBG); *Piehl 62-422&62-512; Philbrick s.n.,* in 1969; *Philbrick s.n.,* in 1970].

Lavatera assurgentiflora

Special emphasis is given here to a particularly interesting island plant, the Island Mallow, *Lavatera assurgentiflora*. This plant has been known botanically and horticulturally for over 125 years [*Parry s.n.,* March 1850 (NY)], and by 1918 was cultivated as far south as Ecuador [*Pachano 68* (US)]. It has been documented for several of the California Islands and is extensively grown in mainland California and Mexico.

San Miguel Island *Lavatera* was described in 1874 as "a small grove of malva-trees, whose green leaves and penciled blossoms refresh the eyes" (Dall 1874:524). Then E. L. Greene collected *Lavatera* on this island in September 1886 (A, GH, JEPS, NDG, NY, UC), and reported (Greene 1887:77-78) these plants as being restricted to two separate colonies, as follows:

> [N]ear the western extremity, in an open grassy valley looking southward there is a group of some thirty small trees of . . . *Lavatera assurgentiflora*. . . . The other specimens seen by me were three or four depressed and straggling bushes growing on an open slope fully exposed to the winds, at the very western end of San Miguel; and these although stunted by exposure were flowering and fruiting.

Not until E. R. Blakley's collection of 1961 (SBBG) were any Island Mallows again reported for San Miguel. He found about 20 shrubs, some up to 1.2 m tall, that formed a colony 6 m in diameter. These plants were located in a flat sandy area adjacent to a blowout in the dunes north of Adams Cove, near the western end of the island. This is probably fairly close to the location of Greene's larger population, with some modification of the habitat by subsequent wind erosion and grazing. Greene's "open grassy valley" also may have been a result of the heavy rains of 1886 (Johnson 1972:278).

Subsequent observations in 1966 and 1978 show this population to be basically unchanged since 1961, although there are presently more than 20 mature plants.

From 1969 through 1974, Richard S. Peterson, Robert L. DeLong, and George A. Antonelis, Jr., all biologists studying San Miguel Island marine mammals, transplanted seedling Island Mallows from the only known remaining natural population, north of Adams Cove, to two other higher locations in this same general part of the island (R. DeLong, pers. comm.; G. Antonelis, pers. comm.).

Then in 1978, one mature *Lavatera* shrub (2 m tall, 3 m across, and with a basal diameter of 13 cm) was found at the opposite end of the island at an elevation of about 6 m, roughly 1 km southeast of the mouth of Willow Canyon, between Bay Point and Triangulation Point Fish (*Philbrick et al. B78-376*). Under the canopy of this shrub were about two dozen thin seedlings up to 15 cm tall. It is presumed that this shrub, which was not known to have been there in the 1960s, was intentionally or unintentionally established, perhaps from the Adams Cove population.

Brandegee (1890b) lists *Lavatera assurgentiflora* for four islands, including Santa Rosa; however, this does not agree with his more detailed discussion of the same year (1890a). Parish (1890) notes the same four islands, yet I know of no specimens of *Lavatera* for Santa Rosa prior to F. H. Elmore's collection in August of 1938 at "Becher's Bay" (AHFH). M. B. Dunkle made a similar collection one year later that he labeled as coming from "Streambank, Ranch Canyon" (AHFH, LAM). I suspect that both of these collections were from the same general area in the gully at the Vail Ranch headquarters where J. R. Haller and I collected two Island Mallows in 1965. Plants persist in this location to the present, where they are suspiciously near the ranch buildings and have the appearance of having been introduced there. According to C. F. Smith (1976:191) they were "planted at the main ranch on Santa Rosa Island, the source from (?) a native stand on the island." Smith's insertion of a question mark in this quotation indicates his uncertainty; no such native stand, or substantive clue thereof, is known.

According to Brandegee (1890a:109-110) *Lavatera* "has been found on . . . various islets and rocks about Santa Catalina and Santa Cruz"; however, we have searched extensively on Santa Cruz Island and adjacent islets and have found no Island Mallows in the wild, although they are presently cultivated at the Stanton Ranch and at the University of California Field Station.

Evidence of *Lavatera* on Anacapa Island begins with Kellogg's type description of *L. assurgentiflora* "from the island of Anacapa off the coast of Santa Barbara and now to some extent cultivated. . ." (Kellogg 1854). It was reported by Brandegee (1890a:109) that "the species was described from a cultivated specimen obtained by Dr. Trask from a garden in Santa Barbara." He further states, "The seed he [she] was told came from the island of Anacapa. . . ." According to Lyon (1886:204) "sealers reported that once abundant upon Anacapa and San Nicolas, it is now scarce. . . ." Then in 1930 Ralph Hoffmann collected "4 or 5 plants on steep hillside above old sheep landing . . . Anacapa Island" (SBM). None were found on this island by M. B. Dunkle in the late 1930s or early 1940s, nor by subsequent collectors, until in 1978 two live and four dead Island Mallows were found at the top of a 100-m sea bluff on West Anacapa near Portuguese Rock (*Timbrook & Philbrick 652 & 653*). Then in 1979 one small young plant was found near the top of a similar sea bluff on Middle Anacapa (*Junak & Amick MA-36*).

Early mention of *Lavatera* on San Nicolas Island is sketchy. In 1853 Nidever "found some high bushes, called by the natives *malva real* . . . " (Ellison 1937:79), and 33 years later Lyon mentioned the sealers' report as given above. No further San Nicolas record is known until 1978, when both Marla Daily (*Daily 86*) and R. M. Beauchamp collected cultivated specimens from that island.

For Santa Catalina Island *Lavatera,* the known history begins with Lyon's (1886:204) report for "Bird Island [probably Bird Rock, off Fisherman's Cove]." By 1890 Brandegee (1890a:109) had seen this Island Mallow on "a small rock . . . near the isthmus" and reported that it was also known from a second islet to the northwest. It is likely that the second islet was Indian Rock, off Emerald Bay, where *Lavatera* was collected by Moran (LAM, SBBG) in 1941. However, in contrast to this restricted distribution, Parish (1890:301) wrote that *Lavatera* "occupied within the memory of living men, a large part of the island, only yielding to the overstocking of it with sheep and goats." Island Mallow was cultivated in the Avalon area at least as early as 1908 when Jepson collected a San Clemente Island plant grown by Blanche Trask, and, at present, northern island *Lavatera* is naturalized in this same part of the island (Thorne 1967).

On San Clemente Island, *Lavatera* has been documented from three general areas. At the northwest end of the island, natural and transplanted populations have been found near West Cove (*Blakley 6414*, in 1963; *Boutin 1623*, in 1967; *Murbarger 208*, in 1936, cultivated; Raven 1963:330) and near Wilson Cove (*Benedict s.n.*, in 1971, cultivated; Raven 1963:330). Trask also collected "one tree near sea edge . . . West End" (*Trask 282*, in 1903); this collection was reported the next year as follows: "in a region of Pot's Valley . . . it was a foot in diameter and twelve feet high; low and bent and splitting at base" (Trask 1904:94).

The second *Lavatera* area on San Clemente is Seal Cove, near the middle of the outer coast of the island. The label of the Nell Murbarger specimen mentioned above states that her West Cove collection was from a tree moved from Seal Cove by a fisherman; this would date a Seal Cove location prior to 1936.

Lavatera was documented for the southeast portion of the island by a second Trask collection (*Trask 283*, in 1903). The following year this collection was described as "one tree eight inches in diameter—looking into the sea from a cliff near Mosquito Harbor. . ." (Trask 1904:94).

Lyon (1886:204) reported that about 1874, *Lavatera* "constituted unbroken forest, extending for miles upon the high plateaus." And Trask (1904:94-95) wrote that "Johnny [Robearts, a 20-year resident of the island] tells me that formerly there were many 'Malva Rosas' as he calls them; some even on the south coast; mostly eaten by cattle in years when feed was scarce. He recalls these forming groves." Therefore, the historic record for San Clemente Island makes it clear that we can now study only a fragment of a once very extensive population of *Lavatera*.

A single *Lavatera* shrub was found on Todos Santos del Sur in 1965 (*Philbrick & Benedict B65-1554*) at the base of an inland cliff in the northeastern portion of the island. This plant was estimated to be 1.5 m tall, and in 1968 a basal diameter of 20 cm was recorded. Ten years later a basal diameter of 25 cm was noted for the largest of nine plants that ranged from 0.5 to over 2 m high.

The Todos Santos Island population was most likely planted in recent decades. This hypothesis is supported by three facts: (1) no *Lavatera* was noted for the Anthony, Brandegee, and Stockton collections of 1897 (Brandegee 1900) or for the Moran, Lindsay, Thomas, and Wiggins collections of 1948 and 1949 (Moran 1950); (2) the number of individual Island Mallows has increased markedly since these plants were first collected in 1965; and (3) this population is morphologically very similar to mainland cultivated material.

From the above information it can be assumed that *Lavatera assurgentiflora* is native to at least San Miguel, Anacapa, Santa Catalina, and San Clemente Islands. It was possibly also native to Santa Rosa and San Nicolas Islands. Of these six islands, sufficient study material is available for all except San Nicolas. The *Lavatera* from San Miguel, Santa Rosa, and Anacapa Islands, and nearly all the cultivated populations (including those on Todos Santos), differ from the native populations of Santa Catalina and San Clemente Islands by consistently having a pubescent upper leaf surface, a subentire petal apex, and a pubescent staminal tube. The Santa Catalina and San Clemente taxon is characterized by a glabrous or subglabrous upper surface of the leaf and usually by an erose petal apex and a glabrous or subglabrous staminal tube.

Lavatera assurgentiflora is thus divided here into two subspecies, *L. assurgentiflora* Kell. subsp. *glabra* subsp. nov., and *L. assurgentiflora* Kell. subsp. *assurgentiflora*. A formal description of the new subspecies follows.

Lavatera assurgentiflora Kell. subsp. *glabra* subsp. nov., including *Saviniona clementina* Greene (Leafl. Bot. Observ. Crit. 2:160-161, 1911) and *S. reticulata* Greene (Leafl. Bot. Observ. Crit. 2:161, 1911). Superficies folii glabra usque subglabra, viridis vivide; apex petali plerumque erosus; tubus staminalis glaber usque subglaber.

Upper surface of leaf glabrous to subglabrous, bright green; petal apex usually erose;

staminal tube glabrous to subglabrous.

Type.—Bird Rock, Santa Catalina Island, Los Angeles County, California, U.S.A., 23 September 1961, *E. R. Blakley 4739* (SBBG).

Known distribution.—Santa Catalina and San Clemente Islands, California.

Specimens examined.—United States: California, Los Angeles County, Santa Catalina Island: one locality, flowers pale rose color, May 1896, *Blanche Trask s.n.* (US); one tree, buds and flowers snow white, February 1898, *Blanche Trask s.n.* (isotype of *S. reticulata,* US); two localities, March 1898, *Blanche Trask s.n.* (NY); on islets off north coast, March 1898, *Blanche Trask s.n.* (US); on two islets, March 1899, *Blanche Trask s.n.* (A); Indian Rock, 26 February 1941, *Reid Moran 625* (SBBG); Indian Rock, 4 October 1962, *E. R. Blakley 5415* (SBBG); preceding collection in cultivation, 20 April 1966, *R. N. Philbrick s.n.* (SBBG); Bird Rock, 22 May 1931, *F. R. Fosberg 7167* (UC, US); Bird Rock, 23 September 1961, *E. R. Blakley 4739* (type, SBBG); in cultivation from Bird Rock, 20 April 1966, *R. N. Philbrick s.n.* (SBBG); San Clemente Island; no definite locality, April 1885, *Nevin & Lyon s.n.* (GH); in cultivation, July 1908, *W. L. Jepson 14050* (JEPS); no definite locality, no date, received October 1911, *Blanche Trask s.n.* (A); one tree near sea edge, West End [northwest portion of island], June 1903, *Blanche Trask 282* (isotypes of *S. clementina,* A, NY, US); between Driggs and West Rock, 11 April 1962, *P. H. Raven 17303* (SBBG); SW of airstrip runway, 23 April 1967, *F. C. Boutin 1623* (SBBG); West Cove in cultivation, May 1936, *Nell Murbarger 208* (UC); West Cove, 8 December 1963, *E. R. Blakley 6414* (SBBG); preceding collection in cultivation, 20 April 1966, *R. N. Philbrick s.n.* (SBBG); Wilson Cove in cultivation, 27 June 1971, *M. R. Benedict s.n.* (SBBG); one tree, East End [southeast portion of island], June 1903, *Blanche Trask 283* (A, NY, US).

Therefore, *Lavatera assurgentiflora* becomes another example of an endemic plant with different subspecies on different islands.

DIFFERENCES AT THE SPECIES LEVEL

About 100 species are restricted to the California Islands, and a few such endemic plants are present as different species on different islands. These include species of *Arctostaphylos, Astragalus, Castilleja, Dudleya, Eriogonum, Eschscholzia, Haplopappus, Hemizonia, Lavatera, Lotus, Malacothrix,* and *Senecio.*

The tomentose maritime Locoweeds, *Astragalus miguelensis, A. nevinii,* and *A. traskiae,* are good examples of such a pattern of distribution. *A. miguelensis* occurs on the four northern islands from San Miguel to Anacapa, plus San Clemente Island, where it grows sympatrically with the San Clemente endemic *A. nevinii.* This latter *Astragalus* is very closely related to *A. traskiae,* which is restricted to Santa Barbara and San Nicolas Islands.

The genus *Dudleya* probably contains more island endemic taxa than any other. These include about nine published and unpublished island species, illustrated by *D. candelabrum* of Santa Rosa and Santa Cruz Islands, *D. traskiae* of Santa Barbara Island, and *D. greenei (sensu lato)* of San Miguel, Santa Rosa, and Santa Cruz Islands, and perhaps once from Santa Catalina Island.

Buckwheats of the genus *Eriogonum* have also evolved into a number of different island species, including the northern island *E. arborescens* and the southern island *E. giganteum.* The narrow-leaved *E. arborescens* occurs on Santa Rosa, Santa Cruz, and Anacapa, while the broad-leaved *E. giganteum (sensu lato)* is on Santa Barbara, Santa Catalina, and San Clemente.

The insular *Haplopappus* shrubs have also evolved into northern and southern island species (Raven 1963). *Haplopappus detonsus* occurs on Santa Rosa, Santa Cruz, and Anacapa; it has thick, coarsely serrate, pubescent leaves and densely white-woolly phyllaries. *Haplopappus canus,* on the other hand, has nearly glabrous phyllaries and relatively thin, finely serrate leaves that are glabrate on the upper surface. The known distribution of the latter species is restricted to San Clemente and Guadalupe Islands.

DIFFERENCES AT THE GENERIC LEVEL

Although no plant family is restricted to the California Islands, four genera, *Baeriopsis, Hesperelaea, Lyonothamnus,* and *Munzothamnus,* occur only on these islands. Three are known from only a single island. The same three are each considered to consist of a single species. Two are members of the family Compositae. Two are woody trees. Two are known only from Guadalupe Island, and two occur on San Clemente Island.

One of these four insular endemic genera, *Hesperelaea,* is a member of the Olive family, found only on Guadalupe Island, and now thought to be extinct; this extinction is not surprising in view of the devastation by goats on that island and in view of Watson's 1876 (p. 118) description and comment:

> A rather compact tree, twenty to twenty-five feet high, flowers lemon-color. Only three living trees were found in a canyon on the east side, no young trees seen, but many dead ones.

Baeriopsis, the other Guadalupe Island endemic, is reported to be quite rare (R. Moran, pers. comm.), and this herbaceous member of the Compositae is in danger of being further reduced by goats. In spite of the implication of its name, *Baeriopsis* is morphologically very different from *Baeria* (now included within the genus *Lasthenia*).

Munzothamnus is a larger, semi-woody endemic of San Clemente Island where it, too, is in danger of reduction by goats. It is generally recognized as a distinct genus, but is a close relative of *Malacothrix.*

The only wide-ranging endemic genus on the California Islands is *Lyonothamnus* of the Rosaceae. As discussed above under subspecific differences, this tree occurs on Santa Rosa, Santa Cruz, Santa Catalina, and San Clemente Islands. It differs from many of its woody relatives by having opposite leaves.

EVOLUTIONARY TENDENCIES AMONG ISLAND PLANTS

Ten evolutionary trends and processes that are particularly conspicuous among island plants are discussed here.

Pink flower color. —A striking trend among both the endemic and nonendemic plants of the California Islands is the occurrence of pink-flowered forms in plants that usually have other flower colors throughout most of their range. Although frequencies need to be calculated and compared for island and mainland locations and the genetics and pollination biology must be worked out, preliminary information is given here for several interesting examples.

The island endemic Morning Glory, *Calystegia macrostegia macrostegia* (see Philbrick 1972), usually has white flowers; however, a few plants on Anacapa and Santa Cruz have a light pink cast to their flowers (*Blakley 3951 & 4407*).

The shrubby Paintbrush, *Castilleja hololeuca,* is also endemic to the islands. Nearly all San Miguel and Santa Rosa populations have yellow flowers. Yellow, red, and pink flowers occur on Santa Cruz, and red and pink predominate on Anacapa.

The island populations of several nonendemic species are of equal interest. The Yarrow, *Achillea borealis,* usually has white ray petals; however, both pink- and white-flowered forms are abundant on San Miguel. A few pink forms also appear on Santa Rosa, for example in Cow Canyon (*Philbrick & Broder B65-1036*), and in scattered locations on Santa Cruz, such as Sauces Canyon, Lower Embudo, and above China Harbor (*Philbrick B66-187, Philbrick et al. B68-269, Philbrick & Benedict B65-1390*). In all of these pink-flowered populations the color is variable, but the original color persists under cultivation on the mainland.

The Santa Cruz Island Buckwheat, *Eriogonum grande grande*, occurs on the northern islands, plus Santa Catalina, San Clemente, and Todos Santos, and in a very limited way on mainland Baja California. All of the San Miguel Island plants, some of those on Santa Rosa, and a few of those on Santa Cruz are short in stature and have gray foliage and intense rose pink to light pink flower clusters. These have been treated by some as a distinct species, *E. rubescens;* however, they intergrade in all these characters with the taller, green-leaved, whitish-flowered taxon.

A few plants of Indian Pink, *Silene laciniata*, found near Ragged Mountain and East Twin Harbor on Santa Cruz Island, have pink flowers (*Benedict s.n.*, in 1967, *Philbrick & Benedict B65-1307, B65-1309, & B65-1329*). These are in sharp contrast to the usual intensely red flowers seen in this species on the mainland and in numerous other island populations.

The prevalence of such evolutionary experimentation among island populations of predominantly mainland plants suggests incipient speciation in these groups leading possibly to further adaptive radiation on the islands.

Variability in leaf shape. —Variation in vegetative structures, such as leaves, is usually more extreme than variation in reproductive structures. Nevertheless, it is of interest to note that the leaf shape of such island endemics as *Eriophyllum nevinii* and *Lyonothamnus floribundus asplenifolius* differs markedly from island to island.

The leaf shape of island populations of the widespread Toyon, *Heteromeles arbutifolia*, varies in a different way. This Toyon undoubtedly exhibits a certain amount of variability in nearly all of its populations, mainland and island; however, the amount of variation within and between various populations on the same and on different islands is remarkable even when these variants are grown together in cultivation. Leaf characters that vary include: the length/width ratio, the angle of folding along the midrib, the shape of the base and apex, and the amount of serration along the margin.

Gray foliage. —A third trend noted particularly among island plants is the predominance of gray foliage, especially among insular endemics in strictly maritime habitats.

This tendency is exemplified by a Pine, *Pinus torreyana;* a Century Plant, *Agave sebastiana;* a grass, the *Elymus condensatus* from Prince Island; several Buckwheats, including *Eriogonum giganteum;* various Poppies, including *Eschscholzia ramosa* and insular races of *E. californica;* the related Bush Poppy, *Dendromecon;* a number of *Dudleya* endemics; legumes such as *Lotus cedrosensis*, insular subspecies of *L. argophyllus*, and *Astragalus miguelensis* and its relatives; *Ceanothus arboreus; Lavatera assurgentiflora assurgentiflora;* the Santa Cruz Island *Garrya;* members of the Snapdragon family, *Castilleja hololeuca* and *Galvezia speciosa;* and several Compositae including *Artemesia californica insularis, Eriophyllum nevinii*, and *Haplopappus detonsus*.

Thomas Mulroy (1976, 1979) has made an extensive study of the glaucous gray foliage in *Dudleya*. His work establishes a genetic basis for this glaucousness and correlates the waxy surface with reduced herbivore damage, increased leaf longevity, and probably with reduced nutrient loss due to leaching.

Nancy Vivrette (pers. comm.) has been particularly interested in a number of maritime plants with pubescent gray leaves. In these cases the gray coloration is correlated with a slower rate of growth; it is speculated that selective advantages may involve increased water collection and protection from predation, fungus, and salt spray, especially by the pubescent underside of developing leaves in the bud stage.

Gray and green foliage races. —If the assumptions regarding the selective advantages of gray-leaved insular plants are valid, it is somewhat surprising that races with both gray and green leaves occur within several island species. This is true, for example, with nearly sympatric races of both the succulent *Dudleya* and the shrubby *Galvezia*. Several different island Dudleyas exhibit this phenomenon, for example *D. albiflora* as it occurs on Cedros, the *D. candida* of Los Coronados, *D. greenei* on the three most westerly islands, and *D. traskiae* on Santa Barbara. Mulroy (1976) has carefully studied the habitat preferences of the gray and green races of *D. brittonii*, a primarily mainland relative of *D. candida;* although these taxa are superficially sympatric, he has established subtle differences in their microhabitats. Perhaps, then, this type of evolutionary divergence allows for the exploitation of different microhabitats by very closely related taxa.

Insular plants with relatively large habit, leaves, or fruit. —Carlquist (1966) nicely documented the occurrence on islands of large plants with relatively large plant parts. This phenomenon has been studied in detail by Hochberg (1980) for the leaves of three California Island plants.

The following partial list suggests the prevalence of such gigantism among woody and semi-woody island endemics of the flora under consideration: a Buckwheat, *Eriogonum giganteum;* Bush Poppy, *Dendromecon; Ceanothus arboreus* and *C. megacarpus insularis; Lomatium insulare;* Island Morning Glory, *Calystegia macrostegia macrostegia;* a Paintbrush, *Castilleja hololeuca;* Island Coastal Sage, *Artemisia californica insularis; Eriophyllum nevinii;* and *Haplopappus detonsus.*

Prostrate races of nonendemic island plant species. —Again, as with flower color variants, the prostrate races of California Island plants seem to be mostly among widespread nonendemic species that usually occur as nonprostrate plants on both the mainland and the islands. Transplant culture at the Santa Barbara Botanic Garden has demonstrated a genetic dwarfing for the following perennials, all originally collected in windy island habitats: Blue-eyed Grass, *Sisyrinchium bellum;* California Buckwheat, *Eriogonum fasciculatum;* Chamise, *Adenostoma fasciculatum;* and Coastal Sagebrush, *Artemisia californica.* It will also be important to compare genetic and environmental factors for mainland dwarfs. However, it seems possible that the insular or maritime habitat may be conducive to such incipient speciation through the selective advantage of dwarfing mutations.

Hybridization. —Open habitats and nonrigorous selection probably play a major part in increasing the frequency of apparent hybridization on these islands.

On Santa Catalina Island a few relictual plants of the Island Mountain Mahogany, *Cercocarpus betuloides traskiae,* persist in a depauperate hybrid swarm with *C. betuloides blancheae* (Thorne 1969a).

A surprising intersectional *Opuntia* hybrid was found on San Clemente Island by Nell Murbarger (UC). Morphologically this plant is an *F1* hybrid between two nonendemic cacti, a Cholla, *O. prolifera,* and a Prickly-pear, either *O. littoralis* or *O. oricola.* This plant represents the only known evidence for such a wide cross (either natural or artificial) in the genus *Opuntia.*

Another remarkable hybrid swarm occurs among the Cuyler Harbor Chicories on San Miguel Island (*Philbrick B74-157, Philbrick & Benedict B68-316* through *B68-322, Philbrick & Ricker B73-301 & B73-302*). Here the caespitose Beach Chicories, *Malacothrix incana* (*sensu stricto*) and *M. succulenta,* hybridize freely with *Malacothrix implicata.* These particular crosses are so remarkable to those familiar with *Malacothrix* that W. S. Davis, biosystematic specialist in this genus, at first rejected our report as impossible. Subsequent examination of the specimens, however, offers at least preliminary supporting evidence (W. S. Davis, pers. comm.). Two other similar hybridizing populations have recently been found on San Miguel.

One of the most fascinating island hybrids is a single arborescent shrub of *Ceanothus* found by Michael Benedict on Santa Cruz (*Benedict s.n.,* in 1969; *Philbrick et al. B78-2; Philbrick & Benedict, B69-114*). It shares many characteristics with the Santa Cruz Island *C. arboreus* but differs in a number of ways (Tables 1 and 2). Regardless of its precise parentage, this unusual shrub is most probably of hybrid origin. With sample sizes of 500 to 1,000 pollen grains from

TABLE 1. A comparison of the Santa Cruz Island hybrid *Ceanothus* with *Ceanothus arboreus* and *Ceanothus spinosus*.

	Ceanothus arboreus	Ceanothus hybrid	Ceanothus spinosus
Burl	absent	present	present
Color of new bark	gray	gray with green cast	bright yellow-green
Petiole length	7 to 15 mm	6 to 11 mm	2 to 9 mm
Leaf blade shape	broadly ovate to elliptic	ovate to elliptic	elliptic to oblong
Maximum leaf blade length	8 cm	6 cm	4 cm
Leaf margin	serrulate to serrate	serrulate, lower 1/3 subentire	mostly entire, sometimes toothed near apex
Leaf apex	acute to obtuse	acute to obtuse	obtuse to emarginate
Leaf venation	3-veined	3-veined	3-veined only on burl sprouts
Upper leaf surface	puberulent	glabrous to subglabrous	glabrous
Lower leaf surface	canescent	strigose along veins	glabrous or somewhat strigose on midrib
Fruit shape	3-sided	globose	globose
Fruit width	5.5 to 6.5 mm	4.5 to 5.5 mm	4.0 to 6.0 mm

single plants, the Santa Cruz Island *C. arboreus* has 96 per cent stainable pollen, mainland *C. spinosus* has 98 per cent, and mainland *C. thyrsiflorus* has 99 per cent, yet the Santa Cruz Island shrub has only 40 per cent stainable pollen.

The hybrid shrub grows adjacent to *C. arboreus* in a mesic phase of island chaparral. A few feet away a 1-m seedling, which looks very much like the original hybrid, has become established. In addition to this natural seedling, about 200 seedlings have been grown in cultivation from open-pollinated seed collected in the wild from the original shrub. These progeny range from some approaching *C. arboreus* to some with the bark, leaf, and fruit characteristics of the Greenbark Ceanothus, *C. spinosus,* a species which is not known from the fossil or current record of any of the California Islands. It is of interest to note, however, that Axelrod (1967:290) lists a "species similar to" *C. spinosus* among the mainland fossil associates of the now insular *Lyonothamnus* and *Quercus tomentella*.

Chaney and Mason (1930) reported fossil seed of *C. thyrsiflorus* from Santa Cruz Island, and it is tempting to consider the possibility that the hybrid shrub is a cross between *C. arboreus* and a now extinct island population of *C. thyrsiflorus*. However, we have studied the size and shape of seeds of *C. arboreus, C. thyrsiflorus,* and *C. spinosus,* as well as the actual Chaney and Mason fossils; we find no evidence to support the hypothesis. Furthermore, one cannot argue that the fossil seeds are actually representative of *C. spinosus* or the Santa Cruz Island hybrid, for the fossil seeds match rather closely those of contemporary *C. thyrsiflorus*. The average fossil seed length × width is 1.18 × 1.07 mm. Adding 25 per cent to restore live dimensions (15 to 25 per cent proposed by Chaney and Mason), these fossil seeds would reflect a live seed size

TABLE 2. Simplified comparison of the Santa Cruz Island hybrid with *Ceanothus arboreus* and *Ceanothus spinosus*.

	Like *C. arboreus*	Intermediate	Like *C. spinosus*
Burl	—	—	X
Bark color	—	X	—
Petiole length	—	X	—
Leaf blade shape	X	—	—
Leaf blade length	—	X	—
Leaf margin	—	X	—
Leaf apex	X	—	—
Leaf venation	X	—	—
Upper leaf surface	—	X	—
Lower leaf surface	—	X	—
Fruit shape	—	—	X
Fruit width	—	X	—

of about 1.5 × 1.3 mm, which compares favorably with 1.8 × 1.5 mm for contemporary *C. thyrsiflorus* but definitely not with the 2.4 × 2.4 mm of the Santa Cruz Island hybrid or the even larger-seeded *C. spinosus*.

All available morphological data considered, it seems to us that *C. spinosus* is the more probable absent parent, especially because of the *C. spinosus*-like progeny and the intermediate nature of so many salient characteristics of the Santa Cruz Island shrub (Tables 1 and 2).

In addition to hybridization in the wild, island taxa also have a propensity to hybridize when brought into cultivation. *Eriogonum giganteum giganteum* from Santa Catalina Island and the native *E. arborescens* have been grown together for several years at the Stanton Ranch on Santa Cruz. In 1971 apparent *F1* hybrids were noted at this same location and have since been found elsewhere on the island. These hybrids appear to be morphologically intermediate between the two rather different looking Buckwheats (*Philbrick B71-46* through *B71-48*). Similar hybridization has also been found in cultivation on the mainland (*Philbrick s.n.*, in 1979).

Mahonia pinnata insularis from Santa Cruz Island has been grown in cultivation with the mainland subspecies *M. p. pinnata*, and the two collections remain morphologically distinct. However, volunteer seedlings growing under a plant of the smooth leaflet insular subspecies produced the spiny leaflets characteristic of mainland populations. Apparently cross-pollination occurred in cultivation, and the spiny leaflet margin is genetically dominant.

Island species of the genus *Lavatera* offer another example of interspecific hybridization in cultivation. Volunteer seedlings have resulted from uncontrolled cross-pollination between *L. venosa* and both *L. assurgentiflora* and *L. occidentalis* [*Hall s.n.*, in 1903 (UC), *Philbrick s.n.*, in 1971].

Such hybridization in cultivation suggests that these island endemics have resulted from morphological evolution that has not been accompanied by the evolution of intrinsic reproductive barriers.

Reduction and extinction.—For 16 relatively small islands we can easily list 21 insular endemic plants that have been eliminated or drastically reduced on at least some of these islands. This is a result of both the fragility of these plants and the vulnerability of their habitats. It is an especially discouraging trend for those who are interested in the study of island endemic plants. There is, however, always the possibility that some of these plants may again be found where they are now thought to have been eliminated.

The grass *Dissanthelium californicum* has yielded to grazing pressures and is extinct throughout its known range which once included at least three of the larger southern islands.

Mahonia pinnata insularis was probably never abundant anywhere during the past century and has not been collected again on Santa Rosa or Anacapa Island in recent decades. This leaves only a few small populations on Santa Cruz to perpetuate this ornamental island shrub.

Three insular members of the Mustard family have been reduced or eliminated. *Arabis hoffmannii* can no longer be found on Santa Cruz, nor *Sibara filifolia* on Santa Cruz or Santa Catalina. The Santa Cruz Island endemic *Thysanocarpus conchuliferus* is reduced to a small fraction of its original distribution on this island; now it is usually found only on relatively inaccessible rocky ledges.

Succulent Dudleyas are especially vulnerable. *Dudleya candelabrum* is rare on Santa Rosa Island and presently even harder to find on Santa Cruz. The Santa Barbara Island *Dudleya traskiae* was thought to be extinct as of 1969 (Philbrick 1972). Since 1974, however, reduction in the feral rabbits on Santa Barbara Island has allowed a few scattered plants to become re-established in areas in and around Cave, Middle, and Cat Canyons. There is also a thriving colony, probably of several hundred plants, recently discovered by Molly Hunt on the nearly vertical westerly face of Signal Peak (*Philbrick & Cummings B76-1*). This population has apparently been inaccessible to the rabbits, but could be eliminated by landsliding.

The herbaceous Saxifrage, *Lithophragma maximum*, has been collected only on San Clemente Island, and there only once, in 1936 (Bacigalupi 1963).

Only a very few individual plants of the endemic Mountain Mahogany, *Cercocarpus betuloides traskiae*, now occur on Santa Catalina Island.

Two subspecies of *Lotus argophyllus*, *L. a. adsurgens* of San Clemente Island and *L. a. niveus* of Santa Cruz Island, are extremely rare and apparently vulnerable to grazing. A third legume, *Trifolium palmeri*, is reported as extinct for Santa Catalina Island (Thorne 1967); it is known otherwise only from four other southern islands.

Lomatium insulare cannot now be found on San Clemente Island, where it is known only from a 1918 collection (Raven 1967, Thorne 1969b). Apparently this plant has been extinct on San Clemente for several decades.

The extinction of *Hesperelaea*, the endemic tree from Guadalupe Island, is discussed above under generic endemics and again emphasizes the irreversible destruction of uncontrolled grazing on islands.

One endemic species of *Phacelia* and two of *Lycium* have not been collected since the 1930s or earlier. *Phacelia cinerea* is known only from San Nicolas Island, where it was collected only once or twice [*Trask s.n.* (GH), in 1901, not seen; *Trask s.n.* (UC), no date]. *Lycium hassei* is known only from one plant each on Santa Catalina and San Clemente Islands. The San Clemente plant was reported as dead in 1936 and that on Santa Catalina was intentionally removed by 1908 (Raven 1963). *L. verrucosum* is known only from San Nicolas Island and is another of those plants collected only by Blanche Trask [*Trask s.n.* (CAS), in 1897; *Trask s.n.* (LAM), in 1901]. It has not been seen since.

The genus *Mimulus* contains three small, fragile island Monkey Flowers that have not been found by any contemporary botanist and must be assumed to be extinct. These three are *M. brandegei* from Santa Cruz Island, *M. latifolius* from Guadalupe Island, and *M. traskiae* from Santa Catalina Island. The most recent collection of these annual Monkey Flowers was in 1932.

Abundance. —Diametrically opposed to extinction is a trend among some island endemic plants to be extremely abundant where they do occur. This may result from the presence of favorable habitats within a nonsaturated flora and from appropriate plant adaptations.

Examples of such abundant endemics are: Buckwheats, including *Eriogonum arborescens* and *E. grande; Dudleya,* such as *D. greenei* on San Miguel Island; a Locoweed, *Astragalus miguelensis;* a White Popcorn Flower, *Cryptantha maritima cedrosensis;* Paintbrushes, such as *Castilleja hololeuca* on Anacapa Island; *Haplopappus detonsus* on West Anacapa; a Tar Weed, *Hemizonia clementina;* and *Malacothrix foliosa (sensu lato)* on Santa Barbara Island.

Widespread distribution. —A few plants that are known only from the California Islands have a remarkably wide distribution within that limit. An annual, *Gilia nevinii;* an herbaceous perennial, *Jepsonia malvifolia;* and a tree, *Quercus tomentella,* each occur on six of these islands. All three occur on Santa Cruz, Santa Catalina, San Clemente, and Guadalupe. In addition, the *Gilia* is known from Anacapa and Santa Barbara Islands; the *Jepsonia,* from Santa Rosa and San Nicolas Islands; and the oak, from Santa Rosa and Anacapa Islands.

The Island Morning Glory, *Calystegia macrostegia macrostegia,* has an even wider distribution; it occurs on 10 islands from San Miguel to Guadalupe.

The Island Poppy, *Eschscholzia ramosa,* has recently been collected on San Nicolas Island by Mitchel Beauchamp (pers. comm.). This collection, plus previously overlooked reports for Natividad Island (Brandegee 1900) and for Anacapa Island (Dunkle 1942:131 as "Eschscholtzia elegans Greene"), extends the reported distribution for this delicate annual endemic to all of the California Islands except San Miguel.

Such extensive distributions for strictly insular plants may be related to a relatively uniform climate over broad distances and to successful plant adaptations.

SUMMARY

Among the plants discussed in this paper are a new subspecies of *Lavatera assurgentiflora* and a hybrid related to *Ceanothus arboreus.*

Many plants are restricted to the California Islands and differ from their mainland relatives and those on other islands. Some of these plants have minor differences of a few trivial characters; at the opposite extreme, others differ by the aggregation of numerous characters, resulting in generic endemics.

Of particular interest are the morphological and physiological experimentations, which play a part in allowing endemic island organisms to exploit the favorable, open habitats of these islands.

ACKNOWLEDGMENTS

The plants of the California Islands are available for field study to all qualified botanists with sufficient patience, hardiness, and flexibility who obtain the necessary private and governmental permission. Some of the most interesting island plants have been well documented in herbarium collections such as those of the University of California, California Academy of Sciences, Santa Barbara Botanic Garden, Santa Barbara Museum of Natural History, Los Angeles County Museum of Natural History, Rancho Santa Ana Botanic Garden, San Diego Museum of Natural History, University of Notre Dame, and the Smithsonian Institution.

Our island plant research at the Santa Barbara Botanic Garden has resulted from the field and herbarium work of several botanists, but special credit is due Michael R. Benedict, Botanic Garden Research Associate, for extensive collecting, especially on Santa Cruz Island, and for discovering, rediscovering, or making repeated field observations on the island *Arbutus* and the *Ceanothus* hybrid discussed here. Steven A. Junak, Botanic Garden Botanist, has contributed careful herbarium study of *Lavatera assurgentiflora,* the Prince Island *Elymus,* and the hybrid *Ceanothus* and its presumed parents. The Latin translation was provided by Robert W. Patterson.

In addition, manuscript suggestions have been received from Mary H. Allcott, Martha J. Cummings, Mary C. Hochberg, and Steven L. Timbrook.

REFERENCES

AXELROD, D. I. 1967. Geologic history of the Californian insular flora. Pp. 267-315 *in* R. N. Philbrick, ed., Proceedings of the symposium on the biology of the California Islands. Santa Barbara Botanic Garden, Santa Barbara, Calif.

BACIGALUPI, R. 1963. A new species of *Lithophragma* from San Clemente Island, California. Aliso 5:349-350.

BRANDEGEE, T. S. 1889 [1890]. A collection of plants from Baja California, 1889. Proc. California Acad. Sci., ser. 2, 2:117-216.

———. 1890a. The plants of Santa Catalina Island. Zoe 1:107-115.

———. 1890b. Flora of the Californian Islands. Zoe 1:129-148.

———. 1900. Voyage of the Wahlberg. Zoe 5:19-28.

CARLQUIST, S. 1965. Island life. Natural History Press, Garden City, N.Y.

———. 1966. The biota of long-distance dispersal. I. Principles of dispersal and evolution. Quart. Rev. Biol. 41:247-270.

CHANEY, R. W., and H. L. MASON. 1930. A Pleistocene flora from Santa Cruz Island, California. Carnegie Inst. Publ. 415:1-24.

COCKERELL, T. D. A. 1937. The botany of the California Islands. Torreya 37:117-123.

DALL, W. H. 1874. The lord of the isles. Overland Monthly 12:522-526.

DUNKLE, M. B. 1942. Contributions from the Los Angeles Museum—Channel Islands biological survey. 27. Flora of the Channel Islands National Monument. Bull. So. California Acad. Sci. 41:125-137.

ELLISON, W. H., ed. 1937. The life and adventures of George Nidever (1802-1883). University of California Press, Berkeley, Calif.

GREENE, E. L. 1887. A botanical excursion to the island of San Miguel. Pittonia 1:74-85.

———. 1911. The genus *Saviniona*. Leafl. Bot. Observ. Crit. 2:159-163.

HECKARD, L. R. 1973. A taxonomic re-interpretation of the *Orobanche californica* complex. Madroño 22:41-70.

HOCHBERG, M. C. 1980. Factors affecting leaf size of chaparral shrubs on the California Islands. Pp. 189-206 *in* D.M. Power, ed., The California Islands: proceedings of a multidisciplinary symposium. Santa Barbara Museum of Natural History, Santa Barbara, Calif.

HOOVER, R. F. 1970. The vascular plants of San Luis Obispo County, California. University of California Press, Berkeley, Calif.

JOHNSON, D. L. 1972. Landscape evolution on San Miguel Island, California. Ph.D. thesis, University of Kansas, Lawrence, Kan.

KELLOGG, A. 1854. [Type description of *Lavatera assurgentiflora*]. Proc. California Acad. Sci. 1:14.

LYON, W. S. 1886. The flora of our south-western archipelago. I-II. Bot. Gaz. 11:197-205, 330-336.

MORAN, R. 1950. Plants of the Todos Santos Islands, Baja California. Leafl. West. Bot. 6:53-56.

———. 1969. Twelve new dicots from Baja California, Mexico. Trans. San Diego Soc. Nat. Hist. 15:265-295.

MULROY, T. W. 1976. The adaptive significance of epicuticular waxes in *Dudleya* (Crassulaceae). Ph.D. thesis, University of California, Irvine, Calif.

———. 1979. Spectral properties of heavily glaucous and non-glaucous leaves of a succulent rosette-plant. Oecologia 38:349-357.

MUNZ, P. A. 1935. A manual of southern California botany. Claremont College, Claremont, Calif.

PARISH, S. B. 1890. Notes on the naturalized plants of southern California. VII. Zoe 1:300-303.

PHILBRICK, R. N. 1972. The plants of Santa Barbara Island, California. Madroño 21:329-393.

RAVEN, P. H. 1963. A flora of San Clemente Island, California. Aliso 5:289-347.

———. 1965. Notes on the flora of San Clemente Island, California. Aliso 6:11.

———. 1967. The floristics of the California Islands. Pp. 57-67 *in* R. N. Philbrick, ed., Proceedings of the symposium on the biology of the California Islands. Santa Barbara Botanic Garden, Santa Barbara, Calif.

RAVEN, P. H., and D. I. AXELROD. 1978. Origin and relationships of the California flora. Univ. California Publ. Bot. 72:1-134.

SMITH, C. F. 1976. A flora of the Santa Barbara region, California. Santa Barbara Museum of Natural History, Santa Barbara, Calif.

THORNE, R. F. 1967. A flora of Santa Catalina Island, California. Aliso 6:1-77.

———. 1969a. The California Islands. Ann. Missouri Bot. Gard. 56:391-408.

———. 1969b. A supplement to the floras of Santa Catalina and San Clemente Islands, Los Angeles County, California. Aliso 7:73-83.

TRASK, B. 1904. Flora of San Clemente Island. II. Bull. So. California Acad. Sci. 3:90-95.

WATSON, S. 1876. Botanical contributions. Proc. Amer. Acad. Sci. 11:105-148.

Factors Affecting Leaf Size of Chaparral Shrubs on the California Islands

M. C. Hochberg[1]

Department of Biological Sciences, University of California,
Santa Barbara, California 93106

INTRODUCTION

Correlations between leaf size and environmental factors have been well documented (Gates 1968, Vogel 1970, Parkhurst and Loucks 1972, Givnish and Vermeij 1976, Grier and Running 1977, Smith and Nobel 1977, Smith 1978, Werger and Ellenbroek 1978), and interest in this subject dates to studies by Theophrastus in the 4th century B.C. (Hort 1916). In recent years, the concept of water-use efficiency has become the focus of considerable experimental research on the interrelationships between leaf characteristics and the environment (Ehrler 1969, Meinzer and Rundel 1973, Schultze *et al.* 1975, Ehleringer *et al.* 1976). Results from these studies suggest that there is an optimum balance between the photosynthetic gain by a leaf and the concomitant water loss from transpiration and evaporation. This loss is strongly coupled with environmental variables such as air temperature, relative humidity, solar radiation, and convective and conductive forces. Biotic variables include leaf temperature and leaf resistance to transpirational losses, both of which are a direct function of leaf dimension.

In general, plants native to arid habitats are characterized by small, thick leaves with small cells, thick cuticles, and well-developed mechanical tissues. In contrast, plants native to mesic areas bear large, thin leaves with large cells, thin cuticles, and poorly-developed mechanical tissues (Shields 1951, Kummerow 1973). However, the leaf characteristics of a single species may vary in response to seasonal patterns and exposure to intense solar radiation (Bjorkman and Holmgren 1963, Kummerow 1973, Smith and Nobel 1977).

I have observed distinct leaf size differences in chaparral shrubs common to the Santa Ynez Mountains on the mainland of Santa Barbara County and to the California Islands, where leaf size correlations with environmental parameters are not obvious. Although many shrub species are common to the two areas, the physiognomy of island and mainland stands of chaparral is drastically different. Chaparral on the mainland consists of dense, impenetrable stands of sclerophyllous shrubs with very little understory (Cooper 1922, Hanes 1977, Mooney *et al.* 1977). Light, nutrients, and moisture availability may be extremely limited in mature chaparral vegetation, and, coupled with fire, these factors play a major role in controlling the development of seedlings, herbs, and understory shrubs (McPherson and Muller 1967, Hanes 1977, Schlesinger and Gill in press). In addition, the build-up of allelopathic toxins may interfere with seedling establishment in older stands (Muller 1966, Muller *et al.* 1968). In contrast, insular chaparral vegetation often forms an open woodland of large-leaved, arborescent shrubs intermingling with grassland and coastal sage scrub on south-facing slopes, and a more dense aggregation of oaks and mesic chaparral associates on north-facing slopes (Philbrick and Haller 1977, Bjorndalen 1978).

The observed variation of shrub density in the chaparral of the Santa Ynez Mountains and Santa Cruz Island has been documented elsewhere (Hochberg 1980). Mainland sites are dominated by an essentially complete overstory of large shrubs (83.9 to 99.1 per cent cover),

---

[1] Present address: Santa Barbara Botanic Garden, 1212 Mission Canyon Road, Santa Barbara, California 93105.

with small shrubs and a few herbs scattered in pockets or among rocky outcrops in the chaparral. Island sites, on the other hand, are covered by an open shrubland in which large shrubs are aspect dominant and form 40.9 to 47.0 per cent cover. Small shrubs, herbs, and grasses grow around and under the large shrubs and actually represent the majority of cover.

There are several factors which may contribute to the openness of island chaparral. Unlike chaparral on the mainland, fire does not presently play a major role in the vegetation dynamics of the California Islands. As a result, altered nutrient-cycling patterns, potential accumulation of allelopathic toxins, and the dependence of many chaparral shrubs on fire for seed germination may result in decreased shrub density. It is not presently known what effects these variables have on island plants. Furthermore, the higher incidence of intensive grazing by feral animals on the islands may interfere with seedling establishment and longevity. Hobbs (1978) contrasts the relative openness and the difference in age structure of the grazed northern pine forests on Santa Cruz Island with the dense tangle of trees and chaparral underbrush of the fence-protected western and eastern pine forests.

In this paper, environmental factors are briefly summarized and differences in leaf dimensions between island and mainland habitats are documented. A preliminary attempt is made to isolate those factors which make the largest contributions to the uniqueness of island chaparral shrubs and their environment.

METHODS

Meteorological data. — In order to examine the role of climatic factors on island and mainland chaparral, coastal and interior collecting and climate monitoring sites were established in the Santa Ynez Mountains and on Santa Cruz Island in January of 1977, as described in Hochberg (1980). All sites are typical chaparral habitats on southerly slope exposures at elevations between 225 and 400 m.

The mainland coastal study area consists of two sites on a ridge above Maria Ygnacio Creek. The mainland interior site is located above Kelly Creek in Los Laureles Canyon. The island coastal site occupies a ridge above Albert Anchorage. The island interior site is located on the slopes above Islay Canyon.

Meteorological data from the mainland coastal monitoring stations have been supplied by Dr. W. H. Schlesinger and are also reported in Schlesinger and Gill (in press) and Schlesinger and Hasey (1980). A total of five meteorological stations has been established in a transect from 350 m to 1,050 m (Schlesinger and Hasey 1980); pertinent data from the sites at 350 m and 560 m are reported here. Meteorological data from the mainland interior site are on file at the Los Prietos Ranger Station.

Meteorological stations were established at the island sites to record precipitation, wind speed, temperature, relative humidity, and solar radiation. Precipitation was measured using a Tru-Chek wedge-shaped rain gauge. Both a Taylor maximum-minimum thermometer and a Weather Measure hygrothermograph, model H311, were utilized for temperature data. Relative humidity was recorded on weekly hygrothermograph charts and checked periodically with a wet and dry bulb sling psychrometer. Average wind speed was determined with a Belfort Instrument Company anemometer. A Weather Measure solar radiometer (model R401) was added to the island interior site in June 1978. In addition, vapor pressure deficits were calculated according to methods described in Hochberg (1980). Insufficient data were available for determinations of vapor pressure deficits at the island coastal site or minimum vapor pressure deficit levels at the mainland interior site.

In order to assess the frequency and extent of fog cover at the four study areas, a series of satellite images was reviewed. Landsat satellite images, such as those shown in Figures 8 and 9, are available at the Department of Geography, University of California, Santa Barbara for selected dates between 1972 and the present. The satellite orbits over the Santa Barbara area every 14 days at 9:30 to 10:00 a.m. and records existing cloud cover using a multispectral optical scanner. All four study areas on both the mainland and island are clearly visible in these images; however, it is not possible to distinguish the two sites within the mainland coastal study area. Tallies of clear, partly overcast, and overcast "days" (at 9:30 a.m.) have been made from examination of these images.

Soils.—Three soil samples were collected at each study site for soil textural analysis utilizing methods described by Bouyoncos (1936). This process was repeated twice during the study. The approximate proportion of organic matter in the soil was established by ashing three 2-g samples of dry soil in a muffle furnace for four hours at 500°C. This procedure was also repeated twice during the study.

Leaf size.—For this investigation, three taxonomically unrelated chaparral shrub species were chosen in order to quantify the general trend of differential leaf size. Each species has an island and a mainland subspecies. The three pairs of subspecies being studied are: *Ceanothus megacarpus* Nutt. subsp. *megacarpus* from the mainland (Fig. 1), and *Ceanothus megacarpus* Nutt. subsp. *insularis* (Eastw.) Raven from the California Islands (Fig. 2); *Prunus ilicifolia* (Nutt.) Walp subsp. *ilicifolia* from the mainland (Fig. 3), and *Prunus ilicifolia* (Nutt.) Walp subsp. *lyonii* Raven from the California Islands (Fig. 4); and *Dendromecon rigida* Benth. subsp. *rigida* from the mainland (Fig. 5), and *Dendromecon rigida* Nutt. subsp. *harfordii* (Kell.) Raven from the Northern Channel Islands (Fig. 6). All of these have been classified as separate species at one time or another based on numerous morphological distinctions. In addition, all three pairs of subspecies have maintained their differences in common garden environments at both the Santa Barbara Botanic Garden and the University of California at Santa Barbara.

Thirty plants of each species were sampled, when present, in each of the four study areas. Sixty leaves were removed per shrub from low, medium, and high branches in each cardinal compass direction. Care was taken to sample only mature leaves and leaves not damaged by insect predation. The sample leaves were placed in a bag and mixed together; a subsample of 30 leaves was then randomly drawn from each bag. Petioles were clipped off each leaf, and leaf profiles were recorded on contact photographic proof paper. Leaf length and width were measured directly from the photographic images within 0.1 cm, and leaf area was determined using a polar planimeter with an accuracy of 99 per cent for leaves greater than 10 cm^2 and 95 per cent for leaves smaller than 10 cm^2. The leaves were also weighed so that correlations between leaf area and leaf weight could be made for use in dimension analysis studies.

In addition to the shrub samples taken at the four major study sites, 10 shrubs of each species were sampled at several other subjectively selected localities (including Santa Rosa Island) in order to show the range of variation in leaf size in both island and mainland populations. Student's *t*-tests were used to determine the significance levels of all leaf dimensions.

Dimension analysis.—Dimension analysis studies were undertaken during November-December 1977 and January 1978 for comparative measurements of total leaf area for each of the species pairs (Schlesinger and Gill 1978). Fifteen branches were collected from different individuals of each pair of subspecies on both the island and the mainland (seven from *Prunus* due to branch size and the corresponding impact on the island chaparral habitat). Branch diameters of all stems originating at or below 15 cm above the ground were also measured. Dead wood was removed and woody and foliar components were separated, dried, and weighed. Total leaf area per plant was determined by use of the formula:

$$\text{total leaf area} = \frac{\text{mean leaf area of 30 leaves}}{\text{mean leaf weight of 30 leaves}} \times \text{total leaf weight.}$$

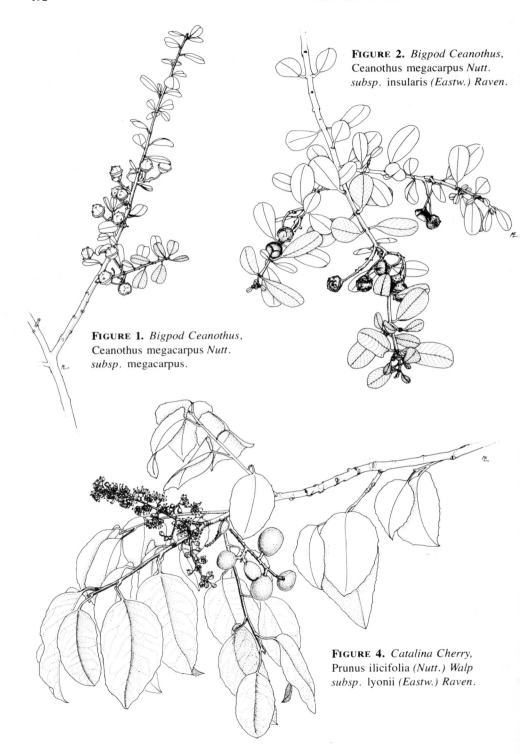

FIGURE 2. *Bigpod Ceanothus,* Ceanothus megacarpus *Nutt.* *subsp.* insularis *(Eastw.) Raven.*

FIGURE 1. *Bigpod Ceanothus,* Ceanothus megacarpus *Nutt.* *subsp.* megacarpus.

FIGURE 4. *Catalina Cherry,* Prunus ilicifolia *(Nutt.) Walp* *subsp.* lyonii *(Eastw.) Raven.*

FIGURE 3. *Hollyleaf Cherry,* Prunus ilicifolia *(Nutt.) Walp subsp.* ilicifolia.

FIGURE 6. *Island Bush Poppy,* Dendromecon rigida *Benth. subsp.* harfordii *(Kell.) Raven.*

FIGURE 5. *Bush Poppy,* Dendromecon rigida *Benth. subsp.* rigida.

TABLE 1. Summary of climatic data for coastal and interior sites on Santa Cruz Island and in the Santa Ynez Mountains (1978 data for all sites except the island coastal site, where only 1977 data are available).

	Santa Cruz Island		Mainland		
	Coastal	Interior	Coastal		Interior
Elevation (m)	229	225	350	560	306
Precipitation (mm)					
1977-1978	1113	1115	1352†		1006
10-year average	509*	509*	495†		521
Temperature (°C)					
Mean annual	19.3	19.0	18.6	18.9	17.3
Mean January minimum	19.0	11.3	11.4	9.4	7.5
Mean July maximum	31.2*	27.2	30.4	32.5	33.5
Extremes	2.0 - 42.2	2.1 - 43.3	3.0 - 44.0	0.0 - 42.5	−7.8 - 41.0
Relative humidity (%)					
Mean annual	N.A.	68.9	67.4	62.6	N.A.
Mean July minimum	40.3*	48.1	40.7	34.8	31.8
Wind velocity (kph)					
Mean annual	5.3	2.3	1.4		10.6

N.A. = not available.

*Sufficient data not available; determined by linear regression.

†Data from Santa Barbara Botanic Garden.

Leaf anatomy.—In May 1978, six one-year-old leaves were collected from each subspecies for anatomical studies. Prepared slides of leaf cross-sections were made and the following parameters were measured: upper and lower surface cuticle thickness, upper and lower surface epidermal cell thickness, and leaf thickness at the immediate periphery of the central midvein. Epidermal peels were made during June 1979 for stomatal counts. Five leaves per subspecies, with six peels per leaf, were mounted on slides, and stomata were counted within a standard area. Because *Ceanothus megacarpus* stomata occur in crypts, the stomatal frequency was not determined. Also in June 1979, 15 leaves from each subspecies were randomly collected, weighed, and subsequently oven-dried and reweighed to calculate leaf water content. The significance of all measurements was tested using Student's *t*-tests.

RESULTS AND DISCUSSION

Meteorological data.—Results from the environmental monitoring stations are summarized in Table 1. Precipitation totals from all sites are comparable and none of the data is significantly different at $P < 0.05$. Mean wind velocity is affected primarily by local topography and is not consistently high or low on either the island or mainland. Mean annual temperatures differ by only 1 to 2°C at the various sites; the mean annual temperature at the mainland interior site appears lower than that of the other sites because of significantly lower temperature minima during the winter months (Hochberg 1980). Mean annual relative humidity figures are also insignificantly different. However, during the months of July through October, substantial

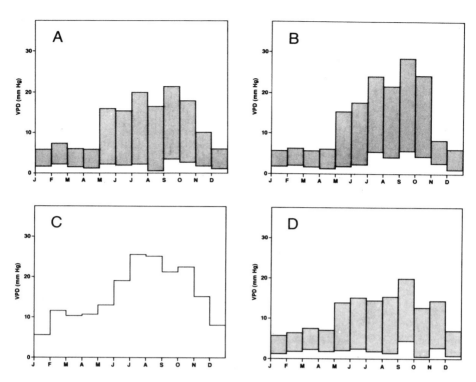

FIGURE 7. *Range in vapor pressure deficits in mm Hg on the mainland and island.* **a:** *lower mainland coastal site.* **b:** *upper mainland coastal site.* **c:** *mainland interior site (maximum values available only).* **d:** *island interior site.*

differences in relative humidity (Table 1) and vapor pressure deficits exist between the various sites (Fig. 7).

The highest vapor pressure deficit values are recorded during July through October at the mainland sites. At the upper mainland coastal site and the mainland interior site, the maximum vapor pressure deficit for July through October varies from 21.7 to 28.0 mm Hg. During the same time period, the maximum vapor pressure deficit at the lower mainland coastal site and the island interior site fluctuates from 11.8 to 20.7 mm Hg. Although averages of the vapor pressure deficits during the entire 12-month period at each site are not statistically significant at $P < 0.05$, maximum vapor pressure deficit values from the July through October period are significantly higher at the upper mainland coastal site and the mainland interior site than at either the lower mainland coastal site or the island interior site (Mann-Whitney test: $P < 0.01$). Dr. W. H. Schlesinger (pers. comm.) has observed that the lower coastal mainland site is frequently within the fog inversion layer, while the upper mainland coastal site often remains above the fog zone or at least clears off earlier in the day.

The relative frequency of clear, partly overcast, and overcast days at the various sites is shown in Table 2. In addition to yearly totals, the data have been subdivided into two additional categories to distinguish overcast days during winter storms from summer overcast due to fog.

TABLE 2. Summary of cloud cover in Landsat satellite imagery for the period 1972-1978.

	Clear		Partly overcast		Overcast		
	no. days	%	no. days	%	no. days	%	
Mainland							
Coastal:							
Total	78	66.1	8	6.8	32	27.1	$n = 118$
June-October	34	65.4	5	9.6	13	25.1	$n = 52$
November-May	44	66.7	3	4.5	19	28.8	$n = 66$
Interior:							
Total	92	78.0	7	5.9	19	16.1	$n = 118$
June-October	44	84.6	3	5.8	5	9.6	$n = 52$
November-May	48	73.7	4	6.1	14	21.2	$n = 66$
Santa Cruz Island							
Coastal:							
Total	68	57.6	18	15.3	32	27.1	$n = 118$
June-October	25	48.1	9	17.3	18	34.6	$n = 52$
November-May	43	65.2	9	13.6	14	21.2	$n = 66$
Interior:							
Total	80	67.8	12	10.2	26	22.0	$n = 118$
June-October	37	71.2	4	7.7	11	21.2	$n = 52$
November-May	43	65.2	8	12.1	15	22.7	$n = 66$

During the months of November through May, the cloud cover at the two island sites is virtually identical, whereas the mainland interior site averages slightly more clear days and fewer overcast days than the mainland coastal site. During June through October, the mainland interior site again experiences the greatest proportion of clear days. The island interior site records more clear days and fewer overcast days than the island coastal site and approximately the same number of clear and overcast days as the mainland coastal site. In fact, during June through October there is at least some cloud or fog cover at the island coastal site 52 per cent of the time; this figure drops to 35 per cent at the mainland coastal site, 29 per cent at the island interior site, and 15 per cent at the mainland interior site. However, it is also important to point out that the proportion of overcast days at all sites is artificially high since the Landsat images are taken in the morning before the fog has dissipated at most sites. Figures 8 and 9 illustrate fairly typical summer fog patterns, with dense fog in the Santa Barbara Channel and the coastal lowlands, but clear skies in the interior and at higher elevations near the coast.

Soils.—Soil textures and organic matter at the four study areas are shown in Table 3. The proportion of clay in the soil is similar at the two island sites and at the mainland coastal site but is somewhat lower at the mainland interior site. The ratio of sand to silt is noticeably different between the island and mainland sites, however. This ratio is always less than one on the island (coastal = 0.71:1; interior = 0.44:1), whereas on the mainland it varies from 3.5:1 (coastal) to 5.7:1 (interior). These results are not too surprising since the mainland interior site is located on the Coldwater Sandstone Formation and the mainland coastal site is located on the Sespe Formation, a sedimentary deposit containing high proportions of sand (Dibblee 1966). The island sites, on the other hand, are both situated on Santa Cruz Island Schist, a volcanic formation containing lower proportions of sand and correspondingly higher proportions of silt (Weaver 1969). The percolation of water out of the root zone of plants down to lower levels is

FIGURE 8. *Distribution of fog on 1 August 1974 along the Santa Barbara coast and Northern Channel Islands.*

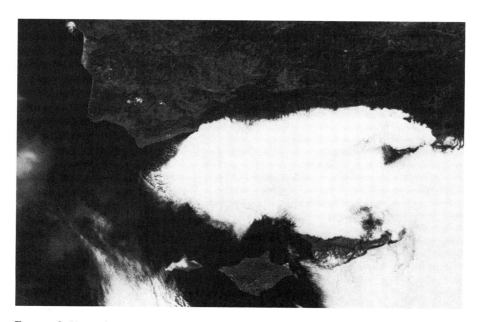

FIGURE 9. *Heavy fog on 13 September 1976 along the Santa Barbara coast and around Santa Cruz Island.*

TABLE 3. Characteristics of island and mainland soils (percentage composition).

	Clay	Silt	Sand	Organic matter
Mainland				
Coastal	23.0	17.0	60.0	4.3
Interior	13.0	13.0	74.0	10.3
Island				
Coastal	21.2	46.1	32.7	7.5
Interior	22.0	54.3	23.7	5.4

TABLE 4. Leaf dimensions of *Ceanothus megacarpus*. (Mean with standard error; numbers in parentheses indicate the range in leaf size.)

	Leaf area (cm^2)	Leaf length (cm)	Leaf width (cm)
Santa Ynez Mountains			
Coastal sites:			
Primary coastal site	1.55 ± 0.08	1.58 ± 0.05	1.05 ± 0.03
(n = 30)	(0.5 - 3.0)	(0.7 - 2.4)	(0.6 - 1.4)
Rattlesnake Canyon	2.10 ± 0.18	1.98 ± 0.10	1.10 ± 0.05
(n = 10)	(0.7 - 3.1)	(0.7 - 2.6)	(0.6 - 1.5)
San Roque Canyon	1.50 ± 0.15	1.61 ± 0.09	1.03 ± 0.04
(n = 10)	(0.6 - 3.0)	(0.6 - 2.2)	(0.5 - 1.5)
Santa Cruz Island			
Coastal sites:			
Primary coastal site	4.50 ± 0.12	2.73 ± 0.06	1.79 ± 0.03
(n = 30)	(2.5 - 6.6)	(2.1 - 4.1)	(1.2 - 2.4)
Laguna Canyon	3.53 ± 0.16	2.79 ± 0.10	1.65 ± 0.04
(n = 10)	(1.8 - 3.5)	(1.8 - 4.6)	(1.2 - 2.0)
Interior sites:			
Primary interior site	3.88 ± 0.13	2.85 ± 0.06	1.76 ± 0.04
(n = 30)	(1.6 - 7.0)	(1.9 - 4.3)	(1.2 - 2.9)
Central Valley	3.59 ± 0.22	2.62 ± 0.07	1.54 ± 0.05
(n = 10)	(1.9 - 6.0)	(2.0 - 3.8)	(1.2 - 2.1)
Santa Rosa Island			
Black Mountain	3.01 ± 0.15	2.78 ± 0.07	1.68 ± 0.05
(n = 10)	(1.8 - 3.5)	(1.5 - 5.2)	(1.2 - 2.1)

accelerated in sandy soils. Hence, the water-holding capacity of the island soils should be higher due to the more favorable sand-to-silt ratios there. In general, island soils are deeper as well (R. Brumbaugh, pers. comm.). Results from the organic matter analysis are inconclusive.

Leaf size.—Results from the leaf size study reveal significant differences (P < 0.0001) between the three island and mainland pairs of chaparral shrubs (Tables 4 to 6). Leaves from island plants are at least one and one-half to three times larger than leaves from mainland plants.

Comparative data for *Ceanothus megacarpus* (Table 4) indicate an average leaf area of 3.8 cm^2 from Santa Cruz Island sites and 1.8 cm^2 from mainland sites. The variation in leaf size

TABLE 5. Leaf dimensions of *Prunus ilicifolia*. (Mean with standard error; numbers in parentheses indicate the range in leaf size.)

	Leaf area (cm²)	Leaf length (cm)	Leaf width (cm)
Santa Ynez Mountains			
Coastal sites:			
Primary coastal site	9.49 ± 0.27	4.12 ± 0.17	2.69 ± 0.06
(*n* = 30)	(3.6 - 18.1)	(1.8 - 5.4)	(1.5 - 4.3)
Mission Canyon	9.05 ± 0.40	3.38 ± 0.18	2.48 ± 0.06
(*n* = 10)	(3.8 - 17.2)	(2.1 - 8.0)	(1.6 - 3.7)
Interior site:			
Primary interior site	9.32 ± 0.34	3.60 ± 0.16	2.62 ± 0.03
(*n* = 30)	(4.1 - 15.6)	(2.1 - 5.4)	(1.6 - 3.4)
Santa Cruz Island			
Coastal site:			
Primary coastal site	25.36 ± 0.80	7.04 ± 0.20	4.31 ± 0.09
(*n* = 30)	(8.7 - 62.3)	(4.3 - 12.3)	(1.8 - 7.5)
Interior sites:			
Primary interior site	22.07 ± 0.71	5.98 ± 0.22	3.48 ± 0.11
(*n* = 30)	(10.1 - 48.3)	(4.5 - 10.6)	(1.8 - 6.2)
Central Valley	23.56 ± 1.37	6.32 ± 0.42	3.56 ± 0.17
(*n* = 10)	(9.2 - 53.4)	(4.8 - 13.3)	(2.0 - 8.1)
Santa Rosa Island			
Cherry Canyon	22.51 ± 1.43	6.43 ± 0.39	3.50 ± 0.19
(*n* = 10)	(8.7 - 56.1)	(4.2 - 15.0)	(1.8 - 8.1)

between plants at coastal and interior island sites is not significant. Mainland leaf sizes averaging 1.3 cm² were obtained by Gill (unpubl. data) in the Santa Ynez Mountains. The leaf sizes of Santa Rosa Island *Ceanothus megacarpus* are also significantly larger than any of the mainland populations, albeit somewhat smaller than Santa Cruz Island *Ceanothus*. The ratio of leaf length to width remains between 1.63:1 and 1.65:1 at all sites, indicating that the leaf shape retains similar proportions in spite of the variance in leaf area.

Leaf size comparisons of island and mainland *Prunus ilicifolia* follow a pattern similar to those of *Ceanothus megacarpus* (Table 5). Leaves of *Prunus ilicifolia* subsp. *ilicifolia* from the mainland have an average area of 9.2 cm² at the three sites sampled; Harrison *et al*. (1971) report a mean leaf area of 9.3 cm² in the Santa Monica Mountains. Leaves of *Prunus ilicifolia* subsp. *lyonii* from Santa Cruz and Santa Rosa Islands are larger with an average area of 24.1 cm². As before, there are no significant differences in leaf size between plants at coastal and interior sites. The leaf length-to-width ratio is somewhat larger in the island populations (1.71:1 to 1.84:1) than in mainland populations (1.42:1), reflecting the more narrowly ovate, pointed leaves representative of *Prunus ilicifolia* subsp. *lyonii*.

As in the other two subspecies pairs, the island populations of *Dendromecon rigida* have significantly larger leaves than the mainland population (Table 6). The island plants have a mean leaf area of 18.5 cm² for all sites, in contrast to 3.9 cm² for the one site sampled on the mainland. Furthermore, there are no significant differences between the leaf dimensions of *Dendromecon* at the insular coastal or interior sites. The leaf length-to-width ratio is smaller on the islands (Santa Cruz Island = 2.1:1; Santa Rosa Island = 1.86:1) than the length-to-width

TABLE 6. Leaf dimensions of *Dendromecon rigida*. (Mean with standard error; numbers in parentheses indicate the range in leaf size.)

	Leaf area (cm²)	Leaf length (cm)	Leaf width (cm)
Santa Ynez Mountains			
Coastal sites:			
Primary coastal site	3.94 ± 0.47	4.51 ± 0.10	1.51 ± 0.10
(*n* = 30)	(1.6 - 9.9)	(1.5 - 10.2)	(0.8 - 3.2)
Santa Cruz Island			
Coastal sites:			
Primary coastal site	18.26 ± 0.78	6.89 ± 0.16	3.41 ± 0.11
(*n* = 30)	(6.3 - 52.3)	(3.5 - 10.6)	(1.8 - 5.1)
Laguna Canyon	17.34 ± 1.58	6.36 ± 0.31	3.15 ± 0.15
(*n* = 10)	(10.1 - 60.3)	(4.0 - 12.6)	(1.9 - 6.0)
Coches Prietos	21.90 ± 1.80	7.27 ± 0.21	3.58 ± 0.21
(*n* = 10)	(9.4 - 56.3)	(4.1 - 11.5)	(2.0 - 5.1)
Interior sites:			
Primary interior site	15.49 ± 1.01	5.71 ± 0.18	3.06 ± 0.11
(*n* = 30)	(5.0 - 55.1)	(3.8 - 11.7)	(1.8 - 6.2)
Central Valley	14.92 ± 1.64	7.01 ± 0.21	3.01 ± 0.18
(*n* = 10)	(4.9 - 40.2)	(3.6 - 10.2)	(1.8 - 3.9)
Santa Rosa Island			
Black Mountain	17.58	6.08	3.27
(*n* = 1)	(6.5 - 25.0)	(4.2 - 6.8)	(2.0 - 4.5)

ratio of 2.99:1 recorded from mainland plants. Thus, island leaves of *Dendromecon rigida* are proportionately wider as well as larger than mainland leaves (Figs. 5 and 6).

Because the initial island and mainland samples of *Dendromecon rigida* had been taken at different times of the year and because of the unexpectedly small leaf size of the mainland population, a new mainland sample was taken from five shrubs in May 1979. The mean leaf area of the new sample is 8.3 cm² (s.e. ±0.77), the mean leaf length is 7.99 cm (±0.38), and the mean leaf width is 1.99 cm (±0.07). However, these dimensions are still significantly smaller than those from island material. The larger leaf area in 1979 undoubtedly is a reflection of the timing of the sampling period. The initial sample was taken in fall 1977 following two years of drought, and the later sample was taken in spring following two years of substantial precipitation. These results suggest that prevailing climatic conditions have a major effect on the mean leaf size of this chaparral species and may affect the other species in a similar manner. Since island and mainland samples of *Prunus* and *Ceanothus* were taken at the same time of year, however, an examination of seasonal changes in leaf area for these species will be deferred until future studies. Seasonality in leaf characteristics has been documented by several authors for other xerophytic shrubs (Orshan 1964, Cunningham and Strain 1969, Smith and Nobel 1977).

Dimension analysis.—One interesting question raised early in this study was how the total leaf surface area per plant, or per branch, compared between island and mainland populations, and, more importantly, if differences in this total leaf area were a function of area per leaf or of the number of leaves per plant. The total photosynthetic surface area could be identical in both

TABLE 7. Total shrub size for species pairs from Santa Cruz Island and the Santa Ynez Mountains.

	Dendromecon rigida		Ceanothus megacarpus		Prunus ilicifolia	
	Island	Mainland	Island	Mainland	Island	Mainland
Mean number of branches/shrub at 15 cm above ground	16.2	3.5	7.4	1.3	6.0	21.6
Range in measured branch diameters (cm)	0.5 - 15.0	0.5 - 4.0	0.5 - 10.2	0.5 - 3.5	0.5 - 30.0	0.1 - 6.8
Total leaf area/shrub (cm^2)	127,574	2,331			728,347	206,193
Open canopy:			57,983	3,685		
Closed canopy:				1,660		
Total leaf number/shrub	8,236	792			28,720	22,064
Open canopy:			14,937	2,378		
Closed canopy:				1,071		

habitats, maintained by fewer larger leaves on the islands and numerous small leaves on the mainland. As a consequence, a dimension analysis study was initiated to establish comparative measurements of total leaf area per shrub for each of the species pairs.

Table 7 summarizes the total branch number, leaf area, and leaf number per shrub calculated for *Dendromecon, Ceanothus,* and *Prunus.* The island subspecies of both *Ceanothus* and *Dendromecon* have more branches originating at or below 15 cm above the ground when compared with the mainland subspecies. The arborescent island *Prunus,* on the other hand, generally has only a single main trunk with a few slender sprouts at the base, whereas the mainland *Prunus* is shrubbier with many basal branches. Each of the island subspecies has a much greater total leaf area per shrub, which, in *Ceanothus* and *Dendromecon*, can be attributed both to increased area per leaf and to the greater number of branches. The mainland *Ceanothus* is the only plant which shows significant changes in total leaf area depending on whether branches have been collected in an open site, such as a fuel break, or in a closed canopy of dense chaparral. However, shrubs of mature *Dendromecon* and *Prunus* were most frequently encountered at the open margins of dense stands.

Table 8 compares branches of the same diameter in the three subspecies pairs. The data for *Dendromecon* clearly indicate that for a given branch of the same diameter, leaf number remains constant while leaf size increases on the island. The results for *Ceanothus* are more difficult to interpret, however; island *Ceanothus* tends to grow in open habitats while the mainland type does not. Thus, results comparing island *Ceanothus* from an open habitat and mainland *Ceanothus* from a dense canopy are similar to *Dendromecon,* with striking similarities in leaf numbers but increased surface area per leaf in insular environments. For the *Ceanothus* growing in the two open habitats, however, total leaf area per branch is relatively constant for island and mainland forms, while leaf number roughly doubles for the mainland type. Hence, for equivalent branch diameters, mainland *Ceanothus* growing in open environments has approximately twice as many leaves and the same total leaf surface area as the island form, while mainland *Ceanothus* growing in a closed canopy has the same number of leaves and half the total leaf surface area when compared to the island form.

TABLE 8. Leaf area comparisons for branches of the same diameter between species pairs.

	Dendromecon rigida		*Ceanothus megacarpus*		*Prunus ilicifolia*	
	Island	Mainland	Island	Mainland	Island	Mainland
Branch diameter = 2.0						
Leaf area (cm²)	2,084	460	2,059		9,369	7,440
Open canopy:				1,826		
Closed canopy:				723		
Leaf number	145	156	530		387	800
Open canopy:				1,178		
Closed canopy:				467		
Branch diameter = 3.0						
Leaf area (cm²)	7,710	1,383	4,647		17,700	14,008
Open canopy:				4,650		
Closed canopy:				2,135		
Leaf number	498	470	1,197		731	1,506
Open canopy:				3,000		
Closed canopy:				1,380		

Unlike either of the other two species, the mainland *Prunus* has many more major stems than the island *Prunus,* elevating the total leaf area appreciably. In addition, the mainland *Prunus* has about double the leaf number per branch, bringing the total leaf area per branch closer to the island form, much like the *Ceanothus megacarpus* in the open canopy.

Hence, in all three pairs of subspecies the island plants have both larger leaves and total shrub leaf area. Island *Prunus* has fewer branches per shrub and fewer leaves per branch when compared with mainland *Prunus.* In addition to its larger leaves, however, it reaches much greater proportions and has more leaves per plant than the mainland form. Island *Ceanothus* and *Dendromecon,* on the other hand, have both larger leaves and more branches and leaves per shrub than their mainland counterparts.

Leaf anatomy. — A comparison of five anatomical leaf characteristics known to be correlated with moisture availability (Stocker 1960, Kummerow 1973) shows several differences between island and mainland leaves (Table 9). Cuticle thickness measurements do not appear to follow any pattern. Island leaves of *Ceanothus megacarpus* have significantly thicker cuticles on the upper leaf surface than mainland leaves, but mainland leaves of *Prunus ilicifolia* have significantly thicker cuticles on the upper leaf surface than island leaves; no statistical differences were indicated for cuticle thicknesses of leaves from *Dendromecon rigida.* Furthermore, the cuticle thicknesses reported from *Prunus* and *Dendromecon* are somewhat misleading since the leaf surfaces of both species are covered with additional layers of wax not included in this measurement.

Both smaller leaves and decreased cell size are often associated with plants from xeric habitats. Coupled with a reduction in cell size is an increase in the number of stomata per unit area (Stocker 1960). The epidermal cell widths in island leaves of both *Ceanothus* and *Prunus* are statistically greater than their mainland counterparts, and island *Prunus* has lower stomatal

TABLE 9. Comparisons of five xeromorphic characters between species pairs (* = differences statistically significant at $P < 0.05$).

	Ceanothus megacarpus		Prunus ilicifolia		Dendromecon rigida	
	Mainland	Island	Mainland	Island	Mainland	Island
Leaf thickness (mm)	0.39	0.37	0.28	0.28	0.32	0.38
Cuticle thickness (μ)						
Upper leaf	6.9	8.1*	2.9	2.3*	1.8	2.0
Lower leaf	3.4	3.2	1.4	1.5	1.5	1.5
Epidermal cell width (μ)						
Upper	17.8	30.7*	20.0	24.6*	27.7	29.5
Lower	8.8	10.9*	15.5	15.4	24.1	26.0
Stomatal frequency (no. per mm²)			452	321*	191	178
Per cent water content	48.0	46.0	51.7	54.1*	30.7	34.7*

frequencies than mainland *Prunus* as well. Per cent water content is significantly greater in island leaves of *Dendromecon* and *Prunus*. The range of expression of xeromorphy in island and mainland leaves needs to be examined more thoroughly in order to elucidate seasonal and long-term trends. In a similar study, Krause and Kummerow (1977) report few differences in the xeromorphic structure of leaves collected from species common to north- and south-facing slopes.

CONCLUSION

Measurements of leaf length, width, and area for the chaparral shrubs *Ceanothus megacarpus, Dendromecon rigida*, and *Prunus ilicifolia* show that populations on the Northern Channel Islands have significantly larger leaves than the mainland populations. In addition, the total leaf area per plant is consistently greater for the island subspecies.

An examination of island and mainland climates at or above 225 m indicates a number of similarities. Variables such as precipitation, mean annual temperatures, and yearly temperature extremes are essentially the same at all sites, and wind velocity averages reveal no sharp distinctions between the island and mainland, although these differences do exist on occasion. In spite of these similarities, humidity and vapor pressure deficit figures and, to a lesser degree, cloud cover show that the islands may be significantly moister. In addition, the presence of deep soils with enhanced water-holding capacities may provide island chaparral with more available moisture year-round, and, in particular, decreased moisture stress during the warm months.

Energy budget analysis of the effects of environmental factors on leaf dimensions indicate that lower stomatal resistances are required by the large-leaved island plants than by mainland plants in order to maintain leaf temperatures at biological optima (Hochberg 1980). Reduced evapo-transpiration rates, greater soil moisture retention, and decreased competition from other woody shrubs may all contribute towards enhanced water availability in island chaparral habitats. In addition, the larger leaves on island plants may reflect an adaptation to even more mesic conditions during the late Pleistocene (Axelrod 1967).

ACKNOWLEDGMENTS

I am grateful to the Sigma Xi Foundation, the Scientific Research Society of North America, for a Grant-in-Aid supporting this research. Special appreciation is due J. R. Haller for his valuable help and support throughout my study. Many other people also provided me with both their time and advice during this project. On Santa Cruz Island, M. Daily, H. Duffield, L. Fausett, L. Laughrin, and C. Stanton were especially helpful. C. Magagnosc, W. H. Schlesinger, R. Steele, and J. Wyss provided crucial information on computer programming. M. Hasey assisted with the soil analysis and I. Morrow with anatomical slide preparations. I am extremely grateful to my numerous field assistants, who cheerfully exchanged a weekend of work for a chance to visit Santa Cruz Island. I also wish to thank J. R. Haller, S. A. Junak, B. E. Mahall, and R. N. Philbrick for their helpful review of the manuscript. M. Emerson drew the illustrations and J. Spickelmier prepared the graphs.

REFERENCES

AXELROD, D. I. 1967. Geologic history of the Californian insular flora. Pp. 267-316 in R. N. Philbrick, ed., Proceedings of the symposium on the biology of the California Islands. Santa Barbara Botanic Garden, Santa Barbara, Calif.

BJORKMAN, O., and P. HOLMGREN. 1963. Adaptability of the photosynthetic apparatus to light intensity in ecotypes from exposed and shaded habitats. Physiol. Plantarum 16:889-914.

BJORNDALEN, J. E. 1978. The chaparral vegetation of Santa Cruz Island, California. Norwegian J. Bot. 25:255-269.

BOUYONCOS, G. J. 1936. Directions for making mechanical analyses of soils by the hydrometer method. Soil Sci. 42:225-230.

COOPER, W. S. 1922. The broad-sclerophyll vegetation of California—an ecological study of the chaparral and its related communities. Carnegie Inst. Washington Publ. 319.

CUNNINGHAM, G. L., and B.R. STRAIN. 1969. An ecological significance of seasonal leaf variability in a desert shrub. Ecology 50:400-408.

DIBBLEE, T. W. 1966. Geology of the central Santa Ynez Mountains, Santa Barbara County, California. California Div. Mines Geol. Bull. 186.

EHLERINGER, J., O. BJORKMAN, and H. A. MOONEY. 1976. Leaf pubescence: effects on absorptance and photosynthesis in a desert shrub. Science 192:376-377.

EHRLER, W. L. 1969. Daytime stomatal closure in Agave americana as related to water-use efficiency. Pp. 239-248 in C. C. Hoff and M. L. Riedesel, eds., Physiological systems in semi-arid environments. University of New Mexico Press, Albuquerque, N.M.

GATES, D. M. 1968. Transpiration and leaf temperature. Ann. Rev. Plant Physiol. 19:211-238.

GIVNISH, T. J., and G. J. VERMEIJ. 1976. Sizes and shapes of liane leaves. Amer. Natur. 110:743-778.

GRIER, C. C., and S. W. RUNNING. 1977. Leaf area of mature northwestern coniferous forests: relation to site water balance. Ecology 58:893-899.

HANES, T. L. 1977. California chaparral. Pp. 417-469 in M. G. Barbour and J. Major, eds., Terrestrial vegetation of California. John Wiley & Sons, New York, N.Y.

HARRISON, A. T., E. SMALL, and H. A. MOONEY. 1971. Drought relationships and distribution of two Mediterranean-climate California plant communities. Ecology 52:869-875.

HOBBS, E. 1978. The effects of grazing on Bishop Pine (Pinus muricata) forests, Santa Cruz Island, California. M.A. thesis, University of California, Los Angeles, Calif.

HOCHBERG, M. C. 1980. Factors affecting leaf size of the chaparral shrubs Ceanothus megacarpus, Prunus ilicifolia, and Dendromecon rigida on the California Islands. M.A. thesis, University of California, Santa Barbara, Calif.

HORT, S. A. 1916. Theophrastus: inquiry into plants, Vols. I and II. G. P. Putnam & Sons, New York, N.Y.

KRAUSE, D., and J. KUMMEROW. 1977. Xeromorphic structure and soil moisture in the chaparral. Oecologia Plantarum 12:133-148.

KUMMEROW, J. 1973. Comparative anatomy of sclerophylls of Mediterranean climatic areas. Pp. 157-167 in F. Di Castri and H. A. Mooney, eds., Mediterranean type ecosystems. Origin and structure. Springer-Verlag, New York, N.Y.

MCPHERSON, J. K., and C. H. MULLER. 1967. Light competition between Ceanothus and Salvia shrubs. Bull. Torrey Bot. Club 94:41-55.

MEINZER, F. C., and P. W. RUNDEL. 1973. Crassulacean acid metabolism and water-use efficiency in Echeveria pumila. Photosynthetica 7:358-364.

MOONEY, H. A., J. KUMMEROW, A. W. JOHNSON, D. J. PARSONS, S. KEELEY, A. HOFFMAN, R. I. HAYS, J. GILIBERTO, and C. CHU. 1977. The producers—their resources and adaptive responses. Pp. 85-143 in H. A. Mooney, ed., Convergent evolution in Chile and California Mediterranean climate ecosystems. Dowden, Hutchinson, and Ross, Stroudsburg, Penn.

MULLER, C. H. 1966. The role of chemical inhibition (allelopathy) in vegetational composition. Bull. Torrey Bot. Club 93:332-351.

MULLER, C. H., R. B. HANAWALT, and J. K. MCPHERSON. 1968. Allelopathic control of herb growth in the fire cycle of California chaparral. Bull. Torrey Bot. Club 95:225-231.

ORSHAN, G. 1964. Seasonal dimorphism of desert chamaephytes and their significance as a factor in their water economy. Pp. 245-254 in A. J. Rutter and F. H. Whitehead, eds., The water relations of plants. Blackwell, Oxford.

PARKHURST, D. F., and O.L. LOUCKS. 1972. Optimal leaf size in relation to environment. J. Ecol. 60:505-537.

PHILBRICK, R. N., and J. R. HALLER. 1977. The Southern California Islands. Pp. 893-906 in M. G. Barbour and J. Major, eds., Terrestrial vegetation of California. John Wiley & Sons, New York, N.Y.

SCHLESINGER, W. H., and D. S. GILL. 1978. Demographic studies of the chaparral shrub Ceanothus megacarpus in the Santa Ynez Mountains, California. Ecology 59:1256-1263.

————. Biomass, production, and changes in the availability of light, water, and nutrients during the development of pure stands of the chaparral shrub, Ceanothus megacarpus, after fire. Ecology (in press).

SCHLESINGER, W. H., and M. M. HASEY. The nutrient content of precipitation, dry fallout, and intercepted aerosols in the chaparral of southern California. Amer. Midl. Natur. 103:114-122.

SCHULTZE, E.D., O. L. LANGE, M. EVENARI, L. KAPPEN, and U. BUSCHBOM. 1975. The role of air humidity and temperature in controlling stomatal resistance of Prunus armeniacca L. under desert conditions. III. The effect on water-use efficiency. Oecologia 19:303-314.

SHIELDS, L. M. 1951. Leaf xeromorphy in dicotyledon species from a gypsum sand deposit. Amer. J. Bot. 38:175-190.

SMITH, W. K. 1978. Temperatures of desert plants: another perspective on the adaptability of leaf size. Science 201:614-616.

SMITH, W. K., and P. S. NOBEL. 1977. Influences of seasonal changes in leaf morphology on water-use efficiency for three desert broadleaf shrubs. Ecology 58:1033-1043.

STOCKER, O. 1960. Physiological and morphological changes in plants due to water deficiency. Pp. 63-104 *in* Arid zone research. XV. Plant-water relationships in arid and semi-arid conditions. UNESCO, Paris.

VOGEL, S. 1970. Convective cooling at low airspeeds and the shapes of broad leaves. J. Expt. Bot. 21:91-101.

WEAVER, D. W. 1969. Geology of the Northern Channel Islands. Amer. Assoc. Petroleum Geologists Soc. Econ. Paleontologists and Mineralogists (Pacific Section).

WERGER, M. J. A., and G. A. ELLENBROCK. 1978. Leaf size and leaf consistence of a riverine forest vegetation along a climatic gradient. Oecologia 34:297-308.

Zonation of Coastal Plant Species and their Correlation with Salt Levels in the Soil

Nancy J. Vivrette[1]

*Botany Department, University of California,
Berkeley, California 94720*

INTRODUCTION

This study was an investigation of the processes leading to the establishment of a coastal vegetation pattern, and the factors which maintain or change a vegetation pattern over time. The simplest explanation for a zoned or banded distribution of species is the presence of an environmental gradient coupled with differential tolerance of the species to environmental factors in the gradient. An example is the banding of species at a right angle to onshore winds in exposed coastal regions. Onshore winds carry high levels of salt aerosol, and the strongest wind occurs closest to the ocean. This results in the deposition of high levels of salt aerosol and, consequently, leads to higher salt levels in the soil closest to the ocean. As the wind moves inland it carries less aerosol and the soil is less saline. Along this gradient the more salt-tolerant plant species would be expected in the regions close to the coast and less salt-tolerant forms would be expected in the interior soils.

Support for this hypothesis has been given in some preliminary work by Barbour *et al.* (1973), who found a strong association between species distributions and soil salinities. Lugo and Snedaker (1974) tested the hypothesis that soil salinities were responsible for zonation in mangrove regions and found that differential salt tolerance could not account for the zonation of species in mangroves. The present study was designed to test the hypothesis that differential salt tolerance can account for species distribution along a salt gradient on coastal headlands. To do this, I describe the zoned pattern along coastal headlands, examine the correlation of the distribution pattern with soil salinities, test salinity tolerances of the species involved in the pattern, and test these correlations with field manipulations.

DESCRIPTION OF THE STUDY SITE

The study was conducted on Fraser Point, the extreme western (and windward) end of Santa Cruz Island, 35 km off the coast of Santa Barbara, California. The study site was on the coastal headland 20 m above sea level, bounded on three sides by cliffs. The substrate is rocky with a shallow layer of soil varying in texture from clay to sand. Vegetation is a low-lying assemblage of annuals and perennials that appears to be sorted into bands paralleling the edge of the sea bluff.

The zonation of vegetation was quantified using two continuous line transects running from the seaward cliff (west) to the interior (east). Species were recorded at 10-cm intervals for 240 m (Fig. 1). A marked zonation is apparent for the three annual species. *Mesembryanthemum crystallinum* L. is found along the seaward edge of the headland. *Hordeum leporinum* Link. is found in the central portion of the headland, and *Lasthenia chrysostoma* (F. and M.) Greene is found in the most interior portion. The perennial species do not show as striking a zonation pattern. *Frankenia grandiflora* Cham. and Schlecht. is associated with the *Mesembryanthemum* and *Hordeum* zones. *Atriplex semibaccata* R. Br. is found in greatest abundance in the *Hordeum* zone. *Atriplex californica* Moq. in DC. and *Salicornia subterminalis* Parish. are

---

[1]Present address: Ransom Seed Laboratory, 747 Knapp Dr., Santa Barbara, California 93108.

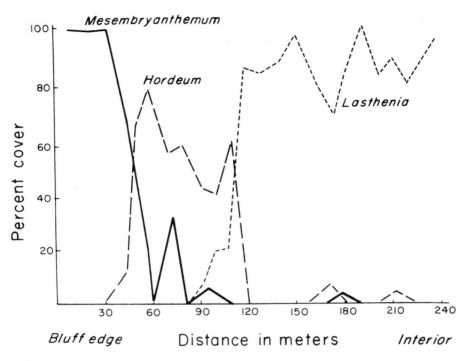

FIGURE 1. *Distribution of annual species from the seaward edge of the bluff to the interior. Values are average per cent cover over 10-meter intervals.*

associated with the *Lasthenia* zone. The annual species were chosen for further study since they must re-establish the banded pattern each season and are therefore suitable for experimental manipulation.

CORRELATION OF VEGETATION DISTRIBUTION WITH SOIL SALT LEVELS

If the zonation of the annual species is the result of differential salt deposition and accumulation from salt aerosol, there should be a correlation between the level of salt in the soil and the pattern of zonation. The expected salt levels would be high at the seaward edge and lower further inland. To measure salt levels in the soil, 100-g soil samples were taken to a depth of 2 cm at 10-m intervals from the seaward edge of the headland to the interior for 240 m. The soil was sifted to remove rocks, pulverized with a mortar and pestle, and then sifted again through a 0.01-mm pore soil screen. Two 20-g subsamples from each samples were shaken with 80 g of water for two hours. The extract was filtered through Whatman #1 filter paper and analyzed for total salts using freezing point depression with an Advanced Instruments Osmometer. Total salts are measured as milliosmols (mOsm) in the extract. Using this method, a one-molal solution of a nondissociating compound will have one osmol (Osm) activity or 1,000 milliosmols. Sea water is approximately 900 mOsm.

There is no correlation between soil salt levels and distance from the seaward edge of the bluff (Fig. 2). Up to a one hundredfold difference in soil salinity was exhibited at the same distance from the seaward edge of the transect.

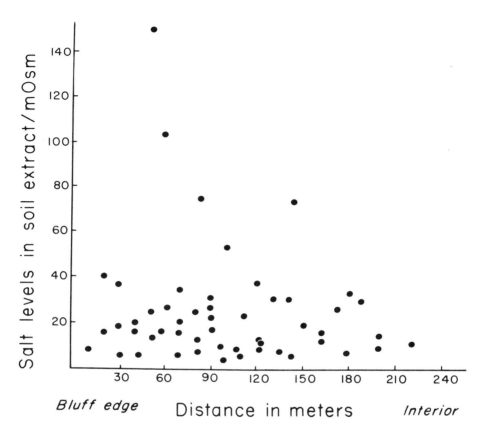

FIGURE 2. *Soil salinity as a function of distance from the seaward edge of the bluff to the interior.*

Mesembryanthemum crystallinum is known to greatly influence salinities in the surrounding soil (Vivrette and Muller 1977). To control for this influence, the soil samples were separated according to the species occupying them. The same gradient of high salinities on the seaward edge and lower salinities toward the interior would be expected for the soil beneath each species. Again, no decreasing gradient was observed (Fig. 3). On the other hand, there was a close association between the soil salinities and particular species. The variation in soil salinity found beneath the same species was much smaller than the variation in soil salinity between species. The large variation in soil salinity shown in Figure 3 can be explained in large part by the differential salinity associated with the various species.

I propose that the close association between soil salinity and the species occupying the soil is caused by species-specific mechanisms of salt uptake and release. Since the soil salinities are similar beneath a given species whether it is growing at the seaward edge or interior portion of the headland, differential salt recycling by the plants appears to have a greater influence on the soil salt levels than salt deposition from aerosol. If the soil salinities found beneath each species are used to plot their placement along a gradient of high to low salinities, the resultant species distribution appears as in Figure 4. However, this pattern does not match the actual distribution

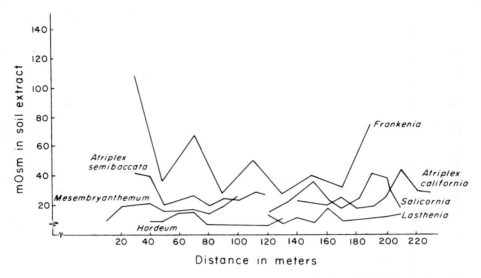

FIGURE 3. *Soil salinity as a function of species from the seaward edge of the bluff to the interior.*

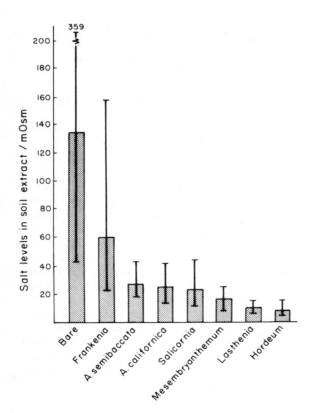

FIGURE 4. *Salt levels in soils from bare ground and from beneath plant species ranked in order of average soil salinity (e.g., highest average salt concentrations were found in soil beneath* Frankenia, *lowest beneath* Hordeum*). The order of species is therefore the distribution of species expected on the basis of soil salinities alone.*

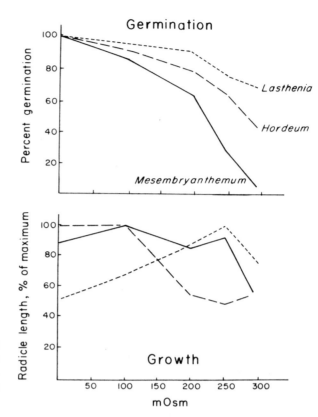

FIGURE 5. *Germination and growth of the annual species under various levels of salinity. Each value is the average of 90 seeds.*

of species observed on the headland. From this figure it is clear that the annual species have lower salinities than the perennials; the highest salinities are found beneath *Frankenia* and in bare soil.

SALT TOLERANCE OF THE ANNUAL SPECIES

It is possible that the differences in salinity associated with each species could be responsible for the distribution of the other species. Such a case has been described for *Mesembryanthemum crystallinum* (Vivrette and Muller 1977). Salt tolerances of the three annual species were tested using germinating seeds. Ten seeds were placed on a substrate of sand in each of a series of Petri dishes. The dishes were watered with either distilled water, 100-mOsm, 200-mOsm, 250-mOsm, or 300-mOsm NaCl solutions, representing the range of salinities observed in the soil extracts in the previous experiments. Each test consisted of three dishes, and the tests were repeated three times, for a total of 90 seeds per treatment.

Per cent germination and radicle elongation were measured (Fig. 5). The salt tolerances of all three annual species are very broad. *Lasthenia* had the highest tolerance for salinity, although it is found on the interior portion of the headland. The distribution of species along the headland cannot be accounted for by differential salt tolerance. The close association between soil salinities and the species occupying the soil is more a function of the plants producing the salinity than the plants responding to a gradient of salinity.

TABLE 1. Seedling establishment in *Hordeum* and *Lasthenia* zones. Each value is the average of four subsamples.

	Average number of seedlings (range)		
	Control	Seed added	Seed added and clipped
Hordeum zone			
Mesembryanthemum	0	0.5 (0-2)	2 (0-3)
Hordeum	49 (40-62)	56 (33-80)	69 (52-94)
Lasthenia	0	8 (0-31)	47 (8-78)
Other	0	0	0
Lasthenia zone			
Mesembryanthemum	0	2 (0-12)	7 (0-19)
Hordeum	0	2 (0-5)	3 (0-10)
Lasthenia	145 (72-250)	159 (54-238)	207 (134-292)
Other	4 (0-10)	2 (0-5)	3 (0-10)

BIOTIC INTERACTIONS

The species distribution pattern seems to have no simple explanation. The sharp drop in occurrence of one annual species in the presence of another suggests that biotic interactions may play a role in zonation. If this hypothesis is correct, then each of the species should be able to grow in the other zones in the absence of the dominant species. To test this hypothesis, reciprocal transplants were performed. One control and two treatments were applied in the experiment, and each had two replicates. The control in each zone was an untreated 1-m² plot. The first treatment was a 1-m² plot with seed of the other zones added. The second treatment was a plot in which the dominant species was clipped to the ground, the clippings removed, and seeds of the other species added. A similar experiment had already been performed for the *Mesembryanthemum* zone (Vivrette and Muller 1977), so only the *Hordeum* and *Lasthenia* zones were included in the present experiment. The treatment was performed during the dry summer season when only the dead remains of plants were present. The results were recorded the following spring, after the winter rains had produced a new crop of plants. Seedling counts were taken in 10-cm diameter subsamples at the four cardinal compass points within the experimental plots.

The results of the transplant experiments are given in Table 1. When no manipulation is made, each zone is maintained by the dominant species. *Hordeum* grew in the zone it had occupied the year before; *Lasthenia* did the same within its zone. This persistent dominance was overcome slightly with the addition of seed from the other zones. Seed dispersal is apparently part of the explanation for the maintenance of the pattern over time. The clipped plots with seed added showed the strongest increase in seedling establishment of the other species. In the *Hordeum* clipped plot *Lasthenia* greatly increased in number. In the *Lasthenia* zone the increase in numbers of *Hordeum* and *Mesembryanthemum* seedlings was not as great, but the seedlings were large and occupied up to a quarter of the plot. This increase in the number and size of plants from the other zones following removal of the biomass of the dominant species suggests a strong biotic control of the pattern observed. These findings were reinforced during the drought year of 1976-1977. The *Lasthenia* zone was only sparsely occupied and the biomass was greatly reduced. Under these conditions, *Mesembryanthemum* invaded the *Las-*

thenia zone and now shares dominance with the *Lasthenia*. Experiments are in progress to characterize the nature of this biotic interaction.

CONCLUSIONS

Differential salt tolerance of species along a salt gradient cannot account for the banded pattern observed for the annuals on Fraser Point, Santa Cruz Island. The soil salt levels remained in the range characteristic for each species regardless of the distance the species was found from the edge of the bluff. This close association between each species and the soil salt levels is due to characteristic mechanisms of salt recycling by the species growing in the soil, rather than to the species responding to a salt gradient.

ACKNOWLEDGMENTS

I wish to thank Mary Lu Arpaia, Linda Fox, J. Robert Haller, Deborah Mangis, and Robert Sheets for field and laboratory assistance. I also thank Dr. Carey Stanton and the Santa Cruz Island Co., and the staff of the University of California Santa Cruz Island Reserve. Illustrations are by Charlotte Mentges.

REFERENCES

BARBOUR, M. G., R. B. CRAIG, F. R. DRYSDALE, and M. T. GHISELIN. 1973. Coastal ecology. Bodega Head. University of California Press, Berkeley, Calif.

LUGO, A. E., and S. C. SNEDAKER. 1974. The ecology of mangroves. Pp. 39-64 *in* R. F. Johnston, ed., Annual review of ecology and systematics, v.5. Ann. Reviews, Inc., Palo Alto, Calif.

VIVRETTE, N. J., and C. H. MULLER. 1977. Mechanism of invasion and dominance of coastal grassland by *Mesembryanthemum crystallinum*. Ecol. Monogrs. 47:301-318.

Evidence of Hybridization Between
Rhus integrifolia and *R. lentii* (Anacardiaceae) on
Cedros Island, Baja California, Mexico

David A. Young

*Department of Botany, University of Illinois,
Urbana, Illinois 61801*

INTRODUCTION

The tendency among island plants to hybridize has been noted by many authors (*e.g.*, Carlquist 1966) and this phenomenon is exemplified by several plants of the California Islands (Thorne 1969). Examples of hybridization on the California Islands can be found in genera such as *Quercus* (Muller 1967), *Rhus* (Young 1974a), *Opuntia, Dudleya, Salvia, Helianthemum, Cercocarpus,* and *Ceanothus,* to mention a few. At the same time, even though the California Islands, like most fringing archipelagos, often serve as refugia for relict plant taxa (Axelrod 1967, Thorne 1969), they also are possible sites of autochthonous evolution, although they certainly are not comparable in this respect to oceanic islands (Carlquist 1974). Some possible examples of autochthonous evolution in plants of the California Islands can be found in *Hemizonia* (Carlquist 1965) and *Dudleya* (Moran 1959), as well as in *Lavatera, Solanum, Eriogonum,* and *Malacothrix.* The objective of this study was to determine whether *Rhus integrifolia* (Nutt. in T. & G.) Brew. & Wats. var. *cedrocensis* Barkl., an endemic of Cedros Island, represents an example of autochthonous insular evolution or whether it actually is of hybrid origin, representing a hybrid between *R. integrifolia* and *R. lentii* Kell., as suggested by Barkley (1937).

Cedros Island is the largest of the California Islands, with a total land area of 348 km² (134 mi²) (Philbrick 1967); it is located 23 km (14 mi) off the coast of Baja California near Punta Eugenia (Fig. 1). In 1967, the total number of native plant taxa on Cedros Island was estimated at 205 (Raven 1967). Although probably a conservative estimate, it is still a fairly low number of taxa, given the size of the island, compared with the other large California Islands. For example, Santa Cruz Island (249 km² or 96 mi²) has approximately 420 native plant taxa (Raven 1967). The depauperate nature of the flora of Cedros Island probably is due to the very arid nature of the Vizcaino Desert that covers most of the island and the adjacent mainland (Shreve and Wiggins 1964).

Rhus integrifolia, a perennial shrub with typically simple evergreen leaves, is a prominent member of the coastal sage scrub and chaparral communities of coastal southern California and Baja California (Fig. 1). On Cedros Island, *R. integrifolia* occurs on the west side and northern end of the island in a vegetation type that would best be termed island coastal sage scrub-chaparral. *Rhus lentii* also is a perennial shrub with simple evergreen leaves and is another example of a near island endemic (Axelrod 1967) (Fig. 1). On Cedros Island, *R. lentii* is a distinctive element of the Vizcaino Desert vegetation that covers the island at lower elevations.

MATERIALS AND METHODS

Population samples.—Field studies on Cedros Island were conducted in March and April of 1972 and 1973. Collections of "pure" *R. lentii* were made from lower elevations around the village and on the southwest and southeast ends of the island. A previously studied population of *R. integrifolia* from Santa Barbara County, California (Young 1974a; population 4, nos. 711-725) was used to represent a "pure" population of this taxon. In addition, collections of

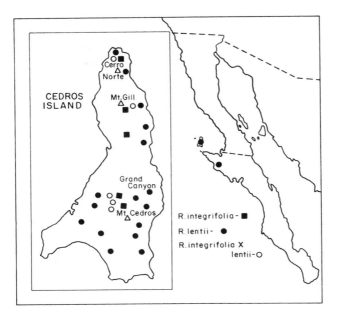

FIGURE 1. *Distribution of* R. lentii, R. integrifolia, *and the putative hybrid* R. integrifolia x R. lentii *on Cedros Island (based upon herbarium specimens and personal collections).*

both taxa were made on the west side of the island (near the main water-pumping station) along a transect that began in coastal sage scrub-chaparral (*R. integrifolia*), descended through transitional or ecotonal vegetation, and ended in the lower elevation Vizcaino Desert vegetation (*R. lentii*). Voucher specimens of the plants sampled from Cedros Island are deposited at Rancho Santa Ana Botanic Garden; duplicates are located at the University of Illinois. Vouchers of *R. integrifolia* from Santa Barbara County, California are deposited in the California State University at Fullerton.

Comparative morphology.—Based upon examination of numerous herbarium specimens and analysis of descriptions of the two taxa, several morphological features were selected that could be used to characterize them. Features considered to be diagnostic were: leaf length/ width ratios, leaf pubescence (mean number of simple trichomes per mm^2 on the lower leaf surface), sepal color and pubescence, and inflorescence morphology. Values for each quantitative feature consisted of an average of three measurements per plant. The number of trichomes per mm^2 was determined by making collodion peels of leaves and counting the number of trichomes using a compound microscope. In addition, cuticular relief patterns for the two taxa were observed using scanning electron microscopy (SEM). Dried leaves were obtained from herbarium specimens for SEM studies. The portion of each leaf examined came from an area midway between the base and apex and extending laterally from the midvein to the margin of the leaf. Leaf specimens were prepared in two ways. Leaf surfaces were peeled using cellulose acetate paper and acetone (Payne 1968). Both the peeled leaf surface and the peel (cast) of the surface were examined. Leaf surfaces also were examined directly as obtained from the herbarium sheets. All specimens were affixed to aluminum stubs with silver conducting paint or Microstik prior to coating with gold-palladium. SEM micrographs were made on a Cambridge Mark II Stereoscan, operated at 15KV. Populational variation of these morphological features was analyzed with the aid of pictorialized scatter diagrams and hybrid index (*HI*) values (Table 1) (Anderson 1949).

TABLE 1. Characters used and values assigned to them in constructing the morphological hybrid index (*HI*).

Character	Hybrid index value		
	0	1	2
Sepal color	green	pinkish	deep rose
Leaf pubescence (= mean no. trichomes/mm² on lower leaf surface	< 10	10-150	> 150
Mean leaf length/width ratio	1.45-2.00	1.31-1.44	1.15-1.30
Sepal pubescence	glandular trichomes	mixed glandular/ simple trichomes	simple trichomes
Inflorescence	compact spike	intermediate	open panicle

Pollen stainability.—Pollen stainability was determined for functionally male individuals (see Young 1972) of each species and their putative hybrids. Pollen was stained in 1 per cent aniline blue in lactophenol ("cotton blue") for 24 hours. Three different flowers from each plant were utilized and a minimum of 600 grains (per plant) counted. Those pollen grains that stained dark blue were assumed to be viable and those that stained faintly or not at all, inviable (however, see Jones 1976).

RESULTS AND DISCUSSION
Comparative Morphology and Analysis of Population Samples

Although the two species superficially are quite similar, several features distinguish them. Distinctive features of *R. integrifolia* include: (1) its leaves, which are generally elliptic in shape (length/width ratio ≥ 1.5), glabrous (usually < 10 simple trichomes/mm² on the lower leaf surface; Fig. 6), entire to serrate, and simple (rarely trifoliolate [Young 1974a]); (2) its flowers, which are sessile and borne in dense, terminal, compact spikes (with persistent bracts); and (3) its sepals, which are greenish in color and ciliate with an abundance of orange, glandular, uniserriate, multicellular trichomes (Fig. 8). Characteristic features of *R. lentii* include: (1) its leaves, which are more or less deltoid in shape (length/width ratio ≤ 1.3), densely hairy on the lower leaf surface (usually > 200 simple trichomes/mm²; Fig. 2), entire, and always simple; (2) its flowers, which are pedicellate and borne in short, somewhat open panicles (with deciduous bracts); (3) its sepals, which are deep rose in color and ciliate with uniserriate, unicellular, simple trichomes (Fig. 9); and (4) its large fruits (11 to 14 mm in diameter compared with 8 to 10 mm in *R. integrifolia*), which are the largest in the genus (Young 1975).

Variation of morphological features measured for the population samples is presented in Figures 12 and 13. Based upon the morphological features analyzed in this study, the two species are easily distinguished and morphologically are quite distinct. Those individuals which were morphologically intermediate between the two species were found growing in the transitional, or ecotonal, vegetation along the elevational transect. The results of pollen stainability studies supported the interpretation that these morphologically intermediate individuals were putative hybrids between *R. integrifolia* and *R. lentii*. Pollen of individuals of *R. integrifolia* (*HI* = 0) and *R. lentii* (*HI* = 10) was 95 to 99 per cent stainable (viable), whereas

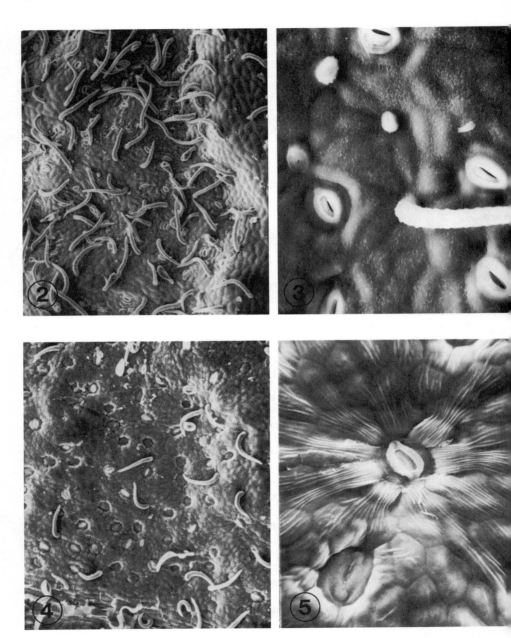

FIGURES 2-7. *SEM photographs of the lower leaf surfaces of the* Rhus *taxa studied.* **Figures 2-3:** R. lentii, *"peeled" surface (see text for explanation of "peeled" and "unpeeled"); Figure 2* ca. *200×; Figure 3* ca. *600×.* **Figures 4-5:** R. integrifolia × R. lentii; *Figure 4 "unpeeled" surface,* ca. *200×; Figure 5 "peeled" surface,* ca. *700×.* **Figures 6-7:** R. integrifolia *"peeled" surfaces; Figure 6* ca. *300×; Figure 7* ca. *600×.*

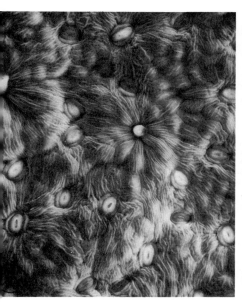
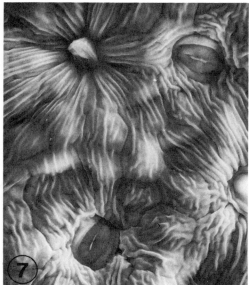

that of the putative hybrids (HI = 4 to 7) was 50 to 60 per cent stainable. Reduced pollen viability, indicating partial sterility, is a well-known indicator of hybridization (*e.g.*, Anderson and Woodson 1935, Chapman and Jones 1971, Stebbins 1958, Young 1974a).

Putative hybrids between the two taxa are generally intermediate in leaf morphology (mean length/width ratio = 1.15 to 1.52) and pubescence (mean no. trichomes/mm^2 = 7 to 162) (Figs. 4 and 11). In addition, several of the hybrids had trifoliolate leaves (Fig. 11). It would appear that trifoliolate leaves in these taxa is a recessive character that, for some unknown reason, is more commonly expressed in the hybrids than in either of the parents. Hybrids also were intermediate in terms of their cuticular relief pattern. Cells of the lower leaf epidermis of *R. lentii* are smooth in appearance (Figs. 2 and 3), whereas those of *R. integrifolia* are striate (Figs. 6 and 7). The lower leaf epidermis of hybrids had both striate and smooth cells (Figs. 4 and 5).

The inflorescences of putative hybrids tended to possess both pedicellate and sessile flowers, and were generally much more elongated than those of either parent (Fig. 11). Sepal pubescence in hybrids consisted of a mixture of simple trichomes and a few glandular (often malformed) trichomes (Fig. 10). Sepal pubescence was one of the most reliable characteristics for detecting hybridization between *R. integrifolia* and *R. lentii,* and was usually correlated with an intermediate type of leaf morphology.

Nearly all of the morphological features characteristic of these putative hybrids also are characteristic of *R. integrifolia* var. *cedrocensis.* This suggests that the latter is actually of hybrid origin.

There was no indication of introgression between the two species on the island (Fig. 13). Two possible explanations may account for this situation. The first is that the hybrids are sterile and are not reproducing. Pollen stainability data indicated that male fertility in the hybrids was greatly reduced compared with that of the parental species. However, many of the putative hybrids found during the course of the field studies were female plants. These plants did produce some seed, which appeared to have normally developing embryos, but no seedlings

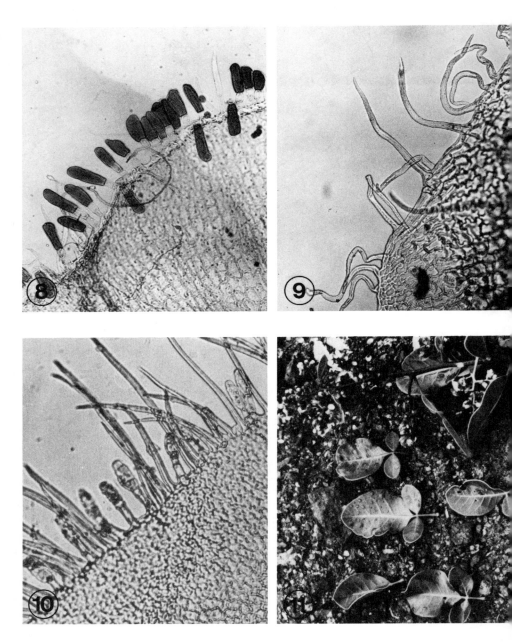

FIGURES 8-11. *Whole mounts of sepals showing characteristic pubescence of taxa and leaves of the putative hybrid.* **Figure 8:** R. integrifolia *(725,* HI=1*) with predominantly glandular trichomes.* **Figure 9:** R. lentii *(125,* HI=10*) with simple trichomes only.* **Figure 10:** *Putative hybrid (108,* HI=5*) with mixture of malformed glandular and simple trichomes.* **Figure 11:** *Leaves of the putative hybrid; note the trifoliolate shape.*

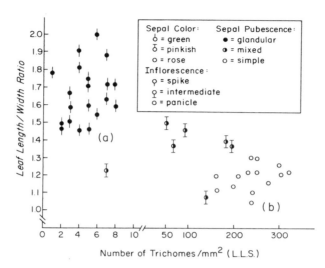

FIGURE 12. *Pictorialized scatter diagram for the populations of* R. integrifolia *and* R. lentii *studied. Grouping* (a) *represents* R. integrifolia; *grouping* (b) *represents* R. lentii. *(L.L.S. = lower leaf surface.)*

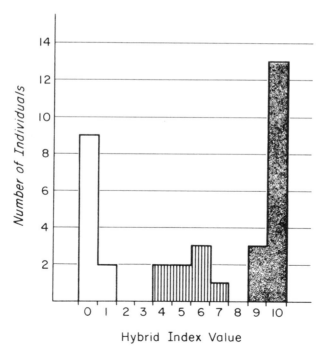

FIGURE 13. *Histogram of hybrid index values for "pure"* R. integrifolia *(clear), "pure"* R. lentii *(dotted), and the putative hybrid (vertical lines).*

were discovered. It has been shown that introgression between *R. integrifolia* and *R. ovata* probably occurs via fertilization of female hybrids with pollen from either of the parental species, due to decreased pollen viability of the hybrids (Young 1974a). It seems likely that this also is the case in *R. integrifolia* and *R. lentii*. The degree of fertility of female hybrids is not known; while it probably is lower than that of either of the parents, some viable introgressive seeds are likely to be produced by female hybrids. A second possible explanation for the absence of introgression may be that there simply are not any habitats available for the establishment of introgressive types. One of the characteristics of introgression is that the recombinant types ("hybrid swarms") typically are found in disturbed habitats which are often intermediate between the habitats of the parental taxa. In those regions on Cedros Island where *R. integrifolia* and *R. lentii* are sympatric there is relatively little disturbance and consequently few disturbed habitats. Clearly, the putative hybrids that were present occurred in a *natural* habitat that appeared to be intermediate between those of the parents. However, this habitat was not extensive and appeared to be occupied primarily by F_1 (or perhaps F_2) morphotypes (Figs. 12 and 13). In my opinion, the lack of suitable, *available* habitats for the establishment of introgressive types is the primary reason for the absence of introgression between *R. integrifolia* and *R. lentii* on Cedros Island.

Evolutionary Significance of Hybridization

The ultimate evolutionary importance of hybridization depends directly on the environment in which it takes place. For example, hybridization between *R. integrifolia* and *R. ovata* in coastal southern California has occurred under changing environmental conditions, most recently due in large part to manmade disturbances, which have afforded new habitats for the establishment and stabilization of recombinant types through introgression (Young 1974a). In this instance, hybridization probably has played, at least to some extent, a role in the evolutionary history of these species. However, hybridization between well-established and well-adapted taxa in a stable environment will generally have no significant effect on the evolutionary history of the taxa involved (Stebbins 1950). The most obvious effect of hybridization under such conditions is the breakdown or blurring of the distinctions between the species involved. This certainly appears to be the case concerning hybridization between *R. integrifolia* and *R. lentii* on Cedros Island.

TAXONOMIC TREATMENT

The results of this investigation indicate that *R. integrifolia* var. *cedrocensis* is actually of hybrid origin (*R. integrifolia* × *R. lentii*), and not the result of autochthonous insular differentiation. Formal taxonomic recognition of this hybrid seems unwarranted and is, in fact, misleading. The following taxonomic treatment is presented to help clarify the relationships between these taxa.

Key to *R. integrifolia*, *R. lentii*, and Their Hybrids

1. Leaves generally elliptic and glabrous; inflorescence a dense, terminal spike with persistent bracts; flowers sessile; sepals green, ciliate with orange, glandular trichomes
   . . . . *R. integrifolia*
1. Leaves deltoid to elliptic, puberulent to densely tomentose; inflorescence a terminal panicle or spike-like with deciduous bracts; flowers pedicellate or sessile; sepals pinkish to deep rose, ciliate with simple and orange, glandular trichomes.
   2. Leaves deltoid, glaucous, puberulent above, densely tomentose below; inflorescence a terminal panicle, with deciduous bracts; flowers short pedicellate; sepals deep rose, ciliate with short, simple trichomes . . . . *R. lentii*

2. Leaves more or less elliptic, more or less glabrous above, pubescent below; inflorescence intermediate between spike and panicle, with more or less deciduous bracts; some flowers short pedicellate; sepals pinkish, ciliate with a mixture of simple and orange, glandular (often malformed) trichomes .... *R. integrifolia* × *R. lentii*

Rhus integrifolia (Nutt. in Torr. & Gray) Brewer and Watson. Bot. California 1: 110. 1876. HOLOTYPE: San Diego, *Nuttall s.n.* (BM!). [A complete discussion of the nomenclature, synonyms, and description of *R. integrifolia* can be found elsewhere (Young 1974b).]

In order to conserve space, a list of representative specimens examined will not be included for *R. integrifolia,* but are presented only for *R. lentii* and hybrids. Upon written request to the author, a complete list may be obtained.

Rhus lentii Kellogg, Proc. California Acad. Sci. 2: 16. 1863; Just's Bot. Jahresb. 21: 158. 1893, as *R. leutii* [sic].—*Schmaltzia lentii* (Kell.) Barkley, Amer. Midl. Natur. 24: 650. 1940.—*Toxicodendron lentii* (Kell.) Kuntze, Rev. Gen. Pl. 1: 154. 1891.—HOLOTYPE: Cedros Island, *Veatch s.n.,* 1859 (CAS! Photo: MO!).

Rounded evergreen shrub, 1 to 3 m high, with stout, often red-maroon, puberulent twigs with scattered reddish-brown lenticels. Leaves simple, coriaceous, entire, often with subrevolute, whitish margins, distinctly pallid-veined with a fine reticulum of distinctly visible smaller veins, upper surface brownish-green to gray-green, glaucous, lower surface lighter green to tan, less often glaucous; lvs. 2.0 to 6.0 cm long, 1.5 to 4.5 cm wide, deltoid, orbicular to subovate, apex rounded-obtuse to subacute, base rounded-obtuse, less often cordate, upper surface minutely pubescent, lower surface densely tomentose-villous. Petioles often reddish-maroon, stout, pubescent, 2.0 to 8.0 mm long. Inflorescence a terminal, open panicle, *ca.* 5 cm long, slightly narrower; bracts deciduous, ovate, *ca.* 3 mm long, *ca.* 2 mm wide, whitish, pubescent, apex acute; flowers short pedicellate, pedicel *ca.* 2.5 mm wide, pilose on outer surface and ciliate with simple trichomes; petals whitish-pink to deep rose (rose to yellow when dried), ovate-deltoid, *ca.* 3 mm long and 3.5 mm wide in hermaphrodites, glabrous on outer surface, pilose at base of inner surface, ciliate with simple trichomes; stamens shorter than sepals in female flowers, slightly exserted in hermaphrodites. Fruit a drupe, *ca.* 14 mm in diameter, pubescent with red, glandular and simple trichomes.
Representative specimens:
MEXICO: Baja California Sur: Cedros Island: *Anthony 98 & 305* (MO, SD, UC); *Brandegee s.n.* (SD, UC); Grand Canyon, 3 mi E from coast, *Haines & Hale s.n.* (LA, UC); wash bottom 0.5 mi W of village, *Haines & Hale 183* (CAS, LA, MO, SD, UC); North Head, *Lindsay 2151* (SD, UC); spring above village, *Moran 10600* (SD, UC); arroyo in middle of E coast, *Moran 10695* (SD); canyon on E side 4 mi from N end, *Moran 15167* (SD, UC). Mainland: Aguaje de San Andrés S of Cerro Elefante, *Gentry 7465* (ASU, SD, UC); mountains SE of Aguaje de San José, *Gentry 7786* (SD, UC); arroyo 4 mi N of San Andrés, *Moran & Reveal 19809* (RSA, SD).

Rhus integrifolia (Nutt. in Torr. & Gray) Brew. & Wats. × Rhus lentii Kell.
Rhus integrifolia var. *cedrosensis* Barkley, Ann. Missouri Bot. Gard. 24: 363. 1937.—*Schmaltzia integrifolia* var. *cedrosensis* (Barkl.) Barkley, Amer. Midl. Natur. 24: 651. 1940.—HOLOTYPE: Cedros Island, Baja California, Mexico, 11 March 1911, *Rose 16134* (NY! Photo: MO!).

Hybrids between the species are similar in general habit to that of the species. Major diagnostic features are: leaves simple to trifoliolate, coriaceous, entire, more or less intermediate in shape to that of parents, subglabrous to puberulent, 3.0 to 6.0 cm long, 2.0 to 4.0 cm wide. Petioles 3 to 12 mm long. Inflorescence much looser and more elongate than in either parent, with more or less deciduous bracts; flowers short pedicellate to sessile. Sepals pinkish-rose and ciliate with simple and glandular (often malformed) trichomes. Occasional on the west side and northern end of Cedros Island at the interface of the Vizcaino Desert and chaparral-coastal sage scrub vegetations.

Representative specimens:

MEXICO: Baja California: Cedros Island: Mt. Katherine, *Haines & Hale s.n.* (UC); edge of pine grove near summit of main divide, *Haines & Hale s.n.* (UC); *Mason 2039* (CAS).

SUMMARY

Populations of *Rhus integrifolia* (Nutt. in T. & G.) Brew. & Wats. and *Rhus lentii* Kell. on Cedros Island were studied and, based upon morphological features, a number of putative hybrids were found in areas where the two species were sympatric. On the west side of the island, hybrids were almost entirely restricted to an ecotone (intermediate habitat) between island chaparral-coastal sage scrub (*R. integrifolia*) and Vizcaino Desert vegetation (*R. lentii*), and there was little evidence of introgression. Diagnostic features of value in distinguishing the species and their hybrids are leaf pubescence and morphology, sepal pubescence, and inflorescence morphology. Although this interspecific hybrid has been formally recognized as a variety (*Rhus integrifolia* var. *cedrosensis* Barkl.), as was true for the hybrid between *R. integrifolia* and *R. ovata* Wats. on Santa Catalina Island (*Rhus ovata* var. *traskiae* Barkl.), such recognition is misleading.

ACKNOWLEDGMENTS

I wish to thank Ralph Philbrick and Michael Benedict for their company during our visits to Cedros Island, and the village officials for their hospitality during my stay on the island. Special thanks are due Linda Oestry-Stidd for her technical assistance in performing the SEM work, and I am grateful for the use of facilities of the Center for Electron Microscopy at the University of Illinois. I also thank P. Lowry for criticizing a preliminary draft of the manuscript, and the curators of the following herbaria for the loan of herbarium specimens: Arizona State University, British Museum, California Academy of Sciences, University of California at Los Angeles, New York Botanic Garden, Missouri Botanic Garden, San Diego Museum of Natural History, and University of California at Berkeley.

REFERENCES

ANDERSON, E. 1949. Introgressive hybridization. John Wiley & Sons, New York, N.Y.

ANDERSON, E., and R. E. WOODSON. 1935. The species of *Tradescantia* indigenous to the United States. Contrib. Arnold. Arb. 9:1-132.

AXELROD, D. I. 1967. Geologic history of the Californian insular flora. Pp. 267-315 *in* R. N. Philbrick, ed., Proceedings of the symposium on the biology of the California Islands. Santa Barbara Botanic Garden, Santa Barbara, Calif.

BARKLEY, F. A. 1937. A monographic study of *Rhus* and its immediate allies in North and Central America, including the West Indies. Ann. Missouri Bot. Gard. 24:256-500.

CARLQUIST, S. 1965. Island life. Natural History Press, Garden City, N.Y.

———. 1966. The biota of long-distance dispersal. I. Principles of dispersal and evolution. Quart. Rev. Biol. 41:247-270.

———. 1974. Island biology. Columbia University Press, New York, N.Y.

CHAPMAN, G. C., and S. B. JONES. 1971. Hybridization between *Senecio smallii* and *S. tomentosa* (Compositae) on the granitic flatrocks of the southeastern United States. Brittonia 23:209-216.

JONES, A. G. 1976. Environmental effects on the percentage of stainable and presumed normal pollen in *Aster* (Compositae). Amer. J. Bot. 63:657-663.

MORAN, R. 1959. *Dudleya*. Pp. 344-359 *in* H. Jacobsen, ed., A handbook of succulent plants. Blandford Press, London.

MULLER, C. H. 1967. Relictual origins of insular endemics in *Quercus*. Pp. 73-77 *in* R. N. Philbrick, ed., Proceedings of the symposium on the biology of the California Islands. Santa Barbara Botanic Garden, Santa Barbara, Calif.

PAYNE, W. W. 1968. The use of cellulose acetate film for the production of epidermal casts. Ward's Bull. 7:6-7.

PHILBRICK, R. N. 1967. Introduction. Pp. 3-8 *in* R. N. Philbrick, ed., Proceedings of the symposium on the biology of the California Islands. Santa Barbara Botanic Garden, Santa Barbara, Calif.

RAVEN, P. H. 1967. The floristics of the California Islands. Pp. 57-67 *in* R. N. Philbrick, ed., Proceedings of the symposium on the biology of the California Islands. Santa Barbara Botanic Garden, Santa Barbara, Calif.

SHREVE, F., and I. WIGGINS. 1964. Vegetation and flora of the Sonoran Desert. Stanford University Press, Stanford, Calif.

STEBBINS, G. L. 1950. Variation and evolution in plants. Columbia University Press, New York, N.Y.

————. 1958. The inviability, weakness and sterility of interspecific hybrids. Adv. Genet. 9:147-215.

THORNE, R. F. 1969. The California Islands. Ann. Missouri Bot. Gard. 56:391-408.

YOUNG, D. A. 1972. The reproductive biology of *Rhus integrifolia* and *Rhus ovata* (Anacardiaceae). Evolution 26:406-414.

————. 1974a. Introgressive hybridization in two southern California species of *Rhus* (Anacardiaceae). Brittonia 26:241-255.

————. 1974b. Taxonomic and nomenclatural notes on *Rhus integrifolia* and *Rhus ovata* (Anacardiaceae). Madroño 22:286-289.

————. 1975. Systematics of *Rhus* subgenus *Lobadium* section *Styphonia*. Ph.D. thesis, Claremont Graduate School, Claremont, Calif.

Distribution of *Malacothrix* (Asteraceae) on the California Islands and the Origin of Endemic Insular Species

W. S. Davis

*Department of Biology, University of Louisville,
Louisville, Kentucky 40208*

INTRODUCTION

Malacothrix DC. consists of approximately 20 species of annual and herbaceous perennial plants distributed in the western United States and Mexico, with disjunct populations of one species, *M. coulteri* Harv. and Gray, in Chile and Argentina. Ten taxa have been collected on the California Islands. Some of them are insular endemics and some also have a mainland distribution.

A study of the island *Malacothrix* was begun following a taxonomic revision of *M. clevelandii* Gray which resulted in the establishment of three new species, *M. stebbinsii, M. sonorae,* and *M. similis* (Davis and Raven 1962). The latter species is a tetraploid with both mainland and insular distributions and it was speculated that other taxa of *Malacothrix* now endemic to the islands might have participated in its alloploid origin. In addition, there was disagreement in the literature concerning the taxonomic status and circumscription of most of the island endemics of *Malacothrix* (Williams 1957, Ferris 1960, Munz 1974). It seemed probable, therefore, that a thorough study of all of the insular *Malacothrix* would be a fruitful one and that a more stable taxonomy might result.

CURRENTLY RECOGNIZED SPECIES ON THE ISLANDS

Malacothrix clevelandii Gray is an autogamous annual with a chromosome number of $2n = 14$ and has been collected on Guadalupe of the Baja California Islands (see Thorne 1969 for a description of the island groups). It is also distributed on the mainland from northern Baja California to Tehama County in California. Closely related to *M. clevelandii,* and most certainly derived from it, is *M. similis* Davis and Raven, an autogamous annual. It is a tetraploid ($2n = 28$) and has been collected on Todos Santos, Cedros, and Los Coronados of the Baja California Islands. It also occurs on the mainland in northwestern Baja California and perhaps in Ventura County, California. Specimens of *M. clevelandii* and *M. similis* from the islands fall within the range of variation found in populations of their respective species on the mainland and there is no evidence of adaptive radiation by either species on the islands. Dispersal over water is certainly the route by which *M. clevelandii* arrived on Guadalupe, but *M. similis* may have reached its island habitats via land connections to the mainland or by over-water dispersal.

Malacothrix coulteri var. *cognata* Jepson, an annual that is probably autogamous and diploid, has been collected on Santa Rosa and Santa Cruz of the Northern Channel Islands. It has been collected rarely on the mainland; there have been single collections recorded from Contra Costa, Kern, Los Angeles, and San Diego Counties in California. It differs from *M. c.* var. *coulteri,* which has a widespread mainland distribution, by its modally smaller achenes and by its dissected leaves. The two varieties are very similar in achene micromorphology (Fig. 1).

From the populations making up the white-flowered, self-incompatible, herbaceous perennial *Malacothrix,* which have a chromosome number of $2n = 18$, six species have been described: *M. arachnoidea* McGregor, *M. altissima* Greene, *M. commutata* T.&G., *M.*

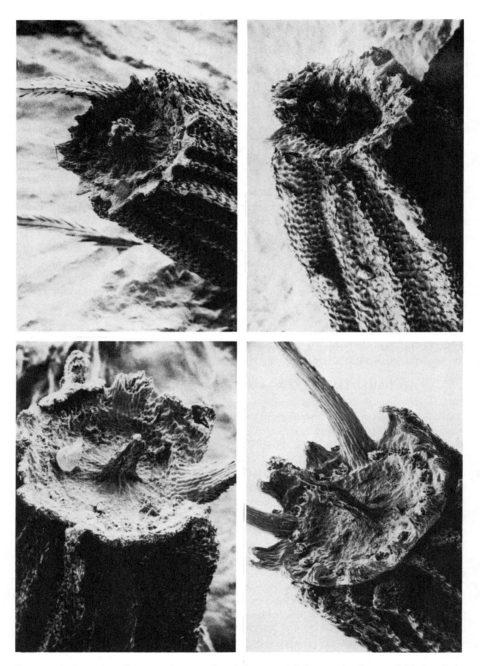

FIGURE 1. *Scanning electron micrographs of the apical 0.3 mm of achenes of* M. insularis *(upper left);* M. squalida *(upper right);* M. coulteri var. cognata *(lower left);* M. coulteri *var.* coulteri *(lower right).*

saxatilis (Nutt.) T.&G., *M. tenuifolia* (Nutt.) T.&G., and *M. implicata* Eastwood. The most recent treatments of *Malacothrix*, however, consider all of these as varieties of *M. saxatilis* (Williams 1957, Ferris 1960). Only two of the taxa have island distributions. *M. tenuifolia* has been collected on Santa Catalina Island and is distributed in mainland California as far north as Santa Barbara County, as far west as Riverside County, and as far south as San Diego County. *M. implicata* is restricted to the islands and has been collected on Anacapa, San Miguel, Santa Cruz, and Santa Rosa of the Northern Channel Islands, and on San Nicolas of the Southern Channel Islands. In the herbarium, *M. implicata* is easily distinguishable from all of the other perennial taxa but is closest to *M. tenuifolia* in overall morphology. *M. tenuifolia* is sometimes difficult to distinguish from *M. altissima*, *M. commutata*, and *M. saxatilis*. All four taxa occupy mainland habitats that are generally more xeric than the island habitats of *M. implicata* and, when all of the evidence is considered, it appears that *M. implicata* may be the most primitive of the group and that its island distribution is relictual.

The next two species, *M. insularis* Greene and *M. squalida* Greene, are obviously closely related and have been considered conspecific by some taxonomists (Williams 1957, Ferris 1960). Both are annuals and both are endemic to the California Islands. *M. insularis* has been collected at least four times on Los Coronados but there have been no recent collections. *M. squalida* has been collected on Santa Cruz Island (the type locality) and recently on Anacapa Island. On the basis of pollen size, both species are assumed to be polyploid and both are probably autogamous. Gray (1886) suggested that *M. insularis* was intermediate between *M. coulteri* and *M. incana*, an herbaceous perennial that will be discussed later. Evidence from my work supports a relationship of *M. insularis* and *M. squalida* to *M. coulteri*. The three species are similar in most aspects of leaf morphology, in their scarious-margined outer involucral bracts, and in the presence of unbarbed receptacular bristles (many in *M. coulteri*, but fewer in *M. insularis* and *M. squalida*). Details of achene micromorphology also suggest that all three species are related but at the same time distinct (Fig. 1). The outer pappus of *M. insularis* and *M. squalida* is evenly dentate while that of *M. coulteri* is more dissected and ragged. As many as five long, persistent bristles are found as part of the outer pappus of *M. coulteri*, while *M. insularis* possesses only one bristle and *M. squalida* generally has none. In all three species the five most prominent ribs of the achene extend above the other, weaker, intermediate ribs at the apex, which is constricted only in *M. squalida*. The mean lengths of the achenes of the three taxa are: *M. coulteri*, 2.5 mm; *M. insularis*, 2.1 mm; and *M. squalida*, 1.7 mm.

The taxa that have been described to this point possess achenes with both an inner pappus and a well-developed outer pappus (as do all but one of the exclusively mainland species). The remaining insular taxa that will be considered in this paper have achenes that have only an inner pappus; they also share other characteristics that, in combination, distinguish them from most other species of *Malacothrix*. The formal taxa are: *M. incana* (Nutt.) T.&G., *M. foliosa* Gray, and *M. indecora* Greene.

M. incana is an herbaceous perennial that blooms at the end of its first year of growth. The single representative that I have grown in cultivation is self-compatible. *M. incana* has been collected on Santa Rosa, Santa Cruz, and San Miguel of the Northern Channel Islands, and on San Clemente of the Southern Channel Islands. The type collection is from "an island in the bay of San Diego" but, as far as I know, it has not been collected again from that region. On the mainland, its distribution is more to the north, and it is restricted to sand dune areas along the coast of California in the counties of San Luis Obispo and Santa Barbara.

M. foliosa is a self-incompatible annual that is endemic to the islands. It has been collected on Santa Barbara and San Clemente of the Southern Channel Islands, and on Los Coronados of the Baja California Islands.

The third species, *M. indecora*, is an annual island endemic that has been collected on San

Miguel and Santa Cruz (the type locality) of the Northern Channel Islands. Based on the size of the pollen, it is assumed to be a diploid and it is probably autogamous.

NEW TAXA AND THEIR RELATIONSHIPS

In the course of my studies of *M. incana, M. foliosa, M. indecora,* and specimens referred to the latter two species, living material has been obtained from the islands and representatives of various populations have been grown for the past several years in an environment room at the University of Louisville. In addition, conclusions regarding the distribution and taxonomy of the *foliosa*-related taxa have been influenced by a thorough study of herbarium specimens and by firsthand information regarding the appearance, relative blooming times, and habitats of some of the taxa as they occur on the islands (R. Philbrick and P. Raven, pers. comm.). I have concluded that there are at least three undescribed population groups on the islands that, although related closely to *M. foliosa* and *M. incana,* are sufficiently distinct to be given formal taxonomic status. A detailed taxonomic treatment of these taxa will be published elsewhere; the remainder of this paper will be confined to a brief description of the salient features within the groups.

The first entity is a self-incompatible annual from Santa Barbara Island which shall be referred to as Species A. The second, Species B, is an autogamous annual occurring on Anacapa Island. The third, Species C, is a self-compatible annual from San Nicolas Island. All three taxa share the following characteristics with *M. foliosa* and *M. incana:* (1) a chromosome number of $2n = 14$ and chromosomes that are the smallest in *Malacothrix;* (2) achenes that have no outer pappus; (3) a bristleless receptacle; and (4) well-developed cauline leaves. Although the chromosome number of *M. indecora* is unknown, it shares the remainder of the characteristics with the others. On the basis of comparative studies of several sorts, I suggest the following: (1) that Species C from San Nicolas is closely related to, and has been derived rather recently from, *M. foliosa;* (2) that Species B from Anacapa has been derived from Species A; (3) that *M. indecora* is more closely related to Species A and B than to *M. foliosa* and Species C; and (4) that *M. incana* has been involved in the origin of Species A and perhaps Species B. Evidence on which these conclusions are based has come from comparative studies of flower color, leaf morphology, growth habit under uniform conditions, length of time from germination to flowering, and number of heads per plant.

In addition, scanning electron microscope studies have disclosed a number of useful aspects of achene micromorphology (Figs. 2 and 3). For example, the apex of the achene in Species C and *M. foliosa* has a flattened area within which the stumps of the inner pappus are situated. This characteristic is lacking in Species A, Species B, and *M. indecora,* which have, instead, a cup-shaped area at the achene apex which is deeper than that of the former two taxa. The achene of *M. incana* differs in several details from the achenes of the other taxa. The involucres of Species A, Species B, and *M. indecora* differ from those of Species C and *M. foliosa* (Fig. 4), and the involucre of *M. incana* is most similar to the A-B-*indecora* group. A close relationship among all the taxa is also suggested by the fact that fertile hybrids have been produced from the several possible pairs of *M. foliosa,* Species A, Species B, and Species C. In addition, fertile hybrids have been produced between *M. incana* and *M. foliosa,* and between *M. incana* and Species A. In general, F_1 progeny have been self-compatible, even when both parents have been self-incompatible. When the perennial *M. incana* has been one of the parents, none of the F_1 progeny has maintained the perennial habit. Intercrosses between F_1 plants have produced some individuals with a perennial habit, and different levels of sterility have been found in the F_2. In nature, *M. foliosa* is isolated from Species B and Species C by its distribution, and from Species A and *M. incana* by differences in flowering time.

The present distribution of *M. foliosa* on three widely separated islands whose geologic pasts

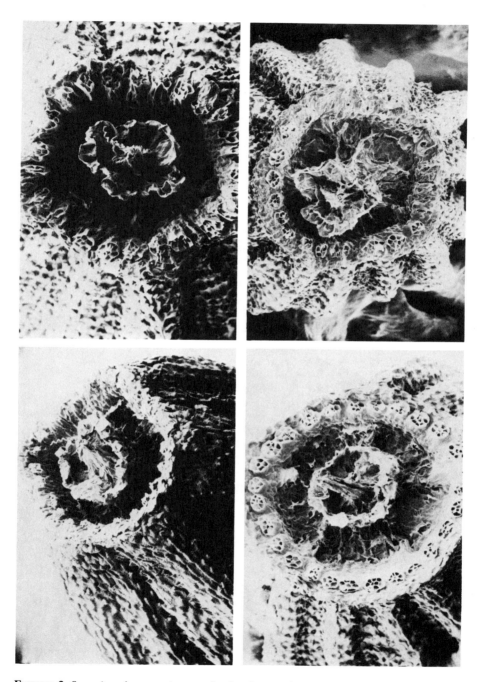

FIGURE 2. *Scanning electron micrographs showing a polar view of the achenes of Species B (upper left);* M. foliosa *(upper right); Species A (lower left); Species C (lower right).*

FIGURE 3. *Scanning electron micrographs of the apical 0.3 mm of the achenes of Species B (upper left);* M. indecora *(upper right);* M. incana *(lower left); Species C (lower right). The magnification of* M. incana *is half that of the others.*

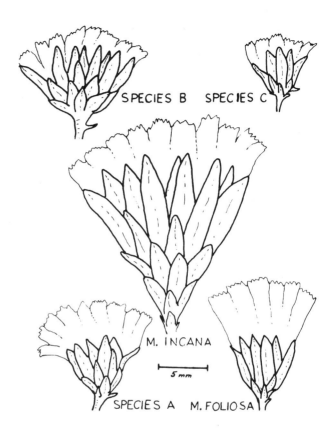

FIGURE 4. *Camera lucida drawings of typical pressed flower heads of* Malacothrix.

are apparently different suggests that it was once a mainland species and that its present island distribution is relictual. The restricted distributions of Species B and Species C and their probable derivative origin from the self-incompatible taxa suggest that they are autochthonous endemics.

SUMMARY

With the exception of four of the eight Baja California Islands, at least one representative of *Malacothrix* is found on all of the California Islands. Six taxa occur on the Northern Channel Islands, six occur on the Southern Channel Islands, and four are found on the Baja California Islands. Two taxa, *M. implicata* and *M. incana,* are found on the major islands of the Northern Channel Islands and on different single islands of the Southern Channel Islands. *M. foliosa* has been collected from two of the Southern Channel Islands and one of the Baja California Islands. So far as the insular distribution of *Malacothrix* is concerned, Los Coronados appear to be the most important of the Baja California Islands, with three species occurring there.

Of the thirteen taxa now documented on the islands, five are known to be self-compatible and four others are assumed to be on the basis of floral morphology. Of the four self-incompatible taxa, two are perennials and two are annuals.

Nine of the thirteen taxa are either strictly insular or primarily insular: *M. foliosa, M. implicata, M. incana, M. indecora, M. insularis, M. squalida,* Species A, Species B, and

Species C. The distributions of *M. tenuifolia, M. similis, M. clevelandii,* and *M. coulteri* var. *cognata* are primarily on the mainland. Where taxa have both an island distribution and a mainland distribution, the latter is now well to the north of the former.

The pattern of variation in insular endemics related to *M. foliosa, M. indecora,* and *M. incana* is a complex one but some progress has been made by the recognition of three reasonably coherent formal groups. Hybridization may have played a role in the origin of these new taxa, and a shift from self-incompatibility to self-compatibility has accompanied the origin of at least two of them.

REFERENCES

DAVIS, W. S., and P. H. RAVEN. 1962. Three new species related to *Malacothrix clevelandii*. Madroño 16:258-266.

FERRIS, R. S. 1960. Illustrated flora of the Pacific states, IV. Stanford University Press, Stanford, Calif.

GRAY, A. 1886. Synoptical flora of North America. Supplement to v. 1, pt. 2. Smithsonian Institution, Washington, D.C.

MUNZ, P. A. 1974. A flora of southern California. University of California Press, Berkeley, Calif.

THORNE, R. F. 1969. The California Islands. Ann. Missouri Bot. Gard. 56:391-408.

WILLIAMS, E. W. 1957. The genus *Malacothrix* (Compositae). Amer. Midl. Natur. 58:494-517.

BIOGEOGRAPHY, EVOLUTION, AND ECOLOGY OF MARINE ORGANISMS

Eddies of the California Current System: Physical and Ecological Characteristics

R. W. Owen

*National Oceanic and Atmospheric Administration,
National Marine Fisheries Service,
Southwest Fisheries Center, La Jolla, California 92038*

INTRODUCTION

This paper reviews eddies and their ecological effects in the California Current System (CCS). The importance of eddies lies in the physical properties of eddy motion and the effect on what we can identify to be systematic in flow patterns and in patterns of organism distribution. The Southern California Eddy (SC Eddy), which owes at least its character and perhaps its existence to the island and bank system off southern California, receives special attention because it is the most resolvable and ecologically significant eddy known in the CCS.

Many terrestrial populations as well as littoral and planktonic marine communities may prove to be continuously or temporarily maintained by eddy processes in otherwise marginal habitats. The fate of manmade products (MacGregor 1974) and their effect on island coastal and oceanic populations are also in part determined by the flow perturbations of the CCS. Formation of eddies in the flow is of particular interest since organisms and substances in transit become rather differently distributed in space and time in gyre-like circulations. Concentrations of organisms and substances are maintained in eddies at higher levels and for longer periods, their trajectories are markedly different, and populations which would not otherwise interact are juxtaposed. Recirculation by eddies further affects such local environmental conditions as temperature and nutrient distribution in the water, and humidity, temperature, and cloud cover in the atmosphere. My purpose is to give examples of eddy circulation—both free and stationary—and to show that large eddies are more a rule than an exception in the CCS, particularly in the Southern California Bight (SC Bight). I wish also to support the hypothesis that eddies larger than 10 km in diameter and longer than a week's duration have a major role in sustaining the high biological productivity which is characteristic of the inshore 200 km of the CCS.

Baroclinic eddies, meaning those identifiable from their effect on the mass field, have the interesting property of deforming the observable density field. A cyclonic eddy of sufficient size and intensity exhibits a detectable dome in surfaces of constant density to the depth where the eddy motion vanishes. This signals that the thermocline layer, which marks a sharp increase in water density with depth, has risen and displaced surface mixed-layer water, which is stripped of nutrients and usually poor in phytoplankton as well. In regions such as the CCS, where the thermocline is nutrient-laden and close to the bottom of the photic zone, this elevation results in a vertical flux of nutrients which affects growth of phytoplankton stocks. The new availability of nutrients is augmented and sustained by upwelling (here meaning upward flow across the eddy's density surfaces) in and near the eddy center and by mixing and stripping from shear flow across the thermocline layer of the eddy. Additional nutrients are supplied in episodic fashion during storm activity long or severe enough to erode the dome, with its relatively exposed pate (*e.g.*, Blackburn 1966). If such an eddy is associated with a boundary, it will also collect and conserve populations and nutrients washed down from the boundary layer of the obstacle. Seed populations in such eddies appear to respond to this major niche modification by increasing their production and biomass and thus rapidly create new

237

sequences of community structure (*e.g.*, Sargent and Walker 1948). Closer examination of biological effects of eddies seems warranted to determine, for example, whether eddy processes can affect production and survival of the commercially and ecologically significant anchovy, *Engraulis mordax*. This may occur by eddy effect on phytoplankton community structure or on productivity, both important factors in determining survival of the large numbers of anchovy spawned in the region (Lasker 1975, Smith 1978).

THEORY AND PHYSICS OF EDDY FORMATION

A fluid of a given viscosity impinging on an obstacle produces eddies if the obstacle is large enough or if the flow is fast enough. These eddies can be stationary, "attached" to the lee side of the obstacle, or, with increased flow or obstacle size, may be shed in a series similar to a von Kármán vortex street. A vortex street, in air or water, extends as a series of paired eddies downstream from the obstacle. There exists a large body of theory on transitions from laminar flow to stationary eddy formation to eddy street formation for simple obstacle geometries in ideal fluids. Island profiles and ocean flow are neither simple nor ideal, however. In view of the complex and hazily perceived behavior of island-ocean systems of the Pacific, it is scarcely worth reviewing theory beyond the degree to which it has been helpful in describing large eddies in the sea. Irregularities in the flow impinging on the obstacle in question cause part of the complexity. In addition, interaction of small perturbations with larger ones, changes in depth and degree of density stratification, and irregular geometry of islands and shoals all contribute to the difficulty of verifying theory by measurement.

Van Dorn *et al.* (1967) investigated circulation downstream from two small, mid-Pacific islands using direct current measurements. They described from somewhat limited observations what appears to be stable shedding of eddies in the wakes of the islands. Choosing a relatively simple system, Barkley (1972) examined flow past Johnston Atoll, a small, mid-Pacific barrier, using direct current measurements by drogues and his ship's drift. He found remarkable agreement between observed current patterns and von Kármán's physical-mathematical model of flow past long cylinders, considering the simplifying assumptions that were necessary (constant impinging current velocity, no vertical motion, and constant wake characteristics). His observations demonstrated perhaps the first obstacle-induced vortex street to be detected in the sea (Fig. 1). As Barkley pointed out, islands in clusters may act as a single obstacle to flow and extend wake effects far beyond that expected for the sum of the single islands. Also, a small change in speed or direction of the impinging current may affect not only the partitioning of energy in the system but also distributions of physical, chemical, and biological properties within island clusters and for hundreds of kilometers downstream.

Patzert (1970) fitted a complex model of flow (the Rankine vortex; Rouse 1963) to the observed structure of a frequent free-eddy phenomenon west of the islands of Hawaii, although the impinging flow and obstacle geometry there is correspondingly more complicated than in the Johnston Atoll case. In this instance the ocean responded to atmospheric forcing. Impingement of the trade winds on the profile of this high island group evidently created vortices or jets in the wind, which caused eddy formation in the water.

In a study of subsurface flow past island groups, White (1971a, 1971b, 1973a, 1973b) examined the wake of the Equatorial Undercurrent (or Cromwell Current) downstream from the Galapagos island group, which is comparable in scale to the Hawaiian island group. The unique position of the Galapagos, on the equator and obstructing an east-flowing current, suggested that the observed meanders in the flow constituted a barotropic Rossby wake, which differs from a von Kármán street in that it is time-independent and owes its existence to variations of the earth's rotation with latitude as well as to the presence of an obstacle and impinging current. Due to the usual vagaries of the impinging undercurrent, White could not distinguish between

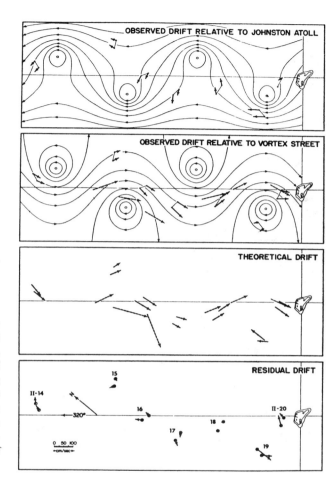

FIGURE 1. *Eddies in the wake of Johnston Atoll (Barkley 1972, fig. 3). Streamlines were derived from von Kármán vortex street model fitted to direct current measurements (arrows). Degree of success of the model is evident from comparison of the two lower panels.*

wake mechanisms. However, as the Rossby wake phenomenon requires an eastward flow, it is unlikely to occur in the flow past islands of the Californias (Baja California, Mexico and California, U.S.A.) because the impinging currents usually have no eastward component.

An obstacle is not a prerequisite for generation of surface eddies in the ocean. Barkley (1968) was able to account for a variety of observed flow patterns in the open-ocean boundary between the Kuroshio and Oyashio Currents by their resemblance to a type of flow consisting of two vortex streets lying side by side. In this instance, the vortices were apparently generated by the convergence of the two currents in the absence of fixed boundaries. That baroclinic eddies can be independent of islands, coasts, or strong current convergences has not been demonstrated, yet various studies confirm their commonplace occurrence in the open sea in general (*e.g.,* Bernstein and White 1974), and in the CCS in particular (Sverdrup and Fleming 1941, Wyllie 1966, Bernstein *et al.* 1977).

In the vicinity of island systems of the Californias, we must expect that a combination of effects of wind, current, and topography must be invoked to understand patterns of circulation (Pavlova 1966, Reid 1965). The flow impinging on the islands is as complex as island/bank

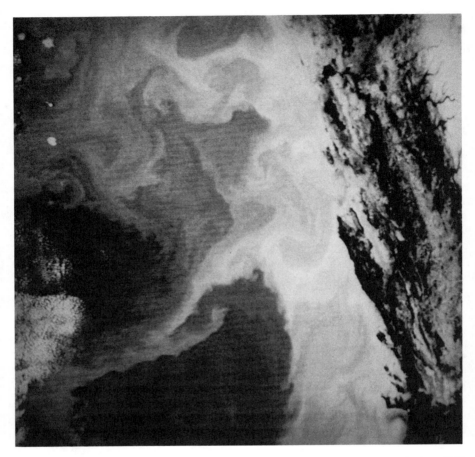

FIGURE 2. *Satellite photograph of sea-surface thermal patterns off California on 14 June 1975 (NOAA-3 satellite). Lighter shades represent cooler surfaces (Scripps Institution of Oceanography, Remote Sensing Facility).*

topography. Wind patterns exercise significant control, on the large scale, in producing the impinging flow and, on a local scale, in augmenting the perturbation of flow by the island and bank complex. Local winds are in turn affected by the islands and coastline. It is easy to understand why no simple theoretical treatment of the flow in this region can consistently account for observed current patterns downstream of the islands and banks of the Californias.

WIND

Wind stress on the sea surface is the primary source of the ocean's surface currents. The main theoretical approaches employed to account for the ocean's response to varying wind stress are those of Ekman (1905) and Sverdrup (1947), which, respectively, relate upper layer flow to temporal change in wind stress on the sea surface, and total water transport to spatial gradients of wind stress. These models have been applied to the California Current System. Bakun

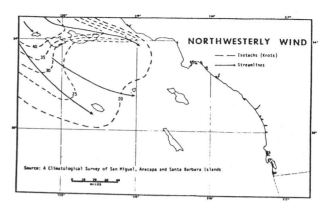

NORTHWESTERLY WIND

——— Isotachs (Knots)
⟶ Streamlines

Source: A Climatological Survey of San Miguel, Anacapa and Santa Barbara Islands

FIGURE 3. *Wind speed and direction over the SC Bight during northwest winds (U.S. Dept. Interior 1978, p. 65).*

(1973), for example, used Ekman's theory and computed upwelling intensity and timing regionally along the coastline of the Californias and farther north. These indices apply over distances too great to resolve localized phenomena. They may, however, be quite useful together with satellite thermal imagery in identifying regions and times of eddy activity associated with upwelling, should they prove to be commonplace. Sverdrup and Fleming (1941) found such eddies at the edge of an upwelling zone off Point Conception. Such an event appears again in a satellite photograph of thermal patterns in the sea off central California (Fig. 2). A cold plume and eddy extend seaward from a coastal upwelling zone, and the lower limb of a still larger eddy or meander is apparent—activity at least qualitatively similar to the upwelling edge-eddy found by Sverdrup and Fleming 42 years earlier off Point Conception.

Winds which affect local processes in the ocean off the Californias are predominantly out of the northwest and reach maximum velocity at a distance of about 200 km off the southern California coastline (Reid *et al.* 1958, Nelson 1977). Munk (1950), on the basis of his Sverdrup-based model of wind-driven circulation, found the offshore maximum in downcoast California winds to be consistent with the southward offshore flow and northward near-shore flow that seem to be prerequisites for strong SC Eddy development. Munk's meridional solution of the wind model also exhibits the weak and variable character of the main California Current.

In a more recent application of Sverdrup's theory, Nelson (1977) analyzed monthly mean values of wind stress in one-degree squares of latitude and longitude using surface wind observations from ships. This sampling grid was smaller (about 100 km) than those previously used for such wind studies, but still marginal for single eddy detection. His transport calculations from mean wind stress fields show flow directions consistent with the offshore equatorward transport of the California Current, near-shore poleward transport of the Countercurrent, and patterns south of Point Conception that are consistent with the SC Eddy.

The distribution of wind speed and direction over the region of the Channel Islands during northwest wind conditions is shown in Figure 3 (U.S. Dept. Interior 1978). It exhibits a two-jet system, consistent with wind retardation by the Northern Channel Islands of a single jet impinging from the north. High wind zones also are characteristic west and southwest off Point Conception (Reid *et al.* 1958, Allan Hancock Foundation 1965), but their role in eddy genesis is unassessed.

Sverdrup and Fleming (1941) discuss the possibility of coupling of atmospheric and oceanic eddies and raise the question of whether oceanic eddies are generated by the inherent ocean

FIGURE 4. *Vortices in the atmospheric wake of Guadalupe Island off Baja California from Skylab on 6 September 1973 (NASA photograph SL-3 #121-2371).*

current characteristics or are secondarily impressed on the ocean by the atmosphere. That this can happen elsewhere was shown by Patzert (1970), as noted above. Except for an eddy detected in the wind shadow of Cedros Island by Scripps Institution of Oceanography (SIO 1962), wind-induced ocean eddies have not been shown to occur in the CCS, although it is likely that they do occur.

Reports of atmospheric perturbations due to islands, and of von Kármán-like vortex wakes in particular, have been well documented in recent years. This is due, as Barkley (1972) notes, to "a special combination of circumstances: the wind, an obstacle, the right kind and quantity of cloud cover at the proper level, and a satellite overhead taking pictures; all must be present." Figure 4 is one such picture. Guadalupe Island is shown as seen from the orbiting Skylab satellite in September 1973. The cloud patterns clearly show a vortex street in the atmosphere downwind of the island. Such vortex wakes and other types of eddies are apt to be common in both ocean and atmosphere. Berger and Wille (1972) and Chopra (1973) review these phenomena and their dynamics. Additional examples of atmospheric flow perturbations by islands, and further discussion of their characteristics, are provided in Chopra's (1973) review of island effects on oceanic and atmospheric flow as known through 1970. Of obstacles in the CCS, only Guadalupe Island receives direct mention, but Chopra also reports effects of both smaller and larger islands which show that obstacles of virtually any size may produce systematic flow deviations. When the proper observations have been applied in the CCS, eddies are virtually always detected. Closer inspection of eddy systems may reveal that local coupling of atmosphere and ocean is responsible for the free eddies and meanders of the CCS as well as the previously established large-scale atmospheric coupling to which the main California Current owes its existence.

CALIFORNIA ISLAND AND BANK OBSTACLES

The islands and banks of the Californias are large enough relative to the impinging flow to induce or modify eddies of baroclinic scale. In full detail, the island/bank/basin topography of the Californias surpasses the complexity of most continental shelf systems of the world, leading Shepard and Emery (1941) to classify it as a "continental borderland," to distinguish it from ordinary continental shelves. The 100-m depth contour roughly describes a major break in the shelf slope (Emery 1958). At this depth, the northern group of Channel Islands (San Miguel, Santa Rosa, and Santa Cruz) may be considered a single obstacle to the flow, whereas the islands of the southern group (Santa Catalina, San Clemente, Santa Barbara, and San Nicolas) act individually. At the 500-m depth contour, the northern island group, San Nicolas, the Santa Rosa-Cortez Ridge, and Cortez and Tanner Banks act as a somewhat leaky, 200-km extension of the coastline north of Point Conception; as such, they would act on eddies the size of the SC Eddy. The direct effects of the California island and bank systems on flow have not been quantitatively specified in the literature.

It should be noted that islands and other obstacles to flow in the CCS can induce upwelling that is independent of wind. A theoretical treatment of eastern boundary currents by R. S. Arthur (1965) identified the importance of change of flow vorticity to upwelling in the boundary layer downstream of westward obstructions to southward flow in the CCS. Where the thermocline and nutricline are shallow, the result of such upwelling is cool, enriched water at the surface south of such promontories (Reid *et al.* 1958).

Examples of records exhibiting eddy patterns from direct current measurements near California islands are shown in Figure 5. Drogues released at 10-m depths were tracked in the Southern Channel Islands (Panel A). The circular trajectories shown were downstream of San Clemente and Santa Catalina Islands and depict eddies with diameters somewhat greater than 30 km and circuit times of about 3 days at 10 cm/sec. These eddies were probably caused by flow perturbation by the islands since the measurements were made under calm wind conditions (SIO 1962). On the other hand, the eddy defined by drogue trajectories near Cedros Island (Fig. 5, Panel B) was probably caused by wind forcing; northwest winds impinged on Cedros and Bahía Sebastián Vizcaíno during the measurement period. This 30-km eddy was located on the edge of the wind shadow of Cedros (labeled "calm area"), and may be the only documented case in the CCS of the wind's role in eddy genesis.

On a larger scale, eddies can be detected in the lee of the Channel Islands and banks during an offshore wind from thermal image patterns of the sea surface photographed by satellite (Fig. 6) the day before it photographed the patterns shown in Figure 2. The downstream eddy and meander patterns range from 30 to 100 km in diameter, and an eddy (< 30 km) appears near an upwelling zone off northern Baja California. Upwelling and eddy activity were apparent north of Point Conception, as well.

The effects of islands on flow as described for somewhat simpler systems elsewhere thus apply to the California Islands and associated banks, as well; they are capable of generating and shedding eddies of a variety of sizes. They may also alter the eddy patterns of the impinging flow by attenuating small eddies and deforming large ones.

EDDY PATTERNS OF THE CALIFORNIA CURRENT SYSTEM

It is likely that eddies, or eddy-like motion, impart to the flow of the California Current its characteristic large variability, in which excursions from the mean flow are at least as large as the mean flow itself. Flow is usually treated as the net motion resulting from superimposition of three main components: that due to, or balanced by, the internal distribution of mass (baroclinic mode); that due to wind stress on the sea surface, a barotropic mode under changing wind

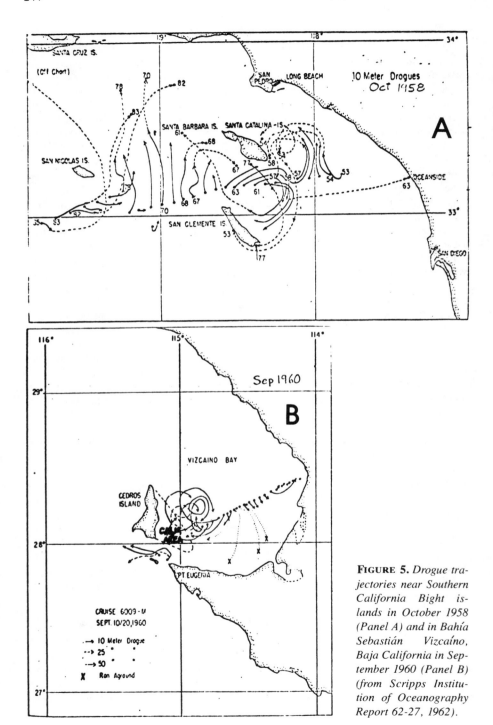

FIGURE 5. *Drogue trajectories near Southern California Bight islands in October 1958 (Panel A) and in Bahía Sebastián Vizcaíno, Baja California in September 1960 (Panel B) (from Scripps Institution of Oceanography Report 62-27, 1962).*

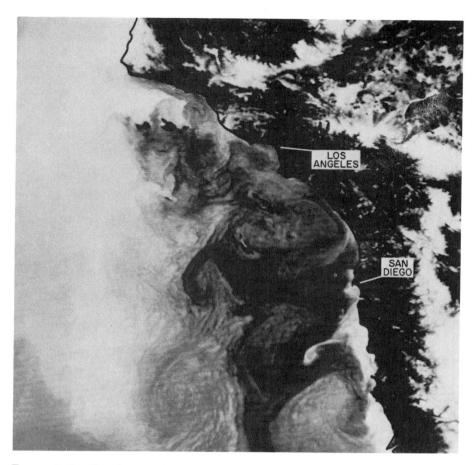

FIGURE 6. *Satellite photograph of sea-surface thermal patterns in the Southern California Bight on 19 September 1979 (NOAA-6 satellite). Lighter shades represent cooler surfaces (Scripps Institution of Oceanography, Remote Sensing Facility).*

conditions; and that due to tides and other cyclic internal motions, also barotropic. Direct determinations of currents are sensitive to all components, whereas currents depicted from the internal mass field (*i.e.*, from a spatial array of depth-integrated density profiles derived from temperature and salinity measurements) reflect only the mass-balanced baroclinic component of flow. Cyclical barotropic motions such as those due to tides or internal waves can, however, confuse interpretation of net motion using short-term direct current measurements. Internal wave displacements may also produce or suppress the appearance of small eddies in the baroclinic representation of flow (Knauss 1962). Local accelerations, *e.g.*, from storm activity, can cause poor estimates of flow velocity from the baroclinic representation.

Due to California Cooperative Oceanic Fisheries Investigations (CalCOFI) sample spacing (nominally a 30 to 60-km grid, at 30 to 90-day intervals), we can consistently identify baroclinic eddies larger than approximately 100 km in diameter and those persisting for more

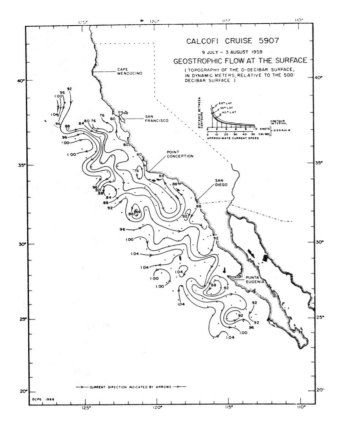

FIGURE 7. *Baroclinic representation of surface flow off the Californias in July 1959 (Wyllie 1966, p. 124). Eddies large enough to deform the density field and to be detected by the sampling grid (dots) appear as closed isobars; meanders appear as loops.*

than a month. We can resolve eddies 20 to 100 km in diameter, but at the risk of misidentifying them because of interference due to internal waves, meanders, error of measurement, and too few data points. Eddies of 20 to 100 km diameter and of less than one month's duration thus are known to exist, but their incidence and size distribution remain underestimated.

Relevant to this important range of eddy sizes is the work of Bernstein *et al.* (1977) on infrared imagery from the NOAA-3 satellite of thermal patterns in the California Current. Their work demonstrates the possibility of using thermal imagery for following eddy development and surveying their incidence, and confirms for a wide region what is observed in the field of mass and at current meter and drogue stations: most of the California Current is rich in eddies, including the flow impinging on the Channel Islands. A much more complete understanding of the distribution, persistence, and size of eddies can be anticipated from use of such satellite data to identify eddies upward of 20 km diameter and to document their genesis and decay.

Direct measurements of current speed and direction in the region off the Californias which are appropriate to eddy structure are made with difficulty and are not sufficiently numerous to support general conclusions on eddy incidence. Direct measurements made in the CCS by following parachute drogues (*e.g.,* SIO 1962) or by moored, recording current meters (*e.g.,* Lam 1972, Hendricks 1979) demonstrate flow variations consistent with effects of eddies of 10 to 50 km diameter which persist in deep and shallow waters for a few days to a few weeks. On the larger scale, baroclinic eddies from 100 to 1,000 km diameter and of months to years

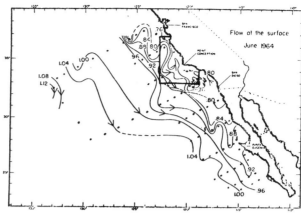

FIGURE 8. *Baroclinic surface flow as represented from the CalCOFI grid (top panel) and from an intensified grid (lower panel) in June 1964 (from Reid 1965, figs. 41, 42).*

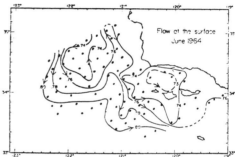

duration are identifiable from the somewhat systematic coverage of the CCS region by surveys of the CalCOFI program. Tests of the hypothesis that flow in the CCS is balanced by the mass field have been conducted and the geostrophic method was shown to agree with various direct current measurements and to afford a somewhat better estimate of direction than of magnitude (Reid 1961, 1963, Reid and Schwartzlose 1962).

The geostrophic method also has been shown to apply in particular to eddy flow in the CCS. Baroclinic representation of an isolated eddy of about 80 km diameter was shown to agree well with drogue trajectories (Reid *et al.* 1963). This demonstrated the coherence of the velocity and mass fields and thus confirmed the adequacy of the baroclinic mode for representing eddy flow on the 100-km scale and for identifying smaller eddies, as well. Reid *et al.* (*op. cit.*) point out, perhaps as a cautionary note, that the particular eddy they describe would have "slipped through the mesh of the [CalCOFI] station grid" used for the geostrophic description had not a hydrographic station been added to the grid after discovery of the eddy by drogue work.

The incidence of baroclinic eddies and meanders in the main flow of the CCS and in the SC Bight is high. Virtually every chart of the baroclinic mode of flow given by Wyllie (1966) exhibits irregularities upstream of the island and bank system and in the CCS in general (Fig. 7). The California Current System, including flow impinging on islands, is probably rich in eddies smaller than 100 km, as well. Though some are known to be missed by the CalCOFI grid, small eddies nevertheless are often sampled and are common features in the baroclinic flow of the CCS (Wyllie 1966). Irregularities and eddies of small extent are apparent in charts of geostrophic flow off Point Conception for both January and June of 1964 (Fig. 8), periods when

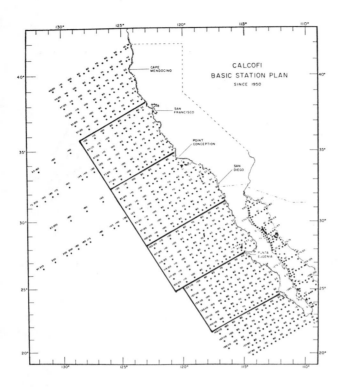

FIGURE 9. *Sectors of the CalCOFI grid used to enumerate baroclinic eddies of the California Current System. The sector containing the SC Bight covers 25 per cent more area than the others.*

the observation grid was augmented to give twice the resolution of the standard grid. As Reid (1965) notes, closer-spaced grids always seem to show proportionately smaller, but no less numerous, eddies.

Eddies in the California Current System, as defined by one or more closed streamlines of baroclinic flow, were enumerated from the charts of Wyllie (1966) by season in four size classes and four sectors off the Californias. I chose the sectors defined in Figure 9 to represent segments of the coastline between San Francisco Bay (38° N), Point Conception (35° N), Cabo Colnett (31° N), Punta Eugenia (28° N), and Bahía Magdalena (25° N). The sectors were covered, in part or totally, by 112 CalCOFI survey periods from 1949 to 1965. Separate counts were made of cyclonic and anticyclonic eddies because of their presumably different biological effects and modes of genesis. As a matter of convenience, eddy incidence is expressed as the mean number occurring in ten years, although the record used was 16 years in duration. Mean ten-year eddy incidences, corrected for gaps in coverage, are shown in Table 1. As noted above, the incidences of 20 to 100-km eddies are minimum estimates because at least some eddies of this size range were missed by the CalCOFI surveys. Larger eddies were missed when survey frequency was reduced.

Table 1 defines the level of eddy incidence in the CCS, demonstrating that eddies of all detectable sizes usually are present throughout the region off the Californias. It is also evident that there are times which show a low incidence of eddies of a given size or type. Eddy incidence demonstrates no significant seasonal variation except perhaps in the southernmost sector. Large eddies are rarer than small eddies in the Baja California sectors, but off California, eddies >200 km occur more often than those of 100 to 200 km diameter. In all areas and

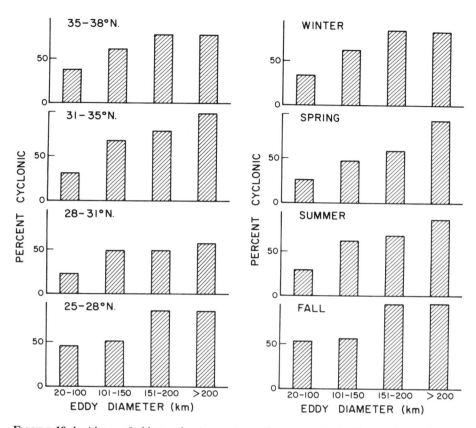

FIGURE 10. *Incidence of eddy type by size, sector, and season in the California Current System from Table 1. Panel A, by sector; Panel B, by season.*

seasons, eddies <100 km occur most frequently. In the sector containing the SC Bight, eddy incidence is dominated by the consistent (but not constant) presence of the SC Eddy. In this sector there is a corresponding paucity of both large anticyclonic eddies and small cyclonic eddies. The high incidence of small anticyclonic eddies in this sector, as well as in the two adjacent sectors, indicates that the small eddies could have been spawned by larger and more predominantly cyclonic eddies as a result of flow instabilities.

The dominance of cyclonic over anticyclonic eddies is seen in Figure 10 to occur progressively with increasing eddy size in each of the four sectors (Panel A) and in all four seasons (Panel B). The progression is most pronounced in the SC Bight (Panel A), due to the SC Eddy. This preponderance of cyclonic eddies may be ascribed to lateral friction augmented by planetary vorticity. Eddies created by lateral friction of the southward flow of the California Current against the coastal topography would be predominantly cyclonic due to inshore drag in the boundary zone. Perhaps more effective on smaller scales, the decrease in wind velocity between the coastline and the offshore maximum (discussed below) favors formation of cyclonic eddies. Wind stress gradients may be seen (charts 37 to 48 *in* Nelson 1977) to impart torque in the proper direction to favor cyclonic eddy formation in all months of the year in each

TABLE 1. Mean 10-year incidence of eddies by size, type, area, and season in the California Current System, 1949 - 1965, coast to 300 nautical miles offshore.

Eddy diameter (km)		20-100		101-150	
		a	c	a	c
Eddy type*					
Sector/season†					
	Winter	0.4	0.4	0.4	1.7
	Spring	2.8	0.9	1.3	1.3
35-38° N	Summer	3.6	2.3	0.9	1.9
	Fall	0.6	1.0	2.7	3.3
	Annual	7.4	4.6	5.3	8.2
	Per cent c		38.3		60.7
	Winter	5.0	2.0	1.0	1.1
	Spring	3.7	2.3	0.2	1.3
31-35° N	Summer	6.2	1.9	0.3	1.6
	Fall	3.0	2.1	1.6	2.4
	Annual	17.9	8.3	3.1	6.4
	Per cent c		31.7		67.4
	Winter	2.1	0.7	0.4	0.4
	Spring	4.1	1.5	2.8	2.4
28-31° N	Summer	3.1	0.6	1.4	1.7
	Fall	1.6	0.5	1.6	1.3
	Annual	10.9	3.3	6.2	5.8
	Per cent c		23.2		48.3
	Winter	1.1	1.4	0.7	1.0
	Spring	3.2	0	1.8	0.5
25-28° N	Summer	4.0	2.2	1.8	2.1
	Fall	3.3	6.1	2.3	3.3
	Annual	11.6	9.7	6.6	6.9
	Per cent c		45.5		51.1
All areas **25-38° N**		47.8	25.9	21.2	27.3
	Per cent c		35.1		56.3

* a = anticyclonic; c = cyclonic.
†Winter = January, February, March; spring = April, May, June; summer = July, August, September; fall = October, November, December.

151-200		>200		All sizes		Per cent c = $100\dfrac{c}{a+c}$
a	c	a	c	$\sum$ a	$\sum$ c	
0	1.9	2.4	3.7	3.2	7.7	
0.9	0.3	0	1.8	5.0	4.3	
0.9	0.9	0	2.0	5.4	7.0	
0	2.9	0.6	2.7	3.9	10.0	
1.8	6.0	3.0	10.2	17.5	29.0	
76.9		77.3				62.3
1.0	3.7	0	7.2	7.0	13.9	
0.9	2.6	0	6.4	4.9	12.7	
0	1.0	0.3	9.2	6.7	13.6	
0	0	0	7.3	4.6	11.9	
1.9	7.3	0.3	30.1	23.2	52.1	
79.3		99.0				69.2
1.1	0	1.5	1.2	5.1	2.3	
1.0	1.1	0.4	1.6	8.3	6.6	
2.0	2.2	1.4	0.6	7.9	5.1	
0.3	1.0	0	1.1	3.5	3.9	
4.4	4.3	3.3	4.5	24.8	17.9	
49.4		57.7				41.9
0	0.7	0.3	0.3	2.1	3.4	
0.7	0.9	0.3	0.3	6.0	1.7	
0.3	2.7	0.3	1.0	6.4	8.0	
0	2.0	0	3.8	5.6	15.2	
1.0	6.3	0.9	5.4	20.1	28.3	
86.3		85.7				58.5
9.1	23.9	7.5	50.2	85.6	127.3	
72.4		87.0				59.8

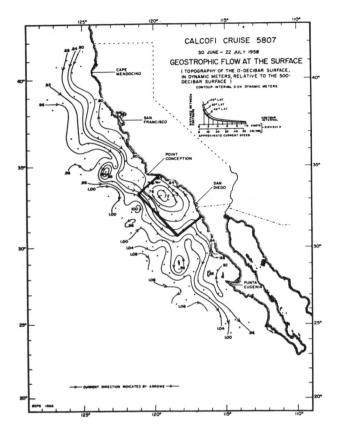

FIGURE 11. *Baroclinic representation of surface flow off the Californias in July 1958 (from Wyllie 1966, p. 111). The SC Eddy pattern (boxed) appears as a depression in the field of dynamic height anomaly.*

sector examined (Fig. 9), with the consistent exception of the southern half of the sector from 28° to 31° N off Baja California. This exception is important, as it helps explain the reduced incidence of cyclonic eddies in this one sector (Fig. 10, Panel A).

Finally, predominance of cyclonic over anticyclonic eddies is favored by their equatorial transport by the California Current due to conservation of angular momentum. Weak augmentation of cyclonic eddies and suppression of anticyclonic eddies occur by the Coriolis Effect (*cf.* von Arx 1962). With the exception of the SC Eddy, discussed below, the intensity (circulation strength) of eddies detected by CalCOFI surveys cannot be as well assessed as their incidence and type. This is due to the somewhat ephemeral nature of the eddies and to the inaccuracies of the geostrophic approximation of the baroclinic representation of flow. An intense eddy can thus appear weak in the charts analyzed, and *vice versa*.

SOUTHERN CALIFORNIA EDDY

The SC Eddy is the most resolvable of the eddies in the California Current System by virtue of its large scale and degree of permanence, which usually exceed the mesh and frequency of CalCOFI grid observations. Examples of eddies at least as large and intense as the SC Eddy are found in the main flow of the California Current (*e.g.*, Wyllie 1966), but have not been measured in further detail because of their transitory character.

One of the better examples given by Wyllie (1966) from the CalCOFI data is shown in Figure

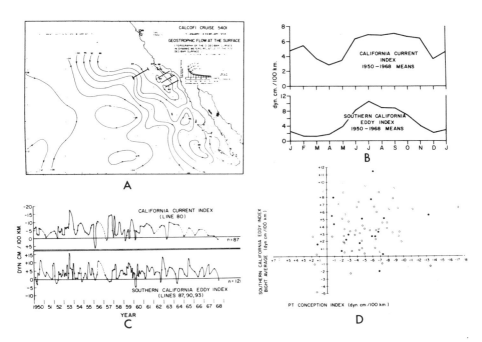

FIGURE 12. *Indices of baroclinic flow across sections (Panel A) off Point Conception (Panel B and C upper) and in the SC Eddy (Panel B and C lower), and the relationship between individual index pairs (Panel D). Indices derived from Wyllie (1966) by the author.*

11. The pattern of the SC Eddy (boxed) was augmented by the surfaced coastal countercurrent in this period (July 1958). Offshore, the eddy was augmented by a southwest-flowing, jet-like intensification of the California Current, which appears to have spawned two offshore eddies (one 200 km west of Point Conception and one centered near Guadalupe Island).

The SC Eddy, from Wyllie (1966) and Figure 12, Panel C, was present in every year (1949 to 1964) from July through January. From February through May, the time of the spring phytoplankton boom and the spawning of the northern anchovy (*Engraulis mordax*), the SC Eddy may periodically disappear for a month or more, flushing the surface waters of the SC Bight. Flushing is episodic in character, but most frequent in April (3 of 13 cases). The eddy may also "dissolve" in the baroclinic representation to an indeterminate field of weak flow. Such dissolution occurs in the same season as does flushing (again, 3 of 13 cases are in April). The eddy usually persists, however, in the absence of the surface countercurrent. This typically occurs in April to May, a period when the intensified California Current overrides the coastal countercurrent, to paraphrase Wyllie (1966). This pattern of events is supported by independent conclusions from drift bottle release and return statistics (Schwartzlose 1962, Squire 1977), and by the intensity of the SC Eddy, as I will now discuss.

The SC Eddy affords the best conditions for estimating changes in eddy flow intensity. Its stationary location and usual large size permit use of CalCOFI survey measurements to characterize two aspects of its flow: southward impinging flow off Point Conception, and the return flow of the inshore limb of the eddy. I computed indices of circulation strength from CalCOFI cruise measurements of the baroclinic slope of the sea surface (0/500 db; Wyllie 1966) across sections defined in Figure 12, Panel A. I chose these sections to show variations of strength of the California Current off Point Conception (northernmost section) and of the inshore limb of the SC Eddy and SC Countercurrent, when present (mean value of seaward slope across the three lower sections). Slopes shoreward of the index sections were not included in the eddy slope means to avoid effects of boundary instabilities associated with upwelling, nor were those off Point Conception to avoid including as well the effect of the Davidson Current, when present. The average annual cycle of flow past Point Conception in the period 1950 to 1968 (Fig. 12, Panel B, upper) is seen to be regular and to agree with the cycle and magnitude of circulation of the SC Eddy (Panel B, lower), which might be expected if the impinging flow drives the eddy, as noted by Pavlova (1966). The seasonal cycle of average surface flow impinging on the SC Bight (Panel B, upper) is in essential agreement with results of Reid (1965); offshore southward flow occurs all year off Point Conception and is strongest from May through November and weakest in spring. Circulation strength of the SC Eddy, as measured by flow of its inshore limb, is seen in Panel B to be greatest from June through October and least from December through April. Reid (1965) notes that the eddy's inshore limb develops to such a degree that it rounds Point Conception from October through January, and then constitutes a coastal countercurrent. He also shows that the Northern Channel Islands usually experience seasonal reversals of current direction due to their inclusion in the eddy's inshore limb from July through February.

Examination of flow across these sections month by month and year by year adds a perspective of the effects of eddies and meanders on flow estimation and indicates a high frequency of eddies imbedded in the mean flow to and through the Channel Island system. The time sequence of individual flow estimates, shown in Panel C of Figure 12, reveals a degree of variation in both incident and eddy flow intensity which is not apparent in the plots of averaged flow values of Panel B. This is because transient baroclinic-scale eddies and meanders detected in the flow are suppressed upon averaging. The fluctuations of individual indices in Panel C are caused by perturbations large enough to affect the field of mass, since the flow estimates were derived from the distribution of mass. Eddies or meanders of less than about 10 km radius (of curvature) or 5 days duration are unlikely to produce a detectable change in the mass field. The plots of Figure 12, therefore, reflect the abundance of eddies exceeding these dimensions.

Owing in part to the effects of eddies and meanders *not* reflected in the indices, it is difficult to predict flow intensity at a particular time and to specify the particular response of the SC Eddy to changes in impinging flow intensity. This is shown by the scatter of data points in Panel D of Figure 12.

PACIFIC EDDY COMPARISONS

It is of interest to compare SC Eddy characteristics with those of large eddies elsewhere in the Pacific, some of which have been investigated more intensively. A documented example of baroclinic doming and upwelling is provided by the Costa Rica Dome, produced by a major northward deflection of the North Equatorial Countercurrent as it impinges on the American continent (Wyrtki 1964). The dome is located in the bight of this deflection in a region where nutrients and thermocline both are close to the photic depth (Brandhorst 1958, Thomas 1970, Owen and Zeitzschel 1970a). Its physical characteristics denote a stationary, cyclonic eddy large enough to demonstrate nutrient enrichment effects (Brandhorst 1958, Broenkow 1965, Thomas 1970, 1977) and the responses of phytoplankton, zooplankton, and small nekton stocks (Blackburn *et al.* 1970, Owen and Zeitzschel 1970b, and references above).

A contrasting case is provided by the Hawaii Eddy phenomenon described previously. Despite the large vertical displacement (50 to 150 m) of the thermocline that is attributable to doming by the eddy (Patzert 1970), nutrient-rich waters lie deep. For enrichment of the photic zone to occur, water deeper than about 300 m would have to be raised more than 200 m to reach the bottom of the photic zone. McGary (1955) consequently found no evidence for photic zone enrichment that could be attributed to the Hawaii Eddy. Other significant biological processes are, however, evidently affected by the Hawaii Eddy; Sette (1955) describes evidence for the effect of the eddy on local fish populations.

Uda and Ishino (1958) have identified patterns of enrichment resulting from eddy systems off Japan comparable in scale and persistence to those off the Californias and Costa Rica. Areas of high concentrations of commercially and ecologically important fish, squid, whales, plankton, and benthic fauna were found to coincide with areas of high eddy activity, both near and far from land boundaries. Uda and Ishino distinguished between topographical eddy systems (those affected by topography) and dynamic eddy systems (those affected by current "collision").

Table 2 gives estimated magnitudes of various properties of the SC Eddy, together with reported magnitudes of California coastal upwelling and of other large eddy systems in the Pacific. As may be seen in the geostrophic flow atlas (Wyllie 1966), the SC Eddy may deviate from Table 2 values of size and circulation strength.   This is caused in part by change in the obstacle profile confronting the current when changes occur in either the direction or depth span of the impinging flow.

Several comparisons of magnitude estimates in Table 2 are worth comment. Despite the varying eddy sizes, intensities, and vertical velocities, transport by upwelling is of the same order of magnitude in the SC Eddy, Hawaii Eddy, Costa Rica Dome, and in a segment of the coastal upwelling domain 200 km in length (the same distance along the California coast usually subtended by the SC Eddy). As may be seen from ambient nutricline and photic depths, nutrients are readily available for transfer up through the photic zone in all areas considered, except off Hawaii. The degree of enrichment and subsequent productivity of the SC Eddy is probably comparable, therefore, to that of other major eddy systems. The SC Eddy appears only slightly less effective in total transport of nutrients into the photic zone than does upwelling along a comparable length of the California coastline, although SC Eddy nutrients are transported into about three times the volume. Such ecological impact is enhanced by the role of the SC Eddy as an oceanic reservoir for washout of coastal and upwelling products from the Southern California Bight, as well as from Point Conception and farther north.

ECOLOGICAL EFFECTS OF THE SOUTHERN CALIFORNIA EDDY

Several biological effects of the SC Eddy have been identified in studies of phytoplankton concentrations and communities, zooplankton, and fish populations. Allen (1945) examined vernal distribution of diatom populations and abundances in the upper 60 m over the SC Bight in relation to baroclinic flow and bathymetry. The area of the Santa Rosa-Cortez Ridge system above 200 m depth is treated as an obstacle. Allen indicates local topographic control of both current patterns and of diatom abundance on a relatively intensified sampling grid (25-km spacing, six cruises in three months). He presents spatial variations of diatom concentrations ranging over five orders of magnitude in patterns which support his hypothesis that higher diatom concentrations occur off the Santa Rosa-Cortez Ridge axis, partly due to washdown of coastal upwelling from the north. The ridge axis usually defines that of the SC Eddy.

Sargent and Walker (1948), from a similar data set, examined patterns of abundance of several diatom populations sampled in the upper 60 m in and beyond the SC Bight. They considered these populations to be closely associated with what they treated as "cyclonic eddies of freshly upwelled water entering the area of observation from the north" (off Point Conception), which appear identical in size and persistence to the SC Eddy. Greater abundance of

TABLE 2. Parameters of Pacific eddies and California coastal upwelling.

	Southern California Eddy[1]	Johnson Atoll[2]	Hawaii Eddy[3]	Costa Rica Dome[4]	Small CCS Eddy[5]	California coastal upwelling[6]
Obstacle diameter (km)	200	26	100 (wind) 300 (current)	—	—	200 (length†)
Eddy type	stationary, topographic-dynamic	vortex street	wind-forced	free, stationary	free, stationary	(edge eddies)
Ambient* or incident flow (cm/sec)	20	60	30	55	20	20
Eddy flow (cm/sec) at 1/2 radius	30	80	50	40	20	—
Radius (km)	100	30	65	200	40	—
Decay time (days to 1/e)	100	16	>65	—	>14	14
Vertical velocity (m/day)	0.3	—	0.8 (initial)	0.1	—	1.0
Upwelling volume (m³/day)	10^{10}	—	10^{10}	10^{10}	—	10^{10}†
Pycnocline elevation $\left(\frac{\text{ambient-dome}}{\text{ambient}}\right)$	0.3-0.5	—	0.4	0.7	0.1	0.4-0.6
Ambient* photic depth (m)	60	100	100	70	70	60
Ambient* nutricline depth (m)	30-70	75	300	40	40	20-60

Sources: [1] McEwen 1948; Wyllie 1966; Wyllie and Lynn 1971; Owen 1974.
[2] Barkley 1972; Frederick 1970.
[3] Patzert 1970; McGary 1955; Frederick 1970.
[4] Wyrtki 1964; Broenkow 1965; Bennett 1963; Owen and Zeitzschel 1970a.
[5] Reid et al. 1963; Owen and Sanchez 1974.
[6] Bakun 1973; Walsh et al. 1974; McEwen 1948; Wyllie and Lynn 1971; Arthur 1965; Sverdrup and Fleming 1941; Owen and Sanchez 1974.
* "Ambient" refers to condition in absence of phenomenon.
† 200-km coastal strip 50 km wide for comparison with SC Eddy.

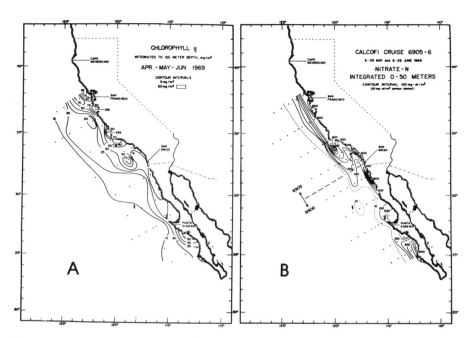

FIGURE 13. *Total chlorophyll* a *(mg/m²) to 150 m depth (Panel A, Owen 1974, p. 107) and total nitrate-nitrogen to 50 m depth (Panel B, Thomas and Seibert 1974, p. 37) off the Californias in spring 1969.*

several diatom populations in the offshore limb of the eddy was attributed to entraining of upwelled water north of Point Conception. Diminished abundances in the inshore limb were ascribed to nutrient depletion and grazing as the phytoplankton circuited the eddy. Change in phytoplankton community composition was also detected as the populations circuited the eddy, consistent with Allen's (1945) distinction between diatom communities inshore and seaward of the Santa Rosa-Cortez Ridge.

Spatial variation of community structure and of population densities is enhanced by the SC Eddy. Succession of community composition occurs along flow streamlines; where such streamlines are closed, as in the SC Eddy, successive communities are inevitably juxtaposed. This is apparent from the work cited above, which suggests a change in time and space from a diatom species ensemble characteristic of recent coastal upwelling to an ensemble characteristic of older surface-layer waters. Due to the SC Eddy, these ensembles were spatially juxtaposed in what may prove to be a characteristic state. This state demonstrates (perhaps more crudely than actually occurs) the creation of community patchiness by stirring, as defined by Eckart (1948), and is not necessarily confined to the phytoplankton alone.

Patterns of high phytoplankton concentration which correspond to those of the SC Eddy are shown by Owen (1974) and by Owen and Sanchez (1974) in terms of surface and depth-integrated chlorophyll *a* concentrations (Fig. 13, Panel A). These corresponded with patterns of surface-layer nutrient distribution of Thomas and Seibert (1974) at times when the SC Eddy was fully developed (Panel B). Together with the evidence for high persistence of the SC Eddy, these studies confirm that the effects observed by Allen and by Sargent and Walker are characteristic (rather than episodic) in the SC Bight. Primary production measurements in the SC Bight are too sparse to demonstrate an enrichment effect of the SC Eddy. A single transect of such measurements across the SC Bight (Owen 1974) showed primary production to be about six times greater in the SC Eddy than beyond it.

Brinton (1976) studied the population biology of *Euphausia pacifica*, the dominant species among the larger zooplankton of the SC Bight. He identified the SC Eddy and its associated upwelling regimes as a productive refuge for an identifiable population of the species.

Benthic-dwelling organisms with planktonic life history stages (usually larval) depend for population maintenance on being deposited, at the end of their planktonic stage, in waters shoal enough to permit their survival on the sea bottom. Off the Californias, where flow frequently diverges from the coast, such populations must depend on eddies and meanders in the mean flow to return a sufficient number of their meroplankton to the habitat. Although the SC Eddy is not cited in particular, examples include populations of the spiny lobster, *Panulirus interruptus* (Johnson 1960), and the red crab, *Pleuroncodes planipes* (Longhurst 1968). Both organisms spend extended periods as plankton in their early life history.

During spawning in the 1941 season, a population of the now decimated California sardine (*Sardinops caerulea*) was shown from plankton surveys (Sette and Ahlstrom 1948) to have concentrated its eggs and larvae in an area corresponding closely to that of the SC Eddy and its elevated diatom densities (Sargent and Walker 1948). Figure 14 shows this striking local correspondence, which suggests the possible sensitivity of the sardine stock to the SC Eddy. The surveys did not cover the entire range of spawning, however, and it is possible that other eddies beyond the SC Bight may have supported undetected spawning areas.

Since the replacement of the California sardine stocks by those of the northern anchovy (*Engraulis mordax*), CalCOFI plankton surveys have covered the spawning time and area of the anchovy. These have revealed (Smith 1978) that the region inclusive of the SC Eddy, comprising about 12 per cent of the spawning area of the anchovy's central subpopulation, contained, on the average, 48 per cent of the spawned larvae during the period 1951 to 1975; since 1966 this region has contained 64 per cent.

Berner (1959), in his study of food of anchovy larvae, noted that areas where larvae were found to be actively feeding corresponded to those of the copepod nauplii maximum, as described by D. K. Arthur (1956). Comparison of areas of active larval feeding in the SC Bight with corresponding charts of baroclinic flow (Wyllie 1966) shows that the area of feeding larvae corresponded with the inshore limb of the SC Eddy, although D.K. Arthur (1977) subsequently showed that the copepod nauplii maximum may also lie on the SC Eddy axis or in its offshore limb.

SUMMARY

Owing to the rapid attenuation of sunlight with water depth, over half of the total primary production of food in the offshore CCS occurs in the surface mixed layer, 10 to 60 m deep. The primary supply of inorganic nutrients to the mixed layer is from below. Lateral transport in the mixed layer imports virtually no inorganic nutrients, except directly from coastal upwelling zones, because the phytoplankton communities of the northeastern Pacific can strip the mixed layer of extant nutrients in only a few days. Local regeneration of nutrients from mixed-layer organics is known to be a nutrient source for sustaining phytoplankton growth under otherwise impoverished conditions, but has not been proposed to sustain the higher levels of production characteristic of the CCS off California. Southward transport of the California Current imports nutrients at depth and, at the same time, creates the shoreward upslope of the thermocline layer that makes possible enrichment of the mixed layer and photic zone. Actual transfer of nutrients

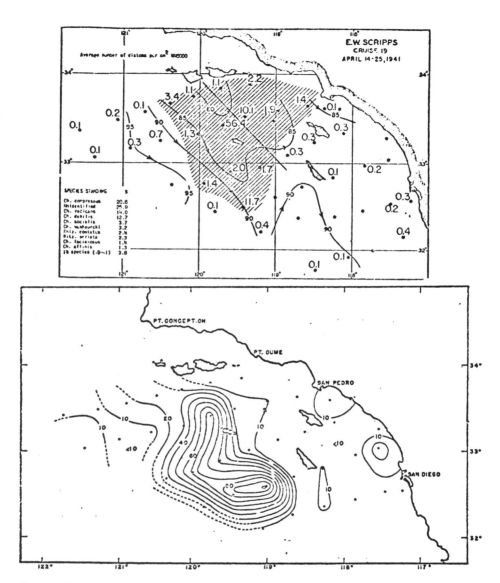

FIGURE 14. (*top*) *Distribution of diatoms and baroclinic flow in April 1941. Hatching denotes area of higher diatom abundance. Per cent contribution to total diatoms given beside each sampling location (Sargent and Walker 1948, fig. 1). (* **bottom***) Distribution and concentration of sardine eggs over the spring 1941 spawning season. Values on isopleths are number of eggs under 10 m² of sea surface (Sette and Ahlstrom 1948, fig. 4).*

to the mixed layer at high rates is episodic. The best known episodic fertilization process is wind-driven coastal upwelling; direct effects of strong upwelling are detectable to 50 km offshore, farther off capes, and perhaps farther yet if edge-eddies transport large, cold volumes offshore. The upward transport of nutrients in the SC Eddy can evidently approach that of the coastal upwelling strip. Although injected into a larger volume of water than in coastal upwelling, nutrient enrichment by the SC Eddy is continuous rather than episodic since the SC Eddy is a persistent feature of the region. Eddies of comparable enrichment potential are usually present elsewhere in the CCS, and small eddies are commonplace. Due to their transitory nature, they are difficult to study and their ecological impacts are thus undocumented. The cyclonic eddies of the CCS nevertheless are likely to be an important and variable determinant of the standing stocks, productivity, and community structure of life in the CCS, and particularly in the SC Bight.

ACKNOWLEDGMENTS

I wish to thank the following people for their help with this work and their interest in it: R. Lynn, R. Lasker, J. Hunter, P. Smith, S. Commerford, C. Kimbrell, and K. Coleman. I wish also to acknowledge the technicians and administrators of the Data Collection and Processing Group of Scripps Institution of Oceanography and their counterparts at NOAA-Southwest Fisheries Center, who have provided high-quality data since the 1940s on the physical and biological behavior of the ocean off the Californias.

REFERENCES

ALLAN HANCOCK FOUNDATION, UNIVERSITY OF SOUTHERN CALIFORNIA. 1965. An oceanographic and biological survey of the southern California mainland shelf. California State Water Quality Control Board, Publ. 27.

ALLEN, W. E. 1945. Vernal distribution of marine plankton diatoms offshore in southern California in 1940. Bull. Scripps Inst. Oceanogr. 5:335-369.

ARTHUR, D. K. 1956. The particulate food and the food resources of the larvae of three pelagic fishes, especially the Pacific sardine, *Sardinops caerulea* (Girard). Ph.D. thesis, University of California, Scripps Institution of Oceanography, La Jolla, Calif.

———. 1977. Distribution, size and abundance of microcopepods in the California Current System and their possible influence on survival of marine teleost larvae. Fish. Bull., U.S. 75:601-611.

ARTHUR, R. S. 1965. On the calculation of vertical motion in eastern boundary currents from determinations of horizontal motion. J. Geophys. Res. 70:2799-2803.

BAKUN, A. 1973. Coastal upwelling indices, west coast of North America, 1946-71. NOAA Tech. Rep. NMFS SSRF-671.

BARKLEY, R. A. 1968. The Kuroshio-Oyashio front as a compound vortex street. J. Marine Res. 26:83-104.

———. 1972. Johnston Atoll's wake. J. Marine Res. 30:201-216.

BENNETT, E. B. 1963. An oceanographic atlas of the eastern tropical Pacific Ocean, based on data from EASTROPIC expedition, Oct.-Dec. 1955. Bull. Inter-Amer. Trop. Tuna Comm. 8:33-165.

BERGER, E., and R. WILLE. 1972. Periodic flow phenomena. Ann. Rev. Fluid Mech. 4:313-340.

BERNER, L., JR. 1959. Food of the larvae of the northern anchovy *Engraulis mordax*. Bull. Inter-Amer. Trop. Tuna Comm. 4:3-22.

BERNSTEIN, R. L., and W. B. WHITE. 1974. Time and length scales of baroclinic eddies in the central north Pacific Ocean. J. Phys. Oceanogr. 4:613-624.

BERNSTEIN, R. L., L. BREAKER, and R. WHRITNER. 1977. California Current eddy formation: ship, air and satellite results. Science 195:353-359.

BLACKBURN, M. 1966. Biological oceanography of the eastern tropical Pacific: summary of existing information. U.S. Fish Wildl. Serv. SSRF-540:1-18.

BLACKBURN, M., R. M. LAURS, R. W. OWEN, and B. ZEITZSCHEL. 1970. Seasonal and areal changes in standing stocks of phytoplankton, zooplankton, and micronekton in the eastern tropical Pacific. Marine Biol. 7:14-31.

BRANDHORST, W. 1958. Thermocline topography, zooplankton standing crop, and mechanisms of fertilization in the eastern tropical Pacific. J. Cons. Perm. Int. Explor. Mer. 24:16-31.

BRINTON, E. 1976. Population biology of *Euphausia pacifica* off southern California. Fish. Bull., U.S. 74:733-762.

BROENKOW, W. W. 1965. Nutrient distribution in the Costa Rica Dome in the eastern tropical Pacific Ocean. Limnol. Oceanogr. 10:40-52.

CHOPRA, K. P. 1973. Atmospheric and oceanic flow problems introduced by islands. Adv. Geophysics 16:297-421.

ECKART, C. 1948. An analysis of the stirring and mixing processes in incompressible fluids. J. Marine Res. 7:265-275.

EKMAN, V. W. 1905. On the influence of the earth's rotation on ocean currents. Ark. Mat. Astr. Fys. 2:1-52.

EMERY, K. O. 1958. Shallow submerged marine terraces off southern California. Geol. Soc. Amer. Bull. 69:39-60.

FORSBERGH, E. D. 1964. Biological production in the eastern Pacific Ocean. Bull. Inter-Amer. Trop. Tuna Comm. 9:479-527.

FREDERICK, M. A. 1970. An atlas of Secchi disc transparency measurements and Forel-Ule color codes for the oceans of the world. Thesis, U.S. Naval Postgraduate School.

HENDRICKS, T. 1979. *In* City of San Diego application to EPA for waiver of secondary treatment requirements for ocean discharges of municipal wastewaters.

JOHNSON, M. W. 1960. Production and distribution of the larvae of the spiny lobster *Panulirus interruptus* (Randall) with records on *P. gracilis* Streets. Bull. Scripps Inst. Oceanogr. 7:413-462.

KNAUSS, J. A. 1962. Observations of internal waves of tidal period made with neutrally-buoyant floats. J. Marine Res. 20:111-118.

LAM, R. K. 1972. Current measurements off the California coast—1972. Scripps Inst. Oceanogr. Ref. 74/12.

LASKER, R. 1975. Field criteria for survival of larval anchovy: the relation between inshore chlorophyll maximum layers and successful first feeding. Fish. Bull., U.S. 73:453-462.

LONGHURST, A. R. 1968. Distribution of the larvae of *Pleuroncodes planipes* in the California Current. Limnol. Oceanogr. 13:143-155.

MACGREGOR, J. S. 1974. Changes in the amount and proportions of DDT and its metabolites, DDE and DDD, in the marine environment off southern California, 1949-1972. Fish. Bull., U.S. 72:275-293.

MCEWEN, G. F. 1948. The dynamics of large horizontal eddies (axes vertical) in the ocean off southern California. J. Marine Res. 7:188-216.

MCGARY, J. W. 1955. Mid-Pacific oceanography. Part VI. Hawaiian offshore waters, Dec. 1949-Nov. 1951. U.S. Fish Wildl. Serv. SSRF-152.

MUNK, W. H. 1950. On the wind-driven ocean circulation. J. Meteorol. 7:79-93.

NELSON, C. S. 1977. Wind stress and wind stress curl over the California Current. NOAA Tech. Rep. NMFS SSRF-714.

OWEN, R. W. 1974. Distribution of primary production, plant pigments and Secchi depth in the California Current region, 1969. *In* A. Fleminger and J. G. Wyllie, eds., California Coop. Oceanic Fish. Invest. Atlas 20.

OWEN, R. W., and C. K. SANCHEZ. 1974. Phytoplankton pigment and production measurements in the California Current region, 1969-1972. NOAA-NMFS Data Rep. 91.

OWEN, R. W., and B. ZEITZSCHEL. 1970a. Phytoplankton standing stocks and production. Pp. 9-10 *in* C. M. Love, ed., EASTROPAC Atlas. NOAA-NMFS Circ. 330(4).

——. 1970b. Phytoplankton production: seasonal change in the oceanic eastern tropical Pacific. Marine Biol. 7:32-36.

PATZERT, W. C. 1970. Eddies in Hawaiian waters. Hawaii Inst. Geophys. Rep. 69-8.

PAVLOVA, YU. V. 1966. Seasonal variations of the California Current. Oceanology 6:806-814.

REID, J. L., JR. 1961. On the geostrophic flow at the surface of the Pacific Ocean with respect to the 1000-decibar surface. Tellus 13:489-502.

——. 1963. Measurements of the California Countercurrent off Baja California. J. Geophys. Res. 68:4819-4822.

——. 1965. Physical oceanography of the region near Point Arguello. Univ. California Inst. Marine Res., Ref. 65-19.

REID, J. L., JR., G. I. RODEN, and J. G. WYLLIE. 1958. Studies of the California Current System. California Coop. Oceanic Fish. Invest. Rep., 1 July 1956 to 1 Jan. 1958.

REID, J. L., JR., and R. A. SCHWARTZLOSE. 1962. Direct measurements of the Davidson Current off central California. J. Geophys. Res. 67:2491-2497.

REID, J. L., JR., R. A. SCHWARTZLOSE, and D. M. BROWN. 1963. Direct measurements of a small surface eddy off northern Baja California. J. Marine Res. 21:205-218.

ROUSE, H. 1963. On the role of eddies in fluid motion. Amer. Sci. 51:284-314.

SARGENT, M. C., and T. J. WALKER. 1948. Diatom populations associated with eddies off southern California in 1941. J. Marine Res. 7:490-505.

SCHWARTZLOSE, R. A. 1962. Nearshore currents of the western United States and Baja California as measured by drift bottles. Part 2. Scientific contributions. California Coop. Oceanic Fish. Invest. Rep., 1 July 1960 to 30 June 1962.

SCRIPPS INSTITUTION OF OCEANOGRAPHY. 1962. Results of current measurements with drogues. Data rep., Scripps Inst. Oceanogr. Ref. 62-27.

SETTE, O. E. 1955. Consideration of midocean fish production as related to oceanic circulatory systems. J. Marine Res. 14:398-414.

SETTE, O. E., and E. H. AHLSTROM. 1948. Estimations of abundance of the eggs of the Pacific pilchard (*Sardinops caerulea*) off southern California during 1940 and 1941. J. Marine Res. 7:511-542.

SHEPARD, F. P., and K. O. EMERY. 1941. Submarine topography off the California coast: canyons and tectonic interpretations. Geol. Soc. Amer., Spec. Paper 31.

SMITH, P. E. 1978. Central subpopulation northern anchovy: first order corrections for missing region and month survey effort. NMFS-Southwest Fisheries Center Admin. Rep. LJ-78-2.

SQUIRE, J. L., JR. 1977. Surface currents as determined by drift card releases over the continental shelf off central and southern California. NOAA Tech. Rep. NMFS SSRF-718.

SVERDRUP, H. U. 1947. Wind-driven currents in a baroclinic ocean; with application to the equatorial currents of the eastern Pacific. Proc. Natl. Acad. Sci. 33:318-326.

SVERDRUP, H. U., and R. H. FLEMING. 1941. The waters off the coast of southern California, March to July 1937. Bull. Scripps Inst. Oceanogr. 4:261-378.

THOMAS, W. H. 1970. Nutrient chemistry. *In* C. M. Love, ed., EASTROPAC Atlas. NOAA-NMFS Circ. 330.

————. 1977. Nutrient-phytoplankton interrelationships in the eastern tropical Pacific Ocean. Bull. Inter-Amer. Trop. Tuna Comm. 17:173-212.

THOMAS, W. H., and D. L. R. SEIBERT. 1974. Distribution of nitrate, nitrite, phosphate and silicate in the California Current region, 1969. *In* A. Fleminger and J. G. Wyllie, eds., California Coop. Oceanic Fish. Invest. Atlas 20.

UDA, M., and M. ISHINO. 1958. Enrichment pattern resulting from eddy systems in relation to fishing grounds. J. Tokyo Univ. Fish. 44:105-129.

U.S. DEPARTMENT OF THE INTERIOR. 1978. Draft environmental statement, OCS sale no. 48. Proposed 1979 outer continental shelf oil and gas lease sale, offshore southern California, v. 1.

VAN DORN, W. G., P. W. HACKER, and R. K. LAM. 1967. Circulation around oceanic islands. Scripps Inst. Oceanogr. Ref. 67-34.

VON ARX, W. S. 1962. Introduction to physical oceanography. Addison-Wesley, London.

WALSH, J. J., J. C. KELLEY, T. E. WHITLEDGE, and J. J. MACISAAC. 1974. Spin-up of the Baja California upwelling ecosystem. Limnol. Oceanogr. 19:553-572.

WHITE, W. B. 1971a. A Rossby wake due to an island in an eastward current. J. Phys. Oceanogr. 1:161-165.

————. 1971b. Reply. J. Phys. Oceanogr. 1:285-289.

————. 1973a. An oceanic wake in the equatorial undercurrent downstream from the Galapagos Archipelago. J. Phys. Oceanogr. 3:156-161.

————. 1973b. Reply. J. Phys. Oceanogr. 3:351-352.

WYLLIE, J. 1966. Geostrophic flow of the California Current at the surface and at 200 meters. California Coop. Oceanic Fish. Invest. Atlas 4.

WYLLIE, J. G., and R. J. LYNN. 1971. Distribution of temperature and salinity at 10 meters, 1960-1969, and mean temperature, salinity and oxygen at 150 meters, 1950-1968, in the California Current. California Coop. Oceanic Fish. Invest. Atlas 15.

WYRTKI, K. 1964. Upwelling in the Costa Rica Dome. Fish Bull., U.S. 63:355-372.

Overview of the Rocky Intertidal Systems of Southern California

Mark M. Littler

Department of Ecology and Evolutionary Biology,
University of California, Irvine, California 92717

INTRODUCTION

The Southern California Bight (Fig. 1) has been defined (SCCWRP 1973) as the open embayment of the Pacific Ocean bounded on the east by the North American coastline extending from Point Conception, California, to Cabo Colnett, Baja California, Mexico, and on the west by the California Current. The climate of the Southern California Bight has been amply studied in quantitative terms and is relatively well known (for physical, air, and seawater data, see Kimura 1974). Wind conditions are extremely important in that major reversals occur predominantly throughout late fall and winter. This results in strong, hot, and dry "Santa Ana" winds from the inland desert regions at the time of low tides during the daylight hours, thereby causing extreme heating, desiccation, and insolation stress to intertidal organisms. Another important ecological factor is the protection of certain mainland shores and the mainland sides of islands from open ocean swell and storm waves. This leads to a higher wave-energy regime on the unprotected outer island shores with marked effects on their biological communities. Nearly all of the southern California mainland coastline is protected to some degree by the outlying islands (Ricketts, Calvin, and Hedgpeth 1968). The only mainland sites receiving direct westerly swell are near the cities of Los Angeles and San Diego. A number of substrate types were present among the 10 rocky intertidal habitats studied (Fig. 1), ranging from hard, irregular flow breccia to smooth sandstone or siltstone. Some sites were heavily influenced by sand which inundates and removes organisms. The presence of extensive loose boulder fields at some habitats constitutes another form of environmental instability limiting community development. The existence of such natural disturbances has important implications in interpreting changes associated with petroleum exploration and development. Cockerell (1939) was among the first to point out that the region, especially near the Northern Channel Islands, is remarkable for the impingement and mixing of both cold and warm waters, and is thus comparable in certain respects to such diverse regions as the Galapagos Islands. For example, Santa Cruz Island is periodically exposed to both cold and warm currents, San Clemente Island lies in relatively warm southern waters, while the cold California Current impinges on San Nicolas Island throughout much of the year (Neushul, Clarke, and Brown 1967). These climatic, physical, and hydrographic variations result in a complex intermingling of environmental conditions that are reflected in the diversity of marine biota in the Bight.

The rocky intertidal shoreline of southern California's mainland is subjected to exceptionally intense usage by a concentrated, recreation-oriented human population; this creates some unique conservational problems. The often excessive usage (*e.g.*, collecting, beachcombing, tidepooling, field trip outings) may stress this interface between land, sea, and air, making it particularly sensitive to additional forms of disturbance.

Previous compilations of review data on the Southern California Bight included information on intertidal macrophytes (Murray 1974) and macroinvertebrates (Bright 1974). These reviews pointed out the remarkable paucity of information regarding the ecology of southern California's rocky seashores. Of the limited data base, the most widely used information was generated during the studies of Dawson (1959, 1965) on marine macrophytes. Dawson noted

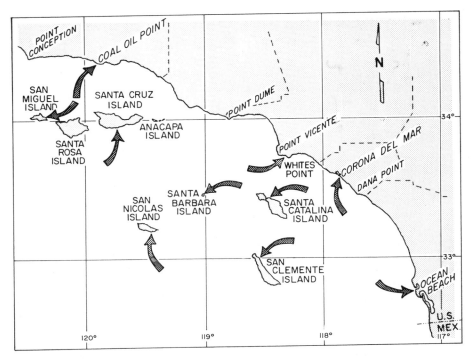

FIGURE 1. *Location of the 10 study areas (arrows) within the Southern California Bight.*

reductions in species numbers ranging from 50 to 70 per cent at sites near sewage outfalls. Others (*e.g.,* Nicholson and Cimberg 1971, Widdowson 1971, Thom 1976) have since measured further declines in macrophyte species numbers at some of the same sites studied by Dawson. They attributed such declines to human influence but presented only correlative evidence as documentation. Such declines do not seem to have been instantaneous, as pointed out by Nicholson (1972), but probably are the result of human pressures that have been increasing markedly since the turn of the century. With the further expansion of the human population in southern California, even the marine communities of some of the relatively inaccessible offshore Channel Islands (*e.g.,* Anacapa Island) are being altered by visitor trampling and collecting (Littler 1978).

The marine ecosystems of the Southern California Islands are virtually unknown to science. Although limited taxonomic lists have been published for Anacapa, Santa Catalina, Santa Cruz, and San Clemente Islands (Hewatt 1946, Dawson and Neushul 1966, Neushul, Clarke, and Brown 1967, Sims 1974, Seapy 1974, Dawson 1949, Nicholson and Cimberg 1971), quantitative data are available only for San Nicolas Island (Caplan and Boolootian 1967), Anacapa Island (Neushul, Clarke, and Brown 1967), and San Clemente Island (Littler and Murray 1974, 1975, 1978, Murray and Littler 1978, Kindig and Littler in press).

The cumulative effects of environmental degradation and a general lack of proper baseline information have posed severe problems, particularly during the last 10 years when attempts have been made to assess the immediate effects of specific pollutants on southern Californian coastal organisms. These problems were glaringly obvious (*e.g.,* Nicholson and Cimberg 1971,

Straughan 1971, Foster, Neushul, and Zingmark 1971, Cimberg, Mann, and Straughan 1973) in the attempts to evaluate effects of the Santa Barbara oil spills of 1969 on mainland intertidal populations. The research reported here was explicitly responsive to the specifications and requirements dictated by the Bureau of Land Management, U.S. Department of the Interior. The ongoing purpose of this program is to establish quantitatively reliable and reproducible baseline assessments of the distribution and abundance of rocky intertidal organisms. Both field and laboratory efforts were directed toward the determination of the kinds and levels of biological variation shown by six island and four mainland ecosystems. Within this framework, sites were selected to reflect the major ecological systems throughout the Bight.

This paper is the product of comprehensive investigations during 1975-76 into the following three aspects of study: (1) taxonomic and systematic studies of the macroepibiota, (2) determinations of the seasonal distribution and abundance patterns in macrophyte and macroinvertebrate standing stocks, and (3) temporal and spatial analysis of variation in community organization. No comparable spectrum of rocky intertidal systems has been examined with the level of sampling effort and resolution of data undertaken in this research program. The scope of this work is such that temporal and spatial variations of the macroinvertebrate and macrophyte populations have been assessed in terms of tidal location, cover, frequency, density, wet weight, dry weight, ash-free dry weight, species diversity, evenness, richness, and species assemblages. These descriptive parameters were used at each of 10 representative sites during four separate quarters of the year to characterize a range of intertidal systems and to relate important aspects of distribution and abundance to possible causal (biotic and abiotic) features of the environment.

This paper attempts to place in perspective the salient features within each study area, contrasts the 10 sites, and discusses overall patterns and trends. In the last regard, it is appreciated that habitats having markedly different substrates, environmental regimes, and levels of human stress would be expected to differ greatly; comparisons or interpretations without supportive experimental data must be viewed as preliminary.

The design of the study was such that trends and correlative insights might begin to be drawn through intensive seasonal studies of a few sites selected to be as representative as possible. Generalizations concerning the specific degree to which our study sites are characteristic of intertidal systems throughout the Bight are contingent upon a more synoptic approach to sampling. Such an approach has been taken during our 1977-78 program and it has become apparent that the 10 sites reported here are characteristic of the major intertidal systems. The mainland areas studied were exposed to relatively more human-induced stresses, but we felt that, with few exceptions, this is characteristic of the more prominent rocky mainland sites in general. A baseline has not yet been established, particularly due to the exceptionally warm and dry winter experienced during 1975-76; under wetter or colder winter conditions, we would expect different patterns of seasonality.

METHODS AND MATERIALS

The intertidal study of mainland and island rocky shores consisted of: (1) taxonomic and systematic studies of the macroepibiota, (2) determinations of the seasonal distribution and abundance patterns of macrophyte and macroinvertebrate standing stocks, and (3) temporal and spatial analyses of variation in community organization. We have also developed programs to predict the ecological effects of disturbances as well as experimental studies that include: (1) the responses of intertidal communities to natural catastrophic events (such as storms, high surf conditions, sedimentation, and floods), (2) recovery rates and patterns of various communities at different times of the year at contrasting tidal heights following artificial disturbances (harvesting), (3) manipulative assessments of the role of possible key species populations, and

(4) the synoptic surveying of all island intertidal communities during daytime low tides by means of helicopter overflights and mapping techniques. This last study gives us considerable confidence that our 10 sites are indeed representative of major intertidal systems within the Southern California Bight. Although we have extensively used all of these methods over the last several years, only those methods and the data resulting from the 1975-76 baseline analysis of standing stock will be presented in this paper because of space limitations.

Standing Stock Data

Much of our knowledge of benthic marine organisms is based upon subjective observations, although some studies have employed "quasiquantitative" methods. Among such methods used previously in the field are those in which diagrammatic sketches within sample units are made and subsequently used to obtain estimates of abundance (e.g., Manton 1935, Abe 1937), those in which transect lines are used to visually estimate cover (e.g., Nicholson and Cimberg 1971, Widdowson 1971), and those that utilize metal grids (e.g., Caplan and Boolootian 1967) to assess visually the abundance of organisms. Such in situ assessments are usually time-consuming and often physically exhausting, thereby severely limiting the number of samples that can be taken within the field time available (e.g., during the low-tide cycle). A significant problem with all of these visually based in situ techniques is that of parallax (due to movement of the observer and organisms relative to the sampling devices) which has been shown (Littler 1971) to be an unsatisfactorily large source of error when measuring the cover of organisms.

The principal method of assessing the standing stocks of intertidal organisms during this study was a photographimetric technique of undisturbed sampling (modified from Littler 1971) which yields parallax-free samples that can be used to generate precisely detailed and highly reproducible quantitative information, i.e., cover, density (number of individual organisms per unit area), and frequency (percentage of sample plots in which a given species occurs). This method has the advantage of being rapid and simple to use, thus enabling a greater number of samples to be taken per unit of time. This technique, when used with infrared film, permits the quantification of blue-green algal cover, the predominant cover taxon in most rocky intertidal habitats. The system also permits a high degree of quality control because photo-samples scored by various individuals can be reviewed by the entire staff, including senior taxonomic personnel, to assure standardization and accuracy in the quantification process. The infrared photographs also emphasize unhealthy thalli (which have reduced chlorophyll contents that are often masked by accessory pigments) which would otherwise not be visible by color photography or to the unaided eye. Another important feature of the technique is that the photo-samples are permanent historic data sets which depict the status of the biota at a given point in time. Changes can easily be documented by direct comparison of photo-samples taken of the same quadrats at different times.

Quarterly sampling was accomplished at the 10 general areas shown in Figure 1. An overview of the tasks involved during each of the 40 site visits is elaborated upon in the account that follows. Two to four belt transects, 4 to 70 m apart as dictated by the steepness of the shoreline and topography, were laid perpendicular (by means of a sighting compass) to the waterline at each site from immediately above the highwater level of intertidal organisms to just below the waterline at low tide to provide locations for a minimum of 40 samples. The general location of each study site was determined by consulting aerial photographs and maps of the area. After extensive reconnaissance of each area, the precise location of the upper end of each transect was determined, by consensus of several experienced marine biologists, along a biologically representative part of the shoreline. To provide permanent sample locations, holes were drilled and eyebolts cemented into the substrate at the upper and lower ends of the transect tapes; this enabled the precise replacement of the transects during seasonal studies. A sampling optimization analysis employing the Poisson statistic (Wilson 1976) revealed that a minimum of 30 0.15-m² samples was required to adequately assess a typical rocky intertidal site. Consequently, no fewer than 40 rectangular quadrats, 30 cm x 50 cm (0.15 m²), and 40 square quadrats, 1.0 m x 1.0 m (1.0 m²), were placed along the transect tapes at 1.0 to 3.0-m intervals, depending upon the steepness of the shoreline, thereby providing permanent, stratified plots for sampling temporal and spatial distributions of organisms. To furnish statistically adequate representation, no fewer than four replicate quadrats of each size were represented in a given 0.3-m tidal interval whenever possible. This was done after the first site visit by adding quadrats to the immediate right and left sides (in some cases upper and lower sides) of quadrats known to be at tidal heights that were "under-sampled" due to the steepness of the shoreline. Tidepools were not discriminated against in positioning any of the quadrats; however, space does not permit their treatment here. The 1.0-m² quadrats were used to sample large macrophytes and the rarer forms of large invertebrate species. Quadrat locations were permanently marked with metal studs, epoxy putty, or eyebolts set in "hard-rock" cement.

Relative vertical tidal heights for each quadrat were measured from permanent reference points by means of a vertical leveling rod and a standard (20-power) surveyor's transit. A permanent reference point was established at each of the 10 study sites for surveying the tidal heights of the individual quadrats. The height of this reference point was determined in relation to mean lower low water (MLLW) by measuring, at six or more places along the shoreline, the midpoint between low and high wave peaks at the time of the predicted low tides (U.S. Department of Commerce 1975, 1976).

Repeatability of measurements checked on different site visits was ± 0.1 m. Throughout the program, considerable care was taken to minimize trampling and other forms of disturbance to the biotic communities under study.

Physical descriptions of each study site, including date, time, tidal stages, wave heights, air and water temperature, cloud cover, and salinity, were recorded at the time of each visit. Oceanographic literature and climatological data were used (Table 1), where available, to further characterize the respective environmental features of each study site.

Undisturbed Samples

Samples were obtained by photographing the numbered quadrats at right angles to the substrate with two cameras equipped with electronic flashes. Each quadrat contained a grey plastic label affixed to the upper left corner that was marked with a wax pencil to permanently identify each of the photo-samples. One camera contained 35-mm Kodachrome-64 slide film and the other contained Ektachrome infrared (IR) slide film.

Two miniature tape recorders and waterproof (polypropylene) data forms were used as a rapid method of taking field notes on the contents of the photo-samples. For every disturbed and undisturbed sample, a taxonomist recorded the taxa, counted the individual macroinvertebrates, and visually estimated the cover of each species in a detailed section-by-section format; each quadrat was subdivided into 20 equal subsections. It is worthwhile noting that most previous studies stopped at this level of quantification. We found that such estimates usually could not be repeated precisely (e.g., within ± 25 per cent for dominant organisms) because of parallax problems and differences between observers and even between observations by the same person. Observer differences were influenced by varying degrees of field distractions and stresses, which were especially pronounced during heavy surf and nighttime low-tide conditions. Recorded in situ information was transcribed in the laboratory and used for density counts of small animals and to minimize taxonomic and other problems encountered while interpreting the photo-samples in the laboratory.

The method as applied here does not allow for the quantification of microalgae, small

Table 1. Physiographic attributes of the 10 rocky intertidal habitats studied.

Study area	Latitude and longitude	Water temperature	Substrate	Tidal range (m)	Wave exposure	Disturbance source	Sand cover
San Miguel Island	34°02'55"N 120°20'08"W	cold	Irregular volcanic flow breccia	−0.3 to +2.7	exposed (moderate)	none	lower intertidal
Santa Cruz Island	33°57'43"N 119°45'16"W	intermediate	Irregular volcanic flow breccia	+0.3 to +4.0	surge	none	none
San Nicolas Island	33°12'54"N 119°28'22"W	cold	Sandstone	−0.3 to +1.5	exposed (moderate)	none	extensive
Santa Barbara Island	33°28'43"N 119°01'36"W	intermediate	Vesicular volcanic rock	+0.3 to +3.7	surge (heavy)	none	none
Santa Catalina Island	33°26'47"N 118°29'04"W	warm	Vesicular volcanic rock	−0.6 to +3.0	protected	none	none
San Clemente Island	33°00'06"N 118°33'03"W	warm	Stable volcanic boulders	−0.3 to +2.1	protected	none	none
Coal Oil Point	34°24'27"N 119°52'40"W	cold (moderate)	Monterey Shale/siltstone	−0.6 to +0.9	exposed (moderate)	oil seeps	extensive
Whites Point	33°43'11"N 118°19'39"W	warm to intermediate	Diatomaceous Monterey Shale and unstable boulders	−0.3 to +0.9	exposed (moderate)	domestic wastes	upper intertidal cobbles
Corona del Mar	33°35'14"N 117°51'54"W	warm to intermediate	Unstable granitic boulders on sandstone/siltstone	−0.3 to +0.9	exposed (moderate)	human usage (extensive)	upper intertidal
Ocean Beach	32°44'35"N 117°15'15"W	warm to intermediate	Poorly-consolidated friable sandstone	+0.3 to +4.0	exposed	none	none

epifauna, or infauna when they occur in low abundances. We realize that these may be metabolically very active, but including them requires special techniques and expertise which constitute separate problems in themselves. For this reason, our measurements were restricted to macroepibiota that could be discerned with the unaided eye. However, we did quantify microbiota (*e.g.*, turfs of filamentous algae) when it occurred in high abundances, and most of the residual infaunal organisms from disturbed sampling have been identified and retained for future analyses. These latter samples never exceeded 1.0 per cent of the biomass in a given quadrat.

In the laboratory, the developed pairs of transparencies (color and IR) were projected simultaneously through a panel of glass (45 x 55 cm) onto two sheets (each 21 x 28 cm) of white bristol paper taped and glued to the glass. The paper contained a grid pattern of dots at 2.0-cm intervals on the side of the transmitted light; this has been shown (Littler and Murray 1975) to be an appropriate density (*i.e.*, 1.0 per cm^2) for consistently reproducible estimates of cover. Red dots were found to contrast best with the biological detail shown by the projected color transparencies; black dots were used in conjunction with the IR transparencies. The transparencies were aligned and focused onto the paper from the side opposite the field of dots (out of view) to assure unbiased assessments. The number of dots superimposed on each species was then scored twice (*i.e.*, replicated after movement of the grid) with the per cent cover values expressed as the number of "hits" for each species divided by the total number of dots contained in the quadrats. Reproducibility was high and seldom varied more than ± 5 per cent cover for a given species. Species that were not abundant enough to be scored by the replicated grid of point intercepts were assigned a cover value of 0.1 per cent.

The IR transparency was found to be instrumental in the delineation of the various species of primary producers and in assessing the state of their health. Blue-green algae, for example, are dominant forms that can only be discerned reliably on dark, wet substrate by use of IR photography. Each species fluoresces differently in the infrared band depending on its chlorophyll content and the percentage of dead branches on an algal thallus. In cases of multilayered communities, more than one photograph per quadrat was taken to quantify each stratum after upper strata had successively been moved aside, often yielding total biotic cover values of greater than 100 per cent. The only organisms removed from the permanent undisturbed quadrats were very small samples occasionally taken for taxonomic purposes.

Disturbed Samples

Biomass measurements of the standing stock give information contributing to community description and provide an additional set of variables to be examined with time; we used the wet weight, dry weight, and ash-free weight data in the same manner as the cover, density, and frequency data from the undisturbed method. The nonpermanent disturbed quadrats were selected for their biological similarity to the photo-quadrats and the organisms within each were harvested quantitatively by means of nylon or metal scrapers and fixed in formalin for subsequent sorting in the laboratory. All portions of algae having holdfasts within a given quadrat were taken. If most of the holdfast of an alga was outside the quadrat, it was not harvested. Organisms half in and half out of a quadrat were harvested only from the left and upper sides of the quadrat. Disturbed plots (0.15 m^2 for complexes of small organisms and 1.0 m^2 for larger organisms) were photographed and harvested within the high, middle, and lower intertidal regions. Approximately 12 plots of each size were harvested per visit at each intertidal site.

In the laboratory, the harvested specimens were identified, packaged, and catalogued. After sorting to species, the samples were rinsed quickly in distilled water to remove salt deposits, shaken to remove excess water, and weighed in tared aluminum foil containers. The samples were then dried to constant weight at 50°C, wrapped and sealed in heavy-duty aluminum foil, cooled to room temperature in desiccators, and weighed to 0.001 g. For those organisms having large inorganic components (such as calcium carbonate), ash-free dry weights were determined following 24 hours of combustion at 400°C in a muffle furnace. We feel that ash-free dry weight is the best measure of biomass, but because of the time constraints of the study only representative calcifying species were combusted. All fleshy organisms (such as frondose algae) were analyzed for wet and dry weight. Consequently, the results of this study expressed as organic dry weight will include ash-free dry weights for organisms with hard parts and dry weights for noncalcareous species.

All biomass data were considered by 0.3-m tidal intervals to formulate an overall picture of the distribution of standing stocks for each study site. Mean wet and dry organic biomass were averaged for each species in each tidal interval and the wet and dry organic weights per square meter for all species were summed to yield a distributional pattern of biomass as a function of tidal height. Values over all of the various tidal heights were averaged to produce a mean standing stock number (in wet and dry organic weight) per average square meter of substrate; these values were then used to compare all 10 study sites.

Collection of Floristic and Faunistic Data

Additional representative organisms were collected in duplicate, catalogued, and archived as permanent taxonomic voucher specimens. These were listed by site for disturbed samples, undisturbed samples, and collections outside the study quadrats. Each site was sampled sufficiently to provide a comprehensive species list of all taxa identifiable by recognized taxonomic experts during the course of the study. Some taxa (*e.g.*, *Chthamalus fissus/dalli*) include more than one species that could not be accurately separated and are treated here as single species complexes. An effort was made to relate variations in the environmental and biological conditions to changes in the composition and organization of intertidal associations.

Analyses of Data

Information obtained by the photographimetric sampling method (undisturbed) and by the harvest method (disturbed) provided quantitative data on the distribution of standing stocks in relation to tidal height. Species cover, frequency, and density distributions were calculated for 0.3-m vertical intervals throughout the intertidal zone. Biomass data were computed each season for wet weight (including hard parts) and organic dry weight (minus hard parts) in grams per square meter of substrate.

Species diversity indices are of particular value in assessing community changes with time: *i.e.*, Margalef's (1968) Index D', which stresses richness; Pielou's (1975) Index J', stressing evenness; and the Shannon and Weaver (1949) Index H', incorporating both richness and evenness. Diversity indices, calculated using natural logarithms and based on cover and biomass, were used to quantify seasonal changes in compositional patterns of the biota at each site and to provide between-site comparisons of community structure. Poole (1974) has indicated that in most ecological cases natural logarithms should be used in the Shannon-Weaver Index; however, the base of the logarithms is very much open to choice. By simply multiplying our H'_e diversity values by the factor 1.443, interested readers can obtain H'_2 numbers.

To characterize objectively natural, within-site assemblages of organisms in an unbiased manner, the quarterly, undisturbed cover data for each quadrat were subjected to cluster analyses by an adaptation of the weighted pair-group method (Sokal and Sneath 1963). This produced a dendrogram of assemblages based on correlation coefficients that were then characterized by their cover dominants and used to label the quadrats along their respective transect lines to produce maps of the prevalent zonal patterns for the various sites (see Figs. 2 and 3). All of the sites combined were also examined by cluster analysis based on overall combined macrophyte and macroinvertebrate species wet weight, organic dry weight, frequency, and cover to reveal common between-site ecological patterns and similarities.

SITE-SPECIFIC FEATURES
Island Study Areas
San Miguel Island Site

The Cuyler Harbor study area on San Miguel Island (34°02'55"N, 120°20'08"W) is the westernmost of all of the rocky intertidal zones studied and is consistently bathed by the cold California Current. The highly irregular volcanic flow breccia substrate of the study area extends over a 3.0-m intertidal range (from -0.3 to $+2.7$ m). A 0.7-m-wide band of aged bituminous residues of unknown source was present at the high-water line. The biota was reflective of a cold-water habitat and this site appeared more closely aligned taxonomically with San Nicolas Island than with the other eight sites. Macrophytes with the greatest mean cover throughout the year were *Gigartina canaliculata* (17.2 per cent), blue-green algae (9.9 per cent), and *Pelvetia fastigiata* (8.8 per cent). Macrophytes occurred maximally in the -0.3 to $+0.3$-m interval, with *P. fastigiata* establishing another smaller peak at $+1.5$ m. Only the lower samples were affected by sand movement, which appeared to be a minor environmental influence on the rocky intertidal community at this site. *Pelvetia fastigiata* had reduced cover during the spring while *G. canaliculata* showed spring and summer maxima. *Corallina vancouveriensis* declined in close association with the increases of *G. canaliculata*. *Gigartina canaliculata* and *C. vancouveriensis* dominated the macrophyte wet biomass with the peak in their standing stocks occurring at the $+0.6$-m level. Along with Santa Cruz Island, this site represented one of the few island areas lacking a large standing stock of *Egregia*. Macroinvertebrates with the highest densities were *Chthamalus fissus/dalli* (1,407/m^2), *Balanus glandula* (378/m^2), and *Littorina planaxis* (140/m^2). *Phragmatopoma californica* (9.2 per cent cover), *Dodecaceria fewkesi* (4.4 per cent), *C. fissus/dalli* (3.9 per cent), and *Mytilus californianus* (3.4 per cent) had the highest yearly mean macroinvertebrate cover. Invertebrate cover was highest at $+0.9$ m and showed little seasonal variability. An April peak in macroinvertebrate densities resulted from increases in *C. fissus/dalli* which recruited at that time. The greatest macrophyte wet and dry biomass constituents were *P. fastigiata* (894 g/m^2) and *G. canaliculata* (862 g/m^2). Macroinvertebrates with the highest wet biomass were *Tegula funebralis* (138 g/m^2) and *Anthopleura elegantissima* (100 g/m^2); considerable dry organic weight also was contributed by these species (15 g/m^2 and 21 g/m^2, respectively), along with a brown encrusting sponge (21 g/m^2). *Anthopleura elegantissima* declined slightly in February and April, but otherwise dominated the low intertidal invertebrate wet biomass.

The total flora and fauna of 116 taxa included 61 macrophytes and 55 macroinvertebrates discernible in the quadrat samples. San Miguel Island contained many species assemblages (11) arranged in 6 seasonally constant zones (Fig. 2). In general, seasonal trends at this site were minimal and were attributable more to populations with inherent annual cycles than to major environmental events. The San Miguel biota had the highest Shannon-Weaver diversity ($H' = 2.95$) of all sites studied and consisted predominantly of perennial organisms characteristic of mature, constant communities (*e.g.*, *Pelvetia*, *Mytilus*, *Phyllospadix*); species normally found (see Murray and Littler 1978) in early seral stages (*e.g.*, *Porphyra*, *Scytosiphon*, *Ulva*) were uncommon.

Santa Cruz Island Site

The study area on the west side of Willows Anchorage (33°57'43"N, 119°45'16"W) is located near the central portion of the southern shore of the island and receives a consistently strong

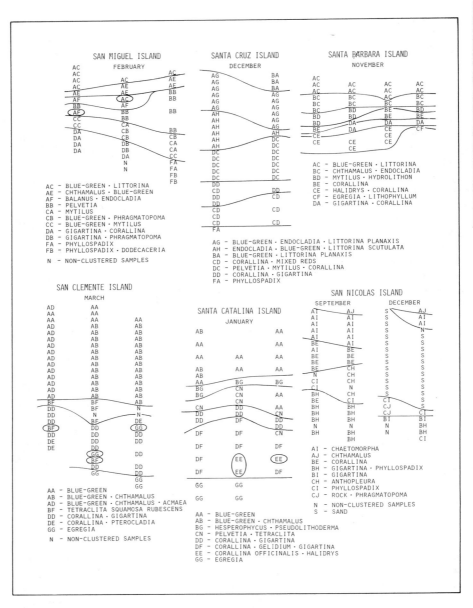

FIGURE 2. *Representative distributional patterns of dominant species assemblages (as determined by cluster analyses based on cover) in relation to positions of transects and locations of quadrats in which they occurred for each of the six island study areas. For each island, columns of letters represent line transects, with the most landward samples at the top and the most seaward at the bottom. Combinations of letters represent specific quadrats within transects, each letter combination specifying certain dominant species, according to the legends. Contour lines are drawn between transects to delineate assemblages in common.*

wave surge. The substrate consists of very rough volcanic breccia extending over a 3.7-m interval (+0.3 to +4.0 m). This site receives afternoon shade and is relatively protected from the prevailing waves and surf. Strong, dry, warm Santa Ana winds recorded during February apparently had been blowing for some time prior to that visit, judging from the desiccated state of the upper intertidal algae. With 77 macrophytes and 100 macroinvertebrates, the Santa Cruz Island site had considerably more taxa (177) in the quadrats throughout the year of study than any of the other sites. Blue-green algae contributed the most cover (29.6 per cent), followed by *Lithophyllum proboscideum* (7.6 per cent), *Corallina officinalis* var. *chilensis* (6.5 per cent), *Endocladia muricata* (4.4 per cent), *Pelvetia fastigiata* (2.6 per cent), and *Gigartina canaliculata* (2.5 per cent). There was a December peak in macrophyte cover due to increases in blue-green algae in the high intertidal region and a low in February correlated with the condition of desiccating winds. The macrophyte species reduced in February included *E. muricata, P. fastigiata, C. officinalis* var. *chilensis,* and *C. vancouveriensis.* Only four species of macroinvertebrates had an average mean cover greater than 1.0 per cent: *Anthopleura elegantissima* (2.6 per cent), *Mytilus californianus* (1.6 per cent), *Tetraclita squamosa rubescens* (1.2 per cent), and *Strongylocentrotus purpuratus* (1.2 per cent). *Littorina planaxis* had the highest average mean density (532 individuals/m²), followed by *Chthamalus fissus/dalli* (386/m²), *T. squamosa rubescens* (310/m²), and *L. scutulata* (254/m²). Density data showed striking increases (*i.e.,* recruitment) of *C. fissus/dalli* and *T. squamosa rubescens* during February and May. In terms of species composition, it is surprising that this site more closely approximated the intermediate biota of Santa Barbara Island than the colder-water communities of either San Nicolas or San Miguel Island. *Pelvetia fastigiata* (96 g/m²) was the highest dry organic biomass contributor, followed by *Halidrys dioica* (75 g/m²), *Egregia menziesii* (27 g/m²), *Gelidium coulteri* (16 g/m²), and *C. officinalis* var. *chilensis* (16 g/m²). The macroinvertebrate contributing the highest dry organic weight was *A. elegantissima* (47 g/m²), along with *S. purpuratus* (44.3 g/m²) and *M. californianus* (33.8 g/m²). This site warrants special mention as one of the few island sites lacking a large stock of *E. menziesii.* The mean yearly Shannon-Weaver diversity (H') was 2.58, richness (D') was 28.86, and evenness (J') was 0.53. None of these measures of species diversity varied appreciably over the year. Cluster analysis resolved seven biological zones and subzones with seven assemblages (Fig. 2) that did not vary throughout the year. These zones, like those at Ocean Beach and Santa Barbara Island, were shifted upward relative to most other sites, indicating consistently strong wave surge conditions. The intertidal biota generally lacked marked seasonal patterns and presented a temporally constant and relatively mature ecosystem dominated by long-lived organisms (Fucales, *Endocladia, Tetraclita,* acmaids). This interpretation was supported by the consistent patterns of zonation shown by the cluster analyses for each quarter.

San Nicolas Island Site

The San Nicolas Island study area represents an intertidal sandstone bench (33°12'54"N, 119°28'22"W) strongly influenced by sand movements (particularly in the upper intertidal region) and has a 1.8-m tidal range from −0.3 to +1.5 m. This site is exposed to the cold California Current most of the year. Although the cold-water species composition of this site had the closest affinity with that of San Miguel Island, the patterns of distribution and abundance of dominant forms were closest to those recorded for Coal Oil Point, which also is subjected to comparable levels of sand movement. There were 120 taxa in the sample plots, of which 69 were macrophytes and 51 were macroinvertebrates. The greatest cover of both macrophytes and invertebrates occurred low in the intertidal zone and decreased upward. Macrophytes with the greatest mean cover throughout the year were *Gigartina canaliculata* (19.8 per cent), *Phyllospadix scouleri* (8.8 per cent), and *Chaetomorpha linum* (8.5 per cent). Of the prominent macroinvertebrates, *Dodecaceria fewkesi* (8.2 per cent), *Anthopleura elegantissima* (5.5 per cent), and *Chthamalus fissus/dalli* (5.4 per cent) had the greatest mean cover. Macroinvertebrates with the highest densities were *C. fissus/dalli* (2,183 individuals/ m²), *A. elegantissima* (136/m²), *Littorina scutulata* (91/m²), and *Mytilus californianus* (62/m²). Seasonal fluctuations among the major species were apparent (cover and density were lowest in winter) with the exceptions of *M. californianus, D. fewkesi,* and *P. scouleri*. For example, total macrophyte cover, particularly of *G. canaliculata* and *C. linum,* declined sharply in winter. There was little seasonality in invertebrate cover except for a *C. fissus/dalli* settlement in May. The low intertidal cover peak of macroinvertebrates (mostly *Phragmatopoma californica* and *D. fewkesi*) was unique among the 10 sites studied. The wet biomass peak for macroinvertebrates occurred at +0.6 to +0.9 m, mostly due to *M. californianus, C. fissus/dalli,* and *Haliotis cracherodii*.

Community mean yearly biomass was very high at San Nicolas Island (4,659 g/m² wet weight, 896 g/m² organic dry weight) and was exceeded only at Santa Catalina Island. *Phyllospadix scouleri* (343 dry organic g/m², 1,173 wet g/m²) and *Halidrys dioica* (149 dry g/m², 846 wet g/m²) had the greatest biomass of the macrophytes; among the macroinvertebrates, *Mytilus californianus* (20 dry organic g/m², 218 wet g/m²) and *Anthopleura elegantissima* (47 dry g/m², 212 wet g/m²) were predominant. Sand movement during winter caused large alterations in the six species assemblages that were somewhat arranged into five indistinct zones (Fig. 2). By early spring, the macrobiota exhibited nearly complete recovery; richness, evenness, and Shannon-Weaver diversity indices were highest in spring. This recovery and the high abundance of *Anthopleura* clones and *Chaetomorpha* suggest, hypothetically, that much of the intertidal biota at the study site was comprised of environmentally-stressed communities adapted to periodic conditions of sand inundation.

It seems that raised portions of the intertidal bench serve as islands of refuge upon which mature abalone and mussel-dominated communities develop. These raised pinnacle communities are of interest in that their lower limits may be determined by the physical smothering action of sand movement rather than by the kinds of biological factors so well documented in the literature (see Paine 1966, Connell 1972).

Santa Barbara Island Site

The study site is located on the east side of the island near the mouth of Cave Canyon (33°28'43"N, 119°01'36"W). The intertidal region extends over a steep, vesicular volcanic rock shoreline which is very rough in texture and has a 3.4-m tidal range (from +0.3 to +3.7 m). Comparable biotic zones were considerably elevated relative to most of the other sites, probably due to the predominant wave surge effect and a high degree of shading during the afternoon. The macrophytes sampled numbered 88 taxa, while macroinvertebrates numbered 69; macrobiota totaled 157 taxa. The macrophytes contributing the highest per cent cover averaged over the tidal intervals sampled were blue-green algae (37.0 per cent), *Halidrys dioica* (5.7 per cent), *Corallina officinalis* var. *chilensis* (5.5 per cent), *Gigartina canaliculata* (5.0 per cent), *Egregia menziesii* (4.6 per cent), *Lithophyllum proboscideum* (4.5 per cent), *C. vancouveriensis* (2.6 per cent), and *Hydrolithon decipiens* (2.4 per cent). Macroinvertebrates contributing the highest average cover were *Chthamalus fissus/dalli* (3.0 per cent), *Mytilus californianus* (3.0 per cent), *Pseudochama exogyra* (2.8 per cent), *Petaloconchus montereyensis* (1.8 per cent), and *Tetraclita squamosa rubescens* (1.8 per cent). *Chthamalus fissus/dalli* were by far the most numerous macroinvertebrates (1,475 individuals/m²), followed by *T. squamosa rubescens* (350/m²), *Littorina planaxis* (240/m²), *M. californianus* (214/m²), *P. montereyensis* (181/m²), and *Pollicipes polymerus* (140/m²). Invertebrates showed little seasonality in cover and reached their maximum in the +0.9 to +2.1-m interval. Total macrophyte cover was highest in January due to large increases in blue-green algae above +1.8 m; frondose forms low on the shore reached their maximum in the fall. Juvenile barnacles (*T. squamosa rubescens* and *C. fissus/dalli*) were most numerous in January, then showed a steep decline in the spring.

Total mean biotic cover changed dramatically between the November visit (88 per cent) and the January visit (107 per cent), largely due to increased blue-green algae above +1.5 m. Biotic cover below +1.8 m exceeded 100 per cent with most of the biomass resulting from large algal stocks below +1.5 m. Biomass was relatively high at this site (6,775 g/m² wet weight, 876 g/m² organic dry weight) and 86 per cent consisted of macrophytes. On the basis of organic dry weight, *Egregia menziesii* was the dominant macrophyte with an average of 299 g/m², followed by *Gigartina canaliculata* (179 g/m²), and *Halidrys dioica* (174 g/m²). Only three macroinvertebrates had an average equal to or greater than 10 dry organic g/m², including *Pseudochama exogyra* (44 g/m²), *Mytilus californianus* (25 g/m²), and *Strongylocentrotus purpuratus* (10 g/m²). Seven relatively complex biotic zones (Fig. 2), as characterized by seven different assemblages, were present on the shore. There were a number of organisms usually associated with colder waters which were present at this site that were not found on nearby Santa Catalina and San Clemente Islands to the south; consequently, this site showed closer affinities with the area studied on Santa Cruz Island than with any of the other eight sites. An abundant population of the pulmonate gastropod *Siphonaria brannani*, as well as lesser numbers of the holothurian *Cucumaria pseudocurata*, were found exclusively on Santa Barbara Island during the present study.

Santa Catalina Island Site

The Santa Catalina Island site is on the north point of Fisherman Cove (33°26′47″N, 118°29′04″W) about 1.3 km northeast of Isthmus Cove and shielded from the direction of the prevailing swell. The study area extends over a 3.6-m range (−0.6 to +3.0 m) and consists of a vesicular volcanic rock substrate (middle Miocene) with many surface irregularities. A total of 169 taxa was present in the quadrats taken during the study (73 macrophytes and 96 macroinvertebrates). At this site, macrophyte abundance was highest between MLLW and +0.6 m; the macroinvertebrate maximum was localized between +0.3 and +0.6 m. Based on the yearly average, blue-green algae provided the greatest macrophyte cover (25.1 per cent), followed by *Egregia menziesii* (10.6 per cent), *Pelvetia fastigiata* f. *gracilis* (8.0 per cent), *Hesperophycus harveyanus* (6.8 per cent), *Gelidium purpurascens* (6.6 per cent), *Lithophyllum proboscideum* (6.4 per cent), and *Corallina officinalis* var. *chilensis* (5.9 per cent). Less than 5.0 per cent cover was contributed by each of 63 additional macrophytes. Total macrophyte cover was minimal during August due to large reduction in blue-green forms; however, several other macrophytes reached abundance peaks at this time. Most of the macrophyte seasonality was shown by turf species and their epiphytes, many of which can be characterized as summer annuals. For example, *Colpomenia sinuosa*, *Sargassum agardhianum*, and *Gelidium coulteri* grew rapidly from spring through summer to a fall maximum. During winter, *Gelidium pusillum* was most abundant, while the fucalean forms *P. fastigiata* f. *gracilis* and *H. harveyanus* remained directly constant over the year. The greatest macroinvertebrate cover was furnished by *Dendropoma lituella/rastrum* (3.6 per cent), *Tetraclita squamosa rubescens* (3.2 per cent), *Chthamalus fissus/dalli* (2.1 per cent), and *Serpulorbis squamigerus* (1.2 per cent). Less than 1.0 per cent cover was provided by each of 90 additional macroinvertebrates. *Chthamalus fissus/dalli*, with 802 individuals/m², was by far the most numerous macroinvertebrate, followed by *T. squamosa rubescens* (450/m²), *D. lituella/rastrum* (341/m²), *Littorina planaxis* (157/m²), *Brachidontes adamsianus* (102/m²), *Balanus tintinnabulum californicus* (97/m²), and *Littorina scutulata* (80/m²). Diversity was high at this site with the maximum occurring during August. Wet and dry organic biomass (8,078 and 1,458 g/m², respectively) were very high at this site, concentrated between −0.6 and MLLW, and from +0.6 to +1.3 m, and comprised mostly of Phaeophyta. Thirteen taxa contributed 99.3 per cent of the mean macrophyte organic dry weight. The greatest dry organic biomass was provided by *Eisenia arborea* (558 g/m²), *P. fastigiata* f. *gracilis* (350 g/m²), *E. menziesii* (273 g/m²), and *H. harveyanus* (110 g/m²). Eleven species of macroinvertebrates contributed 91.8 per cent of the mean dry organic biomass; the bulk of this was supplied by *T. squamosa rubescens* (24 g/m²), followed by *Pseudochama exogyra* (10 g/m²), *B. adamsianus* (6 g/m²), a white sponge (4. g/m²), and *C. fissus/dalli* (4 g/m²). There were eight discrete assemblages on the shore, forming six constant major zones throughout the year (Fig. 2).

San Clemente Island Site

This site is located 450 m to the south of Wilson Cove (33°00′06″N, 118°33′03″W) on the northeast portion of the island. The study area has a 2.4-m tidal range extending from −0.3 to +2.1 m over a field of large, volcanic rocks. The Corona del Mar site also consists of a habitat mosaic of slopes, angles, and crevices from large rocks; however, the substrate on the leeward side of San Clemente Island is characteristically much more stable than at Corona del Mar and little movement of substrate occurred during the year of study. This warm-water site is the calmest of all the sites studied and receives afternoon shade during the winter. A total of 129 taxa was recorded in the quadrats (64 macrophytes and 65 macroinvertebrates). Blue-green algae provided the greatest macrophyte cover (26.8 per cent), followed by *Egregia menziesii* (13.4 per cent), *Corallina officinalis* var. *chilensis* (8.0 per cent), *Gigartina canaliculata* (7.5 per cent), and *Pterocladia capillacea* (7.3 per cent). The barnacles *Chthamalus fissus/dalli* (3.6 per cent) and *Tetraclita squamosa rubescens* (1.2 per cent) furnished nearly three-fourths of the total macroinvertebrate cover based on annual averages. Less than 1.0 per cent was contributed by each of 62 additional macroinvertebrates. *Chthamalus fissus/dalli* (1,528 individuals/m²) provided 74 per cent of all macroinvertebrate individuals based on annual averages and was one order of magnitude more abundant than the second most abundant taxon (*Acmaea [Collisella] scabra*). Although this site showed the least seasonality of all 10 areas, there was a slight tendency for higher macrophyte cover in December and June, with a small reduction of invertebrate cover in June.

San Clemente Island's intertidal biota was very similar to that of Santa Catalina Island, but the latter showed more seasonal fluctuation. *Egregia menziesii,* which was most abundant in October, was observed to decrease in March, although many juvenile thalli were present. *Halidrys dioica* reached a cover peak in March. As was the case at most sites, blue-green algae were more abundant in December and March. *Pterocladia capillacea, Sargassum agardhianum, Colpomenia sinuosa, Laurencia pacifica,* and *L. snyderae* reached their peak during the warmer months of summer and fall. Biomass (mostly Phaeophyta) was greatest between MLLW and +0.3 m with invertebrate dominance above +0.8 m. Fourteen macrophytes provided 98.9 per cent of the dry organic biomass, including *E. menziesii* (181 g/m²), *H. dioica* (62 g/m²), *S. agardhianum* (58 g/m²), *Phyllospadix torreyi* (47 g/m²), and *P. capillacea* (41 g/m²). Six macroinvertebrates contributed 96.2 per cent of the total macroinvertebrate dry biomass; the majority was provided by *Tetraclita squamosa rubescens* (6 g/m²), *Chthamalus fissus/dalli* (5 g/m²), and *Acmaea (Collisella) scabra* (2 g/m²).

Invertebrates at San Clemente Island were found to contribute less to the intertidal community composition than those at the other nine sites. This site, as well as leeward San Clemente Island in general, is notable in its paucity of large mobile macroinvertebrates. Although March samples contained the most taxa (103), there was no marked seasonality in Shannon-Weaver diversity (2.55 yearly mean). Cluster analysis revealed seven assemblages of species distributed into four major intertidal zones (Fig. 2) that did not vary over the period of study.

Mainland Study Areas

Coal Oil Point Site

The Coal Oil Point study area (34°24′27″N, 119°52′40″W) is located approximately 3.0 km west of Goleta Point, which is part of the University of California, Santa Barbara campus. The rocky intertidal region consists of a sandstone substrate usually covered by sand above the +0.9-m tidal level. The habitat studied is quite flat, extends over a 1.5-m tidal range of −0.6 to +0.9 m, and has marked winter influxes of sand affecting most of the area. Sampling was restricted to the low to mid-intertidal zone, which has an important bearing on interpretations relative to most of the other study sites; that is, we would expect macrophyte and, hence, total standing stocks to be overemphasized (with macroinvertebrates underemphasized) since the high zone typically dominated by macroinvertebrates was not available for sampling. Historically, this site has received oil from nearby offshore seeps that release from 50 to 70 barrels per day into the sea.

One hundred and twenty-seven taxa, comprising 71 macrophytes and 56 macroinvertebrates, were present in the samples. Macrophytes with the greatest mean cover were *Phyllospadix torreyi* (23.0 per cent), rhodophycean turf (15.6 per cent), *Egregia menziesii* (11.1 per cent), and *Gigartina canaliculata* (8.1 per cent). The macroinvertebrate cover dominants were *Anthopleura elegantissima* (15.4 per cent) and *Mytilus californianus* (8.2 per cent). Macroinvertebrates with the highest densities were *Chthamalus fissus/dalli* (1,651 individuals/m²), *Lacuna* spp. (1,255/m²), and *A. elegantissima* (412/m²). The peak in biotic cover occurred in the −0.3 to +0.3-m interval, mostly due to macrophytes. The macroinvertebrates (mostly *A. elegantissima*) reached their maximum from +0.6 to +0.9 m.

A significant portion of the macrophyte cover was a rhodophycean turf (including three species of *Polysiphonia*, *Tiffaniella snyderae*, and *Pterosiphonia dendroidea*) that was attached on substrate beneath sand. In general, macrophytes showed a winter decline, especially *Egregia menziesii* and *Gigartina canaliculata*. *Phyllospadix torreyi* (131 dry organic g/m²) contributed the most wet biomass, which was highest in winter. *Egregia menziesii* stocks were low at this site, a trend noted for most of the northern study areas. *Anthopleura elegantissima* (169 dry organic g/m²) dominated the macroinvertebrate biomass and apparently reproduced by asexual budding to give rise to extensive clonal populations, a form apparently (Francis 1973) adapted to environmental stresses.

Similar populations were recorded only from the site on San Nicolas Island, a habitat also influenced by sand movements. The distribution and abundance patterns at the San Nicolas site were more similar to Coal Oil Point than to any of the other eight areas studied. Probably owing to the lack of a high intertidal region, Coal Oil Point had a large number of species assemblages (nine) but a low number of discrete zones (three); these varied considerably in association with sand movement (Fig. 3). Although Coal Oil Point was the northernmost site studied, it did not contain as many cold-water organisms as did the San Miguel Island and San Nicolas Island sites.

Whites Point Site

The study site at the base of the Palos Verdes Hills (33°43′11″N, 118°19′37″W) and about 4 km northwest of Los Angeles Harbor was chosen as representative of a mainland habitat exposed to human usage and municipal wastes. Whites Point, as in the case of Coal Oil Point, also appeared to receive a certain amount of petroleum pollution; aged bituminous residues were present as a continuous band along the high tide line. This area lies just shoreward of the site of the world's largest release of sewage into the ocean (over one billion gallons per day). The substrate is both silty and diatomaceous Monterey Shale (middle Miocene). The habitats selected as representative were two tilted, bedded planes that extend shoreward from −0.3 to

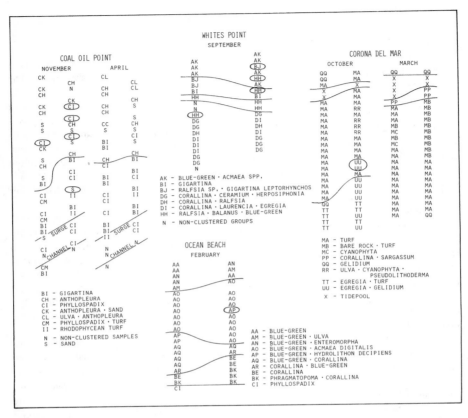

FIGURE 3. *Representative distributional patterns of dominant species assemblages (as determined by cluster analyses based on cover) in relation to positions of transects and locations of quadrats in which they occurred for each of the four mainland study areas.*

+0.9 m; above this they become covered by an unstable boulder-cobble beach. Since the middle to high zones (regions of invertebrate maxima) were not available for study, one would expect that macrophyte stocks would be overemphasized and invertebrates underemphasized relative to all of the other sites except Corona del Mar, Coal Oil Point, and San Nicolas Island.

There was a total of 125 taxa sampled by quadrats, including 36 macrophytes and 69 macroinvertebrates. Five macrophytes accounted for more than half of the annual cover. Blue-green algae provided the greatest macrophyte cover (14.8 per cent) based on annual averages, followed by *Corallina officinalis* var. *chilensis* (14.0 per cent), *Gigartina canaliculata* (7.4 per cent), *Ralfsia* sp. (7.0 per cent), and *C. vancouveriensis* (6.2 per cent). Less than 6.0 per cent cover was contributed over the year by each of 50 additional macrophytes. The following three macroinvertebrates provided almost two-thirds of the total animal cover based on annual averages: *Balanus glandula* (1.6 per cent), *Anthopleura elegantissima* (1.4 per cent), and *Strongylocentrotus purpuratus* (1.1 per cent). Less than 1.0 per cent cover was provided over the year by each of 58 additional macroinvertebrates. *Balanus glandula* (582 individuals/m²) was the most numerous macroinvertebrate, followed by *Acmaea*

(*Collisella*) *conus/scabra* (336/m²), *Chthamalus fissus/dalli* (238/m²), and *A.* (*Collisella*) *strigatella* (118/m²). The maximum biotic cover (99 per cent) occurred during September but decreased in winter due to declines in algal turf species and their epiphytes. Two filamentous Rhodophyta, *Herposiphonia verticillata* and *Ceramium eatonianum*, were important epiphytes on the turf community, a relationship not pronounced at any of the other sites. *Gigartina canaliculata* formed a turf distinct from the *Corallina* turf and grew mainly on rock (unlike most of the other sites where these two usually were strongly intermingled in turfs). Kelp at Whites Point was patchy in the lower intertidal region. *Egregia menziesii* reached a peak in autumn, then declined in winter, as was the case at nearly all of the sites where it was important. Twelve macrophytes supplied 99.0 per cent of the mean macrophyte organic dry weight. The majority was contributed by *E. menziesii* (433 g/m²), which furnished 72.6 per cent of the macrophyte total, followed by *G. canaliculata* (70 g/m²), *C. vancouveriensis* (24 g/m²), *C. officinalis* var. *chilensis* (23 g/m²), and *Ralfsia* sp. (11 g/m²). Eleven species, including *Mytilus californianus* (22 g/m²), *A. elegantissima* (17 g/m²), and *S. purpuratus* (8 g/m²), comprised 95.7 per cent of the macroinvertebrate dry organic biomass; considerable contributions were also made by *Pugettia producta*, *Nuttallina fluxa*, *B. glandula*, and *Tegula funebralis*. The peak in macrophyte biomass occurred in the −0.3-m to MLLW interval and comprised mostly Phaeophyta. Most of the macroinvertebrate wet biomass was between +0.6 and +0.9 m and consisted primarily of *M. californianus*, *A. elegantissima*, and *S. purpuratus*. *Balanus glandula* recruited strongly in May.

There were seven species assemblages and four zonal communities (Fig. 3) that varied considerably during the study. Species numbers and richness (*D'*) were maximal during May, while Shannon-Weaver diversity (*H'*) at this site was highest in winter due to an increased macrophyte evenness associated with sand movement. Sand and gravel were important perturbatory factors at this site; a winter inundation of many of the quadrats, particularly along the north transect line, resulted in the predominance of a blue-green algal-limpet community in February.

Corona del Mar Site

The site selected for study at Corona del Mar lies near the mouth of Morning Canyon (approximately 33°35′14″N, 117°51′54″W), located 1.4 km southeast of the entrance channel to Newport Bay. The intertidal zone examined extends over a tidal range of only 1.2 m (from −0.3 to +0.9 m) and consists of loose, granitic boulders lying on a sandstone/siltstone substrate. Of the sites studied, Corona del Mar represents one of the most disturbed by both human usage (including tidepooling, rock turning, trampling, and handling of organisms) and natural disturbances (such as heavy surf which causes movement of the boulder substrate). Because of sandy beach cover above +0.9 m, sampling was restricted to only the low intertidal zone where, at comparable tidal heights in most rocky habitats, macrophytes and total standing stocks are at their greatest. Therefore, care must be taken in comparing this site with other sites sampled at high levels, *i.e.*, where barnacles and littorine populations (usually low in biomass) are typically dominant.

Quadrat samples analyzed from Corona del Mar contained 137 taxa of macroorganisms, including 66 macrophytes and 71 macroinvertebrates. The greatest overall macrophyte cover based on yearly means was contributed by *Egregia menziesii* (14.4 per cent), followed by *Corallina officinalis* var. *chilensis* (12.0 per cent), *Ulva californica* (10.4 per cent), blue-green algae (8.0 per cent), and *Pseudolithoderma nigra* (7.8 per cent). *Chthamalus fissus/dalli* and *Anthopleura elegantissima* contributed most of the macroinvertebrate cover (1.0 per cent each). *Lithophyllum proboscideum* was the most widespread species (90.4 per cent of the samples) as a result of the mosaic of crevices (its primary habitat) created by the boulder substrate. *Chthamalus fissus/dalli* was considerably more numerous (408 individuals/m²) than other significant species, which ranged from 59 individuals/m² to 10 individuals/m². Biological cover at this site averaged 91 per cent throughout the year, of which macroinvertebrates accounted for only 4 per cent. Biotic cover exceeded 95 per cent below +0.3 m due to large stands of macrophytes that were maximal (126.4 per cent) in the lowest interval sampled. *Egregia menziesii* contributed the most cover (14.4 per cent) when averaged over the year but was greatly reduced during late winter. Overall community dry organic biomass was exceptionally low at this site (361 g/m²), with the majority (83 per cent) contributed by macrophytes. Most of the macrophyte biomass occurred at the lowest level sampled (2,822 g/m² wet weight and 471 g/m² organic dry weight). *Egregia menziesii* provided 56 per cent of the total macrophyte wet weight, while the remainder consisted mostly of turf formers. Most of the macroinvertebrate biomass was *Strongylocentrotus purpuratus* (372 g/m² wet weight) and *A. elegantissima* (76 g/m² wet weight), along with several other mobile forms.

There were no sharp zonal communities at this site and most of the quadrats showed changes in dominant assemblages during each quarter (Fig. 3). The bigger forms of invertebrates predominated, with their biomass largely attributable to *Strongylocentrotus purpuratus, Anthopleura elegantissima,* and *Aplysia californica.* These animals were able to move into the crevices between boulders before, during, and following substrate movement, making them less likely to be damaged by the smaller cobbles. The instability of substrate at this site was probably responsible for the predominance of early successional and eurytopic algal forms. Other abundant macrophytes were those characteristic of shaded crevices, a habitat abundantly represented throughout the study site. Nearly all of the population and community parameters recorded from the upper surfaces of boulders suggest a general subclimax system at Corona, perhaps maintained by substrate instability.

Ocean Beach Site

The study area is located on a broad section of wave-exposed coastline at Ocean Beach, San Diego (32°44′35″N, 117°15′15″W) and covers a 3.7-m intertidal range (+0.3 to +4.0 m) over a substrate of poorly consolidated, friable sandstone. This site consistently receives more wave shock than any of the other habitats. A strong seasonal pattern occurred due to the increase in winter high surf and wave splash in the upper intertidal region. This resulted in a rapid winter colonization of blue-green algae, *Ulva* sp., and *Enteromorpha* sp. on previously bare substrate.

A total of 150 taxa was present in the sample plots at this site, with 92 macrophytes and 58 macroinvertebrates. Mean cover of macrophyte species averaged over all of the tidal intervals sampled was highest for blue-green algae (38.8 per cent), *Corallina officinalis* var. *chilensis* (8.4 per cent), *Hydrolithon decipiens* (5.3 per cent), *C. vancouveriensis* (4.8 per cent), *Cryptopleura corallinara* (4.4 per cent), *Phyllospadix torreyi* (4.1 per cent), *Rhodoglossum affine* (1.9 per cent), and *Enteromorpha tubulosa* (1.6 per cent). Mean cover by macroinvertebrates was highest for the tube worm *Phragmatopoma californica* (4.8 per cent), followed by *Mytilus californianus* (2.3 per cent), *Acmaea (Collisella) digitalis* (1.6 per cent), *Chthamalus fissus/dalli* (1.0 per cent), *Pollicipes polymerus* (0.9 per cent), and *Nuttallina fluxa* (0.6 per cent). *Chthamalus fissus/dalli* was the most abundant macroinvertebrate at Ocean Beach (annual mean of 997 individuals/m²), followed by *A. (Collisella) digitalis* (274/m²), *P. polymerus* (274/m²), *P. californica* (183/m²), and *M. californianus* (134/m²). Eleven additional macroinvertebrates were represented by average annual densities of 6 to 97 individuals/m² and 23 other macroinvertebrates contributed a mean of 37 individuals/m². Macroinvertebrates attained their maximum cover between +0.6 and +1.8 m, largely owing to extensive populations of *P. californica* and *M. californianus.* For macrophytes, the rank order using dry organic weight was *P. torreyi* first (97 g/m²), followed by *C. corallinara* (29 g/m²), *C. vancouveriensis* (24 g/m²), *C. officinalis* var. *chilensis* (19 g/m²), and *Gigartina canaliculata* (10 g/m²). Among the macroinvertebrates, *M. californianus* had the highest dry organic weight (116 g/m²),

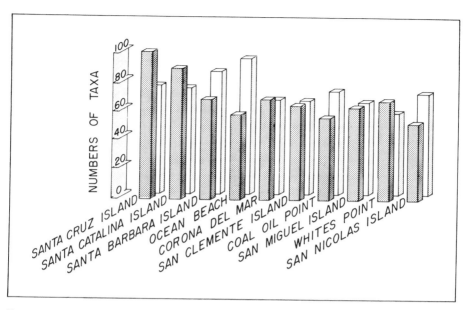

FIGURE 4. *Mean annual numbers of macrophyte taxa (histograms in rear) and macroinverte-brate taxa (dark histograms in front) found in quadrats for each study area.*

followed by *Septifer bifurcatus* (42 g/m²), *N. fluxa* (10 g/m²), and *Strongylocentrotus purpuratus* (9 g/m²). Maximum biomass (mostly *Mytilus*) occurred between +0.9 and +2.1 m, with another peak, dominated by *Corallina* and *Phyllospadix,* at +0.3 to +0.9 m. The lack of large *Egregia* and *Eisenia* stocks here could be related to the friable nature of the substrate, as demonstrated by the relative ease with which these algae could be pulled loose during harvesting and collecting. Overall community biomass was low (421 g/m² organic dry weight) at this site. Five biotic zones made up of a large number of species assemblages (10) were present on this shore (Fig. 3) throughout the year. The flora and fauna at Ocean Beach, our most southerly site, contained no elements unique to cold-water systems, but had many forms associated with warm-water environments.

COMPARISONS BETWEEN SITES
Numbers of Taxa

More taxa occurred in the communities sampled at Santa Cruz Island (177), Santa Catalina Island (169), Santa Barbara Island (157), and Ocean Beach (150) than at any of the other six sites (Fig. 4). The fewest total taxa were sampled at San Miguel Island (116), San Nicolas Island (120), and Whites Point (125); the last two of these sites exhibited stress by sand or pollutants. Inspection of the data (Fig. 4) shows that the Ocean Beach and Santa Barbara Island sites had by far the greatest number of macrophyte taxa (92 and 88, respectively); Santa Cruz Island had considerably more species (13 more) than did San Clemente Island and four more than Santa Catalina Island, both of which are somewhat protected from wave swell. As indicated elsewhere, Ocean Beach has the greatest exposure to surf, and the communities at Santa Barbara Island were displaced upward owing to the heavy surge present there. The increase in macrophyte species, therefore, may have been due to less desiccation stress because of the

Table 2. Seasonal and mean annual macrophyte cover percentage comparisons between study areas.

Study areas	Months				
	MJJA	SON	DJ	FMA	Mean
Island sites					
San Miguel Island	66	66	64	76	68
Santa Cruz Island	82	56	80	54	68
San Nicolas Island	81	84	45	66	69
Santa Barbara Island	76	71	92	74	78
Santa Catalina Island	86	104	102	108	100
San Clemente Island	94	88	104	89	94
Island Means	81	78	81	78	80
Mainland sites					
Coal Oil Point	90	58	74	91	78
Whites Point	66	94	67	63	72
Corona del Mar	87	110	81	71	87
Ocean Beach	93	67	81	79	80
Mainland means	84	82	76	76	79

greater surge allowing a greater number of normally subtidal species to inhabit higher regions. There were far more macroinvertebrate taxa in quadrats sampled at Santa Cruz Island (100) and Santa Catalina Island (96) than at the other study sites. The lowest numbers of invertebrate taxa occurred at San Nicolas Island (51) and Coal Oil Point (56), where sand movement was clearly associated with the dominance of stress-resistant clonal aggregates of *Anthopleura elegantissima* (Francis 1973), a form that our preliminary data (Taylor and Littler 1979) indicate is capable of excluding such colonial space occupiers as *Phragmatopoma californica*.

Cover

Macrophyte per cent cover (seasonal and mean annual) for all sites is presented in Table 2. The yearly mean for overall intertidal cover of macrophytes was clearly greatest at Santa Catalina Island (100 per cent), followed by San Clemente Island (94 per cent) and Corona del Mar (87 per cent). The remainder of the sites contained from 80 to 68 per cent macrophyte cover, with San Miguel and Santa Cruz Islands having the least. All 10 sites displayed seasonality in macrophyte cover, except for San Clemente Island (annual range of only 5 per cent), which is the most sheltered of all the sites. Many of the geographically southern sites (San Clemente Island, Santa Catalina Island, Santa Barbara Island, and Corona del Mar) showed high macrophyte cover from late fall to winter, mainly due to an increase in blue-green algal cover. However, the general tendency for many of the other macrophytes (particularly turf species, epiphytes on turf species, and the large brown kelp *Egregia menziesii*) was to begin an increase of cover in the spring, reach their peak in fall, and then show marked declines associated with the stressful daytime low-tide periods of late fall and winter. This trend may have been especially pronounced during the 1975-76 winter when desiccating "Santa Ana" wind conditions prevailed for at least two weeks during December and January, coinciding with early afternoon low tides. Other factors, such as preferential grazing (Vadas 1977, Lubchenco

Table 3. Seasonal and mean annual macroinvertebrate cover percentage comparisons between study areas.

| Study areas | Months | | | | |
---	MJJA	SON	DJ	FMA	Mean
Island sites					
San Miguel Island	23	31	28	24	26
Santa Cruz Island	9	10	8	9	9
San Nicolas Island	21	24	26	33	26
Santa Barbara Island	17	17	15	15	16
Santa Catalina Island	13	14	12	9	12
San Clemente Island	4	7	8	7	6
Island means	16	17	16	16	16
Mainland sites					
Coal Oil Point	37	29	26	18	28
Whites Point	9	5	6	6	6
Corona del Mar	4	5	2	3	4
Ocean Beach	9	15	12	14	12
Mainland means	15	14	12	10	12

1978), environmentally controlled alterations in life history stages (Wynne and Loiseaux 1976), or seasonal growth strategies (Hatcher *et al.* 1977), could also be important.

The overall intertidal macroinvertebrate cover (Table 3) was highest at Coal Oil Point (28 per cent), followed by San Miguel Island (26 per cent) and San Nicolas Island (26 per cent); these sites were all affected to varying degrees by winter sand movements. The lowest macroinvertebrate cover occurred at Corona del Mar (4 per cent), San Clemente Island (6 per cent), and Whites Point (6 per cent). At half of the 10 study areas, little macroinvertebrate seasonality was apparent; however, seasonal trends were apparent at Coal Oil Point, Ocean Beach, Whites Point, San Nicolas Island, and San Clemente Island. Seasonal periodicity appeared to be closely related to the inundation of parts of the rocky intertidal zone by onshore/offshore sand movements at three of these sites (Whites Point, Coal Oil Point, and San Nicolas Island). Many of the sites showed a late winter to early spring increase of macroinvertebrate cover associated with the decline in frondose algal cover and the recruitment of juvenile barnacles.

Macroinvertebrate Densities

Seasonal and mean yearly macroinvertebrate densities (individuals per square meter) are presented for all sites in Table 4. Coal Oil Point (3,609/m²) had higher invertebrate densities than any other site, owing to large numbers of *Lacuna* spp. and clonal populations of *Anthopleura elegantissima*. Corona del Mar and Whites Point were by far the most depauperate sites in terms of animal numbers, with 583 and 1,494 per square meter of intertidal substrate, respectively. This is surely due, in part, to sand inundation in the upper rocky intertidal zone where invertebrate numbers usually tend to be very high, but it also may be due to disturbances such as sand and rock abrasion that are particularly stressful to barnacles and other sessile organisms. Very marked seasonality of opportunistic species such as barnacles occurred at all sites; it is felt that the density data are the most useful for depicting seasonal patterns of the

Table 4. Seasonal and mean yearly macroinvertebrate density (nos./m²) comparisons between study areas.

Study areas	Months				Mean
	MJJA	SON	DJ	FMA	
Island sites					
San Miguel Island	3492	1609	2620	1472	2298
Santa Cruz Island	2850	1420	2050	1897	2054
San Nicolas Island	4338	2433	2566	1370	2677
Santa Barbara Island	1483	3232	4301	3574	3148
Santa Catalina Island	1792	2528	2246	2560	2282
San Clemente Island	1890	1901	2676	1816	2071
Island means	2641	2187	2743	2115	2422
Mainland sites					
Coal Oil Point	4645	5233	3536	1022	3609
Whites Point	2709	1094	1082	1092	1494
Corona del Mar	448	665	632	587	583
Ocean Beach	3259	2080	1765	2532	2409
Mainland means	2765	2268	1754	1308	2024

majority of invertebrate taxa. Most of the sites showed a late winter or spring recruitment of barnacle spat during 1975-76.

Wet Biomass

Figure 5 provides mean biomass determinations of wet weight (including hard parts) for macrophytes and macroinvertebrates at each study site. Overall wet biomass was greatest at the Santa Catalina Island site (8,078 g/m²), followed closely by Santa Barbara Island (6,775 g/m²) and Ocean Beach (5,334 g/m²). The disturbed sites, Corona del Mar (2,430 g/m²) and Coal Oil Point (2,661 g/m²), contained by far the lowest standing stocks of all areas sampled. This point is even more significant when one considers that upper intertidal samples (which usually are low in biomass) could not be taken at these two sites because of sand inundation; consequently, only regions characteristic of high standing stocks were sampled. For this reason, Whites Point and San Nicolas Island must be considered areas of only moderate biomass and not directly comparable to sites with high intertidal zones.

Macrophytes dominated the wet biomass at all sites except Santa Cruz Island and Ocean Beach, where large stands of mussels were sampled; *Egregia menziesii* stocks were also very sparse at these two sites. Macrophytes reached a wet biomass maximum at Santa Catalina Island (7,049 g/m²), followed by Whites Point (4,653 g/m²), Santa Barbara Island (4,405 g/m²), San Nicolas Island (3,703 g/m²), and San Clemente Island (3,146 g/m²); all four of these island sites are in the Southern Channel Islands geographic group. Wet macrophyte standing stock was lowest at the oil-polluted Coal Oil Point study area (1,728 g/m²) and at Santa Cruz Island (1,750 g/m²), both of which lacked well-developed brown algal stocks.

Macroinvertebrates had the greatest wet standing stocks at those sites where wave surge was highest (shown by the characteristic upward displacement of zones), namely, Ocean Beach (3,253 g/m²), Santa Barbara Island (2,370 g/m²), and Santa Cruz Island (1,942 g/m²), mostly due to *Mytilus californianus*. The lowest macroinvertebrate standing stock occurred on San Clemente Island (309 g/m²), where mussel beds were not present and wave action was minimal.

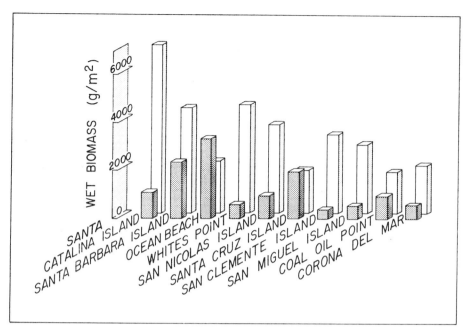

FIGURE 5. *Mean annual wet biomass of macrophytes (histograms in rear) and macroinvertebrates (dark histograms in front) for each study area.*

Dry Organic Biomass

The ash-free dry weight or organic biomass (ODW) is a much better measure of standing stock than is wet biomass (WW) because the latter includes large amounts of inorganic shell and other hard parts. Consequently, a somewhat different picture of the standing stock emerges when dry organic biomass is considered (Fig. 6). The highest dry organic standing stocks were recorded on Santa Catalina Island (1,458 g/m^2), followed by San Nicolas Island (896 g/m^2), Santa Barbara Island (876 g/m^2), Whites Point (659 g/m^2), and San Miguel Island (659 g/m^2). The last site was very low in wet biomass (Fig. 5). Four sites with low stocks of *Egregia*— Corona del Mar (361 g/m^2), Ocean Beach (421 g/m^2), Santa Cruz Island (463 g/m^2), and Coal Oil Point (466 g/m^2)—had considerably lower dry organic standing stocks than any of the other study areas.

In terms of dry organic biomass, the macrophytes overshadowed the macroinvertebrates at all sites (Fig. 6). Macrophytes had their dry organic biomass maximum at Santa Catalina Island (1,396 g/m^2), followed by San Nicolas Island (798 g/m^2) and Santa Barbara Island (756 g/m^2). The macrophyte ODW minimum occurred at Ocean Beach (225 g/m^2), with similar low readings from Coal Oil Point (282 g/m^2), Santa Cruz Island (288 g/m^2), and Corona del Mar (300 g/m^2).

Ocean Beach (196 g/m^2), Coal Oil Point (184 g/m^2), and Santa Cruz Island (174 g/m^2) had the largest standing stocks of macroinvertebrates in terms of dry organic biomass. The smallest ODW totals were from San Clemente Island (16 g/m^2), Corona del Mar (61 g/m^2), Santa Catalina Island (62 g/m^2), and Whites Point (63 g/m^2). The site with the greatest yearly wave shock exposure (Ocean Beach; Table 1 and Ricketts, Calvin, and Hedgpeth 1968) had a

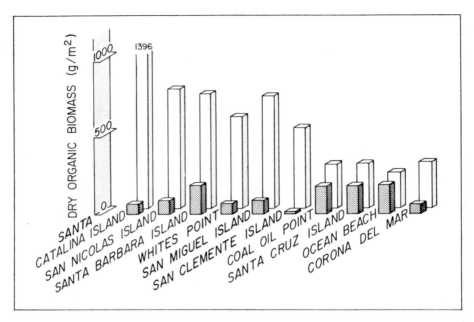

FIGURE 6. *Mean annual dry organic biomass of macrophytes (histograms in rear) and macroinvertebrates (dark histograms in front) for each study area.*

considerably lower proportion of brown algal biomass and a higher proportion of animal biomass (~46 per cent of total mean ODW) than all other sites except Santa Cruz Island (a site also high in wave surge). The two sites on protected leeward sides of islands (*i.e.*, San Clemente Island and Santa Catalina Island) had low macroinvertebrate biomass components (3 and 4 per cent of total mean ODW, respectively).

Richness (D′)

Richness indices (D') using combined macroinvertebrate and macrophyte data gave information that closely paralleled the counts of total taxa (Fig. 7). Santa Cruz Island, which appeared to be a stable climax community dominated by long-lived perennials, was considerably richer ($D' = 28.86$) than the other sites. Richness at Coal Oil Point ($D' = 15.42$), a community stressed by both oil and sand inundation, was very much lower than at the other sites. Seasonal trends in richness were less at San Miguel Island, Santa Cruz Island, and Ocean Beach than at the other sites.

Evenness (J′)

The evenness index (J') combining macrophyte and macroinvertebrate cover data was a most revealing parameter (Fig. 7). Sites high in richness and numbers of taxa were often low in evenness (*e.g.*, Ocean Beach and Santa Cruz Island). San Miguel Island ($J' = 0.66$), San Nicolas Island ($J' = 0.62$), Whites Point ($J' = 0.63$), and Santa Catalina Island ($J' = 0.62$) had the most equitably distributed biota. Ocean Beach, although it had many taxa and a high richness index, had the lowest evenness index ($J' = 0.52$). Seasonality in evenness was apparent at Corona del Mar, Santa Catalina Island, Coal Oil Point (peaks in summer), Santa Cruz Island, Ocean Beach (peaks in fall), and Whites Point (peak in winter). The aforemen-

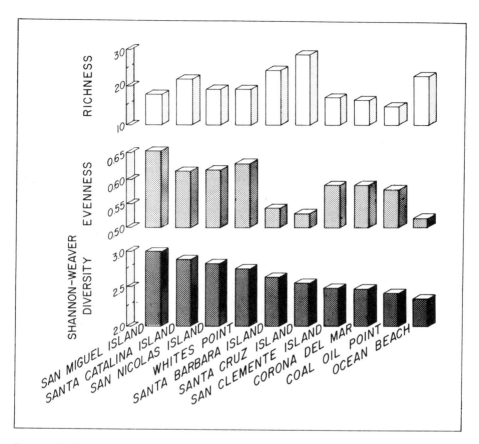

FIGURE 7. *Mean annual richness (D'e), evenness (J'e), and Shannon-Weaver diversity (H'e) for each study area using combined macrophyte and macroinvertebrate cover data.*

tioned sites represent a mixture of pristine, stable sites and sites perturbed by pollution and sand movement. Evenness indices, at least in terms of the levels recorded, do not appear to be particularly indicative of environmental disturbance (to which the populations sampled in this study may have become somewhat adapted).

Shannon-Weaver Diversity (H')

The mean Shannon-Weaver cover diversity (H') for all seasons was greatest at San Miguel Island ($H' = 2.95$) and Santa Catalina Island ($H' = 2.87$), both quite stable systems with many taxa showing high cover values (Fig. 7). Low diversities were found at Ocean Beach ($H' = 2.43$) and the heavily perturbed Coal Oil Point ($H' = 2.45$), where relatively few taxa dominated most of the substrate. For example, rhodophycean turf, *Phyllospadix,* and *Anthopleura* constituted the bulk of the cover at Coal Oil Point, while blue-green algae, *Corallina,* and *Mytilus* were dominant at Ocean Beach. Seasonal shifts in diversity were apparent at Coal Oil Point (high in summer), Santa Cruz Island (high in fall), Ocean Beach (high in fall), and Whites Point (high in winter). The H' index incorporates both richness and evenness compo-

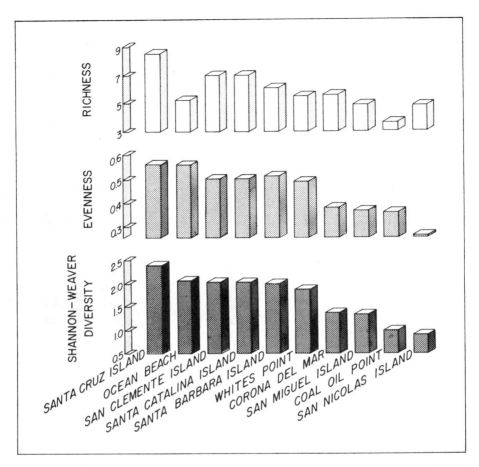

FIGURE 8. *Mean annual richness (D'e), evenness (J'e), and Shannon-Weaver diversity (H'e) for each study area using macroinvertebrate density data.*

nents but stresses evenness. Consequently, as mentioned above for J', our data do not show a clear-cut relationship between the levels of environmental disturbance we observed and Shannon-Weaver diversity, as has been shown by Littler and Murray (1975) for a pristine *versus* disturbed community on San Clemente Island. However, the sand and rock movement forms of disturbance are more localized and intertidal systems may show increased diversity (Levin and Paine 1974) as a result of patches containing successional seres.

Shannon-Weaver indices employing macroinvertebrate density as the evenness component (Fig. 8) revealed that Santa Cruz Island ($H' = 2.34$) far exceeded other sites in animal diversity; this finding agrees with simple counts of taxa. The two seasonally sand-inundated sites (Coal Oil Point and San Nicolas Island) had considerably lower macroinvertebrate diversities than the other sites ($H' = 1.08$ and 0.91, respectively), reflecting the predominance of sea anemones and *Lacuna* spp. at the former and sea anemones and littorines at the latter.

Cluster Analysis

Sites having the greatest number of seasonally constant species assemblages or subassemblages (revealed by the cluster analyses) were San Miguel Island with 11, Ocean Beach with 10, and Santa Catalina Island with 8 (Figs. 2 and 3). Corona del Mar and San Nicolas Island had only six assemblages and these changed in close association with environmental features at each site. The greatest zonational complexity was observed at Santa Cruz Island (seven zones), Santa Barbara Island (seven zones), San Miguel Island (six zones), and Santa Catalina Island (six zones). Greater zonational complexity occurred over relatively even flows of very rough-textured volcanic rock. The least zonation was evident at Corona del Mar (two zones), Coal Oil Point (three zones), Whites Point (four zones), and San Clemente Island (four zones). Reductions in zonal patterns appear to be related to lack of a high intertidal zone, mosaic habitat patterns, instability of boulder substrates, and environmental stresses such as sand inundation.

All 10 sites were subjected to cluster analysis based on the combined overall mean abundances of both macrophyte and macroinvertebrate populations. The wet weight dendrogram (Fig. 9) indicated a close grouping between the two mainland sites, Whites Point and Corona del Mar, both of which are subjected to high levels of stress from substrate instability and human disturbance. The next most closely correlated sites, Santa Barbara Island, Santa Cruz Island, and Santa Catalina Island, all have uniformly sloping volcanic rock substrates. San Miguel Island and San Nicolas Island, both of which are relatively cold-water sites, were also grouped together.

The dendrogram based on organic dry weight (Fig. 9) showed groupings similar to the aforementioned. It is somewhat enigmatic that, based on both wet weight and organic dry weight, the most northern site (Coal Oil Point) and the most southern site (Ocean Beach) are more similar to one another than either is to any other cluster. This was mostly due to the large biomass contributions by mussels and *Phyllospadix,* large species found abundantly in both warm and cold water, at these otherwise dissimilar sites. The San Clemente Island site was not closely correlated with the other nine sites because of its substantially lower macroinvertebrate biomass.

Cluster dendrograms using frequency and cover (Fig. 10) are more revealing and statistically more reliable because they are based on a greater number of samples (*i.e.,* the photo-samples). Frequency distributions showed groupings between the two warm-water biotas (Santa Catalina and San Clemente Islands), the two biologically intermediate islands (Santa Barbara and Santa Cruz), and the two sites most heavily affected by sand inundation (San Nicolas Island and Coal Oil Point).

Because space and light have been shown (see Connell 1972) to be limiting resources in the rocky intertidal zone, cover is ecologically the most meaningful parameter for comparison between sites. The cover dendrogram (Fig. 10) produced groupings that agreed closely with our opinions (based on subjective observation) regarding the similarities and dissimilarities between sites. For example, the island sites having mixtures of cold-water and warm-water biotas (Santa Barbara and Santa Cruz) clustered together with the Ocean Beach habitat, which also had large amounts of macroinvertebrate cover. The two leeward warm-water sites (Santa Catalina and San Clemente Islands) were next most similar to these two, while the two disturbed mainland sites (Whites Point and Corona del Mar) were correlated with the aforementioned to a lesser extent. The two cold-water sites (San Miguel and San Nicolas Islands) formed a second cluster group, while the oil-polluted site (Coal Oil Point) was not closely correlated with any of the other sites. The above patterns are basically similar to those determined independently from binary (presence/absence) data for the island macrophytes (Murray, Littler, and Abbott 1980) and macroinvertebrates (Seapy and Littler 1980).

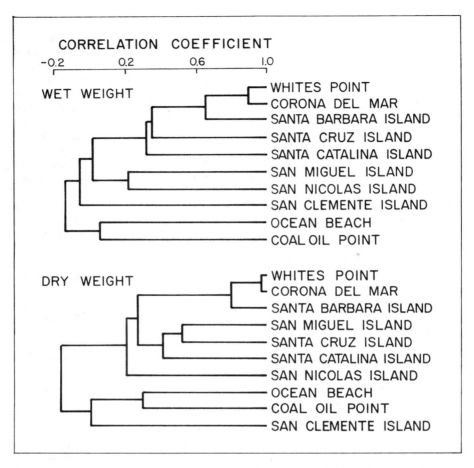

FIGURE 9. *Dendrogram displays of differential clustering for all 10 study areas using combined macrophyte and macroinvertebrate wet biomass and dry organic biomass data.*

OVERALL PATTERNS

Overall, it would appear that water temperature determined by oceanic currents accounts for much of the broad-scale, biogeographic pattern (Fig. 10, Seapy and Littler 1980, Murray, Littler, and Abbott 1980). Operating at a less coarse level are factors such as wave action and coastal upwelling, which usually lead to richer intertidal communities in moderate quantities. As indicated below, a still finer (site-specific) level of organization would seem to be related to factors such as substrate stability, sand inundation, substrate hardness and heterogeneity, desiccation stress, human-induced disturbances, and natural disturbances such as storm waves, floods, and sedimentation. Within this framework, biological interactions (*i.e.,* predation, competition, diseases) have been shown (Paine 1966, Connell 1972, Dayton 1971, 1975, Lubchenco 1978) to play an important role in determining local patchiness. It is well known that limpets and littorine snails significantly reduce algal cover in the upper intertidal zone (Cas-

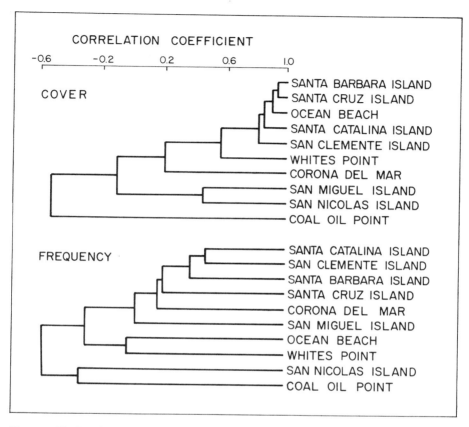

FIGURE 10. *Dendrogram displays of differential clustering for all 10 study areas using combined macrophyte and macroinvertebrate per cent frequency and cover data.*

tenholz 1961, Haven 1973, Lubchenco 1978), that urchins devastate algal stocks in pools (Paine and Vadas 1969) and shallow subtidal habitats, and that *Pisaster* plays a key role in maintaining community diversity by reducing the competitively dominant mussel beds (Paine 1966). These same biological interactions were clearly present throughout the Southern California Bight, but, in addition, we observed many others which will be analyzed in subsequent papers. For example, we currently have manipulative studies under way (Taylor and Littler 1979) which are beginning to show that large populations of *Haliotis cracherodii*, still abundant on some islands (San Nicolas, San Miguel, Santa Rosa, San Clemente), are able to cross the barnacle-dominated zone at night during high tides and severely reduce the conspicuous *Gigartina* and *Endocladia* stocks in the upper intertidal region. Also, at sand-inundated sites (San Nicolas Island, Coal Oil Point) where clonal colonies of *Anthopleura elegantissima* predominate, presumably because of their ability to "stretch" through shallow sand layers to avoid burial, they are able to prevent the settlement and development of *Phragmatopoma californica* colonies (Taylor and Littler 1979). An extremely important organism in the lower intertidal zone at most sites would seem to be the angiosperm *Phyllospadix*. This macrophyte was

Table 5. Number of taxa by major taxonomic groups collected at all 10 study areas during 1975-76.

Major groups	Number of taxa collected	Major groups	Number of taxa collected
Macrophytes		Macroinvertebrates	
Bacillariophyta	1	Annelida - Polychaeta	12
Chlorophyta	27	Arthropoda - Crustacea	27
Cyanophyta	4	Cnidaria - Anthozoa	6
Phaeophyta	34	Cnidaria - Hydrozoa	10
Rhodophyta	152	Chordata - Ascidiacea	4
Spermatophyta	2	Echinodermata - Asteroidea	8
Total	220	Echinodermata - Echinoidea	2
		Echinodermata - Holothuroidea	2
		Ectoprocta (Bryozoa)	8
		Mollusca - Bivalvia	15
		Mollusca - Cephalopoda	1
		Mollusca - Gastropoda	97
		Mollusca - Polyplacophora	12
		Platyhelminthes - Turbellaria	3
		Porifera - Calcarea	2
		Porifera - Demospongiae	18
		Total	227

observed over the course of the study to overgrow *Strongylocentrotus purpuratus* populations, which appear unable to graze it, and to smother the bigger algal forms by its invasive root and rhizome system which traps and binds sand, producing anaerobic conditions that are lethal to algal holdfast systems. The competitive dominance of *Phyllospadix* seems to be prevented in the intertidal zone by its relatively great susceptibility to periods of desiccation during daytime low-tide periods.

A total of 447 taxa was recorded during 1975-76 (Table 5). The number of macrophyte taxa (220) was about equal to the number of macroinvertebrate taxa (227). Over half of the macrophytes recorded were Rhodophyta, but Phaeophyta (especially *Egregia menziesii*) was the major contributor of biomass. Of the macroinvertebrates, gastropods contained by far the most taxa (97), while bivalves dominated the biomass.

As mentioned, biological cover in the rocky intertidal zone is of considerable interest because space and light are often limiting resources. Major macrophytic cover throughout the 10 sites was contributed predominantly by blue-green algae (overall mean of 20 per cent), *Corallina* spp. (9 per cent), *Gigartina canaliculata* (8 per cent), *Egregia menziesii* (6 per cent), and *Phyllospadix* spp. (4 per cent). Most of these were important at many of the sites, except for *Phyllospadix* spp. which was abundant only at Coal Oil Point and San Nicolas Island (the two sites most affected by sand), while blue-green algae were important at all other sites. In terms of cover, the dominant macroinvertebrates were the anemone *Anthopleura elegantissima* (3 per cent overall cover), the mussel *Mytilus californianus* (2 per cent), and the barnacles *Chthamalus fissus/dalli* (2 per cent). These four were present at most sites; however, *A. elegantissima* was predominant only at Coal Oil Point and San Nicolas Island.

Organic dry weight is also an ecologically significant parameter because it represents the

Table 6. Seasonal and mean annual population and community attributes averaged for all 10 study areas.

Parameters	Months				
	MJJA	SON	DJ	FMA	Mean
Macrophyte cover (%)	82	80	79	77	80
Macroinvertebrate cover (%)	15	16	14	14	15
Macroinvertebrate density (nos./m²)	2691	2220	2347	1719	2244
Richness (D'_e)	18.96	19.78	21.14	22.47	20.59
Evenness (J'_e)	0.59	0.60	0.58	0.57	0.58
Combined Shannon-Weaver diversity (cover)	2.62	2.71	2.69	2.62	2.66
Macroinvertebrate Shannon-Weaver diversity (density)	1.77	1.58	1.77	1.64	1.69

standing stock of organically bound energy potentially available to higher trophic levels. In regard to biomass, *Egregia menziesii* was by far the predominant organism, with an overall mean of 155 g/m², followed by *Pelvetia fastigiata* (70 g/m²), *Phyllospadix* spp. (70 g/m²), *Eisenia arborea* (57 g/m²), *Gigartina canaliculata* (56 g/m²), *Halidrys dioica* (48 g/m²), and *Corallina* spp. (29 g/m²). All of these exhibited widespread importance except *Phyllospadix* spp. (abundant at four sites), *Pelvetia fastigiata* (predominant only at three sites), and *Eisenia arborea* (dominant only at Santa Catalina Island). Macroinvertebrate biomass throughout the 10 sites resided mainly in *Anthopleura elegantissima* (33 g organic dry weight/m²), *Mytilus californianus* (22 g/m²), the purple urchin *Strongylocentrotus purpuratus* (9 g/m²), and the barnacles *Tetraclita squamosa rubescens* (4 g/m²) and *Chthamalus fissus/dalli* (2 g/m²). All of these exhibited widespread abundance except *T. squamosa rubescens* which was an important contributor of biomass at only four of the sites; most of the *A. elegantissima* biomass occurred at Coal Oil Point, while Santa Cruz Island and Corona del Mar contained most of the *S. purpuratus* biomass.

Three nearly ubiquitous intertidal zones have been broadly defined by Stephenson and Stephenson (1972) based on their extensive worldwide studies: (1) an upper littorine-blue-green algal zone, (2) a middle barnacle zone, and (3) a wetter, lower zone covered by coralline algae with abundant Phaeophyta at the lowest margin. These same generalized zones are clearly recognizable at all of the sites we investigated that have a continuous rocky slope. As indicated earlier, we were able to further differentiate from three to seven subzones and six to eleven subassemblages (depending on the particular site) within these three generalized zones by means of cluster analysis (Figs. 2 and 3).

When the seasonal means are averaged for all 10 sites and compared (Table 6), the general lack of any widespread or consistent patterns, except for a very slight lowering of most parameters following the winter months, strongly suggests that local or even site-specific conditions tended to predominate most often and obscure any broad climatic effects. This agrees with other descriptive studies (Stephenson and Stephenson 1972) of rocky intertidal systems that have also demonstrated a high degree of autonomy. Climatic conditions appeared to influence the subtler but more widespread populational declines in late fall and winter manifested by such macrophytes as *Egregia menziesii*, *Phyllospadix torreyi*, *Laurencia pacifica*, *Sargassum agardhianum*, and *Gigartina canaliculata;* this tendency may have been particularly noticeable because 1975-76 was characterized by pronounced drought conditions

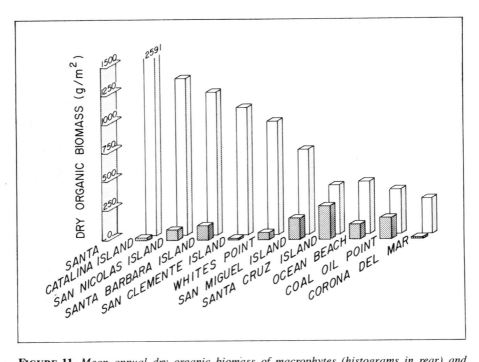

FIGURE 11. *Mean annual dry organic biomass of macrophytes (histograms in rear) and macroinvertebrates (dark histograms in front) for the lowest three 0.3-m intervals sampled at each study area.*

when winter desiccating ("Santa Ana") winds prevailed, coinciding with early afternoon low tides. Additionally, such catastrophic mortalities also have been observed for populations of upper intertidal limpets (Sutherland 1970) due to heat and desiccation when low tides occur during midday. Macrophytes and most macroinvertebrates recruited strongly during the winter-spring period, while the sea hare *Aplysia californica* was observed producing abundant egg masses in late July at Corona del Mar. Numerous workers (*e.g.*, Emery 1960, Jones 1971) have pointed out that the Southern California Bight is a very unusual system located within the overlapping boundaries of two major biogeographic regions containing a complex oceano-graphic and climatological regime. Throughout the Southern California Bight there exists a mosaic of frequently changing water temperatures, substrates, upwelling conditions, wave exposures, water transparencies, levels of natural and human-induced disturbances, and nutrient concentrations. It is not very surprising, therefore, that "representative" intertidal systems should show a high degree of site-specific individuality.

The data appear to suggest a trend in regard to substrate type. For example, those sites (San Miguel, Santa Cruz, Santa Barbara, and Santa Catalina Islands) having relatively even slopes created by flows of the very rough-textured volcanic rock (which holds small pockets of moisture) had considerably more macroinvertebrate taxa (mean of 80) than the other six sites (mean of 62); San Miguel Island was an exception with only 55. Corona del Mar (71), Whites Point (69), and San Clemente Island (65) were reasonably high in macroinvertebrate taxa, possibly due to the relatively structured nature of the substrate at these sites (*i.e.*, nearby

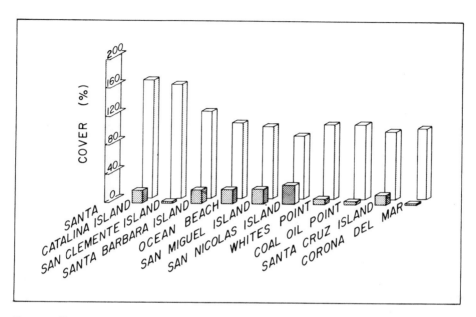

FIGURE 12. *Mean annual cover of macrophytes (histograms in rear) and macroinvertebrates (dark histograms in front) for the lowest three 0.3-m intervals sampled at each study area.*

boulder habitats having a broad spectrum of sizes and stabilities). The three remaining sites, which were entirely smooth sandstone or siltstone, contained a mean of only 55 macroinvertebrate taxa. Also, the greatest zonal complexity and constancy was observed for the same four volcanic island sites (mean of 6.5 zones), followed by siltstone/sandstone habitats (Coal Oil Point, San Nicolas Island, Whites Point, and Ocean Beach), which have an average of 4.2 zones, and boulder habitats (Corona del Mar and San Clemente Island), with the mean number of zones being only 3.0. Sites shown to be periodically inundated by sand (Coal Oil Point, San Nicolas Island, and Whites Point) had an average of 4.0 zones that were altered seasonally; areas lacking a high intertidal zone (Coal Oil Point, San Nicolas Island, Whites Point, and Corona del Mar) had a mean of 3.5 zones. Reductions in zonal pattern were most closely related to a reduction in vertical extent of the rocky shoreline, to the mosaic-like habitat distribution in the case of boulder beaches (noted also by Seapy and Littler 1978), to instability of boulder substrates, and to environmental perturbations such as sand inundations. These last two factors were shown to have especially dramatic effects, a point not very well documented in the existing literature on intertidal ecology (see Cimberg, Mann, and Straughan 1973, Daly and Mathieson 1977).

It is interesting and quite revealing to compare island with mainland rocky intertidal habitats. First, a direct comparison was made between sites, taking into consideration only the lower portions of the shoreline. The means for the lowest three 0.3-m intervals that could be sampled intertidally throughout the year were determined for each of the 10 sites and are presented in Figures 11 and 12. The average lower zone dry organic biomass (Fig. 11) for the island habitats studied (1,355 g/m^2) was more than double that for mainland sites (620 g/m^2). The bulk of this biomass was contributed by macrophytes (1,238 and 527 g/m^2 for island and mainland sites,

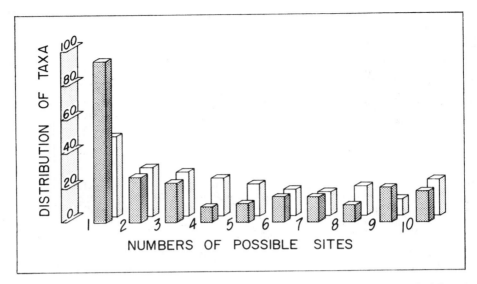

FIGURE 13. *Numbers of macrophyte (histograms in rear) and macroinvertebrate (dark histograms in front) taxa as a function of the number of sites at which they were collected.*

respectively) and mostly resided in the larger brown algae (*e.g., Egregia, Halidrys, Eisenia*) and surf grasses (*Phyllospadix* spp.). The same trend held for comparisons between lower intertidal macrophytic cover (118 per cent island *vs.* 102 per cent mainland) but the differences were not as pronounced as in the case of biomass (Fig. 12). Lower intertidal island dry organic biomass (116 g/m^2) exceeded mainland values (92 g/m^2) for macroinvertebrates and the same was true for the cover data (17 per cent island macroinvertebrate *vs.* 9 per cent mainland).

Even considering that there were more island sites sampled (six *vs.* four), the higher numbers of taxa, particularly of macroinvertebrates, that occurred only on islands are striking. Of the macrophytes taken in the quadrat samples, 117 were common to both island and mainland sites, 25 were from mainland sites only, and 39 were found uniquely in island samples. For macroinvertebrate taxa, 86 were common to both islands and mainland, 33 were only in mainland samples, and 86 were sampled only from islands.

Relatively more taxa (45 to 140) were sampled at three or less sites (Fig. 13), while many fewer (15 to 28) were found at more than five sites; this relationship applied to both macrophytes and macroinvertebrates. There were 15 macrophytes and 13 macroinvertebrates that occurred in samples at all 10 of the study areas (Table 7) and another somewhat smaller group (6 macrophytes and 12 macroinvertebrates) was sampled at 9 of the 10 sites. It is quite revealing that the site where most (66 per cent) of these otherwise ubiquitous macrophytes did not occur was Whites Point. There were two other sites where certain widespread macroinvertebrates also were not sampled: Coal Oil Point, where one-half of these were not present, and San Clemente Island, where one-third were absent.

Coal Oil Point samples, on the other hand, contained the largest number of macrophyte taxa (nine) found only at one site, while Corona del Mar and San Nicolas Island had the fewest (two). Santa Cruz Island had far more site-specific macroinvertebrates (27) and San Nicolas Island had the least (three), followed by Coal Oil Point and San Miguel Island (four). This leads

Table 7. Taxa common to all 10 sites.

Macrophytes	Macroinvertebrates
Benthic diatoms	*Acmaea (Collisella) conus*
Blue-green algae	*Acmaea (Collisella) digitalis*
Bossiella orbigniana ssp. *dichotoma*	*Acmaea (Collisella) limatula*
Ceramium eatonianum	*Acmaea (Collisella) pelta*
Corallina officinalis var. *chilensis*	*Acmaea (Collisella) scabra*
Corallina vancouveriensis	*Acmaea (Collisella) strigatella*
Egregia menziesii	*Anthopleura elegantissima*
Gelidium coulteri	*Chthamalus fissus*
Gelidium pusillum	*Chthamalus dalli*
Gigartina canaliculata	*Cyanoplax hartwegii*
Gigartina spinosa	*Littorina planaxis*
Lithophyllum proboscideum	*Mytilus californianus*
Petrospongium rugosum	*Pachygrapsus crassipes*
Pterocladia capillacea	*Pugettia producta*
Pterosiphonia dendroidea	*Tetraclita squamosa rubescens*

us to hypothesize that the presence of oil may act at Coal Oil Point to eliminate certain widespread species while providing a unique habitat for other more uncommon forms.

Samples could not be obtained from the upper vertical zones because of sand inundation at San Nicolas Island and at Coal Oil Point, Whites Point, and Corona del Mar on the mainland. On the assumption that these sites, as well as the six others, are reasonably representative of their respective habitats (island shorelines are much less subject to sand and gravel inundation than mainland shorelines), we felt that cautious comparisons of tendencies between all of the mainland and island zones sampled would be instructive. In other words, it was essential to document mainland rocky intertidal systems, which often had their upper shorelines inundated by sand and gravel and were thereby poor in upper intertidal fauna. Similarly, it was just as essential to represent the island intertidal systems with stations having well-developed high intertidal faunal assemblages. Also, it should be re-emphasized that two of the mainland sites selected as representative (Whites Point and Corona del Mar) have had considerable histories of human disturbance.

The mean grand totals of all parameters measured for the six island sites and four mainland sites showed the island sites to have higher values than the mainland sites in nearly every respect. One general trend shown by the data is that the southeastern Southern California Islands geographical group (Fig. 1) contains larger macrophyte stocks than the northwestern Southern California Islands geographical group, and mainland sites contain lower stocks than island sites (Fig. 6). For example, islands averaged 813 dry organic g/m² (719 dry organic g/m² macrophytes and 94 dry organic g/m² macroinvertebrates) while mainland sites averaged only 477 dry organic g/m² (351 dry organic g/m² macrophytes and 126 dry organic g/m² macroinvertebrates). A considerable discrepancy existed between the sizes of the island and mainland lower intertidal brown algal standing stocks (*i.e., Egregia menziesii, Eisenia arborea,* and *Halidrys dioica*); these were relatively depauperate and patchy at nearly all mainland sites (although they still dominated the biomass). The apparent reduction of mainland brown algal biomass is likely to be attributable to environmental stress; the data of Littler and Murray (1975) showed a similar considerable reduction in stocks of large brown algae near a sewage outfall on San Clemente Island directly correlated with sewage-induced environmental stress. The greater macrophyte stocks found on the southeastern Southern California Islands geographical group are due primarily to the biomass of *E. menziesii* and *E. arborea* on the warm-water islands (Santa Catalina and San Clemente).

Also, while extensive algal turf communities were prevalent in the middle to low intertidal zones at nearly all sites, the island turfs were composed of larger and more robust populations (mostly coralline algae) with epiphytes primarily of medium-sized frondose algae (*e.g.*, *Gigartina canaliculata*, *Laurencia pacifica*, *Colpomenia sinuosa*). However, mainland turf communities (corallines with *Gelidium pusillum*, *G. coulteri*, or filamentous Rhodophyta) tended to be lower-growing, more compact, and often heavily coated with a predominance of fine, filamentous epiphytes such as: blue-green algae, ectocarpoids, diatoms, and *Ceramium eatonianum* at Corona del Mar; *Herposiphonia verticillata* and *C. eatonianum* at Whites Point; and *Polysiphonia* spp., *Tiffaniella snyderae*, and *Pterosiphonia dendroidea* at Coal Oil Point. The exception on the mainland was Ocean Beach (with a robust coralline turf containing foliose algal epiphytes), a site that apparently has shown few effects of environmental degradation over the last three decades; the biota there closely approximates that found (Stephenson and Stephenson 1972) at a rocky platform north of Scripps pier and nearby Bird Rock during 1947. The only island site with a community of fine, filamentous forms (*C. eatonianum* and *Centroceras clavulatum*) epiphytic on *Corallina* turf (*C. officinalis* var. *chilensis* and *C. vancouveriensis*) was San Nicolas Island, which received considerable perturbation by sand inundation. It is suggested, therefore, that the highly epiphytized compact turf morphology— represented by algal populations having relatively great surface area-to-volume ratios, high reproductive capacities, high growth rates, simple thallus forms, and mechanisms for short and simple life histories (*e.g.*, continuous and rapid output of spores and gametes, perennation, vegetative fragmentation)—may be characteristic of communities in stressed environments. Such populations, particularly at the lower intertidal levels, may in fact make up intermediate seral communities maintained in subclimax by lack of environmental constancy and/or pollution stress.

Other parameters (Figs. 4 and 7) for which island sites exceeded mainland sites were the following: number of taxa (islands 145, mainland 134), richness (islands $D' = 21.90$, mainland $D' = 18.62$), evenness (islands $J' = 0.60$, mainland $J' = 0.58$), and Shannon-Weaver Diversity (islands $H' = 2.74$, mainland $H' = 2.54$).

One important consideration (Table 2) involves the lack of any difference between overall macrophyte cover on islands (80 per cent) compared with mainland sites (79 per cent). Average macroinvertebrate cover (Table 3) on islands was not much greater than on mainland sites (16 *vs.* 12 per cent), but average macroinvertebrate density (Table 4) was considerably lower at mainland sites (2,024 individuals/m^2) than on islands (2,422/m^2).

Several workers (*i.e.*, Dawson 1959, 1965, Nicholson and Cimberg 1971, Widdowson 1971, Thom 1976, Thom and Widdowson 1978) have documented large reductions in the number of macrophytic species over time through human influences (*e.g.*, pollution) on the southern California mainland. We found (Fig. 4), contrastingly, that the average number of macrophyte species occurring in our sample plots at the six relatively unpolluted island sites (72) was nearly equal to the average number at our four mainland sites (71). If it can be assumed that the islands have remained relatively unpolluted and that they historically contained roughly at least as many species as the mainland (both highly likely), then this similarity of species numbers (72 *vs.* 71) could lead to the interpretation that many, if not most, of the species recorded by the above authors as "lost" due to pollution on the mainland must have been rare or uncommon forms that would not be likely to be found even by extensive quadrat sampling. Another more probable interpretation is that the transect sampling procedures used first by Dawson (1959) on the mainland (*i.e.*, techniques that are appropriate for the measure of abundance [cover or frequency] but which were used instead to report presence and absence of taxa) were such that only very abundant species could be recorded. This would seem to be the case because our methods, which also were not designed to "find" species but to measure distributional patterns, were considerably more effective in recording greater numbers of macrophyte taxa present at Corona del Mar, Coal Oil Point, and Whites Point than were those of either Dawson (1959, 1965) or Nicholson and Cimberg (1971). Thus, if human effects caused declines but not disappearances, as our data contrasting island with mainland biomass indicate, subsequent use of the Dawson method would record fewer species, although the original number could still be present in the area. It is likely that both declines in abundance and actual loss of rare forms explain the results recorded by workers who repeated Dawson's (1959) original sampling methods.

Some of the differences we found between island and mainland community parameters— such as total species numbers, richness, evenness, and Shannon-Weaver diversity—can be attributed to the absence of samples from the sand-inundated high intertidal habitat, usually dominated by animals, at three of the four mainland sites. On the other hand, the absence of a high intertidal zone makes the lower values of overall mean macrophyte dry organic biomass and macrophyte cover for mainland sites even more striking because only the low to middle zones, which normally contain the bulk of the macrophyte stocks, were sampled. The observation that overall mean macroinvertebrate biomass was higher for the mainland sites is not surprising because the lower zones contain macroinvertebrates with relatively high biomass.

SUMMARY

The data presented are the product of intensive research during 1975 and 1976 into the taxonomy, distribution, and abundance patterns shown by rocky intertidal macrophytes and macroinvertebrates at 10 representative study sites within the Southern California Bight. Temporal and spatial variations of the biota were analyzed in terms of tidal location, cover, frequency, density, wet weight, dry weight, ash-free dry weight, species diversity, evenness, richness, and species assemblages to characterize a spectrum of intertidal ecosystems and to relate salient aspects of changes in standing stocks to possible causal factors. The attempt has been made to describe the important features within each study area, to compare the 10 sites, and to emphasize overall patterns and general trends. The methodology used has been explained in considerable detail since some of it is new or has not appeared elsewhere.

A total of 447 taxa was recorded. The number of macrophyte taxa (220) was about equal to the number of macroinvertebrate taxa (227). Major macrophytic cover throughout the 10 stations was contributed predominantly by blue-green algae (overall mean of 20 per cent), *Corallina* spp. (9 per cent), *Gigartina canaliculata* (8 per cent), *Egregia menziesii* (6 per cent), and *Phyllospadix* spp. (4 per cent). In terms of cover, the dominant macroinvertebrates were the anemone *Anthopleura elegantissima* (3 per cent overall cover), the mussel *Mytilus californianus* (2 per cent), and the barnacles *Chthamalus fissus/dalli* (2 per cent). In regard to biomass, *Egregia menziesii* was by far the most predominant organism, with an overall mean of 155 dry organic g/m², followed by *Pelvetia fastigiata* (70 g/m²), *Phyllospadix* spp. (70 g/m²), *Eisenia arborea* (57 g/m²), *Gigartina canaliculata* (56 g/m²), *Halidrys dioica* (48 g/m²), and *Corallina* spp. (29 g/m²). Macroinvertebrate biomass throughout the 10 sites resided mainly in *Anthopleura elegantissima* (33 g organic dry weight/m²), *Mytilus californianus* (22 g/m²), the purple urchin *Strongylocentrotus purpuratus* (9 g/m²), and the barnacles *Tetraclita squamosa rubes-*

cens (4 g/m²) and *Chthamalus fissus/dalli* (2 g/m²). In regard to abundance patterns, site-specific conditions tended to predominate most often and obscure any broad climatic effects. Climatic conditions appeared to influence the subtler but more widespread population changes manifested by such macrophytes as *Egregia menziesii, Laurencia pacifica, Sargassum agardhianum,* and *Gigartina canaliculata.* Macrophytes and most macroinvertebrates recruited strongly during the winter-spring period. Those sites (San Miguel, Santa Cruz, Santa Barbara, and Santa Catalina Islands) having relatively even slopes created by flows of the very rough-textured volcanic rock (which holds small pockets of moisture) had considerably more macroinvertebrate taxa (mean of 80) than the other six sites (mean of 62); San Miguel Island was an exception with only 55. Corona del Mar (71), Whites Point (69), and San Clemente Island (65) were reasonably high in macroinvertebrate taxa, possibly related to the relatively structured nature of the substrate at these sites (*i.e.,* nearby boulder habitats having a broad spectrum of sizes and stabilities). Reductions in zonal pattern were most closely related to a decreased vertical extent of the rocky shoreline, mosaic-like habitat distribution in the case of boulder beaches, instability of boulder substrates, and environmental disturbances such as sand inundation. The mean grand totals of all parameters measured for the six island sites and four mainland sites showed the island sites to have higher values than the mainland sites in nearly every respect. Considerable variation existed in the size of the lower intertidal brown algal standing stocks (*i.e., Egregia menziesii, Eisenia arborea,* and *Halidrys dioica*), which were relatively depauperate and patchy at nearly all mainland sites (although they still dominated the biomass). Also, while extensive algal turf communities were prevalent in the middle to low intertidal zones at nearly all sites, the island turfs comprised larger and more robust populations (mostly coralline algae) with epiphytes primarily of medium-sized frondose algae. Mainland turf communities (corallines with *Gelidium pusillum, G. coulteri,* or filamentous Rhodophyta) tended to be lower-growing, more compact, and often heavily coated with a predominance of fine, filamentous epiphytes. Other parameters for which island sites exceeded mainland sites were the following: number of taxa (islands 145, mainland 134), richness (islands $D' = 21.90$, mainland 18.62), evenness (islands $J' = 0.60$, mainland 0.58), and Shannon-Weaver Diversity (islands $H' = 2.74$, mainland 2.54). It is likely that both declines in abundance of many species and the actual loss of uncommon forms due to disturbances have occurred at mainland habitats near large human population centers.

ACKNOWLEDGMENTS

Funding for the work presented here was provided by the U. S. Department of the Interior, Bureau of Land Management as part of their Outer Continental Shelf Program.

This project would not have been possible were it not for the high level of skills, dedication, and perseverance shown by: Jerry Abajian, Joyce Cook, Charles Currie, Jr., Cally Curtis, Stephen Fain, Jack Fancher, William Fitt, Jr., Steve Gaines, Roxanna Hager, Mark Hay, Maurice Hill, Andrew Kindig, Rob Kleban, David Martz, Martina McGlynn, Wayne McMahon, Ronald Mizusawa, Mark Schildhauer, Robert Sims, James Stretch, Peggy Trabue, Mark Tapley, Carol Ungemach, Lynnette Vesco, Janet Wheeler, Susan Yamada, and Karen Yoshihara.

Patrick Y. O'Brien coordinated the overall field and laboratory efforts while Diane S. Littler served very ably as administrative and materials organizer, as well as project illustrator. Bill Fitt devoted much effort and personal time to the tidepool fish studies. Special acknowledgments are given to my colleagues Dr. S. N. Murray and Dr. R. R. Seapy, who identified macrophyte and macroinvertebrate specimens, respectively, throughout the project and also provided technical and scholarly expertise which contributed immeasurably to overall quality control of the data produced. The credibility of the information gathered was elevated greatly by the contributions of Dr. Isabella Abbott, who personally annotated and confirmed nearly all of our algal identifications. Special thanks are given to the following people for verification and identification of invertebrate species: Dr. Gerald Bakus (Porifera), Dr. Gilbert Jones (Mollusca and Crustacea), and Dr. Charles Lambert (Ascidiacea). We are indebted to Cecil W. Robinson for the time and care he spent characterizing our samples of substrate from each of the 10 study areas.

REFERENCES

ABE, N. 1937. Ecological survey of Iwayama Bay, Palao. Palao Trop. Biol. Station Stud. 1:217-324.

BRIGHT, D. B. 1974. Benthic invertebrates. Pp. 10-1 to 10-291 *in* M. D. Dailey, B. Hill, and N. Lansing, eds., A summary of knowledge of the southern California coastal zone and offshore areas. Bureau of Land Management, U.S. Dept. Interior, Washington, D.C.

CAPLAN, R. I., and R. A. BOOLOOTIAN. 1967. Intertidal ecology of San Nicolas Island. Pp. 203-217 *in* R. N. Philbrick, ed., Proceedings of the symposium on the biology of the California Islands. Santa Barbara Botanic Garden, Santa Barbara, Calif.

CASTENHOLZ, R. W. 1961. The effect of grazing on marine littoral diatom populations. Ecology 42:783-794.

CIMBERG, R., S. MANN, and D. STRAUGHAN. 1973. A reinvestigation of southern California rocky intertidal beaches three and one-half years after the 1969 Santa Barbara oil spill: a preliminary report. Pp. 697-702 *in* Proceedings of joint conference on prevention and control of oil spills. American Petroleum Institute, Washington, D.C.

COCKERELL, T. D. A. 1939. The marine invertebrate fauna of the Californian islands. Proc. 6th Pac. Sci. Congr. 3:501-504.

CONNELL, J. H. 1972. Community interactions on marine rocky intertidal shores. Ann. Rev. Ecol. Syst. 3:169-192.

DAWSON, E. Y. 1949. Contributions toward a marine flora of the Southern California Channel Islands, I-III. Occas. Pap. Allan Hancock Found. Publs. 8:1-57.

————. 1959. A primary report on the benthic marine flora of southern California. Pp. 169-264 *in* Oceanographic survey of the continental shelf area of southern California. Publs. California State Water Pollution Control Board 20.

————. 1965. Intertidal algae. Pp. 220-231, Appendix 351-438 *in* An oceanographic and biological survey of the southern California mainland shelf. Publs. California State Water Quality Control Board 27.

DAWSON, E. Y., and M. NEUSHUL. 1966. New records of marine algae from Anacapa Island, California. Nova Hedwigia 12:173-187.

DAYTON, P. K. 1971. Competition, disturbance, and community organization: the provision and subsequent utilization of space in a rocky intertidal community. Ecol. Monogrs. 41:351-389.

————. 1975. Experimental evaluation of ecological dominance in a rocky intertidal algal community. Ecol. Monogrs. 45:137-159.

DALY, M. A., and A. C. MATHIESON. 1977. The effects of sand movement on intertidal seaweeds and selected invertebrates at Bound Rock, New Hampshire, USA. Marine Biol. 43:45-55.

EMERY, K. O. 1960. The sea off southern California. John Wiley & Sons, New York, N. Y.

FOSTER, M., M. NEUSHUL, and R. ZINGMARK. 1971. The Santa Barbara oil spill, pt. 2: initial effects on intertidal and kelp bed organisms. Environ. Pollut. 2:115-134.

FRANCIS, L. 1973. Clone specific segregation in the sea anemone *Anthopleura elegantissima*. Biol. Bull. 144:64-72.

HATCHER, B. G., A. R. O. CHAPMAN, and K. H. MANN. 1977. An annual carbon budget for the kelp *Laminaria longicruris*. Marine Biol. 44:85-96.

HAVEN, S. B. 1973. Competition for food between the intertidal gastropods *Acmaea scabra* and *Acmaea digitalis*. Ecology 54:143-151.

HEWATT, W. G. 1946. Marine ecological studies on Santa Cruz Island, California. Ecol. Monogrs. 16:186-208.

JONES, J. H. 1971. General circulation and water characteristics in the Southern California Bight. Southern California Coastal Water Research Project, SCCWRP TR 101.

KIMURA, J. C. 1974. Climate. Pp. 2-1 to 2-70 *in* M. D. Dailey, B. Hill, and N. Lansing, eds., A summary of knowledge of the southern California coastal zone and offshore areas. Bureau of Land Management, U.S. Dept. Interior, Washington, D.C.

KINDIG, A. C., and M. M. LITTLER. Growth and primary productivity of marine macrophytes under exposure to domestic sewage effluents. Marine Environ. Res. (in press).

LEVIN, S. A., and R. T. PAINE. 1974. Disturbance, patch formation, and community structure. Proc. Natl. Acad. Sci. 71:2744-2747.

LITTLER, M. M. 1971. Standing stock measurements of crustose coralline algae (Rhodophyta) and other saxicolous organisms. J. Exper. Marine Biol. Ecol. 6:91-99.

_____. 1978. Assessments of visitor impact on spatial variations in the distribution and abundance of rocky intertidal organisms on Anacapa Island, California. U. S. Natl. Park Serv. Rep.

LITTLER, M. M., and S. N. MURRAY. 1974. The primary productivity of marine macrophytes from a rocky intertidal community. Marine Biol. 27:131-135.

_____. 1975. Impact of sewage on the distribution, abundance and community structure of rocky intertidal macro-organisms. Marine Biol. 30:277-291.

_____. 1978. Influence of domestic wastes on energetic pathways in rocky intertidal communities. J. Appl. Ecol. 15:583-595.

LUBCHENCO, J. 1978. Plant species diversity in a marine intertidal community: importance of herbivore food preference and algal competitive abilities. Amer. Natur. 112:23-39.

MANTON, S. M. 1935. Ecological surveys of coral reefs. Sci. Rep. Great Barrier Reef Exped. 3:273-312.

MARGALEF, R. 1968. Perspectives in ecological theory. University of Chicago Press, Chicago, Ill.

MURRAY, S. N. 1974. Benthic algae and grasses. Pp. 9-1 to 9-61 *in* M. D. Dailey, B. Hill, and N. Lansing, eds., A summary of knowledge of the southern California coastal zone and offshore areas. Bureau of Land Management, U.S. Dept. Interior, Washington, D.C.

MURRAY, S. N., and M. M. LITTLER. 1978. Patterns of algal succession in a perturbated marine intertidal community. J. Phycol. 14:506-512.

MURRAY, S. N., M. M. LITTLER, and I. A. ABBOTT. 1980. Biogeography of the California marine algae with emphasis on the Southern California Islands. Pp. 325-339 *in* D.M. Power, ed., The California Islands: proceedings of a multidisciplinary symposium. Santa Barbara Museum of Natural History, Santa Barbara, Calif.

NEUSHUL, M., W. D. CLARKE, and D. W. BROWN. 1967. Subtidal plant and animal communities of the Southern California Islands. Pp. 37-55 *in* R. N. Philbrick, ed., Proceedings of the symposium on the biology of the California Islands. Santa Barbara Botanic Garden, Santa Barbara, Calif.

NICHOLSON, N. L. 1972. The Santa Barbara oil spills in perspective. California Marine Res. Comm., California Cooperative Oceanic Fisheries Investigations [CalCOFI] Rep. 16:130-149.

NICHOLSON, N. L., and R. L. CIMBERG. 1971. The Santa Barbara oil spills of 1969: a post-spill survey of the rocky intertidal. Pp. 325-399 *in* D. Straughan, ed., Biological and oceanographical survey of the Santa Barbara Channel oil spill. 1969-1970, v. I. Allan Hancock Foundation, University of Southern California, Los Angeles, Calif.

PAINE, R. T. 1966. Food web complexity and species diversity. Amer. Natur. 100:65-75.

PAINE, R. T., and R. L. VADAS. 1969. The effects of grazing by sea urchins, *Strongylocentrotus* spp., on benthic algal populations. Limnol. Oceanogr. 14:710-719.

PIELOU, E. C. 1975. Ecological diversity. John Wiley & Sons, New York, N.Y.

POOLE, R. W. 1974. An introduction to quantitative ecology. McGraw-Hill, New York, N.Y.

RICKETTS, E. F., J. CALVIN, and J. W. HEDGPETH. 1968. Between Pacific tides. Stanford University Press, Stanford, Calif.

SEAPY, R. R. 1974. Macro-invertebrates. Pp. 19-22 *in* S. N. Murray and M. M. Littler, eds., Biological features of intertidal communities near the U.S. Navy sewage outfall, Wilson Cove, San Clemente Island, California. U.S. Naval Undersea Center, San Diego, Calif., TP 396.

SEAPY, R. R., and M. M. LITTLER. 1978. The distribution, abundance, community structure, and primary productivity of macroorganisms from two central California rocky intertidal habitats. Pac. Sci. 32:293-314.

————. 1980. Biogeography of rocky intertidal macroinvertebrates of the Southern California Islands. Pp. 307-323 *in* D.M. Power, ed., The California Islands: proceedings of a multidisciplinary symposium. Santa Barbara Museum of Natural History, Santa Barbara, Calif.

SHANNON, C. E., and W. WEAVER. 1949. The mathematical theory of communication. University of Illinois Press, Urbana, Ill.

SIMS, R. H. 1974. Macrophytes. Pp. 13-17 *in* S. N. Murray and M. M. Littler, eds., Biological features of intertidal communities near the U.S. Navy sewage outfall, Wilson Cove, San Clemente Island, California. U.S. Naval Undersea Center, San Diego, Calif., TP 396.

SOKAL, R. R., and P. H. A. SNEATH. 1963. Principles of numerical taxonomy. W. H. Freeman, San Francisco, Calif.

SOUTHERN CALIFORNIA COASTAL WATER RESEARCH PROJECT. 1973. The ecology of the Southern California Bight: implications for water quality management. SCCWRP TR 104.

STEPHENSON, T. A., and A. STEPHENSON. 1972. Life between tidemarks on rocky shores. W. H. Freeman, San Francisco, Calif.

STRAUGHAN, D. 1971. What has been the effect of the spill on the ecology in the Santa Barbara Channel? Pp. 401-426 *in* D. Straughan, ed., Biological and oceanographical survey of the Santa Barbara Channel oil spill. 1969-1970, v. I. Allan Hancock Foundation, University of Southern California, Los Angeles, Calif.

SUTHERLAND, J. P. 1970. Dynamics of high and low populations of the limpet, *Acmaea scabra* (Gould). Ecol. Monogrs. 40:169-188.

TAYLOR, P. R., and M. M. LITTLER. 1979. The effects of *Anthopleura elegantissima* and *Haliotis cracherodii* on rocky intertidal community structure. Bureau of Land Management, U.S. Dept. Interior, Rep. II, Section II-4.0.

THOM, R. M. 1976. Changes in the intertidal flora of the southern California mainland. M. A. thesis, California State University, Long Beach, Calif.

THOM, R. M., and T. B. WIDDOWSON. 1978. A resurvey of E. Yale Dawson's 42 intertidal algal transects on the southern California mainland after 15 years. Bull. So. California Acad. Sci. 77:1-13.

U.S. DEPARTMENT OF COMMERCE. 1975. Tide tables. National Ocean Survey, Rockville, Md.
————. 1976. Tide tables. National Ocean Survey, Rockville, Md.
VADAS, R. L. 1977. Preferential feeding: an optimization strategy in sea urchins. Ecol. Monogrs. 47:337-371.
WIDDOWSON, T. B. 1971. Changes in the intertidal algal flora of the Los Angeles area since the survey by E. Yale Dawson in 1956-1959. Bull. So. California Acad. Sci. 70:2-16.
WILSON, J. L. 1976. Data synthesis. Southern California baseline study, final report, vol. III, Rep. 5.2. Bureau of Land Management, U.S. Dept. Interior, Washington, D.C.
WYNNE, M. J., and S. LOISEAUX. 1976. Recent advances in life history studies of the Phaeophyta. Phycologia 15:435-452.

Biogeography of Rocky Intertidal Macroinvertebrates of the Southern California Islands

Roger R. Seapy[1] and Mark M. Littler[2]

[1]*Department of Biological Science,
California State University, Fullerton, California 92634*

[2]*Department of Ecology and Evolutionary Biology,
University of California, Irvine, California 92717*

INTRODUCTION

The macroinvertebrate fauna of the rocky intertidal zone on the Southern California Islands is incompletely known; consequently, it has not been possible to determine zoogeographical relationships among the various islands or between the islands and the mainland. Three studies (Hewatt 1946, Caplan and Boolootian 1967, Littler and Murray 1975) have been published on the rocky intertidal biotas for three of the islands, although only one of these (Hewatt 1946) is a comprehensive faunistic study. Based on extensive collections from rocky and sandy beaches at six stations around Santa Cruz Island, Hewatt (1946) recorded a total of 297 invertebrate species. It is noteworthy that, of this total, many were small, inconspicuous forms that dwell among and beneath macrophytes (*e.g.*, articulated corallines) and macroinvertebrates (*e.g.*, mussels). After assembling the latitudinal distribution records for the various species, Hewatt concluded that Santa Cruz Island was located in a transitional area between northern and southern faunas. This conclusion was based, in part, on the determination that nearly equal percentages of the island's rocky intertidal species occurred mainly to the north (30 per cent) or south (27 per cent) of Point Conception, while the remaining species (43 per cent) were broadly distributed along the mainland. The vertical distribution of the 19 predominant rocky intertidal macroinvertebrates at two sites on the southeastern portion of San Nicolas Island was assessed by Caplan and Boolootian (1967). Their analyses are of little biogeographical value, however, since they were concerned with only those species whose densities exceeded $100/m^2$ from any quadrat sampled. Rocky shore species on the leeward, east-facing side of San Clemente Island near Wilson Cove were reported by Littler and Murray (1975). However, since the inception of the intensive Bureau of Land Management intertidal baseline studies (Littler 1977, 1978, 1979, 1980), our knowledge of the fauna there has greatly expanded.

Historically, Point Conception has been considered an important marine biogeographical boundary along the Pacific coast of North America (reviewed by Hedgpeth 1957 and Valentine 1966), with the cold-temperate Oregonian Province lying to the north and the warm-temperate Californian Province to the south (Fig. 1). The Oregonian Province and the Aleutian Province are included in the East Pacific Boreal Region (Fig. 1), while the Californian Province describes a warm-temperate region separate from the East Pacific Tropical Region, which includes the Mexican and Panamanian Provinces. The Cortezian Province in the Gulf of California probably should not be considered warm-temperate (as Briggs [1974] has suggested), but rather as having tropical affinities (W. Newman, pers. comm.). The biogeographical boundary at Point Conception does not appear to be sharp. Instead, it can be considered to represent an overlap area, with cold-temperate species ranging two to three degrees in latitude to the south and warm-temperate species ranging two to three degrees to the north. The existence of this overlap zone was clearly described by Newell (1948) using the molluscan range data of Schenck and Keen (1936) and Keen (1937). The area of overlap, termed the Californian Transition Zone, delineates the latitudinal range of a number of short-range endemic species (Newman in press).

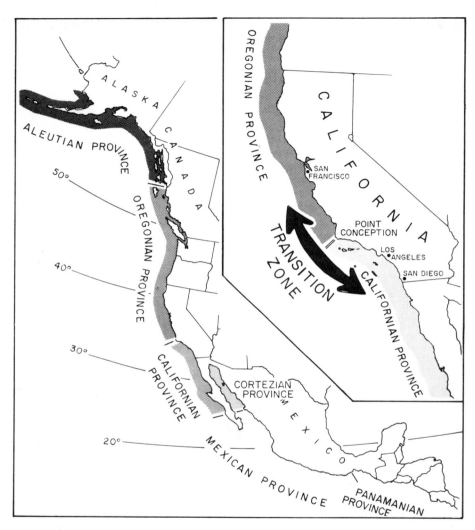

FIGURE 1. *Zoogeographical provinces of the Pacific coast of North America (modified from Briggs 1974).*

The reason Point Conception is important biogeographically is clearly related to patterns of oceanic circulation. Off central California, the broad and sluggish California Current generally flows southeastward along the coast (Wyllie 1966) and near-shore waters are maintained at cold temperatures through spring and summer due largely to the extended upwelling period between about April and August (Bolin and Abbott 1963). At Point Conception, the coastline turns sharply to the east. California Current flow does not follow the shoreline, however, but continues southeastward (Reid *et al.* 1958) to the west of the Santa Rosa-Cortez Ridge, the submerged peninsula that extends from Point Conception to Cortez Bank and includes Santa Rosa and San Nicolas Islands. South of Cortez Bank, the California Current turns eastward in a

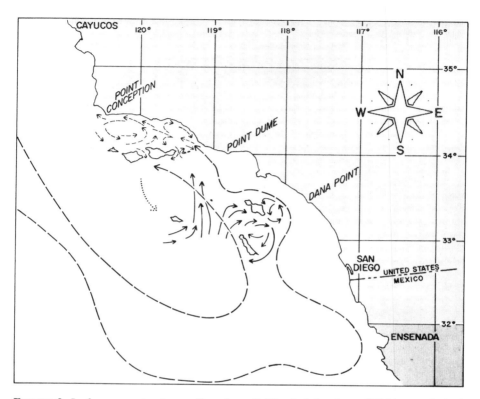

FIGURE 2. *Surface current patterns off southern California (after Seapy 1974). Long dashed lines represent mean geostrophic flow contours for the month of August, averaged for a 16-year period between 1950 and 1965 (Wyllie 1966). Short dashed lines indicate surface current flow during August 1969 based on drift bottle studies (Kolpack 1971). The solid lines are surface currents derived from 10-m drogue releases during October 1958 (Scripps Inst. Oceanogr. 1962), while the single dotted line between Santa Rosa and San Nicolas Islands is based on Neushul* et al. *(1967).*

broad arc (Fig. 2), forming the Southern California Eddy or Countercurrent (Sverdrup and Fleming 1941). This eddy is most strongly developed during the summer months (Wyllie 1966), a finding supported by the recent drift card studies of Squire (1977). For this reason, the 16-year mean geostrophic flow contours of Wyllie (1966) for the month of August were used to illustrate this general flow (Fig. 2). This pattern of flow, including several of the counterclockwise-flowing eddies, has been substantiated by recent satellite thermal imagery done in late June 1976 (Hendricks 1977). The northwesterly-flowing arm of the Southern California Eddy is generally a weak flow (Reid *et al.* 1958). Consequently, the near-shore waters remain along the coast for an extended period and become much warmer than the offshore waters which are continuously replaced by cold California Current water (Reid *et al.* 1958). The warm, northwesterly-flowing coastal waters move along the southern California mainland as far north as Point Conception, where they encounter the cold, southeasterly-flowing waters of the California Current. Such markedly different hydrographic histories and physical-chemical properties of the coastal waters to the northwest and southeast of Point Conception lead to the prediction of a biogeographical break between cold-temperate and warm-temperate faunas at Point Conception.

In light of the above hydrographic patterns, the Southern California Islands should, hypothetically, exhibit intermediate biogeographical affinities with biotas on the mainland to the north and south of Point Conception. This was indeed the conclusion of Hewatt (1946) concerning Santa Cruz Island. Because San Miguel Island lies on the eastern edge of the southeasterly-flowing California Current, we predict that it should show the strongest northern affinity of all the islands. San Nicolas Island should also have strong northern affinities since it is bathed directly by the California Current; however, because it is located to the southeast of San Miguel Island, it receives waters that should be somewhat warmer. San Clemente and Santa Catalina Islands, located in the pathway of the warm, northerly-flowing Southern California Eddy (Fig. 2), are hypothesized to show the strongest affinities of all the islands with the southern mainland biota. Santa Barbara Island should show intermediate affinities, as should Anacapa Island and the southern sides of Santa Cruz and Santa Rosa Islands, because the waters impinging on them should represent a mixture of cold and warm waters from the California Current and Southern California Eddy, respectively (Fig. 2). The northern sides of Santa Rosa and Santa Cruz Islands are bathed by colder, eastward-flowing waters of the counterclockwise gyre in the Santa Barbara Channel. This gyre is fed by California Current water (Fig. 2) deflected into the Channel by San Miguel Island (Kolpack 1971, Hendricks 1977), and the northern sides of these two islands are generally colder than the southern sides (Neushul et al. 1967). The biogeographical relationships hypothesized above for the islands are basically similar to those proposed by Neushul et al. (1967), who also utilized oceanographic data from the California Cooperative Oceanic Fisheries Investigations (CalCOFI) program in developing a biogeographical model for the islands.

MATERIALS AND METHODS

Rocky intertidal macroinvertebrates were collected from nine sites on the eight Southern California Islands (Fig. 3) between August 1975 and February 1978 as part of the Bureau of Land Management's Outer Continental Shelf research program in the Southern California Bight (Littler 1980). These species records are included in technical reports (Littler 1977, 1978, 1979) for the Bureau of Land Management. In these studies, quarterly standing stock assessments were made for six of the island sites (San Miguel, southeast end of San Nicolas, Santa Cruz, Santa Barbara, Santa Catalina, and San Clemente) over a two-year period; Santa Rosa Island was assessed over a one-year period, while the sites on Anacapa Island and the west end of San Nicolas Island were sampled during single visits. However, the level of actual faunistic sampling and taxonomic effort was comparable at each site.

For comparative zoogeographical purposes, macrofaunal records from mainland sites that could be considered northern and southern were desired. For a southern site, we chose the Bureau of Land Management study area at Ocean Beach, which has been sampled quarterly over a two-year period (Seapy and Littler 1977, 1978a). For a northern site, we used Cayucos Point in central California, which we sampled intensively in 1973 (Seapy and Littler 1978b) and on two subsequent occasions in 1976 and 1977.

Species records for each of the eleven sites were compiled as a presence-absence data matrix. Records for two taxonomic groups were excluded: the bryozoans, because our tentative identifications and unknowns have not been resolved, and the hydroids, because identification below the generic level is not presently reliable for the common forms (Rees and Hand 1975). For the remaining taxa, a literature search was conducted to determine the latitudinal ranges for as many of the species as possible, with the result that ranges were assigned to all of the

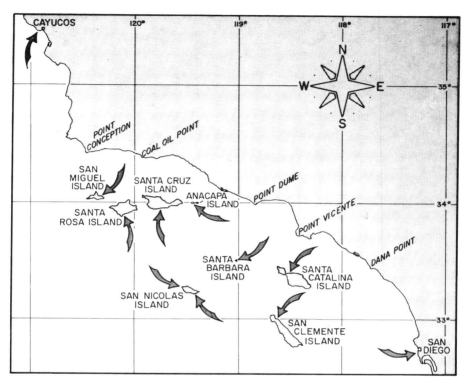

FIGURE 3. *Location of the sampling sites on the Southern California Islands and on the mainland at Ocean Beach (near San Diego) and Cayucos Point.*

represented species of anthozoans, polychaetes, molluscs, crustaceans, and echinoderms, but were only partially completed in the cases of the ascidians (10 of 13 species) and poriferans (8 of 23 species). In determining the latitudinal ranges, the most recent authority was accepted and a variety of sources were used: Porifera (de Laubenfels 1932); Anthozoa (Ricketts, Calvin, and Hedgpeth 1968); Polychaeta (Hartman 1969); Gastropoda (Dall 1921, Oldroyd 1925-1927, Morris 1966, McLean 1978, Keen 1971, Abbott 1974, D. Lindberg, pers. comm., G. Mac-Donald, pers. comm.); Polyplacophora (Burghardt and Burghardt 1969, McLean 1978); Bivalvia (Dall 1921, Oldroyd 1925-1927, McLean 1978, Keen 1971); Crustacea (Schmitt 1921, Menzies 1948, Garth 1958, Haig 1960, Ricketts, Calvin, and Hedgpeth 1968, McLaughlin 1974, Haig and Wicksten 1975, Nations 1975, Newman 1975); Echinodermata (Fisher 1911, Ricketts, Calvin, and Hedgpeth 1968); and Ascidiacea (Van Name 1945). Perusal of the range data suggested that the species could be grouped into four categories: northern, southern, widespread, and transitional. Species classified as northern range northward from Point Conception through the Oregonian Province, and often through the Aleutian Province, as well. However, the southern limit for most of these species was not Point Conception but San Diego or northern Baja California. Southern species are those that range southward from Point Conception through the Californian Province and possibly into the Cortezian, Mexican, and, in a number of cases, the Panamanian Provinces. As with the southerly limits of the northern

TABLE 1. Macroinvertebrate species present at all eleven study sites.

Mollusca: Gastropoda (10 species)	Mollusca: Polyplacophora (2 species)
Acmaea (Collisella) digitalis	*Cyanoplax hartwegii*
Acmaea (Collisella) limatula	*Mopalia muscosa*
Acmaea (Collisella) pelta	
Acmaea (Collisella) scabra	Cnidaria: Anthozoa (1 species)
Acmaea (Collisella) strigatella	*Anthopleura elegantissima*
Fissurella volcano	
Littorina planaxis	Arthropoda: Crustacea (6 species)
Littorina scutulata	*Balanus glandula*
Lottia gigantea	*Chthamalus dalli*
Ocenebra circumtexta	*Chthamalus fissus*
	Pollicipes polymerus
	Pugettia producta
Mollusca: Bivalvia (2 species)	*Tetraclita squamosa rubescens*
Mytilus californianus	
Septifer bifurcatus	Echinodermata: Echinoidea (1 species)
	Strongylocentrotus purpuratus

category, the northerly limit of the southern species was not usually Point Conception but some area in central California, most commonly near Monterey. Species classified as widespread range broadly through at least the Californian and Oregonian Provinces. Many of the species in this category occur farther northward and/or southward of the Oregonian and Californian Provinces, respectively. Finally, a special category, termed transitional, was required to account for the ranges of about 15 per cent of the species that ranged narrowly through the area of latitudinal overlap for the northern and southern categories—approximately through central and southern California. The existence of such a transitional species grouping, extending over an approximate four-degree latitudinal range, has been recognized for benthic barnacles by Newman (in press), who termed the area the Californian Transition Zone. Recently, a "coastal-trend-grid coding system" was developed by Hayden and Dolan (1976) to analyze zoogeographical patterns for the coasts of North and South America. These authors identified several co-range termini along the Pacific coast, including a major one separating the Oregonian and Californian Provinces approximately between San Diego and Monterey. This result is consistent with the present interpretation and with those of Newell (1948) and Newman (in press).

The second analytical approach was to subject the presence-absence data matrix to computer-mediated classification analyses. To emphasize site differences, the 22 species present at all of the sites (Table 1) were deleted from the raw data matrix. A matrix of dissimilarity values for all possible site pairs was first generated, using the Canberra metric

dissimilarity measure: $D = \frac{1}{n} \sum_{1}^{n} |X_{1j} - X_{2j}| / (X_{1j} + X_{2j})$, where n is the number of species

present at sites 1 and 2, X_{1j} is the presence (1) or absence (0) of the *j*th species at site 1, and X_{2j} is the presence or absence of the *j*th species at site 2. The matrix of Canberra metric dissimilarity values was then analyzed in two ways. First, the matrix was subjected to cluster analysis and a dendrogram was generated. The weakness of this approach is that the dendrogram is built by the progressive fusion of sites into site groupings, and misclassifications can occur at higher levels of the clustering (or fusion) process. To counteract this problem, the dendrograms were interpreted in light of results obtained from principal coordinates (PCOORD) ordination analysis. This type of ordination analysis is recommended (Clifford and Stephenson 1975)

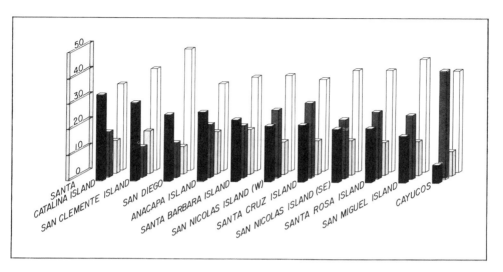

FIGURE 4. *Composition of the macroinvertebrate fauna at each site expressed as per cent of the fauna represented by northern (black bars), southern (dark bars), transitional (light bars), and widespread (clear bars) species.*

when the starting point is a dissimilarity matrix. Cluster and ordination analyses were performed using (1) all of the species (except those 22 species listed in Table 1 as common to all sites), (2) the Gastropoda separately, and (3) a reduced matrix that included only those species whose abundances exceeded one per square meter, averaged over all tidal intervals sampled at a given site. The analysis using the Gastropoda was performed to see whether or not the patterns shown by the total complement of species were supported by the gastropods (the largest major group) alone. The analysis using only those species whose abundances exceeded one per square meter was performed to determine the effect of excluding species that were not relatively common components of the fauna. This analysis was also useful because possible site differences in collection intensity could be eliminated by excluding the rarer species. Such a bias in sampling could have been the case for Anacapa Island and the west end of San Nicolas Island, each of which was visited only once. However, sampling differences would not appear to be likely because the collecting efforts were intensive and resulted in the identification of a comparably large number of species at both sites (98 at Anacapa Island and 82 at the west end of San Nicolas Island).

RESULTS AND DISCUSSION

Analysis of the latitudinal range data for the macroinvertebrate species at the various sites (Fig. 4) indicates that a high percentage of the fauna, averaging 39 per cent and ranging from 34 to 48 per cent, consisted of species displaying widespread distributional ranges. For these species, there were no apparent trends shown between sites. The percentage of the fauna classified as transitional (short-range endemics) averaged 14 per cent and ranged from 10 to 18 per cent, being lowest at the two mainland sites. Among the island sites, the southerly and near-shore islands (San Clemente, Santa Catalina, Santa Barbara, and Anacapa) displayed somewhat higher percentages of transitional species than did the northerly and offshore islands (San Nicolas, San Miguel, Santa Rosa, and Santa Cruz). However, these differences are so

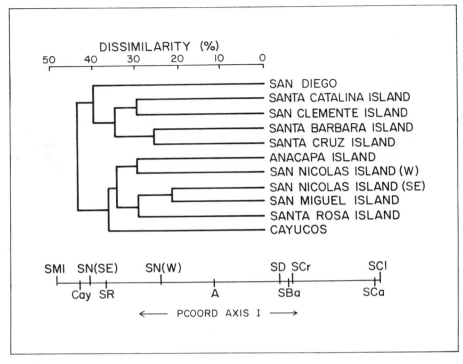

FIGURE 5. *Classification analyses using all species except those common to all sites. Cluster analysis results of per cent dissimilarity between sites and site groupings are displayed as a dendrogram (above). Principal coordinates (PCOORD) ordination results are shown for axis I (below).*

slight as to be of questionable significance and only suggest a possible trend. In combination, the species that were widespread and transitional comprised an average of 53 per cent of the fauna at each site, and ranged from 48 to 60 per cent.

The percentages of the fauna represented by northern and southern species (Fig. 4) are essentially in agreement with the hypothesized inter-island affinities based on hydrographic considerations. The two island sites having the highest proportions of southern species were Santa Catalina (34 per cent) and San Clemente (31 per cent). Both sites had somewhat higher percentages of southern species than the southern mainland site at San Diego (26 per cent), perhaps because such a high proportion of the species at San Diego (48 per cent) was classified as widespread. Anacapa and Santa Barbara Islands had the next highest percentages of southern species (27 and 24 per cent, respectively), although the percentages of northern species at these two sites were only somewhat less (22 per cent at Anacapa and 21 per cent at Santa Barbara). At the remaining sites, the percentage of northern species was greater than the percentage of southern species, ranging from 24 per cent at the southeast end of San Nicolas Island to 29 per cent at Santa Cruz Island. The only historical data against which the present results can be directly contrasted are those of Hewatt (1946) for Santa Cruz Island. The comparison provides quite good agreement, with Hewatt having 1 per cent more northern species, 5 per cent more

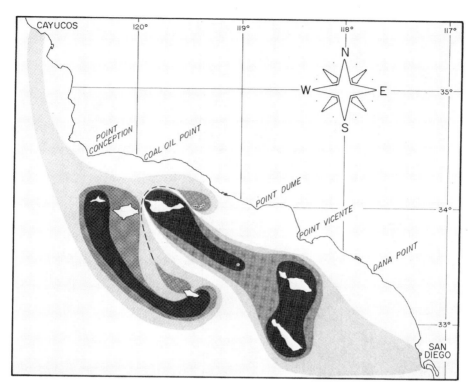

FIGURE 6. *Map overlay of cluster analysis results (Figure 5) using all of the species except those common to all sites.*

southern species, and 6 per cent fewer widespread and transitional species than we recorded at our Santa Cruz Island site.

Only at Cayucos Point was the percentage of the fauna represented by widespread species (40 per cent) exceeded by another category, northern species (43 per cent). It is also noteworthy that Cayucos Point had the lowest percentage (7) of southern species (Fig. 4). One might expect to observe the reverse faunal relationship at the southern mainland site, San Diego. While the percentage of southern species (26) was higher than the percentage of northern species (14) at San Diego (Fig. 4), the difference was not as pronounced as that recorded at Cayucos Point. These data suggest that Point Conception represents a stronger zoogeographical barrier to southern species ranging northward than to northern species ranging southward. Interestingly, this was the conclusion of Van Name (1945) regarding the distribution of ascidians on the Pacific coast of North America, and of Horn and Allen (1978) for California coastal fishes. However, Newell (1948) found that the "nodal point" (where there are equal numbers of species from both the Oregonian and Californian Provinces) was near Point Conception for molluscs, with similar decreases in numbers of Californian and Oregonian species to the north and south of Point Conception. The "nodal point" for barnacle and copepod species from the two provinces (Newman in press) occurred between one and two degrees north of Point

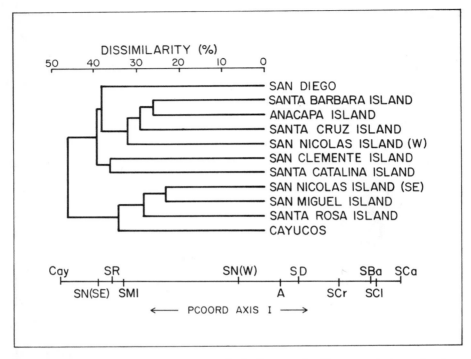

FIGURE 7. *Classification analyses using only the Gastropoda. Cluster analysis results of per cent dissimilarity between sites and site groupings are displayed as a dendrogram (above). Principal coordinates (PCOORD) ordination results are shown for axis I (below).*

Conception. Thus, different taxonomic groups appear to respond somewhat differently to the transition zone.

While the preceding analysis enabled a division of the sites into two groups with predominantly southern and northern affinities, between-site relationships were more clearly revealed by the classification techniques. The cluster analysis using all of the 252 species showed two major groupings (Fig. 5). One group linked San Diego to San Clemente, Santa Catalina, Santa Barbara, and Santa Cruz Islands, and a second group linked Cayucos Point to San Miguel, Santa Rosa, San Nicolas, and Anacapa Islands. Within these two larger groupings, Santa Catalina and San Clemente Islands were paired, as were Santa Barbara and Santa Cruz, and San Miguel and the southeast end of San Nicolas Island. These results are more clearly displayed by overlaying the cluster groupings on a map of the Southern California Islands (Fig. 6). The linkage of Anacapa and the west end of San Nicolas Island by the cluster analysis would appear to represent a misclassification as indicated by the principal coordinates analysis (Fig. 5). The latter shows the two sites to be intermediate in position along the ordination axis, with Anacapa closer to the warm-water site grouping and the west end of San Nicolas Island more closely allied with the cold-water grouping. In this and the two subsequent PCOORD analyses, only projections on axis I are shown because use of axis II did not provide additional information for interpreting the cluster analysis results.

The predominant taxonomic group was the Gastropoda, which contributed nearly half (113)

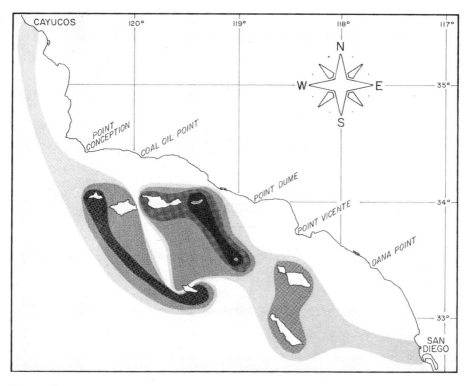

FIGURE 8. *Map overlay of cluster analysis results (Figure 7) using only the Gastropoda.*

of the 252 total species. Because of their numerical dominance, it is revealing to examine the degree of correspondence between the classification analysis using all of the species and that using the Gastropoda alone. The cluster analysis for the gastropods (Figs. 7 and 8) is in basic agreement with results obtained using all of the species (Fig. 5), and also provides strong support for the hypothesized inter-island relationships. For example, Santa Catalina and San Clemente Islands are closely allied, as are Santa Barbara, Anacapa, and Santa Cruz Islands, which together are linked to San Diego as warm-water sites. The west end of San Nicolas Island appears to be misclassified because the principal coordinates analysis (Fig. 7) indicates that it is intermediate in position along the ordination axis between the cold-water and warm-water site groupings. The cold-water cluster group, including Cayucos Point, San Miguel Island, west San Nicolas Island, and Santa Rosa Island, is in perfect agreement with the analysis based on all of the species taken together.

Classification results obtained using only those 59 species whose densities exceeded one per square meter (Figs. 9 and 10) are in general agreement with the results for all 252 species. Cayucos Point is linked with San Miguel Island and the southeast end of San Nicolas Island as cold-water sites. Santa Rosa Island, however, is tied to the warm-water site group, and has a peculiar linkage to San Diego. Principal coordinates analysis (Fig. 9) indicates that this represents a misclassification, because Santa Rosa Island is only peripherally linked with the tightly clumped warm-water site grouping. This interpretation was supported further by the

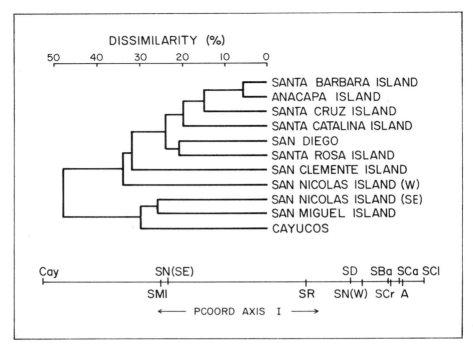

FIGURE 9. *Classification analyses using only those species whose abundances exceeded one per square meter at each site. Cluster analysis results of per cent dissimilarity between sites and site groupings are displayed as a dendrogram (above). Principal coordinates (PCOORD) ordination results are shown for axis I (below).*

relationship of Santa Rosa Island with the other cold-water sites in the total species (Fig. 6) and gastropod (Fig. 8) analyses.

In all three analyses (Figs. 6, 8, and 10), the northern mainland site at Cayucos was grouped with San Miguel Island and the southeast end of San Nicolas Island. This result is strongly supportive of the hypothesized northerly affinities for these two islands. In the total species and gastropod analyses (Figs. 6 and 8), Santa Rosa Island was also related to the northern grouping, while in the principal coordinates analysis which used only those species whose abundance exceeded one per square meter (Fig. 9) it was more closely aligned with the intermediate and warm-water site group. These results are in agreement with the prediction by Neushul *et al.* (1967) that the southern side of the island would be intermediate between the cold-water site at San Miguel Island and the mixed-water area on the southern side of Santa Cruz Island. In all three analyses, a mixed-water island group including Santa Barbara, Anacapa, and Santa Cruz Islands was identified that was linked with the southern islands (San Clemente and Santa Catalina) and the mainland site at San Diego. These results are consistent with the above hypothesized zoogeographical affinities based on hydrographic patterns (Fig. 2). The only site that did not fit the model well was the west end of San Nicolas Island. In the total species analysis (Fig. 6), this site was aligned with the cold-water grouping, but was not closely related to the southeast end of the island. In the gastropod analysis (Fig. 8), it was grouped with the

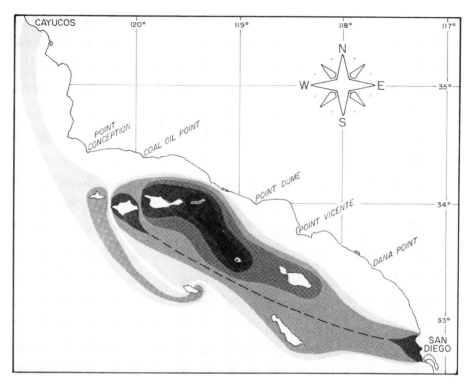

FIGURE 10. *Map overlay of cluster analysis results (Figure 9) using only those species whose abundances exceeded one per square meter at each site.*

intermediate sites, Santa Barbara, Anacapa, and Santa Cruz Islands. The apparent pattern of water circulation in the vicinity of San Nicolas Island affords a possible explanation for the different zoogeographical affinities of the two sites on the island. The southeast end of the island appears to receive cold, offshore California Current waters from the southwest (Fig. 2); these waters flow past the island and are turned northward by the warm, northwesterly-moving Southern California Eddy, which mixes with them to form a large eddy between San Nicolas Island and Santa Rosa and Santa Cruz Islands (Fig. 2). The warmed waters flow southeastward, eventually meeting the west end of San Nicolas Island. Further studies of current flow, such as the thermal imagery study by Hendricks (1977), are needed to substantiate the magnitude and predictability of this large gyre. Its confirmed existence, in addition to records of actual water temperature differences between the west and southeast portions of San Nicolas Island, would afford a plausible explanation for the zoogeographical differences we obtained for the two sites.

SUMMARY

Comparisons were made between the rocky intertidal macroinvertebrate faunas at sites on the eight Southern California Islands and two mainland locations (San Diego in southern California and Cayucos Point in central California). A high percentage (mean 39, range 34 to 48) of the fauna at all of the sites consisted of species with broad latitudinal ranges. An average of 14 per cent (range 10 to 18 per cent) of the species at each site was classified as transitional, with the two mainland localities containing the lowest percentages. The percentages of northern and southern species of the fauna at each site were essentially in agreement with hypothesized inter-island affinities based on hydrographic considerations. Santa Catalina and San Clemente Islands had the highest percentage of southern species (34 and 31 per cent, respectively), followed by Anacapa and Santa Barbara Islands (27 and 24 per cent, respectively). Northern species exceeded southern species at the remaining sites.

Cluster and ordination analyses using (1) all 252 species, (2) the 113 gastropod species alone, and (3) the 59 species whose average densities exceeded one per square meter showed two major groupings: San Miguel Island and the southeast end of San Nicolas Island consistently matched with Cayucos Point, and Santa Catalina and San Clemente Islands formed a southern island group. An intermediate island grouping, including Santa Barbara, Anacapa, and Santa Cruz Islands, was linked with the southern islands and San Diego. Santa Rosa Island was also intermediate, but was aligned with San Miguel and San Nicolas Islands. These grouping patterns strongly support hypothetical affinities developed from hydrographic data, which indicate that (1) San Miguel and San Nicolas Islands are primarily bathed by cold California Current waters, (2) Santa Catalina and San Clemente Islands lie mainly in the pathway of the warm Southern California Eddy flow, and (3) the remaining islands receive differing mixtures of the two waters.

ACKNOWLEDGMENTS

Support for this study was provided by the U.S. Department of the Interior, Bureau of Land Management. We gratefully acknowledge the taxonomic assistance provided by Dr. Gerald Bakus and Ms. Karen Green (sponges), Drs. James Carlton and James McLean (molluscs), Dr. James Villee (ascidians), and Dr. Mary Wicksten (crustaceans). We thank Ms. Peggy Trabue for helping compile the species records for the study sites. Mr. David Lindberg and Mr. Charles Currie assisted in gathering distributional records for the molluscs, and Dr. Mary Wicksten helped in compiling distributional records for the crustaceans. Dr. Robert Smith wrote the computer programs used in the ecological classification analyses. We thank Dr. William Newman for providing valuable comments on the manuscript, Ms. Andrea Braly for assisting in the computer analyses, and Ms. Diane Littler for drafting the illustrations.

REFERENCES

ABBOTT, R. T. 1974. American seashells; the marine Mollusca of the Atlantic and Pacific coasts of North America. Van Nostrand Reinhold, New York, N.Y.

BOLIN, R. L., and D. P. ABBOTT. 1963. Studies on the marine climate and phytoplankton of the central coastal area of California, 1954-1960. California Marine Res. Comm., CalCOFI Rep. 9:23-45.

BRIGGS, J. C. 1974. Marine zoogeography. McGraw-Hill, New York, N.Y.

BURGHARDT, G. E., and L. E. BURGHARDT. 1969. A collector's guide to west coast chitons. San Francisco Aquarium Soc., Spec. Publ. 4.

CAPLAN, R. I., and R. A. BOOLOOTIAN. 1967. Intertidal ecology of San Nicolas Island. Pp. 203-217 in R. N. Philbrick, ed., Proceedings of the symposium on the biology of the California Islands. Santa Barbara Botanic Garden, Santa Barbara, Calif.

CLIFFORD, H. T., and W. STEPHENSON. 1975. An introduction to numerical classification. Academic Press, New York, N.Y.

DALL, W. H. 1921. Summary of the marine shellbearing mollusks of the northwest coast of America, from San Diego, California, to the Polar Sea, mostly contained in the collection of the United States National Museum, with illustrations of hitherto unfigured species. Smithsonian Inst., U.S. Natl. Mus. Bull. 112.

DE LAUBENFELS, M. W. 1932. The marine and freshwater sponges of California. Proc. U.S. Natl. Mus. 81:1-140.

FISHER, W. K. 1911. Asteroidea of the north Pacific and adjacent waters. Part 1, Phanerozonia and Spinulosa. Smithsonian Inst., U.S. Natl. Mus. Bull. 76.

GARTH, J. S. 1958. Brachyura of the Pacific coast of America: Oxyrhyncha. Allan Hancock Pacific Exped. 21.

HAIG, J. 1960. The Porcellanidae (Crustacea, Anomura) of the eastern Pacific. Allan Hancock Pacific Exped. 24.

HAIG, J., and M. K. WICKSTEN. 1975. Field records and range extensions of crabs in California waters. Bull. So. California Acad. Sci. 74:100-104.

HARTMAN, O. 1969. Atlas of the sedentariate polychaetous annelids from California. Allan Hancock Foundation, University of Southern California, Los Angeles, Calif.

HAYDEN, B. P., and R. DOLAN. 1976. Coastal marine fauna and marine climates of the Americas. J. Biogeogr. 3:71-81.

HEDGPETH, J. W. 1957. Marine biogeography. Pp. 359-382 in J. W. Hedgpeth, ed., Treatise on marine ecology and paleoecology. I. Ecology. Geol. Soc. Amer., Mem. 67, New York, N.Y.

HENDRICKS, T. J. 1977. Satellite imagery studies. Pp. 75-78 in Coastal water research project annual report for the year ended 30 June 1977. Southern California Coastal Water Research Project, El Segundo, Calif.

HEWATT, W. G. 1946. Marine ecological studies on Santa Cruz Island, California. Ecol. Monogrs. 16:186-208.

HORN, M. H., and L. G. ALLEN. 1978. A distributional analysis of California coastal marine fishes. J. Biogeogr. 5:23-42.

KEEN, A. M. 1937. An abridged check list and bibliography of west North American marine Mollusca. Stanford University Press, Stanford, Calif.

_____. 1971. Sea shells of tropical west America: marine mollusks from Baja California to Peru. Stanford University Press, Stanford, Calif.

KOLPACK, R. L. 1971. Oceanography of the Santa Barbara Channel. Pp. 90-180 in R. L. Kolpack, ed., Biological and oceanographical survey of the Santa Barbara Channel oil spill, 1969-1970. II. Physical, chemical and geological studies. Allan Hancock Foundation, University of Southern California, Los Angeles, Calif.

LITTLER, M. M., ed. 1977. Spatial and temporal variation in the distribution and abundance of rocky intertidal and tidepool biotas in the Southern California Bight. Bureau of Land Management, U.S. Dept. Interior, Washington, D.C.

LITTLER, M. M. 1978. The annual and seasonal ecology of southern California rocky intertidal and tidepool biotas. Bureau of Land Management, U.S. Dept. Interior, Washington, D.C.

_____. 1979. The distribution, abundance, and community structure of rocky intertidal and tidepool biotas in the Southern California Bight. Bureau of Land Management, U.S. Dept. Interior, Washington, D.C.

_____. 1980. Overview of the rocky intertidal systems of southern California. Pp. 265-306 D. M. Power, ed., The California Islands: proceedings of a multidisciplinary symposium. Santa Barbara Museum of Natural History, Santa Barbara, Calif.

LITTLER, M. M., and S. N. MURRAY. 1975. Impact of sewage on the distribution, abundance and community structure of rocky intertidal macro-organisms. Marine Biol. 30:277-291.

McLAUGHLIN, P. A. 1974. The hermit crabs (Crustacea: Decapoda, Paguridea) of northwestern North America. Zool. Verh. Rijksmus. Nat. Hist. Leiden 130.

McLEAN, J. H. 1978. Marine shells of southern California. Los Angeles Co. Mus. Nat. Hist., Sci. Ser. 24 Zool. 11.

MENZIES, R. J. 1948. A revision of the brachyuran genus *Lophopanopeus*. Allan Hancock Publs., Occas. Paper 4.

MORRIS, P. A. 1966. A field guide to Pacific coast shells including shells of Hawaii and the Gulf of California. Houghton Mifflin, Boston, Mass.

NATIONS, J. D. 1975. The genus *Cancer* (Crustacea:Brachyura): systematics, biogeography, and fossil record. Los Angeles Co. Mus. Nat. Hist., Sci. Bull. 23.

NEUSHUL, M., W. D. CLARKE, and D. W. BROWN. 1967. Subtidal plant and animal communities of the Southern California Islands. Pp. 37-55 *in* R. N. Philbrick, ed., Proceedings of the symposium on the biology of the California Islands. Santa Barbara Botanic Garden, Santa Barbara, Calif.

NEWELL, I. M. 1948. Marine molluscan provinces of western North America: a critique and a new analysis. Proc. Amer. Phil. Soc. 92:155-166.

NEWMAN, W. A. 1975. Phylum Arthropoda: Crustacea, Cirripedia. Pp. 259-269 *in* R. I. Smith and J. T. Carlton, eds., Light's manual: intertidal invertebrates of the central California coast. University of California Press, Berkeley, Calif.

————. Californian Transition Zone: significance of short-range endemics. *In* J. Gray and A. Boucot, eds., Historical biogeography, plate tectonics, and the changing environment. The thirty-seventh annual biology colloquium, April 23-24, 1976. Oregon State University Press, Corvallis, Ore. (in press).

OLDROYD, I. S. 1925-1927. The marine shells of the west coast of North America. Stanford Univ. Publ., Univ. Ser., Geol. Sci. Vols. I and II.

REES, J. K., and C. HAND. 1975. Class Hydrozoa. Pp. 65-85 *in* R. I. Smith and J. T. Carlton, eds., Light's manual: intertidal invertebrates of the central California coast. University of California Press, Berkeley, Calif.

REID, J. L., JR., G. I. RODEN, and J. G. WYLLIE. 1958. Studies of the California Current System. California Marine Res. Comm., CalCOFI Rep. 1 July 1956-1 July 1958:27-56.

RICKETTS, E. F., J. CALVIN, and J. W. HEDGPETH. 1968. Between Pacific tides. Stanford University Press, Stanford, Calif.

SCHENCK, H. G., and A. M. KEEN. 1936. Marine molluscan provinces of western North America. Proc. Amer. Phil. Soc. 76:921-938.

SCHMITT, W. L. 1921. The marine decapod Crustacea of California. Univ. California Publ. Zool. 23.

SCRIPPS INSTITUTION OF OCEANOGRAPHY. 1962. Results of current measurements with drogues, 1958-1961. Data Rep., Scripps Inst. Oceanogr., Ref. 62-27:1-68.

SEAPY, R. R. 1974. Distribution and abundance of the epipelagic mollusk *Carinaria japonica* in waters off southern California. Marine Biol. 24:243-250.

SEAPY, R. R., and M. M. LITTLER. 1977. Biological features of rocky intertidal communities near Ocean Beach, San Diego, California. Pp. 407-514 *in* M. M. Littler, ed., Spatial and temporal variations in the distribution and abundance of rocky intertidal and tidepool biotas in the Southern California Bight. Bureau of Land Management, U.S. Dept. Interior, Washington, D.C.

————. 1978a. Variations in the rocky intertidal biota near Ocean Beach, San Diego, California. Pp. III-1.1.6-1 to III-1.1.6-74 *in* M. M. Littler, ed., The annual and seasonal ecology of southern California rocky intertidal and tidepool biotas. Bureau of Land Management, U.S. Dept. Interior, Washington, D.C.

————. 1978b. The distribution, abundance, community structure, and primary productivity of macro-organisms from two central California rocky intertidal habitats. Pacific Sci. 32:293-314.

SQUIRE, J. L., JR. 1977. Surface currents as determined by drift card releases over the continental shelf off central and southern California. NOAA, Tech. Rep. NMFS (Natl. Marine Fish. Serv.) SSRF 718.

SVERDRUP, H. U., and R. H. FLEMING. 1941. The waters off the coast of southern California, March to July 1937. Bull. Scripps Inst. Oceanogr. 4:261-378.

VALENTINE, J. W. 1966. Numerical analysis of marine molluscan ranges on the extratropical northeastern Pacific shelf. Limnol. Oceanogr. 11:198-211.

VAN NAME, W. G. 1945. The North and South American ascidians. Bull. Amer. Mus. Nat. Hist. 84:1-476.

WYLLIE, J. G. 1966. Geostrophic flow of the California Current at the surface and at 200 meters. California Marine Res. Comm., CalCOFI Atlas 4.

Biogeography of the California Marine Algae with Emphasis on the Southern California Islands

Steven N. Murray,[1] Mark M. Littler,[2]
and Isabella A. Abbott[3]

[1]*Department of Biological Science,
California State University, Fullerton, California 92634*

[2]*Department of Ecology and Evolutionary Biology,
University of California, Irvine, California 92717*

[3]*Hopkins Marine Station of Stanford University,
Pacific Grove, California 93950*

INTRODUCTION

The biogeographical patterns of the marine algal flora of California have received little attention since the classical studies by Setchell (1893, 1917, 1935). This has been due in part to a lack of adequate floristic records, a long-standing obstacle (see Svedelius 1924) to advances in understanding worldwide distributions of marine algae. In the past, as indicated by Hayden and Dolan (1976), coastal marine faunistic patterns have served to delineate biogeographical provinces. Unfortunately, most of the previous distributional analyses have considered only the biota and quantitative attempts to define the physical factors controlling biological patterns have been unsuccessful. Of the physical parameters hypothesized to determine or strongly influence species distributions, temperature has been proposed most frequently as being of greatest importance (*e.g.,* Ekman 1953, Hedgpeth 1957, Briggs 1974). Setchell (1893, 1915, 1917, 1920a, 1920b, 1935), in a series of papers, attempted to explain the global distributions of marine algae, particularly the Laminariaceae, on the basis of temperature. More recently, Abbott and North (1972) discussed temperature influences on the California coastal flora in an effort to advance our understanding of the effects of thermal discharges. However, attempts to statistically correlate temperature with biogeographical patterns have been unsuccessful due to difficulties in selecting an appropriate single "temperature factor" (see Valentine 1966).

Two major distributional boundaries in the eastern north Pacific, the first near Point Conception (34°27′N) and the second near Monterey Bay (36°35′ to 36°57′N), have been identified along the California coastline in recent biogeographical studies (*e.g.,* Valentine 1966, Hayden and Dolan 1976, Horn and Allen 1978). The region near Point Conception has historically been recognized as an important distributional boundary (Dall 1899, 1909, Bartsch 1912) and has commonly been reported as separating northern cold-temperate (Oregonian) from southern warm-temperate (Californian) biogeographical provinces (*e.g.,* Newell 1948, Hall 1960, Valentine 1966). Monterey Bay, however, has not been consistently recognized as a distributional barrier, although recent studies have established its biogeographical significance (Hall 1964, Valentine 1966, Hayden and Dolan 1976, Horn and Allen 1978).

Biogeographical studies have always been plagued by the necessity of interpreting distributional data which may be incomplete or affected by different levels of taxonomic study. For the California algae, further work is required before a complete understanding of species distributions is obtained. This is particularly crucial for portions of the California coastline that have received little scientific attention (*e.g.,* 35-36° and 39-42°N) and for southern California, where significant changes in species composition have occurred during this century (Widdowson 1971, Thom and Widdowson 1978). Yet, it is important to construct models, where sufficient data exist, so that advances can be made in interpreting complex distributional patterns. The newly published comprehensive treatment of the marine algae of California (Abbott and Hollenberg 1976) has at last provided the necessary distributional data, thus enabling preliminary biogeographical assessment. The present study was undertaken to analyze these distributional records and to examine the degree to which they correlate with the previously recognized faunal boundaries near Point Conception and Monterey Bay. This research complements a recent study of patterns of latitudinal overlap of congeneric seaweed species of the Pacific coasts of the Americas (Pielou 1978) through an intensive analysis of algal distributions along the biogeographically important California coastline.

The Southern California Islands begin just to the south of the major distributional boundary at Point Conception and are of central importance to the understanding of the eastern north Pacific biogeography (Neushul et al. 1967). Until lately, the islands have received little scientific attention despite their biogeographical importance and the fact that they contain most of the pristine coastal habitats remaining in southern California. The biological significance of the complex surface currents in the vicinity of the Southern California Islands (see Seapy and Littler 1980) was recognized by Neushul et al. (1967) in their studies of the shallow-water benthic biota of Anacapa Island. The islands are in a region of variable mixing between cold California Current water from the north and west and the warm Southern California Countercurrent water from the south (Schwartzlose 1963, Reid et al. 1958). Neushul et al. (1967), although providing no supportive data, indicated that the shallow-water benthos of the islands reflected prevailing oceanographic conditions and hypothesized that the affinities of each of the Southern California Islands could be characterized by its proportion of northern and southern biotic elements. Anacapa, Santa Barbara, and Santa Cruz Islands and the eastern portion of Santa Rosa Island were believed to be subject to variable mixing of cold and warm surface waters and to have both northern and southern biotic elements. Greater northern (San Miguel, San Nicolas, western Santa Rosa Island) or southern (San Clemente, Santa Catalina Islands) affinities were expected for the other islands based on their more consistent exposure to colder or warmer water, respectively.

Previous algal research on the Southern California Islands has been reviewed by Murray (1974); with the exception of the extensive studies directed by Littler (1977, 1978, 1979), additional work has been limited to ecological research on San Clemente Island (Littler and Murray 1974, 1975, 1978, Murray and Littler 1978) and Santa Cruz Island (Foster 1975a, 1975b). Littler (1977, 1978) has reported the seasonal distribution and abundance of marine macrophytes and macroinvertebrates for intertidal sites on all but Anacapa Island; the biota of Anacapa Island has recently been assessed, however (Littler 1979). These studies have greatly increased our knowledge of the island marine algal floras and have provided the data necessary for distributional analysis. A major contribution of this paper is the first thorough quantitative algal biogeographical analysis of the Southern California Islands. Additionally, the floristic affinities of each of the islands are interpreted with respect to the biogeographical boundary at Point Conception.

METHODS AND MATERIALS

Abbott and Hollenberg (1976) was used to provide the distributional data for the biogeographical analyses of the California algal flora. Records for 668 algal species were examined and ranges along the 1,287-km California coastline were determined. Distributional data for a subspecies, variety, or form were considered as part of the records for the species concerned, while entries reported as alternate life history phases (e.g., Falkenbergia hillebrandii) were excluded from analyses. Treatments were restricted to the Chlorophyta (72 species), Phaeophyta (137 species), and Rhodophyta (459 species). Distributions were recorded according to presence or absence for each one-degree latitudinal interval. A species was said to occur

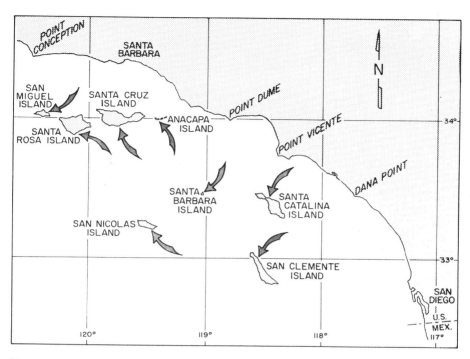

FIGURE 1. *Location of the rocky intertidal sites on the Southern California Islands used for the distributional analyses.*

within an interval if collection records were listed for any geographical location within that one-degree section of coastline, or if the species' range included that interval (*e.g.*, any report between 32°00′N and 32°59′N was assigned to the 32°N interval). We began with latitude 32°00′N and proceeded in one-degree increments through 42°00′N, the range of latitudes for California, Species with seemingly disjunctive ranges, presumably owing to incomplete collection data (about 10 per cent), were assumed to exhibit continuous distributions.

Species restricted to single latitudinal intervals (one-degree endemics) were also identified and eliminated from our distributional analyses to partially offset bias due to disproportionate intensity of taxonomic study. Floral richness was determined by plotting numbers of species as a function of latitudinal interval. Species with northern or southern range terminations (exclusive of one-degree endemics) were also distinguished and their range end-points plotted by latitudinal interval to reveal major biogeographical barriers. For the latitudinal interval 41-42°N, species with southern range terminations were distinguished from one-degree endemics using Phinney's (1977) records for the Oregon coast; Dawson (1961) was similarly employed to estimate the number of species with northern range terminations in the 32-33°N interval.

Distributional data for the Southern California Islands were obtained for Chlorophyta, Phaeophyta, and Rhodophyta from the sites (Fig. 1) studied by Littler (1977, 1978, 1979). Generic and familial categories including more than one species were not utilized in the analyses. The data obtained by Littler (*op. cit.*) comprise approximately 70 per cent of the island records (see Murray 1974 for previous records) and were used exclusively in our distributional analyses because they represent relatively comparable levels of study for each

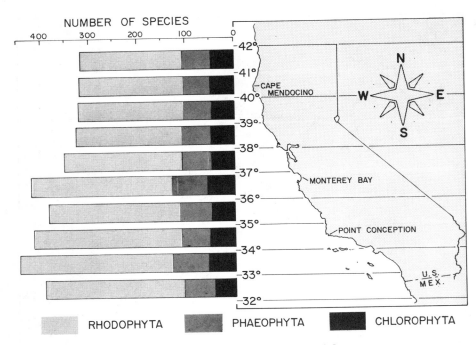

FIGURE 2. *Latitudinal richness of the California marine algal flora.*

island. The available historical data (Murray 1974) have been characterized by disproportionate research; consequently, Anacapa, Santa Catalina, and Santa Cruz Islands have larger known algal floras than the other five islands.

The Jaccard coefficient (Jaccard 1908, Sokal and Sneath 1963), the most widely-used measure in bio-associational studies (Cheetham and Hazel 1969), was used to measure the degree of similarity between the island floras. We then employed single-level similarity comparisons of all possible island pairs, separate computer-mediated classification, and principal coordinates ordination analysis. Computer analyses were performed using the programs described by Smith (1976).

The insular algal floras were also compared with the mainland distributional patterns derived from Abbott and Hollenberg (1976). The degree of overlap with the floras for the California mainland north and south of Point Conception was established for each island.

RESULTS

Maximal floral richness was obtained at 33-34°N (446 species), while the fewest species (318) occurred at 40-41°N (Fig. 2). Floral diversity increased southward and was significantly correlated ($r = -0.87$, $P < 0.01$) with latitude. This increase was due to the greater numbers of red (Rhodophyta) and brown (Phaeophyta) algal species reported for the southerly California latitudes; both Rhodophyta ($r = -0.93$, $P < 0.01$) and Phaeophyta ($r = -0.63$, $P < 0.05$) exhibited significant correlations between floral richness and latitude. In contrast, the green algae (Chlorophyta) showed little latitudinal variability in species number (Fig. 2); hence, a significant correlation between richness and latitude was not obtained.

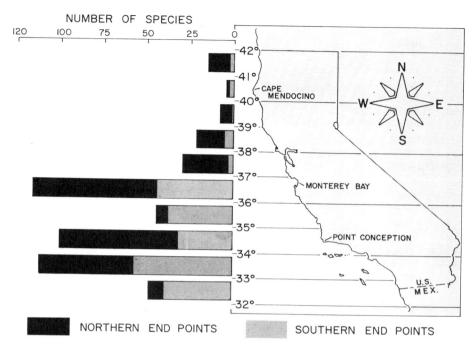

FIGURE 3. *Range terminations of California marine algae as a function of latitude.*

Major California distributional barriers were identified by plotting species' range terminations by latitude (Fig. 3). These data revealed two probable floral disjunctions—the first near Monterey Bay (36-37°N) and the second near Point Conception in southern California (33-35°N)—however, the latter was less sharp and stretched over 2° latitude. The California distributions of 115 species were reported to terminate at 36-37°N, with 71 species reaching their northern limits and 44 their southern limits at this latitude. A total of 211 species recorded range terminations between 33 and 35°N, a zone containing Point Conception and the Southern California Islands. The majority of these range end-points (123) were also northern limits, suggesting that this region of the coastline, like Monterey Bay, presents a more significant barrier to species with distributional centers south of these biogeographical boundaries.

Biogeographical relationships of the Southern California Islands were interpreted from quantitative comparisons of species composition. These included individual similarity determinations of all possible island pairs, hierarchical classification (cluster) analysis, and ordination analysis by principal coordinates. These assessments revealed a consistent pattern of three distinct island groups:

Group I: Anacapa, San Clemente, and Santa Catalina Islands

Group II: Santa Barbara and Santa Cruz Islands

Group III: San Miguel, San Nicolas, and Santa Rosa Islands

The trellis diagram (Fig. 4) presents the similarity comparisons for all possible island pairs. Inter-island similarity averaged 45.4 per cent, with highest floral affinities for Santa Catalina and San Clemente Islands (64.2 per cent) and Santa Barbara and Santa Cruz Islands (62.3 per cent). Least similarity (32.6 per cent) was determined between Santa Catalina and San Miguel

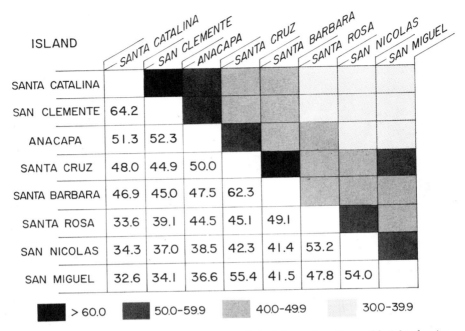

ISLAND	SANTA CATALINA	SAN CLEMENTE	ANACAPA	SANTA CRUZ	SANTA BARBARA	SANTA ROSA	SAN NICOLAS	SAN MIGUEL
SANTA CATALINA								
SAN CLEMENTE	64.2							
ANACAPA	51.3	52.3						
SANTA CRUZ	48.0	44.9	50.0					
SANTA BARBARA	46.9	45.0	47.5	62.3				
SANTA ROSA	33.6	39.1	44.5	45.1	49.1			
SAN NICOLAS	34.3	37.0	38.5	42.3	41.4	53.2		
SAN MIGUEL	32.6	34.1	36.6	55.4	41.5	47.8	54.0	

> 60.0   50.0-59.9   40.0-49.9   30.0-39.9

FIGURE 4. *Similarity (per cent) comparisons of algal floras for all possible island pairs.*

Islands. Anacapa, San Clemente, and Santa Catalina Islands (55.9 per cent) averaged slightly greater floral association than did San Miguel, San Nicolas, and Santa Rosa Islands (51.7 per cent). Members of Group II showed close floral affinities with both Groups I (47.0 per cent) and III (45.8 per cent), while the last two groups had the least overall similarity (36.7 per cent).

The associations of the insular algal floras determined by hierarchical classification and principal coordinates analyses substantiated the trends established by the individual site-pair comparisons and more clearly established the relationships of the three island groups. Based on the classification analysis (Fig. 5), floral similarity was again greatest between Santa Catalina and San Clemente Islands and between Santa Barbara and Santa Cruz Islands. Anacapa Island clearly exhibited greatest association with Santa Catalina and San Clemente Islands (Group I), while San Miguel, San Nicolas, and Santa Rosa Islands (Group III) formed a distinct unit. The floristic affinities of Santa Barbara and Santa Cruz Islands (Group II) were more clearly defined by classification analysis, because greater association occurred with Anacapa, San Clemente, and Santa Catalina Islands (Group I) than with members of Group III. Principal coordinates analysis provided further support for the composition of the three island groups (Fig. 6) since identical site assemblages were obtained in the two-dimensional space resulting from the first two ordination axes. Santa Barbara and Santa Cruz Islands (Group II) again occupied an intermediate position with respect to Groups I and III.

The percentage of algal species in common with the California mainland was determined for each of the islands to compare the relative affinities of island floras with the coastal algal floras north and south of Point Conception. Overall, the algal floras of all eight islands were more closely associated with the mainland California algae south of Point Conception, averaging 95.4 per cent overlap compared with only 80.1 per cent for the central California flora (Table 1).

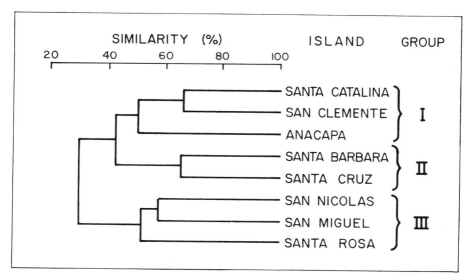

FIGURE 5. *Dendrogram (cluster analysis) depicting the percentage of similarity between sites and site groupings of the algal floras for the Southern California Islands.*

The percentage of species in common with the northern mainland flora was much more variable among the islands and was generally supportive of the previously established affinities. San Nicolas Island (93.6 per cent) had the greatest number of species in common with the central California flora and San Clemente Island (67.5 per cent) had the least. Group I averaged only 71.1 per cent overlap with the mainland algal flora north of Point Conception, while greater association was evident for Groups II (77.3 per cent) and III (91.0 per cent).

DISCUSSION

Richness of the California algal flora was significantly correlated ($P < 0.05$) with latitude and increased from north to south; maximum diversity was below Point Conception (Fig. 2). Greater species richness south of Point Conception has previously been indicated for the California algal flora (Abbott and Hollenberg 1976) and has similarly been reported for shallow-water benthic molluscs (Valentine 1966) and near-shore fishes (Horn and Allen 1978). Additionally, Horn and Allen (1978) reported a significant correlation between latitude and mean maximum and minimum surface sea-water temperatures, based on data taken from Eber, Saur, and Sette (1968), suggesting a relationship between temperature and richness of coastal fishes. For benthic marine algae, southern California provides more potential habitats per latitudinal degree due to the east-west nature of a large portion of the coastline and the presence of the Southern California Islands. Horn (1974) has suggested that the greater environmental heterogeneity of southern California is expressed by the relative richness of its fish fauna. It has been frequently pointed out (*e.g.*, Schwartzlose 1963, Jones 1971) that the Southern California Bight is a very unusual system, situated within the overlapping boundaries of two major biogeographic regions, containing extremely complex and varied oceanographic and climatological regimes. For the marine algae, this heterogeneity includes the availability of shallow-water habitats subjected to a diversity of temperature ranges due to the complex

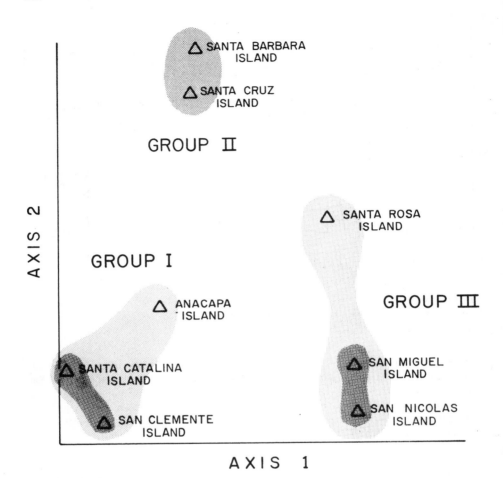

FIGURE 6. *Ordination analysis by principal coordinates of the algal floras of the Southern California Islands; sites are depicted in two-dimensional space resulting from relationships with the first two ordination axes.*

oceanographic conditions, compounded by the variable exposures of the Southern California Islands to the cold waters of the California Current and the warm waters of the Southern California Countercurrent.

Separate analyses of floral richness for each of the algal divisions indicated that diversity increased from north to south and was significantly correlated with latitude for both the Phaeophyta and the Rhodophyta; however, numbers of Chlorophyta did not change significantly with latitude (Fig. 2). The Chlorophyta generally reach maximal development in warm tropical waters (Dawson 1966) where larger, structurally complex species are conspicuous elements of the flora. For California, the green algae, other than *Codium,* are represented by smaller, generally eurytolerant forms with high surface-to-volume ratios (see Littler and Murray 1974). Additionally, 43 per cent of the California Chlorophyta are reported (Abbott and

TABLE 1. Percentage of Southern California Island algal species in common with mainland distributional records north and south of Point Conception.

Coastline from Point Conception	San Clemente	Santa Catalina	Anacapa	Santa Barbara	
South	97.5	95.7	97.7	94.7	
North	67.5	70.2	75.6	76.6	

	Santa Cruz	Santa Rosa	San Nicolas	San Miguel	Mean
South	96.7	94.5	93.6	92.8	95.4
North	78.0	87.7	93.6	91.8	80.1

Hollenberg 1976) to occur in coastal waters along the entire state, *vs.* 31 per cent of the Rhodophyta and 18 per cent of the Phaeophyta, suggesting a tendency for broad distributions and wide tolerances to physical factors. Greater species richness in warmer southern California waters was expected for the Rhodophyta. Phaeophyta also showed increased species richness southward, even though maximum brown algal floristic development has typically been described for more northerly latitudes (Dawson 1966). Cheney (1977) proposed that the ratio of green and red algae to brown algae could be used to describe the nature of an algal flora. A ratio of 3.0 or less would indicate a temperate or cold-water flora, while a value of 6.0 or greater would signify a tropical flora; ratios between 3.0 and 6.0 are characteristic of intermediate floras. For California, the Cheney index ranged from 4.2 at 41-42 °N to 5.3 at 32-33 °N—both values for an intermediate flora; nevertheless, a significant correlation ($r = -0.90$, $P < 0.01$) between the index and latitude was observed, due to the marked southerly increases in Rhodophyta.

Probable distributional barriers for California algae, based on range end-points, occur near Point Conception and Monterey Bay (Fig. 3), regions recognized as biogeographical boundaries for shallow-water benthic molluscs (Valentine 1966), ascidians, crabs, and molluscs (Hayden and Dolan 1976), and coastal fishes (Horn and Allen 1978). The largest percentage (42.5) of algal range terminations occurred near Point Conception and the Southern California Islands (33-35°N), the regions of greatest floral richness. However, the coastline between 33 and 34 °N revealed more species range terminations than did the latitudinal interval actually containing Point Conception (34-35 °N), thus suggesting that the entire southern California area represents a transitional region. This interpretation is supported by the data of Newell (1948), who previously determined high rates of change (= total end-points/total species) in eastern north Pacific marine Mollusca at both 33°N and 34°N. The biogeographical barriers for the marine algae near Point Conception and Monterey Bay appear to be more significant to species with southern distributional centers; 61.7 per cent of the range terminations near Monterey Bay and 58.3 per cent near Point Conception represented northern range limits. Oceanic currents appear to be of paramount importance in determining this pattern. For example, the coastline runs east-west south of Point Conception, thus removing the southern California mainland from the direct influence of the California Current, whose colder waters flow southeast, extending towards Cabo Colnett in Baja California (see Seapy and Littler 1980). These patterns no doubt permit a considerable extension southward of colder-water species into habitats proximal to California Current waters (*i.e.*, San Miguel, San Nicolas, and Santa Rosa Islands). In addition, southern California locales subjected to persistent upwelling would

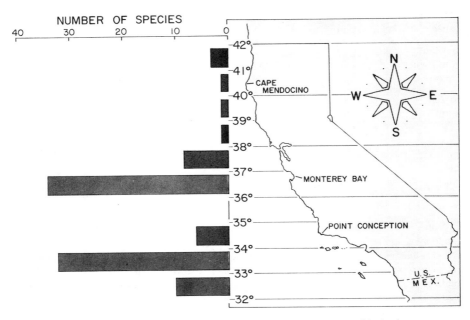

FIGURE 7. *Numbers of "one-degree" endemic species as a function of latitude.*

provide habitats in southern California for cold-water forms, as suggested by Valentine (1966). The warm Southern California Countercurrent, on the other hand, terminates its northward flow abruptly near Point Conception, thereby severely restricting the northerly extension of warm-water species. This greater influence of the area near Point Conception on southern species has also been noted by Valentine (1966), Neushul *et al.* (1967), and Horn and Allen (1978). Mean minimum surface water temperatures have been determined (Horn and Allen 1978) to decrease most sharply (2°C) at Point Conception, and mean maximum temperatures to drop most significantly (2°C) near both Point Conception and Monterey Bay, possibly providing an explanation as to why these regions seem to function as major biogeographical barriers.

A total of 97 algal species was recorded in only one degree of latitude; these species have been referred to as one-degree endemic forms (Fig. 7). These were far more frequent at 36-37°N and 33-34°N, regions of the coastline most closely investigated by Abbott and Hollenberg (1976), suggesting that the distributional data in other localities are relatively incomplete. Additionally, the numbers of one-degree endemic species correspond well with species disjunction patterns based on range end-point analysis (Fig. 3), thus suggesting the possibility that the different levels of taxonomic effort along the California coastline have contributed somewhat to the biogeographical patterns discussed above. However, previous research on Mollusca (Newell 1948, Valentine 1966) has also demonstrated considerable overlap between the frequency distribution of one-degree endemic forms by latitude and biogeographical boundaries determined by range end-point analysis. The fact that species richness and the Cheney (1977) index show significant correlations with latitude lends credence to the interpretation that factors other than the level of taxonomic effort are operating. Furthermore, studies on benthic invertebrates (Newell 1948, Valentine 1966, Hayden and

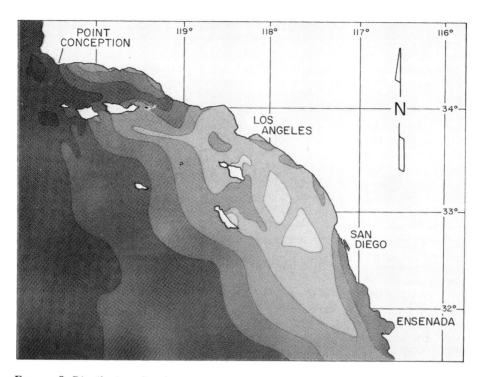

FIGURE 8. *Distribution of surface water temperatures within the Southern California Bight based on remote sensing satellite imagery (redrawn from the 23 June 1976 NOAA-3 satellite imagery in Hendricks 1977); darkest tones represent coldest water temperatures with temperature increases of about 1.4 °C with each successively lighter tone.*

Dolan 1976) have independently offered the same interpretation. *i.e.*, that major biogeographical breaks occur near Point Conception and Monterey Bay; Pielou (1978) has also observed that the number of seaweed species whose distributions span the Point Conception area is small compared with other eastern Pacific regions. However, further studies of species distributions are required before our interpretations merit complete acceptance.

Quantitative comparisons of the floristic composition of the Southern California Islands revealed three distinct assemblages (Figs. 4, 5, and 6): Anacapa—San Clemente—Santa Catalina (Group I); Santa Barbara—Santa Cruz (Group II); and San Miguel—San Nicolas—Santa Rosa (Group III). These groups were comparable to those predicted by Neushul *et al.* (1967), with the exception that our study showed that Anacapa had greatest floristic affinities with San Clemente and Santa Catalina Islands. Based on an understanding of the complicated surface circulation patterns in the vicinity of the Southern California Islands (Schwartzlose 1963, Reid *et al.* 1958), the algal floras appear to be influenced most by temperature (Fig. 8). Neushul *et al.* (1967) emphasized the variability in oceanic circulation near the Northern Channel Islands and reported greater exposure of San Clemente and Santa Catalina Islands to warmer water throughout the greater part of the year. San Miguel, San Nicolas, and the western half of Santa Rosa Island were said to be strongly under the influence of the colder waters of the

California Current, while Anacapa, Santa Barbara, Santa Cruz, and eastern Santa Rosa Island were reported to lie in a region of variable mixing between cold- and warm-water currents. This pattern of surface water circulation has been quantitatively substantiated (Hendricks 1977) using satellite thermal imagery. Hendricks' data (Fig. 8) interestingly reveal a tongue of warm water extending toward Anacapa Island from the south, which may account for its floristic affinities with Santa Catalina and San Clemente Islands.

All of the Southern California Islands had a higher percentage of species in common with the mainland flora south of Point Conception, but a pattern of variable association was determined with the species to the north (Table 1). Greatest affinities with the central California algal flora were determined for the San Miguel, San Nicolas, and Santa Rosa Island sites, reflecting a higher proportion of colder-water species for these islands. San Clemente and Santa Catalina Islands had lowest cold-water floral affinities, and Anacapa, Santa Barbara, and Santa Cruz Islands occupied somewhat intermediate positions. A temperature-based characterization of the Southern California Island algal floras is further suggested by the principal coordinates ordination analysis (Fig. 6), where the orientation of the insular sites, with respect to the first ordination axis, agrees well with interpretations derived from our species overlap comparisons (Table 1), previous studies (Neushul et al. 1967), and available temperature data (Fig. 8).

Our results clearly substantiate the previously-held opinions (e.g., Hewatt 1946, Caplan and Boolootian 1967, Neushul et al. 1967) that the Southern California Islands contain biotic elements transitional between colder-water locales to the north and warmer-water regions to the south of Point Conception. These data emphasize the importance of the islands to a full understanding of the biogeography of the eastern north Pacific and suggest that environmental heterogeneity increases markedly in California coastal areas south of Point Conception (see Horn 1974).

SUMMARY

Richness of the California algal flora increased southward and was significantly correlated with latitude, mostly due to the Rhodophyta and Phaeophyta. Probable distributional barriers for marine algae, interpreted from range end-point analysis, occurred near Monterey Bay and Point Conception, in agreement with previous studies of coastal faunas. The range distributions of 115 species terminated near Monterey Bay, while 211 algae had northern or southern range end-points near Point Conception and the Southern California Islands. The majority of these terminations represented northern limits, suggesting that the proposed biogeographical boundaries represent greater barriers to species with more southerly distributional centers.

Quantitative assessments of the algal floras of the Southern California Islands using individual similarity comparisons, hierarchical classification analysis, and principal coordinates ordination analysis revealed three distinct island groups: (I) Anacapa, San Clemente, and Santa Catalina Islands; (II) Santa Barbara and Santa Cruz Islands; (III) San Miguel, San Nicolas, and Santa Rosa Islands. The island floras appeared to be influenced mainly by temperature; this assumption is based upon an understanding of the reported oceanic circulation patterns, comparisons of floristic components with the mainland floras north and south of Point Conception, and interpretations of the principal coordinates ordination analysis. All of the island floras had greatest overlap with the mainland algae south of Point Conception; nevertheless, a pattern of variable association (presumably temperature-based) was shown with the central California flora. Our results substantiate the previously-held viewpoint that the Southern California Islands contain biotic elements transitional between colder-water locales to the north and warmer-water regions to the south of Point Conception and emphasize the importance of the islands to understanding eastern north Pacific biogeography.

ACKNOWLEDGMENTS

We are grateful to Robert H. Sims and Peggy J. Trabue for assistance with the compilation of the algal species lists for the Southern California Islands, and to Margaret L. Hummer, Paul S. Kramsky, Brian R. Oates, and Märie T. Polis for assistance in extracting the distributional data from *Marine Algae of California* (Abbott and Hollenberg 1976). Robert W. Smith made available the computer programs and Robert N. Lockwood assisted with the analyses. We particularly thank Michael H. Horn for valuable comments during the development of this manuscript and both him and Larry G. Allen for providing a copy of their distributional paper on California coastal fishes prior to its publication. Diane S. Littler contributed the illustrative work.

REFERENCES

ABBOTT, I. A., and G. J. HOLLENBERG. 1976. Marine algae of California. Stanford University Press, Stanford, Calif.

ABBOTT, I. A., and W. J. NORTH. 1972. Temperature influences on floral composition in California coastal waters. Pp. 72-79 *in* K. Nisizawa, ed., Proceedings of the seventh international seaweed symposium. John Wiley & Sons, New York, N.Y.

BARTSCH, P. 1912. A zoogeographic study based on the pyramidellid mollusks of the west coast of America. Proc. U.S. Natl. Mus. 42:297-349.

BRIGGS, J. C. 1974. Marine zoogeography. McGraw-Hill, New York, N.Y.

CAPLAN, R. I., and R. A. BOOLOOTIAN. 1967. Intertidal ecology of San Nicolas Island. Pp. 203-217 *in* R. N. Philbrick, ed., Proceedings of the symposium on the biology of the California Islands. Santa Barbara Botanic Garden, Santa Barbara, Calif.

CHEETHAM, A. H., and J. E. HAZEL. 1969. Binary (presence-absence) similarity coefficients. J. Paleont. 43:1130-1136.

CHENEY, D. P. 1977. R&C/P—a new and improved ratio for comparing seaweed floras. J. Phycol. 13 (Suppl.):12.

DALL, W. H. 1899. The mollusk fauna of the Pribilof Islands. Pp. 539-546 *in* D. S. Jordan, ed., The fur seals and fur-seal islands of the north Pacific Ocean. Part III. Special papers relating to the fur seal and to the natural history of the Pribilof Islands. U.S. Govt. Printing Office, Washington, D.C.

————. 1909. Report on a collection of shells from Peru, with a summary of the littoral marine Mollusca of the Peruvian zoological province. Proc. U.S. Natl. Mus. 37:147-294.

DAWSON, E. Y. 1961. A guide to the literature and distributions of Pacific benthic algae from Alaska to the Galapagos Islands. Pacific Sci. 15:370-461.

————. 1966. Marine botany, an introduction. Holt, Rinehart, and Winston, New York, N.Y.

EBER, L. E., J. F. T. SAUR, and O. E. SETTE. 1968. Monthly mean charts: sea surface temperature, north Pacific Ocean 1949-62. U.S. Fish Wildl. Serv. Circ. 258:1-168.

EKMAN, S. P. 1953. Zoogeography of the sea. Sidgwick & Jackson, London.

FOSTER, M. S. 1975a. Algal succession in a *Macrocystis pyrifera* forest. Marine Biol. 32:313-329.

————. 1975b. Regulation of algal community development in a *Macrocystis pyrifera* forest. Marine Biol. 32:331-342.

HALL, C. A., JR. 1960. Displaced Miocene molluscan provinces along the San Andreas fault, California. Univ. California Publ. Geol. Sci. 34:281-308.

————. 1964. Shallow-water marine climates and molluscan provinces. Ecology 45:226-234.

HAYDEN, B. P., and R. DOLAN. 1976. Coastal marine fauna and marine climates of the Americas. J. Biogeogr. 3:71-81.

HEDGPETH, J. W. 1957. Marine biogeography. Pp. 359-382 *in* J. W. Hedgpeth, ed., Treatise on marine ecology and paleoecology. I. Ecology. Geol. Soc. Amer. Mem. 67, New York, N.Y.

HENDRICKS, T. J. 1977. Satellite imagery studies. Pp. 75-78 *in* Coastal water research project annual report for the year ended 30 June 1977. Southern California Coastal Water Research Project, El Segundo, Calif.

HEWATT, W. G. 1946. Marine ecological studies on Santa Cruz Island, California. Ecol. Monogrs. 16:186-208.

HORN, M. H. 1974. Fishes. Pp. 11-1 to 11-124 *in* M. D. Dailey, B. Hill, and N. Lansing, eds., A summary of knowledge of the southern California coastal zone and offshore areas. II. Biological environment. Bureau of Land Management, U.S. Dept. Interior, Washington, D.C.

HORN, M. H., and L. G. ALLEN. 1978. A distributional analysis of California coastal marine fishes. J. Biogeogr. 5:23-42.

JACCARD, P. 1908. Nouvelles recherches sur la distribution florale. Bull. Soc. Vaud. Sci. Nat. 44:223-270.

JONES, J. H. 1971. General circulation and water characteristics in the Southern California Bight. Southern California Coastal Water Research Project, El Segundo, Calif.

LITTLER, M. M., ed. 1977. Spatial and temporal variations in the distribution and abundance of rocky intertidal and tidepool biotas in the Southern California Bight. Bureau of Land Management, U.S. Dept. Interior, Washington, D.C.

_____. 1978. The annual and seasonal ecology of southern California subtidal, rocky intertidal and tidepool biotas. Bureau of Land Management, U.S. Dept. Interior, Washington, D.C.

_____. 1979. The distribution, abundance, and community structure of rocky intertidal and tidepool biotas in the Southern California Bight. Bureau of Land Management, U.S. Dept. Interior, Washington, D.C.

LITTLER, M. M., and S. N. MURRAY. 1974. The primary productivity of marine macrophytes from a rocky intertidal community. Marine Biol. 27:131-135.

_____. 1975. Impact of sewage on the distribution, abundance and community structure of rocky intertidal macro-organisms. Marine Biol. 30:277-291.

_____. 1978. Influence of domestic wastes on energetic pathways in rocky intertidal communities. J. Appl. Ecol. 15:1-13.

MURRAY, S. N. 1974. Benthic algae and grasses. Pp. 9-1 to 9-61 *in* M. D. Dailey, B. Hill, and N. Lansing, eds., A summary of knowledge of the southern California coastal zone and offshore areas. II. Biological environment. Bureau of Land Management, U.S. Dept. Interior, Washington, D.C.

MURRAY, S. N., and M. M. LITTLER. 1978. Patterns of algal succession in a perturbated marine intertidal community. J. Phycol. 14:506-512.

NEUSHUL, M., W. D. CLARKE, and D. W. BROWN. 1967. Subtidal plant and animal communities of the Southern California Islands. Pp. 37-55 *in* R. N. Philbrick, ed., Proceedings of the symposium on the biology of the California Islands. Santa Barbara Botanic Garden, Santa Barbara, Calif.

NEWELL, I. M. 1948. Marine molluscan provinces of western North America: a critique and a new analysis. Proc. Amer. Phil. Soc. 92:155-166.

PHINNEY, H. K. 1977. The macrophytic marine algae of Oregon. Pp. 93-115 *in* R. W. Krauss, ed., The marine plant biomass of the Pacific northwest coast. Oregon State University Press, Corvallis, Ore.

PIELOU, E. C. 1978. Latitudinal overlap of seaweed species: evidence for quasi-sympatric speciation. J. Biogeogr. 5:227-238.

REID, J. L., JR., G. I. RODEN, and J. G. WYLLIE. 1958. Studies of the California Current System. California Marine Res. Comm., California Cooperative Oceanic Fisheries Investigations [CalCOFI] Rep. 1 July 1956 to 1 January 1958:27-56.

SCHWARTZLOSE, R. A. 1963. Nearshore currents of the western United States and Baja California as measured by drift bottles. California Marine Res. Comm., CalCOFI Rep. 9:15-22.

SEAPY, R. R., and M. M. LITTLER. 1980. Biogeography of rocky intertidal macroinvertebrates of the Southern California Islands. Pp. 307-323 in D.M. Power, ed., The California Islands: proceedings of a multidisciplinary symposium. Santa Barbara Museum of Natural History, Santa Barbara, Calif.

SETCHELL, W. A. 1893. On the classification and geographical distribution of the Laminariaceae. Trans. Connecticut Acad. 9:333-375.

————. 1915. The law of temperature connected with the distribution of the marine algae. Ann. Missouri Bot. Gard. 2:287-305.

————. 1917. Geographical distribution of the marine algae. Science 45:197-204.

————. 1920a. The temperature interval in the geographical distribution of marine algae. Science. 52:187-190.

————. 1920b. Stenothermy and zone-invasion. Amer. Natur. 54:385-397.

————. 1935. Geographic elements of the marine flora of the north Pacific Ocean. Amer. Natur. 69:560-577.

SMITH, R. W. 1976. Numerical analysis of ecological survey data. Ph.D. thesis, University of Southern California, Los Angeles, Calif.

SOKAL, R. R., and P. H. A. SNEATH. 1963. Principles of numerical taxonomy. W. H. Freeman, San Francisco, Calif.

SVEDELIUS, N. 1924. On the discontinuous geographical distribution of some tropical and subtropical marine algae. Arkiv. Bot. 19:1-70.

THOM, R. M., and T. B. WIDDOWSON. 1978. A resurvey of E. Yale Dawson's 42 intertidal algal transects on the southern California mainland after 15 years. Bull. So. California Acad. Sci. 77:1-13.

VALENTINE, J. W. 1966. Numerical analysis of marine molluscan ranges on the extratropical northeastern Pacific shelf. Limnol. Oceanogr. 11:198-211.

WIDDOWSON, T. B. 1971. Changes in the intertidal algal flora of the Los Angeles area since the survey by E. Yale Dawson in 1956-1959. Bull. So. California Acad. Sci. 70:2-16.

Biogeographic Patterns in Mussel Community Distribution from the Southern California Bight

Robert G. Kanter[1]

*Institute for Marine and Coastal Studies, University of
Southern California, Los Angeles, California 90007*

INTRODUCTION

The diverse assemblage of organisms associated with *Mytilus californianus* Conrad (Mollusca: Bivalvia) populations is a useful tool for examining biogeographic patterns of intertidal species distributions in the Southern California Bight. Mussels, as members of the genus *Mytilus* are often called, are attached to the underlying substrate and to other mussels by strong byssal threads. This mode of attachment enables mussels to form layered beds up to 20 cm thick (Paine 1976). Sediment, detritus, and debris are trapped in the spaces between mussels, providing food and shelter for a variety of other invertebrates (Reish 1964, Paine 1966, Kanter 1977, Suchanek 1979). This complex association of organisms is referred to as the *Mytilus californianus* community.

The mussel community is extremely rich, often supporting several hundred species (Kanter 1977, Suchanek 1979); its species richness is rivaled only by that of the *Balanus-Endocladia* association described by Glynn (1965). Past studies of mussel beds have dealt only with specific questions concerning succession (Hewatt 1937, Reish 1964, Cimberg 1975) and trophic structure (Paine 1966, Kanter 1977). Questions concerning community distribution patterns over major geographic areas have not been addressed. Large-scale investigations of other intertidal communities have concentrated on macroinvertebrates, macrophytes, or both (Dawson 1959, 1965, Nicholson and Cimberg 1971, Littler 1980); the microbiota occupying interstices in algal turf and mussel beds were generally not considered.

The Southern California Bight contains intertidal mussel beds at mainland and offshore island localities. Prior to the Bureau of Land Management's (BLM) Outer Continental Shelf studies initiated in 1975, no detailed investigations into mussel community structure or distribution had been performed in the bight. This paper discusses some of the findings of the third-year (1977-1978) BLM program, including: (1) mussel community composition, (2) mussel community species richness, and (3) biogeographic patterns and similarities among mussel communities of the bight.

METHODS

This section describes in general terms the methods of data acquisition and analysis employed in the BLM study. A more detailed description and presentation of data is in my BLM report (Kanter 1979).

The *Mytilus californianus* community was sampled at 20 rocky intertidal sites along the southern California coast (Fig. 1). Two study sites were located on each of the following Channel Islands: San Miguel, Santa Rosa, Santa Cruz, Anacapa, Santa Catalina, San Nicolas, and San Clemente. In addition, six mainland localities were sampled: Government Point, Goleta Point, Ventura, Corona del Mar, Carlsbad, and San Diego. Descriptive site references and collection dates are listed in Table 1.

---

[1] Present address: Marine Biological Consultants, Inc., 947 Newhall Street, Costa Mesa, California 92627.

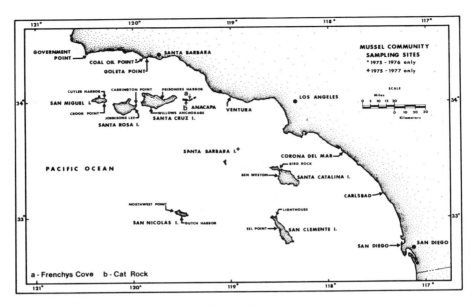

FIGURE 1. *Location of mussel community sampling sites.*

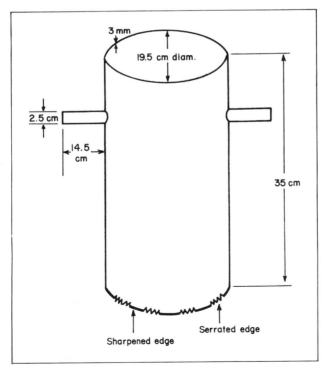

FIGURE 2. *Corer used for sampling.*

TABLE 1. Dates of collection and specific site reference abbreviations.

Collection sites	Abbreviation	Dates
Islands:		
Outer San Miguel Island, Crook Point	SMO	October 26, 1977
Inner San Miguel Island, Cuyler Harbor	MIG	October 27, 1977
Outer Santa Rosa Island, Johnsons Lee	ROS	October 12, 1977
Inner Santa Rosa Island, Carrington Point	SRO	October 11, 1977
Outer Santa Cruz Island, Willows Anchorage	CRU	November 11, 1977
Inner Santa Cruz Island, Prisoners Harbor	SCO	October 13, 1977
Outer Anacapa Island, Cat Rock	ANA	February 23, 1978
Inner Anacapa Island, Frenchys Cove	ANI	November 13, 1978
Outer Santa Catalina Island, Ben Weston	CAO	December 13, 1977
Inner Santa Catalina Island, Bird Rock	BIR	November 25, 1977
Outer San Nicolas Island, Dutch Harbor	SNI	December 9, 1977
Inner San Nicolas Island, Northwest Point	SNO	December 8, 1977
Outer San Clemente Island, Eel Point	CLM	November 9, 1977
Inner San Clemente Island, Lighthouse Point	CLI	November 10, 1977
Mainland:		
Government Point	GPT	December 7, 1977
Goleta Point	GOL	October 14, 1977
Ventura	VEN	October 13, 1977
Corona del Mar	COR	December 12, 1977
Carlsbad	CAR	November 12, 1977
San Diego	SD	November 11, 1977

The accessible extremes of beds at selected sites were sampled to examine the difference between mussel communities occupying different intertidal heights. These sites included Cuyler Harbor (San Miguel Island), Eel Point (San Clemente Island), and Goleta Point. The different intertidal height samples are labeled A and B for reference. The actual vertical height and community differences are discussed in following sections.

An area 1,500 cm² was sampled by collecting five 300-cm² core replicates (Fig. 2). The 1,500 cm² sample size was previously determined to be an optimal size based on species-area curve graphical analysis (Cain 1938) and information loss computations (Smith 1976). The core sample was removed intact, where possible, to include organisms, sediment, detritus, and debris. The sample was preserved in 15 per cent buffered formalin and returned to the laboratory for processing of biotic and abiotic components.

In the laboratory, samples were washed with fresh water and the mussels separated from the rest of the sample. The entire sample was hand sorted to recover all organisms (greater than 0.5 mm) from the sediment, debris, and detritus. All invertebrates and attached algae were identified. The numbers of each animal species were recorded. Algae were not quantified beyond presence or absence. Data were reduced and analyzed to quantitatively describe mussel bed composition, diversity, and community similarity.

Species richness (number of species) was used to refer to the variety of organisms in the mussel community. The number of species represents a cumulative number for a consistent sample size of 1,500 cm² (five 300-cm² replicates). Indices including Shannon-Weaver (H')

TABLE 2. Diversity of biota at each mussel community sampling locality (1977-1978) ranked by faunal richness. (The letters A and B designate separate collections from different intertidal heights.)

Collection sites		Number of species		Diversity H'	Evenness J'
		Fauna	Flora		
Islands:					
Outer Anacapa Island, Cat Rock		174	15	3.218	0.642
Inner Santa Catalina Island, Bird Rock		163	16	3.482	0.694
Inner San Clemente Island, Lighthouse Point		157	14	3.231	0.660
Outer Santa Cruz Island, Willows Anchorage		148	1	2.892	0.579
Inner Santa Cruz Island, Prisoners Harbor		130	17	3.024	0.624
Inner San Nicolas Island, Northwest Point		130	14	2.613	0.560
Inner Santa Rosa Island, Carrington Point		120	15	2.615	0.550
Outer Santa Rosa Island, Johnsons Lee		109	11	2.728	0.583
Outer San Miguel Island, Crook Point	(B)	104	14	1.596	0.344
Outer San Miguel Island, Crook Point	(A)	103	12	1.911	0.412
Outer San Clemente Island, Eel Point	(B)	102	10	2.426	0.526
Outer San Nicolas Island, Dutch Harbor		101	2	3.426	0.745
Outer San Clemente Island, Eel Point	(A)	95	4	2.356	0.521
Inner Anacapa Island, Frenchys Cove		79	7	1.867	0.430
Inner San Miguel Island, Cuyler Harbor	(A)	79	7	1.915	0.454
Inner San Miguel Island, Cuyler Harbor	(B)	72	9	1.517	0.357
Outer Santa Catalina Island, Ben Weston		46	21	1.845	0.508
Mean		112.47	11.12	2.510	0.541
Mainland:					
San Diego		120	23	2.706	0.579
Ventura		107	7	2.487	0.537
Carlsbad		102	13	2.272	0.505
Goleta Point	(B)	91	11	1.862	0.422
Goleta Point	(A)	90	22	1.644	0.369
Corona del Mar		90	6	2.687	0.602
Government Point		77	12	2.472	0.580
Mean		96.7	13.4	2.304	0.513

diversity (Pielou 1966) and Pielou's evenness (J') were provided for comparative purposes only, since their applicability to this study is severely limited.

Intersite and intertidal height comparisons of community similarity were accomplished by classificatory analysis (Clifford and Stephenson 1975). The intersite comparison included only species which occurred in more than 25 per cent of the geographic areas. The Bray-Curtis index (Clifford and Stephenson 1975) was used to compute inter-entity distances. Flexible sorting strategy was employed in the construction of hierarchical dendrograms (Lance and Williams 1966). Species counts were transformed by square root and species mean prior to normal analysis, and by square root and species maximum prior to inverse analysis (Smith 1976). Intrasite intertidal height comparison results were displayed in dendrogram form. The intersite comparison results were displayed in the form of a two-way coincidence table with symbols representing species' relative abundance (Clifford and Stephenson 1975, Smith 1976).

TABLE 3. Mussel community faunal richness and intertidal height separation of collections from the same locality. (The letters A and B designate separate collections from different intertidal heights.)

Locality	Number of species		Differences in intertidal height	
	A	B	(m)	(ft)
Goleta Point	90	91	1.45	4.73
Cuyler Harbor, San Miguel Island	79	72	2.41	7.89
Crooks Point, San Miguel Island	103	104	0.03	0.11
Eel Point, San Clemente Island	95	102	0.33	1.05

RESULTS AND DISCUSSION

Mussel Community Composition and Species Richness

The mussel bed communities in the Southern California Bight are extremely rich. The assemblages examined contained, conservatively, 610 species of invertebrates and 141 species of algae (Table 2). Three invertebrate phyla, the Annelida, Mollusca, and Arthropoda, contributed over two-thirds of all the species recorded.

Sampled mussel beds displayed a large range in faunal richness. The community at Cat Rock on the outer side of Anacapa Island was the most diverse, supporting 174 species. Richness was lowest in the mussel beds at Ben Weston (Santa Catalina Island), which contained only 46 species (Table 2).

The species found in the mussel beds are too numerous to list here (see Kanter 1979). The most common species, however, included the limpets (Mollusca: Gastropoda) *Collisella scabra, C. limatula, C. pelta,* and *C. strigatella;* the barnacles (Arthropoda: Cirripedia) *Chthamalus dalli, C. fissus, Balanus glandula, Tetraclita squamosa,* and *Pollicipes polymerus;* the marine worms (Annelida: Polychaeta) *Arabella semimaculata, Nereis mediator* (= *grubei*), *Typosyllis "fasciata"* sp. D, and *Typosyllis hyalina;* and the nemerteans (Nemertea) *Emplectonema gracile* and *Paranemertes peregrina.*

Algae attached to the surface of the mussels totaled 141 species for all collections combined. The number of algal taxa recorded from a single collection ranged from a low of one at Prisoners Harbor (Santa Cruz Island) to a high of 23 from San Diego (Table 2). The most common attached algal taxa included *Gelidium* spp., *Ulva* spp., *Carpopeltis* spp., *Haliptylon* spp., *Porphyra* spp., *Gigartina* spp., and *Polysiphonia* spp. These groups were represented in several of the mussel beds; in general, more species were found at island than at mainland localities.

There was no apparent relationship between the numbers of floral and faunal species collected at different sites. For example, 15 algal species were recorded at outer Anacapa Island, while 174 animal species were observed in the same samples. However, only one algal species was recorded at Willows Anchorage (Santa Cruz Island), where 148 animal species were observed.

Collections from different intertidal heights at the same locality were very similar with regard to the total number of faunal species (Table 3). The two collections from Goleta Point contained 90 and 91 species, while those from Crooks Point (San Miguel Island) contained 103 and 104 species. A difference of seven species between upper and lower intertidal samples was recorded from mussel beds at Cuyler Harbor (San Miguel Island) and Eel Point (San Clemente

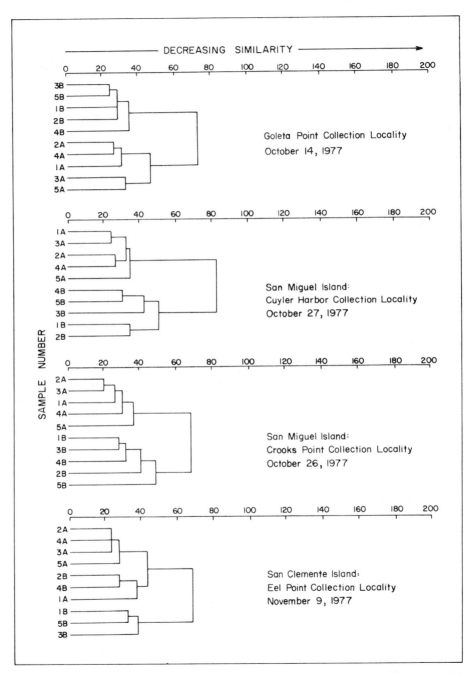

FIGURE 3. *Dendrograms of mussel community samples from different intertidal heights within a locality. Upper intertidal sample replicates labeled* A, *lower samples labeled* B.

Island). Those collections separated by large intertidal height differences did not display a proportionate difference in species richness. For example, Goleta Point samples separated by a distance of 1.45 m (4.73 ft) differed by one species, whereas the Eel Point (San Clemente Island) beds were only 0.33 m (1.05 ft) apart but differed by seven in species count.

Although species richness was similar in samples collected from mussel beds at different intertidal heights within a site, classificatory analysis of the five replicate core samples from each intertidal level revealed that community compositional differences did exist. Analysis of data from Goleta Point and both sides of San Miguel Island produced dendrograms with primary divisions which clearly separated upper and lower collections (Fig. 3).

The separation indicated that upper and lower intertidal samples were dissimilar in species composition and abundance. These results contrasted with those from analysis of Eel Point (San Clemente Island) samples which did not show clear differences between upper and lower intertidal samples (Fig. 3). Thus, the microbiota associated with mussel beds may be vertically stratified, with samples differing in composition depending on bed elevation, but these differences may not be reflected in the community statistical parameters of richness or diversity. Further, samples collected from one intertidal level may not accurately reflect the "total" mussel community at a site unless the entire mussel bed occupies a narrow range in intertidal height.

Mussel Community Similarity Analysis

Classificatory techniques (Clifford and Stephenson 1975) were employed to define similarities and detect biogeographic patterns among mussel communities. The analyses produced normal (site) and inverse (species) dendrograms which were then arranged in a two-way coincidence table. The normal dendrogram clusters localities based on similarity of faunal composition. The inverse dendrogram clusters species with similar distributions. The two-way coincidence table merges the normal and inverse analyses to display species distribution patterns (Fig. 4).

The site groups which resulted from the normal analysis were sequentially numbered for easy reference in subsequent discussions. Species groups were similarly labeled with letters. In order to interpret the species composition of a specific group it was necessary to refer directly to Figure 4. Site abbreviations are listed in Table 1.

The analysis revealed five major patterns which corresponded to characteristic species assemblages occupying the mussel beds of various geographic areas. The observed patterns included: (1) the presence of ubiquitous species groups; (2) clusters of species whose highest abundances characterize particular study sites; (3) clusters of study sites which display a north-south geographic pattern in the similarity of their respective mussel communities; (4) a separation of selected island and mainland communities because of dissimilarities in their species composition; and (5) differences between mussel communities on opposite sides of the same offshore island.

The inverse community similarity analysis yielded six species groups, labeled A through E (Fig. 4). Species group A was a nearly ubiquitous assemblage of organisms found in practically all the mussel beds sampled. Overall abundance of the species in this group was slightly higher in collections from site groups 1, 2, and 3 than in collections from the other site groups. Species group A included the limpets *Collisela scabra*, *C. limatula*, *C. pelta*, and *C. strigatella*, the nemerteans *Emplectonema gracile* and *Paranemertes peregrina*, the crab *Pachygrapsus crassipes*, the barnacles *Chthamalus fissus* and *C. dalli*, the polychaetes *Typosyllis fasciata* sp. D and *Arabella semimaculata*, and the sea anemone *Anthopleura elegantissima*. Other prevalent species were scattered among the remaining species groups including groups C and E. Included among these species were the molluscs *Septifer bifurcatus* and *Lasaea subviridis*, the polychaete *Naineris dendritica*, and the barnacles *Tetraclita squamosa* and *Balanus glandula*.

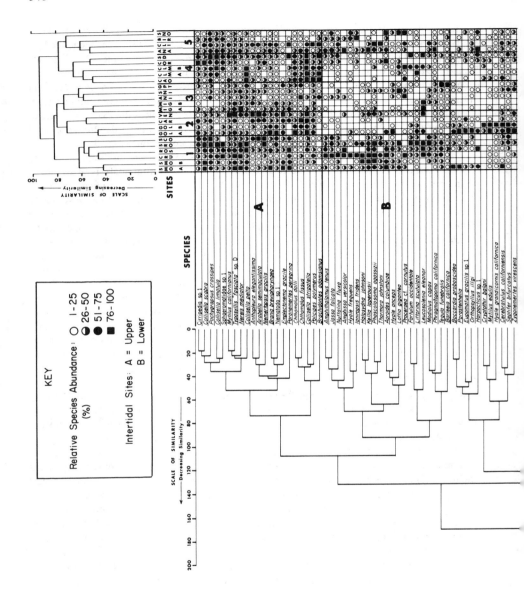

FIGURE 4. *Normal and inverse classification dendrograms with resultant two-way table.*

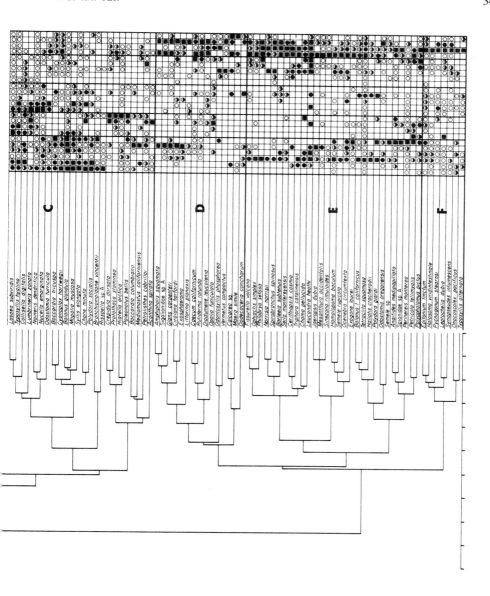

Species in group B characterized Channel Island study areas (Fig. 4). Most of the species occurred in their highest relative abundance at group 1 sites, although some species occurred at sites in other groups but in low or very low numbers. Among the distinctive species in group 1 were the peanut worm *Phascolosoma agassizii* and the bivalve mollusc *Kellia laperousii*.

Site groups 1 and 2 were characterized by high relative abundance of several members of species group C (*e.g.*, the chitons *Mopalia muscosa* and *Cyanoplax hartwegii*, and the barnacle *Balanus glandula*). Other species were present in all mussel beds, with their highest abundance displayed at group 1 mussel beds (*e.g.*, the bivalve *Lasaea subviridis* and the polychaete *Nereis dendritica*).

Species in groups D, E, and F were frequent, abundant, and characteristic of site group 5 mussel beds. Few members of these species groups were found in site group 2, 3, or 4 mussel beds. However, several of the species from groups D, E, and F were encountered in collections from site group 1. Although absent or in relatively low abundance at other sites, species such as the bivalve *Philobrya setosa* and the gastropod *Cerithiopsis cosmia* were found in very high abundance among beds from site group 5.

Species from group F, although present in some abundance at most sites, were notably absent from site group 2 mussel beds.

The normal classification, which includes sites with upper and lower intertidal collections, shows one primary and three secondary divisions on the dendrogram, resulting in five clusters of sites (Fig. 4, Table 1). The primary dendrogram division separates site groups 1, 2, and 3 from site groups 4 and 5. Secondary dendrogram divisions, in turn, separate site groups 1, 2, and 3 from each other and group 4 from group 5. Site group 1 is composed of northern island localities, including the upper and lower intertidal collections from Crooks Point (San Miguel Island), both sampling areas on Santa Rosa Island, and both sampling areas on Santa Cruz Island. Site group 2 contains mainland collection areas from Goleta Point (both upper and lower intertidal samples), Ventura, and Carlsbad. Site group 3 is composed of northern island collections from Cuyler Harbor (San Miguel Island; both upper and lower intertidal samples), Frenchys Cove (Anacapa Island), a more southern island area at Dutch Harbor (San Nicolas Island), and the northernmost mainland site, Government Point. Site groups 4 and 5 contain mixtures of southern island and mainland collection localities. Site group 4 contains the Ben Weston (Santa Catalina Island) collection area, the upper and lower intertidal sampling areas at Eel Point (San Clemente Island), the Corona del Mar locality, and the San Diego collection area. Site group 5 contains one of the more northern collection areas, Cat Rock (Anacapa Island). However, this study site faces the remainder of the southerly collection sites. Also included in site group 5 are collection sites at the northwest point of San Nicolas Island, Lighthouse Point (San Clemente Island), and the Bird Rock site on Santa Catalina Island.

The primary dendrogram split clearly separated the northern collection areas, site groups 1, 2, and 3, from the southern collection areas, site groups 4 and 5. Remembering that clustering of collection sites implies that the mussel communities sampled in these areas were more similar in species composition and relative abundance to each other than to communities outside the cluster, we can elaborate on the resultant biogeographic patterns.

The northern and southern communities appeared to correspond to the "warm-water" and "cold-water" provinces previously described as occurring north and south of Point Conception, California (Johnson and Snook 1967, Light *et al*. 1970). In addition, the results suggested that the "cold-water" provinces should extend south of Point Conception if one considers the mussel community inhabitants when discussing this phenomenon. This pattern was clearly exhibited by the clustering and close similarity displayed among Northern Channel Island and northern mainland communities. There were, within the northern site groupings, additional patterns. Site group 1, for example, was composed entirely of island collection areas from the northernmost localities, whereas site group 2 was composed almost exclusively of northern mainland localities (with the exception of Carlsbad). Site group 3 contained a notable mixture of study areas. The northernmost mainland collection area at Government Point was very similar to the Northern Channel Island site at San Miguel, the north-facing Frenchys Cove site on Anacapa Island, and the Dutch Harbor collection area of San Nicolas Island. This interesting arrangement was best explained by considering the impinging water regimes in the areas, as discussed later.

The southern localities were also clustered according to the similarities of their respective mussel communities. Site group 5 was composed almost exclusively of southern island localities, whereas site group 4 contained a mixture of mainland and island sites. The inclusion of the Cat Rock (Anacapa Island) locality in site group 5 was notable and is discussed later.

The normal dendrogram results illustrated distinct dissimilarities between many of the pairs of collections from the same islands (Fig. 4). The most dramatic differences were displayed by the collections from San Nicolas Island and Anacapa Island. The Dutch Harbor (San Nicolas Island) and Frenchys Cove (Anacapa Island) collections occurred in site group 3; these clustered with the northern study sites, illustrating that these mussel communities resembled the northern mussel communities more than their intra-island counterparts. Conversely, the Northwest Point (San Nicolas Island) and Cat Rock (Anacapa Island) sites contained communities which more closely resembled the mussel beds found at the southern collection areas. Less dramatic but still notable differences were evident in the communities from opposite sides of San Miguel Island and San Clemente Island. Although each study site maintained fidelity to its overall northern or southern geographic group, faunal differences existed which placed Crook Point (outer San Miguel Island) and Cuyler Harbor (inner San Miguel Island) separately in site groups 1 and 3, respectively, and which placed Eel Point (outer San Clemente Island) and Lighthouse Point (inner San Clemente Island) in site groups 4 and 5, respectively (Fig. 4, Table 1).

Dispersal of planktonic larvae by currents and water masses is a hypothesis often put forth to explain biogeographic patterns of species distribution (Johnson 1939, Seapy 1974). Cleve-Eulser (1928, as cited in Johnson 1939) succinctly expressed the underlying principle: "Regular biological analysis of the oceans and of the coastal waters would no doubt give a more thorough knowledge of the sea currents, their movements and their intermingling, than could be expected from hydrographic observations only." This principle has been applied to individual species and should be applied in community studies.

Most mussel community members reproduce either by releasing gametes into the surrounding waters where external fertilization and larval development occurs, or by releasing larvae after partial development in an egg capsule or within the adults. These planktonic larvae drift with prevailing currents and water masses. Passive drifting ends when the larva has matured enough to actively seek out an appropriate substrate (settlement and metamorphosis, however, can only occur when this substrate is within the behavioral and physiological tolerances of the larva). Larvae may drift a considerable distance from source areas prior to settlement, acting as a biological "tracer" in the water mass they occupy. Broad-scale analysis of the community distribution resulting from this dispersal serves as an independent test of hydrographic studies detailing current structure and water mass movement, and allows prediction of community structure in areas not specifically sampled.

A very generalized composite diagram of circulation patterns (Fig. 5) occurring in the southern California area has been constructed from Jones (1971), Pirie et al. (1974), and Bernstein et al. (1977). This figure primarily depicts net surface water circulation and does not include the subsurface currents, localized gyres, or seasonal anomalies which are known to exist (Shepard et al. 1939, Tibby 1941, Reid 1962, Jones 1971, Bernstein et al. 1977). The

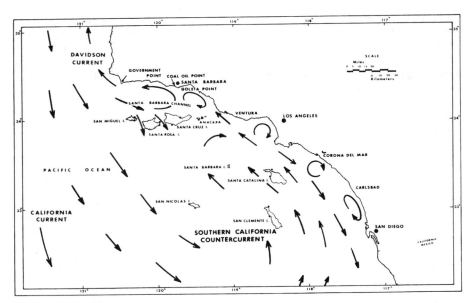

FIGURE 5. *General surface circulation in the Southern California Bight (modified after Jones 1971, Pirie* et al. *1974, and Bernstein* et al. *1977).*

patterns illustrated suggest that cold water arising north of Point Conception flows south and swings in, impinging on the offshore islands in its continued movement down the coast. In addition, movement of warm water arising in lower latitudes flows northward along the mainland coast. Larvae are carried to settlement areas by these two primary current regimes. Mussel community similarities at the various sites suggest that they have received larval recruits from similar source waters (source parental stock). This assumption serves as a basis for delineating and explaining biogeographical patterns among the mussel communities. The similarities of mussel communities illustrated by the classification results (Fig. 4) support the idea of common parental stocks. There is close agreement between the water source to which a site is exposed and the composition of its community. For example, Cat Rock (Anacapa Island) mussel beds closely resemble those communities found on Bird Rock (Santa Catalina Island). The Cat Rock collection area faces due south and is exposed to waters hydrographically similar to those bathing Bird Rock. Conversely, the mussel community at Frenchys Cove (Anacapa Island) is more similar to those found at Cuyler Harbor (San Miguel Island) and Government Point than to species assemblages at Cat Rock, its intra-island counterpart. The Frenchys Cove mussel beds are exposed to almost the same water regimes as mussel beds at Cuyler Harbor and Government Point. Identical arguments could be made in support of the similarities between communities at other sites.

SUMMARY

The community associated with *Mytilus californianus* (mussel) beds from 20 geographic sites in southern California was examined. The study areas included six mainland sites (Government Point, Goleta Point, Ventura, Corona del Mar, Carlsbad, and San Diego) and two sites on opposite sides of seven offshore islands (San Miguel, Santa Rosa, Santa Cruz,

Anacapa, San Nicolas, Santa Catalina, and San Clemente). This large community contains, conservatively, 610 species of animals and 141 species of algae. The richest collection came from Cat Rock (Anacapa Island), where the mussel beds supported 174 species of invertebrates. The lowest diversity was recorded for mussel beds from Ben Weston (Santa Catalina Island), which contained 46 species. In general, the island mussel beds supported a greater variety of both animals and plants. Samples were collected from upper and lower intertidal portions of the beds at several sites. Differences in community composition and abundance were associated with position in the intertidal zone.

Community similarity analysis revealed five major patterns which corresponded to characteristic species assemblages occupying the mussel beds in the various geographic areas. The patterns included: (1) presence of some ubiquitous species groups; (2) clusters of species whose highest abundances characterized selected localities; (3) clusters of localities which displayed a north-south geographic pattern in the similarity of their respective mussel communities; (4) a separation of some island and mainland communities because of dissimilarities in their species composition; and (5) differences between mussel communities on opposite sides of the offshore islands. The results of the community analysis suggest that predictions of the probable mussel community inhabitants of areas not sampled can be made. The observed species distribution patterns appear to correspond in part to known patterns of current flow.

ACKNOWLEDGMENTS

This investigation was a team effort, and I wish to express my gratitude to the many people who contributed to its successful completion. Field collections were made with the help of Lou Fridkis, Jack Kawashima, Glen Yoshida, Richard Rowe, Richard DeLancy, Peggy O'Donnell, and Colleen Cripps. Identification of mussel community inhabitants was performed by Jack Kawashima (almost everything), James McLean and Don Cadien (Mollusca), Barry Wallerstein (Isopoda and tanaids), Mark Crase (Isopoda), Bud Wynn (Isopoda), Mary Wicksten (Crustacea), Jim Wilkins (Amphipoda), Fred Piltz, Rick Rowe, and Pat Bernhardt (Polychaeta), Mary Wright (Echinodermata), Gerald Bakus and Curt Smecher (Porifera), and Valerie Anderson (algae). Sediment size analysis was performed by Gigi Mohamed and Kevin Brown. Sediment carbon analysis was performed by Robert Anderhalt. Data were organized by Louis Fridkis, Janet Helms, Jack Kawashima, and Mike McConnel. Illustrations and figures were drafted by Tom Licari, Diane Hadley, and Cathy Kimmel.

I am particularly indebted to Clyde Henry for his valuable assistance and companionship through the sometimes grueling data-analysis period. I would also like to thank Robert Smith for his great Environmental Assessment Package (EAP) of computer programs. The analyses were performed at the University of Southern California computer facility. Some analyses were completed at Southern California Edison's computer facility, for which I would like to thank Ian Straughan and Nick Condap. The manuscript was typed by Gini Whitt.

I am particularly grateful to Dr. Dale Straughan for her vital support, coordination efforts, and, most of all, for her continued constructive input throughout the entire project.

I also wish to thank Len Cunningham, Bill Lippincott, and others at Science Applications, Inc. for their coordinating efforts. This research was funded by the Bureau of Land Management under contract AA550-CT6-40.

REFERENCES

BERNSTEIN, R. L., L. BREAKER, and R. WHRITNER. 1977. California Current eddy formation: ship, air, and satellite results. Science 195:353-359.

CAIN, S. A. 1938. The species-area curve. Amer. Midl. Natur. 19:573-581.

CIMBERG, R. L. 1975. Zonation, species diversity, and redevelopment in the rocky intertidal near Trinidad, northern California. M.A. thesis, Humboldt State University, Arcata, Calif.

CLIFFORD, H. T., and W. STEPHENSON. 1975. An introduction to numerical classification. Academic Press, New York, N.Y.

DAWSON, E. Y. 1959. A primary report on the benthic marine flora of southern California. Pp. 169-264 *in* Oceanographic survey of the continental shelf area of southern California. Publs. California State Water Pollution Control Board 20.

————. 1965. Intertidal algae. Pp. 220-231, Appendix 351-438 *in* An oceanographic and biological survey of the southern California mainland shelf. Publs. California State Water Quality Control Board 27.

GLYNN, P. N. 1965. Community composition, structure, and interrelationships in the marine intertidal *Endocladia muricata-Balanus glandula* association in Monterey Bay, California. Beaufortia. 148(12):1-198.

HEWATT, W. G. 1937. Ecological studies on selected marine intertidal communities of Monterey, California. Amer. Natur. 18:161-206.

JOHNSON, M. E., and H.J. SNOOK. 1967. Seashore animals of the Pacific coast. Dover, New York, N.Y.

JOHNSON, M. W. 1939. The correlation of water movements and dispersal of pelagic larval stages of certain littoral animals, especially the sand crab *Emerita*. J. Marine Res. 2(3):236-245.

JONES, J. H. 1971. General circulation and water characteristics in the Southern California Bight. Southern California Coastal Water Research Project Publ., Los Angeles, Calif.

KANTER, R.G. 1977. Structure and diversity in *Mytilus californianus* (Mollusca: Bivalvia) communities. Ph.D. thesis, University of Southern California, Los Angeles, Calif.

————. 1978. Mussel community study. Southern California Baseline Study, final report. Vol. III, rep. 1.2. Bureau of Land Management, U.S. Dept. Interior, Washington, D.C.

————. 1979. Mussel community study. Southern California Baseline Study, final report. Vol. II, rep. 7; Vol. III, rep. 2.0; Vol. IV, rep. 2.0. Bureau of Land Management, U.S. Dept. Interior, Washington, D.C.

LANCE, G. N., and W. T. WILLIAMS. 1966. A generalized sorting strategy for computer classifications. Nature 212:218.

LIGHT, S. F., R. I. SMITH, F. A. PITELKA, D. P. ABBOTT, and F. M. WEESNER. 1970. Intertidal invertebrates of the central California coast. R. I. Smith and J. T. Carlton, eds. University of California Press, Los Angeles, Calif.

LITTLER, M. M. 1980. Overview of the rocky intertidal systems of southern California. Pp. 265-306 *in* D.M. Power, ed., The California Islands: proceedings of a multidisciplinary symposium. Santa Barbara Museum of Natural History, Santa Barbara, Calif.

NICHOLSON, N. L., and R. L. CIMBERG. 1971. The Santa Barbara oil spills of 1969: a post-spill survey of the rocky intertidal. Pp. 325-399 *in* D. Straughan, ed., Biological and oceanographical survey of the Santa Barbara Channel oil spill, 1969-1970, v. I. Allan Hancock Foundation, University of Southern California, Los Angeles, Calif.

PAINE, R. T. 1966. Food web complexity and species diversity. Amer. Natur. 100:65-75.

————. 1976. Size limited predation: an observational and experimental approach with the *Mytilus-Pisaster* interaction. Ecology 57:858-873.

PIELOU, E. C. 1966. Species-diversity and pattern-diversity in the study of ecological succession. J. Theor. Biol. 10:370-383.

PIRIE, D. M., M. J. MURPHY, and J. R. EDMISTEN. 1974. California nearshore surface currents. *In* California nearshore processes study, final report. U.S. Army Corps of Engineers, San Francisco District.

REID, J. L., JR. 1962. Measurements of the California Countercurrent at a depth of 250 meters. J. Marine Res. 29:134-137.

REISH, D. J. 1964. Discussion of the *Mytilus californianus* community on newly constructed rock jetties in southern California (Mollusca: Bivalvia). Veliger 7:95-101.

RICKETTS, E. F., J. CALVIN, and J. W. HEDGPETH. 1968. Between Pacific tides. Stanford University Press, Stanford, Calif.

SEAPY, R. R. 1974. Distribution and abundance of the epipelagic mollusc *Carinaria japonica* in waters off southern California. Marine Biol. 24:243-250.

SHEPARD, F. P., R. REVELLE, and R. S. DIETZ. 1939. Ocean-bottom currents off the California coast. Science 89:488-489.

SMITH, R. 1976. Numerical analysis of ecological survey data. Ph.D. thesis, University of Southern California, Los Angeles, Calif.

SUCHANEK, T. 1979. The *Mytilus californianus* community; studies on composition, structure, organization, and dynamics of a mussel bed. Ph.D. thesis, University of Washington, Seattle, Wash.

TIBBY, R. B. 1941. The water masses off the west coast of North America. J. Marine Res. 4:112-121.

Mainland and Insular Assemblages of Benthic Decapod Crustaceans of Southern California

Mary K. Wicksten

Allan Hancock Foundation, University of Southern California,
University Park, Los Angeles, California 90007

INTRODUCTION

Although decapod crustaceans (crabs, hermit crabs, shrimp, and related groups) are among the largest and most familiar invertebrates of southern California, little is known of their distribution according to depth and substrate except in the littoral zone. Many species are known only from isolated collections taken over a span of decades.

During the extensive sampling program from 1975 through 1977 of the "Southern California Baseline Studies and Analysis: Benthic Macrofauna," 80 species of decapods were taken. Examination of the records of these species provided considerable information on their distribution. Recent cataloguing of specimens in the collections of the Allan Hancock Foundation has enabled comparison of these records with those of specimens taken since 1913 off southern California.

METHODS

During 1975-77, specimens were taken at 15 to 1,800 m by the R. V. *Velero IV* and *Thomas G. Thompson* by box cores, rock dredges, and beam trawls as part of the Southern California Baseline Studies and Analysis. During the preliminary direct data inspection, the species of decapods taken at each station were recorded on maps of the stations. The maps were examined to see if any obvious patterns could be detected. This cursory examination indicated that certain species occurred almost entirely either along the islands or near the mainland.

To facilitate comparison of the records, stations are called "mainland" if they are located along the mainland of southern California or in the basins between the mainland and the islands (Fig. 1). Island stations are those taken along the islands, Cortez Bank, or Tanner Bank.

Stations at 100 fathoms (185 m) or less are called shelf stations. The 185-m contour was chosen as the seaward limit of the shelf because it corresponds roughly to the maximum lowering of the sea level during Pleistocene glaciation (Shepard 1963). Stations between 100 and 500 fathoms (185 to 923 m) are labeled slope stations. Those stations between 500 and 1,000 fathoms (923 to 1,846 m) are entitled basin stations, and those deeper than 1,000 fathoms, bathyal stations. These deeper divisions correspond roughly to changes in the composition of the decapod fauna. Sampling stations from a range of depths are listed according to the greatest depth in order to determine the maximum lower limits of the species.

The substrate is recorded according to the description in the field log (*e.g.*, sand, mud, rocks, sand and shell). This descriptive designation (rather than grain size) was used in order to compare the stations sampled in 1975-77 with earlier stations at which no grain size analysis was made. Data on the grain size analysis and organic carbon content of the sediment at the 1975-77 stations will be published elsewhere.

A list was compiled of species taken at 10 or more stations during the sampling program of 1975-77. Additional records of these species were taken from the literature and from records of materials in the collections of the Allan Hancock Foundation. These materials include specimens taken by baited traps, trawls, grabs, dredges, box cores, and by hand. The specimens were from more than 1,000 stations located off San Miguel, Santa Rosa, Santa Cruz, Anacapa,

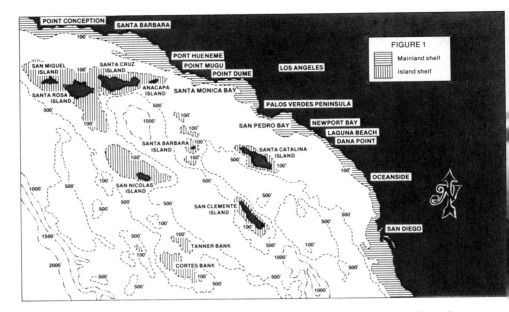

FIGURE 1. *Depth contours and locations of island and mainland shelves off southern California.*

Santa Barbara, San Nicolas, Santa Catalina, and San Clemente Islands, Tanner and Cortez Banks, Point Conception, Santa Barbara, Port Hueneme to Point Mugu, Point Dume, Santa Monica and San Pedro Bays, the Palos Verdes peninsula, Newport to Dana Point, Oceanside, and San Diego (Fig. 1). Collections were made in 1913-26 by the R. V. *Anton Dohrn*, in 1932-42 by the R. V. *Velero III*, in 1948-54 by the R. V. *Velero IV*, since 1970 by researchers at King Harbor and on sandy beaches in southern California, and by private collectors since 1913. Similar information was compiled for the crabs *Cancer anthonyi* and *Cancer gracilis*, the ghost shrimps *Callianassa* spp., and the hermit crab *Orthopagurus minimus*, for which extensive substrate data from previous surveys were available. Data also were compiled for species taken at 546 fathoms (1,000 m) or deeper during 1975-77, although none of these species occurred at as many as 10 stations.

The large variation in the quantity and quality of data for the stations, the gaps in time between periods of sampling, the incomplete lists of species for older stations, and the wide range of techniques used in sampling make numerical analyses of the data by standard statistical methods impossible. Species inhabiting the continental shelves were classified as mainland or insular if twice as many specimens or station occurrences were found in one area as in the other. Because stations from deeper areas were sampled more frequently off the islands, designation of the species at these depths as mainland or insular was not possible. The classification of species by depth is based on the range of the majority of stations at which each species was found (except in the case of *Pandalus platyceros*, which occurs at all depths).

The ranges of the species are recorded as follows: southern (S), reaching their northern limit off southern California; north-south (N-S), extending north and south of the area; or northern (N), reaching their southern limit in this area.

For purposes of this report, only records from southern California (from Point Conception to the U.S.-Mexican border) were examined for depth and substrate. Comparable data for almost all the species examined are not available for central California or Baja California, Mexico.

RESULTS

The ranges, locations, substrates, and depths of the 29 species examined are given in Table 1. Except as indicated, the numbers given are the total numbers of stations in which the species in question occurred in each category.

Of all the species, only the spotted prawn *Pandalus platyceros* was taken at stations ranging from the shelf to bathyal areas. The other species tended to be confined to more narrow ranges of depth.

Among the 14 species found most often on the shelf, six were taken most frequently along the mainland. These six (*Cancer anthonyi, Cancer gracilis, Callianassa longimana, Pinnixa schmitti, Pinnixa occidentalis,* and *Sicyonia ingentis*) usually are found on or in soft substrates (sand, sand and mud, and mud or clay). The high number of *Pinnixa schmitti* recorded at the island stations is due to the occurrence of 116 specimens at a single station off San Miguel Island. Although *Cancer anthonyi* has been collected among rocks at King Harbor, it usually lives in protected areas along and on the inside of the breakwater, not on the exposed outer coast (Straughan 1978). It is noteworthy that the only place on the islands at which both species of *Cancer* as well as *Callianassa* spp. can be taken frequently is Santa Catalina Harbor, which has a quiet, sheltered, silty sand bottom (Straughan 1977).

Six species (*Clythrocerus planus, Crangon zacae, Erileptus spinosus, Orthopagurus minimus, Pagurus setosus,* and *Pylopagurus guatemoci*) usually were collected at island stations. These species are found on bottoms of sand and shell, pebbles, or coarse, clean sand. They were taken along the mainland in rocky areas or in places with swift currents, such as off Point Dume, off Laguna Beach, or among the red sands off Seal Beach.

Two sand shrimp (*Crangon alaskensis elongata* and *Crangon communis*), although taken most often along the islands, also occur frequently along the mainland. These widespread species do not seem to follow the same patterns of distribution as the other 12 shelf species.

Ten species were taken most often on the slopes. Of these, six were taken entirely in trawls or dredges, for which data on substrate usually could not be obtained. Five of these six (*Chorilia longipes turgida, Lopholithodes foraminatus, Munida quadrispina, Paguristes turgidus,* and *Spirontocaris sica*), although most abundant off the islands, also occur frequently along the mainland. These five have a patchy distribution, with a single trawl capturing from one to 86 individuals per tow.

Calastacus quinqueseriatus, Callianassa goniophthalma, and *Munidopsis depressa* were taken along the mainland or on the slopes of the islands facing the mainland. *Calastacus quinqueseriatus* was collected on soft substrates. *Callianassa goniophthalma* favors stagnant bottoms (D. Chivers, pers. comm.). *Parapagurus haigae* and *Argis californiensis,* however, occur most often off the islands on sand or a mixture of sand, shell, and mud.

Chorilia longipes turgida has been taken in dredges along with smooth, round boulders (Garth 1958). One small specimen collected in 1977 was clinging to a large rock. *In situ* benthic photographs, however, show this spider crab crossing a flat, sandy bottom.

Only four species were taken exclusively at stations from the basins and bathyal depths: *Lebbeus washingtonianus, Parapagurus pilosimanus benedicti, Munidopsis diomedeae,* and *Paralomis multispina.* The latter two were collected on muddy bottoms. Smears of mud on specimens of *L. washingtonianus* suggest that it, too, inhabits soft substrates (Wicksten 1978). *Parapagurus pilosimanus* in the Atlantic Ocean lives on silty clay bottoms (Menzies, George, and Rowe 1973).

TABLE 1. Distribution of species.

Species	Range	Number of stations	Number of specimens	Substrate types and number of specimens	Depth in m and number of specimens
			Mainland Shelf		
Cancer anthonyi Rathbun	N-S (Nations 1975)	M: 43 I: 5	M: 214 I: 19	Rock: 2, Gravel: 1, Sand + shell: 4, Sand: 5, Mud: 2, NR: 34	<185: 36 NR: 12
Cancer gracilis Dana	N-S (Nations 1975; AHF records)	M: 52 I: 10	M: 336 I: 36	Rock: 2, Gravel: 1, Sand + shell: 2, Sand + mud: 8, Sand: 13, Mud: 5, NR: 31	<185: 55 NR: 7
Callianassa longimana Stimpson	N-S (Schmitt 1921)	M: 17 I: 3	M: 55 I: 3	Sand: 5, Mud: 4, Clay: 5, NR: 6	<185: 18 185-923: 1 NR: 1
Pinnixa schmitti Rathbun	N-S (Schmitt 1921)	M: 29 I: 8	M: 56 I: 162	Sand + shell: 4, Sand: 12, Mud: 11, Clay: 8, NR: 2	<185: 36 185-923: 1
Pinnixa occidentalis Rathbun	N-S (Schmitt 1921)	M: 17 I: 2	M: 41 I: 2	Sand: 8, Mud: 3, Clay: 8	<185: 18 185-923: 1
Sicyonia ingentis (Burkenroad)	S (AHF records)	M: 27 I: 1 (Word and Charwat 1976)	M: 250 I: NR	NR: 27	<185: 26 185-923: 1

Island Shelf

Species	Status (reference)	M / I	M / I (Island Shelf)	Substrate	Depth
Pagurus setosus (Benedict)	N (McLaughlin 1974)	M: 2, I: 41	M: 10, I: 263	Rocks: 4, Sand + shell or rocks: 24, Sand: 10, Mud: 2, NR: 3	<185: 33, 185-923: 9, NR: 1
Orthopagurus minimus (Holmes)	N (McLaughlin 1974)	M: 16, I: 30	M: 172, I: 26	Sand + shell or rocks: 20, Sand: 10, Sand + mud: 1, Mud: 5, NR: 10	<185: 42, 185-923: 1, NR: 3
Clythrocerus planus Rathbun	S (AHF records)	M: 3, I: 60	M: 6, I: 179	Sand + shell or rocks: 49, Sand: 13, Mud: 1	<185: 63
Erileptus spinosus Rathbun	S (Garth 1958)	M: 21, I: 122	M: 61, I: 1048	Sand + shell or rocks: 14, Sand: 6, Clay + rocks: 1, NR: 122	<185: 131, 185-923: 12
Pylopagurus guatemoci Glassell	S (Walton 1954)	M: 3, I: 41	M: 5, I: 58	Sand + shell or rocks: 21, Sand: 1, Rock + mud: 2, NR: 20	<185: 35, 185-923: 9
Crangon zacae (Chace)	S (Chace 1937)	M: 22, I: 72	M: 114, I: 458	Rock: 8, Sand + shell or rocks: 14, Sand: 23, Sand + mud: 8, Mud + rock or shell: 2, Mud: 15, NR: 24	<185: 57, 185-923: 32, NR: 5

TABLE 1. (Cont.)

Species	Range	Number of stations	Number of specimens	Substrate types and number of specimens	Depth in m and number of specimens
			Both Shelves		
Crangon communis Rathbun	N (Schmitt 1921)	M: 14 I: 27	M: 60 I: 132	Sand + rock: 2, Sand: 4, Mud: 6, NR: 29	<185: 16 185-923: 24 NR: 1
Crangon alaskensis elongata Rathbun	N-S (Schmitt 1921)	M: 79 I: 43	M: 625 I: 529	Rock: 8, Sand + shell or rock: 12, Sand: 28, Sand + mud: 5, Mud: 4, NR: 65	<185: 94 185-923: 4 NR: 24
			Slope		
Calastacus quinqueseriatus Rathbun	N-S (Schmitt 1921)	M: 13 I: 3	M: 16 I: 4	Sand + mud: 1, Mud: 3, Clay: 5, NR: 7	<185: 2 185-923: 14
Munidopsis depressa Faxon	S (Haig 1956)	M: 10 I: 5	M: 39 I: 11	NR: 15	<185-923: 13 923-1846: 1 NR: 1
Callianassa goniophthalma Rathbun	N (Schmitt 1921)	M: 5 I: 1	M: 5 I: 1	Mud = clay: 1, NR: 5	<185: 1 185-923: 5
Parapagurus haigae De Saint Laurent	S (De Saint Laurent 1972)	M: 5 I: 36	M: 5 I: 160	Rock: 5, Sand + shell or rock: 5, Sand: 11, Mud + rock or shell: 5, Mud: 4, NR: 11	<185: 6 185-923: 35

Species	Distribution (source)			Substrate	Depth
Argis californiensis (Rathbun)	S (Wicksten 1977)	M: 3 / I: 14	M: 5 / I: 21	Sand + shell or rock: 3, Sand: 3, Mud + rock or shell: 1, Mud: 3, NR: 8	<185: 6, 185–923: 11
Munida quadrispina Benedict	N-S (Schmitt 1921)	M: 39 / I: 17	M: 81 / I: 312	Sand + rock: 2, Rocks: 2, Rocks + clay: 1, Clay: 1, NR: 50	<185: 3, 185–923: 51, 923–1846: 2
Chorilia longipes turgida Rathbun	N (Garth 1958)	M: 26 / I: 64	M: 60 / I: 209	Dredged with boulders (Garth 1958)	<185: 17, 185–923: 71, 923–1846: 2, NR: 2
Spirontocaris sica Rathbun	N (Butler 1964)	M: 11 / I: 25	M: 73 / I: 150	Sand + shell: 1, NR: 35	<185: 1, 185–923: 33, NR: 2
Pagurites turgidus (Stimpson)	N-S (McLaughlin 1974)	M: 8 / I: 61	M: 16 / I: 489	Rock: 6, Sand + shell or rock: 9, Sand: 18, Mud + shell or rock: 3, Mud: 12, NR: 21	<185: 27, 185–923: 41, 923–1846: 1
Lopholithodes foraminatus (Stimpson)	N (Schmitt 1921)	M: 3 / I: 18	M: 4 / I: 26	Rock: 1, NR: 20	<185: 7, 185–923: 13, NR: 1

TABLE 1. (Cont.)

Species	Range	Number of stations	Number of specimens	Substrate types and number of specimens	Depth in m and number of specimens
			Basin - Bathyal		
Pandalus platyceros Brandt	N (Schmitt 1921)	M: 10 I: 33	M: 19 I: 150	Rock: 1, Mud: 1, Sand: 2, Mud + rock: 1, NR: 38	<185: 21 185-923: 12 923-1846: 3 >1846: 2 NR: 5
Lebbeus washingtonianus (Rathbun)	N (Wicksten 1978)	Total: 5	Total: 10	NR: 5	923-1846: 4 >1846: 1
Parapagurus pilosimanus benedicti De Saint Laurent	N-S (McLaughlin 1974)	Total: 6	Total: 6	NR: 6	185-923: 2 923-1846: 4
Munidopsis diomedae (Faxon)	S (Haig and Wicksten 1975)	Total: 2	Total: 10	Mud: 1, NR: 1	923-1846: 2
Paralomis multispina (Benedict)	N (Schmitt 1921)	Total: 6	Total: 6	Mud: 1, NR: 5	185-923: 1 923-1846: 5

Key to symbols: NR: not recorded.   <: less than.   >: greater than.   M: mainland.   I: island.   AHF: Allan Hancock Foundation.

Of the 29 species examined, only two (*Argis californiensis* and *Crangon zacae*) seem to be confined to the Californian Province (Valentine 1966). *Munidopsis diomedeae* reaches the northern end of a range that extends as far south as Peru. *Pylopagurus guatemoci* ranges south to the Galapagos Islands. *Munidopsis depressa* and *Parapagurus pilosimanus benedicti* extend south to Central America. *Clythrocerus planus, Erileptus spinosus, Sicyonia ingentis, Parapagurus haigae,* and *Cancer gracilis* reach the Gulf of California and the west coast of Mexico. The remaining species range from northern Baja California or southern California to Washington, British Columbia, or Alaska.

DISCUSSION AND CONCLUSIONS

Substrate and its related parameters (organic carbon content, velocity and turbulence of bottom currents, and dissolved oxygen) influence benthic decapods of the shelf to form characteristic insular and mainland assemblages of species. The steep gradients of the bottoms off the islands, the currents around them, and the absence of major sources of silt prevent the accumulation of the soft substrates favored by digging species more common to the mainland. In Santa Catalina Harbor, where protected sand is present, mainland species can occur.

Insular species occur along the mainland only in isolated areas of suitable substrates. Input of large masses of particulate material, whether from large sewage outfalls or dredge tailings, easily could bury suitable habitats for the insular species. Early records have not been analyzed yet to find out if recent human activities, such as the installation of the large sewage outfalls off Los Angeles County, have destroyed some of these patches of coarse sediments. It seems likely, however, that such changes could alter the assemblages of decapods in such areas from insular to mainland types.

More specimens inhabiting the slopes and basins were taken off the islands than along the mainland. This seeming abundance near the islands may be due to the ease of sampling. Because of the sharp drop-offs along the shores of the islands, deep water is available for study closer to shore than it is along the mainland.

On the whole, species of the slopes, basins, and bathyal areas seem to be adapted to soft sediments, which are prevalent in this range of depths (Shepard 1963). I have found that *Chorilia longipes turgida* may stay near isolated outcrops of rock or move from one rocky area to another, as does the shallow subtidal decorator crab *Loxorhynchus crispatus*.

Lopholithodes foraminatus may follow a temperature gradient in its distribution. McCauley (1972) found the crab at 42 to 200 m off Oregon, while Pereyra and Alton (1972) stated that it was most common off Oregon in the outer sublittoral zone, at 50 to 100 fathoms (92 to 185 m). At 14 of the 21 stations where the crab was taken in southern California, it occurred at 190 m or deeper. However, it does range into water as shallow as about 20 m off the Palos Verdes peninsula (L. Ogilvy, pers. comm.).

Unequal distribution of food may cause the patchy distribution of decapods of the slope. Four or more *Chorilia longipes turgida* and *Lopholithodes foraminatus* were taken at a time in baited traps by the R. V. *N. B. Scofield* in 1969 and by the M. V. *Lady Anne* in 1977. *Paralomis multispina* also has been collected in traps (Allan Hancock Foundation unpubl. records).

Of the decapods of the slopes and deeper areas, only *Calastacus quinqueseriatus* and *Callianassa goniophthalma* belong to groups that dig permanent burrows. The other species, taken in baited traps, trawls, and dredges, or photographed *in situ*, seem to be climbers, walkers, shallow diggers, and short-distance swimmers. None are known to be commensals, as are *Pinnixa* spp. Perhaps lack of sufficient concentrations of food in the sediments, or the consistency of the sediments, causes the decapods to be adapted to foraging across wide areas of bottom.

ACKNOWLEDGMENTS

I thank Dustin Chivers, California Academy of Sciences, for information on *Callianassa goniophthalma*. Larry Ogilvy, Claremont College, shared observations of *Lopholithodes foraminatus*. John Fitch, California Department of Fish and Game, donated specimens of *L. foraminatus, Chorilia longipes turgida,* and *Paralomis multispina*. Dale Straughan, University of Southern California, provided use of the records from King Harbor and the sandy beaches. Ginny Mickelson, San Francisco State University, prepared the illustration.

The work in King Harbor was sponsored by the Southern California Edison Company. The survey of the sandy beaches was carried out under sponsorship of the U.S. Bureau of Land Management, U.S. Department of the Interior, contract number AA550-CT7-44. The Southern California Baseline Studies and Analysis was funded by the Bureau of Land Management, contract numbers 08550-CT5-52 and AA550-CT6-40.

REFERENCES

BUTLER, T. H. 1964. Records of shrimps (order Decapoda) from British Columbia. J. Fish. Res. Bd. Canada 21:419-421.

CHACE, F. A., JR. 1937. The Templeton Crocker expedition. VII. Caridean decapod Crustacea from the Gulf of California and the west coast of Lower California. Zoologica 22:109-138.

DE SAINT LAURENT, M. 1972. Sur la Famille des Parapaguridae Smith, 1882. Description de *Typhlopagurus foresti,* gen. nov., sp. nov., et de quinze Especes ou Sous-especes nouvelles de *Parapagurus* Smith (Crustacea, Decapoda). Bijdrager. Tot de Dierkunde 42:97-123.

GARTH, J. S. 1958. Brachyura of the Pacific coast of America: Oxyrhyncha. Allan Hancock Pacific Exped. 21, pt. 1.

HAIG, J. 1956. Notes on two anomuran crustaceans new to California waters. Bull. So. California Acad. Sci. 55:79-81.

HAIG, J., and M. WICKSTEN. 1975. First records and range extensions of crabs in California waters. Bull. So. California Acad. Sci. 74:100-104.

MCCAULEY, J. E. 1972. A preliminary checklist of selected groups of invertebrates from otter-trawl and dredge collections off Oregon. Pp. 409-421 *in* A. T. Pruter and D. L. Alverson, eds., The Columbia River estuary and adjacent ocean waters. Bioenvironmental studies. University of Washington Press, Seattle, Wash.

MCLAUGHLIN, P. A. 1974. The hermit crabs (Crustacea: Decapoda, Paguridea) of northwestern North America. Zool. Verhand. 130, Leiden.

MENZIES, R. J., R. Y. GEORGE, and G. T. ROWE. 1973. Abyssal environment and ecology of the world oceans. John Wiley & Sons, New York, N.Y.

NATIONS, J. D. 1975. The genus *Cancer* (Crustacea: Brachyura): systematics, biogeography, and fossil record. Los Angeles Co. Nat. Hist. Mus. Sci. Bull. 23.

PEREYRA, W. T., and M. S. ALTON. 1972. Distribution and relative abundance of invertebrates off the northern Oregon coast. Pp. 444-474 *in* A. T. Pruter and D. L. Alverson, eds., The Columbia River estuary and adjacent ocean waters. Bioenvironmental studies. University of Washington Press, Seattle, Wash.

SCHMITT, W. L. 1921. Marine decapod Crustacea of California. Univ. California Publ. Zool. 23:1-470.

SHEPARD, F. P. 1963. Submarine geology. Harper and Row, New York, N.Y.

STRAUGHAN, D. 1977. Sandy beaches and sloughs. Southern California Baseline Study, final report III, rep. 2.3 and appendices. Bureau of Land Management, U.S. Dept. Interior, Washington, D.C.

————. 1978. Report on field biology of subtidal rocky shores. *In* Influence of power generating facilities on southern California coastal waters, phase 4: study of environmental conditions in King Harbor April 1, 1977-March 31, 1978. Southern California Edison Research and Development Series 78-RD-108.

VALENTINE, J. W. 1966. Numerical analysis of marine molluscan ranges on the extratropical northeastern Pacific shelf. Limnol. and Oceanogr. 11:198-211.

WALTON, B. C. 1954. The genus *Pylopagurus* (Crustacea: Anomura) in the Pacific with descriptions of two new species. Allan Hancock Pacific Exped. 18:139-172.

WICKSTEN, M. K. 1977. Range extensions of four species of crangonid shrimps from California and Baja California, with a key to the genera. Proc. Biol. Soc. Washington 90:963-967.

————. 1978. The species of *Lebbeus* in California. Occas. Papers Allan Hancock Found. N.S., No. 1.

WORD, J. Q., and D. CHARWAT. 1976. Invertebrates of southern California coastal waters. II. Natantia. Southern California Coastal Water Research Project, El Segundo, Calif.

Ecology of Southern California Island Sandy Beaches

Dale Straughan and Diane Hadley

Institute for Marine and Coastal Studies,
University of Southern California, Los Angeles, California 90007

INTRODUCTION

In 1975 the Bureau of Land Management (BLM) initiated a series of marine studies in the southern California borderland (Straughan 1977b, 1978). These studies were to establish a baseline and to determine "areas of concern" prior to any expansion of the offshore petroleum industry. The baseline was to be one that accounted for natural variability in the region over a period of time so that it could be used to measure any impact of expansion of the petroleum industry. The "areas of concern" included those which have valuable marine resources and might therefore be excluded from larger areas that would be impacted by an increase in oil operations. The following data, concerning sandy beaches on some of the islands in the Southern California Bight, were collected as part of a program to achieve these goals.

The program was designed to establish the abiotic parameters and the distribution and abundance of the biota on the beaches. Surveys were conducted biannually and, at times, quarterly, in order to determine the variability in both abiotic and biotic components. The data were then analyzed to determine if there are correlations that would suggest possible cause-and-effect relationships.

The ultimate aim of the research is to define the physical habitat for each species. This would provide a certain degree of predictability of species distribution based on physical habitat data alone. The ultimate aim is to reach a point where distributional parameters can be extrapolated for nearly all beach areas. Interspecific and intraspecific variables operate within the framework. However, if a species cannot survive within the abiotic limitations in an area there can be no biotic interaction. In the relatively sparsely populated sandy beach habitat, we consider abiotic factors to be more important in limiting the distribution and abundance of species than biotic factors.

The BLM study also includes comparable surveys of mainland sandy beaches and sloughs. While these surveys are outside the scope of the present paper, reference will be made to these data for purposes of comparison.

Six sites were selected to account for many of the variables operating in the area (Table 1). The following factors were considered in selecting sites: (1) geographic variability; (2) the side of an island; (3) the presence of a mammal rookery; (4) exposure to wave action; and (5) disturbance by man.

Geographic variability could be a significant factor because the area is one which is impacted by cold-water currents (California Current) from the north, which flow south past San Miguel Island, and warm-water currents (Davidson Current) from the south. The intrusion of the currents into the Southern California Bight is variable and the current pattern is further complicated by periodic upwelling. However, it could be predicted that there might be a predominance of cold-water species on the more northern islands and a predominance of warm-water species on the more southern islands, with a gradation in between. Therefore, sites were selected ranging from Tyler Bight on San Miguel Island in the north to Dutch Harbor on San Nicolas Island and North West Cove on San Clemente Island in the south (Fig. 1).

The side of the island may be important in that there may be a difference in organisms on the Pacific Ocean side of the islands in comparison with the generally more sheltered mainland side.

TABLE 1. Characteristics of island sites.

Island site	Geographic location	Side of island	Exposure to waves	Mammal rookery	Manmade disturbances
San Miguel (Tyler Bight)	N	P	E	+	−
Santa Cruz (Black Point)	N	P	E	−	−
San Nicolas (Dutch Harbor)	S	P	E	−	−
San Clemente (North West Cove)	S	M	C	−	Military
Santa Catalina (the Isthmus)	S	M	E	−	Boating
Santa Catalina (Cat Harbor)	S	P	C	−	Boating

N = northern side of island.   S = southern side of island.
P = Pacific Ocean side of island.   M = mainland side of island.
E = exposed to wave action.   C = cove sheltered from wave action.

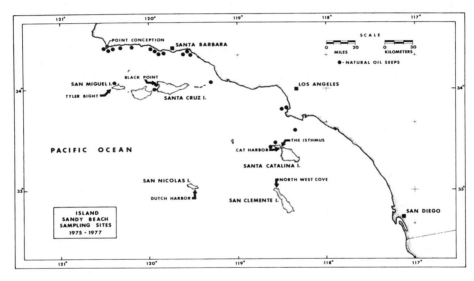

FIGURE 1. *Map of Southern California Bight showing location of island survey sites and recorded areas of natural oil and gas seepage.*

Exposure to wave action is usually related to the sediment parameters on the beach. In previous studies, sites exposed to wave action usually have shorter, more steeply sloping beaches and coarser sediment than sites which are sheltered from wave action. The exposed sites also usually have fewer species and fewer numbers of individuals collected than the sheltered sites.

The mammal rookeries on the islands are expanding. There are particularly large concentrations at the southern and western end of San Miguel Island which include California Sea Lions (*Zalophus californianus*) and Elephant Seals (*Mirounga angustirostris*). The animals traverse and frequently spend a considerable portion of their time in the intertidal areas. This could result in an increase in the organic content of the sediments, which, in turn, may influence the biota in the sand.

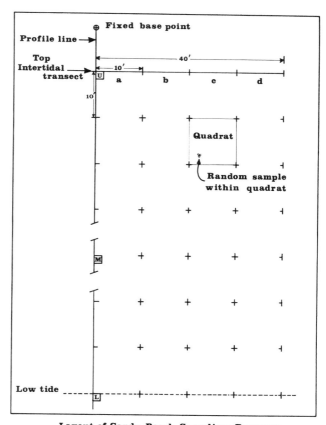

FIGURE 2. *Layout of sandy beach sampling techniques.*

Layout of Sandy Beach Sampling Program

U —Upper Intertidal
M—Middle Intertidal
L —Lower Intertidal

Most of the islands are not heavily impacted by human activities. However, some of the sites are used by the military for training exercises. Massive beach disturbances have been observed at the site at North West Cove on San Clemente Island, for example. Santa Catalina Island is the only site readily accessible to the public. This is a favorite visiting place for the boating public and all areas are heavily used by boaters on fine summer weekends. Data collected at mussel communities on the mainland side of the island at the Isthmus suggested a slight contamination by fuel oil during the summer months, which is thought to be related to these activities (Straughan 1976).

METHODS

A stratified random quadrat method, which takes into account zonation and patchiness in distribution, was used to survey the beaches. Sampling was conducted by taking three cores (7.75 cm diameter and 20 cm deep) at a random point in stratified quadrats across the intertidal area from high tide to low tide level during low spring tides (Fig. 2). Cores were sieved through a 1.5-mm mesh screen; hence, these data include only macrobiota. The large screen size was

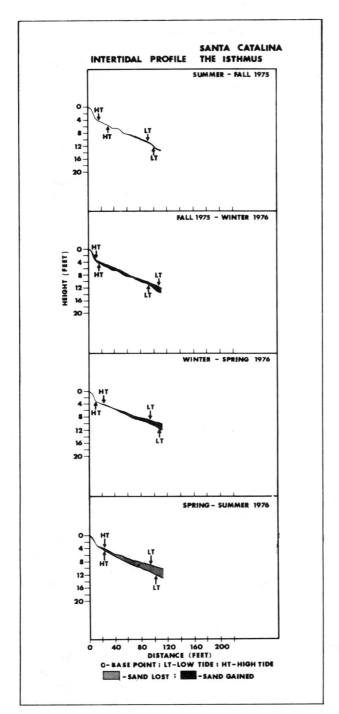

FIGURE 3. *Intertidal beach profiles recorded on quarterly surveys (summer 1975 to summer 1976) at the Isthmus, Santa Catalina Island.*

used so that large samples of sand could be rapidly sieved and large areas surveyed during a spring tide.

Sand samples were collected along the profile line of the grid for laboratory analysis. Grain size analysis was performed using an automatic settling tube (Folk 1968, Pettijohn 1957). Pipette analyses were conducted on a single set of samples from Cat Harbor to determine the amount of silts and clays present (Cook 1969, Gibbs 1974); however, the values were so low that this was discontinued. An Ohaus moisture meter (Model 6020 PG) was used to determine moisture and organic content. This organic content is not the same as total organic carbon (TOC) because it does not include organics incorporated into the sediments. Total organic carbon analyses were performed by Dr. W. E. Reed of the University of California at Los Angeles using the L.E.C.O. technique (Bandy and Kolpack 1963, Kolpack and Bell 1968).

Profiles were measured using an Emery stick method (Emery 1961), and all tar was collected within each sample and at each 10-ft (3.0 m) level down the grid. Temperatures were measured with a Yellow Springs Instrument Telethermometer, and salinity with a refractometer.

In summary, the following abiotic data were obtained from each survey: (1) profile (intertidal height, beach slope); (2) temperature (air, ocean, sand surface, sand subsurface); (3) salinity (ocean, interstitial water); (4) sediment (grain size, moisture content, Ohaus organic content, TOC); and (5) weight of tar.

Ideally, all abiotic parameters should be measured at each sampling point. However, this is prohibitive in cost and time. Research over a nine-year period has indicated that the measurement of abiotic parameters along the profile line adequately reflects abiotic conditions on the 40-ft wide grid where biotic data are collected.

RESULTS

All sites were surveyed quarterly in 1975-76. In 1976-77, sites were surveyed only in summer and winter, except for San Nicolas Island which was surveyed quarterly. Therefore, the summarized data are based on six surveys of most sites and eight surveys at San Nicolas Island.

Tables 2 and 3 summarize the main abiotic characteristics of these island beaches. The water temperatures followed the predicted trend, with colder temperatures being recorded at the more northern sites (e.g., San Miguel Island, 11.0°C to 17.5°C) and warmer temperatures at the more southern sites (e.g., San Clemente Island, 14.0°C to 22°C).

The Isthmus site at Santa Catalina Island had the shortest, steepest beach (Fig. 3) with the coarsest sediment (average mean $\phi = 1.41$), while the Cat Harbor site on the other side of the island had the longest and most gently sloping beach (Fig. 4) with the finest sediments (average mean $\phi = 2.05$). The other four island sites fell in a group somewhat in the middle of these extremes. The beach slope and grain size (Table 2) varied more at Santa Cruz Island and San Nicolas Island than at San Miguel Island and San Clemente Island. The two sites with the greatest variability were more exposed to wave action than the other two sites. Wave action during winter storms at San Nicolas Island resulted in the loss of large amounts of sand from the intertidal area (Fig. 5). While a similar annual pattern of cut and fill was also recorded at San Miguel Island, the loss and gain of sand resulted in smaller changes than those recorded at San Nicolas Island (Fig. 6).

The moisture content of the sediment is related to grain size, intertidal height, and time above water level before samples are collected. The averaging of the data for a site-by-site study reduces the impact of the latter two parameters. Cat Harbor had the finest sediments and the greatest average moisture content (20.1 to 24.5 per cent). The Isthmus, on the other hand, had the coarsest sediments and the lowest average moisture content (9.0 to 15.9 per cent). The other beaches with intermediate grain size characteristics also had intermediate moisture content characteristics.

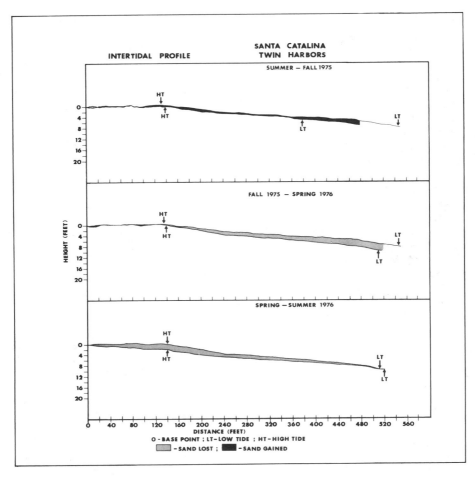

FIGURE 4. *Intertidal profiles recorded on surveys in 1975 and 1976 at Cat Harbor, Santa Catalina Island. (Note: this is referred to as the Twin Harbors site on this figure and in the Bureau of Land Management reports.)*

The Ohaus organic content, which measures plant and waste materials mixed in the sand but not organics incorporated in the sediments, was variable. The highest values were recorded at Tyler Bight on San Miguel Island (Tables 2 and 3). This is the site populated by elephant seals. The highest total organic carbon (6.5 per cent) and Ohaus organic carbon values (0.64 per cent) were also recorded at this site. The survey area is in the sheltered end of the cove and these organic values are interpreted as being waste products from the elephant seal colony.

The Ohaus organic and TOC values for Black Point on Santa Cruz Island and Dutch Harbor on San Nicolas Island are interpreted to mean that organic material such as kelp is mixed with the sand on the beach but very little organic material is incorporated in the sediments. The data at North West Cove suggest relatively higher incorporation of organics in sediments and less organic material mixed with the sediments. Both sites at Santa Catalina Island have relatively

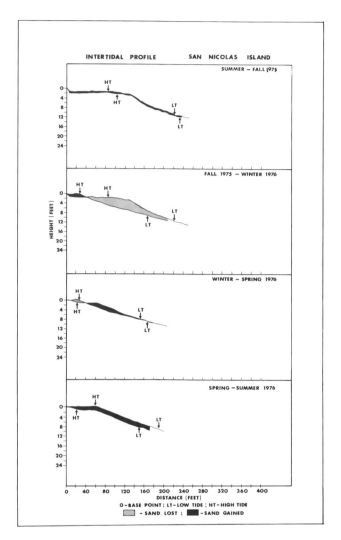

FIGURE 5. *Intertidal profiles recorded on San Nicolas Island (summer 1975 to summer 1976).*

high amounts of organics mixed with, as well as incorporated in, the sediments.

The calcium carbonate data indicate large amounts of shell in the sand at Tyler Bight, Dutch Harbor, North West Cove, and the Isthmus (mean = 10.60 to 13.89 per cent), and very low amounts of shell at Cat Harbor and Black Point (mean = 0.46 and 0.52 per cent, respectively).

No tar was recorded at San Miguel Island or San Clemente Island. Large amounts (an average of 733.95 g per survey) were recorded at the Cat Harbor site. It appeared that, once tar entered the area, ocean currents were not strong enough to move it out of the cove and/or break it into smaller pieces. Small amounts of tar were recorded at the other three sites.

Table 4 shows the number of species recorded at each site for two survey years and Appendix 1 lists all the species recorded at each site. This includes incomplete identifications due to missing taxonomic characters on specimens. It should again be noted that all sites were

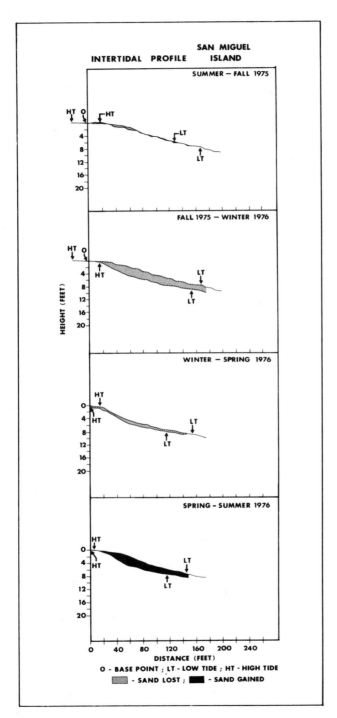

FIGURE 6. *Intertidal profiles at Tyler Bight on San Miguel Island (summer 1975 to summer 1976).*

TABLE 2. Abiotic characteristics measured at island sites, 1975-1977.

Island site	Water temperature (°C)	Salinity range (°/oo)	Grain size* (mean ϕ)	Moisture* (%)	Ohaus organic* (%)	Tar g†
San Miguel (Tyler Bight)	11.0-17.5	32,35	1.72-2.11	14.6-21.0	0.31-0.86	0.0
			1.93	17.90	0.54	
Santa Cruz (Black Point)	13.0-19.0	32,35	1.33-2.45	13.5-21.4	0.17-0.42	0.0-112.5
			1.95	17.70	0.29	22.43
San Nicolas (Dutch Harbor)	13.0-20.0	32,35	1.63-2.14	15.2-17.9	0.27-0.64	0.0-0.2
			1.77	15.90	0.45	0.05
San Clemente (North West Cove)	14.0-22.0	34,35	1.73-2.03	14.7-19.6	0.14-0.53	0.0
			1.89	17.70	0.32	
Santa Catalina (the Isthmus)	14.5-19.0	33,35	1.05-1.60	9.0-15.9	0.29-0.71	0.0-24.5
			1.10	13.05	0.47	9.25
Santa Catalina (Cat Harbor)	17.0-21.0	34,35	1.97-2.08	20.1-24.5	0.39-1.56	545.3-1761.5
			2.05	21.40	0.63	733.95

* Range of average value for each survey and overall average value.
† Range of total amount of tar collected on the survey grid per survey, and average value.

TABLE 3. Organic characteristics measured at island sites, 1976-1977 (range and average values).

Island site	Tar (g)	Ohaus organic (%)	Total carbon (%)	Total inorganic carbon (%)	Total organic carbon (%)	CaCO₃ (%)
San Miguel (Tyler Bight)	0.0	0.66-0.86 0.76	5.24-9.79 6.50	5.12-8.30 5.86	0.05-1.59 0.64	9.36-17.66 13.43
Santa Cruz (Black Point)	4.5-17.6 11.0	0.37-0.42 0.40	0.07-0.20 0.10	0.03-0.16 0.06	0.02-0.10 0.05	0.29-1.36 0.52
San Nicolas (Dutch Harbor)	0.0	0.27-0.64 0.45	1.44-2.20 1.78	1.32-2.04 1.67	0.03-0.32 0.11	10.96-17.03 13.89
San Clemente (North West Cove)	0.0	0.14-0.53 0.34	1.49-3.25 1.88	1.12-2.12 1.61	0.10-1.12 0.27	9.36-17.66 13.89
Santa Catalina (the Isthmus)	0.0-2.0 1.0	0.31-0.71 0.51	0.63-2.05 1.49	0.48-1.84 1.28	0.12-0.33 0.21	3.98-15.36 10.69
Santa Catalina (Cat Harbor)	545.3-1114.5 829.9	0.44-1.56 0.50	0.18-0.51 0.32	0.04-0.10 0.06	0.14-0.46 0.26	0.30-0.84 0.46

TABLE 4. Number of species collected at each site.

Island	1975-1976	1976-1977	1975-1977
San Miguel	33	18	33
Santa Cruz	18	20	25
San Nicolas	26	20	26
San Clemente	18	16	24
Santa Catalina (the Isthmus)	9	7	10
Santa Catalina (Cat Harbor)	121	82	127

surveyed four times in the first year and that only San Nicolas was surveyed four times in the second year. All other sites were surveyed only in the summer and winter of the second year. The most species (127) were recorded at the Cat Harbor site. This was the site with the finest sediments, highest moisture content, and longest, most gradually sloping beach. The fewest species (10) were recorded at the Isthmus, which had the coarsest sediments, lowest moisture content, and the shortest, steepest beach. Ohaus organic content and TOC content were variable but generally high at these sites. The other four sites, which had intermediate abiotic parameters, also had intermediate species numbers (24, 25, 26, and 33), although these were more similar to those recorded at the Isthmus than at Cat Harbor.

During the first survey year, 47 species were collected on the islands and 53 species were collected on the mainland beaches (Straughan 1977b). This number excludes Cat Harbor, where 107 species were collected, of which more than 45 were unique to the site.

Table 5 shows which species were consistently recorded in all surveys at a particular site. Cat Harbor had the largest number of consistently occurring species (13); nine of these are polychaetes. This is also the only site where molluscan species were consistently recorded. All the other sites had only two, three, or four species consistently recorded. Crustacea were found at most sites. Polychaetes were found at all but the coarsest sediment sites, while molluscs occurred only at the finer sediment sites.

Data in Tables 4 and 5 also show that, while each site had specific characteristics, there was a large variability in species occurrence at each site. It should be added that no single species was recorded at all sites.

Most of the island sandy beaches can be characterized by the consistent presence of a crustacean species, which in some instances is the sand crab *Emerita analoga,* sometimes the isopod *Excirolana chiltoni,* and sometimes a beach hopper, *Orchestoidea* sp. San Miguel Island is characterized by the polychaetes *Lumbrineris zonata* and *Nerinides acuta;* Santa Cruz is characterized by the blood worm *Euzonus mucronata;* no polychaete is characteristic of San Nicolas Island; *Hemipodus borealis* is characteristic of the Isthmus site; and *Euzonus dillonensis* is characteristic of San Clemente. The remaining site at Cat Harbor is characterized by a large number of polychaetes and the molluscs *Tagelus californianus* and *Transennella tantilla.*

The biotic characteristics, in terms of numbers of species and numbers of specimens collected, were compared with the abiotic characteristics using the Spearman rank correlation coefficient (Table 6). When $n = 6$, r_s was significant at the 0.05 level when equal to 0.829. The correlation coefficient approached this level of significance with grain size and was significant when the biotic parameters were compared with moisture. Multiple discriminant analyses of data by survey (Straughan 1977b, 1978) showed that the grain size and moisture content explained most of the variation associated with changes in the distribution and abundance of species.

Data in Table 7 show details in the abundance of dominant species at Cat Harbor and further emphasize the variability of each site. However, it should be noted that there are preliminary indications that at least some of the changes at Cat Harbor may be due to contamination by fresh, wet tar in the spring of 1976 (Fig. 7). For example, there was almost a sixfold increase in the population of the polychaete *Capitella capitata* when fresh tar was found at the site. Grassle and Grassle (1974) have recorded large increases in capitellids during the recovery phase following an oil spill. Other abundance patterns which may be influenced by the presence of petroleum include an apparent temporary reduction in numbers of the polychaete *Lumbrineris zonata* and the drastic reduction of the population of the bivalve *Transennella tantilla.* Further analyses over a longer time are required to determine if these are petroleum impacts and, if so, the duration of the impacts. The source of the petroleum is unknown. However, there appears to be a background level of at least 500 g of dry tar in the survey area. This harbor is sheltered so it

TABLE 5. Species found on all surveys at island sandy beach sites.

Species	San Miguel (6)	Santa Cruz (6)	San Nicolas (8)	Santa Catalina, the Isthmus (6)	Santa Catalina, Cat Harbor (6)	San Clemente (6)
Boccardia hamata					+	
Capitella capitata					+	
Euzonus dillonensis						+
Euzonus mucronata		+				
Hemipodus borealis				+		
Lumbrineridae	+					
Lumbrineris zonata	+				+	
Marphysa sanguinea					+	
Neanthes acuminata					+	
Nemertean sp. B					+	
Nothria stigmatus					+	
Notomastus tenuis					+	
Pseudopolydora paucibranchiata					+	
Scolelepis squamata	+					
Callianassa spp.					+	
Emerita analoga	+	+				
Excirolana chiltoni			+			+
Orchestoidea corniculata				+	+	
Orchestoidea juvenile			+	+		
Orchestoidea minor			+			
Tagelus californicus					+	
Transennella tantilla					+	

( ) = number of surveys at site.

TABLE 6. Comparison of biotic and abiotic data using Spearman rank correlation coefficient (r_s).

Island site	Ranking* of data							Numbers of species and specimens†
	Grain size	Moisture	Tar	Ohaus organic	TIC	TOC	CaCO$_3$	
San Miguel (Tyler Bight)	4	5	1.5	6	6	6	4.5	5
Santa Cruz (Black Point)	5	4	4	2	1.5	1	2	3
San Nicolas (Dutch Harbor)	2	2	3	3	5	2	6	4
San Clemente (North West Cove)	3	3	1.5	1	4	5	4.5	2
Santa Catalina (the Isthmus)	1	1	5	4	3	3	3	1
Santa Catalina (Cat Harbor)	6	6	6	5	1.5	4	1	6
r_s with numbers	0.76	0.83	0.13	0.60	0.39	0.26	−0.16	

* Lowest value = 1.
† Same ranking for both variables.

TABLE 7. Number of more abundant species collected on surveys at Cat Harbor, Santa Catalina Island.

Species	1975		1976			1977
	Summer	Fall	Winter	Spring	Summer	Winter
Boccardia hamata	3	16	12	6	2	33
Boccardia proboscidae	2	1	16	57	3	0
Capitella capitata	126	159	53	180	54	96
Lumbrineris zonata	73	80	64	57	27	57
Marphysa sanguinea	16	5	5	9	0	6
Neanthes acuminata	6	9	6	6	1	15
Nothria stigmatus	19	14	13	6	7	1
Notomastus tenuis	7	15	22	23	18	8
Paraeurythoe californica	0	0	10	0	2	17
Prionospio nr. *malmgreni*	0	2	6	4	1	7
Pseudopolydora paucibranchiata	66	1	129	74	40	11
Scyphoproctus oculatus	0	10	16	10	8	0
Callianassa spp.	8	36	49	4	14	29
Hemigrapsus oregonensis	1	2	0	0	4	0
Orchestia georgiana	3	11	0	0	1,340	0
Orchestoidea benedicti	4	2	0	0	1	0
Orchestoidea corniculata	37	29	14	10	19	7
Tylos punctatus	3	2	5	5	5	0
Cryptomya californica	0	0	0	0	2	9
Nassarius tegula	12	10	13	21	27	0
Tagelus californianus	0	2	6	5	3	3
Transennella tantilla	575	271	456	190	71	10

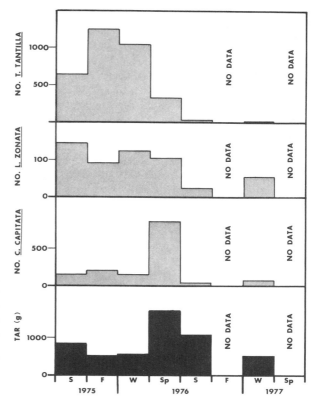

FIGURE 7. *Weight of tar (g), number of* Capitella capitata, *number of* Lumbrineris zonata, *and number of* Transennella tantilla *recorded on quarterly surveys at Cat Harbor, Santa Catalina Island. There were no surveys in fall 1976 or spring 1977.*

is not surprising that when petroleum enters it is not as readily washed away as occurs on the open coast sandy beaches.

DISCUSSION

Distribution and abundance of species are influenced by both abiotic and biotic factors. However, sandy beach populations, which are sparse in comparison with other types of intertidal areas (*e.g.*, rocky shore populations), and which are exposed to large and rapid fluctuations in abiotic parameters, may show primary responses to abiotic changes (*e.g.*, sediment parameters) and secondary responses to biotic changes (interspecific and intraspecific interactions). Such responses are contrasted between the studies of marginal species subject to large climatic changes (Andrewartha and Birch 1954) and studies in dense populations maintained under relatively constant climatic conditions (Nicholson 1957). There have been many attempts to provide a single overall theory which would explain all population regulation. However, regulation of populations both in terms of distribution and abundance will be dominated by different factors under different conditions. Kikkawa (1977) recently demonstrated this ecological problem with reference to terrestrial species. Studies in the marine environment in recent years have concentrated on the biotic interactions either within or at the edge of communities, such as in the case of starfish predation of mussels (Landenberger 1968, 1969) and interspecific competition in barnacles (Connell 1961), giving rise to the general premise that the biotic interactions are paramount in governing the distribution and abundance of marine species.

Connell (1975) documented that competition can occur only where predation and harsh physical conditions are not limiting. However, in a recent article on niche shifts and interspecific competition, Diamond (1978) concedes that the next step in the development of competition theory involves further study of the resources (abiotic parameters) in order to remove the "overwhelming" but sometimes "circumstantial" evidence of interspecific competition as a controlling factor in the distribution and abundance of species.

Sandy beach species are generally sparse in their overall distribution and, as a group, appear to have greater mobility than other marine benthic groups. This overall mobility is demonstrated in their response to changing sediment parameters on a beach. In general, the distribution of the more common species within their intertidal range correlates well with the sediment parameters of the beach. If these species were not mobile they would die off when there was a change in sediment parameters and, because species that otherwise would thrive under the new conditions would not be undergoing larval settlement at the time, there would be no invertebrates on the beach. Therefore, there should be records of relatively fine sand grain beaches, which normally contain most sandy beach organisms, with very few or no organisms. In nine years of surveys of sandy beaches from all latitudes and many parts of the world we have no such records from unpolluted areas. The more abundant and dominant sandy beach species, therefore, must be mobile even after larval settlement and must be able to respond to changes in sediments. Whether this mobility is due to the efforts of the organism, simple transport with the sediments and currents, or a combination of these factors will vary with the species.

Numbers of species and specimens are correlated with the grain size and moisture content of the sediments of sites; these are predictable relationships. Straughan (1975, 1977a, 1977b) has already demonstrated the relationships between some of the more abundant species and these parameters as well as organic content of sediments.

The lack of correlations with organic values, either in terms of Ohaus organics or TOC values, was unpredicted but suggests that grain size and moisture content of sediments may be limiting any response of species to an enriched organic environment, such as at San Miguel Island. However, organic values as a whole fluctuated at each site and it is possible that some species fluctuation will be detected when the data are examined in more detail.

The closeness in overall organic values at the two sites on Santa Catalina Island was not predicted. The Cat Harbor site is a sheltered site with finer grain size and is frequently visited by buffalo. The Isthmus site is exposed with coarser sediments. The reasons for these unpredicted high values are not known.

The data for the island sandy beaches have been compared with the data from the mainland sandy beaches and there is no division between the mainland and island sites (Straughan 1977b, 1978). In both instances, changes in species distribution on each survey correlate with abiotic factors measured on the survey and not with geographic factors in terms of north-south distribution and island-mainland distribution.

The species composition recorded at Cat Harbor differs from that found at the other island sites. The site most similar to it is one inside King Harbor. This is a low, gently sloping, sheltered intertidal area with fine sediments (Straughan 1977a). In other words, again the species distributions are related to abiotic parameters. Wicksten (1980) has also reported similar observations in some groups of Crustacea in that their distribution was related to grain size parameters, not to geography, in the Southern California Bight.

While most species and specimens were consistently recorded at Cat Harbor, this site is the only one to be consistently exposed to large amounts of petroleum. Although this petroleum is mainly dry tar, the area was contaminated by a large volume of fresh tar between winter and spring surveys in 1976. No chemical analyses were performed, so it is not known if this tar is from natural seepage or pollution sources. There are large areas of intermittent natural seepage of oil and gas offshore in southern California (Fig. 1). The nearest documented area of natural oil seepage is several miles to the west of the tip of Santa Catalina Island, which could be a source of the tar in Cat Harbor. While some surveys along mainland sandy beaches have established that most of the stranded tar is of natural seep origin (Allen 1971, Straughan 1973), no similar surveys have been conducted at island sites.

SUMMARY

Sandy beaches on San Miguel Island, Santa Cruz Island, San Nicolas Island, San Clemente Island, and Santa Catalina Island were surveyed at least twice a year, from summer 1975 through summer 1977. Comparable surveys were conducted on mainland beaches. The surveys were designed to collect macrofauna from the sand in a series of randomly selected cores within a grid of quadrats extending across the beach from high tide to low tide. Physical characteristics of the sites at the time of the biotic collections were recorded in the field (*e.g.*, temperatures, salinities, and beach profile). Samples of sediment and tar were also collected in order to determine such characteristics as sediment grain size, moisture and organic content of sediments, and weight of visible tar present in the survey area. The data do not show overall distinctions between the biota at mainland and island sites.

The island sandy beach macrofaunas follow predictable trends of increasing abundance with increasing stability of habitat (finer sediments, more sheltered conditions). There may be some impact of petroleum at the Cat Harbor site, Santa Catalina Island.

ACKNOWLEDGMENTS

This study is very much a large-team effort, in which all personnel have made valuable contributions. Thank you. Field surveys: V. Anderson, P. Bernhardt, A. J. Gaines, D. Ghirardelli, S. Ghirardelli, C. Jones, R. Klink, T. Licari, M. McConnel, J. Martin, L. Masuoka, A. O'Donnell, P. O'Donnell, Patti Pepper, Penny Pepper, F. Piltz, R. Rowe, C. Savage, N. Savage, and M. Wright. Data analysis: C. Savage, N. Savage, and P. Woodland. Sand grain analysis: K. Brown, J. Martin, and G. Mohamed. Computer analysis: L. Fridkis, C. Henry, R. Kanter, and R. Smith. Species identification: polychaetes—P. Bernhardt, P. O'Donnell, F. Piltz, and R. Rowe; crustaceans—R. Kimble, L. McKinney, B. Wallerstein, M. Wicksten, J. Wilkins, and R. Wynn; molluscs—D. Cadien; flora—V. Anderson; Echinoderms—M. Wright; insects and arachnids—R. Klink, and through the efforts of Dr. L. Knutson, U. S. Department of Agriculture; fishes—J. Dock. Illustrations: D. Hadley and T. Licari. Manuscript preparation: B. Allen, P. Smith, and P. Woodland. Surveying: T. Licari and H. Summers.

The following persons identified Insecta and Arachnida: R. L. Smiley, U.S. Department of Agriculture (USDA) (Acarina); W. B. Peck, Systematic Entomology Laboratory, Warrensburg, Missouri (Araneida); D. M. Anderson, USDA, T. L. Erwin, U.S. National Museum (USNM), R. D. Gordon and I. Moore, University of California at Riverside and USDA, P. U. Spangler, USNM, T. J. Spilman, USDA, R. E. Warner, USDA, R. E. White, USDA, and D. R. Whitehead, USDA (Coleoptera); A. B. Gurney, Systematic Entomology Laboratory (Dermaptera); J. Burger, USNM, R. J. Gagne, USDA, L. Knutson, USDA, G. Steyskal, USDA, F. C. Thompson, USDA, and W. W. Wirth, USDA (Diptera); J. L. Herring, USDA (Hemiptera); J. P. Kramer, USDA (Hemiptera Homoptera); S. W. T. Batra, USDA, A. A. Menke, USDA, and D. R. Smith, USDA (Hymenoptera); D. M. Weisman, USDA (Lepidoptera); O. S. Flint, USNM (Neuroptera); O. S. Flint, USNM (Odonata).

This research was funded by the Bureau of Land Management under contracts 08550-CT5-52 and AA550-CT6-40.

REFERENCES

ALLEN, A. A. 1971. Santa Monica Bay natural oil seep investigation. A report from MAR-
    CONSULT Inc. to El Segundo Refinery, Standard Oil Company of California.

ANDREWARTHA, H. G., and L. C. BIRCH. 1954. The distribution and abundance of animals.
    University of Chicago Press, Chicago, Ill.

BANDY, O. L., and R. KOLPACK. 1963. Foraminiferal and sedimentological trends in the
    Tertiary section of the Tecolote Tunnel. California Micropaleon. 9:117-170.

CONNELL, J. H. 1961. The influence of interspecific competition and other factors on the
    distribution of the barnacle *Chthamalus stellatus*. Ecology 42:710-723.

_____. 1975. Some mechanisms producing structure in natural communities: a model and
    evidence from field experiments. Pp. 460-490 *in* M. L. Cody and J. M. Diamond, eds.,
    Ecology and evolution of communities. Harvard University Press, Cambridge, Mass.

COOK, D. O. 1969. Calibration of the U.S.C. settling tube. J. Sed. Pet. 44:583-588.

DIAMOND, J. M. 1978. Niche shifts and the rediscovery of interspecific competition. Amer.
    Sci. 66:332-339.

EMERY, K. O. 1961. A single line method of measuring beach profiles. Limnol. Oceanogr.
    1:90-93.

FOLK, R. L. 1968. Petrology of sedimentary rocks. Hemphill's, Austin, Tex.

GIBBS, R. J. 1974. A settling tube system for sand-size analysis. J. Sed. Pet. 44:583-588.

GRASSLE, J. F., and J. P. GRASSLE. 1974. Opportunistic life histories and genetic systems in
    marine polychaetes. J. Marine Res. 32:253-284.

KIKKAWA, J. 1977. Ecological paradoxes. Australian J. Ecol. 2:121-136.

KOLPACK, R., and S. A. BELL. 1968. Gasometric determination of carbon in sediments by
    hydroxide absorption. J. Sed. Pet. 38:578-583.

LANDENBERGER, D. E. 1968. Studies on selective feeding in the Pacific starfish *Pisaster* in
    southern California. Ecology 49:1062-1075.

_____. 1969. The effects of exposure to air on Pacific starfish and its relationship to
    distribution. Physiol. Zool. 42:220-230.

NICHOLSON, A. J. 1957. The self-adjustment of populations to change. Cold Spring Harbor
    Symp. Quant. Biol. 22:153-173.

PETTIJOHN, F. J. 1957. Sedimentary rocks. Harper and Row, New York, N.Y.

STRAUGHAN, D. 1973. The influence of the Santa Barbara oil spill (January-February, 1969) on
    the intertidal distribution of marine organisms. Report to Western Oil and Gas
    Association.

_____. 1975. Intertidal sandy beach macrofauna at Los Angeles-Long Beach Harbor, pt. II.
    Marine Studies of San Pedro Bay, California, pt. 8. Univ. So. California Publ. :89-107.

_____. 1976. Sublethal effects of natural chronic exposure to petroleum in the marine
    environment. Amer. Petrol. Inst. Publ. 4280.

_____. 1977a. Influence of power generating facilities on southern California coastal waters,
    phase 3. Report on the field biology on sandy beaches. Southern California Edison, Los
    Angeles, 77-RD-63.

_____. 1977b. Sandy beaches and sloughs. Southern California Baseline Study, final report
    III, rep. 2.3 and Appendices. Bureau of Land Management, U.S. Dept. Interior,
    Washington, D.C.

_____. 1978. Baseline study of sandy beaches and sloughs in the southern California
    borderland, 1976-1977. Science Applications Inc., La Jolla, Calif.

WICKSTEN, M. 1980. Mainland and insular assemblages of benthic decapod crustaceans of
    southern California. Pp. 357-367 *in* D.M. Power, ed., The California Islands: proceed-
    ings of a multidisciplinary symposium. Santa Barbara Museum of Natural History, Santa
    Barbara, Calif.

APPENDIX 1. List of species on island sandy beaches.

	San Miguel	Santa Cruz	San Nicolas	San Clemente	Santa Catalina, Cat Harbor	Santa Catalina, the Isthmus
COELENTERATA						
Anthozoa?					+	
NEMERTEA						
Nemertea sp.	+					
Nemertea sp. A	+				+	
Nemertea sp. B				+		
Nemertea sp. C					+	
Nemertea sp. D					+	
NEMATODA						
Unidentified sp.						+
ANNELIDA						
OLIGOCHAETA						
Unidentified sp.		+			+	
ANNELIDA						
POLYCHAETA						
Amphinomidae					+	
Boccardia hamata					+	
Boccardia proboscidea					+	
Boccardia sp.					+	
Boccardia truncata					+	
Branchiomaldane vincentii					+	
Capitella capitata					+	
Capitellidae					+	
Cirratulidae					+	

APPENDIX 1. (Cont.)

	San Miguel	Santa Cruz	San Nicolas	San Clemente	Santa Catalina, Cat Harbor	Santa Catalina, the Isthmus
ANNELIDA						
POLYCHAETA						
Eteone dilatae					+	
Eteone pacifica					+	
Eunicidae					+	
Euzonus dillonensis	+	+	+	+		
Euzonus mucronata	+	+	+			
Exogone lourei					+	
Fabricia sp.					+	
Glycera tenuis					+	
Glyceridae					+	+
Hemipodus borealis	+				+	+
Leitoscoloplos elongatus					+	
Lumbrineridae	+	+	+		+	
Lumbrineris sp. A	+				+	
Lumbrineris sp. B					+	
Lumbrineris zonata	+	+	+		+	
Malmgrenia sp.					+	
Marphysa sanguinea					+	
Mediomastus sp.					+	
Megalomma pigmentum					+	
Neanthes acuminata			+		+	
Nephtyidae		+			+	
Nephtys caecoides					+	
Nephtys californiensis		+	+		+	

ANNELIDA
POLYCHAETA
Nereidae
Nerinides sp.
Nothria iridescens
Nothria stigmatis
Notomastus lineatus
Notomastus magnus
Notomastus precocis
Notomastus tenuis
Onuphidae
Opheliidae
Orbiniidae
Paraonella platybranchia
Paraeurythoe californica
Pherusa capulata
Phyllodocidae
Polydora socialis
Polyopthalmus pictus
Prionospio nr. malmgreni
Prionospio sp.
Pseudomalacoceros maculata
Pseudopolydora paucibranchiata
Scolelepis squamata
Scoloplos acmeceps
Scoloplos armiger
Scyphoproctus oculatus

APPENDIX 1. (Cont.)

	San Miguel	Santa Cruz	San Nicolas	San Clemente	Santa Catalina, Cat Harbor	Santa Catalina, the Isthmus
ANNELIDA						
POLYCHAETA						
Sigalionidae	+					
Spionidae					+	
Spio filicornis				+	+	
Sthenelais verruculosa					+	
Terebellidae					+	
Tharyx sp.						
ARTHROPODA						
CRUSTACEA						
Allomiscus perconvexus			+		+	+
Ampithoe pollex					+	
Ampithoe sp.					+	
Anatanais sp.						
Archaeomysis grebnitzki	+		+			
Archaeomysis sp. ?	+					
Atylus tridens				+		
Betaeus harrimani			+	+	+	
Blepharipoda occidentalis		+				
Callianassa californiensis					+	
Callianassa juvenile					+	
Callianassa longimana					+	
Callianassa sp.					+	
Cancer anthonyi					+	
Corophium sp.					+	
Crustacean eggs					+	

Emerita analoga
Eohaustorius washingtonianus
Excirolana chiltoni
Exosphaeroma inornata
Hemigrapsus oregonensis
Heterophoxus cf. oculatus
Idotea cf. rufescens
Lepidopa californica
Leptochelia dubia
Mandibulophoxus gilesi
Mysidacea
Orchestia georgiana
Orchestia juvenile
Orchestia traskiana
Orchestoidea benedicti
Orchestoidea californiana
Orchestoidea columbiana
Orchestoidea cf. columbiana
Orchestoidea corniculata
Orchestoidea juvenile
Orchestoidea minor
Paranthura elegans
Paraphoxus cf. calcaratus
Paraphoxus lucubrans
Paraphoxus sp.
Proharpinia sp.
Pugettia dalli
Tylos punctatus
Unidentifiable

APPENDIX 1. (Cont.)

	San Miguel	Santa Cruz	San Nicolas	San Clemente	Santa Catalina, Cat Harbor	Santa Catalina, the Isthmus
ARTHROPODA						
INSECTA/ARACHNIDA						
Alleculinae larvae					+	
Amphidora nigropilosa					+	
Anthomyiidae					+	
Bledius sp.	+				+	
Cafius lithocharinus			+			
Cercyon luniger					+	
Cercyon sp. larvae					+	
Chilopoda				+		
Coelopa vanduzeei pupae			+			
Corixidae nymph					+	
Cryptadius inflatus	+	+				
Cyclorrhapha larvae	+		+		+	
Cyclorrhapha pupae		+			+	
Dolichopodidae larvae		+			+	
Eumolpinae					+	
Forcula auricularia		+			+	
Fucellia rufitibia						
Geophiloidea		+				
Gnaphosa maritima immature		+				
Histeridae larvae		+			+	
Leptus sp.		+			+	
Myrmeleontidae					+	
Oxytelinae		+				
Paraclunio alaskensis	+					
Sarcophagidae	+					
Staphylinidae			+		+	
Staphylinidae larvae					+	
Tenebrionidae larvae					+	+

Taxon		
MOLLUSCA		
GASTROPODA		
Acteocina culcitella	+	
Acteocina incluta	+	
Caecum californicum	+	
Littorina scutulata	+	
Nassarius tegula	+	
Norrisia norrisi	+	
Olivella biplicata	+	
Tegula eiseni	+	
MOLLUSCA		
PELECYPODA		
Chione undatella	+	
Cryptomya californica	+	
Cumingia californica	+	
Leporimetis obesa	+	
Macoma nasuta	+	
Parvilucina tenuisculpta	+	
Pelecypoda unidentified	+	+
Protothaca staminea		
Tagelus californianus	+	
Transennella tantilla	+	
ECHINODERMATA		
OPHIUROIDEA		
Amphipholis squamata	+	
PISCES		
Clevelandia ios	+	
Gobiidae	+	
Ilypnus gilberti	+	+
Quietula y-cauda	+	

Genetic Differentiation of the Semi-terrestrial Amphipod *Orchestia traskiana* in an Expanded Habitat on Santa Cruz Island

Ann L. Busath

Department of Biological Sciences,
University of California, Santa Barbara, California 93106

INTRODUCTION

One of the frequently observed characteristics of species on islands is expansion of the range of habitat compared with that of their mainland counterparts. This has most often been attributed to release from biological pressures due to the absence of mainland competitors or predators in the generally depauperate island biota (MacArthur 1972).

Habitat expansion, however facilitated, is presumably the critical precursor of adaptive radiation, a phenomenon commonly seen in island situations (Carlquist 1974). The underlying hypothesis supposes that species arriving on islands move into empty niches (ones they did not occupy on the mainland) and, by natural selection, may become sufficiently adapted to their new habitats to form new species. This end result would be preceded by a stage at which populations in divergent habitats would have accumulated enough genetic differences to distinguish them as ecological races or "ecotypes," but not enough for the establishment of reproductive isolation.

Orchestia traskiana Stimpson, a semi-terrestrial talitrid amphipod, is found on both the Pacific mainland coast and the California Channel Islands. Both the diversity and the number of occupied habitats are much greater on Santa Cruz Island than on the adjacent mainland coast in Santa Barbara County. Populations of *O. traskiana* on the island were found in environments ranging from marine cobble beaches to freshwater stream banks several miles inland and as much as 500 feet above sea level. Furthermore, nearly every island cobble beach, brackish pond, freshwater stream, or cliff-bottom seep that I examined had a population of these animals.

These observations led to the question: How is this species able to exist in such a wide range of habitats; are the animals incredibly ecologically plastic, or are populations in fact genetically adapted to their specific habitats?

Starch gel electrophoresis was the technique chosen to investigate possible genetic variation in *O. traskiana*. Several electrophoretic studies have shown correlations between allele frequency patterns and various ecological variables (Johnson *et al.* 1969, Tomaszewski *et al.* 1973, Rockwood-Sluss *et al.* 1973, McKechnie *et al.* 1975), but only a few have explored genetic variation between populations in specific microhabitats (Tsuno 1975, Saul *et al.* 1978).

The distribution of *O. traskiana* on Santa Cruz Island thus provided a unique opportunity to study both the genetic variation of a species which had apparently undergone habitat expansion and, possibly, adaptive radiation on an island, and the nature and intensity of genotype-microhabitat variation within a species.

MATERIALS AND METHODS

Six populations of *O. traskiana* were chosen, five of them representing three habitats from Santa Cruz Island, and one from the mainland. The locations of the island sample sites are indicated in Figure 1. These include: two cobble beach sites, Prisoners Harbor Cobbles (PHC)

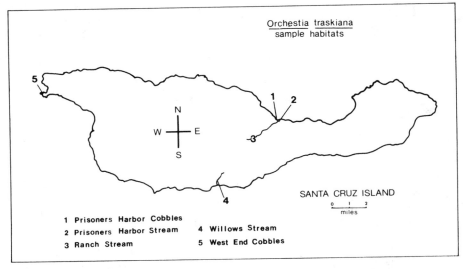

FIGURE 1. *Five sampling sites representing three divergent habitat types for* Orchestia trask-iana *on Santa Cruz Island. Sites 1 and 5 are cobble beach habitats, 2 and 4 are variable brackish pond habitats, and 3 is a freshwater habitat.*

and West End Cobbles (WE); two variable brackish ponds fed by freshwater streams, Prisoners Harbor Stream (PHS) and Willows Stream (W); and a freshwater stream, Ranch Stream (RS). The mainland site was located along the border of the Lagoon Pond of the University of California, Santa Barbara campus, a habitat similar to the PHS island site.

The island sites at PHC, PHS, and RS were chosen, first, because they represented three strikingly different but representative habitat types, and, second, because they were all found along the same drainage. Gene exchange between populations was at least potentially possible. The populations at PHC and PHS are separated by a sand dune only a few meters wide; certainly these populations could exchange individuals. The remaining island sites, W and WE, are similar to PHS and PHC, respectively, but are completely isolated from any other population of *O. traskiana*. Thus, the pattern of genetic variation in isolated habitats could be compared with that found in non-isolated populations from similar microhabitats, and, if the pattern were the same for both, the hypothesis that the animals were being selected on the basis of suitability for survival in a particular habitat would seem rather well supported.

The mainland Lagoon Pond (L) habitat, though not totally analogous to any of the habitats on the island, was chosen to provide information concerning the magnitude of habitat differences in relation to island-mainland differences.

These six populations were surveyed using the technique of starch gel electrophoresis as described in Ayala *et al.* (1972). Two buffer systems and two enzymes were used, as described below.

Buffer systems:
   a) Poulik bridge and gel buffers (system A in Ayala *et al.* 1972).
   b) Borate bridge and gel buffers as follows:
      Electrode buffer: 60.0 g/l boric acid, 60.6 g/l Tris HCl, and 6.0 g/l EDTA;
      Gel buffer: 100 ml electrode buffer, 900 ml distilled water.

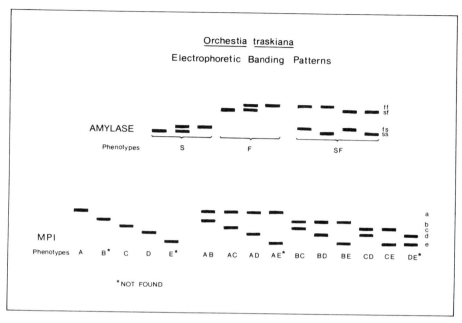

FIGURE 2. *Banding pattern of electromorphs for the enzymes amylase and mannose phosphate isomerase found in* Orchestia traskiana *using starch gel electrophoresis.*

Enzyme assays:

Amylase.—This enzyme required no stain since it digested holes in the starch gel. The reaction was allowed to develop in 50 ml of 0.05 M sodium acetate, pH 4.8, for 30 to 45 minutes. Gels were run on borate buffer.

Mannose phosphate isomerase (MPI).—The stain contained 30 mg mannose-6-phosphate, 12.5 mg NADP, 10 mg MTT, 2.5 mg PMS, 15 units phosphoglucose isomerase, and 20 units glucose-6-phosphate dehydrogenase dissolved in 50 ml 0.05 M Tris HCl pH 8.0. The reaction was incubated at 37°C in the dark. Gels were run on Poulik buffer.

RESULTS

Amylase. —This enzyme showed two banding areas approximately four millimeters apart. If run on a regular thick gel, the enzyme appeared to have only two bands, a fast one and a slow one. If run on a gel one-half the thickness of the regular gel, it became evident that each of these bands was, in turn, composed of one or two bands, a fast-fast and slow-fast, and a fast-slow and slow-slow (Fig. 2). No animal ever had more than two bands, and the pattern suggested a two-allele, single-locus system. Gel results were not consistent enough so that these four bands could always be distinguished. Therefore, animals were scored according to fast or slow *categories.* Sample location, sample size, allele frequencies, and significance of the chi-square test for goodness-of-fit to the Hardy-Weinberg distribution are listed in Table 1. Only one sample showed a significant departure from Hardy-Weinberg equilibrium, which I attribute to sampling error.

It is immediately obvious that there are differences in gene frequencies between these

TABLE 1. Allele frequencies for two enzymes found in *Orchestia traskiana*.

| Sample site | n | Amylase | | |
		Slow	Fast	χ^2
L	78	0.654	0.346	NS
RS	78	0.994	0.006	NS
PHS	72	0.910	0.090	*
W	84	0.821	0.179	NS
PHC	79	0.044	0.956	NS
WE	78	-0-	1.00	NS

n	A	B	MPI C	D	E	χ^2
82	0.079	0.049	0.860	0.006	0.006	NS
84	-0-	0.012	0.982	-0-	0.006	NS
67	-0-	0.007	0.963	0.015	0.015	NS
84	-0-	-0-	1.00	-0-	-0-	NS
62	0.226	0.032	0.621	0.121	-0-	NS
70	0.307	0.014	0.564	0.115	-0-	NS

*$0.01 < P < 0.05$.
NS = not significant.

populations. It is also obvious that some correlation with habitat type exists. The two beach populations both have high frequencies of the fast allele category and very low frequencies of the slow category. In fact, the fast "allele" appears to be fixed in the WE population. The nonbeach populations, including the mainland sample, show high frequencies of the slow "allele," which is nearly fixed in the RS population. In populations from brackish water, a larger proportion of heterozygotes and homozygotes for the fast allele was found. The mainland population, which lives in the most variable and most saline of the brackish habitats, shows the highest incidence of the fast allele.

MPI. —Five alleles were found at this locus (Fig. 2). No animal had more than two alleles, which indicated that this, too, was a single-locus system. Sample size, gene frequencies, and significance of the chi-square test for Hardy-Weinberg equilibrium are given in Table 1.

As shown for amylase, there is a distinction between habitat types for MPI. Allele C was always the most common allele, but was present in a much larger proportion in the stream and brackish pond populations. It is apparently fixed in the isolated population at Willows. Allele A, which was not found in any island fresh or brackish water population and found only in very low frequencies for the mainland population, was present in higher frequencies for both the cobble beach populations. Alleles B and D were present in very low frequencies in all populations, but allele E is apparently absent from both cobble beach populations (and from the Willows population, which is fixed for C).

Figure 3 shows bar graphs with 95 per cent confidence intervals for allelic distributions at both the amylase and MPI loci. There is a clear congruence in the pattern of differences between these populations for both enzymes. Though the enzymes are involved in unrelated metabolic functions—amylase is a digestive enzyme and MPI is involved in glucose metabolism (Christ-

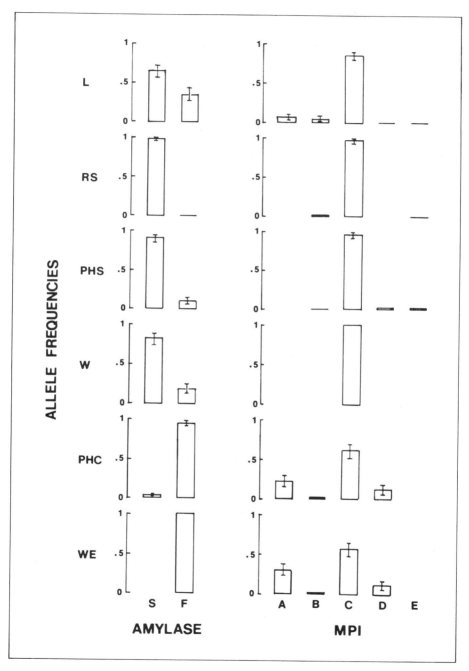

FIGURE 3. *Bar graphs with 95 per cent confidence intervals for allele frequencies at the amylase and MPI loci found in populations of* Orchestia traskiana *from different habitats.*

ensen *et al.* 1974, Nichols *et al.* 1973)—they show the same pattern of habitat differences.

It seems clear that the ecological diversity of *O. traskiana* is due in great part to genetic differences and that these genetic distinctions reflect a selective response to at least the large divergence between beach and nonbeach habitats.

DISCUSSION

The results indicate that populations of *O. traskiana* on Santa Cruz Island can be characterized as either beach or nonbeach "races" which are readily distinguishable electrophoretically. In allele frequencies, the freshwater population is essentially identical to brackish island populations. The mainland population shows a larger proportion of both the fast amylase alleles and allele A at the MPI locus. Whether this is due to geographic isolation between the island and mainland or to the nature of the habitat is not evident. However, the same loci and, except for total absences, the same alleles are present in all populations, which is consistent with the interpretation that they represent a single species.

Hurley (1959) reported that, in a multitude of instances, supralittoral species of *Orchestia* in the Indo-Pacific have given rise to terrestrial endemics on isolated islands. There are approximately 50 recorded terrestrial (by which he means capable of completing the life cycle away from the ocean or other body of water) members of the family Talitridae; almost all of these have very localized distributions. In this region, the forest leaf mold layer descends to the supralittoral zone, so that the transition from beach to land is relatively easy. Terrestrial talitrids apparently have not invaded via fresh water (Hurley 1968).

O. traskiana on Santa Cruz Island showed clear genetic differentiation only between beach and nonbeach (or "terrestrial," in Hurley's terminology) populations. The situation appears analogous to that found in Indo-Pacific island species of *Orchestia* except that: (1) the terrestrial invasion has been confined to the leaf mold margin of ponds and streams in the absence of the tropical forest; and (2) the ecotypes have not differentiated to the point of speciation. Other investigations of this species revealed a similar pattern of ecological variation and absence of reproductive isolating mechanisms, at least prior to maturity of the offspring (Busath 1979). It thus appears that *O. traskiana* may represent an example of incipient speciation enhanced by the unique properties of the island setting.

REFERENCES

AYALA, F. J., J. R. POWELL, M. L. TRACEY, C. A. MOURAU, and S. PEREZ-SALAS. 1972. Enzyme variability in the *Drosophila willistoni* group. IV. Genic variation in natural populations of *Drosophila willistoni*. Genetics 70:113-139.

BUSATH, A. L. 1979. Ecological plasticity vs. incipient speciation in the semi-terrestrial amphipod *Orchestia traskiana* (Crustacea: Amphipoda). Ph.D. thesis, University of California, Santa Barbara, Calif.

CARLQUIST, S. 1974. Island biology. Columbia University Press, New York, N.Y.

CHRISTENSEN, B., B. LOMHOLT, and J. E. JELNES. 1974. Selection and mechanical mixing operating on a two-allele amylase system in *Asellus aquaticus* (Isopoda, Crustacea). Hereditas 77:13-19.

HURLEY, D. E. 1959. Notes on the ecology and environmental adaptations of the terrestrial Amphipoda. Pacific Sci. 13:107-129.

———. 1968. Transition from water to land in amphipod crustaceans. Amer. Zool. 8:327-353.

JOHNSON, F. M., H. E. SCHAFFER, J. E. GILLASPY, and E. S. ROCKWOOD. 1969. Isozyme genotype-environment relationships in natural populations of the Harvester Ant, *Pogonomyrmex barbatus*, from Texas. Biochem. Genetics 3:429-450.

MacArthur, R. H. 1972. Geographical ecology: patterns of distribution of species. Harper and Row, New York, N.Y.

McKechnie, S. W., P. R. Ehrlich, and R. R. White. 1975. Population genetics of *Euphydryas* butterflies. I. Genetic variation and the neutrality hypothesis. Genetics 81:571-594.

Nichols, E. A., V. M. Chapman, and F. H. Ruddle. 1973. Polymorphism and linkage for mannose-phosphate isomerase in *Mus musculus*. Biochem. Genetics 8:47-53.

Rockwood-Sluss, E. S., J. S. Johnston, and W. B. Heed. 1973. Allozyme genotype-environment relationships. I. Variation in natural populations of *Drosophila pachea*. Genetics 73:135-146.

Saul, S. H., M. J. Sinsko, P. R. Grinstad, and G. B. Craig, Jr. 1978. Population genetics of the mosquito *Aedes triseriatus:* genetic-ecological correlation at an esterase locus. Amer. Natur. 112:333-339.

Tomaszewski, E. K., H. E. Schaffer, and F. M. Johnson. 1973. Isozyme genotype-environment associations in natural populations of the Harvester Ant, *Pogonomyrmex badius*. Genetics 75:405-421.

Tsuno, K. 1975. Esterase gene frequency differences and linkage equilibrium in *Drosophila virilis* populations from different ecological habitats. Genetics 80:585-594.

Habitat Groups and Island-Mainland Distribution of Kelp-bed Fishes off Santa Barbara, California

Alfred W. Ebeling, Ralph J. Larson,[1] and William S. Alevizon[2]

Department of Biological Sciences and Marine Science Institute,
University of California, Santa Barbara, California 93106.

INTRODUCTION

The islands off southern California diversify the coastal environment by doubling the length of shoreline and extending coastal habitats (Horn 1974). Geologically, and perhaps biologically, these islands may be classified into northern (bordering the Santa Barbara Channel) and southern groups (Hewatt 1946, Valentine and Lipps 1967, Weaver and Doerner 1967). Yet classification of the insular shore fish fauna is more complex. On a broad scale, distributions of shore fishes are influenced by water temperature and associated currents: the cool, southerly-flowing California Current offshore, and the warmer, inshore countercurrent and eddy (Hubbs 1967, 1974, Neushul *et al.* 1967). Also, the specific assemblage of fishes in a given area will depend very strongly on the habitat structure there. And finally, isolation at islands may be brought about either by differential transport of species having planktonic larvae (Kanter 1980, Seapy and Littler 1980) or by chance transport of species that have no planktonic dispersal stage (*cf.* Haldorson 1980). Our study analyzes the effects of habitat on the composition of one element of the inshore fish fauna, the kelp-bed fishes, and applies this analysis to compare the kelp-bed fish assemblages at Santa Cruz Island with those from the adjacent Santa Barbara mainland.

Some papers in this symposium dealt with large-scale biogeography of inshore organisms on the California Islands (Seapy and Littler 1980, Silva 1978). Even though we do not address this problem directly, we realize that interpretations of habitat effects must consider geographic affinities of the fauna. On the other hand, habitat effects may confound broad-scale geographic effects (*cf.* Kanter 1980, Littler 1980). Our objective, therefore, is to show how assemblages of kelp-bed fishes may be classified into particular habitat groups, and how differences in structural habitat affect the composition of fish assemblages making up such groups.

We did our study off Santa Barbara, at the southern end of a transitional zone between a warm-temperate biota to the southeast and a cool-temperate biota at San Miguel Island and north of Point Conception (*cf.* Hewatt 1946, Hubbs 1948, 1960, 1974, Neushul *et al.* 1967, Quast 1968b, Ebeling *et al.* 1971). The mixed composition of the fauna reflects water temperature and exposure to currents. The California Current carries cool water seaward past Point Conception, although a small branch of this current feeds a counterclockwise eddy in the western part of the Santa Barbara Channel (Reid 1965, Kolpack 1971). This eddy meets warmer currents from the southeast at the eastern end of the Channel, near Santa Barbara and Santa Cruz Island (Kolpack 1971). Therefore, even though oceanographically complex, our study areas are warmer and more exposed to southern currents than is San Miguel Island at the western end of the channel.

Given the geographic affinities of the fish fauna in our study areas, we investigated the influence of structural habitat on the composition of fish assemblages in and about beds of giant

---

[1] Present address: MRC Research Center, 533 Stevens Ave., Solana Beach, California 92075.

[2] Present address: Department of Biological Sciences, Florida Institute of Technology, Melbourne, Florida 32901.

kelp *(Macrocystis)*. In this way, we hoped to explain any "island effect" on these assemblages, as expressed by differences in species abundance and composition between Santa Cruz Island and the Santa Barbara mainland. Inshore habitats vary along several environmental gradients (Limbaugh 1955, North 1963, Quast 1968a, Frey 1971). For example, density of giant kelp varies with depth and several other factors (Neushul *et al.* 1967, North 1963, 1971, Quast 1968a, Pearse and Lowry 1974). A depth-related gradient in dominant plants extends from surfgrass, boa kelp, or *Pterygophora-Eisenia* communities inshore, through giant kelp and red algae at intermediate depths, to depauperate plant communities in deeper water (Clarke and Neushul 1967, Neushul *et al.* 1967). Such biotic gradients follow abiotic gradients in temperature, light, wave surge, and productivity (Quast 1968a, Pequegnat 1964). A gradient in substrate type extends from flat and soft bottoms of sand and/or mud, through flat and hard bottoms, to high-relief rocky reefs; the "turf" of sessile animals and plants that covers these reefs varies with degree of water movement, silting, scouring, light penetration, and grazing (McLean 1962, Pequegnat 1964, Turner *et al.* 1965, 1968, Clarke and Neushul 1967, North 1971, Pearse and Lowry 1974, Neushul *et al.* 1976). Much like a forest, giant kelp provides a vertical gradient along which animals tend to stratify in the water column. Kelp stipes in midwater and the dense canopy near the surface provide shelter, food, and landmarks for a variety of fishes (Hobson 1965, Quast 1968b, Feder *et al.* 1974, Alevizon 1976).

Limbaugh (1955) and Quast (1968b, 1968c) analyzed kelp-bed fish assemblages mainly in the San Diego area of southern California. Miller and Geibel (1973) and Burge and Schultz (1973) analyzed such assemblages off central California, north of Point Conception. These investigators evaluated specific responses of individual species to their natural environment and were concerned with how assemblages may respond to changes in structural habitat. Excepting a few fragmentary observations and species lists (Hewatt 1946, Clarke and Neushul 1967, Neushul *et al.* 1967, Quast 1968c), however, there was almost no published information from the Santa Barbara area.

We supplement these seminal studies of southern and northern regions by taking a more synthetic approach to analyzing species assemblages in the less well-known transitional region off Santa Barbara. Thus, although we must interpret our results in terms of behavior of particular species, our results provide an overall view of changing fish assemblages. Hopefully, our synecological approach reveals general trends not immediately obvious from autecological studies.

We compared kelp-bed fish assemblages sampled at different localities along Santa Cruz Island with assemblages sampled at different localities along the Santa Barbara mainland. We first determined the structure of assemblages by identifying subgroups of species ("habitat groups") that tend to associate with different positions on environmental gradients in and about areas of reef and kelp. We then compared the density, diversity, and composition of assemblages among localities, between mainland and island, and between seasons. With this information, we were better able to distinguish and explain any island effect on the assemblages, in light of the faunal complexity of the region.

METHODS
Cinetransect Samples

We sampled fish populations and associated habitat variables by means of cinetransects. Cinetransects are 2.5-min, Super-8 mm, high-speed color movie films from 15.24-m film cartridges, taken by scuba divers starting out in a randomly chosen direction (Alevizon 1975a, Alevizon and Brooks 1975, Bray and Ebeling 1975, Love and Ebeling 1978, Ebeling *et al.* in press). To take cinetransect samples, we drove our skiff to any open area in the kelp where we could conveniently anchor. Diver photographers then swam with underwater cameras at about

3 m depth below the kelp canopy (canopy transects), or just above the bottom (bottom transects). We sampled in as many different habitats as we could find, but in each transect the photographer tried to stay within the same general depth, terrain, and microhabitat type (*e.g.*, sandy bottom, reef crest, surfgrass beds), so that each cinetransect could be classified by discrete habitat characteristics. For some of our analyses, we divided bottom transects into those made over rocky reefs and those made in inshore or sandy areas at or beyond the reef or kelp-bed margins (sandy-marginal transects). Bottom transects (in kelp beds over rocky reefs) outnumbered canopy and sandy-marginal transects (Table 1). The photographers swam at a fairly constant rate and never doubled back, so as not to photograph fish that tend to follow. The camera was pointed ahead (or slightly downward for bottom transects) and panned in a 10-degree arc as steadily as possible. Occasionally, the camera was pointed to include all fish sighted in a particular school or cluster. Measurement of variables was made *in situ* (*e.g.*, temperature, overcast, surge) or from the movies (*e.g.*, species counts, scored bottom relief, kelp density). Ebeling *et al.* (in press) concluded that cinetransecting is effective for rapidly sampling large, mobile fishes in complex environments where water is reasonably clear. Cinetransects provided permanent records of fish densities and general habitat structure. Compared with destructive sampling such as poisoning, cinetransects provided more realistic counts of larger and stronger fishes, but tended to underestimate densities of small and cryptic species.

During 1970, 175 cinetransects were filmed in reef and sandy-marginal habitats at four localities along the Santa Barbara mainland and five localities along Santa Cruz Island (Fig. 1 and Table 1). Cinetransects served three purposes: first, we used them as a large, heterogeneous sample to identify habitat groups (species with intercorrelated densities, along with associated environmental features). Second, we used them as smaller, homogeneous samples to compare fish assemblages among nearby localities that differed slightly in habitat characteristics, and to compare island and mainland assemblages. We divided the cinetransects into 20 samples, one each for canopy and bottom at each of nine localities, and one each for island and mainland sandy-marginal habitats. Third, we used mainland canopy and bottom cinetransects to see if fish assemblages varied seasonally by comparing samples taken during winter and spring with others taken in summer and fall. Off Santa Barbara, winter-spring (December through May) is an oceanographic period of cooler water, maximum vertical mixing, upwelling, storms, and fish spawning. Summer-fall is a period of warmer and generally clearer water, thermal stratification, calm weather, and rapid fish growth (Brown 1974, Love and Ebeling 1978).

Habitat Group Identification

To identify habitat groups (*i.e.*, to recognize environmentally induced patterns in the co-occurrence of kelp-bed fishes), we carried out a factor analysis of species densities and environmental variables (*cf.* Smith *et al.* 1973). In factor analysis, a large part of the covariation of observed variables is attributed to only a few, presumably causative, factors (Harman 1967). Thus, our factors can be thought of as a smaller number of hypothetical variables (habitat groups) that summarize the relations among a larger number of real variables (fish counts, habitat measures).

After selecting (as described below) 10 environmental variables (*e.g.*, measures of habitat, fish abundance and diversity) and 24 species variables (fish counts), we computed a factor analysis from a correlation matrix of all 34 variables. The analysis was such that factors were not necessarily orthogonal and could be correlated (Program BMDX72, with oblique rotation for simple loadings, from Dixon 1967). Appropriate criteria (Harman 1967, Fisher 1968, Thomas 1968) suggested that five factors were sufficient to describe the major relationships in the system. The degree of relationship between a variable and a factor is expressed by its

TABLE 1. Physical characteristics of 175 cinetransects filmed in kelp-canopy, bottom, and sandy-marginal habitats and grouped by localities along the mainland and Santa Cruz Island off Santa Barbara, California (Fig. 1). *Season* reflects periods of different hydrography: WS (December-May) and SF (June-November). *Bottom depth* is scored: 1 (1.5-4.6 m), 2 (4.8-7.6 m), 3 (7.9-10.7 m), 4 (11.0-13.7 m), and 5 (14.0-17.0 m). *Bottom relief* is scored subjectively from 1 (almost flat) to 5 (high ridges, large boulders, etc.). Each entry represents the number of cinetransects.

Habitat	Area	Locality	Season WS	Season SF	Bottom depth 1	2	3	4	5	Bottom relief 1	2	3	4	5
Canopy	Mainland	HE	3	3		4	2			4	2			
		IV	6	4		4	6			7	3			
		CO	2	5			5	2		7				
		NA	4	3	1		2	4	1			3	2	1
	Island	SC		7		6	1				3	2	1	1
		PE		5			4	1					1	4
		FR		4	1	1		1				1	1	2
		VA		5		2	3					2	2	1
		WI		6		3	3					4	1	1
Bottom	Mainland	HE	5	7		9	3			2	2	5	2	1
		IV	6	5		3	8			1	4	6		
		CO	6	10	5	4	5	1	1	6	8	1	1	
		NA	5	6		1	6	3	1			3	4	4
	Island	SC		11	5	4	1	1				4	2	5
		PE		7	3	4							2	5
		FR		7	1		3		3			2	1	4
		VA		7		2	2	3					4	3
		WI		14		6	8				1		6	7
Sandy margin	Mainland*		6	6	9	3				8	4			
	Island*			10	2	2	6			6	2	2		

* Sandy-marginal cinetransects taken at a variety of mainland and island locations.

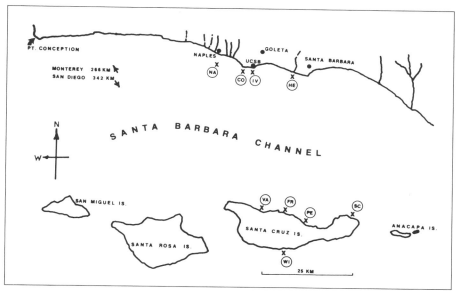

FIGURE 1. *Localities (circled) for cinetransect sampling of fish assemblages in areas of reef and kelp off Santa Barbara, California. Mainland: CO, Coal Oil Point; HE, Hendry's (Arroyo Burro) Beach; IV, Isla Vista; NA, Naples Reef. Santa Cruz Island: FR, Frys Harbor and vicinity; PE, Pelican Bay and vicinity; SC, Scorpion Anchorage; VA, Cueva Valdaze; WI, Willows Anchorage.*

"loading" on the factor. Loadings vary from −1.0 to +1.0 and are analogous to partial regression coefficients (Harman 1967). Because there is no significance test for loadings, we followed Sokal and Daly (1961) and arbitrarily took the absolute value 0.40 as about the lower limit of important loadings. Each of our five habitat groups was defined by the variables loading at least this high on a particular factor. Thus, most species could be unequivocally assigned to the habitat group represented by the factor on which they had the highest loading, although some species were difficult to place because they had intermediate loadings on two or more factors. The latter species may be interpreted as transgressing habitat groups more than is characteristic of the other species (*cf.* Angel and Fasham 1973).

The 24 fish species analyzed were those that occurred at a frequency of about 5 per cent (8 of 175 cinetransects) or more (Table 2). Fish counts per species often included many zeros, so the species' frequency distributions among cinetransects were strongly skewed. Since log-transformations of counts did not normalize most distributions, we used Kendall's rank correlations (instead of the usual parametric product-moment correlations) as the basis for our factor analysis.

Selecting the "best" environmental variables from the huge number observable was more difficult. We began with the largest number we could measure practicably and then, using several criteria, eliminated those considered less important. This large initial set included variables that measured (1) fish abundance and diversity, (2) habitat structure, (3) seasonal progression, and (4) changes in the weather. We subsequently eliminated seasonal and weather variables because their correlations with species densities were relatively small (Table 3).

408

KELP-BED FISH HABITAT GROUPS

TABLE 2. Fish species recorded by 175 cinetransects filmed in areas of reef and kelp off Santa Barbara, California (Fig. 1). *Common names* are arranged alphabetically as in an index (names and classification follow Miller and Lea 1972). *Occurrence* is: *c*, common; *m*, moderately common; *r*, rare but characteristic of such areas; and *u*, rare and uncharacteristic. An *X* marks the species' *inclusion* in the numerical analyses.

Common name	Scientific name	Family	Occurrence	Inclusion
Elasmobranchs				
Guitarfish, shovelnose	*Rhinobatos productus*	Rhinobatidae	u	
Ray				
bat	*Myliobatis californica*	Myliobatididae	u	
Pacific electric	*Torpedo californica*	Torpedinidae	u	
Shark				
horn	*Heterodontus francisci*	Heterodontidae	u[6]	
leopard	*Triakis semifasciata*	Carcharhinidae	u	
swell	*Cephaloscyllium ventriosum*	Scyliorhinidae	u[6]	
Teleosts				
Bass				
barred sand	*Paralabrax nebulifer*	Serranidae	m	X
kelp	*P. clathratus*	Serranidae	c	X
Blacksmith	*Chromis punctipinnis*	Pomacentridae	c	X
Cabezon	*Scorpaenichthys marmoratus*	Cottidae	r[1]	
Croaker, black	*Cheilotrema saturnum*	Sciaenidae	r	
Garibaldi	*Hypsypops rubicundus*	Pomacentridae	c	X
Goby, blackeye	*Coryphopterus nicholsii*	Gobiidae	r[1]	
Greenling				
painted	*Oxylebius pictus*	Hexagrammidae	m	X
kelp	*Hexagrammos decagrammus*	Hexagrammidae	r	
Halfmoon	*Medialuna californiensis*	Scorpididae	m	X
Kelpfish				
giant	*Heterostichus rostratus*	Clinidae	m	X
sp.	*Gibbonsia* sp.	Clinidae	r[1]	
Lingcod	*Ophiodon elongatus*	Hexagrammidae	r	X
Mola	*Mola mola*	Molidae	u	
Opaleye	*Girella nigricans*	Girellidae	c	X
Pipefish	*Syngnathus* sp.	Syngnathidae	r[1]	
Rockfish				
black	*Sebastes melanops*	Scorpaenidae	r	
black-and-yellow	*S. chrysomelas*	Scorpaenidae	m	X[2]
gopher	*S. carnatus*	Scorpaenidae	m	X[2]
blue	*S. mystinus*	Scorpaenidae	c	X
grass	*S. rastrelliger*	Scorpaenidae	r	X[2]
kelp	*S. atrovirens*	Scorpaenidae	c	X
olive	*S. serranoides*	Scorpaenidae	c	X
whitebelly	*S. vexillaris*	Scorpaenidae	r[3]	X[2]
Sculpin, lavender	*Leiocottus hirundo*	Cottidae	r	
Señorita	*Oxyjulis californica*	Labridae	c	X
Sheephead, California	*Pimelometopon pulchrum*	Labridae	c	X

TABLE 2. (Cont.)

Surfperch				
barred	*Amphistichus argenteus*	Embiotocidae	u	
black	*Embiotoca jacksoni*	Embiotocidae	c	X
dwarf	*Micrometrus minimus*	Embiotocidae	r[3]	X
island	*Cymatogaster gracilis*	Embiotocidae	c[4]	
kelp	*Brachyistius frenatus*	Embiotocidae	c	X
pile	*Damalichthys vacca*	Embiotocidae	c	X
rainbow	*Hypsurus caryi*	Embiotocidae	m[5]	X
rubberlip	*Rhacochilus toxotes*	Embiotocidae	m	X
sharpnose	*Phanerodon atripes*	Embiotocidae	r	
shiner	*Cymatogaster aggregata*	Embiotocidae	u	
striped	*Embiotoca lateralis*	Embiotocidae	c	X
walleye	*Hyperprosopon argenteum*	Embiotocidae	u[6]	X
white	*Phanerodon furcatus*	Embiotocidae	m	X
Topsmelt	*Atherinops affinis*	Atherinidae	u	
Treefish	*Sebastes serriceps*	Scorpaenidae	r[2]	
Turbot, C-O	*Pleuronichthys coenosus*	Pleuronectidae	u	
Whitefish, ocean	*Caulolatilus princeps*	Branchiostegidae	r[3]	
Wrasse, rock	*Halichoeres semicinctus*	Labridae	r	

[1] Apparently rare only because small and/or well camouflaged.

[2] All counted in one category of "bottom rockfish."

[3] Apparently rare because its distribution centers on deeper (whitebelly rockfish, ocean whitefish) or shallower (dwarf surfperch) reefs.

[4] Island endemic.

[5] Seasonally (spring, summer) common at Naples Reef.

[6] Active on reef only at night.

We then reduced the set of 20 habitat variables to minimize redundancy. Using the results of a separate, preliminary factor analysis of correlations among the habitat variables, we selected the most representative by the following criteria (Table 3): (1) every habitat factor resolved should be represented by at least one variable, (2) the variable should have a relatively large mean correlation with species densities (*i.e.*, be a likely causative agent), and (3) the variables should have a relatively large "communality" (Table 3) with the other environmental variables (*i.e.*, be most predictive of variation of the factor group as a whole). Hence, most were chosen by weighting the mean correlation (to bring it within the same magnitude as communalities), and adding the communality. For example, all variables loading on habitat factor 1 (Table 3) were highly intercorrelated, but the rocky, high-relief bottom type had the highest mean correlation-communality. Thus, this variable was chosen to represent the factor (and it is likely that variation in bottom relief induces variation in other correlates such as invertebrate and bottom-algal densities). Hence, bottom relief was selected as the best single variable to measure the whole substrate aspect of habitat structure. We made some exceptions: for habitat factor 3, bottom depth and plant density-surfgrass equally met the criteria, so both were included; for habitat factor 2, positional variables were selected, along with plant density-giant kelp (which met the criteria) for better spatial resolution of the groups; and for habitat factor 4, "area" (scored mainland or Santa Cruz Island localities) was omitted because mainland-island faunal and habitat differences were analyzed later.

TABLE 3. Correlative properties of environmental variables measured with each of 175 cinetransects filmed in areas of reef and kelp off Santa Barbara (Table 1). *Mean correlation* is the average of absolute values of correlations of the variable with densities of 24 fish species (Table 2). *Communality*, scaled from 0.0-1.0, measures covariation with others in a subgroup of 20 habitat variables subjected to a preliminary factor analysis. Variables with low communalities do not correlate strongly with others as factors; variables with high communalities and the same *factor number* are intercorrelated relatively strongly. The symbol "(−)" after factor number means that the variable is negatively correlated with others with the same factor number (see text).

Variable	Mean correlation with species variables	Usual sign of correlation	Communality with other habitat variables in factor analysis	Factor number
Abundance-diversity variables				
Number of fish per transect*	0.199	+		
Number of species per transect*	0.270	+		
Mean	0.234			
Habitat variables				
Area (scored localities)	0.205	+	0.80	4
Bottom depth (m)*	0.166	+	0.57	3(−)
Bottom type (score)				
boulders	0.185	+	0.75	1
rocky high relief*	0.185	+	0.84	1
rocky low relief	0.131	−	0.62	4(−)
sand	0.166	−	0.81	1(−)
Invertebrate density (score)				
crabs, etc.	0.175	+	0.81	1
urchins	0.111	+,−	0.67	1
Plant density (score)				
surfgrass*	0.173	+,−	0.54	3
giant kelp*	0.197	+	0.77	2

other brown algae, short	0.135	+	0.49	1
other brown algae, tall	0.122	+, −	0.54	3
red algae	0.144	+	0.72	1
Position of transect relative to kelp bed (score)				
outside of, but near*	0.145	−	0.80	2(−)
outside of, but not near	0.123	−	0.42	3
toward shoreward margin*	0.126	+	0.64	5(−)
toward middle	0.156	+	0.82	2
toward seaward margin	0.114	−	0.67	5
Position of transect in water column (score)*	0.203	+, −	0.37	2
Underwater visibility (m)*	0.129	+	0.42	4
Mean	0.155			
Seasonal variables				
Month (winter-summer)	0.107	+	0.76	
Thermocline depth (m)	0.076	+		
Water temperature (°C)				
bottom	0.095	+		
surface	0.078	+	0.78	
Mean	0.089			
Weather variables				
Overcast (score)	0.116	+		
Surge strength (score)	0.085	−		
Swell height (m)	0.112	−		
Wind				
direction to NW (score)	0.097	−		
speed (mph)	0.113	−		
Mean	0.105			

* Included in final factor analysis based on 10 environmental variables and 24 species.

TABLE 4. Habitat groups of kelp-bed fishes identified by factors relating 34 habitat and species variables from 175 cinetransects filmed off Santa Barbara (Table 1). *Factor loading* measures the contribution of the variable to the factor, and is scaled from −1.0 (correlates negatively with other variables in group) to +1.0 (correlates positively) (see text). *Communality* is explained in Table 3.

Factor number/Habitat group/Variable	Factor loading	Communality
1. Kelp-rock group		
Bottom type: rocky high relief	0.75	0.57
Plant density: giant kelp*	0.51	0.67
Underwater visibility	0.42	0.24
Number of species per transect	0.51	0.72
Number of fish per transect*	0.40	0.57
Blacksmith	0.65	0.52
Opaleye	0.62	0.50
Striped surfperch	0.60	0.45
Halfmoon	0.49	0.29
California sheephead	0.49	0.53
Garibaldi	0.45	0.32
Blue rockfish*	0.40	0.44
2. Canopy group		
Position of transect in water column*	−0.61	0.78
Number of fish per transect*	0.59	0.57
Kelp surfperch	0.56	0.56
Giant kelpfish	0.55	0.39
Señorita	0.41	0.24
Olive rockfish	0.41	0.31
Kelp rockfish*	0.36	0.42
3. Inner-marginal group		
Plant density: surfgrass	0.78	0.60
Bottom depth	−0.67	0.49
Position re. kelp bed: toward shoreward margin	0.56	0.39
Dwarf surfperch	0.64	0.41
Walleye surfperch	0.63	0.54
Rainbow surfperch	0.50	0.32
Black surfperch*	0.39	0.52
4. Commuter group		
Number of fish per transect*	0.51	0.57
Pile surfperch	0.71	0.50
Rubberlip surfperch	0.65	0.44
Kelp bass	0.42	0.37
White surfperch	0.40	0.39
Kelp rockfish*	0.39	0.42
5. Bottom group		
Position re. kelp bed: outside of, but near	0.64	0.63
Plant density: giant kelp*	−0.55	0.67
Position of transect in water column*	0.52	0.78
Lingcod	0.58	0.34
Painted greenling	0.50	0.28

TABLE 4. (Cont.)

"Bottom rockfish"†	0.48	0.31
Sand bass	0.47	0.28
Blue rockfish*	0.40	0.44
Black surfperch*	0.36	0.52

* Variables loading on more than one factor.
† Includes mostly black-and-yellow and gopher rockfishes; more rarely, grass and whitebelly rockfishes and treefish.

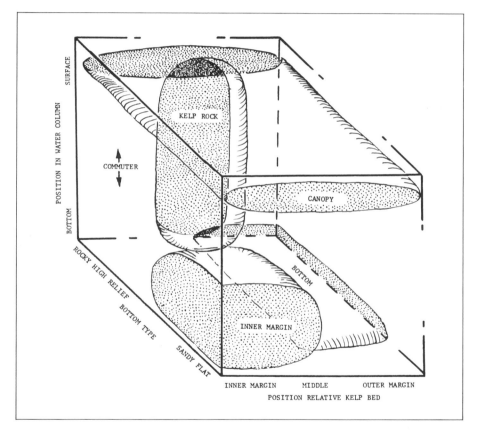

FIGURE 2. *Principal daytime space occupied by habitat groups (Table 4) of kelp-bed fishes identified by factors relating habitat and species variables from 175 cinetransects filmed off Santa Barbara (Fig. 1 and Table 1). Stippling is intersection of a group's principal space with a plane defined by axes of any two habitat variables. For example, species in the inner-marginal group transgress the sandy flat (lower values along transverse axis) beyond the edge of the kelp bed (lower values along horizontal axis) toward shore, so are not necessarily most abundant over well-developed offshore reefs. Species in the commuter group may occur commonly from bottom to canopy throughout the kelp bed.*

In summary, we computed a final factor analysis of rank correlations among 34 variables: density of each of 24 species, total fish and species per transect, and eight measures of habitat structure (Table 4).

Interlocality Comparisons

For canopy and bottom zones, mean fish density (number of individuals/cinetransect), biomass (wet weight estimated from length-weight regressions), and diversity (number of species) were compared among localities by one-way analyses of variance (anovas) for unequal sample sizes, and were compared for localities *vs.* seasons or areas (mainland, island) by two-way anovas for disproportionate, as well as unequal, subclass sizes (Nie *et al.* 1975). For two-way analyses of locality and area main effects, each of four "localities" was made up of a mainland-island pair in the Santa Barbara Channel (see Table 7). Since sample distributions of density and biomass were skewed to the right (relatively few large values), we $\log_{10}$-transformed variates to minimize extremes (Sokal and Rohlf 1969). This corrected for skewness and equalized variances (*cf.* Quast 1969c). Sample distributions of diversity were not significantly different from normal and had equal variances, and were therefore left untransformed. *A posteriori* contrasts between means were made (Table 8) by finding the smallest subgroups of means whose largest and smallest values were not significantly different (Sokal and Rohlf 1969, Dunnett 1970).

Differences in species composition among localities were measured by a similarity index (Whittaker 1960), based on proportionate differences in numbers of individuals: $I = 1.0 - (0.5 \sum_{i=1}^{s} |p_{ij} - p_{ik}|)$, or min (p_{ij}, p_{ik}), where p_{ij} is the proportionate abundance of species i in cinetransect j. Outcomes were similar whether proportionate differences between samples were based on density, biomass, or frequency of occurrence of the included species because the three kinds of arrays were highly intercorrelated. Rank correlations between species arrays based on pooled mainland bottom samples were large and highly significant ($P < 0.001$): 0.60 between biomass and density, 0.64 between biomass and frequency, and 0.78 between frequency and density.

RESULTS

The 175 cinetransects recorded 51 fish species in 23 families, although only about half were common enough to be analyzed (Table 2). This large heterogeneous sample was the basis for identifying habitat groups of species. Showing little or no seasonal variation, subsamples revealed significant differences in kelp-bed fish assemblages among localities, which varied considerably in structural habitat along the mainland. Overall, however, mainland-island differences overshadowed interlocality differences.

Habitat Groups

Factor analysis resolved five factors of intercorrelated species and habitat variables. We interpreted the factors as identifying loose spatial associations or habitat groups of common kelp-bed fishes (Table 4 and Fig. 2): a kelp-rock group (factor 1) of species that co-occurred most abundantly in clear-water areas of high bottom relief and kelp density, where species diversity was greatest; a group (2) of species that co-occurred high in the water column, beneath the kelp canopy; an inner-marginal group (3) of surfperches that co-occurred shoreward at shallower depths, where surfgrass was plentiful; a commuter group (4) of species that co-occurred throughout the water column in areas of high species diversity; and a bottom group (5) of sedentary species that co-occurred most abundantly on the reef bottom, where kelp was less dense.

Correlations between the factors themselves indicated interrelationships among the habitat groups (Table 5). The kelp-rock (factor 1), bottom (5), and commuter (4) groups were positively correlated, while canopy (2) and inner-marginal (3) groups were uncorrelated or negatively correlated with this triad.

TABLE 5. Correlations among five factors relating 34 habitat and species variables from 175 cinetransects filmed off Santa Barbara (see Table 4).

Factor	1. Kelp rock	4. Commuter	5. Bottom	2. Canopy
4. Commuter	0.13			
5. Bottom	0.05	0.12		
2. Canopy	−0.01	0.02	−0.11	
3. Inner margin	−0.13	0.06	0.02	−0.10

TABLE 6. Locality-*vs.*-season analysis of variance of kelp-bed fish density, biomass, and diversity from cinetransects filmed along Santa Barbara mainland and classified by four localities and two semiannual periods, December-May and June-November (Fig. 1 and Table 1).

Source	Degrees of freedom	Density ($\log_{10}$ nos. of individuals)		Biomass ($\log_{10}$ kg)		Diversity (nos. of species)	
		Mean square	F	Mean square	F	Mean square	F
Canopy							
Localities, L	3	0.263	1.73	0.235	1.77	10.279	3.48*
Seasons, S	1	0.037	<1	0.002	<1	1.884	<1
L × S	3	0.387	2.54	0.397	2.99	12.316	4.18**
Error	22	0.152		0.133		2.949	
Bottom							
Localities, L	3	0.677	6.94***	0.784	6.50***	33.476	8.14***
Seasons, S	1	0.090	<1	0.015	<1	0.328	<1
L × S	3	0.037	<1	0.013	<1	7.366	1.69
Error	42	0.097		0.121		4.359	

Significant at: $*0.05<P<0.02$. $**P\cong0.02$. $***P<0.001$.

Interlocality Differences

Habitat structure varied more among mainland than among island localities, and mainland-type habitats as a whole were different from island-type habitats (Table 1). Along the mainland, locality NA (Fig. 1) had a better-developed and deeper reef than the other three localities. All four localities, however, had relatively large expanses of sand and flat rock separating relatively small areas of well-developed reef. In contrast, most of the island localities were segments of a continuous, well-developed reef system.

Within sampling limits, seasonal variation in fish density, biomass, and diversity was nil. Fish densities were but weakly correlated with seasonal variables (Table 3), and no significant differences distinguished semiannual periods (Table 6).

Interlocality variation in density, biomass, and diversity was also nil in the canopy zone. We detected little or no significant differences among canopy means, either within areas or between the mainland and Santa Cruz Island (Table 7). Of all contrasts, in fact, only one mean of one variable was indicated as different from others (Table 8).

In the bottom zone, however, significant differences in these variables, both within areas and between mainland and island (Table 7), reflected differences in habitat type. In general, means from deeper localities with higher bottom relief were significantly greater than the others (Table 8; see NA and HE of mainland, and most island localities, all of which had moderate to high

Canopy:
Localities, L | 3 | 0.101 | <1 | 0.230 | 1.29 | 8.737 | 1.76
Areas, A | 1 | 0.036 | <1 | 0.288 | 1.62 | 9.890 | 1.99
L x A | 3 | 0.262 | 1.20 | 0.097 | <1 | 7.752 | 1.56
Error | 43 | 0.219 | | 0.178 | | 4.957 |

Localities | 8 | 0.141 | <1 | 0.163 | <1 | 8.740 | 1.87*
Error | 48 | 0.232 | | 0.178 | | 4.666 |

Bottom:
Localities, L | 3 | 1.200 | 15.14*** | 1.164 | 13.93*** | 77.56 | 17.01***
Areas, A | 1 | 1.716 | 21.64*** | 2.275 | 27.24*** | 101.58 | 22.28***
L x A | 3 | 0.170 | 2.14 | 0.369 | 4.42** | 7.09 | 1.55
Error | 74 | 0.079 | | 0.084 | | 4.56 |

Localities | 8 | 0.863 | 11.77*** | 1.067 | 13.87*** | 50.70 | 12.38***
Error | 87 | 0.073 | | 0.077 | | 4.10 |

TABLE 7. Locality-*vs.*-area (mainland, island) and among-locality analyses of variance of kelp-bed fish density, biomass, and diversity from cinetransects filmed along Santa Barbara mainland and Santa Cruz Island (Fig. 1 and Table 1). For the two-way analyses, localities are four mainland-island pairs in the Santa Barbara Channel: CO-PE, IV-SC, HE-FR, and NA-VA (WI, on the island's seaward side, is excluded). The one-way analyses include all nine localities.

Source	Degrees of freedom	Density ($\log_{10}$ nos. of individuals) Mean square	F	Biomass ($\log_{10}$ kg) Mean square	F	Diversity (nos. of species) Mean square	F
Canopy							
Localities, L	3	0.101	<1	0.230	1.29	8.737	1.76
Areas, A	1	0.036	<1	0.288	1.62	9.890	1.99
L x A	3	0.262	1.20	0.097	<1	7.752	1.56
Error	43	0.219		0.178		4.957	
Localities	8	0.141	<1	0.163	<1	8.740	1.87*
Error	48	0.232		0.178		4.666	
Bottom							
Localities, L	3	1.200	15.14***	1.164	13.93***	77.56	17.01***
Areas, A	1	1.716	21.64***	2.275	27.24***	101.58	22.28***
L x A	3	0.170	2.14	0.369	4.42**	7.09	1.55
Error	74	0.079		0.084		4.56	
Localities	8	0.863	11.77***	1.067	13.87***	50.70	12.38***
Error	87	0.073		0.077		4.10	

Significant at: $*P=0.09$. $**P=0.006$. $***P<0.001$.

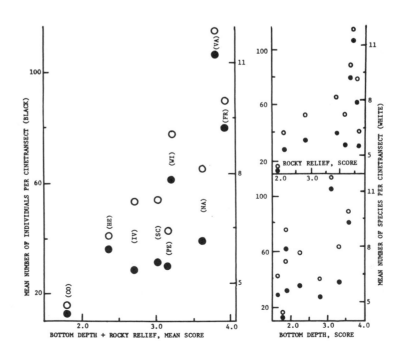

TABLE 8. Among-locality contrasts between means of kelp-bed fish density, biomass, and diversity from *(n)* cinetransects filmed at nine localities *(Loc.)* along Santa Barbara *mainland* and Santa Cruz *Island* (Fig. 1 and Table 1). Mainland observations are pooled between semiannual periods (Table 6). Using the Student-Newman-Keuls procedure, means are ordered by size into subsets (marked by columns of *X*s under *SNK*) judged homogenous by the least significant range (LSR) criterion *(P* = 0.05 level); no subset contains means that differ more than the LSR determined for a subset of that size, so means that differ significantly are in different subsets (Nie *et al.* 1975; see Table 6 and text).

Habitat/ Area	Density (antilog nos. of individuals)				Biomass (antilog kg.)			Diversity (nos. of species)		
	Loc.	*n*	Mean	SNK	Loc.	Mean	SNK	Loc.	Mean	SNK
Canopy										
Mainland	NA	7	43.7	X	IV	7.63	X	NA	4.14	X
	IV	10	46.6	X	NA	8.02	X	IV	4.50	X
	HE	6	54.5	X	HE	8.39	X	CO	6.14	X
	CO	7	95.8	X	CO	15.5	X	HE	6.50	X
Island	FR	4	41.4	X	FR	8.72	X	WI	4.17	X
	PE	5	54.1	X	WI	9.62	X	FR	5.00	X
	WI	6	60.6	X	SC	13.2	X	SC	5.29	X
	SC	7	78.3	X	PE	16.7	X	VA	6.80	X
Bottom										
Mainland	CO	16	12.7	X	CO	4.56	X	CO	4.37	X
	IV	11	28.4	X	HE	11.35	X	IV	6.27	X X
	HE	12	36.6	X X	IV	11.45	X	HE	7.33	X X
	NA	11	38.0	X X	NA	16.6	X X	NA	8.09	X X X
Island	PE	7	29.8	X X	SC	10.8	X	PE	6.43	X X
	SC	11	31.7	X X	PE	15.5	X X	SC	7.27	X X
	WI	14	61.5	X X	WI	28.5	X X	WI	9.07	X X
	FR	7	79.8	X	FR	35.7	X	FR	10.0	X X
	VA	7	107.1	X	VA	41.9	X	VA	12.0	X

FIGURE 3. *Variation of kelp-bed fish density and diversity with bottom depth and degree of rocky relief among bottom assemblages at four mainland and five Santa Cruz Island localities sampled from 175 cinetransects filmed off Santa Barbara (Fig. 1 and Table 1). Vertical axes: left, density (black circles); right, diversity (white circles). Horizontal axes: large graph on left, combined bottom depth and rocky relief; small graphs on right, bottom depth or rocky relief plotted separately. Localities are identified parenthetically between vertical black-white pairs of points on left graph.*

TABLE 9. Relative abundance and frequency of occurrence of 24 species in mainland (*Main.*) and Santa Cruz Island (*Is.*) samples of canopy, bottom, and sandy-marginal assemblages of kelp-bed fishes, as represented in 175 cinetransects filmed off Santa Barbara. Samples are pooled among localities (Fig. 1 and Table 1).

Species	Per cent numbers of individuals						Per cent frequencies of occurrence					
	Canopy		Bottom		Sandy margin		Canopy		Bottom		Sandy margin	
	Main.	Is.	Main.	Is.	Main.	Is.	Main.	Is.	Main.	Is.	Main.	Is.
Bass												
barred sand	-	-	0.83	-	-	-	-	-	12.0	-	-	-
kelp	9.39	3.26	16.00	9.09	4.62	17.28	86.7	66.7	80.0	87.0	33.3	80.0
Blacksmith	8.92	50.44	6.93	23.27	-	3.40	30.0	77.8	26.0	58.7	-	20.0
Garibaldi	-	-	0.36	9.43	-	-	-	-	12.0	67.4	-	-
Greenling, painted	-	-	0.89	0.88	-	-	-	-	16.0	21.7	-	-
Halfmoon	2.02	1.74	0.24	2.42	-	3.40	13.3	29.6	6.0	41.3	-	20.0
Kelpfish, giant	0.65	0.12	0.18	-	0.66	-	33.3	14.8	6.0	-	16.7	-
Lingcod	-	-	0.53	-	-	-	-	-	12.0	-	-	-
Opaleye	0.22	1.34	2.31	15.25	-	0.93	6.7	40.7	24.0	69.6	-	20.0
Rockfish												
blue	5.76	6.25	6.58	7.39	-	1.54	33.3	29.6	38.0	43.5	-	20.0
"bottom"*	-	-	1.01	0.66	-	0.62	-	-	30.0	28.3	-	10.0
kelp	2.20	4.12	1.42	4.21	-	0.62	50.0	66.7	22.0	87.0	-	20.0
olive	0.86	1.19	0.30	1.16	-	-	36.7	51.8	10.0	26.1	-	-
Señorita	6.08	4.30	6.52	3.40	2.64	22.2	63.3	51.8	44.0	43.5	25.0	70.0
Sheephead, California	-	0.24	3.02	10.03	-	11.73	-	11.1	32.0	84.8	-	70.0
Surfperch												
black	1.66	0.12	30.33	5.63	35.97	8.95	16.7	7.4	92.0	84.8	91.7	80.0
dwarf	-	-	-	0.13	3.96	0.93	-	-	-	6.5	25.0	10.0
kelp	35.16	25.74	0.36	0.13	-	0.31	76.7	74.1	6.0	6.5	8.3	10.0
pile	1.44	0.37	7.76	1.95	1.98	1.24	26.7	14.8	66.0	52.2	33.3	30.0
rainbow	-	-	1.30	0.13	7.59	0.31	-	-	22.0	4.35	25.0	10.0
rubberlip	1.04	0.34	5.15	1.95	0.34	1.85	23.3	11.1	46.0	45.6	8.3	30.0

striped	-	50.0	16.0	22.2	-	0.93	-	2.64	0.71	0.21	-
	30.0										23.46
walleye	20.0	33.3	-	6.0	-	10.0	4.32	34.00	-	2.19	-
white	20.0	41.7	6.5	30.0	11.1	23.3	19.44	8.25	0.25	5.09	0.21	1.15
Total number of individuals						324	296	3180	1688	3279	2779
Total number of transects	10	12	46	50	27	30					

* Includes mostly black-and-yellow and gopher rockfishes; more rarely, grass and whitebelly rockfishes and treefish.

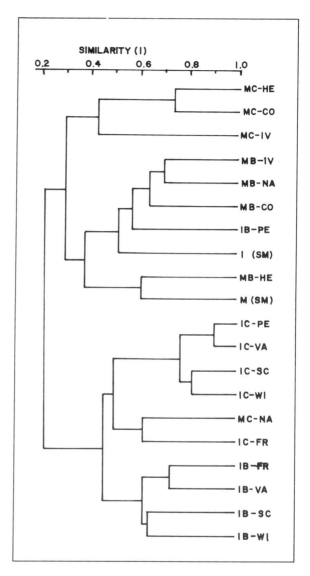

FIGURE 4. *Interlocality cluster analysis of kelp-bed fish assemblages sampled from 175 cinetransects filmed off Santa Barbara. Units are mainland (M) or Santa Cruz Island (I) canopy (C) or bottom (B) samples from the localities (right-hand letter pairs) in Figure 1 and Table 1. The dendrogram was derived from a similarity matrix based on relative species abundances (see text) by means of the unweighted pair-group clustering method using arithmetic averages (Sneath and Sokal 1973).*

bottom relief). Hence, island localities with lowest means (PE, SC) were about as abundant and diverse as mainland localities with highest means (NA, HE). A plot using mean score of depth and bottom relief (from Table 1) revealed the synergistic effect of these two abiotic variables on fish density and diversity, in that plotting either depth or relief separately showed less correlation (Fig. 3). Poorest island localities (PE, SC) were probably the most heavily used and disturbed anchorages. Also, locality SC, like mainland locality CO, had patches of relatively flat, barren rock where turf was sparse.

Species composition differed predictably among localities of different habitat type (Table 9 and Fig. 4). Along the mainland shore, localities HE, CO, and IV (Fig. 1) typically had pockets of sandy, flat bottom interspersed among high-relief reefs or flat pavement rock (Table 1). Many transects were taken near shore, where walleye surfperch schooled during the day. The canopy zone at these near-shore localities also harbored large numbers of such commuter species as kelp bass and pile and rubberlip surfperches. These habitat generalists, including more benthically-oriented, inner-marginal and commuter species (black, rainbow, white, and dwarf surfperches), also frequented sandy-marginal habitats (Table 9 and Fig. 4 [SM]). On the other hand, locality NA was a relatively well-developed reef located farther offshore in clearer water. Its canopy harbored large numbers of kelp-rock species (blacksmith and blue rockfish). Thus, the NA canopy sample clustered with the island samples. Differences between locality NA and the other mainland localities in relative numbers of habitat generalists vs. reef specialists were less clear for bottom samples. Only locality HE contained comparatively large numbers of inner-marginal and commuter species. All island localities were clear-water areas over continuous, high-relief rocky bottom. This was reflected in greater rank concordance in species arrays among island samples (Table 10). Island samples generally contained relatively more individuals of kelp-rock species, although the bottom sample from disturbed locality PE contained more commuter and inner-marginal individuals (kelp bass, pile perch, black surfperch).

The island assemblages differed from those of the mainland not so much in presence or absence of species as in the relative abundance or frequency of occurrence of species. Only two species (rock wrasse and endemic island surfperch) were recorded from Santa Cruz Island but not from mainland localities. Two others occasionally encountered along the mainland (black croaker and lingcod) were not recorded from island localities. Yet we have since seen lingcod during winter-spring, the period unrepresented in island transects.

In the canopy zone, the most obvious island-mainland differences were the absence of island surfperch from the mainland assemblage (Table 2), and the presence of higher densities of tropically-derived kelp-rock species, especially blacksmith, in the island assemblage (Table 9). Also, mainland locality NA had a relative dearth of kelp surfperch, but this dearth was a local phenomenon peculiar to such semi-isolated reefs. Kelp-surfperch populations may be decimated during sporadic decreases in kelp density on such reefs. Also, locality NA, in particular, was swept by relatively strong currents, which often pulled the kelp stipes beneath the surface and may have made it difficult for the small fish to maintain station. Elsewhere along the mainland, kelp surfperch were common in the thicker canopies of inshore kelp beds, where currents were weaker.

Likewise, the island-bottom assemblage had higher densities of tropical derivatives in the kelp-rock habitat group (Table 9). Besides having abundances of California sheephead, opaleye, halfmoon, and garibaldi, it contained rock wrasse (Table 2), which were not recorded from the Santa Barbara mainland. On the other hand, the mainland-bottom assemblage contained higher densities of commuter and inner-marginal species, especially black, pile, white, and rainbow surfperches. The sandy-marginal assemblages also reflected such island-mainland differences. At Santa Cruz Island, kelp-rock species were photographed together

TABLE 10. Among-locality concordance of rank-ordered abundances of 24 species in mainland and Santa Cruz Island samples of canopy and bottom assemblages of kelp-bed fishes, as represented in cinetransects filmed off Santa Barbara (Fig. 1 and Table 1). n represents number of localities; N, range in number of cinetransects at localities (Table 8); W, Kendall's coefficient of rank concordance (Tate and Clelland 1957).

Habitat	Island			Mainland		
	n	N	W	n	N	W
Canopy	5	4-7	0.60**	4	6-10	0.41*
Bottom	5	7-14	0.63**	4	11-16	0.49**

*Significantly different from zero at $0.025 > P > 0.01$.
**Significantly different at $P < 0.005$.

with habitat generalists of the inner-marginal and commuter groups. Such intermingling of specialists and generalists accounted for higher diversity of the island assemblage (Table 9).

DISCUSSION

Southern California kelp beds harbor some 125 fish species, although no more than 20 to 30 are common enough to occur with a frequency of more than 5 to 10 per cent (cf. Quast 1968b, Feder et al. 1974). Hence, the number of species recorded by cinetransect and analyzed in the present study composes a representative array. In the following discussion, we first show how habitat groups merge to form the main fish assemblages of canopy and bottom zones in areas of reef and giant kelp. We suggest that a group composed mostly of reef specialists, many of which retain the more stereotyped behaviors of their close tropical relatives, will be more strongly or weakly represented in the assemblages, depending on habitat structure. We then discount seasonal effects to show that areal differences in assemblages, both among longshore localities and between mainland and island, reflect differences in structural habitat. Therefore, we argue that extensive areas of well-developed reef and clear water, which characterize the island habitats, have an "island effect" on assemblages favoring "tropical derivatives" contributing to higher fish density and diversity, and that this effect is manifest in such habitats whether of the island or mainland shores.

Habitat Groups

In some ways, our habitat groups resemble species associations differentiated subjectively by other authors (cf. Limbaugh 1955, Hobson 1965, Quast 1968b, Feder et al. 1974). Yet our habitat-group classification based strictly on correlations of species abundances does not always coincide with that of Quast (1968b) based on the fishes' behavior and use of different forms of substrate. He distinguished (1) bottom, (2) kelp-holdfast, (3) kelp-column, and (4) canopy habitats, and, within each habitat, species that (a) sit in interstices or on surfaces, (b) continuously roam about surfaces, or (c) use the open-water spaces. Fish behavior contributes indirectly to the formation of our habitat groups, but the prime requisite is that member species coincidentally occupy the same space or volume of water whether they act the same way or not. So, for example, our kelp-rock habitat group contains species of Quast's surface-roaming (b) and open-water (c) categories. However, our bottom habitat group resembles Quast's bottom-surface-sitting category (1, a) because all members are sedentary and limited to one surface in one space, i.e., the reef bottom.

We emphasize that the habitat groups resolved by factor analysis are not the smallest that may occur over the reef. Members of the same group may actually prefer different micro-habitats. For example, gopher and black-and-yellow rockfishes of the bottom group tend to segregate by bottom depth along Santa Cruz Island (Larson 1977). Off Los Angeles, black and rainbow surfperches of the inner-marginal group select different temperature regimes (Terry and Stephens 1976). Whenever the two co-occur abundantly at Naples Reef, rainbow surfperch typically concentrate in depressions, while black surfperch prefer the reef flat (D. Laur, pers. comm.). As in tropical coral reefs, certain species may be mostly restricted to microhabitats distinguishable by their depth and position in the water column, overgrowth and cover structure, height on the reef, consolidation and texture of substrate, currents and surge, and exposure to the open sea (Hiatt and Strasburg 1960, Gosline 1965, Jones 1968, Sale 1968, Talbot and Goldman 1972, Smith et al. 1973, Goldman and Talbot 1976). Yet space may be occupied in ways apparently unrelated to observable microhabitat differences, perhaps by chance (Sale 1974, 1977, Sale and Dybdahl 1975, Bradbury and Goeden 1974).

Most fish bypass the mid-kelp region and occupy the bottom or canopy zones. The kelp canopy and its supports provide a vertical extension of the substrate, allowing fuller use of the entire water column (Quast 1968b, Feder et al. 1974). Many juveniles, like those of olive rockfish, concentrate in the canopy (Quast 1968c, Miller and Geibel 1973, Hobson and Chess 1976), although others, like small juvenile blacksmith, remain close to shelter near the bottom. Bottom and canopy assemblages merge wherever the two habitats meet along the steep, rocky, island shore, and whenever surface disturbance and poor visibility drive the canopy fishes bottomward (cf. Quast 1968a, 1968b, 1968c; pers. obs.). Many canopy and commuter species intermingle, especially over high, rocky areas where kelp bass, opaleye, various surfperches, and blacksmith swim through the water column and extend their zone of activity along the kelp stipes (Limbaugh 1955, Hobson 1965, Alevizon 1975a, 1975b, 1976). Nonetheless, some habitat group members must stay in particular zones; for example, demersal rockfish seldom leave the bottom, and kelp surfperch seldom leave the canopy. In general, therefore, the kelp-bed habitat has an added structural dimension over that of the tropical reef, which supports no canopy of giant algae. But Quast (1968b) observed that even though fish species diversity increases with bottom habitat diversity, it does not increase noticeably with foliage height diversity. He suggested that the kelp forest merely extends the bottom algal zone and does not really provide an entirely new habitat for species diversification. However, our results indicate that a few species, such as the kelp surfperch, occur only when a kelp canopy is present.

Species contributing to more than one factor may be either habitat generalists or species that for some reason congregate near the top and bottom of the water column. An inner-marginal species, the black surfperch, also contributed to the bottom group factor; in fact, it occurs almost everywhere inside and outside the reef. The contribution of blue rockfish to both kelp-rock and bottom group factors supports field observations that their behavior changes markedly with age. Juveniles and subadults usually pick plankton in midwater with aggregations of blacksmith (Love and Ebeling 1978), while larger individuals often approach or rest on the bottom like bottom group species. Yet large blue rockfish may also leave kelp beds to school in midwater over deep reefs (Miller and Geibel 1973). Kelp rockfish contributed almost equally to canopy and commuter group factors. Adults hang motionlessly on or among kelp blades in the canopy or midwater (Alevizon 1976) and occasionally rest on rocks on the bottom. Hobson and Chess (1976) observed that, at Santa Catalina Island, kelp rockfish usually rest on the bottom during the day and rise at night to eat plankton.

Correlations among the factors indicate interrelationships among the habitat groups. The intercorrelated kelp-rock, bottom, and commuter groups compose much of the fish fauna in rocky-bottom kelp beds. Members of kelp-rock and bottom groups differ in their vertical mobility, but are more or less restricted to rocky reefs. Like some kelp-rock species, members of the commuter group occur throughout the water column, but unlike kelp-rock species, they do not depend on the rocky bottom for shelter. Among the commuter species, kelp bass occupy the whole kelp forest from bottom to canopy, where they eat a variety of prey from plankton and small epiphytic animals to small fish and other nekton (Quast 1968d, Love and Ebeling 1978). Pile and rubberlip surfperches, though often foraging over turf-covered bottom (Laur and Ebeling in prep.), also aggregate well up in the water column (Alevizon 1975a). On the other hand, bottom group members usually sit motionlessly, either in the open and camouflaged, ready to ambush relatively large benthic prey (Larson 1972), or hidden in shelters, often to escape heavy surge (Larson 1977). Though confined to rocky reefs, they are not necessarily limited to kelp beds and also occur in deeper water. Canopy group members complete the array of species more or less restricted to areas of reef and kelp. Unlike canopy-dwelling kelp-rock species (blacksmith, halfmoon, blue rockfish), however, canopy species may occupy the kelp-canopy zone whether near rocky reef or not. Kelp surfperch and giant kelpfish are well camouflaged and act to blend in with the moving kelp blades. Señoritas, which are strictly diurnal, actually bury themselves in areas of sand and gravel at night (Ebeling and Bray 1976). Negatively correlated with the other groups, the inner-marginal group contains species of dark or silvery surfperches that are equally at home on the reef, in areas of sand and cobble outside the reef, and in shallow beds of boa kelp and surfgrass farther inshore. These species frequent jetties and piers, where they are caught readily by hook and line (DeMartini 1969, Pinkas *et al.* 1967, Frey 1971).

Most kelp-rock species (Table 4) are members of, or closely allied with, the primarily tropical families of wrasses (Labridae), damselfishes (Pomacentridae), and rudderfishes (Kyphosidae). Like their counterparts on coral reefs, these tropical derivatives actively seek shelter at night, and some (California sheephead and garibaldi) are brightly colored. Their feeding habits also resemble those of their tropical relatives. For example, adult blacksmith congregate upcurrent to eat incoming plankton (Bray in prep.), just like individuals of a tropical congener (Russell 1971). Kyphosid-like opaleye and halfmoon ingest plants, as do tropical rudderfishes, although these temperate species are not strictly herbivorous (Quast 1968c), as are their tropical counterparts (Randall 1967). Tropical derivatives are reluctant to stray far from shelter. Fager (1971) observed that garibaldi and opaleye were among the few kelp-bed fishes that did not colonize experimental reefs made of simple 1-m cubes set out on a sandy bottom some distance from natural reefs off San Diego.

In contrast, the other habitat groups contain, for the most part, members of primarily temperate families or genera such as surfperches (Embiotocidae), rockfishes *(Sebastes)*, and greenlings (Hexagrammidae). In general, these temperate derivatives do not actively seek shelter at night (Ebeling and Bray 1976). Most are generalized carnivores, broad-based microcarnivores, and/or facultative planktivores (Limbaugh 1955, Quast 1968d, 1968e, Bray and Ebeling 1975, Love and Ebeling 1978).

Interlocality Differences

In comparing fish assemblages among localities, we discounted seasonal variation because previous studies support our observations that such variation is relatively small. Miller and Geibel (1973) concluded that most species remain in kelp-bed habitats the year around off Monterey, central California. Fager (1971) observed "surprisingly little" seasonal change in fish abundance and diversity about small experimental reefs, although he noted some changes in species composition of the assemblages. Alevizon (1975a) concluded that four surfperch species (black, striped, pile, and rubberlip) showed no significant seasonal variation in habitat distribution off Santa Barbara. Ebeling and Bray (1976) observed very high seasonal concordance of rank-ordered species abundances in sight-transect samples at Naples Reef.

Kelp-bed fishes, in fact, show little seasonal movement as compared with, for example, bottom fishes in the temperate North Atlantic (*cf*. Tyler 1971, 1972). Adults of many kelp-bed species may spend most of their lives within an area of but a few hundred square meters (Limbaugh 1955, Clarke 1970, Frey 1971, Quast 1968c, Miller and Geibel 1973, Larson 1977, M. Hixon, pers. comm.). In this they resemble herbivores, omnivores, and smaller carnivores of tropical coral reefs (Talbot and Goldman 1972, Goldman and Talbot 1976, review by Ehrlich 1975) and other parochial fish populations (Gerking 1959).

Nonetheless, recent observations show that certain species occur seasonally at Naples Reef (Fig. 1), which is semi-isolated and located 1.6 km offshore (Ebeling and Bray in prep.). Rainbow surfperch and señoritas may disappear during the winter and reappear in the spring. Also, long-term temperature changes may alter the fish assemblages (Carlisle 1969, Mearns and Smith 1976), especially in a transitional zone like the Santa Barbara Channel (Hewatt 1946, Hubbs 1948, 1960, Radovich 1961, Neushul *et al*. 1967, Ebeling *et al*. 1971). Quast (1968d) noted that kelp bass fished out of a particular area of reef and kelp seem to be replaced quickly by immigrants. During our study, however, sportfishing was relatively light in most localities sampled (*cf*. Love and Ebeling 1978).

Interlocality differences in kelp-bed fish density, diversity, and composition reflect differences in habitat structure. Depth and bottom relief may have a synergistic effect on the fish assemblages in that higher densities of more species tend to inhabit deeper parts of rocky, high-relief reef, where water is often relatively clear and calm. More specifically, rocky reefs of greater bottom relief, kelp density, and water clarity harbor habitat specialists in the kelp-rock group, as well as habitat generalists and canopy species in other habitat groups, and the whole heterogeneous assemblage is best represented over deeper, less turbulent areas. Shallow waters show considerable wave action, surge, and increasing turbidity. Thus, especially when surge is strong, fish remaining in water shallower than about 5 m depth may have trouble maintaining station and viewing their immediate environment. Larson (1977) showed that two bottom species, the gopher and black-and-yellow rockfishes, hide in holes and are inactive during periods of heavy surge. Other investigators also observed increases in fish species diversity with greater bottom relief (Limbaugh 1955, Quast 1968a, 1968b, Feder *et al*. 1974). Quast (1968b) showed that diversity increased with depth only over bottoms of moderate to high relief. In a factor analysis of variables affecting the spatial distribution and density of Hawaiian reef organisms in Kaneohe Bay, Smith *et al*. (1973) concluded that the most important determinants of fish distribution are, first, bottom relief, and, second, water circulation and surge.

Island Effect

The island effect we observed is not primarily caused by the varied oceanographic regime of the Northern Channel Islands (*cf*. Hubbs 1967, 1974). Unlike San Miguel Island and the western half of Santa Rosa Island, the north side of Santa Cruz Island, where we did most of our sampling, is not strongly influenced by the cool California Current. Like the mainland, it receives warmer water from the southeast (Hubbs 1967, Neushul *et al*. 1967) and is influenced by local gyres characterizing the surface waters of the Santa Barbara Channel (Kolpack 1971). Therefore, the fish fauna on both sides of the Santa Barbara Channel is mostly southern Californian, with intrusions of central Californian species (Hubbs 1974, Ebeling *et al*. 1971). Tropical derivatives are typical southern, not central, Californian species.

Nor is the island effect primarily caused by isolation. Only one species, the island surfperch, is an island endemic. Furthermore, Ebeling (in prep.) showed that an array of Santa Cruz Island species more closely resembles an array of species from off San Diego, some 340 km to the southeast (*cf*. Quast 1968c), than an array of mainland species from Naples Reef directly across the channel.

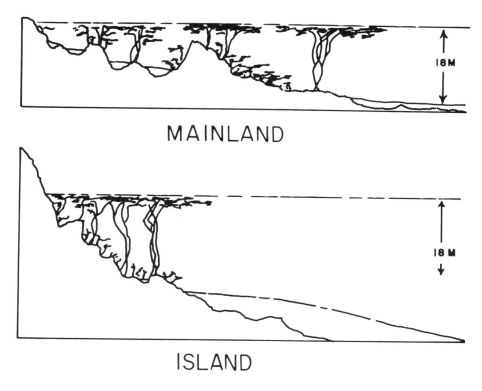

MAINLAND

ISLAND

FIGURE 5. *Vertically exaggerated offshore profiles at the mainland and Santa Cruz Island near Santa Barbara. Off the mainland, broad sand flats (upper bottom lines) separate rocky outcrops (upward extensions of lower bottom lines) between the shore and Naples Reef (highest outcrop) 1.6 km offshore. Off the island, the relatively steep rocky bottom meets sand within only 50 m of shore.*

Hence, the differences in composition between island and mainland species assemblages seem to reflect structural-habitat differences rather than oceanographic or areal differences. The mainland bottom consists of broad sand and pebbly flats between scattered reefs (Fig. 5). Even Naples Reef, the best-developed reef system among the mainland localities, is structurally less complex than the steep, rocky, island bottom, which is strewn with boulders and deeply sculptured with holes and caves. The greater continuity of well-developed reef along the island shore probably accounts for the greater concordance of species abundance among island localities. Underwater visibility averages 1 to 2 m more at Santa Cruz Island than at Naples Reef (Ebeling *et al.* in press). Density of turf, an important source of fish food, is significantly greater at Santa Cruz Island than at Naples Reef (D. Laur, pers. comm.), which may account for island-mainland differences in foraging behavior of striped surfperch (Alevizon 1975b). Clarke and Neushul (1967) emphasized these environmental differences between Anacapa Island, which typifies such areas, and the adjacent mainland. Yet extensive, high-relief, rocky bottoms and clear water also characterize areas of reef and kelp at headlands off La Jolla near San Diego, and these areas also support an island-like biota (Limbaugh 1955, Clarke and Neushul 1967). It seems, therefore, that off southern California it is the island-like habitats, rather than islands *per se,* that attract "island-like" fish assemblages.

The composition of sandy-marginal fish assemblages reflects the mainland-island difference in structural habitat. Typical kelp-rock species commonly venture over the relatively small sandy stretches between extensive rocky reefs. Thus, the precipitous island shore (Fig. 5) leaves little room for a typical shallow, sandy-bottom fauna, and many kelp-rock species were photographed in the sandy-marginal habitat while skirting their favored reefs. Also, we observed some kelp-rock species (*e.g.,* California sheephead) foraging over sandy areas at the bases of reefs.

Perhaps the complex substrate, clear water, and greater food supply of "island-like" environments offer more opportunities for the tropical derivatives to find shelter at night and partition space and food during the day. Several authors have pointed out that the coexistence of tropical-reef fishes depends on the availability of defensible holes and other shelter sites (Randall 1963, Collette and Talbot 1972, Smith and Tyler 1973, 1975, Sale 1974, 1975). Russell *et al.* (1974) showed that experimental reefs made of concrete blocks with holes are more heavily colonized by coral-reef fishes than are reefs made of plain blocks. Smith and Tyler (1975) concluded that a greater variety of hole sizes should provide shelter for a greater variety of sizes of fish. On the other hand, primarily temperate species like surfperches remain mostly exposed at night (Ebeling and Bray 1976). Miller and Geibel (1973) noted that surfperches are usually among the most abundant species on reefs where water is turbid.

In summary, the composition of kelp-bed fish assemblages along Santa Cruz Island reflects the high bottom-relief and clear-water character of island-like habitats. Such habitats support higher densities of kelp-rock species than do simpler and more turbid mainland habitats, and "superimposing" the extra numbers of tropically-derived reef specialists on the usual reef contingent also increases total fish diversity per unit area. This island effect was so profound that fish species sampled from various localities tended to group by area (mainland *vs.* island) rather than by habitat (canopy *vs.* bottom), as they did when sampled only from deeper, well-developed mainland (Naples Reef) and island reefs (Ebeling *et al.* in press).

SUMMARY

The kelp-bed fish fauna off Santa Barbara is mainly warm-temperate, but includes abundances of some primarily cool-temperate species from the north. Using underwater movie strips (cinetransects), we sampled assemblages of this fauna, near the kelp canopy and just over the reef bottom, in nine localities along Santa Cruz Island and the adjacent mainland coast. Factor analysis of these samples indicated that the species are loosely organized into five "habitat groups," which are characteristic of (1) areas of high-relief rock and dense kelp, (2) the kelp canopy, (3) shallow areas at or beyond the margins of reefs and kelp beds, (4) the midwaters, from kelp canopy to bottom, and (5) areas of reef bottom and sparse kelp. Mean fish density, biomass, and diversity varied significantly among localities and between mainland and island, but not between winter-spring and summer-fall. Means increased with rocky relief and bottom depth, and were generally greatest for island localities. Relatively more habitat generalists from the marginal and midwater groups (*e.g.,* surfperches) occurred in areas of mixed bottom types and turbid water. More reef specialists from the kelp-rock group, many of which require shelter holes at night, occurred in areas of extensive rocky bottom and clear water. Phylogenetically, these sheltering species have comparatively close tropical relatives (*i.e.,* are "tropical derivatives"). The island assemblages contained greater abundances of tropical derivatives, which contributed to the higher fish density and diversity. This "island effect" on species composition is probably caused by habitat differences rather than oceanographic differences or isolation between mainland and island. Island habitats, as well as island-like habitats along the mainland, have clearer water, more continuous high-relief rocky bottom, and perhaps more fish food. Thus, they may offer more opportunities for tropical derivatives to shelter at night and to partition the available space and food during the day.

ACKNOWLEDGMENTS

We thank Richard Bray, Milton Love, and Floyd DeWitt for help in taking and viewing cinetransects. Richard Bray, Mark Hixon, and Robert Warner criticized earlier drafts and offered helpful suggestions; Allan Oaten gave valuable statistical advice. Norm Lammer provided invaluable technical help with equipment and boating operations. Administrative personnel of the UCSB Marine Science Institute provided much encouragement, bookkeeping expertise, and stenographic assistance: Robert Holmes and Henry Offen, Directors; Fran Ciluaga, Principal Administrative Assistant; and Mary Ankeny, Jan Hubbel, and Yvonne Pommerville, secretaries. We appreciate use of the UCSB Channel Island Field Station, under agreement with Dr. Carey Stanton, during our island work. Michael Benedict and Lyndal Laughrin provided our island transportation and technical aid, while the U.S. Navy, Pt. Hueneme provided transport to and from Santa Cruz Island. This work was sponsored by NOAA, Office of Sea Grant, Department of Commerce, under grants 2-35208-6 and 04-3-158-22 (Project R-FA-14), by NSF Sea Grants GH 43 and GH 95, and by NSF grants GA 38588 and OCE76-23301. Supplementary funding was provided by a UCSB Faculty Research Grant (No. 369) for Computer Center services, and by the Marine Science Institute, through the courtesy of Henry Offen, for interim project support.

REFERENCES

ALEVIZON, W. S. 1975a. Spatial overlap and competition in congeneric surfperches (Embiotocidae) off Santa Barbara, California. Copeia 1975:352-356.

————. 1975b. Comparative feeding ecology of a kelp-bed embiotocid *(Embiotoca lateralis)*. Copeia 1975:608-615.

————. 1976. Fishes of the Santa Cruz Island kelp forests. Oceans Mag. 9:44-49.

ALEVIZON, W. S., and M. G. BROOKS. 1975. The comparative structure of two western Atlantic reef-fish assemblages. Bull. Marine Sci. 25:482-490.

ANGEL, M. V., and M. J. R. FASHAM. 1973. SOND cruise 1965: factor and cluster analyses of the plankton results, a general summary. J. Marine Biol. Assoc. U.K. 53:185-231.

BRADBURY, R. H., and G. B. GOEDEN. 1974. The partitioning of the reef slope environment by resident fishes. Pp. 167-178 *in* A. M. Cameron, B. M. Campbell, A. B. Cribb, R. Endean, J. S. Jell, O. A. Jones, P. Mather, and F. H. Talbot, eds., Proceedings of the second international coral reef symposium, vol. 1. Great Barrier Reef Committee, Brisbane, Australia.

BRAY, R. N., and A. W. EBELING. 1975. Food, activity, and habitat of three "picker-type" microcarnivorous fishes in the kelp forests off Santa Barbara, California. Fish Bull., U.S. 73:815-829.

BROWN, D. W. 1974. Hydrography and midwater fishes of three contiguous oceanic areas off Santa Barbara, California. Los Angeles Co. Mus. Contrib. Sci. 261:1-30.

BURGE, R. T., and S. A. SCHULTZ. 1973. The marine environment in the vicinity of Diablo Cove with special reference to abalones and bony fishes. California Dept. Fish Game Marine Res., Tech. Rep. 19.

CARLISLE, J. C., JR. 1969. Results of a six-year trawl study in an area of heavy waste discharge: Santa Monica Bay, California. California Fish Game 55:26-46.

CLARKE, T. A. 1970. Territorial behavior and population dynamics of a pomacentrid fish, the garibaldi, *Hypsypops rubicunda*. Ecol. Monogrs. 40:189-212.

CLARKE, W. D., and M. NEUSHUL. 1967. Subtidal ecology of the southern California coast.
    Pp. 29-42 *in* T. A. Olson and F. J. Burgess, eds., Pollution and marine ecology.
    Interscience, New York, N.Y.
COLLETTE, B. B., and F. H. TALBOT. 1972. Activity patterns of coral reef fishes with emphasis
    on nocturnal-diurnal changeover. Pp. 98-124 *in* B. B. Collette and S. A. Earle, eds.,
    Results of the Tektite program: ecology of coral reef fishes. Bull. Los Angeles Co. Nat.
    Hist. Mus. Sci. 14.
DEMARTINI, E. E. 1969. A correlative study of the ecology and comparative feeding mecha-
    nism morphology of the Embiotocidae (surf-fishes) as evidence of the family's adaptive
    radiation into available ecological niches. Wassman J. Biol. 27:177-247.
DIXON, W. D., ed. 1967. BMD computer programs. Univ. California Publ. Automat. Comput.
    2:1-200.
DUNNETT, C. W. 1970. Multiple comparison tests. Biometrics 23:139-141.
EBELING, A. W., and R. N. BRAY. 1976. Day versus night activities of reef fishes in a kelp
    forest off Santa Barbara, California. Fish Bull., U.S. 74:703-717.
EBELING, A. W., R. J. LARSON, W. S. ALEVIZON, and R. N. BRAY. Annual variability of
    reef-fish assemblages in kelp forests off Santa Barbara, California. Fish Bull., U.S. (in
    press).
EBELING, A. W., W. WERNER, F. A. DEWITT, and G. M. CAILLIET. 1971. Santa Barbara oil
    spill: short-term analysis of macroplankton and fish. U.S. Environmental Protection
    Agency Water Pollution Control Res. Ser. 15080EAL02/71.
EHRLICH, P. R. 1975. The population biology of coral reef fishes. Ann. Rev. Ecol. Syst.
    6:211-247.
FAGER, E. W. 1971. Pattern in the development of a marine community. Limnol. Oceanogr.
    16:241-253.
FEDER, H. M., C. H. TURNER, and C. LIMBAUGH. 1974. Observations on fishes associated
    with kelp beds in southern California. California Dept. Fish Game, Fish Bull. 160.
FISHER, D. R. 1968. A study of faunal resemblances using numerical taxonomy and factor
    analysis. Syst. Zool. 17:48-63.
FREY, H. W., ed. 1971. California's living marine resources and their utilization. California
    Dept. Fish Game Spec. Publ.
GERKING, S. D. 1959. The restricted movement of fish populations. Biol. Rev. (Cambridge)
    34:221-242.
GOLDMAN, B., and F. H. TALBOT. 1976. Aspects of the ecology of coral reef fishes. Pp. 125-154
    in O. A. Jones and R. Endean, eds., Biology and geology of coral reefs, vol. 3 (Biol. 2).
    Academic Press, New York, N.Y.
GOSLINE, W. A. 1965. Vertical zonation of inshore fishes in the upper water layers of the
    Hawaiian Islands. Ecology 46:823-831.
HALDORSON, L. 1980. Genetic isolation of Channel Islands fish populations: evidence from two
    embiotocid species. Pp. 433-442 *in* D.M. Power, ed., The California Islands: proceed-
    ings of a multidisciplinary symposium. Santa Barbara Museum of Natural History, Santa
    Barbara, Calif.
HARMAN, H. H. 1967. Modern factor analysis. University of Chicago Press, Chicago, Ill.
HEWATT, W. G. 1946. Marine ecological studies on Santa Cruz Island, California. Ecol.
    Monogrs. 16:185-210.
HIATT, R. W., and D. W. STRASBURG. 1960. Ecological relationships of the fish fauna on coral
    reefs of the Marshall Islands. Ecol. Monogrs. 30:65-127.
HOBSON, E. S. 1965. Forests beneath the sea. Animals 7:506-511.

HOBSON, E. S., and J. R. CHESS. 1976. Trophic interactions among fishes and zooplankters nearshore at Santa Catalina Island, California. Fish Bull., U.S. 74:567-598.

HORN, M. H. 1974. Fishes. Pp. 11-1 to 11-124 *in* A summary of knowledge of the southern California coastal zone and offshore areas. Southern California Ocean Studies Consortium, Contr. No. 08550-CT4-1. Bureau of Land Management, U.S. Dept. Interior, Washington, D.C.

HUBBS, C. L. 1948. Changes in the fish fauna of western North America correlated with changes in ocean temperature. J. Marine Res. 7:459-482.

————. 1960. The marine vertebrates of the outer coast. Syst. Zool. 9:134-147.

————. 1967. A discussion of the geochronology and archaeology of the California Islands. Pp. 337-341 *in* R. N. Philbrick, ed., Proceedings of the symposium on the biology of the California Islands. Santa Barbara Botanic Garden, Santa Barbara, Calif.

————. 1974. Review of "Marine zoogeography" by John C. Briggs. Copeia 1974:1002-1005.

JONES, R. S. 1968. Ecological relationships in Hawaiian and Johnston Island Acanthuridae (surgeonfishes). Micronesica 4:309-361.

KANTER, R. 1980. Biogeographic patterns in mussel community distribution from the Southern California Bight. Pp. 341-355 *in* D.M. Power, ed., The California Islands: proceedings of a multidisciplinary symposium. Santa Barbara Museum of Natural History, Santa Barbara, Calif.

KOLPACK, R. L. 1971. Oceanography of the Santa Barbara Channel. Pp. 90-180 *in* D. Straughan, ed., Biological and oceanographic survey of the Santa Barbara oil spill. Sea Grant Publ. 2. University of Southern California, Allan Hancock Foundation, Los Angeles, Calif.

LARSON, R. J. 1972. The food habits of four kelp-bed rockfishes (Scorpaenidae, *Sebastes*) off Santa Barbara, California. M.A. thesis, University of California, Santa Barbara, Calif.

————. 1977. Habitat selection and territorial competition as the causes of bathymetric segregation of sibling rockfishes *(Sebastes)*. Ph.D. thesis, University of California, Santa Barbara, Calif.

LIMBAUGH, C. 1955. Fish life in the kelp beds and the effects of kelp harvesting. Univ. California Inst. Marine Res. IMR Ref. 55-9.

LITTLER, M. M. 1980. Overview of the rocky intertidal systems of southern California. Pp. 265-306 *in* D.M. Power, ed., The California Islands: proceedings of a multidisciplinary symposium. Santa Barbara Museum of Natural History, Santa Barbara, Calif.

LOVE, M. S., and A. W. EBELING. 1978. Food and habitat of three switch-feeding fishes in the kelp forests off Santa Barbara, California. Fish Bull., U.S. 76:257-271.

MCLEAN, J. H. 1962. Sublittoral ecology of kelp beds of the open coast area near Carmel, California. Biol. Bull. 122:95-114.

MEARNS, A. J., and L. SMITH. 1976. Benthic oceanography and the distribution of bottom fish off Los Angeles. California Coop. Oceanic Fish. Invest. Rep. 18:31-33.

MILLER, D. J., and J. J. GEIBEL. 1973. Summary of blue rockfish and lingcod life histories; a reef ecology study; and giant kelp, *Macrocystis pyrifera,* experiments in Monterey Bay, California. California Dept. Fish Game, Fish Bull. 158.

MILLER, D. J., and R. N. LEA. 1972. Guide to coastal marine fishes of California. California Dept. Fish Game, Fish Bull. 157.

NEUSHUL, M., W. D. CLARKE, and D. W. BROWN. 1967. Subtidal plant and animal communities of the Southern California Islands. Pp. 37-55 *in* R. N. Philbrick, ed., Proceedings of the symposium on the biology of the California Islands. Santa Barbara Botanic Garden, Santa Barbara, Calif.

NEUSHUL, M., M.S. FOSTER, D. A. COON, J. W. WOESSNER, and B. W. W. HARGER. 1976. An *in situ* study of recruitment, growth and survival of subtidal marine algae: techniques and preliminary results. J. Phycol. 12:397-408.

NIE, N. H., C. H. HULL, J. G. JENKINS, K. STEINBRENNER, and D. H. BENT. 1975. Statistical package for the social sciences. McGraw-Hill, New York, N.Y.

NORTH, W. J. 1963. Ecology of the nearshore rocky environment in southern California and possible influence of discharged wastes. Internat. J. Air Water Pollut. 7:721-736.

————. 1971. The biology of giant kelp beds *(Macrocystis)* in California. Verlag J. Cramer, West Germany.

PEARSE, J. S., and L. F. LOWRY, eds. 1974. An annotated species list of the benthic algae and invertebrates in the kelp forest community at Point Cabrillo, Pacific Grove, California. Coastal Marine Lab., Univ. California Santa Cruz Tech. Rep. 1.

PEQUEGNAT, W. F. 1964. The epifauna of a California siltstone reef. Ecology 45:272-283.

PINKAS, L., J. C. THOMAS, and J. A. HANSON. 1967. Marine sportfishing survey of southern California piers and jetties, 1963. California Fish Game 53:88-104.

QUAST, J. C. 1968a. Some physical aspects of the inshore environment, particularly as it affects kelp-bed fishes. Pp. 25-34 *in* W. J. North and C. L. Hubbs, eds., Utilization of kelp-bed resources in southern California. California Dept. Fish Game, Fish Bull. 139.

————. 1968b. Fish fauna of the rocky inshore zone. *Ibid.*, pp. 35-55.

————. 1968c. Estimates of the populations and the standing crop of fishes. *Ibid.*, pp. 57-79.

————. 1968d. Observations on the food and biology of the kelp bass, *Paralabrax clathratus*, with notes on its sportfishery at San Diego, California. *Ibid.*, pp. 81-108.

————. 1968e. Observations on the food of the kelp-bed fishes. *Ibid.*, pp. 109-142.

RADOVICH, J. 1961. Relationships of some marine organisms of the northeast Pacific to water temperature, particularly during 1957 through 1959. California Dept. Fish Game, Fish Bull. 112.

RANDALL, J. E. 1963. An analysis of the fish populations of artificial and natural reefs in the Virgin Islands. Caribbean J. Sci. 3:31-47.

————. 1967. Food habits of reef fishes of the West Indies. Stud. Trop. Oceanogr. Miami 5:665-847.

REID, J. L. 1965. Physical oceanography of the region near Point Arguello. Univ. California Inst. Marine Res. IMR Ref. 65-19.

RUSSELL, B. C. 1971. Underwater observations on the reproductive activity of the demoiselle *Chromis dispilus* (Pisces: Pomacentridae). Marine Biol. 10:22-29.

RUSSELL, B. C., F. H. TALBOT, and S. DOMM. 1974. Patterns of colonisation of artificial reefs by coral reef fishes. Pp. 207-215 *in* A. M. Cameron, B. M. Campbell, A. B. Cribb, R. Endean, J. S. Jell, O. A. Jones, P. Mather, and F. H. Talbot, eds., Proceedings of the second international coral reef symposium, vol. 1. Great Barrier Reef Committee, Brisbane, Australia.

SALE, P. F. 1968. Influence of cover availability on depth preferences of the juvenile manini, *Acanthurus triostegus sandvicensis*. Copeia 1968:802-807.

————. 1974. Mechanisms of coexistence in a guild of territorial fishes at Heron Island. Pp. 193-206 *in* A. M. Cameron, B. M. Campbell, A. B. Cribb, R. Endean, J. S. Jell, O. A. Jones, P. Mather, and F. H. Talbot, eds., Proceedings of the second international coral reef symposium, vol. 1. Great Barrier Reef Committee, Brisbane, Australia.

————. 1975. Patterns of use of space in a guild of territorial reef fishes. Marine Biol. 29:89-97.

————. 1977. Maintenance of high diversity in coral reef fish communities. Amer. Natur. 111:337-359.

SALE, P. F., and R. DYBDAHL. 1975. Determinants of community structure for coral reef fishes in an experimental habitat. Ecology 56:1343-1355.

SEAPY, R. R., and M. M. LITTLER. 1980. Biogeography of rocky intertidal macroinvertebrates of the Southern California Islands. Pp. 307-323 in D.M. Power, ed., The California Islands: proceedings of a multidisciplinary symposium. Santa Barbara Museum of Natural History, Santa Barbara, Calif.

SILVA, P. C. 1978. Geographic distribution of intertidal and shallow subtidal marine algae in the California Islands. Abstracts of papers, a multidisciplinary symposium on the California Islands. Santa Barbara Museum of Natural History, Santa Barbara, Calif.

SMITH, C. L., and J. C. TYLER. 1973. Population ecology of a Bahamian suprabenthic shore assemblage. Amer. Mus. Novitates 2528.

———. 1975. Succession and stability in fish communities of dome-shaped patch reefs in the West Indies. Amer. Mus. Novitates 2572.

SMITH, S. V., R. E. CHAVE, and D. T. O. KAM. 1973. Atlas of Kaneohe Bay: a reef ecosystem under stress. University of Hawaii Sea Grant Program, UNIHI-Seagrant-TR-72-01.

SNEATH, P. H. A., and R. R. SOKAL. 1973. Numerical taxonomy. W. H. Freeman, San Francisco, Calif.

SOKAL, R. R., and H. V. DALY. 1961. An application of factor analysis to insect behavior. Univ. Kansas Sci. Bull. 42:1067-1097.

SOKAL, R. R., and F. J. ROHLF. 1969. Biometry. W. H. Freeman, San Francisco, Calif.

TALBOT, F. H., and B. GOLDMAN. 1972. A preliminary report on the diversity and feeding relationships of the reef fishes on One Tree Island, Great Barrier Reef system. Pp. 425-442 in C. Mukundan and C. S. Gopinadha Pillai, eds., Proceedings of a symposium on corals and coral reefs, 1969. Marine Biological Association of India, Cochin, India.

TATE, M. W., and R. C. CLELLAND. 1957. Nonparametric and shortcut statistics in the social, biological, and medical sciences. Interstate Printers and Publishers, Danville, Ill.

TERRY, C. B., and J. S. STEPHENS. 1976. A study of the orientation of selected embiotocid fishes to depth and shifting seasonal vertical temperature gradients. Bull. So. California Acad. Sci. 75:170-183.

THOMAS, P. A. 1968. Variation and covariation in characters of the rabbit tick, *Haemaphysalis leporispalustris*. Univ. Kansas Sci. Bull. 47:829-862.

TURNER, C. H., E. E. EBERT, and R. R. GIVEN. 1965. Survey of the marine environment offshore at San Elijo Lagoon, San Diego County. California Fish Game 51:81-112.

———. 1968. The marine environment offshore from Point Loma, San Diego County. California Dept. Fish Game, Fish Bull. 140.

TYLER, A. V. 1971. Periodic and resident components in communities of Atlantic fishes. J. Fish. Res. Board Canada 28:935-946.

———. 1972. Food resource division among northern marine demersal fishes. J. Fish. Res. Board Canada 29:997-1003.

VALENTINE, J. W., and J. H. LIPPS. 1967. Late Cenozoic history of the Southern California Islands. Pp. 21-35 in R. N. Philbrick, ed., Proceedings of the symposium on the biology of the California Islands. Santa Barbara Botanic Garden, Santa Barbara, Calif.

WEAVER, D. W., and D. P. DOERNER. 1967. Western Anacapia—a summary of the Cenozoic history of the Northern Channel Islands. Pp. 13-20 in R. N. Philbrick, ed., Proceedings of the symposium on the biology of the California Islands. Santa Barbara Botanic Garden, Santa Barbara, Calif.

WHITTAKER, R. H. 1960. Vegetation of the Siskiyou Mountains, Oregon and California. Ecol. Monogrs. 30:279-338.

Genetic Isolation of Channel Islands Fish Populations: Evidence From Two Embiotocid Species

Lewis Haldorson

Department of Biological Sciences, University of California,
Santa Barbara, California 93106

INTRODUCTION

Islands have provided some of the most fruitful natural laboratories for the study of evolutionary phenomena. Much of the current understanding of processes such as adaptive radiation, character displacement, and speciation has resulted from observation of island populations and species. In particular, understanding of the speciation process has benefited from analyses of island biota. This is not surprising if, as is generally accepted, speciation requires allopatry between diverging groups. Islands are obvious potential isolates for terrestrial plants and animals; consequently, evolutionary literature is endowed with many well-documented examples of terrestrial island endemism and adaptive radiation.

Islands are also important in the production of new marine species. The degree to which any island or island group supports marine endemic species depends on the distance from the nearest source of immigrants, current patterns, and dispersal characteristics of individual species. Fishes are generally regarded as a highly vagile group; however, they often display a considerable degree of endemism at isolated islands. For example, Hawaiian fish species are 34 per cent endemics, Easter Island 29 per cent, Galapagos 27 per cent, and South Georgia 57 per cent (Briggs 1966). Islands that are near shore or in the direct path of currents show lower levels of fish species endemism (McDowall 1968); Bermuda, for example, has 5 per cent endemics, Cape Verde has 4 per cent, and the Azores have none (Briggs 1966).

The Channel Islands off southern California are quite close to the mainland and are in the path of the California Current; it seems unlikely, therefore, that this island group would possess endemic fish species. Under such conditions, immigration would be likely to occur at a rate sufficient to prevent genetic divergence of fish populations in island waters. However, Tarp (1952) has described an endemic species of embiotocid fish, *Cymatogaster gracilis,* from the Channel Islands. On the basis of morphologic divergence from the mainland species, *C. aggregata,* the island perch has been recognized as a distinct species. The family Embiotocidae comprises 23 species, 20 of which occur in California waters, where they are among the most commonly encountered shallow-water marine fishes. The family is particularly distinguished by viviparous reproduction; once a year mature females give birth to broods of between 10 and 50 young that are at an advanced stage of development. Since tagging studies indicate that adult embiotocids are relatively sedentary, and since there apparently is no dispersal stage in their life history, it may not be surprising that an island endemic species has occurred in that family.

Until recently, morphologic variation provided one of the only bases for taxonomic distinctions. The primary difficulty in interpreting morphologic data has always been the problem of separating genetic and environmental effects. In the last decade, the widespread availability and utilization of electrophoretic techniques have provided a source of data on geographic variation that is generally free from direct environmental effects (Avise 1974). These data also allow the direct measurement of allele frequencies at individual gene loci. Consequently, electrophoresis is a powerful tool for use in studies of genetic isolation.

In this study, two other species of embiotocid fishes, the pile surfperch *(Damalichthys vacca)*

TABLE 1. Sample locations (with abbreviations), collection dates, sample sizes, and collection method.

Population	Date	n	Method
Damalichthys vacca			
Puget Sound (PS)	Sept. 74	50	Beach seine
San Francisco (SF)	Aug. 74	50	Angling
Avila (AV)	1975	50	SCUBA
Santa Barbara (SB)	1976	46	SCUBA
Santa Cruz Island (SCI)	1976	38	SCUBA
Redondo (RE)	1976	45	SCUBA
Santo Tomás (ST)	1975	47	SCUBA
Embiotoca lateralis			
Puget Sound (PS)	Oct. 1975	38	Beach seine
San Francisco (SF)	Nov. 1975	49	Angling
Avila (AV)	1975	50	SCUBA
Santa Barbara (SB)	1976	34	SCUBA
Santa Cruz Island (SCI)	1976	43	SCUBA
Santo Tomás (ST)	1975	50	SCUBA

and the striped surfperch *(Embiotoca lateralis)*, were examined electrophoretically to determine if Channel Island populations are genetically isolated from mainland populations. In addition, a number of morphologic analyses were conducted on both species to determine if any form of phenetic variation indicates results similar to those determined electrophoretically.

Materials and Methods

The time, place, sample size, and collection method for each sample are given in Table 1. Figure 1 indicates the species' geographic ranges and identifies sampling locations. The collected fish were frozen immediately on dry ice and were kept frozen until analysis in the laboratory. Horizontal starch gel electrophoresis was conducted following the basic procedures described by Ayala *et al.* (1972) or Selander *et al.* (1971). Seventeen gene loci, determined by nine enzyme assays, were used in electrophoretic analysis. The nine assays were: *general protein* (PT), *lactate dehydrogenase* (LDH), *malate dehydrogenase* (MDH), *glyceraldehyde-3-phosphate dehydrogenase* (GAP), *tetrazolium oxidase* (TO), *glutamate oxalate transaminase* (GOT), *phosphoglucose isomerase* (PGI), *mannose phosphate isomerase* (MPI), and *esterase* (EST). Multiple loci for any assay are designated numerically, and multiple alleles at a locus are designated alphabetically, in order of decreasing anodal mobility. For example, LDH-1B would designate the second fastest allele at the fastest LDH locus.

Each fish was measured for twelve morphometric characters: total length, standard length, head length, maxillary length, snout length, gape, predorsal length, dorsal base length, anal base length, first dorsal spine to pelvic fin, last dorsal ray to anus, and length of ultimate dorsal spine. Measures are based on the descriptions in Lagler *et al.* (1962).

Eight meristic characters were counted on each fish: the numbers of dorsal fin spines, dorsal fin rays, anal fin rays, pectoral fin rays, scales on the lateral line, scales from anus to lateral line, and gill rakers.

Two multivariate techniques were used in analyses of both the morphometric and meristic data sets. Principal components analysis was done with SAS (Statistical Analysis Systems)

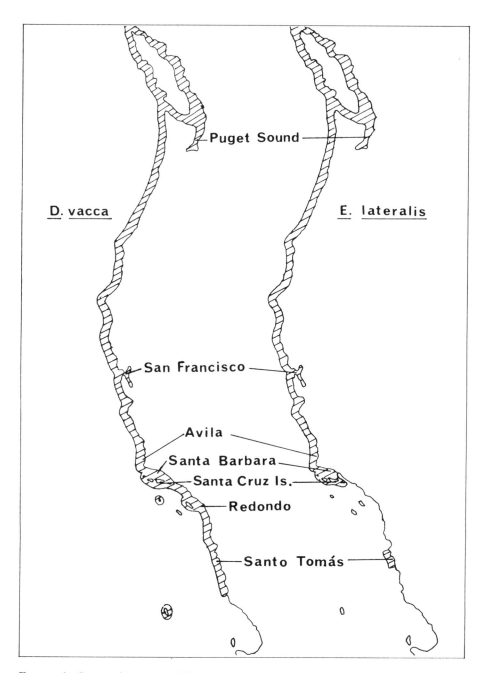

FIGURE 1. *Geographic ranges of* D. vacca *and* E. lateralis *with locations of sampling sites. Ranges extend north to Port Wrangell, Alaska.*

TABLE 2. Allele frequencies of all polymorphic loci in all population samples of *D. vacca* and *E. lateralis*.

Allele	*D. vacca*						
	PS	SF	AV	SCI	SB	RE	ST
TO 1A	.35	.32	.32	.72	.36	.25	.21
TO 1B	.65	.68	.68	.28	.64	.75	.79
PGI 1A	0	0	0	0	.01	.01	0
PGI 1B	1.0	1.0	1.0	1.0	.99	.99	1.0
PGI 2A	.26	.30	.25	0	.20	.22	.24
PGI 2B	.74	.70	.75	1.0	.80	.78	.76

Allele	*E. lateralis*					
	PS	SF	AV	SCI	SB	ST
LDH 1A	1.0	1.0	1.0	.98	1.0	1.0
LDH 1B	0	0	0	.02	0	0
MDH 1A	0	0	0	.02	0	0
MDH 1B	1.0	1.0	1.0	.98	1.0	1.0
PGI 1A	1.0	1.0	1.0	.95	1.0	1.0
PGI 1B	0	0	0	.05	0	0

TABLE 3. Observed (and expected) genotype frequencies at all polymorphic loci in population samples of *D. vacca* and *E. lateralis*.

Genotype	*D. vacca*						
	PS	SF	AV	SCI	SB	RE	ST
TO 1AA	8(6)	6 (5)	5 (5)	20 (19)	5 (6)	3 (3)	1 (2)
TO 1AB	19(23)	20(22)	23(22)	13(15)	26(23)	16(16)	18(16)
TO 1BB	23(21)	24(23)	23(24)	4 (3)	19(21)	25(25)	29(30)
Chi-square	.86	.43	.09	.65	.75	0	.78
PGI 2AA	2 (3.5)	3 (4.5)	2 (3)	0 (0)	1 (2)	3 (2)	2 (3)
PGI 2AB	22(19)	24(21)	22(19)	0 (0)	18(16)	13(15)	20(18)
PGI 2BB	25(26.5)	22(24.5)	27(29)	38(38)	31(32)	28(27)	28(29)
Chi-square	1.20	1.18	.94	0	.78	.67	.37

E. lateralis
(Santa Cruz Island)

LDH 1AA	40(40)	PGI 1AA	38(38)	MDH 1AA	0 (0)
LDH 1AB	2 (2)	PGI 1AB	4 (4)	MDH 1AB	2 (2)
LDH 1BB	0 (0)	PGI 1BB	0 (0)	MDH 1BB	40(40)
Chi-square	0		0		0

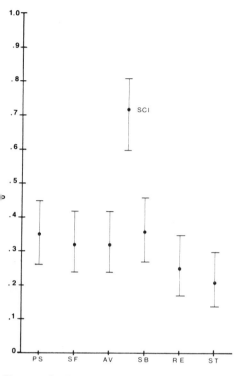

FIGURE 2. *Frequencies (P), with 95 per cent confidence limits, of allele TO-1A in population samples of* D. vacca.

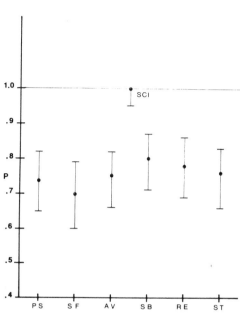

FIGURE 3. *Frequencies (P), with 95 per cent confidence limits, of allele PGI-2B in population samples of* D. vacca.

procedures FACTOR (using principal component and varimax options), SCORE, SCATTER, and MEANS (Barr *et al.* 1976). Canonical variates analysis was done through the use of a stepwise discriminant functions procedure, BMDP program BMDP7M (Dixon 1975).

RESULTS

Enzyme assays for both species produced very even patterns of allele frequencies in all mainland populations. In the striped surfperch all mainland populations were monomorphic for the same allele at all loci examined. In the pile surfperch two loci, TO and PGI-2, were polymorphic and had similar allele frequencies in all mainland populations. Table 2 gives allele frequencies for all observed polymorphic loci in all sampled populations. Table 3 gives genotype frequencies of polymorphic loci in each population. There were no significant deviations from expected Hardy-Weinberg equilibrium genotype frequencies. Figures 2 and 3 display the geographic distributions of allele frequencies at the TO and PGI-2 loci in the pile surfperch.

Both species show evidence of local differentiation in the Santa Cruz Island populations. The pile surfperch population has statistically highly significant ($P < .001$) differences in allele frequencies at the TO and PGI-2 loci. The striped surfperch has three polymorphic loci (MDH-1, LDH-1, and PGI-1) in the Santa Cruz Island population, those being the only

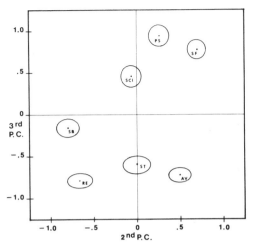

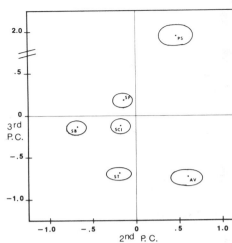

FIGURE 4. *Population samples of* D. vacca *ordinated by second and third principal components of variation of morphometric characters. Ellipses indicate one standard error on either side of sample means.*

FIGURE 5. *Population samples of* E. latera *ordinated by second and third principal components of variation of morphometric characters. Ellipses represent one standard error on either side of sample means.*

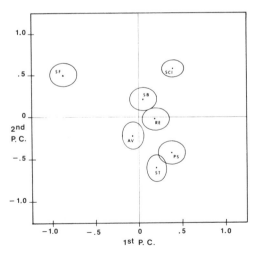

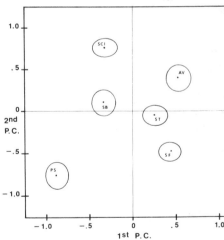

FIGURE 6. *Population samples of* D. vacca *ordinated by second and third principal components of variation of meristic characters.*

FIGURE 7. *Population samples of* E. latera *ordinated by second and third principal components of variation of meristic characters.*

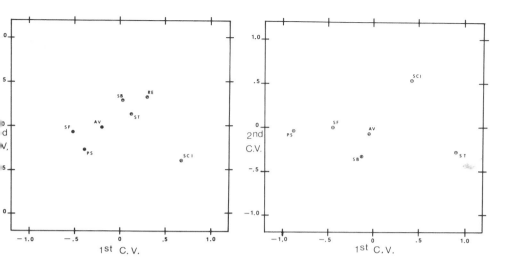

IGURE 8. *Population samples of* D. vacca *ordinated by first and second canonical variates based on discriminant functions analysis of eristic characters.*

FIGURE 9. *Population samples of* E. lateralis *ordinated by first and second canonical variates based on discriminant functions analysis of meristic characters.*

observed polymorphisms in that species.

Principal components and discriminant functions analyses of the morphometric data produced very similar arrangements of the sampled populations of the two species. Only results of the principal components analyses are therefore shown; the mean values of the scores of each population in the two species on principal components 2 and 3 are plotted in Figures 4 and 5. When analyzing morphometric data, the first principal component represents size variation in the sampled individuals and is not used in determinations of shape differences (Blackith and Reyment 1971).

In *D. vacca* principal components analysis of meristic data produces a loose cluster of six populations with a seventh (San Francisco) well separated. In *E. lateralis* analysis produces a loose cluster of five populations with a sixth (Puget Sound) well separated (Figs. 6 and 7).

The results of discriminant functions analyses of meristic characters are displayed in plots of the populations, ordinated by the first and second canonical variates, in Figures 8 and 9 for *D. vacca* and *E. lateralis*, respectively. For *D. vacca* there is a loose cluster of samples with Santa Cruz Island relatively well separated. For *E. lateralis* the Santa Cruz Island and Santo Tomás populations are the most distinct.

DISCUSSION

The extreme geographic uniformity of allele frequencies in widely separated mainland populations of the study species is surprising, and it emphasizes the divergence of the Santa Cruz Island populations. Tagging studies of adult fish indicate low dispersion in embiotocid species (Morgan 1961, Beardsley 1969, Miller and Geibel 1973), and their reproductive biology almost certainly precludes a pre-adult dispersal stage. Low dispersal and a linear or one-dimensional population structure (the Pacific coastline) create a strong tendency toward local differentiation in theoretical models of population structure (Wright 1943, Kimura and Weiss

1964). Large effective population size is a characteristic that tends to promote geographic uniformity in the same models, and the results of reliable density studies of the two study species by Miller and Geibel (1973) and Ebeling *et al*. (1980) indicate that densities are high enough to produce very large effective population sizes—large enough, indeed, to result in the observed geographical uniformity of mainland populations (Haldorson 1978).

The divergence of the island populations of *D. vacca* and *E. lateralis* must be a result of a severe restriction in gene flow with mainland populations, unless prohibitively high selection coefficients are postulated for the individual gene loci (Haldorson 1973). It seems likely, therefore, that the Channel Islands provide an area of genetic isolation for all embiotocid species found there and that the observed morphologic divergence of *Cymatogaster gracilis* described by Tarp (1952) is a genetic effect.

The two procedures used to test concordance of morphologic and electrophoretic variation differ in their assumptions about the data and may provide different interpretations. Principal components analysis makes no *a priori* assumptions about data subgroups. From correlations among real variables, this procedure computes a new set of hypothetical variables that define the principal axes (components) of a multidimensional ellipse (see Blackith and Reyment 1971 for review). Discriminant functions analysis does make *a priori* identification of sample subgroups and investigates the relationship between them by maximizing between-group differences. Variables are added to this analysis in the order of their diminishing ability to distinguish between subgroups until the point at which the next variable does not significantly improve subgroup separation (Blackith and Reyment 1971).

The Santa Cruz Island populations were not in any way unique on the basis of principal components or discriminant functions analyses of morphometric data. There is strong evidence that the morphometric variation observed in this study is the result of some environmental effect, expressed either through some direct developmental phenotype modification or through local selective adaptation to environmental conditions (Haldorson 1978).

Unlike morphometric data, meristic data produced differing results when analyzed by principal components and discriminant functions procedures. In *D. vacca* the San Francisco sample had the highest mean count in six of the seven meristic characters, and diverged in principal components analysis. Discriminant functions analysis of *D. vacca* meristics produced another loose cluster of six populations with separation of a seventh, in this case the Santa Cruz Island population. This result corresponds closely to the electrophoretic results for *D. vacca*.

In *E. lateralis* the Puget Sound sample had the highest mean count in four of the seven meristic characters; in the other three it had the lowest mean count. The Puget Sound sample also clearly separated from the other samples in principal components analysis. Discriminant functions analysis of meristic data in *E. lateralis* produced a loose cluster of four populations and individual separation of two others, Santo Tomás and Santa Cruz Island. There is electrophoretic evidence that Santa Cruz Island is an isolate for *E. lateralis*, and there is observational evidence that the Santo Tomás population is isolated from the rest of the species distribution (Quast 1968). Thus, in both study species there is evidence that discriminant functions analysis of meristic characters is useful in identification of genetically isolated populations.

CONCLUSIONS

Even though the California Channel Islands lie in close proximity to the mainland, it apparently is not reasonable to assume that Channel Island populations of marine organisms are closely associated with mainland populations through migration and genetic similarity. The present study indicates that even species generally regarded as highly vagile, such as fishes, may be genetically differentiated in island waters. Such differentiation may ultimately result in island endemic species. The likelihood of island population differentiation is related to the life history and habits of individual species; consequently, species with low dispersal characteristics, such as the embiotocid fishes studied here, are those where island differentiation may be more pronounced. The various fish species found in the waters of the Channel Islands possess a variety of life history characteristics and dispersal capabilities, and undoubtedly the level of genetic differentiation in those species varies accordingly. It would be valuable to obtain estimated levels of differentiation in island populations of species such as the ovoviviparous rockfishes *(Sebastes)*, as well as species with planktonic eggs and larvae.

SUMMARY

Populations of the pile surfperch and the striped surfperch from Santa Cruz Island waters are genetically differentiated from mainland populations at the biochemical level when analyzed by electrophoresis. In the pile surfperch two loci, tetrazolium oxidase and phosphoglucose isomerase, had highly significant differences in allele frequencies between island and mainland populations. The striped surfperch was monomorphic for all examined electrophoretic loci in all mainland populations, but was polymorphic at three loci in the Santa Cruz Island populations. It is unlikely that the observed allele frequency differences could be maintained unless migration from mainland populations is exceedingly low.

The populations were also examined for signs of morphological differentiation. Analyses of morphometric and meristic data provided disparate results. Principal components and discriminant functions analyses of morphometric data in both species produced very similar arrangements of populations and did not reflect the apparent genetic isolation of the Santa Cruz Island populations.

When the meristic data were analyzed by principal components there was no indication of island population differences; however, discriminant functions analyses of the meristic data showed the Santa Cruz Island populations to be the most distinct in each species. Apparently meristic characters may be useful as indicators of population isolation in these species.

REFERENCES

AVISE, J. C. 1974. Systematic value of electrophoretic data. Syst. Zool. 23:465-481.

AYALA, F. J., J. R. POWELL, M. L. TRACEY, C. A. MOURAO, and S. PEREZ-SALAS. 1972. Enzyme variability in the *Drosophila willistoni* group. IV. Genic variation in natural populations of *Drosophila willistoni*. Genetics 70:113-139.

BARR, A. J., J. H. GOODNIGHT, J. P. SALL, and J. T. HELWIG. 1976. A users guide to SAS 76. Sparks Press, Raleigh, N.C.

BEARDSLEY, A. J. 1969. Movement and angler use of four foodfishes in Yaquina Bay, Oregon. Ph.D. thesis, Oregon State University, Corvallis, Ore.

BLACKITH, R. E., and R. A. REYMENT. 1971. Multivariate morphometrics. Academic Press, New York, N.Y.

BRIGGS, J. C. 1966. Oceanic islands, endemism and marine paleotemperatures. Syst. Zool. 15:153-163.

DIXON, W. J. 1975. BMDP biomedical computer programs. University of California Press, Los Angeles, Calif.

EBELING, A. W., R. J. LARSON, and W. S. ALEVIZON. 1980. Habitat groups and island-mainland distribution of kelp-bed fishes off southern California. Pp.403-431 *in* D.M. Power, ed., The California Islands: proceedings of a multidisciplinary symposium. Santa Barbara Museum of Natural History, Santa Barbara, Calif.

HALDORSON, L. 1973. Genetic variation and population isolation in the pile perch, *Rhacochilus vacca*. M.A. thesis, University of California, Santa Barbara, Calif.

_____. 1978. Geographic variation in two surfperches (Embiotocidae): local differentiation in one-dimensional population structure. Ph.D. thesis, University of California, Santa Barbara, Calif.

KIMURA, M., and G. H. WEISS. 1964. The stepping stone model of population structure and the decrease of genetic correlation with distance. Genetics 49:561-576.

LAGLER, K. F., J. E. BARDACH, and R. R. MILLER. 1962. Ichthyology. John Wiley & Sons, New York, N.Y.

MCDOWALL, R. M. 1968. Oceanic islands and endemism. Syst. Zool. 17:346-350.

MILLER, D. J. and J. J. GEIBEL. 1973. Summary of blue rockfish and lingcod life histories; a reef ecology study; and giant kelp, *Macrocystis pyrifera*, experiments in Monterey Bay, California. California Dept. Fish Game, Fish Bull. 158.

MORGAN, A. R. 1961. Siletz Bay surf perch tagging. Fish Comm. Ore., Res. Briefs 8:5-13.

QUAST, J. C. 1968. Fish fauna of the rocky inshore zone. California Dept. Fish Game, Fish Bull. 139:35-55.

SELANDER, R. K., M. H. SMITH, S. Y. YANG, W. E. JOHNSON, and J. B. GENTRY. 1971. Biochemical polymorphism and systematics in the genus *Peromyscus*. I. Variation in the old-field mouse *(Peromyscus polionotus)*. Studies in Genetics VI. Univ. Texas Publ. 7103:49-90.

TARP, F. H. 1952. A revision of the family Embiotocidae (the surfperches). California Dept. Fish Game, Fish Bull. 88.

WRIGHT, S. 1943. Isolation by distance. Genetics 28:114-138.

Distribution and Abundance of Seabirds Breeding on the California Channel Islands

George L. Hunt, Jr., R. L. Pitman, and H. Lee Jones[1]

Department of Ecology and Evolutionary Biology,
University of California, Irvine, California 92717

INTRODUCTION

The purpose of this paper is to provide an overview of the distribution, abundance, and history of the seabird populations that have bred or currently breed on the Channel Islands of California. Although adjacent to metropolitan Los Angeles and the subject of a large, albeit fragmentary, literature, the marine avifauna of southern California is surprisingly poorly known. Not only are accurate estimates of population size lacking, but often it is difficult to determine whether certain species were breeding or even present on the islands in the past. The recently completed baseline studies of marine birds and mammals of the Southern California Bight, sponsored by the Bureau of Land Management, have provided the first opportunity for a systematic assessment of marine bird populations in this area.

In this paper we (1) provide an update on the status of seabirds nesting in the Southern California Bight; (2) make comparisons of present-day populations with information on prior populations; (3) attempt to assess when and why populations have changed; and (4) discuss some of the interesting zoogeographical aspects of the southern California marine avifauna. It is not our intention that this paper provide the final or complete review of the literature on the history, ecology, or breeding biology of the species in question. Rather, we are providing a synthesis of the results of more detailed studies to be published in the future.

PAST AND PRESENT STATUS OF SEABIRD POPULATIONS

The breeding marine avifauna of the Southern California Bight is surprisingly diverse; 16 species have been recorded nesting there. Two of these species, the Common Murre (*Uria aalge*) and Tufted Puffin (*Lunda cirrhata*), no longer nest on the Channel Islands. Three other species, the Least Tern (*Sterna albifrons*), Elegant Tern (*Thallasseus elegans*), and possibly the Royal Tern (*T. maximus*), nest or have nested at mainland sites but not among the Channel Islands and will not be discussed here. Five families are represented among the marine birds that breed or have bred in recent historical times in the Bight: three storm petrels (Hydrobatidae), three cormorants (Phalacrocoracidae), one Pelican (Pelecanidae), one gull (Laridae), and five alcids (Alcidae).

As seabirds generally restrict their breeding activities to small, isolated islands, colonies are often crowded with thousands, sometimes millions, of birds. However, seabird populations in southern California are relatively small (Table 1); in total, only about 24,000 pairs of marine birds nest on the Channel Islands. Currently, the largest aggregation of nesting seabirds in southern California occurs on San Miguel Island and its two associated islets, Prince Island and Castle Rock (see Figure 1 for place names), where 14,000 to 15,000 pairs of nine species nest. Santa Barbara Island (3,400 pairs, ten species) and Anacapa Island (3,000 pairs, seven species) support the next largest colonies. Other islands support modest populations—San Nicolas (1,200 pairs), Santa Cruz (950 pairs), Santa Rosa (900 pairs)—or miniscule populations—San

---

[1] Present address: Department of Physiology, University of California, Los Angeles, California 90024.

TABLE 1. Estimated numbers of pairs of seabirds breeding in the California Channel Islands, 1975-1977.

Island	Storm Petrels	Brown Pelican	Cormorants	Western Gull	Alcids	Total
San Miguel	400	0	1,450-2,100	580	11,500	14,580
Santa Rosa	?	0	550-750	15	125+	890
Santa Cruz	50+	*0-80	75-150	320	340+	940
Anacapa	-?	*76-417	4-17	2,500	6+	2,940
San Nicolas	-?	0	135-170	900	0	1,170
Santa Barbara	225	0	180-200	800-1,200	1,760	3,385
Santa Catalina	-?	0	0	30	0	30
San Clemente	-?	0	15	60	1+	76

+? - probably present.   -? - probably not present.
 ? - unknown.   0 - not present.
* Data from D.W. Anderson *(in litt.)*, using only high colony counts.

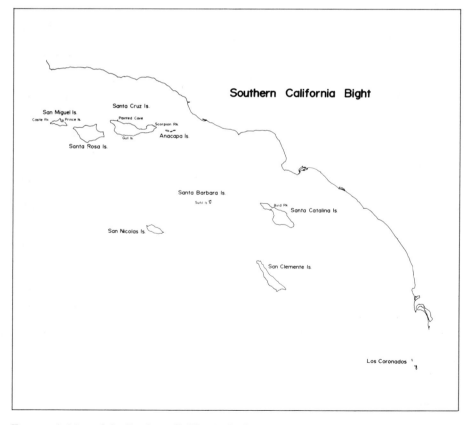

FIGURE 1. *Map of the Southern California Bight.*

445

TABLE 2. Estimated numbers of pairs of storm petrels breeding in the California Channel Islands, 1975-1977.*

Island	Leach's Storm Petrel	Ashy Storm Petrel	Black Storm Petrel
San Miguel	?	+?	0
Castle Rock	+?	100	0
Prince Island	2+	300±100	0
Santa Rosa	?	?	-?
Santa Cruz	?	?	-?
Gull Island	0	1	0
Scorpion Rock	0	20	0
Offshore rocks	0	30+	0
West Anacapa	-?	-?	-?
Middle Anacapa	-?	-?	-?
East Anacapa	-?	-?	-?
San Nicolas	-?	-?	-?
Santa Barbara	+?	125	60
Sutil Island	?	25	15
Shag Rock	?	?	?
Santa Catalina	-?	-?	-?
Bird Rock	0	0	0
San Clemente	-?	-?	-?
Bird Rock	0	0	0

* Symbols as in Table 1.

Clemente (75 pairs), Santa Catalina (30 pairs).

The numerical distribution by species is also uneven; Cassin's Auklet is the most abundant breeding seabird in the Channel Islands with 11,000 pairs, followed by Western Gull (5,600 pairs) and Brandt's Cormorant (3,000 pairs). An additional four species (Leach's and Black Storm Petrels, Double-crested and Pelagic Cormorants) are represented by breeding populations of less than 250 pairs, while the remaining four species (Ashy Storm Petrel, Brown Pelican, Pigeon Guillemot, and Xantus' Murrelet) occur in intermediate numbers.

Species Accounts
Storm Petrels

The distribution and abundance of storm petrels in the Channel Islands remains less well known than for any other group of seabirds (Table 2). Their nocturnal visits to the islands and their distant offshore foraging grounds make detection of the adults difficult, while their nest cavities are inconspicuous and generally inaccessible.

Leach's Storm Petrel (*Oceanodroma leucorhoa*) is the most widespread hydrobatid in the Northern Hemisphere. In the eastern Pacific, it breeds from Alaska south to Islas San Benitos, Baja California, Mexico. Prior to the present study, there were no published reports of Leach's Storm Petrels nesting on the California Channel Islands. In 1976 and 1977, we captured six individuals of this species on Prince Island, one of which was deposited in the San Diego Natural History Museum. One bird caught twice in 1976 had a well-developed brood patch. Upon rechecking storm petrel specimens collected during the Smithsonian Institution's Pacific Ocean Biological Survey Program (POBSP) studies of the Channel Islands, it has been established that one of the storm petrels collected on Castle Rock, San Miguel Island, 14 May 1968, and originally identified as an Ashy Storm Petrel (*O. homochroa*), was in fact a Leach's Storm Petrel (R. B. Clapp *in litt.*). This bird, representing the first known breeding record for the Channel Islands, was taken from a rock crevice and had a brood patch. Leach's Storm Petrels were captured at Santa Barbara Island for the first time in 1978 and may breed there in small numbers. Thus, although we have now established that Leach's Storm Petrels breed in the Southern California Bight, we are left with the puzzling question of why they are present in such small numbers in a region well within the limits of their range. Possibly these islands are too far from the open ocean foraging areas preferred by this species (Ainley *et al.* 1974).

The Pacific coast of the Americas supports a large number of hydrobatids with breeding ranges that are exceptionally limited. Ashy Storm Petrels, for example, breed only on the Farallon Islands in central California and on the California Channel Islands (including Islas Los Coronados in extreme northern Baja California). A few pairs have been found breeding on a rock just north of the Farallons (Ainley and Osborne 1972). The Farallon Islands undoubtedly host the largest colony of breeding Ashy Storm Petrels, although Ainley and Lewis (1974) estimate the population there to be only about 4,000 birds. The entire world population of Ashy Storm Petrels may number only 10,000 to 20,000 individuals.

In the Channel Islands, there are several records for Ashy Storm Petrels breeding on Castle Rock and Prince Island at San Miguel Island and at Painted Cave and Scorpion Harbor, Santa Cruz Island. Although Ashy Storm Petrels have been seen at San Nicolas Island (Grinnell 1897) and collected at Santa Barbara and San Clemente Islands (Miller 1936), there are no historical breeding data for any of the Channel Islands except San Miguel Island, Santa Cruz Island, and their associated rocks and islets.

Field work in 1976-1977 confirmed that Ashy Storm Petrels were scattered in small colonies on many of the offshore rocks along the north side of San Miguel Island and the north side of Santa Cruz Island, and may have nested on San Miguel Island itself. We also captured birds with brood patches and found nests for the first time on both Santa Barbara Island and Sutil Island. The colony at Castle Rock was not inspected closely enough to establish the presence of this species. Instead, an estimate, based on our experience with this species and on Crossin and Brownell's (1968) report, is given in Table 2. On the basis of our present data and data available from the literature and museum records, there is little evidence for any major change in Ashy Storm Petrel population size or distribution within the Bight within historical times.

The Black Storm Petrel (*O. melania*) is another eastern Pacific hydrobatid with a limited breeding range. Before this study, breeding Black Storm Petrels were known only from Mexican islands, where nesting occurs both in the Gulf of California and on the Pacific Ocean side of the Baja California peninsula (Palmer 1962). Dawson (1923) anticipated our findings, however, by stating it was "not known to breed in California, but probably does so." In 1976, Black Storm Petrels were found breeding on Sutil Island, off Santa Barbara Island, for the first time (Pitman and Speich 1976). The population at Sutil Island was estimated at no more than 10 to 15 pairs. This new location is approximately 200 km northwest of Islas Los Coronados, where this species breeds commonly (Crossin 1974). During the 1977 field season, 27 Black Storm Petrels were captured and banded on nearby Santa Barbara Island, including two recaptures. Although no nests were found on Santa Barbara Island, all storm petrels captured had brood patches and were presumed to be breeding there. Using the above information, the entire population of Black Storm Petrels at Santa Barbara Island (including Sutil Island) is estimated to be 75 pairs. Black Storm Petrels were not detected on any of the other Channel Islands. Thus, Santa Barbara Island is probably the only breeding site for this species in the United States.

During this project, two species of storm petrels were found breeding on Santa Barbara

Island and a third species has recently been detected, whereas none had been recorded previously: Ashy Storm Petrel, with the center of its breeding distribution to the north; Black Storm Petrel, with its center to the south; and Leach's Storm Petrel, nesting both north and south of the area. It seems unlikely that any recent change in environmental conditions alone would allow all of these species to expand into the area around Santa Barbara Island unless it is the reduction of predators on the island (see Discussion). Due to the low densities encountered for these species and their habit of frequenting only the extreme periphery of the island at night, it is likely that some or all of these storm petrels were present, but overlooked, in the past.

Brown Pelican and Cormorants

Brown Pelicans (*Pelecanus occidentalis*) breed on both the Atlantic and Pacific coasts of temperate and tropical North and South America. On the Pacific coast, they nest from central South America north to Anacapa Island (Palmer 1962). In former years, Brown Pelicans bred as far north as Bird Island, near Point Lobos, Monterey County, California (Baldridge 1973). The California Brown Pelican (*P. o. californicus*) is presently on California's endangered wildlife list.

The historical record shows that Brown Pelicans have bred, at least intermittently, on Prince Island, Santa Cruz Island (Scorpion Rock), Anacapa Island, and Santa Barbara Island. There is no good evidence of Brown Pelicans having bred on any of the other Channel Islands. At present, varying numbers of pelicans breed regularly on Anacapa Island and occasionally on Scorpion Rock (Gress 1970, Anderson and Hickey 1970, Anderson *in litt.*). Brown Pelicans no longer breed on any of the other Channel Islands. Additionally, their population has declined to perhaps ten per cent of its former maximum in numbers. Since Brown Pelican breeding numbers normally seem to fluctuate in this area at the periphery of their breeding range, it is difficult to know the true extent of their decline. The data available suggest that the major decline occurred in the late 1960s and early 1970s and was accompanied by eggshell thinning and reproductive failure (Gress 1970, Anderson and Hickey 1970, Anderson *in litt.*).

Double-crested Cormorants (*Phalacrocorax auritus*) are widespread as a nesting species in North America, with Pacific coast colonies reported from southwestern Alaska to Baja California (Amer. Ornith. Union 1957). Once a very common breeder in the Channel Islands (Howell 1917), the number of Double-crested Cormorants has decreased over the years until at present only a remnant population persists (Table 3). Gress *et al.* (1973) have presented an overview of the decline of Double-crested Cormorants along the coasts of southern and Baja California. Double-crested Cormorants are still present in small numbers at historically documented colonies (Prince, Anacapa, and Santa Barbara Islands). For example, at Santa Barbara Island in 1939, Sumner (1939) reported approximately 2,000 individuals beginning to nest. In 1977, 67 pairs nested.

The decline probably involves several factors. Grinnell and Miller (1944) commented that the reduction of Double-crested Cormorants in inland California was related to human disturbance (*e.g.,* Willett 1933, Moffitt 1939). Increased human activity in the Channel Islands, including commercial and recreational boating, low-flying private and military aircraft, and increased public access to major colonies, undoubtedly has contributed to what appears to be a long-term decline. Gress *et al.* (1973) documented reproductive failure due to eggshell thinning in the late 1960s in colonies off southern California and in Baja California. This decline in breeding success, correlated with the presence of persistent chlorinated hydrocarbons (DDE) in the ocean environment, apparently caused a recent dramatic, short-term decrease in Double-crested Cormorants. Ainley and Lewis (1974) also suggested that an early beginning of the decline in Double-crested Cormorants may have been related to the disappearence of the fishery-depleted sardine stocks off California.

During 1975-1977, changes in Double-crested Cormorant populations and reproductive

TABLE 3. Estimated numbers of pairs of cormorants breeding in the California Channel Islands, 1975-1977.

Island	Double-crested Cormorant	Brandt's Cormorant	Pelagic Cormorant
San Miguel	0	27-42	100
Castle Rock	0	363-916	15-34
Prince Island	75	860-907	10-20
Santa Rosa	0	500-700	60
Santa Cruz	0	45	4-25
Gull Island	0	23-67	0-4
Scorpion Rock	0	0	0
West Anacapa	3-15	0-1	0-1
Middle Anacapa	0	0-2	0-2
East Anacapa	0	0	0
San Nicolas	0	133-170	0
Santa Barbara	7-10	27-73	0-2
Sutil Island	30-60	70-93	0-2
Shag Rock	0	0	0
Santa Catalina	0	0	0
Bird Rock	0	0	0
San Clemente	0	15	0
Bird Rock	0	0	0

success indicated that this species may be beginning to make a comeback on the four islands (Prince, West Anacapa, Santa Barbara, and Sutil) where it presently nests. Between 1975 and 1977, the number of nests counted on each of these islands increased and adults were successfully fledging young in all colonies. It will be important to monitor these populations carefully to determine if they are in fact beginning to recover their former numbers.

Brandt's Cormorants (*P. penicillatus*) breed along the Pacific coast of North America from Washington south to Baja California (Palmer 1962). They are the most abundant cormorant in the Southern California Bight, where they nest on seven of the eight Channel Islands.

The present numbers and distribution of Brandt's Cormorants in the Channel Islands are given in Table 3. As with Double-crested Cormorants, major historical colonies are still occupied, but with reduced numbers. Wright and Snyder (1913) reported a colony of about 350 pairs of Brandt's Cormorants and another "fair-sized colony" on Santa Barbara Island in 1912, while Crossin and Brownell (1968) estimated 4,000 pairs of cormorants on Prince Island and Castle Rock as late as 1968. Present numbers on these islands are much lower (Table 3). The reasons for this decline are not known, but two factors may have had overriding effects. The deleterious influence of human activity on cormorant colonies cannot be overstated. Incubating adults are quick to abandon nests, thus exposing eggs or young chicks at the slightest disturbance. Western Gulls are equally quick to find a meal in the momentarily abandoned nests. As an example of this behavior, the following observations were reported by Crossin and Brownell (1968) during a survey that POBSP personnel made of Prince Island on 15 May 1968:

Nesting [of Brandt's Cormorant] is still in the egg stage and will likely remain at this stage indefinitely at the rate the eggs are eaten up by Western Gulls. During diurnal survey work on both islets, intensive parasitism was noted. At first sight of the observers, practically every cormorant leaves the colony and lands in the water offshore. Western Gulls then arrive on the scene almost instantaneously from all directions and "scarf up" the eggs. Many birds were noted swallowing the eggs whole, but the usual method is to slash at the egg with the lower mandible and thereby break it open and thus ready to eat. On Castle Rock one newly hatched cormorant was noted, but it also was quickly eaten up by a gull. No cormorant nest was noted with more than two eggs although the species is supposed to lay from four to six eggs. Not only do the cormorants suffer egg and chick loss from the gulls, but when a segment of the colony leaves the area, members of their own species from other segments of the colony rush in and steal nest material from finished nests.

Huber (1968), also working on the POBSP project, visited Prince Island two weeks after the above survey. Regarding Brandt's Cormorant, he reported, "One nest with a medium downy chick and two with one egg found. No other active nests could be found from at least 1500 inactive nests on the N and NE slopes (the only place colonies were found)." From these accounts it can be seen that repeated disturbance of a cormorant colony (or, as in the above case, one poorly-timed disturbance) can have disastrous effects, possibly foiling breeding efforts completely for a season.

Another factor that has probably contributed to the decline of Brandt's Cormorants in the Channel Islands is lowered productivity due to eggshell thinning. Because of the attention Brown Pelicans received during the "pesticide period" in southern California, the plight of Double-crested Cormorants, which often nest in the same colonies, also came to light. While eggshell thinning was not extensively investigated in Brandt's Cormorants, R. Lust (in litt.) reported thin and collapsed eggshells in the San Nicolas Island colony in the early 1970s. It is likely, then, that this species was also affected by the same environmental pollutants that affected the pelican and Double-crested Cormorants.

The Pelagic Cormorant (P. pelagicus) is the smallest of the cormorants that occur in the north Pacific, nesting from Japan through Alaska and south to northern Baja California, Mexico (Palmer 1962). In the eastern Pacific, the Channel Islands are presently the southernmost breeding limit for this species. Nesting may occur on Islas Los Coronados, and possibly on islands further south, but probably not regularly (J. Jehl, pers. comm.). Now, as at the turn of the century (Howell 1917), Pelagic Cormorants are the least numerous of the three species of cormorants which breed in the Bight.

Cormorants, as a rule, received little attention in early accounts. Like Western Gulls, they were ubiquitous along coastal areas and did not capture the attention of ornithologists and egg collectors as did the more obscure pelagic species such as the storm petrels and alcids. Pelagic Cormorants, in particular, do not occur in large, impressive colonies as do the other species of cormorants, making them even less subject to comment. Early accounts (Willett 1910, Howell 1917) reported Pelagic Cormorants breeding commonly among the northern chain, especially at San Miguel Island, and somewhat sporadically at Anacapa and Santa Barbara Islands. There is little or no indication that they bred on any of the remaining southern islands (San Nicolas, San Clemente, or Santa Catalina).

There seems to have been little change in the overall numbers and even less in the breeding distribution of this species in the Channel Islands (Table 3). As with the other two species of cormorants, Pelagic Cormorant colonies are found only on the northern sides of islands.

Western Gull

The breeding range of Western Gulls (Larus occidentalis) extends along the Pacific coast of North America from Washington to Baja California. Western Gulls are strictly coastal, rarely wandering either far out to sea or inland. In former times they may have nested fairly commonly along the mainland of southern California (Evermann 1886, Miller 1936), but they do not do so now (Small 1974).

Western Gulls are the most widespread breeding marine bird in the Channel Islands, nesting on every island and offshore rock of any size (Table 1). Workers in the past rarely did little more than note their presence around colonies, describing them as "common" or "abundant" (*e.g.*, Grinnell 1897, Willett 1910). There seems, however, to have been no shift in the location of colonies and few, if any, obvious changes in population size since the early 1900s. The Western Gull is probably the only marine bird nesting in the Bight that may be benefiting from the advance of civilization, often using refuse from garbage dumps and offal from fishing vessels to enhance their livelihood. Recently, female-female pairing has been found in this species (Hunt and Hunt 1977), the cause of which is presently unknown.

Murres, Guillemots, Murrelets, Auklets, and Puffins

The Common Murre (*Uria aalge*) is a boreal, low-arctic species that breeds in the north Atlantic and eastern Arctic Oceans; in the north Pacific it breeds from Japan to California, including the Bering Sea (Tuck 1960). Nesting murres formerly occurred as far south as San Miguel Island, but the southernmost colony is presently at the Farallon Islands (Small 1974). Common Murres bred in the Channel Islands until at least 1912 (Wright and Snyder 1913), but have not been recorded breeding there since. Nesting was documented only on Prince Island.

No Common Murres were found breeding at Prince Island or any of the other Channel Islands during 1975, 1976, or 1977. On 22 May 1976, an adult murre was seen flying off the precipitous cliffs on the northwest side of Prince Island. No other sightings of murres associated with islands were made during the course of this study.

The disappearance of nesting Common Murres from the Bight parallels the disappearance of nesting Tufted Puffins, another large alcid that once had its southernmost nesting colonies in the Channel Islands. Ainley and Lewis (1974) have attempted to correlate the decline of the Tufted Puffin in California with the demise of the Pacific Sardine during the 1940s. Since Common Murres were already absent by the late 1920s, other factors were undoubtedly responsible for their disappearance. The tiny colony at Prince Island was approximately 470 km south of the closest murre colony at the Farallon Islands. Egg collectors visiting Prince Island in the early 1900s took at least as many as 50 egg sets in some years (Appleton, unpubl. notes in the Western Foundation of Vertebrate Zoology) from a colony that was never reported to have more than 100 nesting pairs. It seems likely that repeated visits by early egg collectors, coupled with the slim possibility of recruitment from other colonies, could have eliminated murres as a breeding species from the Bight. However, changes in the marine environment resulting in a reduction in food availability cannot be ruled out.

Pigeon Guillemots (*Cepphus columba*) breed only in the north Pacific, from the Kuril Islands through the Bering Sea region and south to southern California (Udvardy 1963). The southernmost breeding station in the eastern Pacific is in the Channel Islands, at Santa Barbara Island, although individuals have occasionally been seen as far south as Islas Los Coronados, off northern Baja California (Jehl 1977, D. Povey, pers. comm.).

Pigeon Guillemots are completely absent from the Southern California Bight during the fall and early winter (presumably they disperse northward), but return each spring to breed. Careful estimates of population size have rarely been recorded and, given the secretive nesting habits of Pigeon Guillemots, the available data only give us rough estimates of past abundance. It appears that this species has bred regularly along the northern sides of San Miguel, Santa Rosa, and Santa Cruz Islands, where they nest in damp sea caves. Likewise, Pigeon Guillemots have apparently bred regularly at Santa Barbara Island, having been recorded for at least 11 separate years between 1897 and 1975. Nesting on Anacapa Island seems to have been only sporadic,

TABLE 4. Estimated numbers of pairs of alcids breeding in the California Channel Islands, 1975-1977.*

Island	Pigeon Guillemot	Xantus' Murrelet	Cassin's Auklet
San Miguel	200	+?	10
Castle Rock	100	+?	1,000+
Prince Island	150	75	10,000
Santa Rosa	125+	?	-?
Santa Cruz	200+	?	-?
Gull Island	0	1	75
Scorpion Rock	4	+?	50
Offshore rocks	?	?	10
West Anacapa	0	?	-?
Middle Anacapa	5	?	-?
East Anacapa	0	1+	-?
San Nicolas	0	-?	-?
Santa Barbara	45	1,500	75
Sutil Island	15	75	35
Shag Rock	?	15	0
Santa Catalina	0	0	0
Bird Rock	0	0	0
San Clemente	0	1+	0
Bird Rock	0	0	0

* Symbols as in Table 1.

and apparently they have never bred at San Nicolas, Santa Catalina, or San Clemente Island, despite statements in the literature that they occurred at San Nicolas Island (Evermann 1886).

Estimates of present numbers of breeding Pigeon Guillemots are given in Table 4. As with other primarily northern species, guillemot populations in the California Channel Islands are concentrated in the western portion of the northern islands, with smaller numbers present at Santa Barbara Island. During the present study, no Pigeon Guillemots were found nesting on San Nicolas, Santa Catalina, or San Clemente Island. Despite the somewhat fragmentary nature of the historical record, Pigeon Guillemot numbers and distribution seem to have changed very little in this century.

The entire breeding range of Xantus' Murrelets (*Endomychura hypoleuca*) is restricted to the coast between central Baja California and Point Conception, California (Udvardy 1963); the northernmost colony occurs on San Miguel Island. Jehl and Bond (1975) delimited the breeding ranges of the two well-marked subspecies and suggested they may be acting as distinct species. Generally, only the form *E. h. scrippsi* breeds in the Channel Islands, but a single *E. h. hypoleuca* was recorded nesting on Santa Barbara Island in 1977 and was found in the same nest hole in 1978, paired to a bird intermediate between the *scrippsi* and *hypoleuca* forms (J. Wingfield, pers. comm.) described as typical of San Benitos Island (Jehl and Bond 1975).

Historically, Xantus' Murrelets have been recorded breeding in small numbers on Castle Rock and Prince Island off San Miguel Island and on Scorpion Rock off Santa Cruz Island. They were apparently moderately common at Anacapa Island, with several sets of eggs taken at the beginning of the century. On Santa Barbara Island, early investigators (Cooper 1870,

Grinnell 1897, Wright and Snyder 1913, Sumner 1939) found little or no evidence of this species, suggesting it was very rare there. For the remaining three southern islands (San Nicolas, San Clemente, and Santa Catalina), the only breeding record is on Bird Rock, Santa Catalina Island (D. Bleitz, unpubl. notes 1967).

The present breeding distribution of Xantus' Murrelets in the Channel Islands is similar to that recorded early this century. Small populations persist in the San Miguel Island area and, while only one pair was found on Gull Island, it is likely that a few murrelets may use the cliffs of Santa Cruz Island. The population on Anacapa Island has apparently declined; evidence of but a single pair was found on East Anacapa Island during this study. The presence of introduced rats on Anacapa Island may have been responsible for this drop in numbers. In contrast, the population of murrelets on Santa Barbara Island is probably greater than it has been at any time this century. It is inconceivable that ornithologists exploring the island in the past would not have remarked on the large numbers of birds that visit the island at night and are conspicuous with their loud and frequent calling. On 11 June 1977, a shell of a murrelet egg that had hatched earlier in the season was found in a rocky crevice in the Seal Cove area of San Clemente Island, thereby confirming breeding on this island. However, the almost insignificant murrelet population at San Clemente Island is probably rigorously held in check by the abundant terrestrial predators there and by the lack of offshore rocks. No murrelets were found breeding at San Nicolas or Santa Catalina Island, probably due to the lack of nesting sites safe from terrestrial predators.

Hence, only at Santa Barbara Island have Xantus' Murrelets shown a significant population change since the turn of the century. The dramatic increase recorded there may be related to the disappearance of two predators, one introduced and one natural. According to Howell (1917), cats were introduced on Santa Barbara Island sometime between 1897 and 1908 and subsequently destroyed many of the murrelets. By 1975, when the present study started, the Santa Barbara Island cat population had been substantially reduced, possibly to a single animal, and the Xantus' Murrelet was one of the most abundant breeding birds on the island.

The significant increase in murrelets at Santa Barbara Island in recent years may also be the result of the elimination of the Peregrine Falcon (*Falco peregrinus*). Willett (1933) described the falcon as a "fairly common resident" among the islands, and Howell (1917) indicated they bred on Santa Barbara Island. During 1975-1977, no Peregrine Falcons were definitely known to have bred on the Channel Islands, and certainly none bred at Santa Barbara Island during those years (though single, migratory birds were present there during parts of April and May in 1975 and 1976). In discussing the food preferences of Peregrine Falcons nesting on Langara Island, British Columbia, Nelson and Myers (1976) indicate that Ancient Murrelets were the falcons' major prey species, with a falcon family taking approximately 1,000 murrelets there yearly. Hence, even a single pair of Peregrine Falcons nesting at Santa Barbara Island could exert a tremendous impact on the murrelet population. We suspect that the relatively high number of Xantus' Murralets that now occurs at Santa Barbara Island is a result of the elimination of both cats and falcons from the island.

Cassin's Auklet (*Ptychoramphus aleuticus*) has the most extensive breeding range of any alcid in the eastern Pacific, nesting from the Aleutian Islands of Alaska to Isla San Roque off Baja California (Udvardy 1963). It is the most abundant marine bird breeding in the Southern California Bight.

Historically, Cassin's Auklets have had large colonies at Castle Rock and Prince Island off San Miguel Island, at Scorpion Rock off Santa Cruz Island, and at Santa Barbara Island. The Santa Barbara Island population has undergone a major change within historical times. When Grinnell visited the island in 1897, Cassin's Auklets were "breeding in large numbers" (Grinnell 1897), but they had completely abandoned the island by 1908 when Howell (1917) surveyed it. Willett (1912) visited Santa Barbara Island in 1911 and concluded that Cassin's Auklets "had been exterminated by the cats with which the island is infested." Willett (*op. cit.*) also mentions, however, that he found "a colony of about a hundred pairs of Auklets nesting . . . on a detached rocky islet [Sutil] about a quarter of a mile from the main island." This small population was apparently spared the ravages of introduced cats and persists to this day. Sumner (1939) visited Santa Barbara Island 28 years later and wrote that cats were "decidedly abundant." He added, "At one time large colonies of auklets and murrelets were present on the island but none has been recorded in recent years and it is supposed that they have been exterminated by these feral cats." This colony has yet to regain its former numbers despite the reduction in the number of cats on the island.

Populations in 1975-1977 were high at San Miguel Island, especially at Prince Island and Castle Rock, where over 99 per cent of the Channel Islands population occurs. On all the other islands auklet numbers were relatively low (Table 4). It is not known whether the small colony found at Santa Barbara Island in 1977 is the result of a relatively new invasion or a remnant of the old population.

Ainley and Lewis (1974) have discussed periodic upheavals in the Cassin's Auklet population nesting on the Farallon Islands. During periods of unusually strong countercurrent off the California coast, warm water occurs farther north than usual and is associated with decreased upwelling and productivity. Ainley and Lewis (*op. cit.*) attributed an auklet population crash on the Farallons in the mid-1800s to an especially pronounced and prolonged warm-up period. However, declines in the Channel Islands populations (Santa Barbara Island between 1897-1908, Prince Island possibly during 1919 and 1927) do not appear to be correlated with warm-water periods in the Southern California Bight (summarized in Southern California Coastal Water Research Project, 1973), so other factors may be responsible.

Tufted Puffins are primarily residents of far northern Pacific waters. They breed on rocky coasts and islands of the north Pacific from Japan to California, including the Bering Sea and parts of the Arctic Ocean. Puffins formerly bred in the eastern Pacific as far south as the Channel Islands, nesting on Prince, Santa Cruz, Anacapa, and Santa Barbara Islands (Howell 1917).

Tufted Puffins no longer breed on the Channel Islands, and none were found on or around any of the traditional sites during 1975-1977. At present, they do not breed farther south than the Farallon Islands (Ainley and Lewis 1974).

Formerly, breeding Tufted Puffins were concentrated in the San Miguel Island area, with smaller, more peripheral populations occurring on the remainder of the Northern Channel Islands and Santa Barbara Island. Also, as a corollary, puffins appear to have remained in the San Miguel Island area longer than on other islands in the Bight. Ainley and Lewis (1974) discuss the disappearance of Tufted Puffins from the Channel Islands and their failure to recover from population declines on the Farallon Islands. They suggest these events may have been related to the depletion of sardine stocks off California. As puffins are capable of delivering vicious bites with their enormous bills (Baily 1902, Bent [1919] 1946), and nested in relatively inaccessible cliff areas in the Channel Islands (Streator 1888, Wright and Snyder 1913), it is very unlikely that early egg collectors were entirely responsible for their extirpation from the Channel Islands. It seems more likely that changes in the marine environment may well have been responsible for Tufted Puffins abandoning their southernmost breeding stations in the eastern Pacific. Udvardy (1963) has drawn a parallel between the distribution of Tufted Puffins in the north Pacific and the distribution of the Steller's Sea Lion (*Eumatopias jubata*). The southernmost breeding site of the sea lion is presently at San Miguel Island. This population has declined dramatically since the 1930s and also appears to be losing its foothold in the Channel Islands (Bartholomew and Boolootian 1960, Le Boeuf *et al.* 1976, see discussion in Ainley and Lewis 1974).

DISCUSSION

Distributional Patterns

As Hubbs (1967) and many others have pointed out, the Channel Islands provide a meeting ground for northern and southern species of various diverse faunal groups. Forms that typically occur north of the Bight occur most commonly at the west end of the northern chain of islands, while the east end of the northern chain and the southern islands show a predominance of species with southern affinities.

The reasons for these disjunct distributions and the juxtaposition of "antithetical" ecotypes are directly related to the oceanographic features of the Bight (reviewed by Jones 1971). The westernmost Channel Islands, particularly San Miguel Island, are influenced predominantly by the cool, southward-flowing waters of the California Current. During the spring and summer months, upwelled waters bathe the northwestern islands with cold, nutrient-rich water. This effect becomes less pronounced as one travels east along the northern chain and farther south. The southern and eastern islands are influenced to a greater extent by warmer, more tropical water carried north by the California Countercurrent.

As an indication of the abruptness of the change in these oceanographic conditions, seabirds which, because of their vagility, might not be expected to demonstrate clear zoogeographic patterns over such a small range do, in fact, show a striking parallel with the distribution patterns described above. Of the 13 species of seabirds known to have bred in the Channel Islands, five reach their southern breeding limits and three reach their northern limits within the Channel Islands. The remaining five species occur both north and south of the area (Fig. 2). All of the northern species have their greatest numbers in the San Miguel Island area, while southern species occur almost entirely on the islands of Santa Barbara and Anacapa. Species in the middle of their range are, predictably, more widespread in the Channel Islands, although concentrated in the San Miguel Island area.

Another factor of paramount importance affecting the distribution and numbers of seabirds breeding in the Channel Islands is the presence of the Island Fox (*Urocyon littoralis*) on all the major islands (San Miguel, Santa Rosa, Santa Cruz, San Nicolas, San Clemente, and Santa Catalina). Generally, all of the marine birds breeding in the Bight nest on the small, fox-free islands of Santa Barbara and Anacapa or are crowded onto tiny rocks and islets offshore of the other main islands. A few species that utilize relatively inaccessible habitats do manage to breed on some of the islands despite the foxes. At San Miguel and Santa Rosa Islands, Pigeon Guillemots and Pelagic Cormorants commonly breed in sea caves and on steep sea cliffs, respectively, which offer safety from predators. However, carcasses of guillemots found in fox dens at San Miguel Island suggest that the distributions of these species may also be limited by the foxes. The only island with foxes that supports a sizeable seabird population is San Nicolas Island, where the reason for the persistence of the large gull colony and cormorants breeding at the northwest end is not immediately apparent. The gull colony now appears to be about the largest it has ever been, at a time when Laughrin (1978) reports that the population level for the fox has become "critically low." Seabird populations at San Nicolas Island may fluctuate in response to the fox population, but additional data are needed to determine this.

The most important seabird colonies in southern California are located on three islands. San Miguel Island supports by far the largest and one of the most diverse seabird colonies in southern California, with most of the breeding seabirds concentrated on two small islets: Prince Island and Castle Rock. Sixty per cent of the seabirds nesting in the Channel Islands occur at San Miguel Island and seven of the eleven species that breed in the Bight have their most important colonies there (Leach's and Ashy Storm Petrel, Brandt's, Double-crested, and Pelagic Cormorants, Pigeon Guillemot, and Cassin's Auklet). The largest Xantus' Murrelet

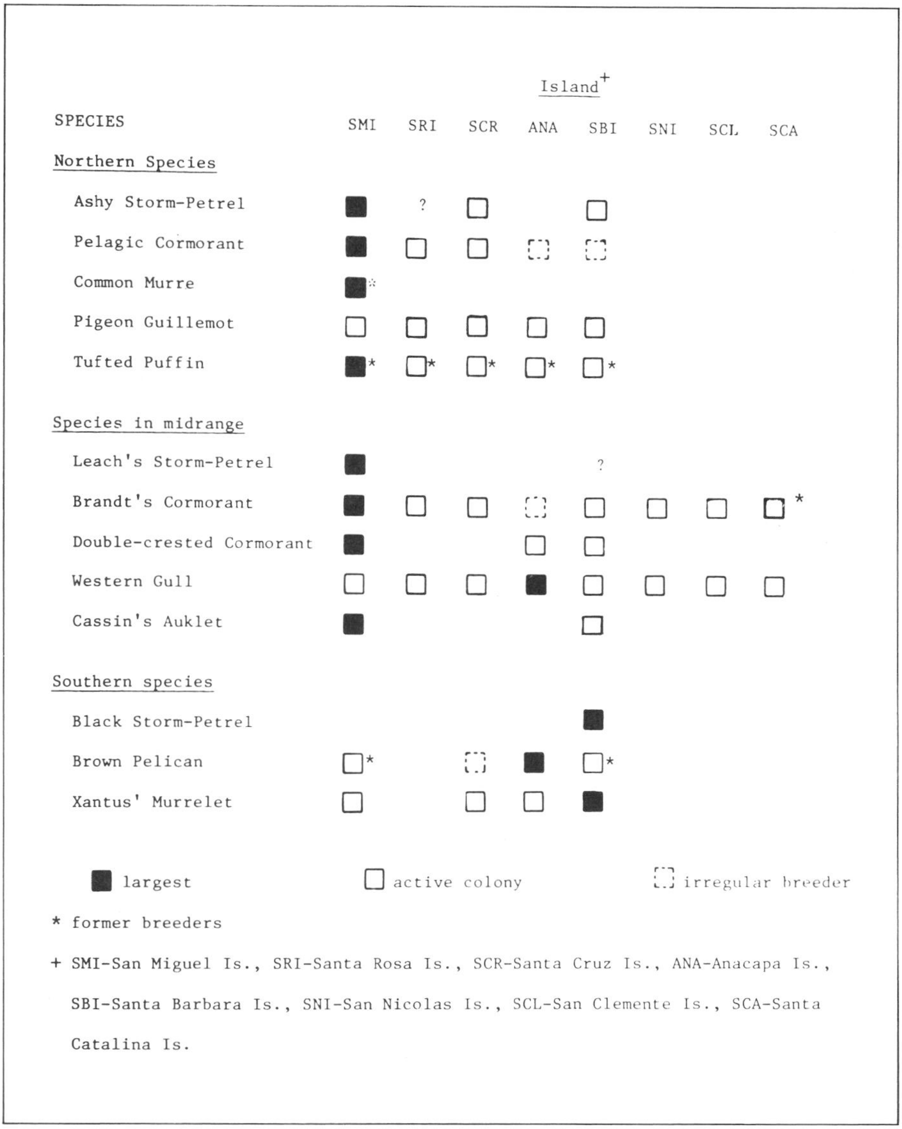

SPECIES	Island+							
	SMI	SRI	SCR	ANA	SBI	SNI	SCL	SCA
Northern Species								
Ashy Storm-Petrel	■	?	□		□			
Pelagic Cormorant	■	□	□	⬚	⬚			
Common Murre	■*							
Pigeon Guillemot	□	□	□	□	□			
Tufted Puffin	■*	□*	□*	□*	□*			
Species in midrange								
Leach's Storm-Petrel	■				?			
Brandt's Cormorant	■	□	□	⬚	□	□	□	□*
Double-crested Cormorant	■			□	□			
Western Gull	□	□	□	■	□	□	□	□
Cassin's Auklet	■				□			
Southern species								
Black Storm-Petrel					■			
Brown Pelican	□*		⬚	■	□*			
Xantus' Murrelet	□			□	□	■		

■ largest   □ active colony   ⬚ irregular breeder

* former breeders

+ SMI-San Miguel Is., SRI-Santa Rosa Is., SCR-Santa Cruz Is., ANA-Anacapa Is., SBI-Santa Barbara Is., SNI-San Nicolas Is., SCL-San Clemente Is., SCA-Santa Catalina Is.

FIGURE 2. *Distribution of seabirds breeding on the Channel Islands, 1975-1977.*

colony in the United States, and possibly the world, occurs on Santa Barbara Island, as does the only colony of Black Storm Petrels in the United States. Anacapa Island is the only place in California where the Brown Pelican breeds regularly and is also the site of the largest Western Gull colony in the Channel Islands. These three islands support the most important seabird colonies in the Southern California Bight.

Population Changes

The populations of a number of seabirds nesting in the Southern California Bight have changed remarkably during historical times. Some of these species, such as the Common Murre and the Tufted Puffin, were northern species at the southern edge of their range. Their demise may have been the result of natural, random fluctuations in a peripheral population, or a response to human disturbance at the colony (in the case of murres) or to diminished food resources (in the case of puffins, see Ainley and Lewis 1974).

Major declines in the Brown Pelican, Double-crested Cormorant, and Brandt's Cormorant undoubtedly find a common cause in their sensitivity to disturbance on the nesting grounds and in reproductive failure due to ingestion of chlorinated hydrocarbons. With the apparent decrease in eggshell thinning following the reduction of environmental pollution by chlorinated hydrocarbons (Anderson *et al.* 1975), these species now have a reasonable chance of regaining their former numbers if their nesting areas are left free of further disturbance.

Major changes in the populations of Xantus' Murrelets and Cassin's Auklets on Santa Barbara Island appear to have been influenced by a combination of changes in predation pressure, particularly the introduction and eventual removal of terrestrial predators and the disappearance of the Peregrine Falcon as a breeding species in the Channel Islands. The causes of apparently large fluctuations in the auklet population at Prince Island, as suggested by the historical record, are not known, however.

It is not at all clear why the murrelets have expanded their population at Santa Barbara Island more rapidly than have the auklets. It is possible that the tendency of Xantus' Murrelets to remain paired throughout the year preadapts them for colonizing an area rapidly; auklets, however, are also capable of rapid recolonization (*cf.* Prince Island with Farallon Island; Ainley and Lewis 1974). It would be most interesting to know the circumstances under which these species managed to reinvade and expand populations on islands from which they were once extirpated. Such information would be valuable for the long-term conservation of seabirds in the Southern California Bight and elsewhere.

Probably by far the greatest single agent of change affecting seabird populations in southern California has been the activities of man. Almost nothing is known about the prehistory of the Channel Islands marine bird populations. However, for thousands of years prior to the earliest Spanish explorations in the area, native California Indians lived on all the larger Channel Islands. In their search for food they undoubtedly used nesting seabird populations, although whether they made regular sorties to the offshore colonies is not known. With the advent of European exploration, starting with the "discovery" of the Channel Islands by Juan Cabrillo in 1542, the seabird fauna of the islands has endured much hardship in its association with man. Prominent in a list of misdeeds has been the introduction of exotic animals. Introduced predators, such as cats and rats, have found easy prey among the seabirds that have little or no defense against terrestrial predators. The numerous herbivores left behind by settlers (*e.g.,* sheep, goats, mules, rabbits) have altered, in some cases radically, the environments of the islands through overgrazing, causing habitat destabilization and loss through erosion.

During the earlier part of this century, numerous egg and specimen collectors made dozens of visits to the colonies during the height of the breeding season to further their avocations. Often colonies were disturbed year after year and declines in some seabird populations were no doubt the result of these activities.

From 1942 until 1965, San Miguel Island was used as an aerial bombing range and missile target area by the U.S. Navy. D. Bleitz (pers. comm.), who visited the area in the 1950s and 1960s, reported seeing the top of Prince Island cindered after one of these exercises. Since 1965, however, the island has not been used as an impact area (Kolipinski 1976). The northwest end of San Nicolas Island has also been used as a target zone.

Adverse impact on the Channel Islands seabird colonies has prevailed even into the present time where applied technology has broadened the effects man is having on his environment. Chemical pollution of ocean waters has threatened the existence of several species nesting on the islands. Oil spills and contamination are ever-present and increasing hazards. Short-sighted fishery policies, which have led to disastrous effects in some parts of the world (*e.g.*, the anchovy fishery of Peru), could, if repeated, have the potential of damaging marine bird populations in the Bight by disrupting food cycles. Increased human activity in the Bight in the form of boat and air traffic has added to the amount of disturbance in the colonies (*e.g.*, foot traffic, shooting, sonic booms).

It is possible now, though, with the three most important seabird colonies in the Bight finally under the protection of the U.S. National Park Service, that these populations will be able to maintain or increase their numbers. Only with adequate protective measures, backed by effective monitoring, can we retain a healthy and diverse marine avifauna in the Channel Islands.

SUMMARY

The Channel Islands of the Southern California Bight presently support breeding colonies of 11 species of primarily marine birds: Leach's Storm Petrel (two or more pairs), Ashy Storm Petrel (600 ±100 pairs), Black Storm Petrel (*ca.* 75 pairs), Brown Pelican (75 to 400 pairs), Double-crested Cormorant (115 to 160 pairs), Brandt's Cormorant (2,075 to 3,025 pairs), Pelagic Cormorant (190 to 250 pairs), Western Gull (2,400 to 2,800 pairs), Pigeon Guillemot (*ca.* 850 pairs), Xantus' Murrelet (*ca.* 1,650 pairs), and Cassin's Auklet (*ca.* 11,150 pairs).

The largest populations of nesting seabirds occur at San Miguel Island (14,000 to 15,000 pairs), with smaller populations on Santa Barbara Island (3,400 pairs) and Anacapa Island (3,000 pairs). In contrast, San Clemente Island and Santa Catalina Island support but 75 pairs and 30 pairs, respectively. Populations of breeding seabirds are generally greatest on the small, fox-free islands and offshore rocks; with the exception of San Nicolas Island, large islands with populations of the Island Fox support few nesting seabirds. The westernmost of the northern islands support many species at or near the southern limits of their range, while species with more southern affinities, except for the pelican, have but small populations north of Santa Barbara Island.

Populations have changed for several species of seabirds in southern California during historical times. Common Murres and Tufted Puffins used to nest on the islands but no longer do so. Numbers of pelicans, cormorants, and Cassin's Auklets have decreased, while numbers of Xantus' Murrelets have increased. Many of these changes can be directly or indirectly linked to the activities of man.

ACKNOWLEDGMENTS

We thank Lloyd Kiff for permission to use museum specimens and unpublished field notes; the United States Navy; and the National Park Service, including, in particular, William Ehorn, Superintendent of the Channel Islands National Monument, who provided access to the islands under their control and a variety of logistical support. Jan Larson was especially helpful to our work on San Clemente Island and provided unpublished field notes. We thank Barbara Burgeson, James Cotton, Paul Kelly, Audrey Martin, Maura Naughton, Steven Speich, Gerald Thompson, John Wingfield, and Kathy Winnett for help with the field work. Audrey Martin provided valuable suggestions for improving the manuscript. The 1975-1977 field work was supported by Bureau of Land Management contracts to the University of California at Santa Cruz and Irvine (K. Norris, G. Hunt, and B. Le Boeuf, Principal Investigators).

REFERENCES

AINLEY, D., and T. J. LEWIS. 1974. The history of Farallon Island marine bird populations, 1854-1972. Condor 76:432-446.

AINLEY, D., S. MORRELL, and T. J. LEWIS. 1974. Patterns in the life histories of storm petrels on the Farallon Islands. Living Bird 13:295-312.

AINLEY, D., and T. OSBORNE. 1972. A Marin County, California, breeding site for Ashy Petrels. California Birds 3:71.

AMERICAN ORNITHOLOGISTS' UNION. 1957. Check-list of North American birds. American Ornithologists' Union, Washington, D.C.

ANDERSON, D. W., and J. HICKEY. 1970. Oological data on egg and breeding characteristics of Brown Pelicans. Wilson Bull. 82:14-28.

ANDERSON, D. W., J. R. JEHL, JR., R. W. RISEBROUGH, L. A. WOODS, L. R. DeWEESE, and W. G. EDGECOMB. 1975. Brown Pelicans: improved reproduction off the southern California coast. Science 190:806-808.

BAILEY, F. M. 1902. Handbook of birds of the western United States. University Press, Cambridge, Mass.

BALDRIDGE, A. 1973. The status of the Brown Pelican in the Monterey region of California: past and present. Western Birds 4:93-100.

BARTHOLOMEW, G., and R. BOOLOOTIAN. 1960. Population structure of the pinnipeds on the Channel Islands, California. J. Mammal. 41:366-375.

BENT, A. C. 1946. Life histories of North American diving birds. (Smithsonian Inst. Bull. 107 [1919]) reprinted by Dover, New York, N.Y.

COOPER, J. G. 1870. The fauna of California and its geographical distribution. Proc. California Acad. Sci., Ser. 1, Zool. 4:61-81.

CROSSIN, R. S. 1974. The storm petrels (Hydrobatidae). Pp. 154-205 in W. B. King, ed., Pelagic studies of seabirds in the central and eastern Pacific Ocean. Smithsonian Contrib. Zool. 158.

CROSSIN, R., and R. L. BROWNELL. 1968. Preliminary report of Channel Islands survey. Eastern area cruise no. 41. Unpubl. rep., Smithsonian Inst., Washington, D.C.

DAWSON, W. L. 1923. The birds of California. South Moulton Co., San Diego, Calif.

EVERMANN, B. W. 1886. A list of the birds observed in Ventura County, California. Auk 3:86-94.

GRESS, F. 1970. Reproductive status of the California Brown Pelican in 1970 with notes on breeding biology and natural history. California Dept. Fish Game, Wildl. Mgmt. Bur. Admin. Rep. 70-6:1-21 (mimeo).

GRESS, G., R. W. RISEBROUGH, D. W. ANDERSON, L. F. KIFF, and J. R. JEHL. 1973. Reproductive failures of Double-crested Cormorants in southern California and Baja California. Wilson Bull. 85:197-208.

GRINNELL, J. 1897. Report on the birds recorded during a visit to the islands of Santa Barbara, San Nicolas, and San Clemente in the spring of 1897. Pasadena Acad. Sci. Publ. 1:1-25.

GRINNELL, J., and A. MILLER. 1944. The distribution of the birds of California. Pacific Coast Avifauna 27:1-608.

HOWELL, A. B. 1917. Birds of the islands off the coast of southern California. Pacific Coast Avifauna 12:1-127.

HUBBS, C. L. 1967. A discussion of the geochronology and archeology of the California Islands. Pp. 337-341 in R. N. Philbrick, ed., Proceedings of the symposium on the biology of the California Islands. Santa Barbara Botanic Garden, Santa Barbara, Calif.

HUBER, L. N. 1968. Preliminary report of San Miguel Island and adjacent islets, Prince and Castle. May 28-June 7, 1968. Unpubl. rep., Smithsonian Inst., Washington, D.C.

HUNT, G., and M. HUNT. 1977. Female-female pairing in Western Gulls (*Larus occidentalis*) in southern California. Science 196:1466-1467.

JEHL, J. R. 1977. An annotated list of birds of Islas Los Coronados, Baja California, and adjacent waters. Western Birds 8:91-101.

JEHL, J. R., and S. BOND. 1975. Morphological variation and species limits in murrelets of the genus *Endomychura*. San Diego Soc. Nat. Hist. Trans. 18:9-23.

JONES, J. H. 1971. General circulation and water characteristics in the Southern California Bight. So. California Coastal Water Res. Proj. Tech. Rep. 101.

KOLIPINSKI, M. C. 1976. San Miguel Island: its resources and recommendations for their protection and management. Report to the Secretary, U.S. Dept. Navy, from the National Park Service, Western Regional Office.

LAUGHRIN, L. 1978. Status report on the San Nicolas Island Fox, January, 1978. Unpubl. rep. to the California Dept. Fish Game, Sacramento, Calif.

LE BOEUF, B. J., M. L. BONNELL, M. D. PIERSON, D. H. DETTMAN, and G. D. FARRENS. 1976. Pinnipedia: numbers, distribution and movements in the Southern California Bight. Final report to the Bureau of Land Management, Marine Mammal and Seabird Survey of the Southern California Bight Area. Vol. III, book 1, Principal Investigators' reports. University of California, Santa Cruz, Calif.

MILLER, L. 1936. Some maritime birds observed off San Diego, California. Condor 38:9-16.

MOFFITT, J. 1939. Notes on the distribution of Sooty Shearwater, White Pelican, and cormorants in California. Condor 41:32-33.

NELSON, R., and M. MYERS. 1976. Declines in populations of Peregrine Falcons and their seabird prey at Langara Island, British Columbia. Condor 78:281-293.

PALMER, R. S., ed. 1962. Handbook of North American birds. I. Loons through flamingoes. Yale University Press, New York, N.Y.

PITMAN, R., and S. SPEICH. 1976. Black Storm-Petrel breeds in the United States. Western Birds 7:71.

SMALL, A. 1974. The birds of California. Winchester Press, New York, N.Y.

SOUTHERN CALIFORNIA COASTAL WATER RESEARCH PROJECT. 1973. The ecology of the Southern California Bight: implications for water quality management, vol. II. SCCWRP, 1100 Glendon Ave., Los Angeles, Calif.

STREATOR, C. P. 1888. Notes on the birds of the Santa Barbara Islands. Ornithologist and Oologist 13:52-54.

SUMNER, E. L. 1939. An investigation of Santa Barbara, Anacapa, and San Miguel Islands. Unpubl. rep., Channel Islands National Monument, Ventura, Calif.

TUCK, C. M. 1960. The murres, their distribution, populations and biology: a study of the genus *Uria*. Canadian Wildl. Serv. Monogr., Ser. 1, Ottawa, Canada.

UDVARDY, M. D. F. 1963. Zoogeographical study of the Pacific Alcidae. Pp. 85-111 *in* J. L. Gressit, ed., Pacific Basin biogeography, a symposium. Bishop Museum Press, Honolulu, Hawaii.

WILLETT, G. 1910. A summer trip to the northern Santa Barbara Islands. Condor 12:170-174.

————. 1912. Birds of the Pacific slope of southern California. Pacific Coast Avifauna 7:1-122.

————. 1933. A revised list of the birds of southwestern California. Pacific Coast Avifauna 21:1-204.

WRIGHT, H., and G. SNYDER. 1913. Birds observed in the summer of 1912 among the Santa Barbara Islands. Condor 15:86-92.

Origin of Homosexual Pairing of Female Western Gulls on Santa Barbara Island

John C. Wingfield,[1] Audrey Martin,[2] Molly W. Hunt,[2]
George L. Hunt, Jr.,[2] and Donald S. Farner[1]

[1]*Department of Zoology, University of Washington,
Seattle, Washington 98195*
[2]*Department of Ecology and Evolutionary Biology,
University of California, Irvine, California 92717*

INTRODUCTION

In 1968, Schreiber (1970) found that 11.3 per cent of the clutches of Western Gulls (*Larus occidentalis wymani*) on San Nicolas Island had more than three eggs. He believed that the low hatching success (0.13 per cent) of these clutches was the result of insufficient heat transfer in incubating four or more eggs. On Santa Barbara Island in 1972, 11 per cent of clutches were found to consist of more than three eggs, with 4.9 per cent hatching success (Hunt and Hunt 1973). It was believed, at first, that these eggs all came from the same female, as the eggs were of similar color and only two adults could be identified on each territory. Between 1972 and 1976, the frequency of clutches with supernumerary eggs varied between 7 and 13 per cent. It also became apparent that these were laid by female-female pairs.

Evidence for female-female pairing found by Hunt and Hunt (1977) is as follows:

(1) In three-egg clutches, 67 per cent of eggs were laid two days apart, whereas in the larger clutches many were laid on consecutive days and 11 per cent on the same day. This suggests that at least two females were laying in the same nest.

(2) Most eggs in the clutches with more than three eggs were infertile. While 81.5 per cent of the eggs of normal clutches showed development, zero to 14 per cent developed in the larger clutches. The few eggs that were fertile resulted from promiscuous, heterosexual matings. Indeed, marked birds have been observed mounting or being mounted by birds other than their mate. In such situations males were off their own territory, and in five of 18 cases females were also off their own territory.

(3) The sex of gulls trapped on nests perhaps provides the most convincing evidence. Hunt and Hunt (1977) trapped 10 male and 15 female adult gulls incubating normal clutches (one to three eggs), and one male and 74 females on larger clutches. Most important, on 23 nests containing larger clutches, two females were captured.

Thus, it appears that on territories where nests contained large clutches, two females are in attendance with no apparent permanent association of males for at least one to two weeks prior to clutch initiation. These females essentially act as though they are heterosexually paired and remain together from one year to the next, although in one instance a female paired to another female in 1976 was found paired to a male in 1977. They engage in most of the usual courtship and territorial behavior but relatively rarely show mounting and copulation behavior normally attributable to males. If given hatching eggs, they are capable of raising young (G. Hunt, M. Hunt, and S. Anthony, unpubl. field notes).

The existence of female-female pairs raises many questions. If the quality of a mate is assessed in courtship, how is the mechanism failing, and how widespread and important is promiscuous, heterosexual mating? Why do female-female pairs form? For the last question we have two working hypotheses, which are not mutually exclusive. These hypotheses are the subject of this paper.

TABLE 1. Sex ratios of Western Gulls caught by cannon-net, 22 April-5 May 1977, and of newly-hatched chicks on Santa Barbara Island.

	Females	Males	Female/male	P^1
All adults	108	46	2.35	<0.005
All immatures	31	25	1.24	>0.05
Breeding adults[2]	88	45	1.95	<0.01
Nonbreeding adults	20	1	20.00	<0.005
Breeding immatures[3]	2	16	0.13	<0.05
Nonbreeding immatures	29	9	3.22	<0.05
Newly-hatched chicks	129	110	1.17	<0.05

[1] χ^2-test for equality of the sexes.
[2] Difference in the percentage of nonbreeders in adult males and females significant at $P<0.01$.
[3] Difference in the percentage of nonbreeders in immature males and females significant at $P<0.005$.

WHY DO FEMALE-FEMALE PAIRS FORM?

The first hypothesis is that the sex ratio is biased in favor of females, thus resulting in female-female pairing owing to a shortage of males. The homosexual pairs formed would have a small chance of raising young (owing to promiscuous, heterosexual matings), whereas an unmated female would have essentially no chance since she would be unable to raise young alone. We have tested the hypothesis that there is a bias in the sex ratio by cannon-netting Western Gulls in "clubs" on Santa Barbara Island during the 1977 breeding season and sexing them by unilateral laparotomy. The breeding status of birds was determined by inspection of the gonads and through the observation of the marked birds following their release after the laparotomy. Results are presented in Table 1, and it appears that there is, indeed, a skewed sex ratio in favor of females. In nonbreeding adults, females outnumbered males twenty to one. In addition, four- and five-year-old birds breeding for the first time were mostly males. These data are consistent with the hypothesis that there is a shortage of males in the breeding population. However, this is the first study of sex ratio in a gull colony, and it is not known if such a biased ratio is unusual. A similar study of a colony with no, or very few, clutches with more than three eggs may resolve this problem. We attempted to determine whether the apparent bias in the sex ratio of the adults originated before or after hatching by sexing newly-hatched chicks. A total of 249 chicks were sexed by laparotomy in 1977 and, although there was an excess of females (Table 1), the difference between the ratio found and a 1:1 ratio was not statistically significant.

The second hypothesis is that female-female pairing is a result of modification of behavior by abnormal plasma hormone levels or cycles. To test this hypothesis, we collected blood samples from both males and heterosexual and homosexual females throughout a breeding season on Santa Barbara Island. Blood was taken from a wing vein using heparinized syringes and was centrifuged in the field using a clinical centrifuge powered by a portable generator. Plasma was stored frozen in a liquid nitrogen refrigerator and transported to Seattle for analysis. Luteinizing hormone, a protein secreted by the pituitary gland and transported via the blood to its target organ, the gonad, was measured by a double antibody radioimmunoassay (Follett et al. 1972). The primary effects of this hormone are on the interstitial cells of both the testis and the ovary, and also on the thecal cells of ovarian follicles, causing them to synthesize and secrete sex steroid hormones (Brown et al. 1975, Lofts and Murton 1973). Of these steroid hormones,

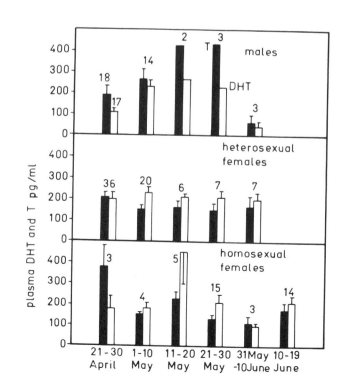

FIGURE 1. *Plasma levels of immunoreactive luteinizing hormone (dark bars) and gonadal size (open bars) in relation to calendar time. Fine bars are standard errors of means. Numbers above bars indicate sample sizes.*

FIGURE 2. *Plasma levels of 5αDHT (open bars) and testosterone (dark bars) in relation to calendar time. Fine bars are standard errors of means. Numbers above bars indicate sample sizes.*

progesterone, 17β-hydroxy-5α-androstan-3-one (5α-DHT), testosterone, estrone, and estradiol-17β were again measured by radioimmunoassay (Wingfield and Farner 1975). The actions of these hormones include control of gametogenesis, secondary sex characteristics, and reproductive behavior (see Lofts and Murton 1973 for review).

Figures 1 and 2 summarize the plasma levels of immunoreactive luteinizing hormone (irLH), gonadal size, plasma 5α-DHT, and testosterone in relation to calendar time. Very little change was seen in females; however, in males, androgen (5α-DHT and testosterone) levels were highest during the peak period of egg laying (May), with lower levels during incubation. As females in May were either about to lay, in lay, or incubating eggs, the data were rearranged according to stages in the cycle, rather than by calendar time (Fig. 3), in order to clarify the relationship between hormone levels and the reproductive cycle. As can be seen, there is a peak in plasma irLH at ovulation in heterosexual females, as has been shown in other species (Furr *et al.* 1973, Donham *et al.* 1976, Wingfield and Farner 1978). The small sample sizes in homosexual females prevent us from making comparisons except for the period of incubation. During incubation, plasma irLH rises in homosexually paired females, whereas a decrease was noted at this time in heterosexual females. Cheng and Follett (1976) found that plasma irLH remained elevated in female Ring Doves incubating infertile eggs compared with those incubating fertile eggs. This they related to renesting attempts by females having infertile eggs. As homosexual gulls are incubating mainly infertile eggs, it is tempting to draw a parallel with Ring Doves even though, to date, none of these females has been recorded as renesting.

From Figure 3 it can also be seen that plasma androgen levels show a maximum at or near ovulation in heterosexual females and that the absolute levels in males and females are remarkably similar (Fig. 2). The ratio of androgen in male plasma to that in female plasma barely exceeds two, whereas in other wild species studied, such as the White-crowned Sparrow, *Zonotrichia leucophrys* (Wingfield and Farner 1978), and the Mallard, *Anas platyrhynchos* (R. S. Donham, pers. comm.), the ratio lies between ten and twenty to one. This difference may be related to the behavior of these species. Male White-crowned Sparrows and Mallards are mainly responsible for territorial defense, and, in the Mallard, the male has no parental responsibilities at all. In the Western Gull, territorial defense and parental duties are more or less equally divided.

Measurements of plasma progesterone, estrone, and estradiol-17β are not yet complete, but preliminary data show apparent maxima in all hormones in females during egg laying. As these hormones have been implicated in the control of vitellogenesis and ovulation, such maxima are to be expected (see Lofts and Murton 1973). Changes , if any, in levels of these hormones in the plasma of males are at present unclear.

From our very preliminary data on hormone levels we can tentatively conclude that plasma androgen and irLH are present at similar concentrations in both males and females. As these hormones are thought to regulate territorial and sexual behavior, and given the fact that females display many behavioral traits normally attributable to males, it is not difficult to rationalize the formation of female-female pairs in a population with a shortage of males. The fate of these "absent" males is at present unknown.

SUMMARY

Clutches of four to six eggs have been found in seven to 13 per cent of Western Gull *(Larus occidentalis wymani)* nests on Santa Barbara Island. Evidence that these larger clutches are the product of female-female homosexual pairings is reviewed and new evidence related to two working hypotheses on the origin of these pairs is presented.

One hypothesis, that female homosexual pairing is associated with a skewed sex ratio, has

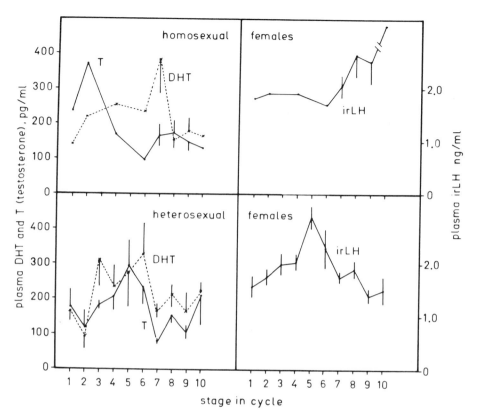

FIGURE 3. *Plasma levels of immunoreactive luteinizing hormone and androgen (± standard errors of means) in relation to stage in cycle. Key to stage numbers is as follows: (1) largest ovarian follicle, 5 mm; (2) largest ovarian follicle, 10 mm; (3) largest ovarian follicle, 15 mm; (4) largest ovarian follicle, 30 mm; (5) largest ovarian follicle > 30 mm, about to ovulate; (6) egg in oviduct; (7) very early incubation; (8) mid-incubation; (9) late incubation; (10) feeding chicks.*

been examined by cannon-netting adults in loafing areas or "clubs" on Santa Barbara Island. We have caught more adult females than males, and found a higher proportion of nonbreeding adult females than males. Among subadult gulls caught, a higher proportion of males was found breeding than females. These data are consistent with the hypothesis that there exists an excess of adult female gulls on Santa Barbara Island; we have no information suggesting the cause of the skewed sex ratio. However, in a population with a predominance of females, female homosexual matings would be favored, if birds so paired could raise young resulting from promiscuous, heterosexual mating. Unpaired females have almost no chance of leaving offspring.

A second hypothesis, not mutually exclusive with the first, is that female-female pairs are the result of abnormal hormonal cycles modifying behavior. This is being tested by quantitative measures of behavior and of plasma levels of hormones. Both homosexually and heterosexual-ly paired females show some behavioral patterns normally attributable to males. It is presently unclear whether there are significant hormonal differences between homosexually and heterosexually mated females.

ACKNOWLEDGMENTS

The investigations described herein are the result of teamwork which included the authors and many undergraduate students. Also, none of these studies would have been possible without the cooperation and help from rangers and officials of the Channel Islands National Monument.

These investigations were supported in part by grant number PCM-7705629 from the National Science Foundation, awarded to Donald S. Farner and George L. Hunt, Jr.

REFERENCES

BROWN, N. L., J.-D. BAYLÉ, C. G. SCANES, and B. K. FOLLETT. 1975. Chicken gonadotro-pins: their effects on the testes of immature and hypophysectomized Japanese quail. Cell Tiss. Res. 156:499-520.

CHENG, M. F., and B. K. FOLLETT. 1976. Plasma luteinizing hormone during the breeding cycle of the female Ring Dove. Horm. Behav. 7:199-205.

DONHAM, R. S., C. W. DANE, and D. S. FARNER. 1976. Plasma luteinizing hormone and the development of ovarian follicles after loss of clutch in female Mallards, *Anas platyrhyn-chos*. Gen. Comp. Endocrinol. 29:152-155.

FOLLETT, B. K., C. G. SCANES, and F. J. CUNNINGHAM. 1972. A radioimmunoassay for avian luteinizing hormone. J. Endocrinol. 52:359-378.

FURR, B. J. A., R. C. BONNEY, R. J. ENGLAND, and F. J. CUNNINGHAM. 1973. Luteinizing hormone and progesterone in peripheral blood during the ovulatory cycle of the hen, *Gallus domesticus*. J. Endocrinol. 57:159-169.

HUNT, G. L., JR., and M. W. HUNT. 1973. Clutch size, hatching success, and eggshell-thinning in Western Gulls. Condor 75:483-486.

_____. 1977. Female-female pairing in Western Gulls *(Larus occidentalis)* in southern California. Science 196:1466-1467.

LOFTS, B., and R. K. MURTON. 1973. Reproduction in birds. Pp. 1-107 *in* D. S. FARNER and J. R. KING, eds., Avian biology, vol. III. Academic Press, New York, N.Y.

SCHREIBER, R. W. 1970. Breeding biology of Western Gulls *(Larus occidentalis)* on San Nicolas Island, California, 1968. Condor 72:133-140.

WINGFIELD, J.C., and D. S. FARNER. 1975. The determination of five steroids in avian plasma by radioimmunoassay and competitive protein-binding. Steroids 26:311-327.

_____. 1978. The endocrinology of a natural breeding population of the White-crowned Sparrow *(Zonotrichia leucophrys pugetensis)*. Physiol. Zool. 51:188-205.

Nesting Success of Western Gulls on Bird Rock, Santa Catalina Island, California

Judith L. Hand

Biology Department, University of California,
Los Angeles, California 90024

INTRODUCTION

In 1965 and 1966, Charles Harper studied aspects of reproductive biology in a colony of less than thirty pairs of Western Gulls *(Larus occidentalis wymani)* on Bird Rock, a small islet approximately 530 m off the east side of the isthmus at Santa Catalina Island, California (Harper 1971). In 1974, I made observations on breeding success at Bird Rock which were comparable to some of the data reported by Harper. This paper presents results of comparison of the two studies.

STUDY SITE AND METHODS

Bird Rock is roughly oval and dome shaped, about 135 m long by 90 m wide. For the most part, the hard surface is smooth and bare with few fissures or prominent contours. A low-growing patch of vegetation ringed by prickly pear cactus *(Opuntia occidentalis)* covers part of the southwest end.

With the exception of a pair of Killdeer *(Charadrius vociferus)* found on 22 June 1975, I saw no other vertebrates on the island. Harper noted a breeding pair of Black Oystercatchers *(Haematopus bachmani)* in 1966 and occasional sea lions *(Zalophus californianus)* resting on the island, but otherwise he also saw no other vertebrates. The Killdeer seen in 1975 performed impressive distraction displays on the south end of the island, suggesting that they were nesting or intended to nest there, but my superficial hunt did not detect the nest. It may have been within the border of the vegetation patch.

The highest part of the islet forms a ridge that runs lengthwise across the top and middle and separates the northeast and southwest slopes. The gulls do not nest on the northeast side, probably because the surface is too steep. Nests are found primarily along the ridge and over the face of the southwest slope (Fig. 1).

The area around Bird Rock is used extensively for human recreation. Access to the islet itself is hindered to some extent because the intertidal zone has numerous jagged rocks and there is always considerable swell, even in calm weather. Difficulties in getting onto the islet, plus its barren and uninteresting appearance, have probably contributed significantly to continued occupation of the gull colony in spite of heavy human traffic in the area. Nevertheless, Harper reported significant mortality in both 1965 and 1966 which he attributed to human disturbances.

Harper visited the colony six times each season, at roughly two-week intervals, beginning in late May and continuing through July. At each visit he counted numbers of nests, eggs, and chicks present. Nests were labeled by painting numbers next to them on the rock. Chicks were banded with temporary bands when about twenty days old.

I made a census of the colony three times in 1974, on 12 May, 19 May, and 13 July. This was sufficient to collect data on nest locations, clutch sizes, and probable hatching success which are comparable to the data collected by Harper. Nests were identified by numbers painted on the rock. Individual eggs and chicks were not marked.

I made no visits during the weeks following completion of clutches or following hatching, so

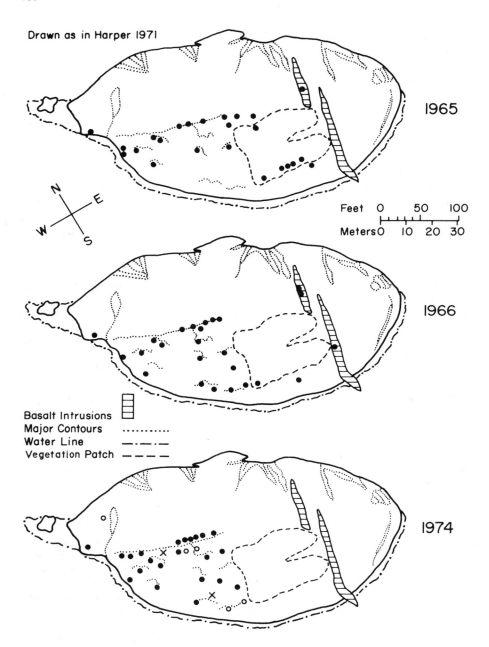

FIGURE 1. *Nest locations on Bird Rock. For 1974 only, solid circles represent three-egg clutches, open circles represent clutches of less than three eggs, and Xs represent clutches exceeding three eggs.*

I have few data on causes of egg loss and no data on causes of chick mortality which might be compared with Harper's observations.

Harper counted the number of young on or around the islet in middle and late July (22 July 1965 and 15 July 1966) and presumed that those young would eventually fledge. I made a similar count on 13 July 1974; the numbers obtained on that date are those used to determine fledging ratios.

RESULTS

Peak of laying. —Harper reports that breeding seasons on Bird Rock in 1965 and 1966 were "nearly identical to those Schreiber reported for 1968" on San Nicolas Island. Schreiber (1970) estimated that the peak of laying by Western Gulls in 1968 occurred between 6 and 16 May. In 1974, 83 per cent of clutches were complete by 12 May, and by 19 May 93 per cent (27 of 29 clutches) were complete. Two new clutches (with three and two eggs) were found on 13 July, possibly representing renesting attempts (one clutch placed very near the high tide line was lost between 12 and 19 May). A member of the University of Southern California Marine Station staff, John Pilger, visited the island in mid-August, checked these two nests, and reported that all eggs from the three-egg nest were absent and that neither of the eggs from the two-egg nest had hatched.

Nest site preference. — Figure 1 shows locations of nests in all three years. A shift occurred between 1965 and 1966. In 1965, hatching was markedly lower in the vegetation patch compared with the rest of the colony (56 *vs.* 76 per cent, respectively), and Harper suggested that birds which had experienced failures there in 1965 avoided the patch in 1966. Birds in 1974 also avoided it; no nests were found in or adjacent to the vegetation. The closest was approximately 2 m from the plants.

In all three years the "preferred" sites were on the central ridge that overlooks the slope where other nests are located (Fig. 1). The territory sizes are generally smaller here than on the slope, having internest distances ranging from 1 to 4 m (Harper 1971, and pers. obs.). The ridge is perhaps more desirable because it provides the most level spots, has some short vegetation (not exceeding 10 cm in height) for nest construction, and some loose soil in which to make a scrape.

In 1965 there were four nests along this prime area, and in 1966 seven pairs were occupying the area (these nests are joined by a dotted line in Figure 1). By 1974, ten pairs were located in this region. Although proportions in Figure 1 make it look more crowded, the placement of nests in 1974 was such that internest distances were similar to those in the other two years, ranging from 1 to 4 m, with a mean of about 2 m.

Clutch size and hatching success. —Table 1 presents data on clutch size and hatching success. Discounting a few known cases of egg loss before hatching, the figures for 1974 are based on the assumption that when I made the census of the colony on 13 July, absence of eggs from the nest was the result of hatching. Although some instances of egg disappearance not attributable to hatching were detected by both Harper and me, visits by neither of us were frequent enough to explain all cases of egg loss. Since some loss invariably occurs in Western Gulls due to predation, particularly by conspecifics, as well as to other minor factors (Schreiber 1970, Coulter 1973, Hunt and Hunt 1975), and because of human disturbance on Bird Rock (Harper 1971), the figures for all three years represent maximum probable hatching values.

Despite these uncertainties, some trends in hatching success are evident. In all three years, three-egg clutches were the most common (67 per cent of all clutches) and generally the most successful, with hatching success ranging from 82 to 96 per cent. The sample sizes for single-egg and two-egg clutches are too small to be meaningful, but they were generally less successful in hatching than were three-egg clutches.

TABLE 1. Clutch sizes and per cent of eggs hatching in 1965, 1966, and 1974.

Year	Size of clutch	Number of clutches	Per cent of clutches	Per cent of eggs hatched
1965	1	6	25.0	33
	2	3	12.5	33
	3	14	58.3	88
	4	1	4.2	75
1966	1	4	16.0	50
	2	3	12.0	100
	3	17	68.0	96*
	6	1	4.0	—*
1974	1	1	3.4	100
	2	4	13.7	50
	3	22	75.8	82
	5	1	3.4	—†
	6	1	3.4	—†

* Per cent hatching of the six-egg clutch was not calculated separately but was treated as two clutches of three eggs.
† See text for explanation.

Supernormal clutches. — Clutches exceeding three eggs, sometimes referred to as supernormal clutches, occurred on Bird Rock in all three years. Because of differences in egg coloration within supernormal clutches of Western Gulls on San Nicolas Island, Schreiber suggested that the eggs might have been laid by more than one female (Schreiber 1970). On Santa Barbara Island, Hunt and Hunt (1977) have found that not only do two females lay eggs in the same nest, they apparently form pairs that exhibit the same kind of territorial behavior used by heterosexual pairs. The phenomena associated with clutches exceeding three eggs in Western Gulls are being studied in detail by G. Hunt and his colleagues on Santa Barbara Island (Hunt and Hunt 1977, Wingfield *et al.* 1980).

Harper reported one of these nests in 1965 (four eggs) and one in 1966 (six eggs). In 1974 I found two, and in 1975 I visited the colony on 22 June and found three such clutches with the eggs still unhatched. Although the increase from one to three nests is small, it is interesting in view of the small size of the colony itself since it suggests that the percentage of supernormal clutches may be increasing. Further observations to verify this possibility seem warranted.

In Table 1, I have not presented a value for per cent hatching in the five- and six-egg supernormal clutches. On 13 July, two eggs were missing from the five-egg clutch and three were missing from the six-egg clutch. Calculation of hatching success in these clutches, based on the assumption that the missing eggs had hatched, would give a 60 per cent hatching rate for the five-egg clutch and 50 per cent for the six-egg clutch. However, Schreiber reported that only one egg hatched out of 74 eggs in supernormal clutches on San Nicolas Island, and Hunt and Hunt (1977) estimated that the number of eggs which were even fertile in such clutches on Santa Barbara Island was slightly less than 15 per cent for 144 eggs from five- and six-egg clutches. It seems most probable that eggs missing from these nests disappeared for reasons other than hatching, such as rolling from the nest, being broken, or being taken by a neighbor. It is for this reason that no estimated value for hatching success appears in Table 1.

Fledging success. —Table 2 summarizes data on breeding at Bird Rock in all three years.

TABLE 2. Summary of nesting success of Western Gulls on Bird Rock in 1965, 1966, and 1974.

Year	1965	1966	1974
Number of nests	24	25	29
Number of eggs	58	67	86
Mean clutch size	2.41	2.68	2.97
Per cent of eggs hatching	76	80	76
Young present (mid-July)	32	24	15
Fledging ratio (young/nest)	1.33	0.96	0.52
Per cent of clutches exceeding 3 eggs	4.16	4.00	6.90

The fledging ratio in 1965 was a healthy 1.33 young/nest, and 0.96 young/nest in 1966. In 1974, this dropped to 0.52 young/nest. The seemingly consistent decline suggests a trend toward reduced fledging success on Bird Rock.

DISCUSSION

I would like to discuss two points of interest. The first concerns supernormal clutches. The presence of these clutches, and presumably the female pairs with which they are associated (as demonstrated on Santa Barbara Island), is of some comparative interest because territory sizes on Bird Rock are quite small, unlike those on Santa Barbara Island (Hunt and Hunt 1975). Data presented by Wingfield *et al.* (1980) show that the adult sex ratio is skewed on Santa Barbara Island, with females outnumbering males. Hunt and Hunt (1977) have suggested that if there were an excess of females in the population, homosexual pairing, combined with polygamous heterosexual mating, would make it possible for excess females to raise offspring. Whatever the causal factors of this phenomenon may be, one might argue that low population density, as seen on Santa Barbara Island, is also a requisite if female pairs are to establish and maintain a territory. Males of the Herring Gull *(Larus argentatus)* group generally carry the bulk of responsibility for defending territories and are certainly more aggressive than females. Western Gulls are no exception (Pierotti 1976, and pers. obs). But territories on Bird Rock are not large, averaging 22.3 m² (Harper 1971), compared with an average of 150 to 214 m² on Santa Barbara Island (Hunt and Hunt 1975). In addition, the barren surface provides no barriers to visibility, which have been shown to reduce tension between neighbors in other gull species (Burger 1974). If the supernormal clutches found on Bird Rock do belong to female pairs, as they do on Santa Barbara Island, it would indicate that low breeding density within the colony is not a necessary condition for the phenomenon of territory establishment by female pairs. This is not meant to suggest that paired females are likely to be able to hold a territory in direct competition with a male. Rather, it may be that as long as all males wishing to breed have some place to do so, even if it is a small territory, female pairs can maintain a territory, as well. Further investigation of the pairs associated with supernormal clutches on Bird Rock might help provide answers to this kind of question.

The second point, one which is also speculative, relates to the reduced fledging success on Bird Rock in 1974. The decline is particularly interesting since mean clutch size increased during this same period (Table 2). Even if the nests containing supernormal clutches are eliminated from calculations, the average clutch size in 1974 was 2.78 eggs/nest, an increase over the two years sampled earlier. The rate of hatching also appears to be similar to what Harper reported, although the number of fledglings was one-third the lowest number reported by Harper (1966) and less than one-half the number in 1965. Total mortality from egg to fledging was 83 per cent in 1974.

The three factors which could contribute to reduced fledging success are decrease in food supply, increase in human disturbance, and problems associated with pesticides. No obvious effects of pesticide poisoning, such as eggshell thinning, were detected by Harper or me. It is difficult to assess the possible effects of human disturbance on the colony. However, Douglas Bombard (pers. comm.), who has operated the Twin Harbor facilities at the isthmus for over fifteen years, stated that the overall recreational activities had not altered significantly in the past ten years, nor did he believe that greater numbers of people were likely to be visiting the island. Furthermore, Harper's values for chick mortality in 1965 and 1966 were already elevated, in his opinion, by human disturbances in those years. Yet values for fledging were much higher than in 1974.

Declines in fledging might stem from the same factor that caused a decline in sport fish abundance, namely, elimination of food items. If these declines represent a genuine trend and are not due to human disturbance, then they may indicate that the area around the isthmus has become so depauperate that there are not enough food alternatives available for gulls at this colony.

Several considerations argue against this explanation, however. First, in view of the flexible nature of gull diets, I find it difficult to imagine that the waters around the isthmus would not provide enough forage for less than 30 pairs of gulls and their young. Furthermore, Hunt and Hunt (1975) found little evidence of starvation (only 6.06 per cent of their sample) in the considerably larger colony of Western Gulls on Santa Barbara Island in 1972. In that colony, 84.8 per cent of chicks reached a weight of 500 g (the Hunts' criterion for chick survival). In addition, since clutch sizes actually increased, food presumably would have to be abundant early in the season but decrease significantly at some point after laying to lead to starvation of young.

Another explanation for the decline in fledging on Bird Rock might be that egg and chick mortality stemming directly from crowding and aggression has increased to a point where fledging is severely reduced. Such conditions would be seriously aggravated by any human visits to such a small colony. This possibility seems plausible in view of the small amount of suitable nesting habitat on Bird Rock and the small and visually exposed spaces between nests. Examination of Figure 1 shows that, in addition to increased numbers of nests in 1974 (29 compared with 24 in 1965), the nests were also less spread out in 1974, resulting in higher density on the preferred slope. At such close internest distances, and without any visual barriers between pairs or cover for chicks, aggressive interactions with several neighbors might keep the birds in sufficient turmoil to facilitate numerous egg thefts. High chick mortality might be even more likely.

On Santa Barbara Island, with roughly 1,200 to 1,500 pairs of gulls, abundant space seems to be available and some other factor or factors are probably limiting colony growth. On Bird Rock, space may be more critical. If this is the case, we have some interesting contrasts in factors affecting Western Gull colonies within the limits of the Channel Island area. Long-term comparative studies of both colonies of this species, located within a few miles of each other, could provide valuable information on gull population dynamics.

SUMMARY

In 1974, data were collected on nest placement, clutch sizes, and rates of hatching and fledging of Western Gulls on Bird Rock, Santa Catalina Island. This paper compares these data with a similar study made at the same site in 1965 and 1966. Judged by the number of nests and eggs laid, the colony appears to be stable or growing, but the number of fledglings in 1974 was significantly reduced below 1965-66 values. This may have been caused by increased nesting density in 1974. "Supernormal" clutches were found in four years: one in 1965, one in 1966, two in 1974, and three in 1975.

ACKNOWLEDGMENTS

I wish to thank friends and acquaintances who donated labor, equipment, and encouragement. These include Margie Chapman, John Pilger, Bobette Nelson, Stacy Hand, Harold M. Hand, Sr., and Harold M. Hand, Jr. The staff and several students at the USC Marine Station were very helpful in providing boat transportation to Bird Rock on several occasions. Gilbert Grant and Thomas Howell read the manuscript and I appreciate their valuable criticisms and suggestions.

REFERENCES

BURGER, J. 1974. Breeding adaptations of Franklin's Gull to a marsh habitat. Anim. Behav. 22:521-567.

COULTER, M. C. 1973. Breeding biology of the Western Gull, *Larus occidentalis*. M.S. thesis, Oxford University, Oxford.

HARPER, C. A. 1971. Breeding biology of a small colony of Western Gulls *(Larus occidentalis wymani)* in California. Condor 73:337-341.

HUNT, G. L., JR., and M. W. HUNT. 1975. Reproductive ecology of the Western Gull: the importance of nest spacing. Auk 92:270-279.

———. 1977. Female-female pairing in Western Gulls *(Larus occidentalis)* in southern California. Science 196:1466-1467.

PIEROTTI, R. 1976. Sex roles, social structure, and the role of the environment in the Western Gull *(Larus occidentalis* Audubon). M.A. thesis, California State University, Sacramento, Calif.

SCHREIBER, R. W. 1970. Breeding biology of Western Gulls *(Larus occidentalis)* on San Nicolas Island, California, 1968. Condor 72:133-140.

WINGFIELD, J. C., A. MARTIN, M. W. HUNT, G. L. HUNT, JR., and D. S. FARNER. 1980. Origin of homosexual pairing of female Western Gulls on Santa Barbara Island. Pp. 461-466 *in* D.M. Power, ed., The California Islands: proceedings of a multidisciplinary symposium. Santa Barbara Museum of Natural History, Santa Barbara, Calif.

Pinnipeds of the California Islands: Abundance and Distribution

Burney J. Le Boeuf and Michael L. Bonnell

Crown College and Center for Coastal Marine Studies,
University of California, Santa Cruz, California 95064

INTRODUCTION

The purpose of this paper is to update George Bartholomew's (1967) article published in the last symposium proceedings on the biology of the California Islands. We will expand on his article by treating the California Islands in a most general sense; by California Islands we mean those islands in western Baja California, Mexico, the Channel Islands in the Southern California Bight, and Año Nuevo and the Farallons in northern California.

It is no small problem to deal with six species of pinnipeds on eighteen islands or island groups. We will have to be brief, severely limit our aspirations, and beg the reader to take some statements on faith. We will dispense with background history, biomedical physiology, esoteric behavior, and cute anecdotes and just plunge into number, distribution, movements, and population trends because we think that understanding the role of pinnipeds in the ecology of the California Islands starts here. We will emphasize changes in various characteristics of pinniped populations which have occurred during the last 13 years—changes in number and distribution and changes in reproductive rate and mortality. Most of the data we present were obtained simply by counting.

It will be helpful to consider three things regarding the animal subjects before presenting data. (1) Pinnipeds are long-lived (15 to 25 years is a reasonable estimate of longevity). This means that some of the animals counted in 1977 were counted by Bartholomew in the early 1960s. The time dimension involved in the study of pinnipeds is quite different from that of most other species on the California Islands. Obviously one cannot talk about the evolution of populations of pinnipeds during the last 13 years. (2) Most pinniped populations were severely depleted during the last century. Thus, we are looking at them during a period of recovery. (3) Many systematic studies of the pinniped populations in Baja California and California have been conducted since Bartholomew's 1967 paper was published.

To justify this last point, and for whatever historical value there may be, we mention five recent and ongoing research efforts: (1) Le Boeuf and numerous collaborators from the University of California at Santa Cruz have studied pinniped populations from Baja California to northern California from 1967 to the present, making approximately one expedition per year to the Baja California islands, to San Miguel Island and San Nicolas Island in southern California, and year-round daily observations on Año Nuevo Island in northern California. (2) Intensive, systematic studies supported by the Bureau of Land Management began in the Southern California Bight in 1974 and were conducted during the period 1974 to 1978 (Le Boeuf, Bonnell, Pierson, Dettman, and Farrens 1976). The census methods used in these studies were more thorough and systematic than those of previous studies in the area. Pinnipeds were counted on all islands in the Southern California Bight eight times per year. Eight aerial and eight ship transects were made over water each year. In addition, detailed observations during the breeding season were made on San Miguel Island and Santa Barbara Island. (3) A long-term study of the northern fur seal population on San Miguel Island by the National Marine Fisheries Service began in 1969 and is still going on. The principal researchers involved in the project have been Robert DeLong and G.A. Antonelis. (4) During 1974 and 1975, Bruce

FIGURE 1. *A photograph of the northern fur seal colony at Adam's Cove, San Miguel Island, taken on 21 July 1968. The adult male is in the center; on the left are some of the females, and on the right are newborn pups. California sea lion males and females are in the background.*

Mate, supported by the Marine Mammal Commission, conducted several aerial censuses of pinnipeds from Vancouver Island south along the coast of Washington, Oregon, California, and Baja California to Cabo San Lucas, and then along several points of the coast in the Sea of Cortez. (5) David Ainley, Harriet Huber, and collaborators from the Point Reyes Bird Observatory have conducted detailed censuses of pinnipeds on the Farallon Islands year-round from 1969 to the present.

In addition, numerous individuals have studied colonies of particular species. For example, Daniel Odell studied northern elephant seals and California sea lions on San Nicolas Island during the early 1970s; Roger Gentry, Finn Sandegren, and Robert Gisiner studied breeding behavior of Steller sea lions on Año Nuevo Island; and Charles Woodhouse and Paul Paulbitski observed harbor seals in southern California and northern California, respectively.

ACCOUNTS OF SPECIES
Northern Fur Seals

Bartholomew (1967) stated that northern fur seals were regular visitors to offshore waters in the Southern California Bight. He noted that the only time these animals were seen on islands or on the mainland was when they were sick, and this was an infrequent occurrence.

Since that time, the northern fur seal has started breeding on San Miguel Island in southern California and has shown signs of being there to stay. In July of 1968, a small colony of approximately 100 fur seals was discovered at Adam's Cove on San Miguel Island (Peterson, Le Boeuf, and DeLong 1968). Photographs taken earlier revealed that the colony had been established before this date, certainly by 1964, and probably as early as 1961. In 1968, the colony on Adam's Cove contained one male, 60 females, and 40 newborn pups (Fig. 1). Tags on several of the females indicated that they had been born on the Pribilof and Komandorski Islands in the Bering Sea. The colony has grown rapidly since that time. Figure 2 shows that the number of pups born annually has increased exponentially. In 1972, another colony was discovered on Castle Rock, only a short distance north of San Miguel Island. It, too, has grown exponentially; 521 pups were born there in 1976. Thus, in 1976, the National Marine Fisheries

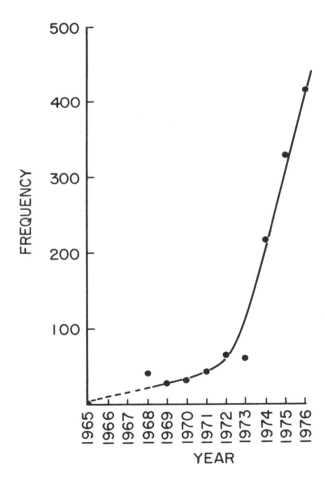

FIGURE 2. *Annual northern fur seal pup production at Point Bennett, San Miguel Island, during the period 1968 to 1976. The dotted line represents a hypothetical extrapolation of the curve to the mid-1960s, when breeding appears to have begun. The curve is plotted from data in Fiscus, DeLong, and Antonelis (1976).*

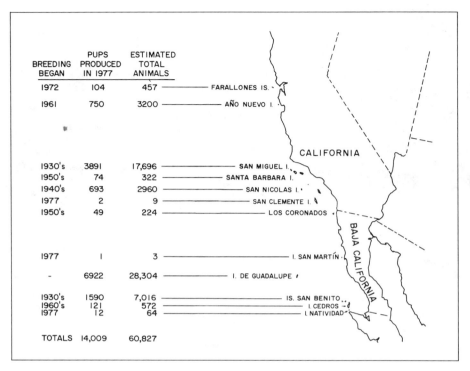

BREEDING BEGAN	PUPS PRODUCED IN 1977	ESTIMATED TOTAL ANIMALS	
1972	104	457	FARALLONES IS.
1961	750	3200	AÑO NUEVO I.
1930's	3891	17,696	SAN MIGUEL I.
1950's	74	322	SANTA BARBARA I.
1940's	693	2960	SAN NICOLAS I.
1977	2	9	SAN CLEMENTE I.
1950's	49	224	LOS CORONADOS
1977	1	3	I. SAN MARTÍN
-	6922	28,304	I. DE GUADALUPE
1930's	1590	7,016	IS. SAN BENITO
1960's	121	572	I. CEDROS
1977	12	64	I. NATIVIDAD
TOTALS	14,009	60,827	

FIGURE 3. *A 1977 summary of northern elephant seal breeding locations, the approximate time that breeding began, pup production, and estimated total population size. Adapted from Le Boeuf (1977) with additional data from Le Boeuf and Mate (1978).*

Service reported that a total of 938 were born on San Miguel Island (Fiscus, DeLong, and Antonelis 1976). The breeding population is estimated to be between two and four thousand animals and rising fast. Recruits continue to come in from the Bering Sea.

Why are these animals here? It is well known that this species migrates from the Bering Sea to as far south as 30°N latitude on both sides of the Pacific during the period from fall to spring (*e.g.*, see Johnson 1975). Le Boeuf *et al.* (1976) noted winter migrants in large numbers beyond the edge of the continental shelf, especially west of San Miguel Island. In addition, many fur seals were seen within the Southern California Bight, especially along the Santa Rosa Ridge and over the San Nicolas Basin near Tanner Bank. Apparently some of these animals failed to make the long trek back to the Bering Sea and started breeding at the farthest point in their migration. The growth of the population in the last decade indicates that the colony is firmly established.

Northern Elephant Seals

The northern elephant seal population reached its nadir in the late 1800s; less than 50 individuals were then living and they were found on only one island, Isla de Guadalupe. By the mid-1960s, Bartholomew (1967) was able to say that northern elephant seals had recovered from near extinction. Approximately 15,000 animals were counted in 1957, and 17,500 in 1965.

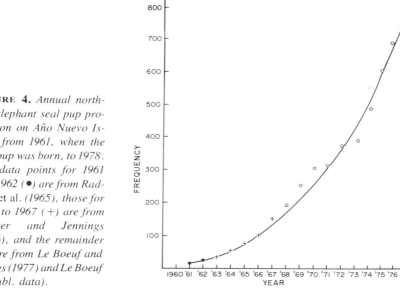

FIGURE 4. *Annual northern elephant seal pup production on Año Nuevo Island from 1961, when the first pup was born, to 1978. The data points for 1961 and 1962 (●) are from Radford* et al. *(1965), those for 1963 to 1967 (+) are from Poulter and Jennings (1966), and the remainder (○) are from Le Boeuf and Briggs (1977) and Le Boeuf (unpubl. data).*

The population was growing logarithmically. The species, all individual descendants from the remnant herd that survived in the latter part of the last century, was reoccupying its former range and was now breeding on Guadalupe, Islas San Benito, San Miguel Island, San Nicolas Island, Islas Los Coronados, and, most recently, Año Nuevo Island. He noted that this was one of the most dramatic demonstrations of population recovery known for any large mammal and he correctly predicted that it would continue.

The remarkable resurgence of the elephant seal has been well documented. Today there are approximately 60,000 elephant seals (Fig. 3). This represents more than a threefold increase in the population since 1965. These data are based on aerial and island censuses; each colony has been monitored very closely. For this species, we know approximately when breeding began at each colony, the number of pups produced, and the rate of growth. As of this writing, only Isla de Guadalupe, the mother colony, and Islas San Benito have populations which have stabilized. All other colonies are increasing in size and show indications of continuing to increase, space permitting (Le Boeuf 1977).

Bartholomew (1967) said that breeding had just begun on Año Nuevo Island. A lot has happened in the interim. Figure 4 shows that pup production was still increasing exponentially in 1978. Over 800 pups were produced on this tiny island. Figure 5 shows that the increase was not specific to pup production, but occurred in the entire colony population during virtually all phases of the annual cycle. By 1978, breeding beaches were so crowded at the peak of the breeding season that many pregnant females had a difficult time landing (Fig. 6). Apparently as a result of crowding, some females started to breed on the Farallon Islands in 1972 (Le Boeuf, Ainley, and Lewis 1974) and on the Año Nuevo mainland in 1975 (Le Boeuf and Panken 1977). The rate of pup production at these two locations has been even higher than the rate of growth described for Año Nuevo Island. Indeed, the annual increase in pup production at several

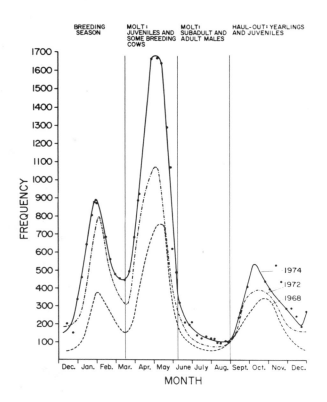

FIGURE 5. *Annual increase in total number of northern elephant seals throughout the annual cycle during the period 1968 to 1974. This annual rate of increment was still continuing in 1978.*

FIGURE 6. *An aerial photograph of the largest breeding aggregation of northern elephant seals on Año Nuevo Island taken on 21 January 1978, near the peak of the breeding season when crowding was greatest. Photograph by Frank McCrary, Jr.*

rookeries in recent years has ranged from approximately 12 to 400 per cent per year. The rate of growth of the total populations on San Miguel Island and San Nicolas Island, shown in Figures 7 and 8, is typical of expanding colonies. On both these islands the animals have not yet exhausted available breeding areas and further growth is expected.

The expansion of breeding areas on islands has proceeded from preferred sandy beaches to peripheral areas. The least preferred areas are cobblestone beaches. Figure 9 shows where elephant seals bred on San Miguel Island in 1976. In 1968, elephant seals bred only on the western tip of San Miguel, the area known as Point Bennett. In subsequent years, harems formed farther eastward each year so that, by 1978, the animals were breeding along virtually the entire southern portion of the island. At present, the animals show signs of starting to breed on the north side of the island, as well. A similar progression has taken place on San Nicolas Island.

We will note briefly some observations on island differences and colony formation which have been made during the last few years. The first concerns the sex and age composition of the breeding animals. This statistic is apparently determined by reproductive competition within each sex. The highest proportion of males at crowded rookeries, such as Isla de Guadalupe, are fully-grown adults. Young males going through puberty have a difficult time landing on breeding beaches and, consequently, many of them migrate to less crowded peripheral colonies, such as that on Año Nuevo Island during the 1960s (Le Boeuf 1974). Consequently, young pubescent males are under-represented at stable colonies like Isla de Guadalupe and are in the majority at peripheral colonies with space to accommodate immigrants. Similarly, the youngest females have a difficult time landing on crowded islands during the breeding season because they are smaller and subordinate to older females. The likelihood that the pups of young females that give birth on a crowded beach will survive is low because of the harassment from the older, larger, more aggressive females (Le Boeuf, Reiter, and Panken, unpubl. data). Consequently, it is the young females that colonize new places such as the Farallon Islands and the mainland across the channel from Año Nuevo Island (Le Boeuf and Panken 1977). Thus, one of the principal differences between an old established rookery and a new one is in the composition of breeding animals.

Island differences in male threat vocalizations, termed dialects, were noted by Le Boeuf and Peterson (1969). Le Boeuf and Petrinovich (1974) explained these differences as resulting from the manner in which the population expanded. To a certain extent, the dialects detected during the late 1960s reflected the direction and the time of dispersal from old established areas to new peripheral ones. Although inter-island differences were still apparent in the vocalizations of breeding-age males in 1978, the differences are decreasing annually as recruitment of individuals from large colonies to peripheral ones continues. If dispersion continues in this direction, the dialects will eventually disappear.

A complete lack of differences between individuals in different colonies was found in a study of genetic variability using blood proteins. Bonnell and Selander (1974) found no polymorphisms in 19 blood proteins at 24 different loci in a sample of 125 elephant seals from five different colonies. This was interpreted as indicating that elephant seals may lack genetic variation, relative to other marine and terrestrial mammals, and that this is, in large part, due to the bottleneck which the population underwent during the latter part of the last century.

Finally, a study of pup mortality by Le Boeuf and Briggs (1977) indicated that the pup mortality rate on Año Nuevo Island varied from 13 to 26 per cent per year during the period 1968 to 1976. This mortality rate was found to be higher than that estimated for San Miguel and San Nicolas Islands. The annual pup mortality rate for the Farallon Islands, on the other hand, has varied from 7 to 71 per cent of pups born during the period 1974 to 1977 (Ainley *et al.* 1978). Le Boeuf and Briggs (1977) concluded that weather was a very important variable which could

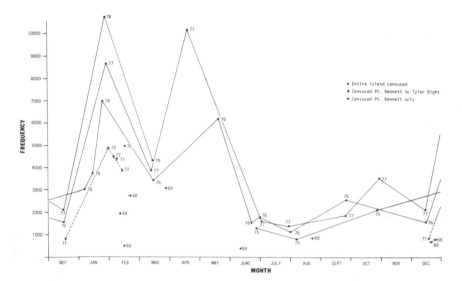

FIGURE 7. *Growth of the northern elephant seal population on San Miguel Island as reflected by censuses of total number of animals. Data points connected by straight lines for different years are from Le Boeuf et al. (1976). The remainder of the data points are from several investigators (see Le Boeuf et al. 1976 for references).*

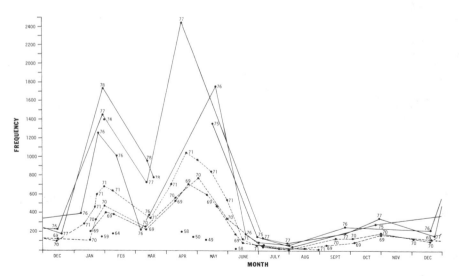

FIGURE 8. *Growth of the northern elephant seal population on San Nicolas Island as reflected by censuses of total number of animals. Data points connected by straight lines for different years are from Le Boeuf et al. (1976), those connected by a dotted line (the years 1969, 1970, and 1971) are from Odell (1972, 1974), and the remainder of the data points are from several investigators (see Le Boeuf et al. 1976 for references).*

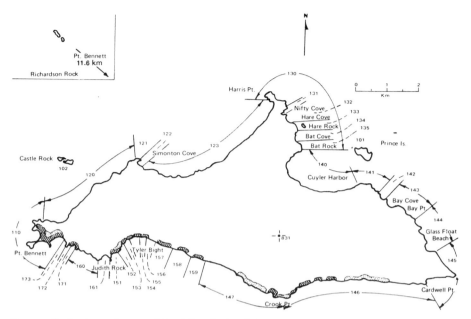

FIGURE 9. *A schematic map of San Miguel Island showing where northern elephant seals bred (crosshatched areas) and the principal resting areas (dotted areas) in 1976. The code numbers are for area identification. Adapted from Le Boeuf et al. (1976).*

interact with other factors to greatly augment mortality. This conclusion was borne out on Año Nuevo Island in 1978 when bad weather caused the pup mortality rate to exceed 40 per cent of pups born.

The present status of northern elephant seals can be summarized as follows: the population is increasing. Breeding space appears to limit population growth more readily than does food. Mainland breeding is an unusual event—a change in breeding habitat which could not have worked 200 years ago because of land predators, but a strategy which is working very well in the 1970s because grizzly bears, wolves, and mountain lions have been virtually eliminated. The extraordinary recovery of the northern elephant seal population continues, but the apparent lack of genetic variation indicated by blood protein studies is a matter of interest and concern (Le Boeuf 1977).

California Sea Lions

In this century, the California sea lion has been known to breed in the Southern California Bight, on islands along the west coast of California, and in the Gulf of California to the Tres Marías Islands. Bartholomew (1967) noted that the number of California sea lions breeding in the Southern California Bight increased exponentially during the first four decades that censuses were taken. The population in 1940 was estimated to be 2,000 animals. By 1964, Bartholomew estimated 17,000 animals and thought that the population was beginning to level off. He indicated that, with no disturbance, the population should remain between 15,000 and 20,000 animals. He further noted that males go north after the breeding season while females remain in the vicinity or move south. He called this species the most conspicuous and abundant pinniped in California and Mexico.

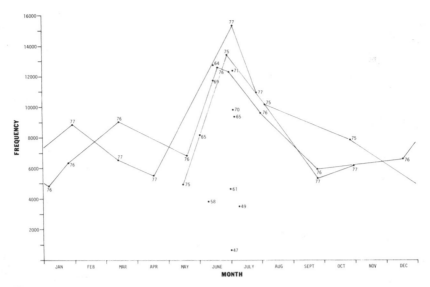

FIGURE 10. *Growth of the California sea lion population on San Nicolas Island as reflected by censuses of total number of animals. Data points connected by straight lines for different years are from Le Boeuf et al. (1976); references for other points can be found in Le Boeuf et al. (1976).*

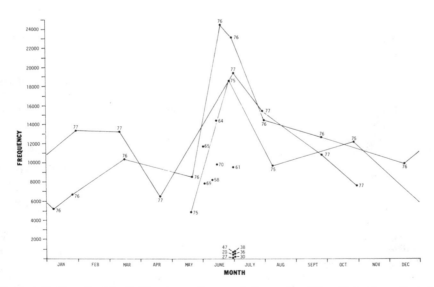

FIGURE 11. *Growth of the California sea lion population on San Miguel Island as reflected by censuses of total number of animals. Data points connected by straight lines for different years are from Le Boeuf et al. (1976); references for other points can be found in Le Boeuf et al. (1976).*

It has turned out that his estimate was low. In 1976, 48,000 California sea lions were counted on the Channel Islands (Le Boeuf *et al.* 1976), the area Bartholomew was referring to. This represents a 40 per cent increase in the population of this species since 1964 (Odell 1971). The population is still growing in the Channel Islands. The two largest rookeries are San Nicolas Island and San Miguel Island; 90 per cent of the California sea lions in southern California breed there. The growth of these two colonies during the last two decades is shown in Figures 10 and 11. Pup production in the Southern California Bight alone in 1976 was at least 13,500 pups, and may have been even greater (Le Boeuf *et al.* 1976). We think it is too soon to say whether the population is leveling off.

The California sea lion breeds on many islands in Baja California. The islands we monitored most closely were Los Coronados, San Martín, San Benito, Cedros, Natividad, and Guadalupe. Islas San Benito represent the largest rookery. Over 10,000 animals can be found there during the peak of the breeding season and approximately one-half that number at other times of the year. Colony size appears to be stable. Similarly, the small population on the distant oceanic island, Guadalupe, also appears to be stable. Colony size has varied from 230 to 750 animals during the last decade.

California sea lions do not breed regularly in northern California; one female was recorded giving birth on the Farallon Islands (Pierotti *et al.* 1977). Even so, thousands of animals haul out on Año Nuevo Island every year. The peak is in the fall during the male migration northward following the breeding season. The number of animals seen at this time of year has decreased considerably from a peak of 13,000 animals in 1961 (Orr and Poulter 1965) to a peak of about 2,000 animals in 1974 (Fig. 12). The peak number of animals was slightly less than 2,000 in 1977. On the other hand, the number of California sea lions sighted on the Farallon Islands has increased from approximately 400 in 1971 to almost 1,600 in 1977. The peak on the Farallon Islands occurs during the month of April (Ainley *et al.* 1978).

Mate (1977) estimates that the total California sea lion population in California and Baja California, including the Sea of Cortez, is approximately 75,000 animals. Le Boeuf *et al.* (1976) put this figure at 125,000 animals. We think that even the latter figure is probably a low estimate.

During the last 10 years, many premature pups have been aborted during the months between January and the beginning of the breeding season in early May (Odell 1970, Gilmartin *et al.* 1976). High pesticide levels, as well as viruses, have been implicated as possible causes (*e.g.*, Le Boeuf and Bonnell 1971, DeLong, Gilmartin, and Simpson 1973, Smith *et al.* 1974, Gilmartin *et al.* 1976). The trend in premature pupping continues, although a complete explanation for this phenomenon is still lacking.

Harbor Seals

Bartholomew (1967) observed that harbor seals were seen in the Southern California Bight throughout the year in groups of a few dozen to over 100 individuals. He remarked that nothing was known about their seasonal movements but they appeared to be more sedentary than other pinnipeds in the area. He estimated the population in southern California to be approximately 500 and he noted that there was no evidence of much change during the previous 20 years.

More recent data by Odell (1971) and Le Boeuf *et al.* (1976) show that the population in southern California has grown slowly. Odell reported a June 1964 census of 645 animals. In June 1975, Le Boeuf *et al.* (1976) counted 1,090 animals, and in June of 1977, 1,656 animals were counted. In these aerial surveys, harbor seals were seen on the following islands: San Miguel, Santa Rosa, Santa Cruz, Anacapa, San Nicolas, Santa Barbara, Santa Catalina, and San Clemente. It was further noted that the number on land varied seasonally, with the highest number of animals being seen in the late spring and early summer during the breeding season

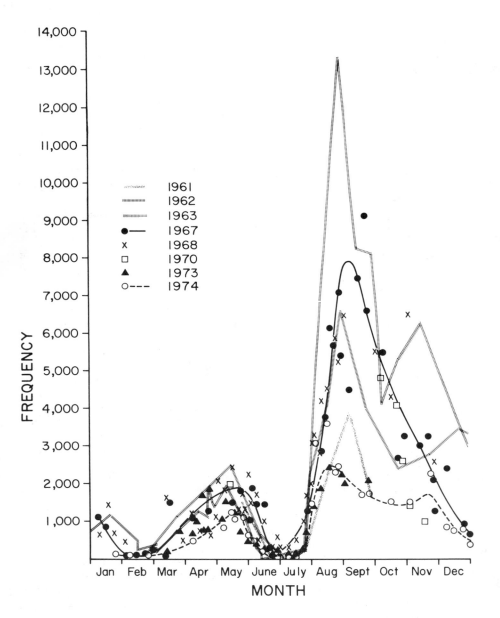

FIGURE 12. *Censuses of California sea lions on Año Nuevo Island, 1961 to 1974. Data from 1961 to 1963 are from Orr and Poulter (1965).*

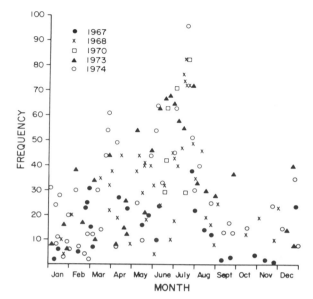

FIGURE 13. *Censuses of harbor seals on Año Nuevo Island from 1967 to 1974. The number of seals counted varied so much with tidal conditions and time of day that it is difficult to compare censuses from year to year. Note that the highest censuses each year were taken in late July.*

(these counts include pups). The average count at other times of the year was approximately 400 individuals. Herds were observed repeatedly in the same areas. The largest numbers were consistently seen on San Miguel Island (*e.g.,* 600 animals in June 1975) and Santa Rosa Island (*e.g.,* 336 in June 1975, 900 in April 1977). Harbor seals were rarely seen at sea; the few sightings were in the Santa Barbara Channel area.

Bartholomew (1967) had no censuses from Baja California. Mate (1977) made aerial censuses in this region during 1974 and 1975, and Le Boeuf and collaborators made periodic censuses in the area from 1968 to 1978. Mate counted 400 harbor seals from the southern California border to the southern tip of Baja California. He found no harbor seals south of Isla Cedros. Our studies reveal that most harbor seals along the west coast of Baja California occur on two islands: Los Coronados and San Martín. On the former, the census counts in the last decade vary from 36 to 136 animals. Pups were seen as early as 11 March in 1974. The highest counts always occurred on the middle island. Isla San Martín may be the southernmost rookery along the west coast of Baja California. Large numbers of harbor seals haul out there in a shallow lagoon on the east side of the island. Three censuses from that area are available: 60 animals with two pups were counted on 21 April 1970, 223 animals with 15 pups were counted on 28 May 1971, and 236 animals with nine pups (three dead) were counted on 19 February 1977. Apparently, breeding in Baja California occurs during February, March, and April. This is somewhat early compared with more northerly places where harbor seals breed.

In northern California, harbor seals breed on Año Nuevo Island, the Farallon Islands, in San Francisco Bay, and at several other locations along the mainland shore. On Año Nuevo Island, as elsewhere, there is great fluctuation in colony number with tide and time of day. The greatest number is seen during the late afternoon and at low tide. Here, these animals breed from April to late May and the greatest number of them is always in July. The peak number in July has steadily increased since the early 1960s (Fig. 13). Eighty-six were counted in 1963 (Orr and Poulter 1965). Le Boeuf and collaborators counted 85 in 1968, 95 in 1970, 162 in 1976, and 183 on 12 July 1977. Evidently the population is increasing slowly.

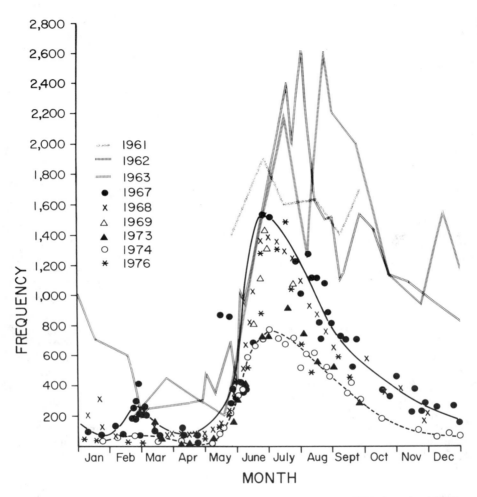

FIGURE 14. *Censuses of Steller sea lions on Año Nuevo Island, 1961 to 1974. Data from 1961 to 1963 are from Orr and Poulter (1965).*

Harbor seals were first seen on the Farallon Islands during the fall of 1971 (Ainley *et al.* 1977). Breeding occurred in 1974. In July of 1977, 26 harbor seals were counted, a 13 per cent increase over 1976 (Ainley *et al.* 1978). These animals are now present there year-round.

Combining the figure of Mate (1977) and those from the Bureau of Land Management studies (Le Boeuf *et al.* 1976), we estimate that the harbor seal population from Año Nuevo Island south to Isla San Martín is at least 2,500 animals. The greatest number ever seen together is approximately 250 animals. We suspect that groups of 100 or more may move *en masse* from one island to the next, or from the island to the mainland (*e.g.*, from Año Nuevo to the mainland, from Los Coronados to an area near Tijuana, from San Martín to an area near San Quintín). We conclude that there are more harbor seals today than there were in the mid-1960s. Harbor seals have been increasing in numbers slowly and consistently throughout their range.

Steller Sea Lions

The Steller sea lion was the most abundant pinniped in southern California during the late 1920s. During the 1930s, 2,000 animals were reported to breed on San Miguel Island alone. However, the number breeding there has been declining ever since. In 1958, Bartholomew (1967) noted that less than 100 animals bred in the Channel Islands, and then only on the western tip of San Miguel Island. In contrast, Bartholomew stated that the population on Año Nuevo Island had been stable for a long time and that approximately 1,000 adults were recorded annually during the breeding season. He mentioned that there was a seasonal separation of sexes similar to that of California sea lions during the nonbreeding season.

During the last 13 years, the Steller sea lion has been seen in the Southern California Bight only on San Miguel Island and in steadily decreasing numbers. Odell (1971) reported 61 adults and seven pups on San Miguel Island in June 1964 and said that they bred there in 1969 and 1970. DeLong (1975) reported that approximately 10 pups were born on San Miguel Island each year since 1969. The highest counts determined by the Bureau of Land Management studies from aerial censuses were four adult males, 12 females, and three pups on 7 August 1975 (Le Boeuf et al. 1976). Steller sea lions have been observed only on Point Bennett, Richardson Rock, and Castle Rock near San Miguel Island. These animals are rarely seen at sea in southern California. Clearly, the decline in southern California continues and there are evidently less than 50 individuals there during the breeding season.

The population of Steller sea lions is four to six times lower than it was 40 years ago on the Farallon Islands. The population peaks in April when migrants haul out briefly. The breeding population is apparently stable at approximately 130 animals. The pregnancy rate is low, approximately 24 per cent; only about 27 pups are born each year. Most of the pups born before the first week in June are stillborn or die shortly after birth. The mortality rate is high, approximately 41 per cent, and is due primarily to premature births. The trend has been very consistent during the last four years (Ainley et al. 1978).

On Año Nuevo Island, the population has fluctuated slightly during the last two decades (Fig. 14). Peak population in 1977 was similar to that in 1974. Pup production has varied from 300 to 600 per year.

We conclude that the population is continuing to decrease in the southern portion of the range and is relatively stable in northern California. Bartholomew (1967) suggests several reasons for the declining numbers in southern California.

Guadalupe Fur Seals

A few years ago, it was not clear whether the Guadalupe fur seal had ever occurred in the Southern California Bight. Bartholomew (1967) knew that the species had occurred on Isla de Guadalupe, Islas San Benito, and on the Farallon Islands before exploitation began. He estimated the 1965 population to be between 400 and 600 animals on Isla de Guadalupe, the only place where these animals bred at the time. He noted that occasional males were seen on San Nicolas Island and on Islas San Benito.

A recent paper by Walker (in press) presents evidence that the Guadalupe fur seal did reside in the Channel Islands before exploitation began. He found that Guadalupe fur seal bones were the most frequent remains in archaeological sites on the west end of San Miguel Island, being more common than those of any other Pacific pinniped or those of the sea otter.

Today, the Guadalupe fur seal still breeds only on Isla de Guadalupe. Winter counts have increased from 350 on 17 February 1969 to 470 on 13 February 1977. The highest summer census was taken in 1977 by Luis Fleischer and Mark Pierson (unpubl. data). They counted 1,073 animals; 400 of them were pups. We estimate, therefore, that the present population of Guadalupe fur seals numbers approximately 2,000 individuals. Fleischer and Pierson con-

FIGURE 15. *An adult female and adult male Guadalupe fur seal photographed against the background of volcanic rock and caves which they inhabit.*

cluded that boat censuses underestimate by at least 50 per cent the number of individuals present. Pup counts from boats may underestimate the true figure by as much as 90 per cent.

It is now evident that Guadalupe fur seals are expanding their range southward on the east side of Isla de Guadalupe. However, they still inhabit only rocky areas where there are numerous caves (Fig. 15). Studies on population dynamics and social and reproductive behavior continue.

In the last few years, DeLong and others have seen occasional male Guadalupe fur seals on San Miguel Island (pers. comm.). One male held a territory against California sea lions in 1973 and 1974 (DeLong 1975).

SUMMARY

The following points characterize the present status of each of the pinnipeds inhabiting the California Islands.

(1) Northern fur seals started breeding on San Miguel Island in southern California during

the 1960s. They show signs of being there to stay. The population numbered at least 2,000 animals in 1976.

(2) The fantastic recovery of the northern elephant seal continues. Dramatic increases in their numbers continue throughout the range and several new colonies are being formed. In 1977, there were approximately 60,000 elephant seals.

(3) There are now twice as many California sea lions on the California Islands as there were 13 years ago. There were 80,000 to 125,000 animals in Californian and Mexican waters in 1976.

(4) There are at least three times as many harbor seals on the California Islands as pinniped researchers thought there were in 1965. Approximately 2,000 harbor seals were counted in 1976.

(5) Steller sea lions continue to decline in southern California, although their numbers have been relatively stable in northern California. There were less than 50 Steller sea lions in the Southern California Bight in 1976 (all on San Miguel Island), and approximately 1,600 breeding individuals in northern California in that same year.

(6) Guadalupe fur seals continue their slow recovery from near extinction. The highest count during a breeding season was in 1977 when 1,073 individuals were seen. The entire world population probably numbers less than 2,000 individuals.

Finally, we would like to note that the perspective one gains from summarizing species by species obscures the rhythm and seasonality of island use by pinnipeds. There is a dovetailing of the activities of different species on land throughout the year, and also variation in patterns of island use within each species with respect to sex and age. For example, northern elephant seal adults breed on San Miguel Island in winter while juveniles are at sea. In spring, juveniles and adult females molt on this island while adult males are at sea. When northern elephant seals breed there are few California sea lions on land—the opposite is true in summer. Again, one will find pinnipeds at Adam's Cove, San Miguel Island, for example, at all times of the year, but the number representing each species, and the sex and age composition within each species, will vary predictably with time of year.

ACKNOWLEDGMENTS

This research was supported in part by NSF grant DEB 77-17063 and Bureau of Land Management contract AA550-CT7-36.

REFERENCES

AINLEY, D. G., H. R. HUBER, R. P. HENDERSON, and T. J. LEWIS. 1977. Studies of marine mammals at the Farallon Islands, California, 1970-1975. Final report to U.S. Marine Mammal Commission, Washington, D.C. (Contract MM4AC002).

AINLEY, D. G., H. R. HUBER, S. MORRELL, and R. H. LE VALLEY. 1978. Studies at the Farallon Islands, 1977. Final report to U.S. Marine Mammal Commission, Washington, D.C. (Contract MM6AC027).

BARTHOLOMEW, G. A. 1967. Seal and sea lion populations of the California Islands. Pp. 227-244 in R. N. Philbrick, ed., Proceedings of the symposium on the biology of the California Islands. Santa Barbara Botanic Garden, Santa Barbara, Calif.

BONNELL, M. L., and R. K. SELANDER. 1974. Elephant seals: genetic variation and near extinction. Science 184:908-909.

DeLONG, R. L. 1975. San Miguel Island management plan. U.S. Marine Mammal Commission, Washington, D.C.

DeLONG, R. L., W. G. GILMARTIN, and J. G. SIMPSON. 1973. Premature births in California sea lions: association with high organochlorine pollutant levels. Science 181:1168-1170.

FISCUS, C. H., R. L. DELONG, and G. A. ANTONELIS. 1976. Population growth and behavior, San Miguel Island. Pp. 40-51 *in* Fur seal investigations, 1976. U.S. Dept. Commerce, National Oceanic and Atmospheric Administration, National Marine Fisheries Service, Northwest and Alaska Fisheries Center, Marine Mammal Division, Seattle, Wash.

GILMARTIN, W. G., R. L. DELONG, A. W. SMITH, J. C. SWEENEY, B. W. DE LAPPE, R. W. RISEBROUGH, L. A. GRINER, M. D. DAILEY, and D. B. PEAKALL. 1976. Premature pupping in the California sea lion. J. Wildl. Diseases 12:104-115.

JOHNSON, A. 1975. The status of northern fur seal populations. Rapp. P-v. Réun. Cons. Int. Explor. Mer. 169:263-266.

LE BOEUF, B. J. 1974. Male-male competition and reproductive success in elephant seals. Amer. Zool. 14:163-176.

_____. 1977. Back from extation? Pacific Discovery 30:1-9.

LE BOEUF, B. J., D. G. AINLEY, and T. J. LEWIS. 1974. Elephant seals on the Farallones: population structure of an incipient breeding colony. J. Mammal. 55:370-385.

LE BOEUF, B. J., and M. L. BONNELL. 1971. DDT in California sea lions. Nature 234:108-110.

LE BOEUF, B. J., M. L. BONNELL, M. O. PIERSON, D. H. DETTMAN, and G. D. FARRENS. 1976. Numbers, distribution and movements of pinnipeds in the Southern California Bight. Final report, 1975-1976, to the Bureau of Land Management, U.S. Dept. Interior, Washington, D.C. (Contract 08550-CT5-28).

LE BOEUF, B. J., and K. T. BRIGGS. 1977. The cost of living in a seal harem. Mammalia 41:167-195.

LE BOEUF, B. J., and B. R. MATE. 1978. Elephant seals colonize additional Mexican and Californian islands. J. Mammal. 59:621-622.

LE BOEUF, B. J., and K. PANKEN. 1977. Elephant seals breeding on the mainland in California. Proc. California Acad. Sci. 41:267-280.

LE BOEUF, B. J., and R. S. PETERSON. 1969. Dialects in elephant seals. Science 166:1654-1656.

LE BOEUF, B. J., and L. F. PETRINOVICH. 1974. Dialects of northern elephant seals, *Mirounga angustirostris:* origin and reliability. Anim. Behav. 22:656-663.

MATE, B. R. 1977. Aerial censusing of pinnipeds in the eastern Pacific for assessment of population numbers, migratory distributions, rookery stability, breeding effort, and recruitment. Final report to U.S. Marine Mammal Commission, Washington, D.C. (Contract MM5AC001).

ODELL, D. K. 1970. Premature pupping in the California sea lion. *In* Proceedings of the seventh annual biosonar and diving mammal conference. Stanford Research Institute, Menlo Park, Calif.

_____. 1971. Censuses of pinnipeds breeding on the California Channel Islands. J. Mammal. 52:187-190.

_____. 1972. Studies on the biology of the California sea lion and the northern elephant seal on San Nicolas Island, California. Ph.D. thesis, University of California, Los Angeles, Calif.

_____. 1974. Seasonal occurrence of the northern elephant seal, *Mirounga angustirostris,* on San Nicolas Island, California. J. Mammal. 55:81-95.

ORR, R. T., and T. C. POULTER. 1965. The pinniped population of Año Nuevo Island, California. Proc. California Acad. Sci. 32:377-404.

PETERSON, R. S., B. J. LE BOEUF, and R. L. DELONG. 1968. Fur seals from the Bering Sea breeding in California. Nature 219:899-901.

PIEROTTI, R. J., D. G. AINLEY, T. J. LEWIS, and M. C. COULTER. 1977. Birth of a California sea lion on Southwest Farallon Island. California Fish and Game 63:64-65.

POULTER, T. C., and R. JENNINGS. 1966. Annual report to the Division of Beaches and Parks, State of California. Stanford Research Institute, Menlo Park, Calif.

RADFORD, K. W., R. T. ORR, and C. L. HUBBS. 1965. Reestablishment of the northern elephant seal *(Mirounga angustirostris)* off central California. Proc. California Acad. Sci. 31:602-612.

SMITH, A. W., C. M. PRATO, W. G. GILMARTIN, R. J. BROWN, and M. C. KEYES. 1974. A preliminary report on potentially pathogenic microbiological agents recently isolated from pinnipeds. J. Wildl. Diseases 10:54-59.

WALKER, P. Archaeological evidence concerning the prehistoric occurrence of sea mammals at Point Bennett, San Miguel Island. California Fish and Game (in press).

BIOGEOGRAPHY,
EVOLUTION,
AND ECOLOGY OF
LAND ANIMALS

Land Vertebrates on the California Channel Islands: Sweepstakes or Bridges?

Adrian M. Wenner[1] and Donald L. Johnson[2]

[1]*Marine Science Institute, University of California, Santa Barbara, California 93106*

[2]*Department of Geography, University of Illinois, Urbana, Illinois 61801*

INTRODUCTION

Often geologists cannot offer much help in telling us the extent of antique land connections, if any, of islands. Most frequently, the best evidence is in the kinds of animals and plants present, if we can perceptively interpret these living archives [Carlquist 1965].

When one visits an island and finds organisms on it, the question, "How did they get here?" is almost inevitable. If islands are close to the mainland, as in the case of the California Islands, the problem is somewhat simplified. Plants (because of their seeds) and birds and insects (because of their wings) are not puzzling, except in some cases. Mayr (1940:201) expressed that idea as follows:

Dispersal across the sea is, of course, most obvious for birds, and ornithologists were among the first who accepted the ideas of the permanency of continents and oceans. Most entomologists are also beginning to realize that they can solve most of their distributional difficulties without land bridges.

On the other hand, land vertebrates, including forms such as elephants, have posed a greater problem because of their larger size and supposed lack of over-water dispersal adaptations. It is little wonder, under the circumstances, that early island researchers favored land bridge hypotheses to explain the migration of nonflying animals between any particular mainland and adjacent islands where those same animals occurred. Massive earth movements can occur and have occurred worldwide, and ocean levels have risen and fallen repeatedly relative to land heights (marine terraces along the California coast provide a striking confirmation in the local area). Under the circumstances, land-island bridges are clearly conceivable, given a sufficiently long span of time.

Unfortunately, biologists have not always been conservative with respect to proposed land bridges. Neither have they always coordinated their efforts well with other biologists or with geological theory, with sometimes rather amusing results. In one case, Zimmerman (1942:282) was led to remark:

So many continents and land bridges have been built in and across the Pacific by biologists that, were they all plotted together on a map, there would be little space left for water.

Zimmerman has not been alone. Biogeographers have consistently objected to an indiscriminate "construction" of land bridges merely to accommodate animal dispersal. Some of the more striking examples of objections which we came across are listed here in chronological order:

It is an established fact that both land plants and land animals cross considerable stretches of water by floating, by carriage on natural rafts, or by wind. . . [Simpson 1940:756].

The means of dispersal of most plants and animals are much more extensive than was formerly realized, and even rather irregular distributions can be explained without the help of land bridges [Mayr 1940:201].

Most of the land bridges suggested to account for the distribution of certain plants and animals in the Pacific create more problems than they solve [Zimmerman 1942:282].

Many zoogeographers used to assume (and a few still do) that if land animals are found on an island . . . they must have reached there by continuous land, across a filter bridge, at least, if not a land corridor. . . . [I]t has become clear that when the whole fauna is taken into consideration the land fauna of some islands cannot be explained by land connections. . . [Simpson 1953:24].

[A]ny mammal may sometimes get across a narrow water gap, and . . . some mammals have crossed fairly wide ones. Rodents seem to be relatively good water crossers [Darlington 1957:322].

Merely because an island has some sedentary mammal or birds, biogeographers should not overrule geological evidence that this island was unconnected [MacArthur 1972:85].

The California Islands host a variety of organisms, some groups of which have now been well studied by many biologists. The 1965 symposium (Philbrick 1967) provided a platform for an exchange of views about island biology and the related geology of those islands. In reading through the resultant symposium volume, we were struck by the rather general acceptance of the land bridge hypothesis, with one notable exception (either that, or participants did not speak to the issue at all).

Since that earlier symposium, new lines of evidence and new attitudes have emerged which bear on the problem of island life, particularly as that evidence relates to the Northern Channel Islands. Information on the geology of the Santa Barbara Channel is becoming available. Plate tectonic theory is increasingly invoked to explain geologic events. Radiometric, paleomagnetic, and amino acid dating have come into more widespread use.

The present symposium is, we think, a most appropriate time for a general overview of the land bridge concept as it relates to land vertebrates on the Northern Channel Islands. We first review the evidence for the hypothesized land bridge, its geological basis, and when it may have existed. We then examine various theoretical ways that animals get to islands. This is followed by a comparison between island and mainland faunas, a biogeographical examination of individual land vertebrate forms, and a discussion of the biogeographical role of Indians. We conclude with an overview of the implications of our theses for island biogeography.

ISLAND-MAINLAND CONNECTION?

If a land bridge did exist between the mainland and the Northern Channel Islands, when did it connect them? We asked this question of the literature and of geologists, but found no consensus. This uncertainty forced us to a rather extensive review of the concept of geological time, past and present geology of the local area, and evolutionary history of elephants in North America. We found answers to some of our questions; others remained unsolved, and a few new ones were raised. We here review our findings on this essential issue before turning to the history of land vertebrates on these islands.

Geological Time and Island Biogeography

Unfortunately, geologic time often is necessarily ill-defined, based as it usually is on the relative age and location of various rock strata and organisms embedded therein. The inherent difficulty in understanding those relationships has been somewhat compounded for nonspecialists by a lack of consistency in the manner in which geologists and biologists refer to given events or time periods. For example, if a stratum was formed somewhat less than a million years ago, one might find its age (plus the fossils contained therein) referred to as mid-Pleistocene, Quaternary, Yarmouth interglacial, Irvingtonian, or late Cenozoic. We found that these terms, though useful when referring to relatively long time spans, have much less

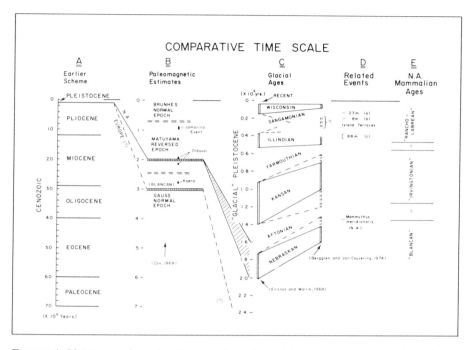

FIGURE 1. *Pleistocene chronology is currently under revision as a consequence of new dating techniques. The traditional estimate of one million years duration for the Pleistocene (column A) has been replaced by other estimates, depending on which deposit or event is being dated (column B). Opinions also are now different with regard to the duration of various glacial ages (column C) and will remain so, apparently, until geologists reach agreement on the dates of various events (we have not addressed the time of the Miocene-Pliocene boundary, which is now estimated to be at about 6 x 10⁶ years). See text for further explanation.*

utility with respect to the biogeography of the California Islands. Neither were the more accurate radiocarbon dates of much value, since they normally apply to events which occurred less than about 40,000 years ago.

Within the past two decades, potassium-argon, magnetic reversal, and amino acid dating techniques have come into general use, affording great potential for dating Quaternary and pre-Pleistocene events (*e.g.*, Berggren and Van Couvering 1974, Cox 1969, Evernden *et al.* 1964, Savage and Curtis 1970), supposedly providing accuracy within about 0.01 million years. Although more research is needed to thoroughly illuminate each time period, we think it is now possible to provide a partial, if tentative, summary of various events and time references as shown in Figure 1.

We must comment about several aspects, assumptions, and sources used in constructing Figure 1, discussed here in the order in which the columns appear in that figure:

(1) At one time, a special committee of the National Research Council specified a chronological sequence for Cenozoic time (Zimmerman 1948). In retrospect, now that more accurate dates and dating techniques are available, reliance on these guidelines does not appear advisable. While the Pliocene-Pleistocene boundary still remains in dispute (Haq *et al.* 1977),

the one million years allowed for the Pleistocene appears to have been far too short. Estimates we obtained from more recent literature considerably exceeded that value. To illustrate, we show three recent estimates, one by Berggren and Van Couvering (1974) of 1.6 x 10⁶ years, one by Ericson and Wollin (1968) of 2 x 10⁶ years, and one by Savage and Curtis (1970) of 3 x 10⁶ years.

(2) Magnetic reversals appear to be fairly well defined now that minor events have been largely clarified (Cox 1969). However, exactly when the Pleistocene began with respect to those magnetic reversals remains unclear to us and others as well. Savage and Curtis (1970), by dating Villafranchian strata in Europe (usually defined as the start of the Pleistocene in that part of the world), settled on about 3 million years for that transition. By contrast, Ericson and Wollin (1968) studied changes in coil direction of a foraminiferan, which are related to changes in ocean temperature, as well as the first abundant appearance of these organisms in ocean sediments. They wrote (1968:1232):

[T]he Pliocene-Pleistocene boundary in our cores, as indicated by the first appearance of abundant *Globorotalia truncatulinoides*, occurs at the base of the Olduvai event, about 2 million years ago.

At least their results would provide a basis for defining the "glacial" Pleistocene, a matter of great importance for North American biogeographers, since glacial ages would have coincided with establishment of the Bering Land Bridge, which permitted animal exchange between Siberia and North America.

Berggren and Van Couvering (1974) later shortened that estimate, placing the start of the Nebraskan ice age at *ca.* 1.6 million years ago and considering that event coincidental with the Pliocene-Pleistocene boundary (Haq *et al.* 1977).

(3) The advance and "retreat" of continental glaciers markedly and repeatedly altered the land vertebrate fauna in North America. Although early geologists thought only one glaciation had occurred, it has become clear that climate changed several times during the Pleistocene, with correlative changes in biota. Climatic changes and a cooling trend apparently occurred prior to each major glacial age (Flint 1971, Ericson and Wollin 1968). We can also follow the lead of Haq *et al.* (1977) and treat the "glacial" Pleistocene as having started with the advent of major glaciation, somewhat less than 2 million years ago.

(4) This column consists of mixed data and remains largely incomplete, but additional pertinent information should soon be available. We can provide some perspective on the items listed.

The oldest mammoth bones known from North America (*Mammuthus meridionalis*) have been dated at 1.36 million years (Evernden *et al.* 1964). This date correlates well with either the beginning of the Kansan glacial age or the end of the Nebraskan glacial age, depending on the scale used (column C). At both times there presumably existed a Bering Land Bridge. *M. meridionalis* was apparently ancestral to the imperial mammoth (*M. columbi*), which lived in southern California (Maglio 1973). (Dates for appearance of the imperial mammoth are not yet known.) *Mammuthus imperator* and *M. columbi* are now believed by many to be the same animal (see discussion in Miller 1971, 1976).

The 88-m marine terrace on San Miguel Island gave an amino acid racemization date of 0.36 to 0.43 million years ago (Wehmiller, pers. comm. 1978), which appears to correspond to an early Sangamon high sea-level stand if one accepts the chronology of Berggren and Van Couvering (1974) (see Fig. 1). When materials from various other terraces are dated, it should be possible to obtain a more complete picture of the relative emergence and submergence of the Northern Channel Island group, as well as correlation among terraces on different islands.

(5) In North America, the Cenozoic has been subdivided into "mammalian ages" primarily defined by the first appearance of certain groups in the fossil record. The "Irvingtonian"

mammalian age is generally recognized as having started in mid-Kansan times (Flint 1971, Hibbard *et al.* 1965), with the appearance of elephants in North America. However, the potassium-argon date for *Mammuthus meridionalis* pre-dates the mid-Kansan by more than 200,000 years (Fig. 1). Moreover, Berggren and Van Couvering (1974) now view the start of the Irvingtonian as coincidental with the K/Ar date of *M. meridionalis* (1.36×10^6 years ago), which places it either in the Nebraskan, Aftonian, or Kansan of column C (Fig. 1), depending on which chronology is used. Under the circumstances, these ill-defined and fluctuating mammalian ages seem to us to be of little value for our studies of island biogeography.

Origin of the Land Bridge Hypothesis

So far we have been unable to find any geological evidence in support of a land bridge hypothesis (a bridge between the Northern Channel Islands and the nearby mainland), at least not for the time that elephants are known to have lived in North America (Junger and Johnson 1980). Rather, the land bridge hypothesis seems to have arisen out of a need to accommodate the elephants, whose bones have been found in abundance on Santa Rosa and San Miguel Islands. As one of us remarked earlier (Johnson 1972):

[I]t is worth recalling that these land bridge reconstructions were principally based on elephant remains, not on structural or tectonic considerations.

Our failure to find such geological evidence surprised us in view of the rather general acceptance of that hypothesis. On the other hand, it is clear how earlier pronouncements could have lulled later workers into believing that the matter was settled. We feel it instructive to repeat and comment upon some of the earlier opinions expressed on the supposed existence of a land bridge.

(1) The beds of mammoth bones is [sic] such conclusive proof of a former land connection that no question can be raised in regard to it [Fairbanks 1897:227].

Comment.—Once one learns that elephants can swim and willingly travel surprising distances at sea (Johnson 1972, 1973, 1978), one is then obliged to question the concept of a land bridge between the mainland and the islands.

(2) The presence of Pleistocene elephants on Santa Rosa Island furnishes apparently a striking confirmation of the view that profound changes in the coast line of southern California have occurred in late geological time [Stock and Furlong 1928:141].

Comment.—Striking changes *have* occurred on the southern California coastline; marine terraces and active faults provide two notable examples. However, the elephant bones found on the islands are not necessary for that conclusion.

(3) The occurrence of elephant material in the Pleistocene deposits of Santa Cruz and Santa Rosa Islands is definite proof of a Pleistocene land connection with the mainland, since elephants are not known on the Pacific Coast before this period [Chaney and Mason 1930:20].

Comment.—This *non sequitur* surprised us. It is true, however, that elephants are not known to have occurred in North America before early Pleistocene and cannot have been on the Pacific Coast before then.

(4) It is clear from the occurrence of proboscidean remains on islands of the Channel Island group that elephants must have gained access to this region, prior to its present insular state, by way of some land-bridge or connection with the mainland [Stock 1935:210].

Comment.—Again, this is clear *only* if one assumes elephants cannot swim.

(5) Living elephants do not swim out to sea and cross marine barriers, and there is no reason for believing that the Californian mammoths of the Ice Age possessed any different habits on that score. On the other hand, it appears much more reasonable to suppose that a former continuous land mass extended westward from what is now the mainland to include the

TABLE 1. References to time of postulated land bridges (approximately oldest to youngest).

Weaver and Doerner (1967, p. 17)	Oligocene-Pliocene (maximum)
Thorne (1969, p. 392)	Oligocene, Miocene, Pliocene
von Bloeker (1967, p. 261)	Entire Pliocene
Weaver (1969, p. 123)	Early Pliocene time ("at least")
Weaver and Doerner (1967, p. 18)	Pliocene
Bremner (1932, p. 32)	Pliocene ("seems possible")
Axelrod (1967, pp. 105, 286)	Pliocene
_____ (1967, p. 292)	Pliocene-Pleistocene transition
Orr (1967, p. 318)	Pre-Illinoin (probably late Pliocene)
Raven (1967, p. 65)	Early Pleistocene
Chaney and Mason (1930, p. 20)	Pleistocene (since the Oligocene)
Valentine and Lipps (1967, p. 32)	Medial Pleistocene
Madden (1978)	Mid-to-late Pleistocene
Gill (1976, p. 845)	Mid-to-late Pleistocene
Thorne (1969, p. 392)	Late Pleistocene
Remington (1971, p. 8)	"A few hundred thousand years ago"
Berger and Orr (1966, p. 1681)	"Earlier connections [than 100,000 years ago]... occurred...."
Stock (1943, p. 8)	20,000 to 100,000 years ago
_____ (1935, p. 211)	Immediately preceding the Recent
Weaver and Doerner (1967, p. 18)	Late Pleistocene and sub-Recent
Weaver (1969, p. 124)	Late Pleistocene and sub-Recent

present island area, and that this represented the terrain over which these animals roamed during certain stages of the Ice Age. As a matter of fact, geologists regard the paleontologic evidence as strongly supporting a view that the islands of San Miguel, Santa Rosa, Santa Cruz and Anacapa were, in the past, an integral part of a land area which extended westerly from the region of the Santa Monica Mountains [Stock 1943:8].

Comment.—This last quotation requires several comments. As mentioned above, elephants *do* swim out to sea. On the next point, Stock provided no citation as to which geologist(s) regarded "the paleontologic evidence as strongly supporting a view that the islands . . . were, in the past, an integral part of a land area. . . ." The comment by Fairbanks was far too early for any definitive work to have been done on the geology of the area. By 1943, Stock could have been referring to two then-current geological works (Reed 1933, Reed and Hollister 1936). However, we searched those references and found no mention of a land bridge. Rather, those geologists wrote of the "structural province of Anacapia," without mention of subaerial or submarine connections.

From all we have been able to glean from the literature, then, it would appear that no geological evidence which supported a land bridge hypothesis existed prior to the 1965 symposium (see Philbrick 1967). Instead, it would appear that earlier workers placed undue reliance on the erroneous assumption (somehow uncritically accepted by both biologists and geologists) that elephants cannot swim out to sea. Only Savage (1967) argued against a land bridge, and then on biogeographical grounds.

Times Proposed for Land Bridges

The foregoing statements reflect certainty about the presence of a land bridge. We then asked, "Did land bridge proponents agree on a time the present gap between islands and

TABLE 2. References to time of postulated island submergence (approximately oldest to youngest).

Weaver and Doerner (1967, p. 17)	Late Oligocene-early Miocene
———— (1967, p. 17)	Middle Miocene
Valentine and Lipps (1967, p. 23)	Pliocene (possible)
———— (1967, p. 26)	Post-Pliocene (maximum)
von Bloeker (1967, p. 262)	Early Pleistocene
Weaver and Doerner (1967, p. 18)	Pleistocene and Recent (great fluctuations)
———— (1967, p. 19)	Between Pleistocene and late Pleistocene or sub-Recent
Orr (1967, p. 318)	Aftonian (maximum submergence)
Johnson (1972, p. 136; 1978, p. 211)	Mid-Pleistocene (maximum)
Axelrod (1967, p. 295)	Mid-Pleistocene (700' terrace)
Norris (1951, p. 73)	Mid-Pleistocene (total submergence of San Nicolas)
Valentine and Lipps (1967, p. 26)	End of mid-Pleistocene (700' terrace)
Raven (1967, p. 65)	Late Pleistocene
Stock (1935, p. 211)	Recent (inferred; after the land bridge)

mainland was spanned by land?" If a bridge had existed, we felt that there should be rather general agreement on the time of its occurrence. To test our supposition, we constructed a list of postulated land bridges (Table 1). The composite list surprised us, as there was virtually no agreement on the time the proposed bridge existed. Any time prior to mid-Pleistocene would have been too early to accommodate elephants, since they are not known to have been in North America before then.

We then constructed a list of proposed island submergences, with essentially the same results (Table 2). The confusion about when a land bridge might have connected the Northern Channel Islands and the mainland becomes compounded when one also considers the various estimates of times for island submergence.

In reviewing the literature with respect to these tables, we found several discrepancies which further blurred the matter. One is an apparent contradiction (emphasis ours):

[I]t should be stated at the outset that present-day Anacapia offers a *paucity of evidence* for Cenozoic connections to the mainland. In general, ancient migratory routes are best delineated by the land animals of the time [Weaver and Doerner 1967:15].

The extent of the Pliocene land mass of Western Anacapia with its *undoubted* connections to the mainland must surely have produced a rich land biota [Weaver and Doerner 1967:18].

We must say "apparent contradiction," because perusal reveals internal consistency in these remarks. The first statement argues that there is basically no geological evidence for a bridge, but that one might conclude a bridge existed because of the animals present on the islands. The second statement merely implies that the presence of a bridge was not seriously doubted by anyone (except by Savage in a later paper during the same symposium).

Another discrepancy relates to a land bridge proposal by Chaney and Mason (1930). They published an illustration of their suggested Pleistocene land bridge (Fig. 2, their fig. 1) and wrote:

Figure 1 shows the suggested landward connection of the Channel Islands, the heavy broken line indicating the approximate position of the shoreline, as estimated from the 50-fathom line on the U.S. Coast and Geodetic Survey map of 1927.

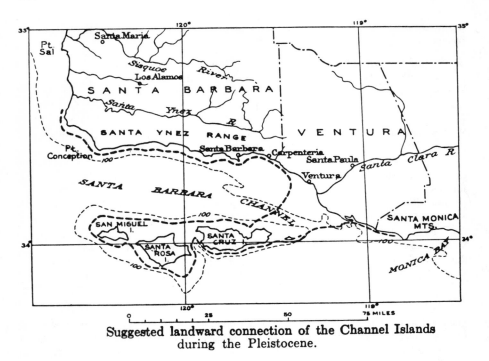

Suggested landward connection of the Channel Islands during the Pleistocene.

FIGURE 2. *Chaney and Mason (1930, their figure 1) were apparently the first to publish a drawing of a postulated land bridge, which apparently served as a model for later researchers. In their drawing (based on 1927 soundings), the 100-fathom line crossed the 50-fathom line.*

Chaney and Mason had the 50-fathom *cross* the 100-fathom line in order to generate their proposed land bridge. Stock (1935, his fig. 1) apparently had much the same figure, for which Chaney and Mason were credited. Later workers omitted, for the most part, the careful reservations expressed by Chaney and Mason (see Stock 1935:205).

Geological Considerations

As mentioned above, geological evidence in support of the land bridge hypothesis seems to be lacking (the Santa Barbara Channel aspects of this subject are treated more extensively in Junger and Johnson 1980). Other geological features, however, have a rather direct bearing on the theme of this paper and deserve treatment at this point.

Marine terraces are one of the most prominent geomorphic features on many of the California Islands. Each supposedly represents a time of relative sea level stability. Although some terraces perhaps reflect glacial and interglacial sea levels, the island area has also experienced a degree of uplift and/or submergence through time. Weaver (1969:123-124) described the situation as follows:

Pleistocene and Recent times saw further orogenic disturbances . . . and great fluctuations in the relative sea levels as evidenced by present day submarine and subaerial terrace deposits.

Those terraces which represent sea levels during glacial and interglacial ages are the ones which interest us most. The advance and "retreat" of glaciers reportedly lowered sea levels by as much as 100 to 140 m and raised sea levels by as much as 20 m, compared with the present

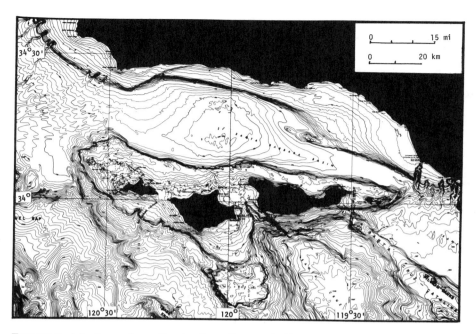

FIGURE 3. *A bathymetric profile clearly outlines probable land areas during the Wisconsin glacial stage, when seas were as much as 140 m lower than at present. We emphasize here the 130-m contour around the Northern Channel Islands as a conservative estimate of the superisland "Santarosae," of Orr (1968). Although the gap between Anacapa Island and Port Hueneme would have narrowed to only 6 km, the water would still have been more than 100 m deep at that time, all other conditions equal. Map from Howell (1976); topography from U.S.G.S. two-degree sheets (Santa Maria, 1956; Los Angeles, 1975; Long Beach, 1970); bathymetry from National Ocean Surveys Maps 1306N-20, 1306N-19, and 1206N-15.*

(Flint 1971). Unfortunately, these values cannot as yet be directly confirmed in the local area, since one cannot discern which component of that change in elevation was due to sea-level fluctuation and which part was due to rising and lowering of land levels. It is worthy of note that a sea level lowered by only 49 m would create the superisland "Santarosae" of Orr (1968). Furthermore, an additional lowering to 130 m less than the present level would reduce the water gap between "Santarosae" and the mainland to a distance of only 6 km (Fig. 3), well within the swimming capabilities of present-day elephants (Johnson 1972, 1978).

To illustrate the markedly different view an elephant on the mainland would have of Anacapa Island, with and without a sea-level lowering, we photographed that island from Pt. Hueneme and obtained an outline of its present-day low profile. We then calculated how much closer we could get if sea level were lowered 130 m, what angle that island would then subtend, and thereby obtained a new profile of the island mass for superimposition on our original photograph (Fig. 4). Compared with the relatively small island of Anacapa, separated from the mainland by a considerable water barrier, "Santarosae" would loom rather large (almost twice as high) and appear quite close (less than one-third the present distance).

By contrast, on the basis of present channel submarine topography, sea level would have to

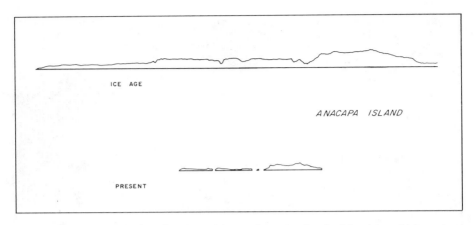

FIGURE 4. *During the glacial ages and lowered sea levels, the islands would have been connected to one another and would have loomed large to an observer (e.g., mammoth) on the mainland. Here we show Anacapa Island as it would have appeared from a greatly extended mainland shoreline.*

lower (or the sea bottom would have to rise, or both) more than 230 m before a land bridge would appear. It is this possibility for which geological evidence is lacking.

Changes in Geological Thought

Plate tectonic theory, new dating techniques, and extensive oil exploration "spill off" collectively have resulted in views considerably changed from those held only ten years ago. One of the more dramatic proposals is that, between middle and late Miocene times, the southern half of Santa Cruz Island moved from a former site west of what is now San Diego to its present location against the northern, volcanic part of the island (Howell 1976:452 and his fig. 2). If correct, the concept of Santa Cruz Island being an extension of the Santa Monica Range then falls into question. Such proposed large-scale land movements gain greater credence when viewed in relation to a more recent report (Graham and Dickinson 1978), which proposes 115 km of right slip along the San Gregorio-Hosgri fault trend during post-early Miocene time. These two movements, coupled with the San Andreas fault and other faults, are viewed as part of a Pacific Plate shear zone (Howell 1976).

Greene (1976:509) addressed the same problem in a comparison of rock structure:

The northern Channel Islands form a complexly folded and faulted anticlinal uplift that appears to be a seaward extension of the Santa Monica Mountains. . . . However, the geology of the north and south parts of Santa Cruz Island differs markedly, suggesting major displacement on the Santa Cruz Island fault (McLean and others, this volume). Rocks in the southern part of Santa Cruz and Santa Rosa Islands do not seem to be the western facies of rocks in the Santa Ynez Mountains (Howell and others, this volume).

Even ideas about the Santa Cruz Island basement complex seem to be in flux. Whereas Reed and Hollister (1936) described the basement complex between the Northern Channel Islands and the Santa Monica Mountains as being similar, Hill (1976:41) recently questioned the relationship:

The Santa Cruz Island basement complex is dissimilar to the basement rocks exposed in . . . the Salinian block, Santa Monica Mountains, and Peninsular Ranges.

Clearly, far more research is needed on the geological history of the Northern Channel Islands before the relationship of those islands to the mainland is clarified.

OTHER WAYS TO GET THERE
Theoretical Considerations

Our search for geological evidence for the land bridge yielded doubt and confusion. The apparent conflict in viewpoints about the time(s) of occurrence of the postulated land bridge between the mainland and Northern Channel Islands strengthened our doubts. (In fact, the longer we studied the geological evidence, the more disturbing the issue became.)

Our failure in the geological realm led us to review theories of biotic dispersal and island colonization proposed earlier by biogeographers (*e.g.*, Simpson 1940, Myers 1949, Darlington 1957). Of the various theoretical formulations, those of Simpson (1940, 1953) seemed most appropriate to the Channel Islands problem. He proposed three ways by which land vertebrates could get from place *A* to place *B*: by a "corridor," by a "filter-bridge," or by a "sweepstakes" route.

Corridors

In describing a "corridor," Simpson (1940:147) conceptualized:

> If no barrier at all exists between two areas, it is to be expected that their faunas will be very similar, or as far as genera or larger groups are concerned practically identical.

Clearly, the "corridor" concept does not apply to the Channel Island-mainland situation, because the faunas on either side of the channel are far from identical.

Filter bridges

The "filter-bridge" concept of Simpson would seem most to resemble what land bridge proponents have suggested for the Northern Channel Islands, that is, that a bridge existed, then disappeared. In that regard, Simpson (1940:148) wrote:

> (1) When two regions are separated by a strong barrier, they develop quite different faunas, the differences being roughly proportional to the lapse of time since the regions were connected.

and (p. 156):

> (2) A filter-bridge permits some animals to pass and holds others back, but in general those that can cross it do cross it and do so fairly soon after the bridge becomes available to them.

and (p. 152):

> (3) The postulation of land bridges on the basis of one or a few mammals is ... very uncertain. Unless there is reasonable possibility that their companions have not been discovered, a theoretical bridge based on such evidence is probably unreal.

Simpson thus provided a fairly complex set of criteria for what one could expect if a bridge had existed at one time between the mainland and an island: (1) island animals should be quite different from mainland forms if separation had been for a long time; (2) an island formerly connected to the mainland should have a wide spectrum of animals, namely those which could pass over the bridge; and (3) the island should have a "balanced fauna," with both herbivores and carnivores represented.

As will be seen, the "filter-bridge" concept does not fit the Northern Channel Islands any more than the "corridor" concept did.

Sweepstakes

The third concept Simpson promulgated was that of the "Sweepstakes Route." This proposal contains two elements absent in the corridor and filter bridge concepts. The first is the notion that the island and mainland were never connected. The second element is the introduction of *chance* into the considerations, an item which requires some clarification.

If an island and nearby mainland have never been connected (an "oceanic" island), then one

TABLE 3. Extreme dispersal among land animals.*

Terrestrial Mammals	
Large mammals	Perhaps 30 miles (48 km) or more†
Small mammals	Possibly 200 miles (322 km) to Madagascar for civets and insectivores
Rodents	500 miles (805 km) to the Galapagos
Amphibians	Perhaps 500 miles (805 km) to the Seychelles; perhaps 1,000 miles (1,609 km) to New Zealand
Reptiles	
Fresh-water turtles	Possibly 200 miles (322 km) to Madagascar
Snakes	500 miles (805 km) or more to the Galapagos
Lizards	1,000 miles (1,609 km) to New Zealand; perhaps more than 1,000 miles (1,609 km) for geckos
Land molluscs	More than 2,000 miles (3,218 km) in Polynesia (to Juan Fernandez Island)
Insects and spiders	More than 2,000 miles (3,218 km)

* Adapted from Carlquist (1965).
† Elephants have been estimated to swim up to 48 km (Johnson 1978). Also, a semiaquatic hippopotamus occurs (or did occur) on Madagascar.

would expect animals to have gotten there by swimming, by rafting, or by some other rather unlikely event. When that is the case, the laws of probability may carry more weight than does logic. For example, an animal which is a good swimmer might never have made it to a nearby island. On the other hand, a poor swimmer may well have succeeded; an event which seems highly improbable may actually have occurred. The result is an unbalanced fauna, as Simpson (1940:154, 156) expressed it:

> The late W. D. Matthew, who was probably the most distinguished and best informed student of problems like this, concluded that insular and highly unbalanced faunas were probably to be accounted for by sporadic transportation of land animals on natural rafts, without the assistance of a dry-land route.

Others have echoed this sentiment. Even rather delicate animals, such as amphibians, easily cross marine barriers. In this regard, Myers (1949:19) wrote:

> Amphibians as a group are delicate creatures, extremely susceptible to salt water, to desiccation, and to the heat of the sun, and since they do not possess wings, it is difficult to imagine how they could cross sea barriers. Recent work, however, suggests that amphibians not only can cross salt-water barriers, but have done so upon many occasions.

Darlington (1957:14) was more forceful on the issue:

> The extent to which animals disperse across physical barriers has been bitterly argued about by zoogeographers. Often the method of argument has been to lay down a law to begin with, find a few cases that seem to support it, and then say that the law applies to all cases. This was done even by Wallace. . ., who ruled that amphibians and terrestrial mammals never (or hardly ever?) reach oceanic islands across barriers of salt water, and that islands on which these animals occur must be continental. This was, I think, the worst mistake Wallace ever made, as a zoogeographer.

From the above comments, it is evident that some rather prominent biogeographers readily accept and provide evidence supporting the notion that various terrestrial vertebrates can reach oceanic islands, given enough time. Dispersal ability would, of course, vary according to the nature of the organism. Carlquist (1965) drafted a rather comprehensive list of examples of biotic dispersal, which we have adapted here as it applies to land animals (Table 3). Upon inspecting this list, it is clear that land animals, given enough time, have done quite well in reaching oceanic islands from continents.

Human Transport of Organisms

While anthropologists and geographers have long been sensitized to the role of aborigines in biotic transport, few biogeographers have addressed this colonization mechanism (usually the matter is relegated to an afterthought). However, it is clear that prehistoric man has had a profound effect on the zoogeography of many lands, including islands. Certain land animals have long been associated with humans as either partial domesticates (*e.g.*, canids, felids, suids, mustelids, viverrids), full domesticates (*e.g.*, bovids, camelids, proboscideans, equids), commensals (*e.g.*, canids, rodents), or as pets (most of the above plus snakes, lizards, and other herpetofauna). Many aboriginal groups are known to have carried some of these forms in their watercraft (Wallace 1869, Carlquist 1965, Darlington 1957). In this regard, Foster (1963, 1965) concluded that the presence of *Peromyscus* on so many of the Queen Charlotte Islands and islets was almost certainly due to the Haida Indians, who visited these islands regularly in their watercraft.

LAND VERTEBRATES ON THE NORTHERN CHANNEL ISLANDS
Mainland and Island Comparisons

Frequent visits to the islands permit one to overcome a natural tendency to focus principally on what organisms are there and how they might differ from the mainland forms. Alternatively, it is perhaps the *missing* forms which prove more interesting—those which should be there (if a land bridge had existed) but are not. Once we began this converse comparison, discrepancies became ever more obvious. We soon found that our assessment of the Northern Channel Island biota matched Thorne's (1969:395) assessment of the biota on the more distant southern (outer) islands:

> A quick examination of the present biotas of the California Islands, at least the offshore islands, suggests that they are mostly depauperate aggregations of plants and animals that have reached the islands by chance over-water dispersal.

For our land vertebrate comparison, we searched the literature and questioned experts in order to find both fossil and historical records of land vertebrate forms (not including birds). The La Brea Tar Pits and other mainland fossil sites proved especially valuable, with approximately 86 species found to date (Table 4, Appendix A). Fossil snakes, however, are poorly represented in the literature at this writing. Within historical times, approximately 83 species of land vertebrates have been found on the nearby California coast (Santa Monica Mountains, Santa Ynez Mountains, Hollywood Hills, and adjacent coastal areas).

By deleting 42 species which represent the overlap between historical and fossil forms, the grand total numbers about 127 mainland species (Table 4, Appendix A). By contrast, only 12 or 13 species have been found on the Northern Channel Islands during historic times (excluding domestic animals), and only three fossil species, all extinct, have been located. Those three fossils are the extinct Anacapa deer mouse, *Peromyscus anyapahensis,* the extinct giant deer mouse, *Peromyscus nesodytes,* and the well-known pygmy mammoth, *Mammuthus imperator* (*exilis?*).

A Depauperate and Unbalanced Fauna

The land vertebrates on the island, as a whole, match an assemblage one would expect on an "oceanic" island colonized via "sweepstakes dispersal." Some specific examples should illustrate this point.

TABLE 4. A comparison of numbers of land vertebrate species on the mainland and the islands.

Group	Mainland		Northern Channel Islands	
	Fossil	Historical	Fossil	Historical
Shrews and moles	3	5		
Rodents	16	16	2	2
Canids	3	3		1
Bears	3	1		
Skunks, weasels, badgers	5	4		1
Raccoons and ringtails	2	2		
Cats	4	2		
Rabbits and hares	3	3		
Horses, tapirs, pigs	3			
Camels and deer	8	2		
Bison, mastodons, elephants	5		2(?)	
Sloths	3			
Amphibians	9	11		3
Turtles	2	1		
Lizards	7	11		3
Snakes	10	22		3

If one chose to ignore the admonitions of Myer (1949) and Darlington (1957) cited earlier, one could argue that the two salamander species *Batrachoseps pacificus* and *B. attenuatus*, being nearly totally intolerant of salt water, could not have gotten to the islands without a dry land bridge. However, a bridge which would accommodate such delicate salamanders would surely have permitted passage of animals such as ground squirrels, moles, and pocket gophers—animals all too well-known for their tenacity of survival in diverse habitats. Furthermore, these burrowing mammals have been found in the mainland fossil record but *Batrachoseps* has not. This fact further argues against the hypothesis that these salamanders crossed via a land bridge, since there is no evidence that they were even present on the mainland during the times suggested for the hypothesized land bridge.

It would appear that the islands are, and have been, large enough to support a variety of herbivores. One might thus further argue that deer might have gotten across a land bridge in the past and then later perished from overpopulation. If deer could have crossed, one would expect that the mountain lion would have crossed the same bridge and kept the deer population in check. Likewise, if mice crossed the land bridge, why did their predators, weasels and rattlesnakes, not follow? If insects crossed, why not shrews?

The absence of other herbivores is even more puzzling. Small mammals such as rabbits, pocket gophers, squirrels, woodrats, and chipmunks should surely be represented if a bridge had existed. Eagles and other birds of prey could have kept their numbers in check and prevented overpopulation. Inconsistencies such as these with respect to amphibians and reptiles led Savage (1967:224) to remark:

> The differences among the island herpetofaunas today derive mainly from the vagaries [vagaries?] of fortuitous distribution, area, distance from shore, and Pleistocene climatic fluctuations. Since no convincing evidence of any Pleistocene land connection between any

of the islands and the mainland is available, as shown by Dr. D. W. Weaver . . . , and since the herpetofaunas now found on the islands are depauperate and composed of vagile forms, it seems probable that all of the islands were invaded by late Pleistocene over-water immigrants. Nothing in the biological evidence speaks strongly for land connections as an explanation of modern distribution patterns, and it seems futile to build imaginary bridges where none are known to have existed and when the facts of the situation do not require it.

The Case for Sweepstakes Dispersal and Indian Transport

Torrential rains occur sporadically in the Santa Barbara-Ventura area. During such times, vast amounts of vegetation and adhering soil get swept out to sea, including trees and logs. Undoubtedly, land vertebrates would not always escape the torrents produced by these rains and might suddenly find themselves ocean-bound. Mice, lizards, tree frogs, and snakes would be particularly susceptible. Skunks and foxes could also be caught by rushing waters, for example, during undermining of stream banks on which they stood or into which they had burrowed. The relatively quiet waters of estuaries (with fresh water in the upper layers during storms) would permit these animals to board floating objects.

Salamanders also are known to inhabit partially decayed logs and would thereby automatically be included among those animals which might be swept out to sea by floods. Even unlikely animals end up at sea; in 1955, for example, a live jack rabbit (*Lepus californicus*) was found on a kelp raft 39 miles (62 km) off the southern California coast near San Clemente Island (Prescott 1959). Additionally, some land animals (*e.g.,* bear, deer, elephants) are good swimmers. These animals could well inadvertently travel too far offshore and end up heading for the wrong landfall, namely, an island instead of the mainland from which they came. During hundreds of thousands of years one would expect some survivors to reach the islands, not once, but several times.

Cockerell (1939), Norris (1951), and Savage (1967) have all discussed the relative merits of sweepstakes dispersal in explaining the Channel Islands biogeographical patterns. Norris (1951), Vedder and Norris (1963), and Orr (1968) also believed that Indian canoe transport of animals was another very real dispersal possibility, transport that was either inadvertent or intentional. Mice, for example, could well have been carried along accidentally amongst Indian food, supplies, or trading goods. Lizards and salamanders could have hidden in baskets or in canoe flotsam, escaping once reaching one or another of the islands. We also think that Indian children (and adults) during Chumash canoe days would have behaved little differently from people today in keeping pets, a quite natural behavioral trait. As other observers have noted (*e.g.,* Stanton *in* McElrath 1967), it is a wonder more species are not found there.

The peculiar assemblage of land vertebrates presently on the islands thus might well be viewed as not just a random assortment when compared to the mainland fauna. Those animals are, for the most part, the sorts of animals one might associate with an Indian culture or which could have rafted to the islands. We now examine the retinue of land vertebrates from the Northern Channel Islands on a case-by-case basis to see how sweepstakes dispersal or Indian transport might apply.

Mammoths and Mice

The only fossil land vertebrates found to date on the Northern Channel Islands are the small mammoth (*Mammuthus exilis*) and its full-size ancestor, the Columbian mammoth (*M. columbi*) (Madden in press), the extinct Anacapa Island deer mouse (*Peromyscus anyapahensis*), and the giant deer mouse (*Peromyscus nesodytes*). Co-occurrence of some of these animals is not without precedent:

The pygmy elephants from both the Mediterranean and Indonesian islands tend to be

associated with giant rodents. . . . This is also so in the Channel Islands of California. . . .
Rodents grow to a large size on islands only when carnivores are absent, as far as can be
established from observations in other parts of the world [Hooijer 1976:224].

Rodents are quite good at crossing water barriers (Carlquist 1965 and Table 3). It has also been
determined that elephants swim well and do so willingly in ocean water for long periods and
distances (Johnson 1972, 1978). Modern elephants swim to islands off Africa and Asia, and
conditions in the Santa Barbara Channel during the late Pleistocene were maximized for
inducing elephants to swim to Santarosae (Johnson 1978, see his fig. 3). Interestingly,
sweepstakes dispersal has been invoked to explain elephant remains found on islands in the
Aegean Sea and elsewhere (see review *in* Johnson 1980):

It is clear that, as Africa is much too far off, Crete was invaded by Pleistocene elephants
from the mainland. Most authors . . . assume land bridges to make this possible, but [we] do
not think these [bridges] necessary. There are several reports of the good swimming abilities
of the Indian elephant. Besides being a good swimmer, it must be an excellent drifter
because of the huge airfilled bones of the back of the head (an additional advantage of the
pneumatic skull). Moreover, the trunk may function like the diving device known as the
snorkel [Sondaar and Boekschoten 1967:562].

It is not possible to find any evidence for land bridges in the geology of the [Aegean] region.
Again analysis of the fauna shows that the existence of land bridges would have led to a
different faunal composition. Of the larger mammals we find only those with good swimming ability (elephant, deer, *Hippopotamus*). . . . Furthermore, endurance, small size,
living in and around trees made [it] possible for animals like mice, rats, and dormice and
insectivores to reach the island by drifting on wood, [floating artificial] islets, etc. On the
islands the animals underwent changes that made them more adaptable to island life. In
general, the larger animals showed a tendency to nanification [dwarfism] while some
rodents showed gigantism [Sondaar 1971].

Altogether the evidence points to elephants and mice obeying what has come to be known as
Foster's (1964:234) Rule:

There is a clear tendency towards gigantism in insular rodents while dwarfism is characteristic of insular [large mammals].

Foster (1964:234) further stated:

The relict hypothesis necessitates the argument that the large size of the insular rodents is a
conservative character, whereas there is abundant evidence that it is more likely to be the
opposite.

The rafting ability of mice, the swimming ability of elephants, the co-occurrence of these
particular animals on various offshore islands throughout the world, and the gigantism-
dwarfism syndrome combined provide a powerful argument in support of the sweepstakes
dispersal explanation for the presence of these animals on the islands.

Another point should be mentioned. When the pygmy mammoths were first described, they
were assigned a new specific name. In a review of elephant evolution, however, Maglio (1973)
synonymized these island elephants with the mainland imperial mammoth (*Mammuthus
imperator*). In a later paper, Hooijer (1976) held to the earlier notion and treated them as a
separate species. Because of this discrepancy, we requested clarification from each of these
experts, whereupon each suggested that the island form might be, at most, a different
subspecies than that on the mainland, on the basis of size alone.

Even there the issue is not clear. Earlier, Stock (1935:213) had pointed out, "Considerable
variation in size exists among the island types, but the difference in stature between island and
mainland forms remains a notable feature." Sondaar and Boekschoten (1967:573) addressed
themselves peripherally to this same question:

TABLE 5. Subspecies of *Peromyscus maniculatus* on the Channel Islands.*

Island	Subspecies
San Miguel	*P. m. streatori*
Prince (islet)	*P. m. streatori*
Santa Rosa	*P. m. sanctaerosae*
Santa Cruz	*P. m. santacruzae*
West Anacapa	*P. m. anacapae*
Middle Anacapa	*P. m. anacapae*
East Anacapa	*P. m. anacapae*
Santa Barbara	*P. m. elusus*
Sutil (islet)	*P. m. elusus*
San Nicolas	*P. m. exterus*
Santa Catalina	*P. m. catalinae*
San Clemente	*P. m. clementis*

*From von Bloeker (1967).

[I]s reduction in size (or, enlargement of size) the single cause for structural changes in the mammal's body? or are other developments primary, and is alteration in size a secondary effect?

The issue thus seems to be still in a state of flux, as Maglio added (pers. comm.), "I think this problem of species names will have to wait for a revision of North American mammoths."

Thus far we have focused on extinct elephants and mice. Two living mice also occur on the Northern Channel Islands, the harvest mouse (*Reithrodontomys megalotis*) and the deer mouse (*Peromyscus maniculatus*)'. The former is uncommon and is known only from Santa Cruz, Santa Catalina, and San Clemente Islands, whereas the deer mouse occurs abundantly on all the Channel Islands (Bills 1969, von Bloeker 1967, Pearson 1951, Gill 1976). Eight subspecies of *P. maniculatus* (Table 5) have been recognized by von Bloeker (1967), based on a study of 840 specimens, but series of mice must be compared to reveal the relatively small morphological differences. According to Gill (1980), the morphological differences are still much greater than the divergence found in the structural genes. Little is known about the harvest mouse except that it is considered a subspecies on Santa Catalina Island (Pearson 1951, von Bloeker 1967), is identical to the mainland population and was probably introduced historically on San Clemente Island (von Bloeker 1967), and is very low in numbers and restricted to certain habitats on Santa Cruz Island (Bills 1969).

As might be expected, the deer mice of the Northern Channel Islands show detectable genetic variability between islands (Gill 1976). In the Santa Cruz Island population, which has been studied in some detail, there exists variability of morphological characters (Bills 1969). The island deer mice, at least on Santa Cruz Island, are bigger than their mainland counterparts (Bills 1969), and thus follow Foster's Rule (Hesse *et al.* 1951 gives general insights on this rule).

Rodents are accomplished sweepstakes dispersers across water (see Table 3), and few biogeographers would deny the high probability of successful over-water dispersal of mice to the superisland Santarosae or Santa Catalina, *given enough time*. During glacially lowered sea-level periods, both islands would have been much larger and considerably closer to the mainland. On the other hand, the presence of deer mice on so many islands and islets (Table 5) suggests to us that humans augmented the natural sweepstakes process, either intentionally or, as is more likely, unintentionally. The Chumash Indians and their predecessors had watercraft, and rodents are well known to be frequent accidental passengers in boats. It is also known that the Indians carried ollas to the mainland in canoes in exchange for grass seeds, acorns, and roots (Yarrow 1879). Canoes or other watercraft hauled up on the back beaches on the mainland and islands must invariably have been inspected by the ever-curious deer mouse. Personal experience supports this conclusion. During the summer of 1969, one of us (DLJ) established a field camp on the back beach in Cuyler Harbor, San Miguel Island. Beginning on the first night, the camp was overrun with curious *Peromyscus*. They got into everything. They even climbed the guy lines that secured the tent and repeatedly clambered over the tent tops. If a canoe had been nearby they would have been in and out of it all night, every night. The frequency of mice being inadvertently transported about the Channel Islands in this way must have been very high indeed, especially in light of the Chumash practice of beaching canoes in tules (Hudson *et al.* 1978), where rodents commonly live (Bills 1969).

Foxes

The Channel Islands fox (*Urocyon littoralis*) occurs on the six largest Channel Islands (San Miguel, Santa Rosa, Santa Cruz, San Nicolas, San Clemente, and Santa Catalina). The morphological and skeletal characters of the island fox have been discussed by Grinnell *et al.* (1937), Dickey (*in* Rogers 1929), and von Bloeker (1967); its behavior and ecology have been studied by Laughrin (1977, 1980). Its small size and other characteristics coupled with its distribution have elicited considerable debate on its origin (Johnson 1975). Stock (1943) entertained the notion that the fox was small before its isolation, and von Bloeker (1967) felt that it more closely resembles the present smaller Central American forms than it does the larger gray fox on the adjacent mainland. However, the fact that the fox populations on the six islands show relatively little divergence from each other but collectively show marked divergence from the mainland gray fox strongly suggests to us (and others) that the island fox was initially isolated on one island for an indefinite time and through inbreeding became reduced in size. This single island presumably provided the parent "small fox" stock for the other island populations that became established only recently (*i.e.*, during the Indian period). The likeliest island candidate is either Santa Catalina or Santarosae, since both were considerably larger and closer to the mainland during glacially induced low sea levels than were other islands. In this regard, Vedder and Norris (1963) suggested that in prehuman times the fox was endemic only to the Northern Channel Islands (Santarosae). Because Santarosae was, in fact, even closer to the mainland and much bigger than Santa Catalina was, the chances of animals reaching it via sweepstakes dispersal, other things being equal, would be far greater. Moreover, there is evidence that the fox has been on the Northern Channel Islands a long time. Orr (1968) tells of a fossil fox skull taken from the upper part of the Tecolote member of the Santa Rosa Island Formation. The age of the upper Tecolote is reportedly 10,400 radiocarbon years B.P. Although the skull was reportedly lost in the sea during transfer to the mainland, there is no reason to doubt the claimed provenance of the fox skull, which shows that the fox has been on the Northern Channel Islands for the last 10,000 years, at least. More recent subfossil fox remains have been found in middens on Santa Cruz Island "throughout the time of Indian occupancy" (Rogers 1929:445).

On the other hand, Grinnell *et al.* (1937:456) were of the opinion that Santa Catalina was the first home of the island fox: "The animals on Santa Catalina are the largest and therefore might be thought of as nearest genetically to the mainland gray foxes. . . ." They further indicated a resemblance gradient among the island foxes. Though qualifying the lineage, they proposed the following sequence: Santa Catalina—San Clemente—San Nicolas—Santa Cruz—Santa Rosa—San Miguel, the implication being that foxes first reached Santa Catalina from the mainland and then later reached the other islands.

Irrespective of whether the initial parent population of small foxes came from Santarosae or Santa Catalina, it is not surprising that the island fox later turned up on San Nicolas, San Clemente, and other islands. We believe, as do others, that Indians were principally responsible for its present far-flung insular distribution. In this regard, Smith (1977:41) commented, "With a little coaxing the fox becomes sociable and one often wonders how this animal had survived through heavy Indian habitation if they were not friendly toward it." The Chumash and Gabrielino Indians and their ancient predecessors traveled about the Channel Islands for a very long time. Man has been on both San Nicolas and Santa Catalina Islands at least 4,000 years (Rozaire 1967, Crane and Griffin 1958) and longer on the Northern Channel Islands (Johnson 1972, see also Berger 1980). Santa Catalina soapstone artifacts occur on San Miguel, Santa Rosa, and Santa Cruz Islands, indicating exchange between the northern and southern island groups. Those who chance to live on the islands, or visit them for extended periods, as we have, find the fox an excellent pet, easily tamed and, for a hunting and gathering people, probably a dependable or emergency source of food (*viz.*, fox remains in middens on Santa Cruz, Santa Rosa, San Miguel, San Nicolas, and Santa Catalina Islands—see Rogers 1929, Grinnell *et al.* 1937, Orr 1968, Vedder and Norris 1963, Meighan 1959, Walker 1978).

Certainly the gray fox was a source of food and pelts for certain aboriginal groups (Landberg 1965, Parmalee 1965, Grinnell 1962 v. I, Munson *et al.* 1971, Baegert 1865, White 1953, Owen *et al.* 1964), including the Chumash Indians who valued and sought "shawls (tapalos) of foxskin" (King 1971). Some aboriginal groups used the fox for ceremonial practices (Grinnell 1962, v. II) and the Chumash practiced the "Zorra (fox) solstice dance on Santa Rosa Island" (King 1971). Others have testified to the adaptability of foxes in general as pets "on account of their gentleness, their intelligence and affectionate behavior, and their ready confidence and alertness" (Allen 1942:199). The association of man and canids in California is traced back at least 4,000 years (Haag and Heizer 1953), and in North America at least 7,500 years, and perhaps considerably longer (McMillan 1970, Lawrence 1967, 1968). The Chumash and Gabrielino Indians ate dogs (Kroeber 1941) and transported them in their watercraft (Bowers 1890, Schumacher 1877, Ellison 1937, Hardacre 1880, see also McKusick and Warren 1959), and there is no reason to think that related (pet?) canines—and perhaps other animals—would not be extended the same honor. In fact, considering how well-traveled the seafaring Indians were it would be surprising had other animals not been introduced.

Getting foxes to the outer islands via watercraft is one thing; getting the initial founding population from the mainland to either Santarosae or Santa Catalina is another. If, for reasons given earlier, we eliminate the land bridge hypothesis, and we assume the foxes did not swim, we are left with two possibilities: natural over-water dispersal and Indian watercraft. Let us assess these two possibilities.

First, given enough time, accidental rafting could well have initially brought the fox to Santarosae or Santa Catalina. Periodic flash floods, prolonged rainy periods, and swollen coastal rivers are, as indicated earlier, common in California, and floods may have been more frequent and intense during glacial periods. It is not difficult to imagine a fox, perhaps a gravid female, being carried on a debris raft down the frequently-swollen Santa Clara, Los Angeles, or Santa Ana Rivers and into the sea, although the probability of this happening with successful dispersal must be low. The fact that the Santa Clara River, one of the largest rivers in southern California, empties into the eastern Santa Barbara Channel increases the probability of successful dispersal to Santarosae. This may, in part, explain how some of the herpetofauna arrived on the Northern Channel Islands. The semipermanent counterclockwise oceanic current gyre present in the Santa Barbara Channel would further tend to increase the probability of success.

Although we do not favor the idea, it is also conceivable that the early aborigines initially brought the first fox to one or another of the superislands as they probably brought them later to the outer islands. We do not know when the earliest people arrived, but it was almost certainly in late Pleistocene time (at least 10,000 to 20,000 years ago, if not earlier; see Berger 1980). This topic was discussed at length earlier (Johnson 1972).

Skunks

The spotted skunk (*Spilogale gracilis amphiala*) presently occurs only on Santa Cruz and Santa Rosa Islands, but also apparently lived on San Miguel until the late nineteenth century (Walker 1978, Voy *ca.* 1893). The morphological and skeletal characteristics of the island skunk have been described by Dickey (1929, and *in* Rogers 1929), Grinnell *et al.* (1937), and Van Gelder (1959, 1965), with comments by von Bloeker (1967). According to Van Gelder (1965), the island skunk *S. gracilis amphiala* differs from *S. gracilis phenax* on the adjacent mainland primarily by its broader face (0.2 cm average) and shorter tail (3 cm average), with lesser variations in tail coloration and body length. The skunks on Santa Cruz and Santa Rosa Islands differ from one another primarily in total length (412 and 426 mm, respectively), but show inconsistent variations in other characters. None of these differences is great. All of them could have developed during post-glacial time, based on reasons cited earlier.

Dickey (1929, and *in* Rogers 1929) and Van Gelder (1965) point out that the Channel Islands skunk resembles *S. gracilis latifrons* of western Oregon and Washington more than *S. gracilis* on the adjacent mainland. It is possible that *amphiala* is a relict from a *latifrons* population which may have ranged further south during the Wisconsin when the climate was cooler and moister. Because Van Gelder has discussed various possibilities for the origin of the Channel Islands skunk it is not necessary to repeat them here. However, certain points made by Van Gelder should be clarified and expanded. For example, he (1965:35) thought:

> [The] burden of evidence . . . fits the idea that they [skunks] occupied the islands when there was a connection to the mainland; it is suited to the existing data, and does not require an accidental rafting or intentional or chance introduction by man.

The burden of evidence cited by Van Gelder primarily reflects his accepting as fact the early Pleistocene land bridge proposed by others. Van Gelder also thought it improbable that Indians brought the skunk since they presumably did not make pets of them, and their smell would have discouraged efforts to transport them to the islands in watercraft. Van Gelder does, however, admit the possibility that the skunk may have been naturally introduced by debris rafting.

A sampling of the literature shows that many aboriginal groups in North America ate skunks (Swanton 1946, Parmalee 1965, Munson *et al.* 1971, Baegert 1865, T. E. White 1953). R. Bruce McMillan (pers. comm.) noted that skunk formed a minor element in the diet of many aboriginal groups in the Great Plains region. Parmalee (1965) showed that the skunk (in this case the striped skunk *Mephitis*) ranked third in importance in food used by peoples living in Tick Creek Cave, Missouri.

Grinnell (1962 v. I) described how important skunks were to the Cheyenne as meat animals: [F]lesh food consisted largely of small animals—skunks are particularly mentioned [p. 6]. [G]eese, ducks, cranes, coons, and skunks constituted a large part of their summer food. . . . Each fall when the skunks were fat, all the people in the camp moved out to the hills and hunted skunks. At the end of the hunt all the skunks were brought in and laid out in rows and then divided—a certain number to each family [p. 51]. In autumn [the Cheyenne moved] to certain hills where these animals [skunks] abounded, and they secured great numbers of them. Such places were visited time after time, and much food secured [p. 248]. [S]kunks are good to eat [p. 256].

In California, skunk occurs as a minor element in the faunal remains of a number of coastal archaeological sites, for example, in the Santa Monica Mountains (Landberg 1965), in Newport Bay in Orange County, and at Diablo Canyon north of Morro Bay (Margaret Weide and Roberta Greenwood in personal communication with Charles Rozaire, April 1972). More intensive and focused research would probably turn up many more such examples.

Skunks were also thought to possess great spiritual powers and were used by some aboriginal groups for medicine, war, and various other purposes (Grinnell 1962, v. II, Feer 1972). For example, "the skunk in almost all Indian groups is endowed with truly phenomenal powers due essentially to the overpowering presence of its scent. The skunk can move mountains and kill people simply by releasing its odors. . ." (Feer 1972, Boas 1918). While we have no way of knowing whether the Chumash and Gabrielino or their predecessors used skunk in similar ways, the fact remains that many recent North American aborigines did (skunk bones occur in middens on San Miguel Island, according to Walker 1978). Van Gelder commented that it was unlikely that the aborigines knew how to de-scent skunks. Yet, the literature shows that the Cherokee used skunk scent bags hung inside their lodges to prevent diseases (Feer 1972, Mooney 1900). This practice also suggests that some aborigines were not as repelled by skunk odor as one might casually think. Moreover, it may well be that very young skunks, which had not yet developed a sense of fear of human beings, were transported about in watercraft. The possibility, therefore, that the founding population of skunks on the Northern Channel Islands arrived by Indian transport is, we believe, very real and cannot be casually dismissed.

Herpetofauna

Very much the same arguments can be formulated for herpetofaunal colonization as have been advocated above for the larger animal forms. Since Savage has already spoken out quite strongly on that issue (Savage 1967), we refer readers to his paper.

IMPLICATIONS FOR ISLAND BIOGEOGRAPHY

If the biological and geological evidence relating to origins of land biota on islands is critically weighed in the context of land bridges *and/or* sweepstakes dispersal *and/or* Indian transport, quite different biogeographic perspectives may emerge. For example, if one assumes that a land bridge once connected the Northern Channel Islands to the mainland, biotic isolation would occur when the bridge subsided below sea level. With the passage of time, those forms remaining on the islands would be "relict" forms, provided that the mainland species became extinct or retreated from the coastal zone. We would also expect that notable endemism would have occurred on the islands after a sufficient lapse of time. On the other hand, not much change should have occurred if the bridge existed only a short time ago.

One could also conclude that *most* of the present island flora and fauna would have been isolated from the mainland for that full time span (after the subsidence of the land bridge). The exception, of course, would be the *very few* species which could have crossed the water gap after the land bridge submergence (if one permits too free a passage, a land bridge hypothesis is not necessary). By assuming that the crossing was very difficult (if not virtually impossible) for a number of species in some major taxon, it should be possible to measure "rate of evolution" in the different subgroups in that taxon, since all animals would have become isolated at approximately the same time.

Before proceeding too far on the assumption that a land bridge once existed, however, we think it prudent for researchers to agree upon a time for the existence of that bridge. It matters a great deal, since it is obvious that the Columbian (or imperial) mammoth could not have used such a bridge before it had even evolved as a species in North America (which probably occurred somewhat less than one million years ago).

If one invokes a sweepstakes approach in assessing Channel Islands biogeographic patterns, the evidence is viewed from a different perspective. For example, one could not know *a priori* how long an organism had been on the islands, not even with forehand knowledge of a particular group's "dispersal ability." That is, the very essence of "sweepstakes" theory is the inclusion of the element of chance into all considerations. Savage (1967) articulated this point in assessing the origin of the Channel Islands herpetofauna. He stressed that the insular herpetofaunas are depauperate chance samples of the adjacent mainland faunas, and that the islands were colonized by fortuitous over-water waif dispersal during the Pleistocene.

Indian transport of biota, on the other hand, could have operated irrespective of whether a land bridge existed, or whether sweepstakes dispersal had occurred. Indian influence, though, would have to have been geologically relatively recent (*i.e.,* Wisconsin-Holocene time). If organisms *had* been transported by Indians, it would, of course, be no easy matter to determine when that event first happened. Detailed analyses of the Indian middens will, we think, ultimately prove invaluable in this regard.

CONCLUSION

A limited number of possibilities exists from which one can draw an explanation for the origin and distribution of land vertebrates on the Northern Channel Islands. Recalling the general caution of Darlington, Simpson, and others, and in light of the factual biogeographic distribution patterns on those islands, we feel that there has been a general and uncritical acceptance of the land bridge hypothesis. A bridge might have existed at some time in the past. But, we argue, if the geological evidence does not unequivocally support that bridge concept, then one must explore the possibility that land animals may well have reached those islands by some means of transport, such as flying, swimming, rafting, or carriage by another organism. We have herein called attention to the lack of geological evidence for a land bridge, at least during the time when it would have been of use for those species which currently inhabit the islands. As an alternative, we have presented an array of biological evidence, anthropological evidence, and interpretation which, we think, strongly suggests that a combination of "sweepstakes" dispersal and Indian transport most plausibly explains the origin and distribution of land animals on the Northern Channel Islands.

ACKNOWLEDGMENTS

We thank P. L. Walker and D. N. Johnson for critically reviewing all or part of this paper; W. A. Berggren, D. A. Hooijer, C. T. Madden, V. J. Maglio, C. A. Repenning, J. J. Saunders, and J. Van Couvering for discussion and comment on elephant taxonomy; W. Akersten, A. Blaustein, B. H. Brattstrom, J. A. Holman, J. M. Savage, and S. Sweet for help with the Appendix; and D. Doerner, A. Junger, and R. Norris for extensive assistance on geology. Above all, we thank C. Stanton and A. Vail for their consistent support of research on the islands. We also thank E. Gustafson for his help on cartography and C. M. Akers for typing the final draft of the manuscript.

REFERENCES

ALLEN, G. M. 1942. Extinct and vanishing animals of the Western Hemisphere. Intelligence Printing Co., Lancaster, Penn.

AXELROD, D. I. 1967. Geologic history of the Californian insular flora. Pp. 267-315 *in* R. N. Philbrick, ed., Proceedings of the symposium on the biology of the California Islands. Santa Barbara Botanic Garden, Santa Barbara, Calif.

BAEGERT, J. 1865. Account of the aboriginal inhabitants of the California peninsula (C. Rau, trans.). Smithsonian Institute, Annual reports 1863:352-369 and 1864:378-399.

BERGER, R. 1980. Early man on Santa Rosa Island. Pp. 73-78 in D.M. Power, ed., The California Islands: proceedings of a multidisciplinary symposium. Santa Barbara Museum of Natural History, Santa Barbara, Calif.

BERGER, R., and P. C. ORR. 1966. The fire areas on Santa Rosa Island, California, II. Proc. Natl. Acad. Sci. U.S.A. 56:1678-1682.

BERGGREN, W. A., and J. A. VAN COUVERING. 1974. The late Neogene: biostratigraphy, geochronology and paleoclimatology of the last 15 million years in marine and continental sequences. Paleogeogr. Paleoclimatol. Paleoecol. 16:1-215.

BILLS, A. R. 1969. A study of the distribution and morphology of the mice of Santa Cruz Island: an example of divergence. M.A. thesis, University of California, Santa Barbara, Calif.

BOAS, F. 1918. Kutenai tales. Bur. Amer. Ethnol. Bull. 59. Smithsonian Institute, Washington, D.C.

BOWERS, S. 1890. San Nicolas Island. California State Min. Bur. Ann. Rep. 9:57-61.

BRATTSTROM, B. H. 1953. The amphibians and reptiles from Rancho La Brea. Trans. San Diego Soc. Nat. Hist. 11:365-392.

———. 1955. Small herpetofauna from the Pleistocene of Carpinteria, California. Copeia 2:138-139.

BREMNER, C. ST. J. 1932. The geology of Santa Cruz Island. Santa Barbara Mus. Nat. Hist., Occas. Papers, 1.

CARLQUIST, S. 1965. Island life: a natural history of the islands of the world. Natural History Press, Garden City, N.Y.

CHANEY, R. W., and H. L. MASON. 1930. A Pleistocene flora from Santa Cruz Island, California. Carnegie Inst. Washington Publ. 415:1-24.

COCKERELL, T. D. A. 1939. Recollections of a naturalist. XII. The California Islands. Bios 10:99-106.

COX, A. 1969. Geomagnetic reversals. Science 163:237-245.

CRANE, H. R., and J. B. GRIFFIN. 1958. University of Michigan radiocarbon dates, III. Science 128:1117-1123.

DARLINGTON, P. J. 1957. Zoogeography: the geographical distribution of animals. John Wiley & Sons, New York, N.Y.

DICKEY, D. R. 1929. The spotted skunk of the Channel Islands of southern California. Proc. Biol. Soc. Washington 42:157-160.

DIXON, J. R. 1967. Amphibians and reptiles of Los Angeles County, Calif. Los Angeles Co. Mus. Nat. Hist. Sci. Ser. 23, Zool. 10.

ELLISON, W. H., ed. 1937. The life and adventures of George Nidever, 1802-1883. University of California Press, Berkeley, Calif.

ERICSON, D. B., and G. WOLLIN. 1968. Pleistocene climates and chronology in deep-sea sediments. Science 162:1227-1234.

EVERNDEN, J. F., D. E. SAVAGE, G. H. CURTIS, and G. T. JAMES. 1964. Potassium-argon dates and the Cenozoic mammalian chronology of North America. Amer. J. Sci. 262:145-198.

FAIRBANKS, H. W. 1897. Oscillations of the coast of California during the Pliocene and Pleistocene. Amer. Geol. 20:213-245.

FEER, M. 1972. The skunk and the smallpox: mythology and historical reality. Plains Anthro. 18:33-39.

FLINT, R. F. 1971. Glacial and Quaternary geology. John Wiley & Sons, New York, N.Y.

FOSTER, J. B. 1963. The evolution of the native land mammals of the Queen Charlotte Islands and the problem of insularity. Ph.D. thesis, University of British Columbia, Vancouver, B.C., Canada.

_____. 1964. Evolution of mammals on islands. Nature 202:234-235.

_____. 1965. The evolution of the mammals of the Queen Charlotte Islands, British Columbia. Occas. Pap. British Columbia Prov. Mus. 14.

GILL, A. 1976. Genetic divergence of insular populations of deer mice. Biochem. Genet. 14:835-848.

_____. 1980. Evolutionary genetics of California Islands *Peromyscus*. Pp. 719-743 *in* D.M. Power, ed., The California Islands: proceedings of a multidisciplinary symposium. Santa Barbara Museum of Natural History, Santa Barbara, Calif.

GRAHAM, S. A., and W. R. DICKINSON. 1978. Evidence for 115 kilometers of right slip on the San Gregorio-Hosgri fault trend. Science 199:179-181.

GREENE, H. G. 1976. Late Cenozoic geology of the Ventura Basin, California. Pp. 499-529 *in* D. G. Howell, ed., Aspects of the geologic history of the California Continental Borderland. Assoc. Amer. Petroleum Geologists, Pacific Sec., Misc. Publ. 24.

GRINNELL, G. B. 1962. The Cheyenne Indians. Cooper Square, Publs., New York, N. Y.

GRINNELL, J., J. S. DIXON, and J. M. LINSDALE. 1937. The fur-bearing mammals of California. University of California Press, Berkeley, Calif. 2:299-301, 452-471.

HAAG, W. G., and R. F. HEIZER. 1953. A dog burial from the Sacramento Valley. Amer. Antiq. 18:263-264.

HAQ, B. V., W. A. BERGGREN, and J. A. VAN COUVERING. 1977. Corrected age of the Pliocene/Pleistocene boundary. Nature 269:483-488.

HARDACRE, E. C. 1880. Eighteen years alone. Scribner's Monthly 20:657-664.

HESSE, R., W. C. ALLEE, and K. P. SCHMIDT. 1951. Ecological animal geography. John Wiley & Sons, New York, N.Y.

HIBBARD, C. W., D. E. RAY, D. E. SAVAGE, D. W. TAYLOR, and J. E. GUILDAY. 1965. Quaternary mammals of North America. Pp. 509-526 *in* H. E. Wright and D. G. Frey, eds., The Quaternary of the United States. Princeton University Press, Princeton, N. J.

HILL, D. J. 1976. Geology of the Jurassic basement rocks. Santa Cruz Island, California, and correlation with other Mesozoic basement terrains in California. Pp. 16-46 *in* D. G. Howell, ed., Aspects of the geologic history of the California Continental Borderland. Amer. Assoc. Petroleum Geologists, Pacific Sec., Misc. Publ. 24.

HOOIJER, D. A. 1976. Observations on the pygmy mammoths of the Channel Islands, California. ATHLON, Festschrift Loris Russell, Royal Ontario Museum, Toronto, Canada.

HOWELL, D. G. 1976. Late-Miocene counterclockwise rotation of the south half of Santa Cruz Island. Pp. 449-454 *in* D. G. Howell, ed., Aspects of the geologic history of the California Continental Borderland. Amer. Assoc. Petroleum Geologists, Pacific Sec., Misc. Publ. 24.

HUDSON, T., J. TIMBROOK, and M. REMPE. 1978. Tomol: Chumash watercraft as described in the ethnographic notes of John P. Harrington. Ballena Press Anthropological Papers, 9.

INGLES, L. G. 1965. Mammals of the Pacific states, California, Oregon and Washington. Stanford University Press, Stanford, Calif.

JOHNSON, D. L. 1972. Landscape evolution on San Miguel Island, California. Ph.D. thesis, University of Kansas, Lawrence, Kan.

_____. 1973. On the origin and extinction of pygmy elephants, Northern Channel Islands, California. Program and abstracts, Geol. Soc. Amer.

_____. 1975. New evidence on the origin of the fox (*Urocyon littoralis clementae*) and feral goats on San Clemente Island, California. J. Mammal. 56:925-928.

_____. 1978. The origin of island mammoths and the Quaternary land bridge history of the Northern Channel Islands, California. Quaternary Res. 10:204-225.

————. 1980. Problems in the land vertebrate zoogeography of certain islands and the swimming powers of elephants. J. Biogeogr. 7 (in press).

JUNGER, A., and D. L. JOHNSON. 1980. Was there a Quaternary land bridge to the Northern Channel Islands? Pp. 33-39 in D.M. Power, ed., The California Islands: proceedings of a multidisciplinary symposium. Santa Barbara Museum of Natural History, Santa Barbara, Calif.

KING, C. 1971. Chumash inter-village economic exchange. The Indian Historian 4:31-43.

KROEBER, A. L. 1941. Culture element distribution: 15-salt, dogs, tobacco. Anthro. Rec. Univ. California 6(1).

LANDBERG, L. C. W. 1965. Chumash Indians of southern California. Southwest Mus. Papers, 19.

LAUGHRIN, L. 1977. The island fox: a field study of its behavior and ecology. Ph.D. thesis, University of California, Santa Barbara, Calif.

————. 1980. Populations and status of the island fox. Pp. 745-749 in D.M. Power, ed., The California Islands: proceedings of a multidisciplinary symposium. Santa Barbara Museum of Natural History, Santa Barbara, Calif.

LAWRENCE, B. 1967. Early domestic dogs. Z. Saeugetierkd. 32:44.

————. 1968. Antiquity of large dogs in North America. Tebiwa 11:43.

MACARTHUR, R. H. 1972. Geographical ecology. Harper and Row, New York, N.Y.

McELRATH, C. 1967. On Santa Cruz Island: the ranching recollections of Clifford McElrath. Santa Barbara Historical Society, Santa Barbara, Calif.

McKEOWN, M. S. 1974. Check-list of amphibians and reptiles of Santa Barbara County, California. Santa Barbara Mus. Nat. Hist. Occas. Paper 9.

McKUSICK, M. B., and C. N. WARREN. 1959. Introduction to San Clemente Island archaeology. Univ. California Los Angeles Archaeol. Surv., Ann. Rep. 1958-1959: 107-183.

McLAUGHLIN, C. A. 1959. Mammals of Los Angeles County, California. Los Angeles Co. Mus. Sci. Ser. 21, Zool. 9.

McMILLAN, R. B. 1970. Early canid burial from the western Ozark highland. Science 167:1246-1247.

MADDEN, C. T. 1978. Elephants of the Santa Barbara Channel Islands, southern California. In Abstracts of papers, a multidisciplinary symposium on the California Islands. Santa Barbara Museum of Natural History, Santa Barbara, Calif.

————. 1980. Earliest isotopically dated Mammuthus from North America. Quaternary Res. (in press).

MAGLIO, V. J. 1973. Origin and evolution of the Elephantidae. Trans. Amer. Phil. Soc., ser. 63, pt. 3.

MARCUS, L. F. 1960. A census of the abundant large Pleistocene mammals from Rancho La Brea. Los Angeles. Co. Mus. Contrib. Sci. 38:1-11.

MAYR, E. 1940. The origin and the history of the bird fauna of Polynesia. Proc. Sixth Pacific Sci. Congr. 4:197-216.

MEIGHAN, C. W. 1959. The Little Harbor site, Catalina Island: an example of ecological interpretation in archaeology. Amer. Antiq. 24:383-405.

MILLER, W. E. 1971. Pleistocene vertebrates of the Los Angeles basin and vicinity (exclusive of La Brea). Bull. Los Angeles Co. Mus. Nat. Hist., Sci. 10:1-124.

————. 1976. Late Pleistocene vertebrates of the Silver Creek local fauna from north central Utah. Great Basin Nat. 36:387-424.

MOONEY, J. 1900. Myths of the Cherokee. Bur. Amer. Ethnol. Annual report 1897-1898, Washington, D.C.

MUNSON, P. J., P. W. PARMALEE, and R. A. YARNELL. 1971. Subsistence ecology of Scovill, a terminal middle Woodland village. Amer. Antiq. 36:410-431.

MYERS, G. S. 1949. Ability of amphibians to cross sea barriers, with especial reference to Pacific zoogeography. Proc. Seventh Pacific Sci. Congr. 4:19-27.

NORRIS, R. M. 1951. Marine geology of the San Nicolas Island region, California. Ph.D. thesis, Scripps Institution of Oceanography, University of California, La Jolla, Calif.

ORR, P. C. 1967. Geochronology of Santa Rosa Island, California. Pp. 317-325 in R. N. Philbrick, ed., Proceedings of the symposium on the biology of the California Islands. Santa Barbara Botanic Garden, Santa Barbara, Calif.

————. 1968. Prehistory of Santa Rosa Island. Santa Barbara Museum of Natural History, Santa Barbara, Calif.

OWEN, R. C., F. CURTIS, and D. S. MILLER. 1964. The Glen Annie Canyon site, SBa 142; an early horizon coastal site of Santa Barbara County. Ann. rep. Archaeol. Surv., University of California, Los Angeles, Calif.

PARMALEE, P. W. 1965. The food economy of Archaic and Woodland peoples at the Tick Creek Cave Site, Missouri. Missouri Archaeologist 27:1-34.

PEARSON, O. P. 1951. Additions to the fauna of Santa Cruz Island, California, with description of a new subspecies of Reithrodontomys megalotis. J. Mammal. 32:366-368.

PHILBRICK, R. N., ed. 1967. Proceedings of the symposium on the biology of the California Islands. Santa Barbara Botanic Garden, Santa Barbara, Calif.

PRESCOTT, J. H. 1959. Rafting of jack rabbit on kelp. J. Mammal. 40:443-444.

RAVEN, P. H. 1967. The floristics of the California Islands. Pp. 57-67 in R. N. Philbrick, ed., Proceedings of the symposium on the biology of the California Islands. Santa Barbara Botanic Garden, Santa Barbara, Calif.

REED, R. D. 1933. Geology of California. Tulsa Amer. Assoc. Petroleum Geologists Bull.

REED, R. D., and J. S. HOLLISTER. 1936. Structural evolution of southern California. Amer. Assoc. Petroleum Geologists Bull. 20:1529-1692.

REMINGTON, C. L. 1971. Natural history and evolutionary genetics of the California Channel Islands. Discovery 7:2-18.

ROGERS, D. B. 1929. Prehistoric man of the Santa Barbara coast. Santa Barbara Museum of Natural History, Santa Barbara, Calif.

ROZAIRE, C. R. 1967. Archaeological considerations regarding the Southern California Islands. Pp. 327-336 in R. N. Philbrick, ed., Proceedings of the symposium on the biology of the California Islands. Santa Barbara Botanic Garden, Santa Barbara, Calif.

SAVAGE, D. E., and G. H. CURTIS. 1970. The Villafranchian stage—age and its radiometric dating. Geol. Soc. Amer. Spec. Paper 124:207-231.

SAVAGE, J. M. 1967. Evolution of the insular herpetofaunas. Pp. 219-227 in R. N. Philbrick, ed., Proceedings of the symposium on the biology of the California Islands. Santa Barbara Botanic Garden, Santa Barbara, Calif.

SCHUMACHER, P. 1877. Researches in the kjokkenmoddings and graves of a former population of the Santa Barbara Islands and the adjacent mainland. Bull. U.S. Geol. Geogr. Surv. Terr. 3:37-56.

SIMPSON, G. G. 1940. Mammals and land bridges. J. Washington Acad. Sci. 30:147-163.

————. 1953. Evolution and geography. Oregon State System Higher Education, Eugene, Ore.

SMITH, C. F. 1977. Random notes on the natural history of San Miguel Island. Noticias 23:41-42.

SONDAAR, P. Y. 1971. Paleozoogeography of the Pleistocene mammals from the Aegean. Pp. 65-70 in A. Strid, ed., Evolution in the Aegean. Opera Botanica 30.

SONDAAR, P. Y., and G. H. BOEKSCHOTEN. 1967. Quaternary mammals in the South Aegean Island Arc; with notes on other fossil mammals from the coastal regions of the Mediterranean I and II. Proc. K. Ned. Akad. Wet., Series B 70:556-576.

STOCK, C. 1935. Exiled elephants of the Channel Islands, California. Sci. Monthly 41:205-214.

————. 1943. Foxes and elephants of the Channel Islands. Los Angeles Co. Mus. Quart., vol. 3, nos. 2, 3, 4:6-9.

————. 1958. Rancho La Brea: a record of Pleistocene life in California. Los Angeles Co. Mus. Sci. Series 20, Paleontol. 11.

STOCK, C., and E. FURLONG. 1928. The Pleistocene elephants of Santa Rosa Island, California. Science 68:140-141.

SWANTON, J. R. 1946. Indians of the southwestern United States. Bur. Amer. Ethnol. Bull. 137, Smithsonian Institute, Washington, D. C.

THORNE, R. F. 1969. The California Islands. Ann. Missouri Bot. Gard. 56:391-408.

VALENTINE, J. W., and J. H. LIPPS. 1967. Late Cenozoic history of the Southern California Islands. Pp. 21-35 in R. N. Philbrick, ed., Proceedings of the symposium on the biology of the California Islands. Santa Barbara Botanic Garden, Santa Barbara, Calif.

VAN GELDER, R. G. 1959. A taxonomic revision of the spotted skunks (genus Spilogale). Bull. Amer. Mus. Nat. Hist. 117:233-392.

————. 1965. Channel Islands skunk. Nat. Hist. 74:30-35.

VEDDER, J. G., and R. M. NORRIS. 1963. Geology of San Nicolas Island, California. Geol. Surv. Prof. Paper 369.

VON BLOEKER, J. C., JR. 1967. The land mammals of the Southern California Islands. Pp. 245-263 in R. N. Philbrick, ed., Proceedings of the symposium on the biology of the California Islands. Santa Barbara Botanic Garden, Santa Barbara, Calif.

VOY, C. D. ca. 1893. San Miguel Island, California. Manuscript, Bancroft Library, University of California, Berkeley, Calif.

WALKER, P. L. 1978. Archaeological evidence for the recent extinction of three terrestrial mammals on San Miguel Island. In Abstracts of papers, a multidisciplinary symposium on the California Islands. Santa Barbara Museum of Natural History, Santa Barbara, Calif.

WALLACE, A. R. 1869. The Malay Archipelago. MacMillan, London.

WEAVER, D. W., ed. 1969. Geology of the Northern Channel Islands. Amer. Assoc. Petroleum Geologists Soc. Econ. Paleontologists Mineralogists, Pacific Secs., Spec. Publ.

WEAVER, D. W., and D. P. DOERNER. 1967. Western Anacapia—a summary of the Cenozoic history of the Northern Channel Islands. Pp. 13-70 in R. N. Philbrick, ed., Proceedings of the symposium on the biology of the California Islands. Santa Barbara Botanic Garden, Santa Barbara, Calif.

WHITE, J. A. 1966. A new Peromyscus from the late Pleistocene of Anacapa Island, California, with notes on variation in Peromyscus nesodytes. Los Angeles Co. Mus. Contrib. Sci. 96:1-8.

WHITE, T. E. 1953. A method of calculating the dietary percentage of various food animals utilized by aboriginal peoples. Amer. Antiq. 18:396-398.

WILSON, R. W. 1936. A new Pleistocene deer-mouse from Santa Rosa Island. J. Mammal. 17:408-410.

YARROW, H. C. 1879. Report on the operations of a special party for making ethnological research in the vicinity of Santa Barbara, California, with a short historical account of the region explored. In Reports upon archaeological and ethnological collections from vicinity of Santa Barbara, California, and certain interior tribes (by F. W. Putnam). In Report upon U.S. geographical surveys west of the one-hundredth meridian in charge of

1st Lieut. G. M. Wheeler. Vol. VII. Archaeology. U.S. Gov't Printing Office, Washington, D.C.

ZIMMERMAN E. C. 1942. Distribution and origin of some eastern oceanic insects. Amer. Natur. 76:280-307.

———. 1948. Insects of Hawaii. I. Introduction. University of Hawaii Press, Honolulu, Hawaii.

APPENDIX A. Land vertebrates of the Santa Barbara-Ventura-Los Angeles coastal zone.[1]

	Mainland		Northern Channel Islands	
	Fossil	Living[2]	Fossil	Living
MAMMALS				
Shrews and Moles				
Sorex ornatus (Ornate (adorned) shrew[3])	+	+		
S. bendirii (Pacific water shrew)		+		
S. trowbridgii (Trowbridge shrew)		+		
Notiosorex crawfordi (Desert shrew)	+	+		
Scapanus latimanus (Broad-footed mole)	+	+		
Rodents				
Thomomys bottae (Botta's pocket gopher)	+	+		
Spermophilus beecheyi (California ground squirrel)	+	+		
Eutamias merriami (Merriam's chipmunk)		+		
Sciurus griseus (Western gray squirrel)		+		
Perognathus californicus (California pocket mouse)	+	+		
Perognathus sp. (Pocket mouse)	+			
P. baileyi (Bailey's pocket mouse)		+		
Microtus californicus (California vole)	+	+		
Reithrodontomys megalotis (Western harvest mouse)	+	+		+
R. humulis (Eastern harvest mouse)	?			+
Peromyscus maniculatus (Deer mouse)	+	+		
P. imperfectus ("Deer" mouse[4,5])	+			
P. crinitus (Canyon mouse)	+			
P. californicus (California mouse)		+		
P. boyli (Brush mouse)		+		
P. eremicus (Cactus mouse)		+		
P. truei (Pinyon mouse)		+		
P. nesodytes ("Giant" deer mouse[4])			+	

APPENDIX A. (Cont.)

		Mainland		Northern Channel Islands	
		Fossil	Living[2]	Fossil	Living
Extinct Anacapa deer mouse[4]	*P. anyapahensis*	+		+	
Southern grasshopper mouse	*Onychromys torridus*	+	+		
Agile kangaroo rat	*Dipodomys agilis*	+	+		
Kangaroo rat	*Dipodomys* sp.	+			
Dusky-footed woodrat	*Neotoma fuscipes*	+	+		
Woodrat	*Neotoma* sp.	+			
Desert woodrat	*N. lepida*		+		
Muskrat	*Ondatra zibethicus*	?			
Wolves, Coyotes, Foxes					
Dire wolf[4]	*Canis dirus*	+			
Gray wolf	*C. lupus*	+	+		
Coyote	*C. latrans*	+	+		
Gray fox	*Urocyon cinereoargenteus*	+	+		
Island fox	*U. littoralis*				+
Bears					
Short-faced bear[4]	*Arctodus simum*	+			
Black bear	*Ursus americanus*	+			
Grizzly bear	*U. arctos*	+	+		
Skunks, Weasels, Badgers					
Striped skunk	*Mephitis mephitis*	+	+		
Western spotted skunk	*Spilogale gracilis*	+	+		+
Skunk	*Spilogale* sp.	+			
Long-tailed weasel	*Mustela frenata*	+	+		
Badger	*Taxidea taxus*	+	+		
Raccoons					
Raccoon	*Procyon lotor*	+	+		
Ringtail	*Bassariscus astutus*	+	+		

Category / Common name	Scientific name	Col. 1	Col. 2
Cats			
Sabretooth[4]	*Smilodon floridanus*		+
American lion[4]	*Panthera leo atrax*		+
Mountain lion	*Felis concolor*	+	+
Bobcat	*F. rufus*	+	+
Rabbits, Hares			
Black-tailed jackrabbit	*Lepus californicus*	+	+
Eastern cottontail	*Sylvilagus floridanus*	+	+
Desert cottontail	*S. auduboni*	+	+
Horses			
Western horse[4]	*Equus occidentalis*		+
Tapirs			
Tapir	*Tapirus sp.*		+
Pigs			
Large peccary[4]	*Platygonus compressus*		+
Camels			
Large camel[4]	*Camelops hesternus*		+
Camel[4]	*Camelops sp.*		+
Slender-limbed camel[4]	*Hemiauchenia macrocephala*		+
Ancient llama[4]	*Paleolama sp.*		
Deer and Pronghorns			
Mule deer[3]	*Odocoileus hemionus*		+
Deer	*Odocoileus sp.*	+	+
Tule elk	*Cervus nannodes*	+	
Pronghorn	*Antilocapra americana*		+
Small antelope[4]	*Capromeryx minor*		+
Bison and Musk Oxen			
Ancient bison[4]	*Bison antiquus*		+
Long-horned bison[4]	*B. latifrons*		+
Musk ox[4]	*Euceratherium collinum*		+
Mastodons			
American mastodon[4]	*Mammut americanum*		+

APPENDIX A. (Cont.)

	Mainland		Northern Channel Islands	
	Fossil	Living[2]	Fossil	Living
Elephants				
Columbian mammoth[4] *Mammuthus columbi* (= *imperator*)	+		+	
Pygmy mammoth[4] *M. exilis*			+	
Sloths				
Harlan's ground sloth[4] *Glossotherium harlani*	+			
Shasta ground sloth[4] *Nothrotheriops shastensis*	+			
Jefferson's ground sloth[4] *Megalonyx jeffersoni*	+			
AMPHIBIANS				
Salamanders				
California newt *Taricha torosa*		+		
Large newt *Taricha* sp.	+			
California tiger salamander *Ambystoma tigrinum californiense*	?			+
California slender salamander *Batrachoseps nigriventris*		+		+
Pacific slender salamander *B. pacificus*		+		
Garden slender salamander *B. major*		+		
Arboreal salamander *Aneides lugubris*	+			
Salamander *Aneides* sp.		+		
Ensatina *Ensatina eschscholtzii*		+		
Toads and Frogs				
Western spadefoot toad *Scaphiopus hammondi*	+			
Nestor toad[4] *Bufo nestor*	+			
Western toad *B. boreas*	+	+		
Southwestern toad *B. microscaphus*		+		
Pacific treefrog *Hyla regilla*		+		+
"Tree" frog *Hyla* sp.	+			
California treefrog *H. cadaverina*		+		

Common name	Scientific name	1	2	3
Red-legged frog	*Rana aurora*			+
Foothill yellow-legged frog	*R. boylei*			+
Frog	*Rana* sp.			
REPTILES				
Turtles				
Pacific pond turtle (Western pond turtle)	*Clemmys marmorata*		+	+
Tortoise	*Gopherus* sp.		+	+
Lizards				
Banded gecko	*Coleonyx variegatus*		+	
Desert spiny lizard	*Sceloporus magister*			+
Western fence lizard	*S. occidentalis*		+	+
Sagebrush lizard	*S. graciosus*	+	?	+
Side-blotched lizard	*Uta stansburiana*		+	
California horned lizard	*Phrynosoma coronatum*	+	+	+
Western skink	*Eumeces skiltonianus*		+	+
Granite night lizard	*Xantusia henshawi*		+	
Orange-throated whiptail	*Cnemidophorus hyperythrus*		+	
Western whiptail	*C. tigris*		+	
Southern alligator lizard	*Gerrhonotus multicarinatus*		+	+
California legless lizard	*Anniella pulchra*	+	+	+
Snakes				
Western blind snake	*Leptotyphlops humilis*		+	
Rosy boa	*Lichanura trivirgata*		+	
Western ringneck snake	*Diadophis punctatus*		+	
Sharp-tailed snake	*Contia tenuis*		?	
Western racer	*Coluber constrictor*		+	+
Coachwhip	*Masticophis flagellum*	+	+	+
Striped racer	*M. lateralis*		+	
Western patch-nosed snake	*Salvadora hexalepis*		+	+
Glossy snake	*Arizona elegans*		+	

APPENDIX A. (Cont.)

		Mainland		Northern Channel Islands	
		Fossil	Living[2]	Fossil	Living
Gopher snake	*Pituophis melanoleucus*	+	+		+
Common kingsnake	*Lampropeltis getulus*	+	+		
California mountain kingsnake	*L. zonata*		+		
Kingsnake	*Lampropeltis* sp.	+			
Long-nosed snake	*Rhinocheilus lecontei*		+		
Common garter snake	*Thamnophis sirtalis*	+			
Western terrestrial garter snake	*T. elegans*		?		
Western aquatic garter snake	*T. couchi*		+		
Garter snake	*Thamnophis* sp.	+			
Western black-headed snake	*Tantilla planiceps*		+		
California lyre snake	*Trimorphodon vandenburghi*		+		
Spotted night snake	*Hypsiglena torquata*		+		
Red diamond rattlesnake	*Crotalus ruber*		+		+
Speckled rattlesnake	*C. mitchelli*		+		
Western rattlesnake	*C. viridis*	+	+		
Rattlesnake	*Crotalus* sp.	+			

[1] Fauna compiled from Savage (1967, pers. comm. 1979), von Bloeker (1967), White (1966), Voy (*ca.* 1893), Johnson (1972, 1978), McKeown (1974), McLaughlin (1959), Dixon (1967), Brattstrom (1953, 1955), Miller (1971), Marcus (1960), Stock (1958), P. Walker (unpubl. ms., pers. comm. 1978), W. Ackersten (pers. comm. 1978), Wilson (1936), Ingles (1965), and E. Anderson (pers. comm. 1978).

[2] "Living" includes those species known to have been present within historic time.

[3] A small piece of skull bone of *Sorex ornatus* and several *Odocoileus hemionus* elements have been found in Indian middens on the Northern Channel Islands. It is probable that these species did not live on the Northern Channel Island group, but were brought in by birds of prey (in the case of *S. ornatus*) or humans (in the case of *O. hemionus*) (Walker 1978).

[4] Extinct.

[5] May not be a valid species.

Biogeography and Distribution of Three Parapatric Salamander Species in Coastal and Borderland California

Kay P. Yanev

Museum of Vertebrate Zoology, University of California,
Berkeley, California 94720

INTRODUCTION

Evolutionary biologists since Darwin have assumed that study of geographic variation provides clues to the history of the evolution of taxa. Such studies often lead to hypotheses concerning the historical and phyletic basis for the distributional patterns that are observed (see Ball 1975). Attempts at reconstruction have been hampered by a lack of objective data concerning the time and rate of phylogenetic events. Starch gel electrophoresis has provided quantitative data on genic differentiation between many taxa (see Ayala 1975); many workers have attempted to reconcile genetic distance information with geological characteristics that may have influenced the divergence of taxa. I am aware of no studies that attempt to reconcile genetic distance with evolution of complex intrageneric patterns of distribution.

Slender salamanders of the genus *Batrachoseps* comprise a morphologically and ecologically specialized group of lungless salamanders that is endemic to the west coast of North America. Within this region they are widely distributed and are one of the most common vertebrates. Although there are several species with particularly localized ranges and relatively generalized morphologies, most of the range of the genus is occupied by a single attenuate form previously assigned to a single species, "*B. attenuatus*," that was thought to be highly variable (Stebbins 1951, Hendrickson 1954, Brame and Murray 1968). Forms living in southern California and on the four Northern Channel Islands are distinctive; Campbell (1931) described sympatry between *B. pacificus* and "*attenuatus*" on Santa Cruz Island and between *B. p. major* and "*attenuatus*" in southern California.

In a recent revision of the genus based on an electrophoretic study, I demonstrated that the attenuate form comprises a complex set of taxonomic units of three sibling species that are distributed through the coastal mountains and the Sierra Nevada of California (Yanev 1978). The distributions of the taxa recognized by me are shown in Figure 1, and the major conclusions from that study were as follows. (1) Populations from the Transverse Ranges and the foothills of the southern Sierra Nevada, formerly referred to *B. attenuatus*, are a distinct species for which the name *B. nigriventris* Cope (1869) is available. (2) The name *B. pacificus* Cope (1865) has priority for a superspecies composed of six semispecies. Two of these, *B. p. pacificus* and *B. p. major*, were formerly regarded as full species. One semispecies (centered in the Gabilan and southern Diablo Ranges) was formerly part of *B. attenuatus*. Three of the four allopatric units that were originally included in *B. relictus* by Brame and Murray (1968) are referred to semispecies of *B. pacificus*; the population on Santa Cruz Island is referable to *B. nigriventris*. In addition to the attenuate complex, several relatively generalized members are recognized in the genus: *B. wrighti*, *B. stebbinsi*, *B. simatus*, *B. aridus*, and an undescribed species from the Inyo Mountains (Marlow *et al.* 1979).

The most striking feature of the distributions of the species of *Batrachoseps* is their parapatric geographic ranges. The three sibling species, *B. attenuatus*, *B. nigriventris*, and *B. pacificus*, are parapatric both in coastal and in Sierran regions. Each of these species is composed of allopatric subunits. *B. attenuatus* and *B. nigriventris* have subunits in the Coast

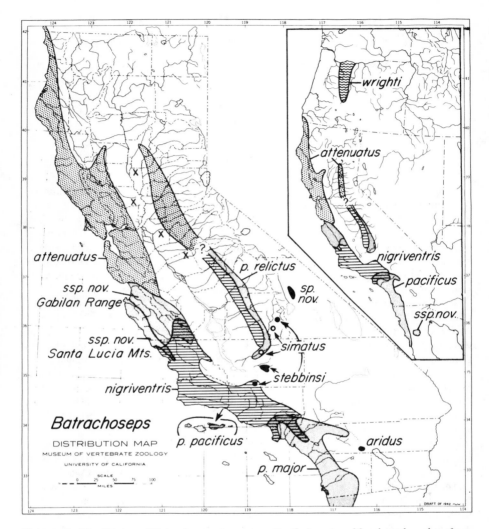

FIGURE 1. *Distribution of* Batrachoseps *in western North America. Map based on data from Yanev (1978). Insert shows isolated position of southern semispecies of* B. pacificus *and northern location of* B. wrighti.

Ranges and in the Sierra Nevada. Four of the six semispecies of *B. pacificus* are allopatric (*B. p. relictus, B. p. pacificus, B. p. major,* and the semispecies in the Sierra San Pedro Mártir) and two are parapatric in the central Coast Ranges (the Santa Lucian semispecies and the Gabilan semispecies). Thus, four parapatric taxonomic units are found in the Coast Ranges—*B. attenuatus,* the Santa Lucian semispecies, the Gabilan semispecies, and *B. nigriventris. Batrachoseps p. major* is a fifth parapatric unit in the Peninsular Range to the south. Populations in the Sierra Nevada form three parapatric units—*B. attenuatus, B. nigriventris,* and *B. p. relictus.*

Species of *Batrachoseps* are morphologically and ecologically specialized for subterranean life. They have elongated bodies with large numbers of vertebrae, markedly reduced limbs and feet, and elongated tails. *Batrachoseps* limit their surface activity to periods of favorable temperature and moisture conditions during the rainy months of winter. They cannot actively burrow and, in order to escape inhospitable surface conditions, rely on passages and spaces excavated by other organisms or produced by agents such as root decay and soil shrinkage. This semifossorial habit allows species of *Batrachoseps* to occupy habitats ranging from moist coastal and montane streamsides to oak and pine savanna and even desert springs.

All *Batrachoseps* are sedentary. Two studies of the movements of marked individuals have been conducted on *B. attenuatus*. Hendrickson (1954) found that adult salamanders moved within a range of 1.5 meters over the two years of his observations, and 59 per cent were found repeatedly under the same cover object. Maiorana (1978) also found evidence of individuals favoring a single cover object during a season of activity. Furthermore, populations of *Batrachoseps* seem to have survived in isolated patches of suitable habitat even though surrounding habitats became unsuitable. For example, *B. aridus* is known from a single spring in the southern California desert (Brame 1970); *B. stebbinsi* is known from several small, scattered localities in the southern California interior; and a recently described species, *B. campi*, is known from isolated springs in the arid Inyo Mountains (Marlow *et al.* 1979).

Stable parapatric distributions of species have been commonly associated with fossorial vertebrates, particularly rodents (see Patton and Yang 1977 for references). Parapatric distributions are also observed in plethodontid salamanders in the eastern United States (see Highton 1972 for closely related species of *Plethodon*). The regular pattern of parapatric distributions among taxa of *Batrachoseps* suggests that this phenomenon is stable and biogeographically significant. Maiorana (unpubl. ms.) has suggested that *Batrachoseps* might face competition for the burrows it needs in order to avoid dry surface conditions. Competition for burrows or other resources may limit the sympatry of closely related congeners. Competition, however, explains neither why there should be so many parapatric units in the genus nor why the units should be distributed as they are.

The thesis of this paper is that the present diversity of the parapatric taxa is related to historical changes in the geographic ranges of their respective ancestral lines. Various factors that may have influenced the establishment of the ranges will be examined in the following sections. Interrelated patterns of variation between the ranges and (1) the amount of genetic differentiation between the taxa and (2) the historical paleogeomorphology of California are described. It is hypothesized that the reconstruction of the evolutionary patterns from the present distributions and genetic relationships of the taxa requires simultaneous examination of the relative tectonic movements of landmasses, shifts in the locations and elevations of seas, mountain building episodes, and changes in paleobotanical and paleoclimatic conditions. I therefore constructed a set of maps showing a time-series of historical reconstructions of the geographical, botanical, and climatic history of California, and then worked backwards from the present patterns of distribution of taxa, superimposing on these maps a scenario of the "potential" divergences of groups inferred from genetic distances between those groups. It is assumed that speciation in salamanders occurred by allopatric mechanisms and that the divergence events occurred in the sequences suggested by the magnitude of the genetic distances between the taxa. A reasonable scenario is sought for the development of the complex parapatric patterns that are observed in *Batrachoseps*, based on the available estimates of the timing and sequence of geological and genic changes. Specific hypotheses concerning the relationship between taxonomic borders and historical geomorphic features may be tested in future studies by examining the concordant or discordant patterns of geographic variation in other genera of amphibians and reptiles.

EVOLUTIONARY HISTORY

Age and Estimates of Divergence Times in the Genus *Batrachoseps*

Batrachoseps is believed to be an old genus. On the basis of osteological and distributional characteristics, Wake (1966) proposed that the ancestors of the tribe Bolitoglossini—which includes *Batrachoseps,* its presumed closest relative, *Hydromantes,* and the Neotropical genera—reached the west coast of North America sometime in the early Tertiary via terrestrial forest corridors from source areas in the Appalachian Mountains. *Hydromantes* and *Batrachoseps* evolved in western North America, while the supergenus *Bolitoglossa* radiated from the northern tropics. Subsequent analyses continue to support the assignment of great age to these groups. Wake *et al.* (1978) report an immunological distance of 75 units between *Batrachoseps* and *Hydromantes.* They estimate that the separation of these lineages occurred around 50 million years (m.y.) ago in the early Eocene. Fossil material for these small animals is scant. A fossil trackway (Peabody 1959) and numerous fossil vertebrae (in the collection of the University of California Museum of Paleontology) from the Miocene of the Sierra Nevada suggest that an attenuate *Batrachoseps* of essentially modern form was present at that time.

In addition to estimating dates from fossil evidence, workers have attempted to infer divergence times from genetic distance. Nei (1972) proposed that genetic distance determined by starch gel electrophoresis is related to time, if it is assumed that most of the observed biochemical changes are effectively neutral or relatively neutral. Studies that examine a diversity of loci with differing evolutionary rates presumably average the discrepancies in evolutionary rates among individual loci. One method of estimating divergence times between taxa as a function of Nei's genetic distance (D) involves albumin immunological distance (for references and full development of this argument see Sarich 1977). Albumin immunological and electrophoretic genetic distances between the same pairs of taxa are highly correlated. On the basis of studies on a variety of taxa, Sarich showed that a genetic distance of 1.0 was approximately equivalent to an immunological distance of 35, which, in turn, predicts a divergence time of 20 m.y. ago; time in m.y. equals $20D$ for an average selection of loci. This method of estimating divergence time from genetic distance has been employed by several workers, including Gorman *et al.* (1976, and references) and Wake *et al.* (1978), who cite geological data supporting the magnitude of their estimates.

Estimates of divergence times within *Batrachoseps,* calculated from genetic distances by Sarich's formula, are large. Mean genetic distances and predicted divergence times between the 15 taxonomic units which I examined (Yanev 1978) are shown in Figure 2. The predicted divergence time between the morphologically generalized species (*B. wrighti* and *B. campi*) and the more derived, attenuate species is on the order of 40 m.y. ago—an early event in the presumed history of the genus. The genetic distances in the original distance matrix from which the dendrogram was derived predict divergence times of 20 to 35 m.y. ago between the three species *B. attenuatus, B. nigriventris,* and *B. pacificus,* and 8 to 10 m.y. ago between the allopatric taxa of *B. nigriventris* and of *B. pacificus.* Identical distances are observed between each of the two isolated taxa on Santa Cruz Island and their mainland relatives (D equals 0.20 between island and mainland populations of *B. nigriventris* and between *B. p. pacificus* and *B. p. major*). These distances predict that separation between the mainland and the island forms occurred on the order of four million years ago.

Paleogeography of California

The topography of California has changed considerably since the genus *Batrachoseps* evolved and its lineages diverged. The late Tertiary was an active geological period and its paleogeography differed from the present geography in several significant respects.

Global tectonic forces have had a primary influence on the geographic history of western

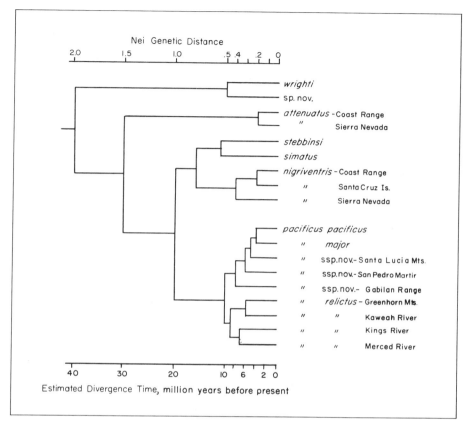

FIGURE 2. *Phenogram of genetic distance between taxonomic units of* Batrachoseps. *Clustering of Nei's D is by the unweighted pair-group method for arithmetic averages.*

North America (Atwater 1970). The recent geologic character of California is governed by the uneasy junction between the Pacific and North American plates that is presently expressed as the San Andreas fault. There have been many studies concerning the historic geology of California with respect to petroleum resources and, more recently, with respect to movement of the major fault systems. These studies report lateral displacements of diverse geologic markers representing a continuum of ages. They indicate that the land to the west of the San Andreas fault, which slices through the central coastal region of California, as illustrated in Figure 3, has moved northwest with respect to the mainland North American plate 190 miles (305 km) during the 12 m.y. since the middle Miocene. (Figure 4 *in* Nilsen and Clarke 1975 is an excellent summary of the movement indicated by these studies.) Some workers have proposed offsets of 350 miles (560 km) or more. However, such movements are now thought to be associated with earlier slipping along the fault system of 135 to 260 miles (220 to 420 km) during the Cretaceous. A thorough bibliography and specific documentation are available in Nilsen and Clarke (1975) and Howell (1976).

Several significant changes in sea-level elevations have occurred during the evolutionary history of *Batrachoseps*. Changes in the surface configurations of the land were due to the occurrence of widespread seas at various times and to episodes of topographic uplifting. Supporting data are derived from a variety of sources, including geologic studies of basins, shoreline deposits, and sedimentation patterns (see Reed 1933, Addicott 1968, Nilsen and Clarke 1975), and the classical geologic determinations of the nature and origins of rocks.

Paleogeographic changes combined with changes in the climate to influence the paleoflora of the region (which also helps, in retrospect, to recognize changes in land configuration). The flora of a region then influenced the dispersal possibilities available to the fauna. In a series of publications (1977, 1976, 1975, 1973, and 1958), Axelrod has discussed the evolution of the flora of California. Axelrod (1973) considers the Mediterranean climate zone to be young, and the flora to be composed of survivors of a richer flora that persisted in California as summer rainfall decreased in the late Cenozoic. By the early Tertiary, three floristic types were present in North America: (1) Neotropical-Tertiary geoflora (in a band across the southern half of the continent), (2) Arcto-Tertiary geoflora (in a band across the northern half of the continent), and (3) Madro-Tertiary geoflora (present south of the Rocky Mountains and in Mexico by the middle Eocene). California's primarily mixed evergreen forest was subjected to warming and drying cycles throughout the Miocene and Pliocene, except for minor perturbations. The cycles enabled Madro-Tertiary floristic elements, including sclerophyllous oak species, to encroach from the southwest. Such changing conditions would have promoted fragmentation of the ranges of mesic-adapted salamanders while promoting the expansion of xeric-adapted salamanders. Cooler and wetter periods from the end of the Pliocene through much of the Pleistocene, assisted by elevational changes produced by mountain building episodes at the end of the Pliocene (Wahrhaftig and Birman 1965), allowed the spread of Douglas-fir, redwood, and mixed conifers on coastal slopes and in the newly-risen Sierra Nevada. These cooler conditions would have promoted the re-expansion of mesic-adapted salamanders.

The age determinations of the geologic time boundaries are subject to variable interpretations; the timing of the boundary between the Miocene and the Pliocene is a relevant example. Most workers continue to follow the stratigraphic correlations of Everenden and Everenden (1970), which are supported by modern dating methods (see Turner 1970), and set this boundary at 12 m.y. ago; this date is used in the present analysis. Others accept the opinion of Berggren (1972), who claims that this boundary is as recent as 5.5 m.y. ago.

Previous Reconstructions of the Evolution of Taxonomic Distributions in Central California

The pioneering work of Peabody and Savage (1958) attempted to integrate paleogeology with the history of the distribution of the herpetofauna of western North America. They proposed a continuous corridor for dispersal that culminated in the Pleistocene. This corridor included the present southern Coast Ranges, but it was blocked and separated from southern California by an extensive seaway which connected to the embayment in the San Joaquin Valley region. Dispersal of animals occurred from the north into the southern Coast Ranges, where gradual differentiation of populations occurred, but animals could not disperse into southern California. When contact was re-established between the northern corridor and the southern regions, subsequent dispersal of taxa into southern California was responsible for the many instances of sympatry and overlap between related forms noted in the herpetofauna of that region.

Our knowledge of the geologic and tectonic history of California has grown in the years since the hypothesis put forth by Peabody and Savage. The seaway is believed to have existed, but the dispersal corridor could not have existed during much of the period when it was hypothesized to have operated. The southern Coast Ranges, which composed the hypothetical corridor, were located to the south of their present position until gradual Pliocene and Pleistocene tectonic movement brought them close to the northern Coast Ranges. The seaway may have served as a barrier to dispersal until the Pleistocene. The model of Peabody and Savage predicts that the affinities of the herpetofauna in the corridor region should be with populations to the north. *Batrachoseps attenuatus* was cited as a primary example of a species that ranged continuously through the corridor and surrounding regions. I (Yanev 1978) demonstrated that this "species" is, in fact, an assemblage of differentiated units, and that the genetic affinities of the populations in the corridor region are more southern than they are northern. A review of the ranges of amphibian species (distribution maps *in* Stebbins 1966) reveals that there are more species whose ranges end abruptly at the northern edge of the present southern Coast Ranges (*Batrachoseps attenuatus, Dicamptodon ensatus, Taricha granulosa, Ambystoma macrodactylum,* and *Aneides flavipunctatus*) than at their southern edge (*Ambystoma tigrinum, Rana boylei*). Unlike the southern boundary zone, this northern boundary is not characterized by sharp climatic and habitat differences. This same northern boundary is also the approximate northern limit of the ranges of a number of xeric-adapted reptilian taxa that are typical of warm, arid regions to the south (*Xantusia vigilis, Crotaphytus wislizenii, Sceloporus magister*), as well as several other forms that extend through the Diablo Range (*Aniella pulchra, Uta stansburiana, Tantilla planiceps,* and *Arizona elegans*). In all instances, if a wide-ranging species is racially or subspecifically divided, the discontinuity between the forms that occur in this region is between populations in northern *vs.* southern areas. The discontinuity never occurs between populations in coastal and inland areas despite major differences in habitat and other ecological features that presently exist between these areas.

Morafka and Banta (1972) extend the hypothesis of Peabody and Savage (*op. cit.*). They correlate the endemism that is observed at the subspecific level in the herpetofauna of the southern Coast Ranges with fragmentation of the Coast Range corridor by invasions of Pliocene seas. They cite particularly the subspecies of *Ensatina eschscholtzii* and *Diadophis punctatus*. As did Peabody and Savage, they propose that the species that were isolated in the Pliocene corridor entered the region from the north. Later, Morafka and Banta (1976) attempted to correlate new geologic data with the distribution of color morphs of a salamander, but they present few data on the level of differentiation of taxa. They propose that a large-spotted *Aneides lugubris* from the Farallon Islands and from the Gabilan Range may represent a common stock that previously had a continuous range on an early Pliocene peninsula. They suggest that large-spotted *Aneides* in these two localities may have been isolated from "mainland" small-spotted *Aneides* on islands that were formed by invasions of Pliocene seas. Several difficulties exist with this hypothesis. Recent geologic evidence does not support the existence of the necessary early Pliocene peninsula, and the Farallon Islands are believed to have been submerged at times. Morafka and Banta suggest that the Farallon Islands and the Gabilan Range were separated by plate movements along the San Andreas fault, but both regions are on the west side of the fault. In addition, other adjacent regions that were insular in the Pliocene do not contain the large-spotted form of *Aneides*. Finally, without some knowledge of the level of genetic differentiation between the large-spotted and the small-spotted forms, it is difficult to accept the magnitude of the time scale that they propose.

A progressive attempt to integrate paleogeology with the history of the distribution of taxa was presented by Axelrod (1978, 1979). He reported that the closest allies of a number of taxa of the California closed-cone pine forest live in western Mexico. Baja California, formerly attached to the western coast of Mexico, was displaced northward to its present position by the San Andreas fault and allied rifts. Axelrod proposed that the California species achieved their present distribution by vicariant northward displacement on, and subsequent dispersal from, this land fragment during a time of spreading aridity.

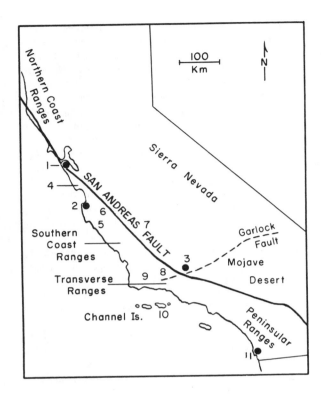

FIGURE 3. *Geographic area of California included in the historical reconstructions of Figures 4 through 7. Numbered features: San Francisco (1); Monterey (2); Bakersfield (3); Santa Cruz Mountains (4); Santa Lucia Mountains (5); Gabilan Range (6); southern Diablo Range (7); Temblor Range (8); San Rafael Mountains (9); Santa Cruz Island (10); San Diego (11).*

A Hypothetical Scenario for the Evolution
of the Patterns of Distribution of *Batrachoseps*

The geographical reconstructions used in the scenario were developed through a three-part procedure: (1) the land lying to the west of the San Andreas fault was shifted southeast (back in geologic time) by linear increments (Atwater 1970) of the total estimated displacement over the presumed period of movement of 15 m.y.; (2) the positions of landmasses that were thought to have been continuously land-positive (from shoreline and depositional analyses), the position of recognized seas, and historical mountain building episodes were then superimposed on (1); and (3) the evolution of the California flora, as traced by Axelrod, and inferences from the floras concerning the evolution of climatic conditions were added to (1) and (2). For comparison, features of the present geography of California are located in Figure 3. The degrees of confidence in the above parameters vary. The relative positions of the land on both sides of the fault are well documented. The limits of the seas and of land-positive areas are uncertain, although the present reconstructions are more reasonable than earlier, convoluted attempts to explain the distribution of geographic features without accounting for land movements (for example, see Reed 1933).

Geography and the distribution of **Batrachoseps** *between 40 and 15 m.y. ago, prior to initiation of movement along the San Andreas fault.* —Several examples suggest that the distribution of the genus has been reduced in Recent times from the range it once occupied. Three specimens of *Batrachoseps* (probably referable to *B. p. major*), reportedly collected in 1875 (Lockington 1880) from La Paz at the southern tip of the Baja California peninsula, are present in the Museum of Vertebrate Zoology, but no specimens have been collected in this century. A single immature specimen collected by Gadow (1905) from the Nevado de Colima, on the western coast of Mexico, is too small to identify but seems to be morphologically similar to *B. p. relictus* or to the unnamed semispecies of *B. pacificus* from the Sierra San Pedro Mártir. No subsequent specimens have been collected despite numerous attempts. Because the genus does not seem to be expanding into the arid regions of southern California and Mexico, these specimens may represent isolated local populations that are remnants of a formerly continuous distribution. *Batrachoseps caudatus* was described by Cope (1889) from southern Alaska, although Brame and Murray (1968) suggest that this may be a locality error for an animal from the northern California coast; they refer the specimen to *B. attenuatus*.

The radiation of *Batrachoseps* must have centered in the southern California interior— probably in Neotropical-Tertiary vegetational associations. Perhaps the ancestral form spread through equitable Neotropical-Tertiary areas and occupied ranges that were fragmented and reduced later. *Batrachoseps campi* in the Inyo Mountains is morphologically the most generalized member of the genus (Marlow *et al.* 1979) and is probably a relict of the period when the genus was generally distributed in the area. *Batrachoseps stebbinsi* and *B. simatus* also have relictual distributions in local regions in the southern interior. Only *B. wrighti* (north-central Oregon) and *B. attenuatus* have distributions that are centered primarily in areas currently dominated by the derivative floras of the Arcto-Tertiary vegetational zone; it is probable that this represents a secondary invasion of that zone rather than the zone of origin for the genus, as has generally been assumed for salamanders (Wake 1966, Peabody and Savage 1958, Lowe 1950). All other taxa of *Batrachoseps* have distributions that are centered in regions currently dominated by derivative floras of the Madro-Tertiary or Neotropical-Tertiary vegetational zones.

Geography and the distribution of **Batrachoseps** *at 10 m.y. ago.* —The first reconstruction in Figure 4 illustrates the central and southern coast of California as it may have looked 10 million years before the present time. The land had been in this position since the end of the earlier episode of tectonic movement in the Paleocene. The Sierra Nevada was present as a range of hills at the western margin of the continent. The partly submerged site of the present city of Monterey was adjacent to the southern end of these hills and west of the San Andreas fault. This site lies at the northern end of the Salinian block of basement rock underlying the Santa Lucia and the Gabilan Ranges; 10 million years ago it was located far to the south of its Recent position (south of the Sierra Nevada, and adjacent to the Transverse Ranges).

Perhaps one morphologically generalized species, the ancestor of *B. wrighti* and the populations in the Inyo Mountains, ranged east of the proto-Sierra Nevada in the interior. A second generalized species, which later differentiated into *B. stebbinsi* and *B. simatus*, ranged over the southern interior around the southern end of the Sierra Nevada region. Three distinct lineages of derived *Batrachoseps* —the sibling species *B. attenuatus, B. nigriventris,* and *B. pacificus* —had already evolved. These taxa probably represent an early radiation in the evolving western North American ecosystems. *Batrachoseps attenuatus* probably ranged in the north along the coast in mixed evergreen forests. *Batrachoseps nigriventris* ranged in the southern interior in the Mojave province, through lowland basins, and onto the (Miocene) coastal lowland west of the Sierra Nevada hills. They probably occupied oak woodland or savanna that had been widespread in these regions since the Oligocene; all present populations of *B. nigriventris* are known from oak habitats in foothill woodland. *Batrachoseps pacificus*, as yet undifferentiated into the assemblage of semispecific taxa, ranged along the Miocene coastal hills in the Sierra Nevada region, throughout the region of the present Transverse Ranges and the Salinian region, and south through the present Peninsular Range. *Batrachoseps pacificus* probably inhabited relatively more mesic sites, such as upland forests, than did *B. nigriventris*.

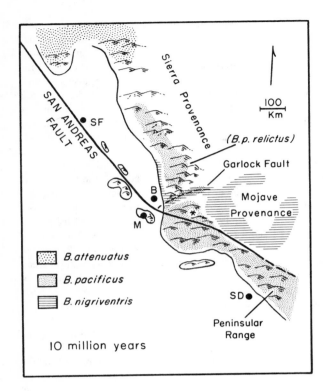

FIGURE 4. *Hypothetical reconstruction of geography of California and distribution of* Batrachoseps *at 10 million years ago. Circles indicate sites of present cities of San Francisco (SF), Monterey (M), Bakersfield (B), and San Diego (SD). Asterisk indicates site of Transverse Ranges at 10 million years ago.*

Sometime around 10 million years ago (corresponding to a genetic distance of 0.5), a barrier arose between the populations of *B. p. relictus* in the Sierra Nevada and the rest of *B. pacificus*. The existence of lowland basins in the present zone of the Garlock fault suggests that the region may have been geologically active (Nilsen and Clarke 1975). Dibblee (1967) suggests that these basins represented long, continuous, and linear lowlands that separated upland areas to the north and south. The upland areas could potentially harbor populations of mesic-adapted salamanders (*B. pacificus*), while the lowlands could be occupied by arid-adapted salamanders (*B. nigriventris*).

Geography and the distribution of Batrachoseps at 8 m.y. ago. —The second reconstruction in Figure 5 illustrates the central and southern coast of California as it may have looked two million years later, or at 8 m.y. ago. Relative motion has occurred along the San Andreas fault. The land to the west of the fault has begun to form a peninsula, or archipelago, which separated into an island several million years later. The seas approached their maximum spread, and there were still a few land-positive areas on the east side of the fault in the vicinity of the incipient Diablo Range.

Differentiation of the semispecies which centered in the Gabilan Range from the rest of *B. pacificus* may have occurred at this time, together with differentiation of the allopatric taxa of *B. nigriventris*. The ancestors of the Gabilan semispecies, in the Gabilan Range west of the San Andreas fault, might have become isolated from other *B. pacificus* by a combination of restriction of populations to mesic upland sites during the drying conditions of the Pliocene and increasing distance of those upland areas from each other as the blocks of land where they were

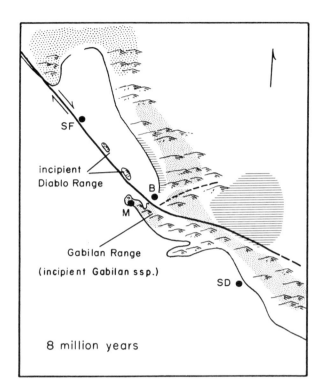

located moved farther apart. Paleobotanical evidence indicates that oak associations were present in the Gabilan region. Freed from genetic contact with the "mainland" *B. pacificus,* those populations in the Gabilan Range may have been under strong selective pressure to adapt genetically to the new conditions. At approximately the same time, the formerly continuous range of *B. nigriventris* may have been split into two disjunct segments in the Mojave region and in the Sierra Nevada foothills.

Geography and the distribution of **Batrachoseps** *between 6 and 5 m.y. ago.* —The geographical changes that occurred by 5 m.y. ago are illustrated in the third reconstruction in Figure 6. Motion continued along the San Andreas fault. The Santa Lucia Range, the Gabilan Range, and the southern Diablo Range landmasses were fully isolated by seas to the east and west and by wide straits to the north and south. The southern strait is that implicated by Peabody and Savage (1958) in preventing dispersal of the herpetofauna to the south from their hypothetical corridor. It has been known that the major drainage from the inland sea or San Joaquin embayment was through the lowland north of the Santa Lucia and Gabilan Ranges, but the importance of this northern strait as a barrier has been underestimated. Throughout much of its history it was a wide seaway, not merely the present continental river valley.

During this time, the Gabilan semispecies became fully isolated on the offshore landmass and drying trends are believed to have been most severe. The most significant geologic event of this mid-Pliocene period was the rise of the Transverse Ranges. The presence of these mountains created a sharp floral boundary between central and southern California by preventing northern storms from reaching southern areas. This climatic stress and the resultant habitat

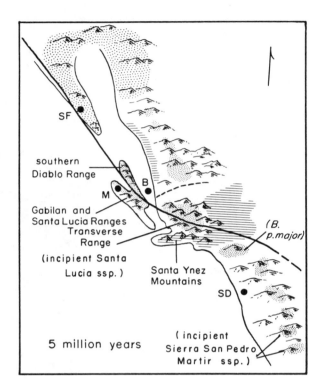

FIGURE 6. *Hypothetical reconstruction of geography of California and distribution of* Batrachoseps *at 5 million years ago.*

stress further split the extensive population of *B. pacificus* into a semispecies in the Transverse Ranges (incipient Santa Lucian semispecies) and populations which ranged south in coastal highlands through the Peninsular Range, into northern Baja California, and perhaps far south along the coast of mainland Mexico. Mesic habitats would still have been available for the Santa Lucian semispecies in the Transverse Ranges and for populations of *pacificus* that happened to be stranded on peaks and ridges to the south (for example, the Sierra San Pedro Mártir). The lowland populations that lived in the rain shadow of the new Transverse Ranges, however, would have been under severe stress to adapt to the increasing aridity. *Batrachoseps p. major* presumably evolved in arid savannas in the lowland basins in the vicinity of Los Angeles. When an arid-adapted form had evolved, it could have begun to spread southward along the coast in similar lowland habitats. With increasing aridity, the mesic habitats in the Transverse Ranges shifted toward the coast, carrying with them the populations of the Santa Lucian semispecies. Similarly, the oak-savanna zones that were inhabited by *B. nigriventris* shifted coastward from the Mojave region into increasingly arid regions of the Transverse Ranges.

Geography and the distribution of **Batrachoseps** *at 4 m.y. ago.* —The paleogeographic map of the late Pliocene of California changed little from the previous map. The landmass that was occupied by the Gabilan semispecies was still isolated by seas and continued to approach the northern Coast Ranges that were occupied by *B. attenuatus*. In the Transverse Ranges, the Santa Lucian semispecies was further restricted by drying conditions to habitats near the coast. *Batrachoseps nigriventris* was abundant throughout the Transverse Ranges and into the Santa

Ynez Mountains, but it no longer inhabited the increasingly arid Mojave province. *Ba-trachoseps p. major,* which is tolerant of dry and unpredictable habitats, continued to expand southward along the coast. It contacted *B. nigriventris* at the southern edge of the Transverse Ranges, where the present parapatric distributions of the two taxa seem to correlate with their habitat preferences. While *B. p. major* presently lives in open, low-elevation grasslands, *B. nigriventris* lives in oak woodlands.

The genetic distance of populations of *B. attenuatus* in the northern Coast Ranges as compared with the northern Sierra Nevada suggests separation at this time, perhaps as cooler temperatures forced populations to move south and into disjunct ranges in the two regions. Forested valley corridors may have maintained limited genetic contact between populations in the two areas.

Establishment of the taxa on the Channel Islands. —The most significant event in the history of *Batrachoseps* at approximately 4 m.y. ago was the establishment of the taxa on the Channel Islands. Excluded from this discussion are populations on Santa Catalina, Los Coronados, and Todos Santos Islands that are referred to *B. p. major.* Presently, populations of *B. p. pacificus* occur on the four Northern Channel Islands, and populations of *B. nigriventris* occur on Santa Cruz Island. I (Yanev 1978) have demonstrated that the two taxa on Santa Cruz Island are most closely related to the two mainland taxa whose present ranges are geograph-ically closest to the islands. Both island taxa have the same genetic distance ($D = 0.2$) from their mainland relatives, which predicts a common divergence time of 4 m.y. ago. Thus, it is inferred that *B. nigriventris* was isolated on Santa Cruz Island and diverged from mainland *nigriventris,* and *B. p. pacificus* from *B. p. major,* at approximately the same time.

These island populations of *Batrachoseps* could have arisen in two ways: (1) by terrestrial range expansion over a land connection which became submerged approximately 4 m.y. ago, or (2) by over-water rafting of the two taxa at approximately the same time. Many geological studies have been conducted recently on the borderlands of southern California (Howell 1976, Vedder and Howell 1980, Junger and Johnson 1980), and there is no support for the hypothesis of a Pliocene land connection between these islands and the mainland. Such a connection has often been erroneously hypothesized in the past, primarily by biologists to explain the presence of terrestrial faunas on the islands (see Wenner and Johnson 1980).

In accordance with these views, Savage (1967) suggested that the modern herpetofauna of the Channel Islands is a depauperate random sample of the herpetofauna of the adjacent mainland and was established during the Pleistocene by over-water distribution of waifs. Circumstantial evidence is in agreement with this hypothesis. Over-water rafting is certainly possible for *Batrachoseps.* Individual salamanders could have been washed out to sea on clumps of debris from mainland rivers, perhaps during periods of torrential rains at the onset of Pleistocene cooling periods. (The power of such storms and their ability to disperse organisms is illustrated by a recent news service report [Anonymous 1978] that a large quantity of fruit was observed floating 10 miles offshore in the Santa Barbara Channel. The fruit, which had been knocked from trees in orchards of central Ventura County by "fierce thunderstorms" the previous week, had floated 20 miles downriver to the ocean.) The minimum distance between the islands and the mainland is believed to have been 7 to 10 km (Junger and Johnson 1980), which is about a quarter of the present distance. In addition, *Batrachoseps* is notably tolerant of saline conditions. Licht *et al.* (1975) report that *Batrachoseps* is one of the most euryhaline amphibians. Furthermore, rafting does not always provide a complete sample of neighboring faunas, which would explain why such generalists as *Ensatina* and *Eumeces* are absent from the islands. The Farallon Islands lie approximately the same distance off the shore of northern California as the Channel Islands do off southern California. Only *Aneides lugubris* is established on the Farallon Islands, even though *Batrachoseps* and other salamanders are

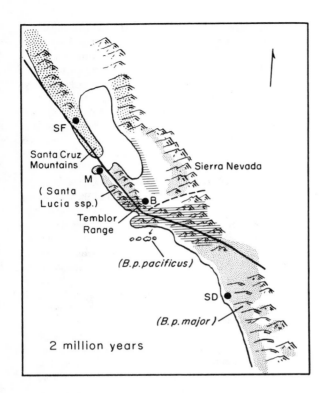

FIGURE 7. *Hypothetical reconstruction of geography of California and distribution of* Batrachoseps *at 2 million years ago.*

abundant on the mainland.

The hypothesis that the island herpetofaunas were established by over-water rafting from the mainland may be tested by comparing the degree of genetic differentiation between other terrestrial island taxa and their mainland relatives. If island populations of different species were established by the submergence of a land bridge, then the genetic distances and the predicted divergence times should be concordant for all pairs of taxa. If the faunas were established by a stochastic process such as rafting, the genetic distances would be expected to be heterogeneous. A parallel test would be to compare the genetic differences between the populations of *B. p. pacificus* on the four Northern Channel Islands with each other and with mainland *B. p. major*. The four northern islands are believed to have been interconnected during the Pleistocene. Thus, these island populations are expected to show small, uniform genetic distances from each other, distances that correspond to divergence times in the late Pleistocene. Analysis of these populations is in progress.

Geography and the distribution of **Batrachoseps** *at 2 m.y. ago.* —The Pleistocene of two million years ago, illustrated in Figure 7, was a time of cyclical cooling with increased moisture. Forested areas spread inland, and temperate areas shifted southward and downslope. The present configuration of the mountain ranges began to emerge. The Sierra Nevada was uplifted rapidly. The uplift of the Temblor Range at the southern end of the Coast Ranges expelled the San Joaquin Embayment from the central valley (through the shrinking seaway north of the Gabilan and Santa Lucia Ranges) and closed the southern seaway that had for so long prevented geographical contact between the Gabilan semispecies of *B. pacificus* on the "moving island" and the Santa Lucian semispecies living in the Transverse Ranges to the south.

The Santa Cruz Mountains at the southern terminus of the northern Coast Ranges also uplifted rapidly and created habitats for populations of *B. attenuatus* in close proximity to populations of the Gabilan semispecies of *B. pacificus*. The ranges of these two taxa remained separated by the major drainage from the Sierra Nevada through the former northern seaway, which is now the Pajaro River; this river was alternately a major river in cool times of low sea level and high continental runoff and a swampy bay in warm times of high seas.

The tectonic and floristic perturbations had several effects on the taxa. Populations of *B. p. relictus* in the Sierra Nevada, and particularly in the northern drainages, were isolated when colder conditions forced them to move lower into river valleys that were separated by arid ridges. This isolation may be responsible for the large genetic heterogeneity that is observed between these populations today. The southerly spread of mixed evergreen and redwood forests along the coast provided a habitat corridor by which the Santa Lucian semispecies of *B. pacificus* may have moved north along forested coastal slopes to occupy its present range in the Santa Lucia Mountains. *Batrachoseps attenuatus* moved south through continuous habitat from the northern Coast Ranges into the Santa Cruz Mountains. *Batrachoseps nigriventris* expanded onto the new geographic connections between the Transverse Ranges and the southern Coast Ranges and occupied the more arid oak-savanna sites surrounding the mesic pockets preferred by the Santa Lucian semispecies. In the southern Diablo Range, the range of *B. nigriventris* contacted the range of the Gabilan semispecies of *B. pacificus* and the two taxa became seemingly microsympatric over the limited area in which they behave as full species. Nothing is known of their interactions, although their overlap is the most extensive between any of the parapatric units of the genus. Populations of *B. p. major* expanded both inland and southward and recontacted the populations of *B. pacificus* that had been left on cooler, wooded ridges of the Peninsular Range by earlier episodes of drying conditions. *Batrachoseps p. major* also spread inland through the San Gabriel and San Bernardino Mountains; *B. aridus* may have been isolated subsequently and may have become a relict of this distribution.

When two taxa of *B. pacificus* came into secondary contact, reproductive isolation does not appear to have developed, and the taxa intergrade despite some accumulated genetic and morphological differences. Intergradation is presently observed where the Santa Lucia semispecies contacts the Gabilan semispecies in the southern Coast Ranges; it also may have occurred where trans-valley migrants may have passed between the Gabilan semispecies and the relatively isolated populations of *B. p. relictus* in the central Sierra Nevada (see Yanev 1978). Intergradation may have occurred where populations of *B. p. major* in the southern California lowlands came into contact with the *B. pacificus* populations on the ridges of the Peninsular Range. Populations in this area are morphologically intermediate and have been taxonomically ambiguous—they have been referred to "*B. attenuatus leucopus*" (Dunn 1926); "intergrades between *B. pacificus* and *B. attenuatus*" (Hendrickson 1954); and "*B. major* Camp" (Brame and Murray 1968, and see maps *in* Brame 1970 and Lowe and Zweifel 1951).

Geography and the distribution of **Batrachoseps** *in the late Pleistocene.* —By the late Pleistocene, the geography of California had assumed its present pattern. The major drainage from the Sierra Nevada shifted to the north, to exit from the valley through San Francisco Bay; this shift brought the ranges of *B. attenuatus* and the Gabilan semispecies into contact. However, this contact is limited and occurs primarily at the base of the Santa Cruz Mountains, where *B. attenuatus* remains in the evergreen forest of higher elevations and the Gabilan semispecies has invaded the alluvial lowlands that support savanna-woodland vegetation. The ranges of these two taxa approach each other at the northern end of the Gabilan Range, but probably do not contact at all in the central Diablo Range. Their potential contact zone in the central Diablo Range is dominated by sterile serpentine outcrops and derived, highly toxic soils that support only limited vegetation (Griffin 1975); no salamanders have been collected there.

DISCUSSION AND PREDICTIONS

A second method of estimating divergence times between taxa, as a function of Nei's genetic distance, was suggested by Nei (1972). Nei and Roychoudhury (1974), in a study of races of man, estimated the parameters necessary to predict that time in m.y. equals $5 \times 10^6 D$. This method predicts divergence times that are lower by a factor of four than those calculated by Sarich's formula which was based on a larger number of taxa of greater and more diverse ages. If a scenario for the evolution of the distribution of *Batrachoseps* is constructed using the shorter time scale, it is not possible to resolve the distributions of the taxa with the geologic data.

Several specific testable hypotheses follow from the predictions of the scenario that was developed for the evolution of the complex distributions observed in *Batrachoseps*. Most significantly, if paleogeographic borders exert a relevant influence on taxonomic diversity, then taxonomic borders ought to be concordant in species of appropriate historical age. Either other species inhabiting the same areas will show electrophoretic evidence of genetic discontinuities at the same paleogeographic borders that were observed in *Batrachoseps,* or the other species will have recently dispersed across the region, which will be apparent in very low levels of genetic differentiation. Appropriate species for this analysis are those with distributions through the coastal and montane regions of California. Such species include *Aneides lugubris, Taricha torosa* and *T. granulosa, Rana boylei, Gerrhonotus coeruleus* and *G. multicarinatus,* and particularly the subdivided species *Ensatina eschscholtzii* and *Diadophis punctatus.* Studies on *Ensatina, Aneides, Diadophis,* and *Gerrhonotus* are in progress.

Few genetic distance comparisons are presently available for other taxa over this geographical region, and none directly concern the paleogeographic borders. The most relevant comparisons involve *Taricha.* The ranges of *Taricha granulosa* and *T. torosa* contact each other in the vicinity of the (former) seaway between the northern and southern Coast Ranges that is hypothesized to have limited the ranges of *B. attenuatus* and the Gabilan semispecies of *B. pacificus.* The hypothesis predicts that taxonomic borders of *Taricha* ought to reflect this biogeographical boundary or demonstrate the low levels of genetic differentiation that would be compatible with recent dispersal across the region. Hedgecock and Ayala (1974) present genetic distance comparisons between five populations of the two species. The range of *T. granulosa* is exactly concordant with this hypothetical boundary, while *T. torosa* ranges primarily to the south but also across this boundary into the southern part of the northern Coast Ranges. The mean genetic distance between the two species equals 0.44, which corresponds to a predicted separation of 8.8 m.y. ago; the seaway may have been a barrier between them. *Taricha torosa* may be regarded as having recently dispersed across this boundary; the genetic distance observed between two populations of *T. torosa* from the northern and southern Coast Ranges equals 0.11, which corresponds to a Pleistocene divergence time within *torosa.*

Some other, more specific predictions from the hypothetical scenario are also testable. (1) The scenario predicts that taxa occupying the southern Coast Ranges will have southern rather than northern affinities. (2) I expect that upland populations in the Peninsular Range will show electrophoretic evidence of past intergradation between *B. p. major* and the undescribed semispecies of *B. pacificus* presently living in the Sierra San Pedro Mártir. (3) The scenario proposed that the present Santa Lucian semispecies of *B. pacificus* moved with shifting mesic habitats from the Transverse Ranges to occupy the Santa Lucia Mountains. The upland Transverse Ranges have not been well sampled. I predict that populations genetically related to the Santa Lucian semispecies and to *B. p. major* may be found and recognized electrophoretically from localized areas. (4) In light of the complex pattern of distribution observed in the semispecific taxa of *B. pacificus,* the distribution of *B. aridus* seems logical for a relict of *pacificus*; I predict that these forms will be found to be close genetic relatives.

SUMMARY

In a recent revision of *Batrachoseps* (slender salamanders) that was based on an electrophoretic survey, it was demonstrated that the attenuate form of the genus comprises a complex set of taxonomic units of three sibling species that are distributed throughout the borderland, the coastal mountains, and the Sierra Nevada of California. The sibling species *B. attenuatus*, *B. nigriventris*, and *B. pacificus* are genetically very different from each other; Nei's genetic distance ranges from 1.0 to 1.5 between them. The superspecies *B. pacificus* is composed of six primarily allopatric semispecies that have genetic distances ranging from 0.2 to 0.5.

The most striking aspect of the distributions of the taxa that were recognized in the revision is the parapatric replacement of morphologically similar taxonomic units. It is proposed in this paper that the present diversity of these parapatric taxa is related to historic changes in the geographic ranges of their respective lineages and that these ranges are predicted by paleogeographic boundaries. A scenario is presented for the evolution of the complex parapatric patterns that are observed in *Batrachoseps*. Divergence times between the taxa are inferred from genetic distance to be 20 to 35 million years ago between the sibling species, and 8 to 10 million years ago between the semispecies. Working backwards from the present patterns of distribution, the possible divergences of lineages are superimposed on a set of maps showing a time-series of reconstructions of the geologic, botanic, and climatic history of California.

Several specific testable hypotheses follow from the predictions of the scenario that is developed for the evolution of the distributions of the taxa of *Batrachoseps*. The relationship between taxonomic borders and historical geomorphic features may be tested in future studies by examining the concordant or discordant patterns of geographic variation in other genera of amphibians and reptiles. Several specific predictions concerning genetic and geographic relationships within *Batrachoseps* also arise from the scenario.

REFERENCES

ADDICOTT, W. O. 1968. Mid-Tertiary zoogeographic and paleogeographic discontinuities across the San Andreas fault, California. Pp. 144-165 *in* W. R. Dickinson and A. Grantz, eds., Proceedings of the conference on geological problems of the San Andreas fault system. Stanford Univ. Publs. Geol. Sci. 11.

ANONYMOUS. 1978. Latest in slicks: a sea of fruit. United Press International. Reprinted 10 March 1978, San Francisco Examiner.

ATWATER, T. 1970. Implications of plate tectonics for the Cenozoic tectonic evolution of western North America. Geol. Soc. Amer. Bull. 81:3513-3536.

AXELROD, D. I. 1958. Evolution of the Madro-Tertiary geoflora. Bot. Rev. 24:433-509.

————. 1973. History of the Mediterranean ecosystem in California. Pp. 225-277 *in* F. di Castri and H. A. Mooney, eds., Mediterranean type ecosystems: origin and structure. Springer-Verlag, New York, N.Y.

————. 1975. Evolution and biogeography of Madrean-Tethyan sclerophyll vegetation. Ann. Missouri Bot. Gard. 62:288-334.

————. 1976. History of the coniferous forests, California and Nevada. Univ. California. Publ. Botany 70.

————. 1977. Outline history of California vegetation. Pp. 139-187 *in* M. G. Barbour and J. Major, eds., Terrestrial vegetation of California. John Wiley & Sons, New York, N.Y.

————. 1978. History of California closed-cone pine forests. Abstracts of papers, a multidisciplinary symposium on the California Islands. Santa Barbara Museum of Natural History, Santa Barbara, Calif.

————. 1979. Age and origin of Sonoran Desert vegetation. Occas. Papers California Acad. Sci. 132.

AYALA, F. J. 1975. Genetic differentiation during the speciation process. Evolutionary Biol. 8:1-78.

BALL, I. R. 1975. Nature and formulation of biogeographical hypotheses. Syst. Zool. 24:407-430.

BERGGREN, W. A. 1972. A Cenozoic time-scale: some implications for regional geology and paleobiogeography. Lethaia 5:195-215.

BRAME, A. H., JR. 1970. A new species of *Batrachoseps* (slender salamander) from the desert of southern California. Nat. Hist. Mus. Los Angeles Co., Contrib. Sci. 200:1-11.

BRAME, A. H., JR., and K. F. MURRAY. 1968. Three new slender salamanders (*Batrachoseps*) with a discussion of relationships and speciation within the genus. Bull. Nat. Hist. Mus. Los Angeles Co. 4:1-35.

CAMPBELL, B. 1931. Notes on *Batrachoseps*. Copeia 1931:131-134.

COPE, E. D. 1865. Third contribution to the herpetology of tropical America. Proc. Acad. Nat. Sci. Philadelphia 17:185-198.

————. 1869. A review of the species of the Plethodontidae and Desmognathidae. Proc. Acad. Nat. Sci. Philadelphia 21:93-118.

————. 1889. The Batrachia of North America. Bull. U.S. Natl. Mus. 34:1-525.

DIBBLEE, T. W., JR. 1967. Areal geology of the western Mojave Desert. U.S. Geol. Surv. Prof. Paper 522.

DUNN, E. R. 1926. The salamanders of the family Plethodontidae. Smith College, Northampton, Mass.

EVERENDEN, J. F., and R. K. S. EVERENDEN. 1970. The Cenozoic time scale. Geol. Soc. Amer. Spec. Paper 124:70-91.

GADOW, H. 1905. The distribution of Mexican amphibians and reptiles. Proc. Zool. Soc. London 2:191-244.

GORMAN, G. C., Y. J. KIM, and R. RUBINOFF. 1976. Genetic relationships of three species of *Bathygobius* from the Atlantic and Pacific sides of Panama. Copeia 1976:361-364.

GRIFFIN, J. R. 1975. A strange forest in San Benito County. Fremontia 2:11-15.

HEDGECOCK, D., and F. J. AYALA. 1974. Evolutionary divergence in the genus *Taricha* (Salamandridae). Copeia 1974:738-747.

HENDRICKSON, J. R. 1954. Ecology and systematics of salamanders of the genus *Batrachoseps*. Univ. California Publ. Zool. 54:1-46.

HIGHTON, R. 1972. Distributional interactions among eastern North American salamanders of the genus *Plethodon*. Pp. 139-188 *in* The distributional history of the biota of the southern Appalachians. Vertebrates. Virginia Poly. Inst. Res. Div. 4.

HOWELL, D. G. 1976. Aspects of the geological history of the California Continental Borderland. Amer. Assoc. Petroleum Geologists, Pacific Sec., Misc. Publ. 24.

JUNGER, A., and D. L. JOHNSON. 1980. Was there a Quaternary land bridge to the Northern Channel Islands? Pp. 33-39 *in* D.M. Power, ed., The California Islands: proceedings of a multidisciplinary symposium. Santa Barbara Museum of Natural History, Santa Barbara, Calif.

LICHT, P., M. E. FEDER, and S. BLEDSOE. 1975. Salinity tolerance and osmoregulation in the salamander *Batrachoseps*. J. Comp. Physiol. 102:123-134.

LOCKINGTON, W. N. 1880. List of California reptiles and batrachia collected by Mr. Dunn and Mr. W. J. Fisher in 1876. Amer. Natur. 14:295-296.

LOWE, C. H. 1950. The systematic status of the salamander *Plethodon hardii*, with a discussion of biogeographical problems in *Aneides*. Copeia 1950:92-99.

LOWE, C. H., JR., and R. G. ZWEIFEL. 1951. Sympatric populations of *Batrachoseps attenuatus* and *Batrachoseps pacificus* in southern California. Bull. So. California Acad. Sci. 50:128-135.

MAIORANA, V. C. 1978. Difference in diet as an epiphenomenon: space regulates salamanders. Canadian J. Zool. 56:1017-1025.

MARLOW, R. W., J. M. BRODE, and D. B. WAKE. 1979. A new salamander, genus *Batrachoseps,* from the Inyo Mountains of California, with a discussion of relationships in the genus. Nat. Hist. Mus. Los Angeles Co., Contrib. Sci. 308:1-17.

MORAFKA, D. J., and B. H. BANTA. 1972. The herpetozoogeography of the Gabilan Range, San Benito and Monterey Counties, California. Wasmann J. Biol. 30:197-240.

————. 1976. Biogeographical implications of pattern variation in the salamander *Aneides lugubris.* Copeia 1976:580-586.

NEI, M. 1972. Genetic distance between populations. Amer. Natur. 106:283-292.

NEI, M., and A. K. ROYCHOUDHURY. 1974. Sampling variances of heterozygosity and genetic distance. Genetics 76:379-390.

NILSEN, T. H., and S. H. CLARKE, JR. 1975. Sedimentation and tectonics in the early Tertiary continental borderland of central California. U.S. Geol. Surv. Prof. Paper 925.

PATTON, J. L., and S. Y. YANG. 1977. Genetic variation in *Thomomys bottae* pocket gophers: macrogeographic patterns. Evolution 31:697-720.

PEABODY, F. E. 1959. Trackways of living and fossil salamanders. Univ. California Publ. Zool. 63:1-72.

PEABODY, F. E., and J. M. SAVAGE. 1958. Evolution of the Coast Range corridor in California and its effect on the origin and dispersal of living amphibians and reptiles. Pp. 159-186 *in* C. L. Hubbs, ed., Zoogeography. Amer. Assoc. Adv. Sci., Washington, D.C.

REED, R. D. 1933. Geology of California. Amer. Assoc. Petroleum Geologists, Tulsa, Okla.

SARICH, V. M. 1977. Rates, sample sizes, and the neutrality hypothesis for electrophoresis in evolutionary studies. Nature 265:24-28.

SAVAGE, J. M. 1967. Evolution of the insular herpetofaunas. Pp. 219-227 *in* R. N. Philbrick, ed., Proceedings of the symposium on the biology of the California Islands. Santa Barbara Botanic Garden, Santa Barbara, Calif.

STEBBINS, R. C. 1951. Amphibians of western North America. University of California Press, Berkeley and Los Angeles, Calif.

————. 1966. A field guide to western reptiles and amphibians. Houghton Mifflin, Boston, Mass.

TURNER, D. L. 1970. Potassium-argon dating of Pacific coast Miocene foraminiferal stages. Geol. Soc. Amer. Spec. Paper 124.

VEDDER, J. G., and D. G. HOWELL. 1980. Topographic evolution of the southern California borderland during late Cenozoic time. Pp. 7-31 *in* D.M. Power, ed., The California Islands: proceedings of a multidisciplinary symposium. Santa Barbara Museum of Natural History, Santa Barbara, Calif.

WAHRHAFTIG, C., and J. H. BIRMAN. 1965. The Quaternary of the Pacific mountain system in California. Pp. 299-331 *in* H. E. Wright, Jr. and D. G. Frey, eds., The Quaternary of the United States. A review volume for the VII Congress of the International Association for Quaternary Research. Princeton University Press, Princeton, N.J.

WAKE, D. B. 1966. Comparative osteology and evolution of the lungless salamanders, family Plethodontidae. Memoirs So. California Acad. Sci. 4:1-111.

WAKE, D. B., L. R. MAXSON, and G. Z. WURST. 1978. Genetic differentiation, albumin evolution, and their biogeographic implications in plethodontid salamanders of California and southern Europe. Evolution 32:529-539.

WENNER, A. M., and D. L. JOHNSON. 1980. Land vertebrates on the California Channel
    Islands: sweepstakes or bridges? Pp. 497-530 *in* D.M. Power, ed., The California
    Islands: proceedings of a multidisciplinary symposium. Santa Barbara Museum of
    Natural History, Santa Barbara, Calif.
YANEV, K. P. 1978. Evolutionary studies of the plethodontid salamander genus *Batrachoseps*.
    Ph.D. thesis, University of California, Berkeley, Calif.

Species Number, Stability, and Equilibrium Status of Reptile Faunas on the California Islands

Bruce A. Wilcox[1]

*Department of Biology, University of California at San Diego,
La Jolla, California 92093*

INTRODUCTION

Island biogeography is the study of species distribution among islands. Its purpose is to develop principles that explain patterns of species distribution and species composition of island biotas through ecological, evolutionary, and historical mechanisms.

The most notable feature of the biogeography of the islands off the coast of southern California and Baja California, Mexico is the paucity of land vertebrate species, especially on the northernmost islands. This pattern was especially noted for reptiles and amphibians in an earlier analysis of the herpetofaunas of these islands by Savage (1967). No causal explanation was offered, save the suggestion that previous land bridge connections to the mainland were nonexistent. At the time of Savage's analysis, our understanding of island biogeography was, in general, poorly developed. The primary purpose of this paper is to re-evaluate the depauperate status of the reptile faunas of the California Islands in light of what is now known of the mechanisms controlling species diversity on islands, and to discuss the significance of the findings in terms of current island biogeographic theory.

THE THEORY OF ISLAND BIOGEOGRAPHY

In the interval between Savage's analysis and the present study, major advances have been made in our understanding of island biotas. Whereas in the past most of the emphasis was on dispersal, many recent studies emphasize the importance of extinction in determining the composition of island faunas. Extinction is apparently not an uncommon event, at least among island vertebrate populations (see Diamond and Jones 1980, Wilcox 1978). Thus, present species distribution on islands may only partially reflect the previous status of land bridge connections or successful over-water colonization events. From a consideration of the processes of extinction and immigration of species on islands, and the characteristics of insular biotas influencing their rates, a general theory of island biogeography has emerged.

The theory of island biogeography centers on the concept of an equilibrium between the rate of addition of new species to an island biota, immigration, and the rate of species loss through extinction (Preston 1962, MacArthur and Wilson 1963, 1967). These authors further proposed that the immigration rate should be dependent on the degree of isolation of an island, which is usually quantified as the shortest distance from an island to the mainland. They proposed that the other important variable, extinction, should be dependent on the size of an island. This is because, on smaller islands with limited habitats, population sizes may be so small that typical population fluctuations imposed by environmental vagaries are more likely to result in extinction. Thus, an island's area and its degree of isolation from other landmasses may largely define the equilibrium number of species. A relationship between species number and area and mainland distance has been established for numerous biotas (see Diamond and May 1976 for the

[1] Present address: Department of Biological Sciences, Stanford University, Stanford, California 94305.

most recent review). Such relationships have also been established for the reptile faunas of the California Islands (Savage 1967) and islands in the Gulf of California (Soulé and Sloan 1966, Case 1975, and Wilcox 1978).

SPECIES NUMBER AND THE CALIFORNIA ISLAND REPTILE FAUNAS
Defining the Problem

Armed with the equilibrium theory of island biogeography, we return to the problem of depauperate reptile faunas on the California Islands. We may now say, *a priori,* that any island biota should be depauperate relative to the adjacent mainland. This is because of the effect of reduced area and isolation from other terrestrial regions. It should hold true regardless of previous land bridge connections since extinction will eliminate at least some land bridge migrants.

The problem of the depauperate reptile faunas can now be more rigorously examined. Our first question is whether the reptile faunas are more depauperate than expected. To help answer this, it should be useful to compare the number of reptile species in these faunas with the number of species in reptile faunas elsewhere.

A Comparison with Islands in the Gulf of California

On the basis of the equilibrium theory, islands with similar areas and mainland distances (given that they are faunistically, ecologically, and historically comparable) should have similar numbers of species. It should be reasonable, therefore, to compare the California Island reptile faunas with similar faunas on islands in the Gulf of California. The two island groups are not strictly ecologically comparable. The regions, however, are zoogeographically similar and share many species.

The comparison will be confined to the eight Channel Islands since they are the most apparently depauperate and form a single biogeographic unit, which will be described later. These will be compared with islands in the Gulf of California which are also beyond the 130-meter depth contour. Thus, these Gulf islands and the Channel Islands are *deep-water* islands. It is assumed that they have had no land bridge connections to the mainland in geologically recent time (*i.e.,* since at least prior to the last glacial stage, the Wisconsin, when eustatic sea-level lowering did not exceed àpproximately 130 meters [Milliman and Emery 1968]).

The biogeographic data are given in Table 1 and island locations in Figure 1. The Channel Islands would be expected to have more species if the Pleistocene land bridge connection from the mainland to the Northern Channel Islands were verified. Nevertheless, the comparison reveals the following. Anacapa of the Channel Islands, for example, with an area of 2.9 km² and a distance to the mainland of 20 km, has only two recorded reptile species. The Gulf islands of Partida Norte, Raza, Salsipuedes, and San Pedro Mártir are all smaller and, on the average, farther from the mainland, yet have four, two, four, and three reptile species, respectively. Comparisons among the larger islands are more striking. Matching Santa Cruz and Santa Catalina of the Channel Islands to the Gulf islands of San Esteban, San Lorenzo, and Santa Catalina, which are roughly equivalent in distance from the mainland but are almost an order of magnitude smaller, shows that all have remarkably similar numbers of reptile species. Darlington (1957) had suggested a rule of thumb now well known to zoogeographers that states a tenfold increase in island size corresponds to a doubling in the number of species. The rule is clearly not upheld in this instance; Santa Cruz and Santa Catalina of the Channel Islands should have twice as many species as the Gulf Islands.

A more systematic comparison is made by plotting the log of the number of species against the log of area for both groups of islands (Fig. 2). The San Benito Islands are included with the

Gulf islands since they are geographically closer and historically more similar, as discussed in detail later. From the regression lines in Figure 2 it can be seen that, for any given size, islands in the Gulf sample have, on the average, two to three times more reptile species than the Channel Islands. In other words, this twofold to threefold difference in the number of reptile species must be explained on the basis of something other than area.

The mean distance to the mainland is twice as great for the Channel Islands (50 km) as for the Gulf island sample (25 km). This undoubtedly accounts for some of the overall deficiency in the Channel Island faunas. As the island-by-island comparison showed, however, the Channel Islands consistently have fewer species than expected for islands of comparable area and distance from the mainland.

The expectation that islands of similar size and isolation should have similar numbers of species assumes that everything else is equal, *i.e.,* evolutionary, ecological, and historical mechanisms have been operating to an equivalent degree on both groups of islands. Each class of mechanisms will be examined to determine whether or not this is the case.

Evolutionary Mechanisms

The equilibrium theory of island biogeography is explicitly an ecological theory and does not account for evolutionary change. Evolutionary mechanisms may affect species diversity on islands in two ways. Species multiplication within a single island or an archipelago can enhance species diversity. Conversely, ecological release in early colonizing species can prevent invasion of new species (MacArthur 1972, Lack 1976), thus limiting species diversity.

Unequal faunal enrichment between the two groups of islands through speciation can be eliminated as a possibility. There is no evidence for speciation events other than those due to the divergence of a single population for any of the islands under consideration here. Further, as an indication of lack of multiple invasions, there are no cases of sympatry between island endemics and the ancestral species from which they were derived. Unequal evolutionary depression of species diversity through ecological release can probably also be eliminated. Ecological release is apparent for some of the island lizard species; however, evidence for such cases exists only for some of the Gulf island populations (Soulé 1966).

Ecological Mechanisms

In the context of equilibrium theory, ecological differences of importance are those which may affect immigration and/or extinction rates characterizing the two groups of islands. The supposition here that islands with similar areas and mainland distances should have similar extinction and immigration rates assumes that numerous ecological variables, including the quality and types of available habitats, are held constant. In general, the Channel Islands and the Gulf islands are ecologically dissimilar. The Gulf islands are arid and characterized by thorn scrub vegetation, while the Channel Islands are characterized by sage scrub and chaparral, including oak woodland on the larger islands. Unfortunately, the ways in which these differences might affect immigration and extinction rates in their respective faunas are unclear, and detailed analyses of the ecological requirements of the species composing these faunas are beyond the scope of this study.

There are, however, at least two identifiable factors that could lead to higher immigration rates for the reptile faunas of the Gulf islands. First, islands in the Gulf can potentially receive immigrants from two mainland regions—the Baja peninsula and Sonora. Second, the number of reptile species available as potential colonists is greater for the Gulf region. According to Stebbins (1966), there are 22 species of lizards and snakes on the mainland adjacent to the northernmost Channel Islands. This number increases to 26 adjacent to the southernmost Channel Islands. Species ranges are not as well established for the Baja peninsula and Sonora;

TABLE 1. Numbers of reptile species and island characteristics.

	Number of reptile species	Area (km²)	Distance from mainland (km)
California Islands			
1 San Miguel	2	37	42
2 Santa Rosa	3	217	44
3 Santa Cruz (Norte)	6	249	30
4 Anacapa	2	2.9	20
5 San Nicolas	2	58	98
6 Santa Barbara	1	2.6	61
7 Santa Catalina (Norte)	8	194	32
8 San Clemente	2	145	79
9 Los Coronados	8	2.5	13
10 Todos Santos	7	1.2	6
11 San Martín	5	2.3	5
12 San Geronimo	3	0.4	9
13 San Benito	2	6.3	66
14 Cedros	12	348	23
15 Natividad	3	7.2	7
Gulf of California Deep-water Islands			
16 Ángel de la Guarda	12	1,001	13
17 Partida Norte	4	2.1	12
18 Raza	2	1.1	18
19 Salsipuedes	4	1.8	19
20 San Esteban	8	43	37
21 Las Ánimas (Norte)	5	7.5	18
22 San Lorenzo	5	44.5	18
23 San Pedro Mártir	3	1.5	48
24 San Pedro Nolasco	5	3.5	10
25 Tortuga	4	6.3	37
26 Santa Catalina (Sur)	9	43	24
27 Santa Cruz (Sur)	4	11.6	17
28 Cerralbo	18	163	9

Note: Guadalupe is omitted since it is not known to have reptiles.

FIGURE 1. *Map of the California and Gulf of California Islands. Numbers refer to island names in Table 1.*

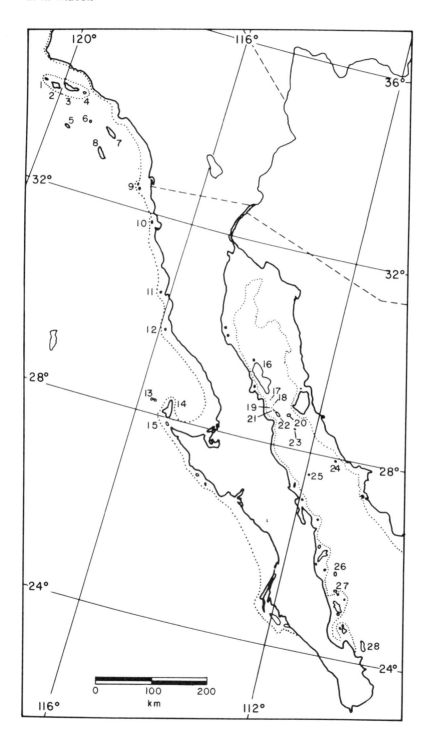

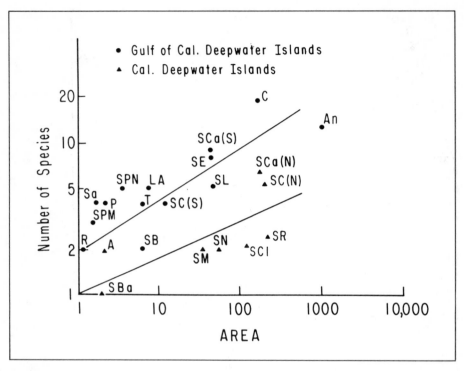

FIGURE 2. *Log of the number of reptile species plotted against the log of island area. SB = San Benitos, An = Ángel de la Guarda, P = Partida Norte, R = Raza, Sa = Salsipuedes, SE = San Esteban, LA = Las Ánimas (Norte), SL = San Lorenzo, SPM = San Pedro Mártir, SPN = San Pedro Nolasco, T = Tortuga, SCa(S) = Santa Catalina (Sur), SC(S) = Santa Cruz (Sur), C = Cerralbo, SM = San Miguel, SR = Santa Rosa, SC(N) = Santa Cruz (Norte), A = Anacapa, SN = San Nicolas, SBa = Santa Barbara, SCa(N) = Santa Catalina (Norte), SCl = San Clemente. The regression equations are as follows. For the Channel Islands, log species number = 0.21 (log area) + 0.02, r = 0.68. For the Gulf of California deep-water islands, log species number = 0.26 (log area) + 0.43, r = 0.80.*

nevertheless, coastal regions in the Gulf of California extending over a distance approximating the length of the southern California coastline may have from 30 to 40 species (Murphy unpubl. data).

It is difficult to estimate the effect these differences should have on immigration rates; it is questionable, however, that they can account for a doubling or tripling in species number. This leads to the third and, in this case, possibly the most important class of mechanisms explaining biogeographic patterns.

Historical Mechanisms: A Climatic Instability Hypothesis

Several reptile species occurring throughout much of mainland coastal southern California and Baja California are relatively uncommon or absent on the Channel Islands. Strikingly, these species—the side-blotched lizard (*Uta stansburiana*), the western whiptail lizard

(*Cnemidophorus tigris*), the night snake (*Hypsiglena torquata*), and the coachwhip (*Masticophis flagellum*)—are among the most common species found on lower-latitude islands, including the islands of the Gulf and the other California Islands. As such, they are demonstrably good colonizers and capable of persisting on islands. The failure of these four species to occur on the Channel Islands with a frequency similar to that on the Mexican islands is virtually sufficient by itself to account for the low levels of reptile species diversity on the Channel Islands. Why are these species less common on these islands?

The present mainland ranges of these species all coincide (Stebbins 1966). While some differences occur east of the coast mountain ranges, along coastal California their distributions are indistinguishable. Their joint range is shown in Figure 3. All are apparently incapable of expanding their ranges into the cool and humid coastal region north of Point Conception.

A cool and humid climate prevailed throughout most of California, including the islands, during periods of Pleistocene glacial maxima (Axelrod 1967). The recurrent climatic and vegetation shifts concomitant with the glacial advances and retreats are estimated to have extended over about 500 miles of latitude (Durham 1950, Chaney and Mason 1930). Thus, a southward retreat of xerophilic reptile forms to desert refugia would have accompanied each glacial advance (Savage 1960). Figure 4 is a reconstruction of the probable mainland distribution of these xerophilic forms at the time of the glacial maxima. There are at least eleven other reptile species presently occurring in coastal southern California which may have been similarly affected, but most do not have ranges extending the length of the Baja peninsula.

The climatic instability during the Pleistocene could have resulted in the reduction of species diversity on the Channel Islands by the exclusion of xerophilic reptile forms in three ways. First, their intermittent displacement from the mainland region adjacent to the Channel Islands would have reduced the rate of immigration to the islands. Second, had any xerophilic species successfully colonized during an interglacial period, as *Uta* and *Hypsiglena* may have done during the present interglacial period, they would have been extirpated with the southward advance of the subsequent glacial environment. Third, the existence of inter-island or island-mainland land bridge connections during periods of glacial maxima when the sea level was at its minimum would have been of little consequence to these species since they would have been absent from the region.

Species distribution on the Channel Islands further supports the hypothesis that climatic instability is responsible for the islands' depauperate nature. Of the 27 occurrences of reptiles (Table 2), only five are of xerophilic forms. The mainland distributions of the remainder (except for the endemic lizard *Klauberina riversiana,* whose ancestral form is not known with certainty) clearly demonstrate their capability of persisting in a cool, humid, glacial environment.

However, if the climatic instability hypothesis is correct in its entirety, then the colonization of five xerophilic forms on the Channel Islands since the present climatic regime stabilized 6,000 to 7,000 years ago must be explained. Considering that four of the five occurrences are of *Uta stansburiana,* the climatic instability hypothesis seems reasonable. Among the local reptiles, *Uta* is unsurpassed in colonizing ability (Case 1975). There are other lines of evidence that specifically suggest that the *Uta* populations on these islands are the result of post-Pleistocene colonization. First, if the Santa Cruz and Anacapa *Uta* pre-date the present interglacial period, the absence of *Uta* on Santa Rosa and San Miguel is surprising since all four islands were presumably connected during the late Pleistocene. Second, according to Ballinger and Tinkle (1972), none of the Channel Island *Uta* are taxonomically distinct, but several subspecies and species are recognized on Mexican islands.

In summary, the Channel Islands appear to have an incomplete assemblage of xerophilic reptile forms. The xerophilic forms that do occur on the islands appear to be the result of

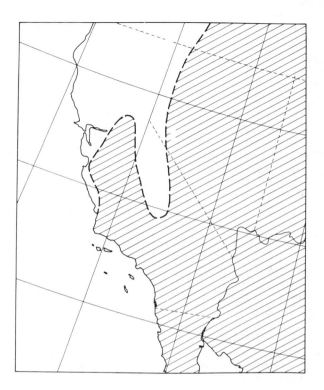

FIGURE 3. *Present joint distribution of several xerophilic reptile forms (see text).*

colonization events since the beginning of the present interglacial period. This implies that the islands will continue to acquire xerophilic forms until they become saturated and the loss of species through extinction balances immigration. Thus, it can be said that the reptile faunas in the Channel Islands are presently below equilibria.

DISCUSSION

Since the equilibrium theory was introduced, biogeographers have not been wholly successful in identifying faunas where species number is the result of a balanced equilibrium between immigration and extinction (Simberloff 1976). There are conditions, however, under which nonequilibrium faunas may actually be anticipated. The conditions depend both upon factors intrinsically characteristic of a taxon (*e.g.*, the specific immigration and extinction rates), and on variables characteristic of a given island (*e.g.*, size, environmental stability, and geologic history). The following considerations of these factors and how they might interact to result in faunas of differing equilibrium status provide the basis for an understanding of biogeographic patterns among the California Islands.

The probability of extinction for an island reptile is presumed to be less than that for an endothermic vertebrate. This was first pointed out specifically for lizards by Williams (1969), and seems reasonable since, because of their lower metabolic demands, reptiles should maintain higher population densities and withstand longer periods of deprivation than birds or mammals. In addition to their ability to persist on islands, reptiles also differ substantially from birds, yet are similar to or slightly superior to land mammals, in their capability for over-water dispersal.

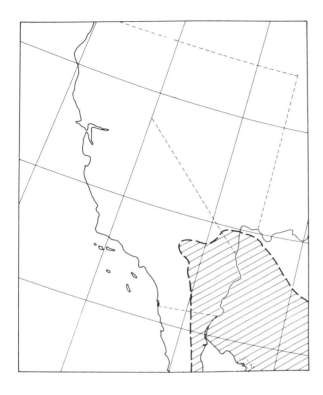

FIGURE 4. *Probable joint distribution of the same xerophilic reptile forms in Figure 3 at glacial maxima.*

The consequences of these probable differences in immigration and extinction rates between the vertebrate taxa are twofold. First, in the case of equilibrium faunas, taxon-specific differences determine relative species numbers on an island. For example, although reptiles and mammals probably have similar dispersal abilities, reptiles, because of lower extinction rates, are expected to produce island faunas which achieve equilibrium at a greater number of species. Second, and of primary interest in this study, nonequilibrium faunas may behave in dynamically predictable ways, differing in the rate of approach to equilibrium, depending on the taxon.

On islands where historical events such as past volcanic activity or changes in climate have reduced biotic diversity, those taxa with poor dispersal ability should take longer to reach equilibrium. Thus, reptile and mammal faunas will be more commonly found below equilibrium, or *subsaturated,* than will avifaunas. Pleistocene climatic fluctuations undoubtedly affected the Channel Island avifaunas and mammal faunas in addition to the reptile faunas. Nevertheless, the avifaunas should have adjusted rapidly to the changing conditions. Studies by Diamond (1969), Diamond and Jones (1980), and Jones and Diamond (1976) suggest these faunas are at their equilibria. Like the reptiles, mammals are also notably depauperate on the Channel Islands; perhaps, having even more limited over-water dispersal capabilities than reptiles, they may be similarly subsaturated. Alternatively, they simply may have attained equilibrium at fewer species because of higher extinction rates and lower immigration rates.

Nonequilibrium faunas have been suggested more frequently to be above equilibrium, or *supersaturated.* These faunas are found primarily on late or post-Pleistocene land bridge islands isolated with the rising sea level. The area is reduced in size and no longer receives the

TABLE 2. Reptile faunas of the California Islands.*

	San Miguel	Santa Rosa	Santa Cruz	Anacapa	Santa Barbara	San Nicolas
Lizards						
Coleonyx variegatus						
Crotaphytus wislizenii						
Uta stansburiana			X	X		
Uta stellata						
Sceloporus magister						
Sceloporus occidentalis	X	X	X			
Phrynosoma cerroense						
Klauberina riversiana					X	X
Cnemidophorus tigris						
Eumeces skiltonianus						
Gerrhonotus cedroensis						
Gerrhonotus multicarinatus	X	X	X	X		X
Anniella geronimensis						
Anniella pulchra						
Snakes						
Salvadora hexalepis						
Chilomeniscus cinctus						
Leptotyphlops humilis						
Lichanura trivirgata						
Thamnophis couchii						
Diadophis punctatus						
Coluber constrictor			X			
Lampropeltis getulus						
Lampropeltis zonata						
Pituophis melanoleucus		X	X			
Hypsiglena torquata			X			
Crotalus exsul						
Crotalus viridis						

*The distributional data are derived largely from Savage (1967); however, there have been the following additions and a deletion. Bostic (1975) records *Salvadora hexalepis* from Todos Santos and San Geronimo, as well as *Chilomeniscus cinctus* from Cedros; a specimen of *Pituophis melanoleucus* was recently collected on Santa Rosa by Paul Collins; the occurrence of *Uta stansburiana* on San Nicolas as reported by Savage (1967) is unsubstantiated (R. Bezy, pers. comm.) and is deleted from this table.

Santa Catalina	San Clemente	Los Coronados	Todos Santos	San Martín	San Geronimo	Cedros	San Benito	Natividad
						X		
						X		
X	X	X	X	X	X	X		X
							X	
						X		
						X		
	X							
		X				X	X	X
X		X	X					
						X		
X		X		X				
					X			
		X	X					
			X		X			
						X		
						X		
								X
X								
X			X	X				
X								
			X					
X		X		X		X		
		X		X		X		
						X		
X		X						

constant influx or recruitment of individuals from adjacent regions. A new, lower equilibrium species number is defined by the reduced immigration and increased extinction rates. The rate of approach to this new equilibrium is inversely proportional to island size (Diamond 1972, Terborgh 1974, Case 1975, Soulé *et al.* 1978) and the taxon-specific extinction rate (Wilcox in prep.). Thus, on similar-sized islands, reptiles are expected to approach equilibrium more slowly than do birds or mammals. The existence of supersaturated faunas is well documented. Studies of land bridge island faunas, including avifaunas of the southwest Pacific (Diamond 1972) and neotropics (Terborgh 1974), lizard faunas (Case 1975, Wilcox in prep.), reptile faunas (Soulé and Sloan 1976, Wilcox in prep.), and mammal faunas (Wilcox in prep.) of the Gulf of California, suggest the importance of geologically recent land bridge connections. These connections clearly can account for the greater number of species on such islands where *relaxation* to equilibrium has not yet been completed. Six of the California Islands (Los Coronados, Todos Santos, San Martín, San Geronimo, Cedros, and Natividad) are potential candidates for supersaturated status since they all occur well within the contour of late Pleistocene minimum sea level. On the basis of Milliman and Emery's (1968) estimates of eustatic sea-level rise, most of these islands were isolated less than 10,000 years ago.

As seen in Table 1, each of these islands has much larger faunas than either the Channel Islands or Gulf islands, considering their sizes. Most are closer to the mainland, so it would seem likely that they should have more species by virtue of higher immigration rates. This, in fact, may not be the case. Studies of lizard faunas (Case 1976, Wilcox 1978) and reptile faunas (Wilcox in prep.) on land bridge islands in the Gulf indicate that immigration influences species numbers only very weakly, if at all, on supersaturated islands.

On islands that have sufficient geological and climatic stability, faunas are expected to have had time to reach equilibrium. Low-latitude, *deep-water* islands, including the Gulf deep-water islands and the San Benitos of the California Islands, may thus have faunas in equilibrium. Historically, then, the San Benitos are more similar to the Gulf islands since they are also of relatively low latitude and probably did not experience severe climatic shifts. That the San Benitos have one of the most divergent populations of island *Uta* (Ballinger and Tinkle 1972) further attests to the relative antiquity of their reptile fauna.

CONCLUSION AND SUMMARY

According to current island biogeographic theory, three types of faunas are possible with regard to equilibrium status: subsaturated, supersaturated, and in equilibrium. The variation in reptile species diversity and the climatic and geological history of the California Islands suggest that each of the types is represented. Climatic instability associated with Pleistocene glacial advances and retreats may be largely responsible for the low diversity of reptile species on the high-latitude California Islands, the Channel Islands. Thus, they are regarded as relatively subsaturated. Geologically recent land bridge connections to the mainland for six of the remaining California Islands inhabited by reptiles may be largely responsible for high reptile species diversity. Thus, they are regarded as relatively supersaturated. The remaining California Island, San Benito, because of its latitude and the depth of the surrounding ocean, should be immune to recent climatic and geological instability. Thus, a balanced equilibrium fauna is more likely.

Most island biogeographic studies stress the role of island size and isolation as factors controlling species diversity at dynamic equilibrium. In this study on numbers of reptile species, historical factors are emphasized and faunas that are apparently not at equilibrium are suggested.

ACKNOWLEDGMENTS

I thank Michael Soulé for providing advice throughout the development of this manuscript. Together with Jared M. Diamond, he is responsible for much of the insight into biogeographic problems upon which this paper is based. I am also grateful to Michael E. Gilpin and Richard H. Rosenblatt for critically reading the final draft, as well as to Pat Carpenter and Mark J. Pomerantz for making suggestions on an earlier version. The author was supported by N.I.H. grant 6M 07242.

REFERENCES

AXELROD, D. I. 1967. Geologic history of the Californian insular flora. Pp. 267-316 *in* R. N. Philbrick, ed., Proceedings of the symposium on the biology of the California Islands. Santa Barbara Botanic Garden, Santa Barbara, Calif.

BALLINGER, R., and D. TINKLE. 1972. Systematics and evolution of the genus *Uta* (Sauria: Iguanidae). Misc. Publ. Mus. Zool. Univ. Michigan, no. 145.

BOSTIC, D. L. 1975. A natural history guide to the Pacific coast and north central Baja California and adjacent islands. Biological Educational Expeditions, San Diego, Calif.

CASE, T. J. 1975. Species numbers, density compensation, and colonizing ability of lizards in the Gulf of California. Ecology 56:3-18.

CHANEY, R. W., and H. L. MASON. 1930. A Pleistocene flora from the asphalt deposits at Carpinteria, California. Carnegie Inst. Washington Publ. 415:45-79.

DARLINGTON, P. J. 1957. Zoogeography: the geographical distribution of animals. John Wiley & Sons, New York, N.Y.

DIAMOND, J. M. 1969. Avifaunal equilibrium and species turnover rates on the Channel Islands of California. Proc. Natl. Acad. Sci.64:57-63.

――――――. 1972. Biogeographic kinetics: estimation of relaxation times for avifaunas of the southwest Pacific islands. Proc. Natl. Acad. Sci. 67:1715-1721.

DIAMOND, J. M., and H. L. JONES. 1980. Breeding land birds of the Channel Islands. Pp. 597-612 *in* D.M. Power, ed., The California Islands: proceedings of a multidisciplinary symposium. Santa Barbara Museum of Natural History, Santa Barbara, Calif.

DIAMOND, J. M., and R. M. MAY. 1976. Island biogeography and the design of nature reserves. Pp. 163-186 *in* R. M. May, ed., Theoretical ecology. Blackwell Scientific Publ., London.

DURHAM, J. W. 1950. Cenozoic marine climates of the Pacific coast. Geol. Soc. Amer. Bull. 61:1243-1264.

JONES, H. L., and J. M. DIAMOND. 1976. Short-time-base studies of the turnover in breeding bird populations on the California Channel Islands. Condor 78:526-549.

LACK, D. 1976. Island biology illustrated by the land birds of Jamaica. University of California Press, Berkeley, Calif.

MACARTHUR, R. H. 1972. Geographical ecology. Harper and Row, New York, N.Y.

MACARTHUR, R. H., and E. O. WILSON. 1963. An equilibrium theory of insular zoogeography. Evolution 17:373-387.

――――――. 1967. The theory of island biogeography. Princeton University Press, Princeton, N.J.

MILLIMAN, J. D., and K. O. EMERY. 1968. Sea levels during the last 35,000 years. Science 162:1121-1123.

PRESTON, F. W. 1962. The canonical distribution of commonness and rarity, pt. II. Ecology 43:410-432.

SAVAGE, J. M. 1960. Evolution of a peninsular herpetofauna. Syst. Zool. 9:184-212.

————. 1967. Evolution of insular herpetofaunas. Pp. 219-228 *in* R. N. Philbrick, ed., Proceedings of the symposium on the biology of the California Islands. Santa Barbara Botanic Garden, Santa Barbara, Calif.

SIMBERLOFF, D. 1976. Species turnover and equilibrium island biogeography. Science 154:572-578.

SOULÉ, M. 1966. Trends in the insular radiation of a lizard. Amer. Natur. 100:47-64.

SOULÉ, M., and A. J. SLOAN. 1966. Biogeography and distributions of the reptiles and amphibians on islands in the Gulf of California, Mexico. Trans. San Diego Soc. Nat. Hist. 14:137-156.

SOULÉ, M., B. A. WILCOX, and C. HOLTBY. 1979. Benign neglect: a model of faunal collapse in the game reserves of East Africa. Biol. Conserv. 15:259-272.

STEBBINS, B. C. 1966. A field guide to the western reptiles and amphibians. Houghton Mifflin, Boston, Mass.

TERBORGH, J. 1974. Preservation of natural diversity: the problem of extinction prone species. Bioscience 24:715-722.

WILCOX, B. A. 1978. Supersaturated island faunas: a species-age relationship for lizard faunas on post-Pleistocene land-bridge islands. Science 199:996-998.

WILLIAMS, E. E. 1969. The ecology of colonization as seen in the zoogeography of anoline lizards on small islands. Quart. Rev. Biol. 44:345-389.

Divergence in the Island Night Lizard
Xantusia riversiana (Sauria: Xantusiidae)

R. L. Bezy,[1] G. C. Gorman,[2] G. A. Adest,[2] and Y. J. Kim[2]

[1]*Section of Herpetology, Los Angeles County Museum of Natural History, Los Angeles, California 90007*

[2]*Department of Biology, University of California, Los Angeles, California 90024*

INTRODUCTION

The island night lizard, *Xantusia riversiana* Cope (Fig. 1), is found only on Santa Barbara, San Clemente, and San Nicolas Islands off southern California (Fig. 2). The species is sufficiently divergent in morphology from its mainland relatives, *X. vigilis* Baird and *X. henshawi* Stejneger (Fig. 1), that it has been placed in the monotypic genus *Klauberina* by Savage (1957, 1963). Regardless of whether it is accorded generic (Savage 1957) or subgeneric (Bezy 1972) rank, *X. riversiana* is clearly more divergent than the other living vertebrates of the California Channel Islands, suggesting that it may have been present longer than other species on one or more of the islands. Moreover, casual observations indicate that there may be greater morphological differences between the island populations of *X. riversiana* than were documented by earlier work (Savage 1951, Smith 1946). In an effort to further clarify the evolutionary history of the species, we have compared electrophoretically determined genetic distances and divergence time estimates between the island populations with those between the species of *Xantusia,* and have reappraised inter-island differences in karyotypes, scalation, coloration, body size, clutch size, and variability.

MATERIALS AND METHODS

Two separate electrophoretic analyses were performed. In the first, 22 presumptive loci were scored for 15 *X. riversiana* from San Clemente Island, 15 from San Nicolas Island, and five from Santa Barbara Island. In the second study, 30 presumptive loci were analyzed for six *X. riversiana* from San Nicolas Island, six *X. riversiana* from San Clemente Island, six *X. henshawi* from the San Jacinto Mountains, and 20 *X. vigilis* from Antelope Valley, California (see Specimens Examined for exact localities). The procedures for preparing the gels, stains, and interpreting alleles follow Selander *et al.* (1971), with minor modifications (Yang *et al.* 1974, Kim *et al.* 1976).

The chromosomal methods utilized were described by Bezy (1972). Scalation was analyzed univariately with the BMDP3D program and multivariately by stepwise discriminant analysis (SDA) utilizing BMDP7M (Dixon 1975).

RESULTS

Electrophoresis

The 22-locus study indicated that 18 presumptive loci are fixed for identical electromorphs (alleles) in all three island samples. Polymorphisms were observed for MDH (San Nicolas Island), PGM-2 (San Clemente and Santa Barbara Islands), and GOT-2 and PGI (San Clemente and San Nicolas Islands) (Table 1). In the 30-locus study, identical alleles were fixed at 27 loci for San Clemente and San Nicolas; polymorphisms occurred for MDH-2 on San Nicolas and for ADH and PGM-2 on San Clemente (Table 2). Allele frequencies were used to compute genetic similarity and distance (Nei 1972). Inter-island genetic distances (Table 3) are, of course,

FIGURE 1. *Living individuals of* Xantusia riversiana *(upper; San Clemente I.)*, X. henshawi *(middle; LACM 127160; California: Riverside Co.: San Jacinto Mts., Snow Creek), and* X. vigilis *(lower; LACM 127154; Mexico: Durango: 6.5 mi NE Pedriceña).*

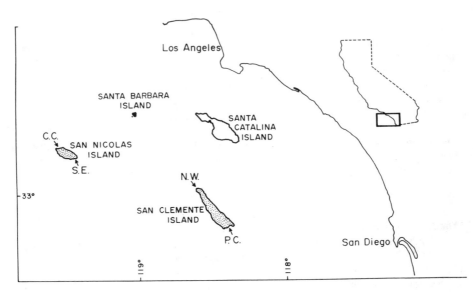

FIGURE 2. *Distribution of* Xantusia riversiana *(three stippled islands). Arrows indicate specific populations sampled.*

TABLE 1. Allelic frequencies at four presumed loci for three island populations of *Xantusia riversiana*. Excluded are 18 presumed loci fixed for electrophoretically identical gene products: GP-1, GP-2, GP-3, GP-4, LDH-1, LDH-2, IDH-1, IDH-2, ADH, Pept-1, Pept-2, ES, GOT-1, PGM-1, MPI, XDH, SDH, and IPO.

Locus	Allele	Island population (Sample size)		
		San Clemente (15)	San Nicolas (15)	Santa Barbara (5)
MDH	a	0	.067	0
	b	0	.033	0
	c	1.0	.900	1.0
PGI	a	.033	.036*	0
	b	.967	.964	1.0
GOT-2	a	.067	.033	0
	b	.933	.967	1.0
PGM-2	a	.167	0	.2
	b	.833	1.0	.8

* Sample size = 14.

extremely small, since identical alleles either predominate or are fixed at all of the loci studied electrophoretically. While genetic distance values are smallest between Santa Barbara and San Clemente Islands (0.0004) and largest between San Nicolas and Santa Barbara Islands (0.0024; Table 3), none differ significantly from zero.

Xantusia riversiana was compared with *X. vigilis* and *X. henshawi* in the 30-locus study (Tables 2 and 3). Fixed differences occur between *X. riversiana* and *X. vigilis* at 10 loci (Nei distance, $\overline{ND} = 0.574$), between *X. riversiana* and *X. henshawi* at 14 loci ($\overline{ND} = 0.830$), and between the two mainland species at 8 loci ($\overline{ND} = 0.409$).

Karyotypes

The chromosomes of lizards from Santa Barbara (1♀, 34 cells) and San Nicolas (1♂, 53 cells) appear identical in number, shape, and relative size to those described by Bezy (1972) for the population on San Clemente (Fig. 3). Utilizing nonbanding techniques, this karyotype also appears identical to that of eastern populations of *X. vigilis* and *X. henshawi* (Bezy 1972).

Scalation

From a total of 217 specimens, data were taken for the following seven scale characters: scales around body (SAB; transverse count of dorsal scales at midbody); gulars (G; longitudinal count along ventral midline from gular fold to postmentals); fourth toe lamellae (FTL; longitudinal count, ventral midline); femoral pores (FP; one leg); ventrals (V; longitudinal count along midline, excluding preanals); preanals (PA; number of enlarged scales along midline between vent and ventrals); preanal enlargement (PAE; sum of diameters of four largest preanals over sum of lengths of four midbody ventrals). These characters were chosen because previous studies suggest they vary geographically in species of *Xantusia* (Bezy 1967, Smith 1946, Webb 1970). Sexual dimorphism was not significant ($P \geqslant 0.05$) in the largest sample (San Clemente, NW, mottled; 20♂, 20♀), and the sexes were combined in subsequent analyses.

Univariate analysis indicates significant ($P < 0.05$) differences between islands for all seven characters, except for ventrals and preanals between Santa Barbara and San Clemente Islands (Table 4). Stepwise discriminant analysis indicates significant separation between island

TABLE 2. Allelic frequencies at 18 presumed loci for four populations of *Xantusia*. Excluded are 12 loci that were fixed identically in all four populations: LDH-1, LDH-2, IDH-1, IDH-2, αGPDH, MPI, PGI, IPO-1, FUM, LAP, AB-2, and AB-3.

		Species, Population, Sample size			
Locus	Allele	*riversiana* San Nicolas 6	*riversiana* San Clemente 6	*henshawi* San Jacinto 6	*vigilis* Little Rock 20
MDH-1	a	0	0	1.0	1.0
	b	1.0	1.0	0	0
MDH-2	a	.167	0	1.0	1.0
	b	.833	1.0	0	0
6PGDH	a	1.0	1.0	.083	0
	b	0	0	.917	1.0
XDH	a	0	0	1.0	0
	b	1.0	1.0	0	0
	c	0	0	0	1.0
ADH	a	1.0	.917	0	0
	b	0	.083	0	0
	c	0	0	1.0	0
	d	0	0	0	1.0
SDH	a	0	0	1.0	0
	b	1.0	1.0	0	1.0
PGM-1	a	0	0	1.0	1.0
	b	1.0	1.0	0	0
PGM-2	a	0	0	.25	.5
	b	0	.33	.75	.5
	c	1.0	.67	0	0
Pept-1	a	0	0	1.0	1.0
	b	1.0	1.0	0	0
ME	a	0	0	1.0	1.0
	b	1.0	1.0	0	0
HEXO	a	0	0	1.0	0
	b	1.0	1.0	0	1.0
AB-1	a	1.0	1.0	0	1.0
	b	0	0	1.0	0
ES-1	a	0	0	1.0	.9
	b	1.0	1.0	0	.1
ES-2	a	0	0	0	.925
	b	0	0	1.0	.075
	c	1.0	1.0	0	0
ES-3	a	1.0	1.0	0	1.0
	b	0	0	1.0	0
IPO-2	a	0	0	0	1.0
	b	1.0	1.0	1.0	0
ES-4	a	0	0	1.0	0
	b	1.0	1.0	0	1.0

TABLE 3. Mean heterozygosity ($\bar{H}$), per cent polymorphic loci (P), and genetic distance (lower left) and similarity (upper right) of Nei (1972) for five populations of *Xantusia*. Figures with asterisks (*) are derived from the 22-locus study (Table 1); those without are based on the 30-locus study (Table 2).

	$\bar{H}$	P	*riversiana* SB	*riversiana* SC	*riversiana* SN	*vigilis*	*henshawi*
riversiana SB	0.92*	4.5*		.9996*	.9976*	—	—
riversiana SC	1.23* 2.87	13.6* 6.8	.0004*		.9983* .9952	.5894	.4529
riversiana SN	1.58* 1.15	9.1* 3.4	.0024*	.0017* .0048		.5864	.4477
vigilis	2.59	10.2	—	.5287	.5338		.6931
henshawi	2.22	6.8	—	.7922	.8036	.3666	

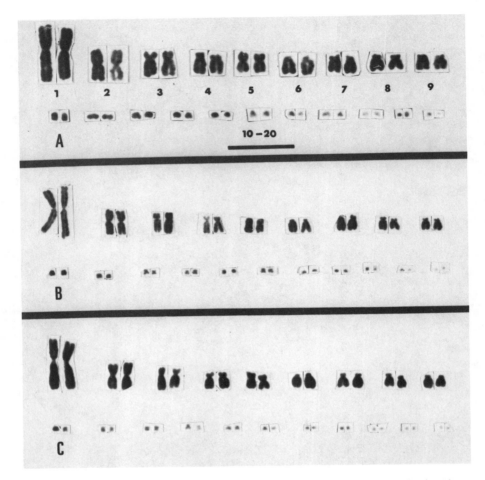

FIGURE 3. *Karyotypes of individuals from three island populations of* Xantusia riversiana: *(A) San Clemente I., University of Arizona 21688,♀; (B) San Nicolas I., LACM 127506, ♂; (C) Santa Barbara I., LACM 125465,♀ .*

TABLE 4. Data for seven scale characters in nine samples of *Xantusia riversiana*. Mean ± standard error (top line), range (middle line), coefficient of variation (bottom line), and sample size (below population) for scales around body (SAB), gulars (G), fourth toe lamellae (FTL), femoral pores (FP), ventrals (V), preanals (PA), and preanal enlargement (PAE) are given.

	SAB	G	FTL	FP	V	PA	PAE
Santa Barbara I. 40	84.15 ±.48	50.47 ±.46	23.28 ±.06	11.23 ±.09	34.00 ±.16	4.98 ±.10	123.64 ±2.29
	79-92	43-58	22-25	10-12	32-37	4-6	105-167
	3.64	5.71	4.29	5.14	2.98	13.26	11.71
San Clemente I. 97	79.55 ±.37	46.98 ±.26	22.67 ±.12	10.50 ±.08	33.67 ±.10	4.89 ±.07	140.44 ±1.87
	70-88	41-54	21-29	9-13	32-36	3-7	98-181
	4.57	5.44	5.39	7.66	2.90	13.82	13.08
San Nicolas I. 80	71.74 ±.37	41.99 ±.26	21.45 ±.13	10.94 ±.10	32.56 ±.11	4.49 ±.06	157.79 ±2.30
	60-79	35-48	19-24	9-13	30-35	3-6	119-226
	4.56	5.64	5.29	8.01	3.12	12.78	13.06
San Clemente I. Pyramid Cove 20	81.25 ±.79	47.15 ±.69	22.20 ±.22	10.45 ±.15	33.95 ±.20	5.00 ±.10	129.80 ±3.25
	75-87	43-54	21-24	10-12	33-36	4-6	108-158
	4.35	6.50	4.52	6.57	2.61	9.18	9.77
Northwest 57	78.65 ±.40	46.91 ±.30	22.70 ±.17	10.46 ±.13	33.50 ±.12	4.73 ±.09	148.98 ±2.11
	70-86	42-52	21-29	9-12	32-36	3-7	114-181
	3.81	4.91	5.71	8.10	2.77	15.21	10.74
mottled 40	79.00 ±.46	47.25 ±.38	22.40 ±.15	10.48 ±.14	33.55 ±.16	4.80 ±.13	148.20 ±2.37
	72-86	42-52	21-25	9-12	32-36	3-7	122-181
	3.70	5.13	4.27	8.37	2.94	16.48	10.12
striped 17	77.82 ±.75	46.12 ±.44	23.41 ±.41	10.41 ±.19	33.41 ±.19	4.59 ±.12	150.82 ±4.49
	70-81	42-49	21-29	9-11	32-35	4-5	114-175
	3.97	3.90	7.25	7.64	2.38	11.06	12.27
San Nicolas I. Carrier Cove 20	70.05 ±.81	41.25 ±.55	21.30 ±.22	10.50 ±.19	32.30 ±.18	4.05 ±.09	158.80 ±6.27
	60-75	35-44	20-23	9-12	31-34	3-5	121-226
	5.17	5.98	4.59	7.88	2.48	9.73	17.65
Southeast 40	72.75 ±.47	42.15 ±.33	21.87 ±.18	11.23 ±.15	32.77 ±.17	4.60 ±.08	159.10 ±2.67
	67-79	37-48	20-24	9-13	31-35	4-6	128-214
	4.06	5.00	5.20	8.19	3.35	11.86	10.60

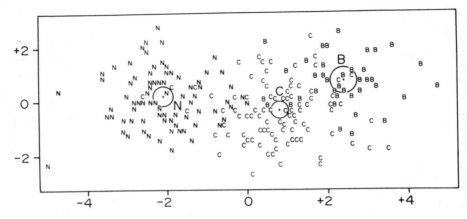

FIGURE 4. *Plot of first two canonical variables separating the three island populations of* Xantusia riversiana: *(B) Santa Barbara I., 40 specimens; (C) San Clemente I., 97; and (N) San Nicolas I., 80. Population centroids (dots) are surrounded by 95 per cent confidence circles. The first variate (abscissa) represents 95 per cent of the observed variance.*

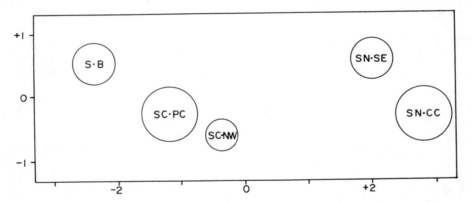

FIGURE 5. *Plot of first two canonical variables separating five populations of* Xantusia riversiana: *Santa Barbara I. (SB); San Clemente I., Pyramid Cove (SCPC) and Northwest (SCNW); and San Nicolas I., Carrier Cove (SNCC) and Southeast (SNSE). Population centroids (dots) are surrounded by 95 per cent confidence circles. First variate (abscissa) represents 86 per cent of observed variance; second (ordinate), 7 per cent. See Figure 2 for location of populations.*

TABLE 5. Inter-island comparisons of airline distance in km (AD), Mahalanobis' distance for scalation ($\sqrt{D^2}$), and genetic distance of Nei, 1972 (ND).

	AD	$\sqrt{D^2}$	ND
Santa Barbara-San Clemente	77	1.91	.0004
San Clemente-San Nicolas	101	2.95	.0017
San Nicolas-Santa Barbara	49	4.66	.0024

TABLE 6. Pooled standard deviations and canonical variate coefficients, with standardized scores in parentheses, for seven characters in the inter-island stepwise discriminant analysis.

	SD	I		II	
SAB	3.403	0.175	(0.596)	-0.025	(-0.085)
G	2.555	0.155	(0.396)	0.081	(0.207)
FTL	1.153	0.220	(0.254)	-0.044	(-0.051)
FP	0.797	-0.245	(-0.195)	1.116	(0.889)
PAE	18.621	-0.010	(-0.186)	-0.017	(-0.317)
V	1.000	0.180	(0.180)	-0.283	(-0.283)
PA	0.634	0.029	(0.018)	-0.586	(-0.372)

TABLE 7. Classification matrix based on stepwise discriminant analysis of 216 *Xantusia riversiana* from Santa Barbara (SB), San Clemente (SC), and San Nicolas (SN) Islands.

			Number of cases classified into group		
	Total	Per cent correct	SB	SC	SN
SB	39	87.2	34	6	0
SC	97	78.4	16	76	5
SN	80	91.2	0	7	73
Total	216	84.7	50	88	78

centroids (Fig. 4). As with the results of the electrophoretic analyses, the order of increasing divergence (Mahalanobis' distance, $\sqrt{D^2}$) was: San Clemente-Santa Barbara (1.91), San Clemente-San Nicolas (2.95), and Santa Barbara-San Nicolas (4.66) (Tables 5 and 6). The *a posteriori* classification scored 91 per cent hits for San Nicolas, 87 per cent for Santa Barbara, and 78 per cent for San Clemente. The classification matrix (Table 7) again emphasizes the intermediate position of San Clemente and its relative closeness to Santa Barbara in the discriminant space.

To test for intra-island geographic variation, samples were compared from two distant localities on both San Clemente (NW and Pyramid Cove) and San Nicolas (SE and Carrier Cove) (Fig. 2). Significant differences were found for SAB and PAE between the San Clemente populations, and for SAB, FP, and PA between the San Nicolas populations (Table 4). For both intra-island comparisons the centroids are significantly different (Fig. 5) and their

FIGURE 6. *Living individuals of* Xantusia riversiana *from Santa Barbara I. (upper two; LACM 127128 and 108835) and San Clemente I. (lower two; LACM 108618 and 108619).*

FIGURE 7. *Living individuals of* Xantusia riversiana *from San Nicolas I. (LACM 108505 through 108509 and 108813).*

Mahalanobis' distances are nearly identical (1.59 and 1.63) and are smaller than for all inter-island comparisons (2.07 to 5.43).

Color Pattern

Color pattern in *Xantusia riversiana* is highly variable (Figs. 6 and 7). Individuals with mottled patterns are found on all three islands; those with longitudinally striped patterns occur on San Clemente and San Nicolas, and a "blank" (uniform tan) pattern was observed only among San Nicolas lizards. There are, however, more subtle island differences in color pattern which we did not attempt to quantify, but which are illustrated in Figures 6 and 7. The color patterns of lizards from San Clemente tend to be more highly contrasting than those of individuals from Santa Barbara (Fig. 6). San Nicolas color patterns are the most variable and include striped, blank, and finely reticulated patterns, as well as many intermediates, often with reddish backgrounds (Fig. 7).

Scale counts were compared between striped and mottled individuals in the NW San Clemente population. Significant differences were detected only for fourth toe lamellae. The population centroids do not differ significantly and only 68 per cent hits were scored in the *a posteriori* classification of the SDA. The apparent association of color morphs with signifi-

TABLE 8. Clutch size from two sources for three island populations of *Xantusia riversiana*. Mean ± standard error, range, and sample size.

	Santa Barbara	San Clemente	San Nicolas
Goldberg and Bezy (1974)	3.50	3.76 ±.23	4.55 ±.50
	3-4	2-6	3-7
	2	25	9
Brattstrom (1951)	—	4.80 ±.37	7.50 ±.65
	—	4-6	6-9
	—	5	4
Total	3.25*	4.03 ±.20	5.46 ±.55
	3-4	2-6	3-9
	4	30	13

* Includes two additional individuals (LACM 125466 and 125467), each with three enlarged eggs.

cant differences in FTL may be a result of minor geographic variation, as the NW San Clemente sample was collected over a 6.5-km² area (Goldberg and Bezy 1974) and local "pockets" of striped individuals were noted in collecting the samples.

All three color morphs occur in mainland populations of *Xantusia vigilis*.

Body Size

The means for snout-vent lengths (SVL) of specimens 75 mm or longer (size at maturity for San Clemente females; Goldberg and Bezy 1974) are: Santa Barbara, 83.35 ±1.31 ($n = 31$); San Clemente, 84.24 ±0.42 ($n = 294$); and San Nicolas, 88.85 ±0.80 ($n = 86$). The differences are significant, except for Santa Barbara *vs.* San Clemente.

Adult *Xantusia riversiana* (SVL = 65 to 109 mm; Goldberg and Bezy 1974) are considerably larger than their mainland relatives *X. vigilis* (SVL = 36 to 60 mm; Bezy 1967, Zweifel and Lowe 1966) and *X. henshawi* (SVL = 47 to 70 mm; Lee 1975) and have been cited as an example of insular gigantism (Carlquist 1965). Large body size may be a primitive character state for xantusiids, retained by *X. riversiana,* and is perhaps associated with a herbivorous diet (Brattstrom 1952, Mautz and Lopez-Forment 1978, Pough 1973, Regal 1968).

Clutch Size

Brattstrom (1951) and Goldberg and Bezy (1974) have presented data on clutch (= litter) size in *X. riversiana* (Table 8). The figures reported by Brattstrom (1951) are considerably higher than those of Goldberg and Bezy (1974), perhaps reflecting annual variations in clutch size. Clutch size is smallest for Santa Barbara Island and largest for San Nicolas Island in both sets of data, but because of sample size limitations the accepted level of significance is achieved only for San Clemente *vs.* San Nicolas, and only when the two sets of data are pooled.

While a correlation between body size and clutch size was not present in the population on San Clemente (Goldberg and Bezy 1974), it appears to hold for comparisons between island populations. This correlation may also hold for the family in general since clutch size in *X. riversiana* is clearly larger than in its smaller mainland relatives *X. vigilis* ($\overline{X} = 1.87$; Zweifel and Lowe 1966) and *X. henshawi* ($\overline{X} = 1.46$; Lee 1975), but similar to that of comparably sized species of *Lepidophyma* (4 to 8; Telford and Campbell 1970, Greene 1970).

TABLE 9. Comparison of eight phenotypic and genotypic characteristics and seven ecogeographical parameters for the three island populations of *Xantusia riversiana*. Color pattern classes are mottled (M), striped (S), and blank (B). Data for last seven parameters (except lizard species number) are from Power (1972).

	Santa Barbara	San Clemente	San Nicolas
Canonical axis I	2.21	0.66	-1.93
Snout-vent length ($\overline{X}$, mm)	83.35	84.24	88.85
Clutch size ($\overline{X}$)	3.25	3.76	4.55
Color pattern	M	M, S	M, S, B
Coefficient of variation ($\overline{CV}_1$)	4.35	5.19	5.32
Coefficient of variation ($\overline{CV}_2$)	4.35	4.99	5.19
Heterozygosity ($\overline{H}$)	0.9	1.2	1.6
Area (km²)	2.6	145	36
Elevation (m)	194	599	253
Latitude (°N)	33.4	32.9	34.0
Mainland distance (km)	61	79	98
Island distance (km)	126	178	150
Plant species number	40	235	190
Lizard species number	1	2	1 (+2?)

Variability

The mean coefficients of variation ($\overline{CV}$) of five scale characters for the island populations are given in Table 9. In computing $\overline{CV}$, PA and PAE were not included because of their unusually high level of variability ($\overline{CV}$ = 13.29 and 12.62, respectively). The order of increasing $\overline{CV}$ of the island populations is Santa Barbara, San Clemente, and San Nicolas, whether $\overline{CV}$ for San Nicolas and San Clemente is computed as the average of the $\overline{CV}$s of their respective intra-island populations ($\overline{CV}_1$), or from the pooled standard deviation for the entire island sample ($\overline{CV}_2$) (Table 9). In comparison with mainland species, *X. riversiana* does not appear to have reduced scale count variability; $\overline{CV}$ for four characters (SAB, FTL, G, and FP) in *X. vigilis* (Bezy 1967) is 5.40, as opposed to 5.47 for *X. riversiana*.

For the 22-locus study, the heterozygosity ($\overline{H}$) figures correspond well to $\overline{CV}$ values, Santa Barbara Island being the least and San Nicolas Island the most variable (Table 3). These data might seem to support the genetic-phenetic variation correlation demonstrated by Soulé *et al.* (1973) for insular *Anolis* and deep-water island populations of *Uta,* and by Patton *et al.* (1975) for Galapagos *Rattus.* That such a correlation exists for *X. riversiana* must, however, remain questionable because the number of islands sampled is necessarily limited to three, our electrophoretic sample sizes are small (20, 20, and 5), and the results of the 30-locus study are contradictory, indicating instead that the larger San Clemente is genetically more variable than the smaller San Nicolas.

Electrophoretic estimates of genetic variability in the two mainland species are similar to those of the island populations (Table 3). All populations of *Xantusia* sampled have low heterozygosity values ($\overline{H}$ = 2.21, 30 loci) when compared with other vertebrates (Selander and Kaufman 1973). Gorman *et al.* (1977) compared heterozygosity estimates for 10 genera of lizards and concluded that the values are low (*ca.* 2 per cent) in fossorial species, intermediate (*ca.* 5 per cent) in territorial, sit-and-wait predators, and high (*ca.* 10 per cent) in vagile, searching predators. These categories presumably influence heterozygosity values through territoriality, population size, and/or mating structure (degree of panmixia).

The heterozygosity levels of *Xantusia* are comparable to those of fossorial species, which these lizards resemble in that they are sedentary, live (often paired) in patchy habitats (*e.g.*, boulder cap rocks and yuccas), and have long lives and low reproductive potentials (Bezy *et al.* 1977, Goldberg and Bezy 1974, Lee 1975, Zweifel and Lowe 1966).

DISCUSSION
Ecological Correlates

That our studies of *X. riversiana* are necessarily limited to three islands precludes any detailed analysis of correlations between the data and island ecological parameters. However, we briefly consider here possible ecological correlates only because a consistent order (Santa Barbara-San Clemente-San Nicolas) occurs in our data for genetic distance, scalation, color pattern, body size, clutch size, heterozygosity, and scale count variability (Table 9). This order contradicts that for island area, elevation, latitude, plant species number, and lizard species number, but corresponds with mainland distance (Table 9; Power 1972). Mainland distance could have affected colonization sequence, which may be reflected in the electrophoretic data. However, for at least scalation, body size, and clutch size, it is likely that the observed pattern of variation is related to climatic factors which are correlated with mainland distance. Other studies have demonstrated that with island area there is a significant negative correlation for dorsal scale number and body size in *Uta* (Soulé 1966), and significant positive correlations for both phenetic and genetic variability in *Uta* (Soulé 1972, Soulé and Yang 1973) and in *Rattus* (Patton *et al.* 1975). None of these parameters appears correlated with island area in our data; plausible explanations for this include the small number of islands, the relatively near-shore position of the islands, the recency of colonization, and possible differences in response to environmental variables related to the secretive lifestyle of xantusiids.

Evolution and Biogeography

On the basis of correlations between electrophoretic data, immunological distance, and the fossil record, Sarich (1977) has estimated that a genetic distance of 1.0 (Nei 1972) indicates a divergence time of approximately 18 million years (m.y.) ago. This correlation would predict that *Xantusia riversiana* diverged from *X. henshawi* about 15 m.y. ago (middle Miocene) and from *X. vigilis* about 10 m.y. ago (late to middle Miocene), while the divergence time between the two mainland species would be approximately 7 m.y. ago (late Miocene).

Schatzinger (1975) has recognized two species of *Paleoxantusia* from the later Eocene (Uintan) of the San Diego region, the larger one sharing characters with *X. riversiana* and the smaller one with *X. henshawi* and *X. vigilis*. The presence of these *Paleoxantusia* species in the Uintan would seem to suggest that the cladistic event that led to *X. riversiana* and *X. henshawi-vigilis* took place over 40 m.y. ago. However, after extensive comparisons among fossil and recent xantusiids, Schatzinger (1975, fig. 9) concluded that these two *Paleoxantusia* species do not represent the divergence between *X. riversiana* (*Klauberina*) and *X. henshawi-vigilis* (*Xantusia*), which he feels took place in the Oligocene or later. Our divergence time estimates based on electrophoretic data support his conclusion.

The genetic distances between the island populations are extremely small compared with those between the species, indicating that at least two, if not all three, of the present island populations are the result of colonization in the last million years. One of the three could conceivably have been in existence for 10 to 14 m.y., the divergence time between *X. riversiana* and its living mainland relatives.

The electrophoretic data appear consistent with the known geological record of the islands (as summarized by J. Vedder, pers. comm.). Pleistocene marine deposits occur on all three islands. On San Nicolas, these are found to the highest present elevation (253 m) and have been estimated to be 0.5 to 0.6 m.y. old. Pleistocene beds that are probably marine cover the highest point (194 m) on Santa Barbara Island, and fossiliferous marine beds occur at the next lower terrace. On San Clemente Island, however, the record of Pleistocene submergence is not as complete. Pleistocene marine beds and wave-cut terraces occur to an elevation of approximately 450 m, leaving 149 m without a conclusive record of Quaternary submergence. Miocene and Pliocene marine beds also occur on San Clemente. While the geological history of the California borderland is highly complex, the evidence would seem to indicate that the colonizations of San Nicolas and Santa Barbara must have been Quaternary events, while it is possible that colonization on San Clemente dates from the late Tertiary.

The occurrence of *X. riversiana* on islands with records of Pleistocene submergence which were not connected by land bridges suggests that the species is at least a moderately effective island colonizer. The recent discovery of the species on Sutil Island off the north end of Santa Barbara Island (R. Wilson, pers. comm.) strengthens this idea. In contrast, *X. vigilis* occurs on none of the islands of the Gulf of California, in spite of its circumgulf distribution, and appears to lack all of the life history attributes that are correlated with successful Gulf island colonization among species of lizards, *i.e.,* habitat generalists having high mainland population densities, potentially high birth rates, and high death rates (Case 1975).

The differences in apparent colonizing abilities between the two species seem consistent with what is known of their ecology and life history. The clutch size of *X. riversiana* is two to three times that of *X. vigilis* (Goldberg and Bezy 1974). The diet of *X. vigilis* consists almost exclusively of insects, while *X. riversiana* is a food generalist, its diet being about evenly divided between plant and animal material (Brattstrom 1952). Although *Xantusia vigilis* achieves high densities in relatively cool desert situations, such as in the Mojave (Zweifel and Lowe 1966) and at localities in Baja California receiving Pacific breezes, it is virtually absent from the hot Gulf coast of Sonora and Baja California (Bezy, pers. obs.). That it does not occur on the Gulf islands is not surprising. While *X. riversiana* no longer occurs on the mainland, its fossil relatives (*Paleoxantusia*) appear to have had a long association with the maritime climates of the California borderland (Schatzinger 1975), and today the species reaches high population densities on at least San Clemente Island (Wilson 1976). It is probably the differences in climate, rather than population parameters, that explain the absence of *X. vigilis* on the Gulf islands and the presence of *X. riversiana* on the California Channel Islands.

One of the more interesting unanswered (and perhaps unanswerable) questions posed by *X. riversiana* is why it does not occur today on the mainland or on other California Islands. Insular shielding from competition, predation (Savage 1967), and harsh climatic factors (Regal 1968) have all been suggested, and with good reason. Compared with *X. henshawi* and *X. vigilis,* the species is morphologically unspecialized (Savage 1967) and its large body size limits its habitat and thermoregulatory options (Regal 1968). All three islands lack snakes as potential predators (Savage 1967), two have no other native lizard species, and San Clemente has only *Uta stansburiana.* (Records for *Uta stansburiana* [Savage 1967] and *Gerrhonotus multicarinatus* [Banta and Wilson 1976] on San Nicolas probably represent introductions.)

However, competition may not have played an important role in the elimination of *X. riversiana* from the mainland or islands since no other extensively herbivorous lizard is known from the California borderland, at least for the Quaternary. The secretive habits of the species would be expected to minimize predation, except by snakes, and it seems unlikely that predation from this source alone could have been a large factor in bringing about extinction. It would appear more reasonable that climatic change has played the dominant role in producing the relictual biogeographic pattern exhibited by several xantusiids, including *X. riversiana* (Bezy 1972). The species has probably persisted on the islands primarily because the greater equability of climate there has offered a substantial buffer against the climatic deteriorations of the Neogene. Among the California Islands, the outer, southern ones would be expected to offer the maximum climatic buffer, and it is to these that *X. riversiana* is restricted. That the mainland extinction of the species may have occurred more than one million years ago is suggested by the general fossil record for mainland North America (north of the Isthmus of Tehuantepec), which indicates virtually no extinction of lizard species since Blancan times (Gehlbach 1965).

In summary, the available evidence suggests that the divergence between *Xantusia riversiana* and *X. henshawi-vigilis* took place in the Miocene. *Xantusia riversiana* could have occurred on San Clemente Island as early as the late Miocene or Pliocene, and its disappearance from the mainland may date to pre-Nebraskan times. In the last half million years or so the species has reached San Nicolas and Santa Barbara Islands, perhaps from San Clemente Island, and the resultant populations have become differentiated in scalation, coloration, body size, and clutch size.

SPECIMENS EXAMINED

Catalogue numbers refer to specimens in the collections of the Los Angeles County Museum of Natural History (acronym, LACM, omitted), the Museum of Vertebrate Zoology (MVZ), and the San Diego Natural History Museum (SDNHM). All localities are in California. Santa Barbara Island is in Santa Barbara County, San Clemente Island in Los Angeles County, and San Nicolas Island in Ventura County.

(A) Electrophoresis.

     X. henshawi: RIVERSIDE CO.: *ca.* 1.3 mi (by road) S Cabezon, 125524-29.

     X. vigilis: LOS ANGELES CO.: 3.5 mi (airline) W Littlerock, 125530-49.

     X. riversiana: SANTA BARBARA I.: vic. Cat Canyon, 125463-67. SAN CLEMENTE I.: vic. dunes, NW side of I., 125470-83, 125506-10; 4.8 mi (airline) SE Wilson Cove, 125468; Horse Cove, 125469. SAN NICOLAS I.: Carrier Cove, SE of W Point, 125486-505; beach along SSE side of I., 125512.

(B) Karyotypes.

     SANTA BARBARA I.: vic. Cat Canyon, 125465. SAN NICOLAS I.: beach along SSE side of I., 127506.

(C) Scalation.

     SANTA BARBARA I.: 3278-85, 3287-88, MVZ 644-45, MVZ 28330, SDNHM 21128, SDNHM 31983-85, SDNHM 44469; vic. Cat Canyon, 108822-38, 125463-67. SAN CLEMENTE I.: *NW Sample*, vic. airport, 108306, 108309-11, 108315, 108319-20, 108322-23, 108327, 108330, 108336, 108347, 108352-56, 108359, 108362-63, 108371-72, 108446, 108449, 108451, 108455-56, 108459, 108462-64, 108470, 108473, 108483-84, 108486-89, 108495-97, 108499-500, 108504, 108563, 108577, 108588, 108618, 108620, 108646, 108654, 108678, 108709, 108734, 108739. *Pyramid Cove Sample*, 3309, 3317, 3330, 3368-69, 3371, 3373, 3377-81, 3383, 3387, 3389-90, 3392-94, 3401. *General Sample*, Mt. Thirst, 119174; Middle Ranch, 26798; Horse Cove, 125469; *ca.* 3 mi W Pyramid Cove, 108607-16; 4 mi S Wilson Cove, 101255-59; 5 mi E Wilson Cove, 101254; 4.8 mi (airline) SE Wilson Cove, 125468. SAN NICOLAS I.: *SE Sample*, 108769-74, 108777-88, 108791, 108793-800, 108802, 108804-09, 108811-12, 108818, 125512-14. *Carrier Cove*

Sample, SE of W Point, 121670-71, 122572, 125486-94, 125496, 125498, 125501-05, 125511. *General Sample,* 3267, 14487, 101262, SDNHM 15487-92, SDNHM 15494-5, SDNHM 17213, SDNHM 17215, SDNHM 36334, SDNHM 36670-71; Army Camp, 3266; Sand Dunes, 3275-77.

SUMMARY

Xantusia (Klauberina) riversiana is endemic to Santa Barbara, San Clemente, and San Nicolas Islands. Electrophoretic analyses of proteins encoded by 22 to 30 presumptive loci indicate that the genetic distances between the island populations are minute ($ND = 0.0004$ to 0.0048), compared with those between the species of *Xantusia* (0.409 to 0.830), and that the heterozygosity levels are low in all the populations ($\overline{H} = 1.80$). The unbanded karyotypes of the three island populations appear identical to each other and to those of certain populations of both mainland species. Stepwise discriminant analysis of seven characters demonstrates both intra-island and inter-island divergence in scalation, with an average of 85 per cent of the specimens being correctly assigned to their home island. The island populations have also diverged in coloration, body size, and clutch size. Electrophoretic data suggest that the divergence time between *X. riversiana* and *X. henshawi-vigilis* is 10 to 15 m.y. ago (*ca.* middle Miocene), while that between the island populations is less than one m.y. ago. *Xantusia riversiana* could have occurred on San Clemente Island from as early as the Miocene or Pliocene and its disappearance from the mainland may date from pre-Nebraskan time.

ACKNOWLEDGMENTS

We thank W. G. Kay and W. S. Myers of the U.S. Department of the Navy, W. H. Ehorn of the U.S. Department of the Interior, and J. M. Brode and K. Ball of the California Department of Fish and Game for issuing collecting permits and/or granting access to the islands; K. Bolles, M. A. Recht, M. G. Ruggles, and J. W. Wright for assistance in collecting specimens; D. B. Wake (MVZ) and T. Fritts (formerly SDNHM) for the loan of specimens under their charge; R. D. Friesen for assistance and advice on data analysis; K. Bolles for preparing illustrations; and J. W. Wright and F. S. Truxal for critically reviewing the manuscript.

REFERENCES

BANTA, B. H., and R. L. WILSON. 1976. On the occurrence of *Gerrhonotus multicarinatus* on San Nicolas Island, Ventura County, California. Bull. Maryland Herp. Soc. 12:99-100.

BEZY, R. L. 1967. Variation, distribution and taxonomic status of the Arizona night lizard (*Xantusia arizonae*). Copeia 1967:653-661.

————. 1972. Karyotypic variation and evolution of the lizards in the family Xantusiidae. Contrib. Sci. Nat. Hist. Mus. Los Angeles Co. 227:1-29.

BEZY, R. L., G. C. GORMAN, Y. J. KIM, and J. W. WRIGHT. 1977. Chromosomal and genetic divergence in the fossorial lizards of the family Anniellidae. Syst. Zool. 26:57-71.

BRATTSTROM, B. H. 1951. The number of young of *Xantusia*. Herpetologica 7:143-144.

————. 1952. The food of the nightlizards, genus *Xantusia*. Copeia 1952:168-172.

CARLQUIST, S. 1965. Island life. Natural History Press, Garden City, N.Y.

CASE, T. J. 1975. Species numbers, density compensation, and colonizing ability of lizards on islands in the Gulf of California. Ecology 56:3-18.

DIXON, W. J., ed. 1975. BMDP Biomedical Computer Programs. University of California Press, Berkeley and Los Angeles, Calif.

GEHLBACH, F. R. 1965. Amphibians and reptiles from the Pliocene and Pleistocene of North America: a chronological summary and selected bibliography. Texas J. Sci. 17:56-70.

GOLDBERG, S. R., and R. L. BEZY. 1974. Reproduction in the island night lizard, *Xantusia riversiana*. Herpetologica 30:350-360.

GORMAN, G. C., Y. J. KIM, and C. E. TAYLOR. 1977. Genetic variation in irradiated and control populations of *Cnemidophorus tigris* (Sauria: Teiidae) from Mercury, Nevada, with a discussion of genetic variability in lizards. Theor. Appl. Genet. 49:9-14.

GREENE, H. W. 1970. Reproduction in a Mexican xantusiid lizard, *Lepidophyma tuxtlae*. J. Herp. 4:85-87.

KIM, Y. J., G. C. GORMAN, T. PAPENFUSS, and A. K. ROYCHOUDHURY. 1976. Genetic relationships and genetic variation in the amphisbaenian genus *Bipes*. Copeia 1976:120-124.

LEE, J. C. 1975. The autecology of *Xantusia henshawi* (Sauria: Xantusiidae). Trans. San Diego Soc. Nat. Hist. 17:259-277.

MAUTZ, W. J., and W. LOPEZ-FORMENT. 1978. Observations on the activity and diet of the cavernicolous lizard *Lepidophyma smithii* (Sauria: Xantusiidae). Herpetologica 34:311-313.

NEI, M. 1972. Genetic distance between populations. Amer. Natur. 106:283-292.

PATTON, J. L., S. Y. YANG, and P. MYERS. 1975. Genetic and morphologic divergence among introduced rat populations (*Rattus rattus*) of the Galápagos Archipelago, Ecuador. Syst. Zool. 24:296-310.

POUGH, F. H. 1973. Lizard energetics and diet. Ecology 54:837-844.

POWER, D. M. 1972. Numbers of bird species on the California Islands. Evolution 26:451-463.

REGAL, P. J. 1968. An analysis of heat-seeking in a lizard. Ph.D. thesis, University of California, Los Angeles, Calif.

SARICH, V. M. 1977. Rates, sample sizes, and the neutrality hypothesis for electrophoresis in evolutionary studies. Nature 265:24-28.

SAVAGE, J. M. 1951. Studies on the lizard family Xantusiidae. II. Geographical variation in *Xantusia riversiana* from the Channel Islands of California. J. Washington Acad. Sci. 41:357-360.

————. 1957. Studies on the lizard family Xantusiidae. III. A new genus for *Xantusia riversiana* Cope, 1883. Zoologica 42:83-86.

————. 1963. Studies of the lizard family Xantusiidae. IV. The genera. Los Angeles Co. Mus. Contrib. Sci. 71:1-38.

————. 1967. Evolution of the insular herpetofaunas. Pp. 219-227 *in* R. N. Philbrick, ed., Proceedings of the symposium on the biology of the California Islands. Santa Barbara Botanic Garden, Santa Barbara, Calif.

SCHATZINGER, R. A. 1975. Later Eocene (Uintan) lizards from the greater San Diego area, California. M.A. thesis, San Diego State University, San Diego, Calif.

SELANDER, R. K., and D. W. KAUFMAN. 1973. Genic variability and strategies of adaptation in animals. Proc. Natl. Acad. Sci. 70:1875-1877.

SELANDER, R. K., M. H. SMITH, S. Y. YANG, W. E. JOHNSON, and J. B. GENTRY. 1971. Biochemical polymorphism and systematics in the genus *Peromyscus*. I. Variation in the old-field mouse (*Peromyscus polionotus*). Studies in Genetics VI, Univ. Texas Publ. 7103:49-90.

SMITH, H. M. 1946. A subspecies of the lizard *Xantusia riversiana*. J. Washington Acad. Sci. 36:392-393.

SOULÉ, M. 1966. Trends in the insular radiation of a lizard. Amer. Natur. 100:47-64.

————. 1972. Phenetics of natural populations. III. Variation in insular populations of a lizard. Amer. Natur. 106:429-446.

SOULÉ, M., and S. Y. YANG. 1973. Genetic variation in side-blotched lizards on islands in the Gulf of California. Evolution 27:593-600.

SOULÉ, M., S. Y. YANG, M. G. W. WEILER, and G. C. GORMAN. 1973. Island lizards: the genetic-phenetic variation correlation. Nature 242:191-193.

TELFORD, S. R., and H. W. CAMPBELL. 1970. Ecological observations on an all female population of the lizard *Lepidophyma flavimaculatum* (Xantusiidae) in Panamá. Copeia 1970:379-381.

WEBB, R. G. 1970. Another new night lizard (*Xantusia*) from Durango, Mexico. Los Angeles Co. Mus. Contrib. Sci. 194:1-10.

WILSON, R. L. 1976. The status of the island night lizard (*Klauberina riversiana*). Pp. 1-10 *in* J. K. Larson, ed., The status of the proposed endangered species on San Clemente Island. Unpubl. document submitted to U.S. Fish and Wildl. Serv. by U.S. Dept. Navy.

YANG, S. Y., M. SOULÉ, and G. C. GORMAN. 1974. *Anolis* lizards of the eastern Caribbean: a case study in evolution. I. Genetic relationships, phylogeny, and colonization sequence of the *roquet* group. Syst. Zool. 23:387-399.

ZWEIFEL, R. G., and C. H. LOWE. 1966. The ecology of a population of *Xantusia vigilis,* the desert night lizard. Amer. Mus. Novitates 2247:1-57.

The Present Status of the Garter Snake on Santa Catalina Island, California

Timothy W. Brown[1]

Department of Biological Sciences,
California State Polytechnic University,
Pomona, California 91768

INTRODUCTION

The status of the garter snake on Santa Catalina Island has long been in doubt. Prior to 1974, only two specimens had ever been reported: one, in the California Academy of Sciences collection, from "Avalon" (Fitch 1940); the other, in the Los Angeles County Museum of Natural History, taken from "Middle Ranch" in 1941. During the ensuing 33 years, no new specimens were reported and the regrettable lack of documentation accompanying the recorded examples gave no additional clues. Even Fitch (1940), after thoroughly describing the single specimen available to him, stated:

> It seems improbable that an endemic population of garter snakes exists on Santa Catalina Island, and the specimen described above may be an abnormally marked individual brought there from the mainland through human agency.

So matters stood for many years, although herpetologists continued to list this species as part of the Santa Catalina Island fauna (Savage 1967, Stebbins 1966, 1972).

On the southern California mainland, the two-striped garter snake (*Thamnophis couchi hammondi*) is strictly confined to the vicinity of fairly permanent fresh water. While not really rare, populations are generally isolated from one another, occurring along canyon streams in the mountain foothills. Garter snakes were also formerly found in rivers, sloughs, and ponds in valleys and along the coast, but these habitats have been largely destroyed by urbanization. Throughout its range, the two-striped garter snake is thoroughly aquatic. It swims and dives well, and, although it may bask at the water's edge, it always takes refuge in the water when alarmed. As might be expected, its food consists of frogs, tadpoles, small fishes, salamanders, and earthworms.

In August 1974, I began a search of possible locations where populations might still occur and made inquiries of various persons familiar with the natural history of Santa Catalina Island. Natural permanent bodies of water are few on Santa Catalina. Although a number of manmade ponds and reservoirs have been constructed, I reasoned that if garter snakes were truly native to the island, they would have had to occupy one of the natural streams or ponds antedating the first arrival of Europeans. Pursuing the "Avalon" record, I was told that the nearest natural body of water was Echo Lake, a small isolated pond in a valley about 315 m above White's Landing (Fig. 1). Whatever Echo Lake once may have been, it has now been grazed barren of vegetation and trampled into a foul, muddy quagmire by goats, bison, and hogs—a totally unsuitable habitat for garter snakes.

A. Douglas Propst, then General Manager of the Wrigley holdings on Santa Catalina and now President of the Santa Catalina Island Conservancy, was extremely helpful in pointing out the canyons with springs and permanent water, all of which drain the west and southwest slopes of the island. These include Little Springs, Big Springs, Cottonwood, Middle, Fern, Bullrush, and Silver Canyons. Later, Mr. Propst visited several of these with me. While making further

---

[1]Deceased, 31 August 1979.

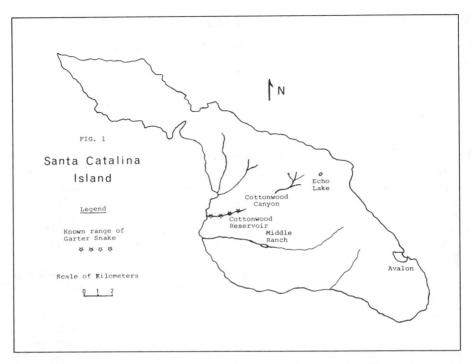

FIGURE 1. *Map of Santa Catalina Island showing range of garter snake (* Thamnophis couchi hammondi*).*

inquiries at Middle Ranch, I was told that children of ranch personnel had occasionally seen "water snakes" at Cottonwood Reservoir in ·Cottonwood Canyon. Everyone seemed quite familiar with the four common species of snake on the island—the ringneck, gopher snake, kingsnake, and rattlesnake—so there could be little question of mistaken identity. In southern California, garter snakes are often called "water snakes," and the fact that these particular snakes had always been seen in the water in Cottonwood Reservoir made this a very promising bit of information.

On the morning of August 4, 1974, my wife, Dr. Patricia Brown, and I captured the third known specimen of garter snake from Santa Catalina. This was a large female found lying in shallow water in the stream about 200 m below the dam at Cottonwood Reservoir.

MORPHOLOGY

To date, I have seen a total of 19 garter snakes in Cottonwood Canyon. Twelve of these, including nine adults and three juveniles (five males and seven females), were caught for meristic measurements. Except for the female specimen caught on August 4, 1974, all of these snakes have been examined in the field and released promptly where captured.

As the quotation from Fitch (1940) has already implied, the garter snakes on Santa Catalina Island look very different from mainland two-striped garters. Actually, the name "two-striped," which has been applied to the subspecies *hammondi,* is totally inappropriate for island specimens, which lack any markings whatever. Instead, they are a uniform olive-brown

FIGURE 2. Thamnophis couchi hammondi—*adult female from Cottonwood Canyon, Santa Catalina Island (dorsal view).*

FIGURE 3. Thamnophis couchi hammondi—*adult female from Cottonwood Canyon, Santa Catalina Island (ventral view).*

on top (Fig. 2); their undersides are also olive-brown, but slightly clouded with orange. Only their chins, lip scales, and throats are pale olive-buff (Fig. 3). By contrast, most mainland specimens are blackish-brown on top with a well-defined yellow stripe along each side. Their lips, chins, and undersides are usually buff-yellow. Occasionally, a dark mainland snake can be found which approaches the coloration of the island specimens, but this is atypical. Aside from coloration, island and mainland forms seem basically alike. Meristics of the Santa Catalina examples fall within the range of *hammondi* as a whole.

Interestingly, there is another species of garter snake, the "Lower California garter snake" (*Thamnophis digueti*), found in a few bodies of fresh water in south-central Baja California that drain into the Gulf of California. This snake is virtually identical in coloration to the garter snakes on Santa Catalina and was originally assigned to *T. couchi hammondi*. The two forms differ only slightly in certain head proportions and average scale counts. It is hoped that biochemical studies will help clarify the relationships between the Lower California garter snake, that on Santa Catalina Island, and the two-striped form on the California mainland.

Very recently, Dr. Glenn Stewart of California State Polytechnic University, who has been studying the distribution and adaptive significance of color morphs in California garter snakes, informed me of a population of brown, patternless garter snakes at the mouth of the Santa Ynez River, about 8 km north of Lompoc in Santa Barbara County. This locality lies approximately 238 km northwest of the mouth of Cottonwood Canyon on Santa Catalina Island. Although I have not personally examined any of these garter snakes, they are said to resemble those of Santa Catalina much more than do snakes from populations in coastal Orange, Los Angeles, and Ventura Counties.

PAST DISPERSAL AND COLONIZATION OF SANTA CATALINA ISLAND

Santa Catalina, a large, topographically diverse island with a mild Mediterranean climate, lies only 32 km from the California mainland. The coastal mainland supports a rich and varied herpetofauna of nine amphibians and 25 reptiles. By contrast, only three amphibians and eight reptiles are native to Santa Catalina, although this well exceeds the number on any of the other Channel Islands (Savage 1967).

Geological and botanical evidence indicates that Santa Catalina has been separated from the mainland as well as from the other Channel Islands since the early Pleistocene (Savage 1967, Thorne 1967). This, plus the peculiar composition of the island's herpetofauna (derived from the mainland fauna, with some notable omissions), indicates chance colonization via over-water dispersal rather than by overland migration across land bridges (Savage 1967). For example, California toads (*Bufo boreas halophilus*), Great Basin fence lizards (*Sceloporus occidentalis biseriatus*), and California striped racers (*Masticophis l. lateralis*) are all very common along the adjacent mainland coast, but are absent from Santa Catalina. Conversely, western skinks (*Eumeces s. skiltonianus*), San Diego ringneck snakes (*Diadophis punctatus similis*), and two-striped garter snakes (*Thamnophis couchi hammondi*) are all rather uncommon on the mainland, but are, nonetheless, present on Santa Catalina. It is likely that, during the Pluvial period some 10,000 years ago, rainfall in southern California was much heavier and stream discharge along the coast much greater. Debris, frequently washed out to sea, could thus have provided dispersal opportunities through rafting—especially for amphibians and reptiles living along watercourses. Rafting was probably responsible for the peculiar herpetofaunal composition of Santa Catalina Island. Based on this assumption, it is likely that the herpetofauna of Santa Catalina consists of comparatively recent arrivals which have differentiated little or not at all from mainland forms.

The Lompoc garter snake population mentioned previously is of special interest since it represents the nearest mainland population with coloration like the garter snakes on Santa Catalina. At first, the likelihood of over-water transport from the Santa Ynez River around Point Arguello to the west side of Santa Catalina seems rather remote. However, studies of ocean currents along the southern California coast (Sverdrup *et al.* 1942, Wyllie 1966) show that the southward-flowing California Current sweeps quite close to shore in the general vicinity of Lompoc. South of San Nicolas Island, some of this water is caught up in a counterclockwise eddy which turns east and then northward, flowing past the shores of San Clemente and Santa Catalina Islands. If one estimates a distance of about 450 km along this

FIGURE 4. *Cottonwood Reservoir.*

"J"-shaped route and a speed of as little as 1 km/hr, such a journey would take a little over three weeks. Surface current velocities of twice this rate do occur, however (Schwartzlose 1963), and could, accordingly, reduce the time in transit.

Reptiles are notoriously able to survive long periods without food or water. They have thus been able to raft to rather remote oceanic islands, such as the Galapagos. Should a gravid garter snake have been carried out to sea on a raft of debris from the Santa Ynez River during a flood, it might well have ended up on the beach at Cottonwood Canyon, none the worse for a three- or four-week ocean journey. This unusual and distinctly colored form of garter snake could then have established a population of nearly identical individuals which has persisted in the absence of any selection against that color. The subsequent degradation of stream habitats by feral animals may well have extinguished garter snake populations elsewhere on Santa Catalina within the past two hundred years. By contrast, San Clemente Island, which completely lacks both suitable habitat and the treefrogs (*Hyla regilla*) which constitute such an important food item for garter snakes, was probably never successfully colonized by them.

ECOLOGY

Despite careful searching in the other stream canyons on Santa Catalina, I have been unable to find garter snakes in any but Cottonwood, nor have ranch personnel noted any elsewhere over the years. Cottonwood is unique in several respects. The permanently "live" portion of its stream flows for roughly 1.6 km from just below Rancho Escondido to a small cove south of Little Harbor. About 0.8 km upstream from where it is crossed by the Little Harbor-Middle Ranch road, there is a concrete dam some 8 m high across a narrow part of the canyon. Cottonwood Reservoir lies behind this dam (Fig. 4). This reservoir is a rather deep, narrow

FIGURE 5. *Stream in Cottonwood Canyon.*

pond about 0.4 ha in extent. The upper end becomes quite shallow where it is fed by the stream. The Cottonwood stream continues "live" for another 0.5 km or so up to a place where ground water wells out below a ledge of metamorphic rock.

Unlike the other canyon streams, Cottonwood is fairly wide and has a rather gentle gradient (Fig. 5). Low falls and riffles are interspersed with long, flat stretches where the water may flow through several channels before joining again. The trees consist of small stands of cottonwoods (*Populus*), willows (*Salix*), and elderberries (*Sambucus*). Scattered clumps of bullrush (*Juncus*) and dense mats of salt grass (*Distichlis*) occur in the flat, open stretches. Various shrubs and herbs, including coyote bush (*Baccharis*), wild grape (*Vitis*), mugwort (*Artemisia douglasiana*), and virgin's bower (*Clematis*), grow along the stream bank. Unlike the other canyons, Cottonwood is quite open and free of the dense thickets of poison oak (*Toxicodendron*), coyote bush, willow, and bullrush which choke considerable stretches of other stream canyons. Behind the dam, Cottonwood Reservoir is lined by a stand of cattails (*Typha*). On the southwest side is a large clump of willows, but elsewhere the embankment is covered by a dense mat of salt grass with scattered clumps of California sagebrush (*Artemisia californica*).

FIGURE 6. *Garter snake habitat at Cottonwood Reservoir.*

This 1.6 km of stream, with Cottonwood Reservoir, constitutes the total known range of the garter snake on Santa Catalina Island (Fig. 1). Although individuals occasionally may be found along the stream, the nucleus of the population is at Cottonwood Reservoir. Garter snakes bask on the mats of salt grass along the embankment and quickly slide into the water at the slightest alarm. Once among the cattails in deeper water, they are almost impossible to see and are quite safe from most predators (Fig. 6).

On Santa Catalina, such predators would include bullfrogs, kingsnakes, red-tailed hawks, ravens, loggerhead shrikes, sparrow hawks (kestrels), marsh hawks, great blue herons, green herons, black-crowned night herons, egrets, burrowing owls, island foxes, feral pigs, feral house cats, domestic dogs, and even ground squirrels. Bison, which frequently drink at the stream and browse streamside vegetation in Cottonwood Canyon, may occasionally kill or maim some snakes by stepping on them. The browsing and trampling of vegetation by bison may actually have a beneficial effect on the garter snake population by preventing dense plant growth from choking the stream. In other canyons, especially in steep, narrow ones less frequented by bison, such overgrowth has resulted in very poor garter snake habitat. By contrast, intense overgrazing by goats in steep, rugged Silver Canyon has removed virtually all of the herbaceous vegetation. The stream in Silver Canyon trickles down through a barren desert-like landscape of eroding rocky slopes with no vegetation except a few very old Catalina cherries (*Prunus*), some scattered tree tobacco (*Nicotiana*), and clumps of prickly pear (*Opuntia*). Here a lack of cover is the problem. Therefore, not only does the garter snake appear to have a very restricted range on Santa Catalina, but I estimate the total population in Cottonwood Canyon to be no more than 25 to 30 individuals. It is thus hovering on the brink of extinction.

A new threat to the garter snake population was the abrupt appearance of bullfrogs (*Rana*

592

Figure 7. *Cottonwood Reservoir during winter drawdown; empty except for narrow stream along exposed bottom.*

catesbeiana) at Cottonwood Reservoir in August 1977. Both adults and tadpoles were seen, although neither had ever been noticed by me or by ranch personnel prior to that time. The nearest source of bullfrogs is Thompson's Reservoir at Middle Ranch. Bullfrogs were introduced into Thompson's Reservoir a number of years ago. However, the intervening terrain of several kilometers of steep, arid, scrub-covered ridges between Middle Canyon and Cottonwood would seem an effective barrier to dispersal.

While the tadpoles might occasionally be eaten by adult garter snakes, adult bullfrogs are voracious predators in their own right, seizing and swallowing any moving object they can engulf. A young garter snake would make an easy meal for an adult bullfrog. Given the low reproductive potential of the small garter snake population at Cottonwood, this new situation appears quite serious. Only the stream habitat will remain unsuitable for and therefore free of bullfrogs.

There is little chance that bullfrogs could have gone unnoticed at Cottonwood until the present time. They are large, and even their tadpoles are easily seen by day. Also, the bellowing calls of the adults at night are unmistakable. They must have been intentionally introduced not many weeks prior to their discovery. Control or elimination of bullfrogs will be quite difficult without seriously disrupting the already tenuous situation at Cottonwood.

HUMAN IMPACT

With the advent of new management policy, a major goal must be to minimize adverse human impact in Cottonwood Canyon. The construction of the dam and formation of Cottonwood Reservoir some 30 years ago greatly helped the garter snakes by creating new habitat for them, despite a great deal of temporary disturbance during construction. Each winter the dam

FIGURE 8. *Stream bed in Cottonwood Canyon during dry period, August 1976.*

spillway is opened to prevent rain runoff from piling up silt behind the dam. This empties the lake for several weeks of each year, leaving only a narrow stream flowing along the exposed lake bottom (Fig. 7).

By 1976, a severe, prolonged water shortage on Santa Catalina Island prompted the drilling of a well 0.5 km up the canyon from Cottonwood Reservoir in a flat, elevated field about 100 m from the stream itself. Under the supervision of Mr. Propst, all possible steps were taken to minimize the impact of construction on the ecology of Cottonwood Canyon. An existing pipeline was reactivated to carry away a projected maximum flow of 60 gallons per minute. This was estimated to be well below the normal recharge rate into the stream from natural springs. Nevertheless, by August 1976, Cottonwood Reservoir was low and much of the stream was dry. Here and there a sluggish trickle ran over surface bedrock, but most of the stream bed consisted of long stretches of dry gravel (Fig. 8). Only a few stagnant pools held any surface water. At this time, only one garter snake was seen in the stream bed itself. Another was found by ranch personnel on the lawn at Rancho Escondido, which lies on a steep, dry, scrub-covered ridge about 0.5 km from Cottonwood Reservoir. If this snake reached Rancho Escondido under its own power, it represents a considerable journey for a semiaquatic snake over very steep, arid terrain. The winter of 1976-77 brought little relief, but with careful monitoring of pumping, water levels in the stream and reservoir rose somewhat.

Fortunately, the drought ended with heavy rains during the winter of 1977-78. The dam spillway at Cottonwood Reservoir is still open because of accumulated flood debris, but there is again normal stream flow and pumping at the well has been discontinued. Despite these seemingly drastic changes, the garter snakes survive; established management procedures at the reservoir can be continued when necessary, therefore, without doing much harm. Any future well pumping should continue to be carefully monitored. A permanent reduction of stream water would have decidedly adverse effects; only close observation can determine what the maximum pumping rate should be.

The two-striped garter snake must be declared a *rare and endangered species on Santa Catalina Island*. The "live" stream portion of Cottonwood Canyon, including Cottonwood Reservoir, must be made off-limits to recreational activities such as hiking, picnicking, or camping. While such activities *per se* would not be harmful, they would attract too many people into the canyon. Informed ranch personnel would not molest snakes, but dogs, small children, snake collectors, vandals, and well-meaning but misguided adults who believe in killing every snake they see would soon extinguish the garter snakes on Santa Catalina. The best policy is to direct all visitors to less sensitive areas offering similar recreational advantages.

Finally, long-term population studies must provide information and recommendations for preserving these interesting reptiles for the future.

SUMMARY

For 33 years, only two specimens of the garter snake (*Thamnophis couchi hammondi*) were recorded for Santa Catalina Island and the status of this species remained unknown. In August 1974, a small population was discovered in the stream and reservoir in Cottonwood Canyon. The species apparently occurs nowhere else on the island.

Unlike most two-striped mainland specimens, garter snakes on Santa Catalina lack any pattern, being a uniform olive-brown with pale buff lips and chins. In this respect they most closely resemble a different species from central Baja California and a conspecific population near Lompoc on the California mainland.

The ecology of Cottonwood and other stream canyons on Santa Catalina is discussed, as are human impacts on garter snakes, and recommendations for conservation measures.

Finally, rafting is proposed as a mechanism by which garter snakes from the Lompoc region might have founded the population on Santa Catalina Island.

ACKNOWLEDGMENTS

I am especially indebted to Mr. A. Douglas Propst, President of the Santa Catalina Island Conservancy, for making this study possible by providing transportation and living quarters on the island and for offering much valuable assistance and encouragement. I also wish to thank Drs. Patricia Brown, Glenn Stewart, Garrett Clough, Russell Zimmer, Alan Grinnell, and Ms. Jeanne Bellemin for assistance in the field and with other aspects of this study. Dr. Stewart also provided the photograph of the garter snake shown in Figure 2.

REFERENCES

FITCH, H. S. 1949. A biogeographical study of the *Ordinoides* artenkreis of garter snakes (genus *Thamnophis*). Univ. California Publs. Zool. 44:1-149.

SAVAGE, J. M. 1967. Evolution of the insular herpetofaunas. Pp. 219-227 *in* R. N. Philbrick, ed., Proceedings of the symposium on the biology of the California Islands. Santa Barbara Botanic Garden, Santa Barbara, Calif.

SCHWARTZLOSE, R. A. 1963. Nearshore currents of the western United States and Baja California as measured by drift bottles. California Cooperative Oceanic Fisheries Investigations (CalCOFI), Reports IX:15-22.

STEBBINS, R. C. 1966. A field guide to western reptiles and amphibians. Houghton Mifflin, Boston, Mass.

_____. 1972. Amphibians and reptiles of California. University of California Press, Berkeley, Calif.

SVERDRUP, H. U., M. W. JOHNSON, and R. H. FLEMING. 1942. The oceans: their physics, chemistry, and general biology. Prentice-Hall, Englewood Cliffs, N.J.

THORNE, R. F. 1967. A flora of Santa Catalina Island. Aliso 6:1-77.

WYLLIE, J. G. 1966. Geostrophic flow of the California Current at the surface and at 200 meters. California Cooperative Oceanic Fisheries Investigations (CalCOFI) Atlas 4:vii-288.

Breeding Land Birds of the Channel Islands

Jared M. Diamond and H. Lee Jones

Department of Physiology,
University of California Medical Center,
Los Angeles, California 90024

INTRODUCTION

Biologists are familiar with the thought that islands have unique scientific value as natural laboratories where the mainland species pool is reshuffled by differential immigration, extinction, and evolution to form new communities of fewer species. As material for studying these natural experiments, birds of the Channel Islands are of special interest. The reason for this interest is not that the birds themselves are unique: Channel Islands birds are far less distinct than those of the Galapagos (*e.g.*, see Power 1980), and they are also less distinct than the Channel Islands plants that Philbrick (1980) has discussed. But birds are the most easily observed, best-studied organisms on the Channel Islands, and hence they are the organisms for which we have the most detailed information on ecological topics such as population dynamics, niche shifts, and competition.

WHAT BIRD SPECIES ARE ON THE CHANNEL ISLANDS?

Table 1 summarizes the status of all breeding land bird species on the eight Channel Islands. Included in the table are the 56 species of birds that do not normally alight on water and that are known to have bred on at least one or more of the Channel Islands. Several additional species, including the Great Blue Heron and Cooper's Hawk (formerly on Santa Cruz), the Sora (Santa Cruz, 1936), the Common Poor-will (Santa Catalina), Lawrence's Goldfinch (occasionally on Santa Rosa), and the Red Crossbill, Lark Sparrow, and Dark-eyed Junco (occasionally on Santa Cruz), may breed occasionally, but convincing evidence is lacking. For a discussion of marine birds on the Channel Islands, see Hunt *et al.* (1980). Published general papers dealing with birds of the Channel Islands are those by Howell (1917), Grinnell and Miller (1944), Diamond (1969), Johnson (1972), Power (1972, 1976), Yeaton (1974), Lynch and Johnson (1974), Jones (1975), and Jones and Diamond (1976). Many other papers dealing with individual islands are cited in these references.

What breeding land bird species are found in island habitats, compared with similar mainland habitats? Many familiar mainland species are present in the same habitats on the islands, such as the Horned Lark in open grassland. Some common mainland species, such as the Wrentit, which is so abundant in mainland chaparral, are completely absent on islands with suitable habitat. Still other mainland species (*e.g.*, the Orange-crowned Warbler and Rock Wren) are greatly increased in abundance or occupy a wider range of habitats on the islands. In all, each island supports between eight and 39 breeding land bird species—far fewer than the 160 species that breed on the adjacent southern California mainland. Fifty-six land bird species have been documented as breeding on one or more islands (Table 1), and nearly 200 other species have been recorded from the islands as migrants, winter visitors, or vagrants.

All these species can be assigned to a list with eight categories, depending on the species' patterns of breeding and occurrence on the islands:

(1) Some species of the adjacent mainland never breed on the islands and have never been recorded on the islands, not even on a single occasion as a vagrant. This list of absentees includes sedentary mainland species that are the commonest species in chaparral: Wrentit,

TABLE 1. Breeding land birds of the California Channel Islands (total of 56 species).

Species	San Miguel	Santa Rosa	Santa Cruz	Anacapa	San Nicolas	Santa Barbara	Santa Catalina	San Clemente
Red-tailed Hawk	O	rB	rB	O			rB	O
Bald Eagle	E	E	E	E	E	E	E	E
Osprey		E	E	E	E	O?	E	E
Peregrine Falcon	E	E	E	E		E	E	E
American Kestrel	rI	rB	rB	rB	O	O	rB	rB
California Quail			rI				rB	
American Oystercatcher								
Black Oystercatcher	rB	rB	rB	rB	O	rB	O	O
Killdeer		rI	rI				rI	
Snowy Plover	rB	rB	?		rB			?
Rock Dove							rB	
Mourning Dove		rB	rB	O		rB	rB	rB
Barn Owl	rB	?	rB	rB		rB	?	rB
Burrowing Owl	E or O	rB or O	rB or O	?	O	rB	rB	rB or O
Long-eared Owl							O	
Saw-whet Owl			rB				rB	
White-throated Swift		rB	rB	rB			rB	rB
Costa's Hummingbird	O?					O		
Anna's Hummingbird			rB				rB	O
Allen's Hummingbird	rI	rB	rB	rB			rB	rB
Common Flicker			rB				rB	
Acorn Woodpecker			rI				rI	
Ash-throated Flycatcher			sI					
Black Phoebe		rB	rB	O			rB	O
Western Flycatcher		sB	sB	sB			sB	sB
Horned Lark	rB	rB	rB	O or E	rB	rB	rB	rB
Barn Swallow	sB	sB	sB	sB	O	O	sB	sB
Scrub Jay			rB					

Species	1	2	3	4	5	6	7
Northern Raven	E	rB	O	O	E or O	rB	rB
Bushtit	rB	rB				E	
Red-breasted Nuthatch		O					
Bewick's Wren	rB	rB	rB	rB		rB	E
Rock Wren	rB	rB	rB	rB	rB	rB	rB
Northern Mockingbird	rB	rB	O	O		rB	rB
American Robin		O					
Swainson's Thrush						O	
Blue-gray Gnatcatcher		rB					
Phainopepla						O	
Loggerhead Shrike	rB	rB	O		O	rB	rB
European Starling	rl	rl	rl	rl	rl	rl	rl
Hutton's Vireo	rB	rB	O			rB	
Orange-crowned Warbler	rB	rB	rB	rl	O	rB	rB
House Sparrow		rB		rl		rl	rl
Western Meadowlark	E	rB	rB	rl		rB	rB
Red-winged Blackbird	rB	O			rB		
Hooded Oriole						O	
Brewer's Blackbird				O			
Black-headed Grosbeak		sl	sl				
House Finch	rB	rB	rB	rB	E	rB	rB
Lesser Goldfinch	O	rB				rB	
Rufous-sided Towhee	rB	rB				rB	E
Rufous-crowned Sparrow		rB	rl or O				
Sage Sparrow		sB				sB	rB
Chipping Sparrow	sB	sB	sl			sB	rB
White-crowned Sparrow		sB	O			sB	sB
Song Sparrow	rB	rB	O		E	E	E

B= breeds every year.
O= has bred on one or more occasions, but not every year.
I= has immigrated and become an established breeder.
E= formerly bred but has not bred recently (extinct).
?= breeding status unclear.
r= present year round (permanent resident).
s= present during the breeding season only.

Brown Towhee, California Thrasher, Plain Titmouse, and Nuttall's Woodpecker. This list also includes some strong overland fliers like the Red-shouldered Hawk, Turkey Vulture, Black-chinned Hummingbird, and American Goldfinch, which simply refuse to cross water and are seldom or never recorded on the islands. The Common Crow is another strong flier that refuses to cross water and is rarely recorded, unlike its relative, the Northern Raven, which has bred on all eight islands. These species do not breed on the islands because they cannot or will not fly there.

(2) There are two species that do breed on a single island as a native, endemic subspecies but for which there are no historical records of individuals dispersing to or between islands: the Scrub Jay and California Quail. These are sedentary species that somehow reached an island by a rare chance event in the distant past (Wenner and Johnson 1980).

(3) Many species occur abundantly on the islands at some season but never breed because the islands do not offer the appropriate breeding habitat. This category includes numerous Sierran coniferous forest species, such as the Hermit Thrush and Fox Sparrow, which are common winter visitors on the islands.

(4) Some species occur rarely on the islands (or on some particular island) and do not breed, despite the presence of suitable habitat, because the occasional individual that reaches an island does not find a mate there. For instance, Cañon Wrens rarely reach the islands. A single Cañon Wren has been present on Santa Cruz Island since at least August 1973, without a mate having arrived.

(5) Several species reach the islands in numbers every year and find suitable breeding habitat there, but nevertheless do not breed. These species present one of the most puzzling problems in the Channel Islands avifauna. Examples of such species are the House Wren, Warbling Vireo, Northern Oriole, Ash-throated Flycatcher, Black-headed Grosbeak, and Brown-headed Cowbird, which flood the islands in spring migration each year. None bred on the islands until the Ash-throated Flycatcher and Black-headed Grosbeak recently began breeding on Santa Cruz Island, although they are still not breeding in similar and equally suitable habitats on Santa Catalina and Santa Rosa. Our guess is that these are highly philopatric species which tend to return each year to the mainland area where they were born, even if they migrate through other areas with similar habitat.

(6) Several species reach the islands but breed rarely or only in low numbers, evidently because of competition from a related species. For example, Anna's Hummingbird breeds in low numbers on two islands, was once recorded breeding on a third island, and has been recorded from other islands only as a vagrant, yet it is an abundant breeder in similar mainland habitats. We attribute its rareness as a breeder on the islands to competition from the abundant insular populations of Allen's Hummingbird.

(7) Numerous species reach islands where they breed in some years but not in other years. For example, a pair of Northern Mockingbirds bred on San Nicolas in 1968, but not in 1969, 1970, or 1971, bred again in 1972, not in 1973, and bred in 1974, 1975, and 1976. There are many similar cases of bird species that breed on a particular island on this sporadic basis.

(8) Finally, there are dozens of species that breed on some particular island every year (e.g., the Rock Wren and House Finch on Santa Catalina).

DYNAMICS OF LAND BIRD POPULATIONS

The breeding bird fauna of an island is not fixed forever but changes, often from year to year, as local populations immigrate and die out. The word "turnover" is used to refer to these changes in local species composition. It is an important general problem in population biology to estimate turnover rates and to estimate population lifetimes. These rates surely differ among islands and among plant and animal groups. The rates are of theoretical interest to biologists, and of much practical interest to conservationists.

To measure turnover rates in Channel Islands bird species, one of us (J.M.D.) carried out breeding bird surveys on the islands in 1968, and the other of us (H.L.J.) began doing annual breeding surveys in 1973. In these surveys, we have been helped by many resident and visiting observers on the islands. Our goal was to obtain virtually complete lists of the breeding bird species on each island in successive years. A detailed account of our methods has already been published (Jones and Diamond 1976). We shall only mention briefly here that we have developed efficient survey procedures to reduce the chance of overlooking breeding populations and to prove, by finding nests, eggs, or fledglings, that species observed were actually breeding. We have calculated turnover conservatively; the numbers given below may slightly underestimate actual turnover rates. For comparison, we shall cite qualitatively similar but much more detailed results from breeding surveys on European islands (Diamond and May 1977, Reed 1977). For example, on some European islands it is known not only which species bred but also how many pairs of each species bred in each year for the past several decades.

Turnover rates T for the Channel Islands have been calculated from surveys conducted between 1973 and 1977 (from 1972 for Santa Barbara Island) and computed as: $T = 100(I + E)/(S_1 + S_2)(t)$ where I and E are the number of species that immigrated and went extinct, respectively, between two survey years; S_1 and S_2 are the number of breeding species present in the first and second survey years, respectively; and t is the time interval (in years) between surveys. In most instances, $t = 1$ (surveys conducted every year); in a few instances, however, $t = 2$ when we failed to obtain a complete survey in a given year, as on Santa Catalina in 1974. For example, the average yearly turnover rate ($\overline{T}$) for Santa Catalina is 1.8 per cent per year, computed as follows:

1973-1975 $100(0 + 1)/(33 + 32)(2) = 0.8$
1975-1976 $100(2 + 0)/(32 + 34)(1) = 3.0$
1976-1977 $100(1 + 0)/(34 + 35)(1) = \underline{1.5}$
                                     5.3 $\overline{T} = 5.3/3 = 1.8$

The average yearly turnover rates (per cents) for the other islands are: Santa Barbara, 5.6; Anacapa, 3.0; San Miguel, 2.2; San Nicolas, 5.7; San Clemente, 2.4; Santa Rosa, 0.6; Santa Cruz, 1.3.

Figure 1 illustrates the detailed population fluctuations revealed by the annual breeding surveys of European islands, in this case on the British island Calf of Man. Qualitatively similar fluctuations have been observed for Channel Islands bird populations, although the available data are less dramatic because fewer survey years and less precise breeding population estimates were available. In Figure 1, the fluctuations in breeding populations of four ground-dwelling species in consecutive survey years from 1959 to 1974 are shown. The uppermost depicted species, the Wheatear, did not breed in the first survey year, 1959; one pair bred in 1960; none bred in the next three years; one pair bred in 1964; two bred in 1965; none bred in 1966; and from 1967 the population gradually crept upwards from two pairs and then fluctuated between five and eight pairs. Between 1959 and 1974 the Wheatear immigrated three times and disappeared twice on Calf of Man. Had the censuses been made on the island only in 1959 and 1974, one could have concluded that there had been only a single case of turnover and a single immigration (because the species was absent in 1959 and present in 1974); one would have been unaware that two additional immigrations were offset by two extinctions in the intervening years.

The next species depicted in Figure 1, the Stonechat, bred in good numbers from 1959 to 1962, until the harsh winter of 1963 eliminated the whole population. Not until 1965 did a

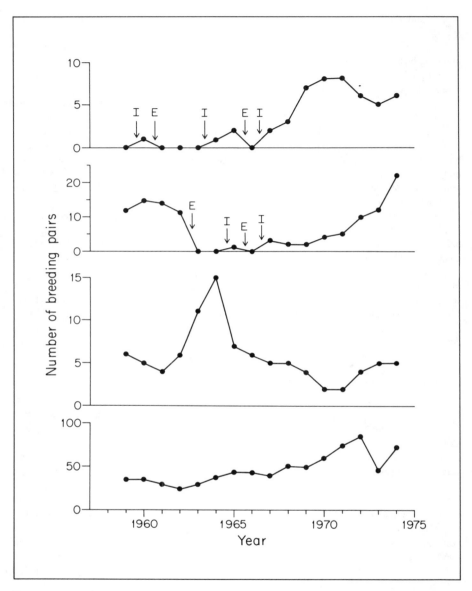

FIGURE 1. *Number of breeding pairs of four ground-dwelling bird species on Calf of Man, a small British island in the Irish Sea, as revealed by annual breeding censuses from 1959 to 1974. From top to bottom the species are: Wheatear, Stonechat, Skylark, and Meadow Pipit. An arrow marked E indicates an extinction of a local population (i.e., an instance in which there was a breeding population one year but not in the succeeding year). An arrow marked I indicates an immigration (i.e., an instance in which there was a breeding population in one year but not in the preceding year).*

single pair again breed. The pair did not return in 1966, but in 1967 breeding resumed with three pairs, gradually increasing to 22 pairs by 1974. Had only the censuses of 1959 and 1974 been available, one would have concluded that the Stonechat did not turn over on Calf of Man, since it bred in both census years. One could not have guessed that four cases of turnover had occurred in the intervening years: two extinctions reversed by two immigrations.

The two remaining species shown in Figure 1, the Skylark and Meadow Pipit, bred in every survey year and exhibited no turnover. Nevertheless, their populations went through large fluctuations, especially in the case of the Skylark, which ranged from two to 15 breeding pairs and came close to disappearing in 1970 and 1971.

We have observed numerous similar cases of population fluctuations for Channel Islands birds. The on-again, off-again breeding of the one or two pairs of Northern Mockingbirds on San Nicolas between 1968 and 1976, already mentioned, resembles the fluctuations in the Wheatear on Calf of Man between 1959 and 1967. House Finches on Anacapa have gone through large fluctuations in recent years that, at one point, reduced the population to four breeding pairs but did not quite produce an extinction; this is similar to the history of the Skylark on Calf of Man. As is true for the Meadow Pipit on Calf of Man, the Northern Mockingbird and Orange-crowned Warbler on Santa Rosa have gone through large population fluctuations, but the population has always remained large enough that it was not in danger of extinction.

Figure 1 emphasizes one of the main practical problems in turnover studies. If the available information consists only of a pair of surveys spaced many years apart, one is likely to underestimate turnover because of immigrations offset by subsequent extinctions (or *vice versa*) in the intervening years. That is, breeding populations appear and disappear repeatedly between survey years. Figure 2 depicts the magnitude of error that this sporadic breeding introduces into turnover studies. The British island of Lundy was surveyed almost every year from 1922 to 1974. We have calculated turnover from all pairwise combinations of censuses and plotted the apparent turnover rate as a function of the number of years between censuses. For example, turnover at a 20-year interval was calculated by comparing the species lists for 1949 and 1969, or 1950 and 1970, or 1951 and 1971, *etc.* The true turnover rate for Lundy calculated from censuses at one-year intervals is 9.4 per cent per year. That is, every year, on the average, 9.4 per cent of Lundy's breeding populations fail to survive until the next year and are replaced by a similar number of new breeding species that did not breed in the previous year. With an increasing interval between surveys, the apparent turnover rate plummets and is 1 per cent per year or less for survey intervals of 23 years or more. Even for a census interval of three years, the apparent turnover rate is barely half of the true value. We previously published a figure analogous to Figure 2 depicting the decline in apparent turnover rate with increasing census interval for Anacapa, one of the Channel Islands (Jones and Diamond 1976).

All of the several dozen European islands that we have analyzed, and all eight Channel Islands, exhibit this drastic decline in the apparent turnover rate with increasing census interval due to sporadic breeding. Census intervals of a decade or more underestimate the turnover rate by about an order of magnitude. The true turnover rates, based on one-year intervals, range from less than one to nearly six per cent per year for the Channel Islands, and from two to twenty per cent per year for islands of northern Europe.

Figure 3 summarizes our turnover results for the eight Channel Islands. This figure depicts the fluctuations in breeding species number for each island, based on all years since 1897 for which adequate breeding surveys were available. Three conclusions can be drawn from the figure. (1) Species number is not fixed on each island, but fluctuates as populations immigrate and go extinct. For example, the number of species breeding in a given year fluctuates on Santa Cruz from 35 to 39; on Anacapa, from 15 to 19; on San Nicolas, from 8 to 12. These

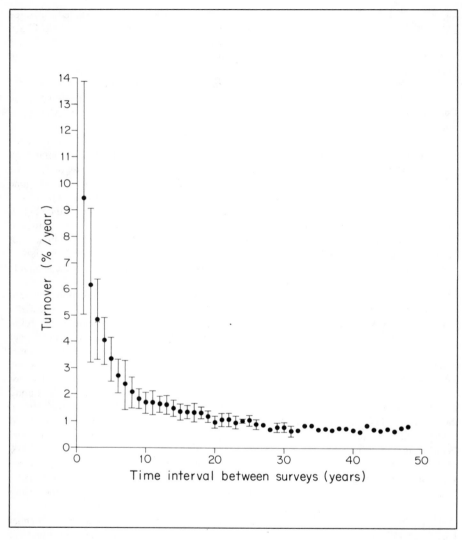

FIGURE 2. *Apparent turnover rate of the breeding land bird community on the British island of Lundy as a function of time interval between surveys. Lundy has been surveyed nearly annually from 1922 to 1974. For each pairwise combination of census years, turnover (in units of per cent/year) was calculated as* $100(I + E)/(S_1 + S_2)t$, *where* I *is the number of apparent immigrations and* E *the number of apparent extinctions revealed by comparison of species lists for the two years;* S_1 *and* S_2 *are the numbers of breeding species in the earlier and later census years, respectively; and* t *is the number of years between censuses. The calculation was carried out for all pairs of census years corresponding to a given time interval; the resulting average value and standard deviation of the turnover rates were plotted as the solid point and vertical bars, respectively.*

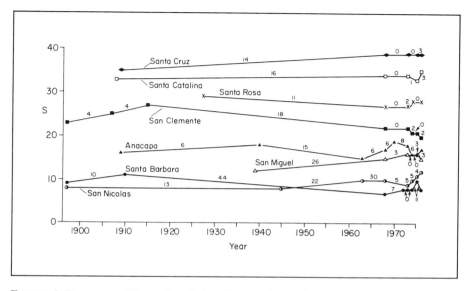

FIGURE 3. *Turnover and fluctuations in breeding species number on the Channel Islands. For each Channel Island, and for each year since 1897 in which the number of breeding land bird species (S) was adequately determined, S is plotted on the ordinate against the survey year on the abscissa. The number on the line connecting each pair of censuses is the absolute turnover in units of per cent of the island's breeding species turning over between surveys: i.e., 100(I + E)/(S_1 + S_2); see legend of Figure 2 for explanation of these symbols.*

fluctuations remain within modest limits unless island habitats are much altered, as happened on Santa Barbara between the 1910 and 1968 surveys (Philbrick 1972). Thus, the number of breeding species on an island is set by a dynamic equilibrium between immigrations and extinctions. (2) The numbers on the line connecting each pair of points in Figure 3 represent the absolute turnover (percentage of island species turning over between surveys), *not* the turnover rate in per cent per year. A zero means that there was no turnover. It can be seen that between most survey years there is some turnover, even in one-year periods. (3) There can be turnover even if species number remains constant. This occurs if the number of immigrations happens to equal the number of extinctions. For example, on San Nicolas between 1963 and 1968, the number of breeding species remained constant at 10, but turnover was 30 per cent because three populations disappeared and three new ones immigrated.

What populations turn over? As illustrated by Figure 4, the populations most prone to extinction are smaller populations: species such as big raptors with large territories, species living in specialized habitats, or any species on a small island. In Figure 4, we have grouped Channel Islands bird populations by the approximate number of breeding pairs and calculated for each group the fraction of the populations in the group that disappeared during the time that surveys have been made. It will be seen that no population exceeding 1,000 pairs has disappeared and that nearly half of the populations numbering just a few pairs have disappeared. The larger a population, the lower its probability of extinction and the longer its probable lifetime. There are also characteristic differences between species in proneness to

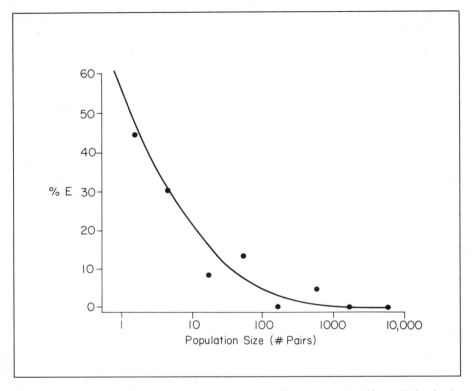

FIGURE 4. *Probability of extinction as a function of population size on the Channel Islands. On each island, the average breeding population of each species was estimated as falling into one of nine size classes (1 to 3 pairs, 4 to 10 pairs, 11 to 30 pairs, etc.). For each breeding population size class (abscissa), the ordinate gives as a percentage the number of populations in that class that became extinct since the first surveys, divided by the total number of populations in that class.*

extinction, independent of population size. For example, an island breeding population of Northern Ravens consisting of just two or three pairs can persist year after year, while equally small populations of a warbler would repeatedly go extinct and recolonize in the same length of time.

At this point, let us consider three common misconceptions that frequently arise in discussions of turnover.

(1) Some of the foregoing results could be misconstrued to mean that there are two types of populations: common species that breed regularly and do not turn over, and rare species that breed occasionally and do turn over. Is turnover only a constant churning of the rare species and a phenomenon of little importance to the bulk of the community? We do not believe that this is the case. Rather than there being two distinct types of species, there is, instead, a continuous decrease in risk of extinction with increasing population size (Fig. 4), and this rate of decrease differs for every species. A small population may last one year; a big one, 10 years; a still larger

one, 50 years. A very large population becomes limited by its temporal coefficient of variation, rather than by population size itself, and may last a thousand or a million years. On a large island, many populations survive for a long time. That is why the oldest and most distinct endemic bird subspecies of the Channel Islands, the Island Scrub Jay, is on the largest island, Santa Cruz. On a small island, few populations survive for a long time. For example, on the smallest Channel Island, Anacapa, 24 species have bred at least once in this century, but, on the average, only 17 of these species breed in a given year, and only two of these species have populations currently exceeding 100 individuals; all the remaining populations on Anacapa are likely to have short lifetimes.

(2) So far, we have not said anything about the effects of man. One can ask if it is not true that much of this turnover is due to man and his fires, DDT, goats, sheep, and rabbits. To answer this question, we reviewed all the cases of turnover documented for the islands in relation to the history of habitat alteration, man's effect on the islands, and our experience with island birds and habitats (Jones and Diamond 1976). Some of the cases of turnover we observed are probably, or surely, due to the effects of man: the extinctions of Osprey, Peregrine Falcon, and Bald Eagle on all islands (see Kiff 1980); immigrations of European Starling and House Sparrow on some islands; and some extinctions due to habitat destruction, especially on Santa Barbara and San Clemente. However, the majority of the cases of turnover do not appear to be reasonably attributable to man. Instead, they seem to represent merely the fluctuations that one expects in any small population. For example, there is no obvious man-related reason why the Northern Mockingbird bred on San Nicolas in 1968, 1972, 1974, 1975, and 1976, but not in 1969, 1970, 1971, or 1973. As only one or two breeding pairs were involved, one could expect a large element of chance in determining whether a pair happens to breed in any particular year. The overall effect of man in this century may have been to decrease rather than to increase turnover rates by eliminating species that have rapid turnovers under natural conditions (*e.g.*, big raptors living at low densities) and by introducing species that have slow turnover rates (*e.g.*, the European Starling and House Sparrow).

This is partially, but not completely, offset by the long-term stability of raptor populations, despite their small size. Hunt and Hunt (1974) and Jones (1975) have shown, nevertheless, that carnivores on the Channel Islands have a higher turnover rate than do noncarnivores.

(3) The islands have endemic subspecies that may have taken a long time to evolve. Does this fact argue against several per cent of an island's species turning over every year? No, because different populations turn over at different rates. Some, like the Northern Mockingbird on San Nicolas, turn over almost every other year. Other populations, like some of the endemic subspecies, may last for tens of thousands of years. To illustrate species differences in turnover frequency, Figure 5 depicts the distribution of species among turnover frequency categories for two British islands. A turnover frequency of 0.5 would mean that a population immigrated or went extinct every other year, on the average. A turnover frequency of zero means that a population bred every year and never went extinct during the several decades for which censuses were available for these islands. This figure is based on the small island of Hilbre, which has only six breeding species in an average year, and on the larger island of Bardsey, with 26 breeding species in an average year. As the bar graphs illustrate, each island has some populations which turned over very rapidly (0.2 to 0.5/year, or once every several years), some populations which turned over slowly (0.1/year, once every ten years), and some populations which did not turn over at all within the span of censuses. There are many more populations with zero turnover frequency on the larger island than on the smaller island because almost all populations on Hilbre consist of too few breeding pairs to escape extinction for long.

Patterns similar to those shown in Figure 5 also apply to the Channel Islands and were

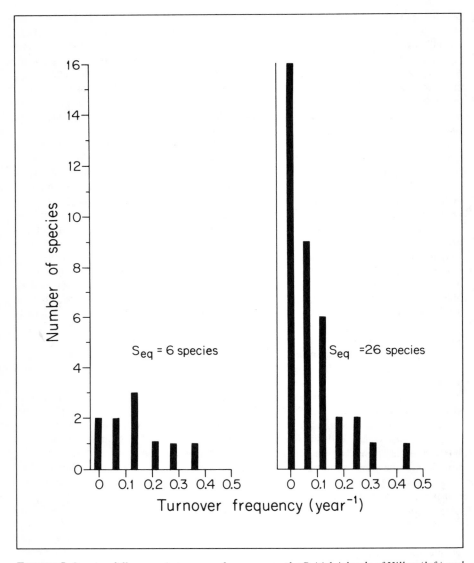

FIGURE 5. *Species differences in turnover frequency on the British islands of Hilbre (left) and Bardsey (right). Annual breeding surveys on each island for 16 or 17 consecutive years were analyzed. For each species that bred on the island during this period, the turnover frequency was calculated as the number of turnover events (immigrations or extinctions) over this 16- or 17-year period, divided by 16 or 17 years. Populations were then grouped according to turnover frequency; the bars indicate the number of species with a given turnover frequency. For example, a frequency of 0.2 year⁻¹ means that a species exhibited three cases of turnover (immigration - extinction - immigration, or extinction - immigration - extinction) on the island in 15 years. On the average, the number of breeding species is six on Hilbre, 26 on Bardsey.*

illustrated previously (figs. 2 and 5 of Jones and Diamond 1976). For example, on San Nicolas, where the Northern Mockingbird turned over almost every year, the Horned Lark and House Finch have bred in every year of observation since at least 1897. On Santa Cruz, the Scrub Jay population has probably persisted for thousands or tens of thousands of years, while the Red-breasted Nuthatch has apparently immigrated and gone extinct repeatedly.

In the light of these observations, let us reconsider the favorite questions of island biogeographers: Why do islands have fewer species than the adjacent mainland? Why do small islands have fewer species than larger islands? Unfortunately, there is not just one simple answer. For Channel Islands birds, as for other species on other islands, there are at least three major explanations: (1) islands have fewer types of habitats than mainlands and small islands have fewer types of habitats than large islands; (2) some species never or rarely disperse over water to reach islands; and (3) local populations go extinct more often on islands than on the mainland, so that in a given year a smaller fraction of the island's species pool is present as breeders.

Other organisms may not necessarily show the same patterns as birds. Turnover rates must differ greatly among species groups, as pointed out by Wilcox (1980) in other contexts. Immigration rates are far lower for mammals, lizards, millipedes, and pine trees than for birds, butterflies, and annual weeds. For the former four groups of species, decades, centuries, or perhaps even millenia may elapse between immigration events. Extinctions may be much less frequent in small plants and insects than in birds, because there are many more individual plants and insects than birds per acre. Low extinction rates mean that a population may survive long enough to become an endemic species or subspecies. This may be why there are more striking endemics among Channel Islands plants and beetles than among birds: many plant and beetle populations, but few bird populations, have survived for a long time on the islands.

THE ENDEMIC BIRDS

While the islands have striking endemic species of plants and insects, there is no bird species confined to the Channel Islands. However, there are some endemic subspecies, as summarized by Johnson (1972). Of the 56 land bird species that breed or have bred on the islands, 13 are represented by one or more endemic races. In all, there are 18 currently recognized endemic races of birds on the Channel Islands, because some species are represented by two (Loggerhead Shrike) or three (Bewick's Wren, Song Sparrow) endemic races. The largest islands have the largest number of endemic populations.

The most distinctive endemic subspecies on the Channel Islands is the Scrub Jay population confined to Santa Cruz Island. Some other endemic races, such as those of the Orange-crowned Warbler and Horned Lark, are fairly distinct. Others are only weakly differentiated.

An interesting feature of the endemic avifauna is that two of the endemic subspecies, the island races of the Orange-crowned Warbler and Allen's Hummingbird, have established local breeding colonies on areas of the California mainland coast opposite the islands.

NICHE SHIFTS

The phenomenon of niche shifts is familiar from island studies elsewhere in the world and has contributed importantly to the rediscovery of interspecific competition in the past several decades (Diamond 1978). Briefly, island populations are often observed to occupy broader niches than populations of the same species on the mainland. For example, a species may occupy a wider range of habitats and occupy or forage over a broader altitudinal range on an island than on the mainland. The accepted interpretation of this phenomenon is based on the fact that there are fewer competing species on the islands. On the mainland, one species may be excluded by competing species from habitats and vertical zones in which its competitors are superior. On islands where these competitors are absent, the species is able to occupy these habitats and zones. Yeaton (1974) has published a detailed analysis of niche shifts on Santa Cruz Island, and Diamond (1970) has described other examples.

Compare, for example, the breeding bird communities in chaparral on Santa Cruz or other Channel Islands and on the mainland. The total number of breeding bird pairs per acre of chaparral is similar on Santa Cruz and on the mainland. Yet Santa Cruz chaparral has only two-thirds as many breeding species as mainland chaparral has, and some of the commonest species found in mainland chaparral are completely absent on Santa Cruz: the Wrentit, Brown Towhee, California Thrasher, Plain Titmouse, and Nuttall's Woodpecker. Other Channel Islands are even more impoverished, lacking the Scrub Jay and Bushtit of Santa Cruz Island and mainland chaparral. What makes up for the missing species on Santa Cruz? Which Santa Cruz birds utilize the extra resources made available by the absence of mainland competitors?

In part, the resources are used by species that also occur in mainland chaparral but are more abundant in Santa Cruz chaparral. For example, Bewick's Wren is twice as common and Hutton's Vireo four times as common in Santa Cruz chaparral as in mainland chaparral.

The resources are also used by species that are confined to habitats other than chaparral on the mainland. Excluded from mainland chaparral by competitors, they are able to move into Santa Cruz chaparral because of the absence of these competitors.

For example, on the mainland, Allen's Hummingbird breeds in the coastal zone and is largely excluded from chaparral by Anna's Hummingbird. On the islands, Anna's Hummingbird is uncommon or absent, while Allen's Hummingbird is common in chaparral.

On the mainland, the Scrub Jay occupies chaparral and oak woodland communities. On Santa Cruz Island, it can also be found in Bishop Pines, which lack the similar Steller's Jay of Bishop Pine communities on the mainland.

The common insectivores of mainland chaparral are the Wrentit, Bushtit, and Plain Titmouse. They are replaced in island chaparral by the Orange-crowned Warbler, which is uncommon or absent in mainland chaparral, and by a superabundance of the Bewick's Wren, Hutton's Vireo, and Blue-gray Gnatcatcher, compared with the numbers found in mainland chaparral.

The common mimic thrush of mainland chaparral is the California Thrasher. On Santa Cruz, it may be replaced partly by the Northern Mockingbird, which is uncommon or absent in mainland chaparral, and, perhaps, partly by the island race of Scrub Jay, which has been described as spending much time feeding on the ground, as the California Thrasher does on the mainland.

These are some of the examples of niche shifts that become apparent if one compares communities in the same habitat on an island and on the mainland, or on different islands. All these niche shifts illustrate the same point: those species that reach islands successfully may increase their abundance or broaden their niches by utilizing resources that would have been pre-empted by mainland competitors.

SUMMARY

Fifty-six species of land birds are known to breed, or to have bred, on the eight California Channel Islands. Based on information in the literature and on our own field surveys conducted in 1968 and from 1973 through 1977, we categorize these species according to breeding status and to whether or not they have recently immigrated and established breeding populations or have formerly bred and become extinct. Populations on the islands are not static but are in a dynamic equilibrium (*i.e.*, species composition varies through time). Average annual turnover of island populations is one to six per cent per year. True turnover rates must be based on one-year census intervals. Data from the Channel Islands and certain European islands exhibit a drastic decline in *apparent* turnover rate with increasing census interval; census intervals of a decade or more underestimate the turnover rate by about an order of magnitude.

There is a continuous decrease in risk of extinction with increasing population size. Smaller, more extinction-prone populations are commonly those species with large territories (*e.g.*, large raptors), species in specialized habitats, and species on small islands. Different populations turn over at very different rates. Furthermore, the majority of cases of turnover do not appear to be attributable to the effects of man.

Turnover rates are higher and the degree of endemism is lower for more mobile species, such as birds, than for less mobile organisms, such as most mammals, reptiles, amphibians, and plants. There are a number of cases of increased densities and niche shifts for island birds. Those species that succeed in reaching islands may increase their abundance or broaden their niches by using resources that would have been pre-empted by competitors on the mainland.

ACKNOWLEDGMENTS

It is a pleasure for us to acknowledge the help of numerous colleagues in studying the Channel Islands and their birds. We thank the Lievre Memorial Fund for support of field work.

REFERENCES

DIAMOND, J. M. 1969. Avifaunal equilibria and species turnover rates on the Channel Islands of California. Proc. Natl. Acad. Sci. 64:57-73.

————. 1970. Ecological consequences of island colonizations by southwest Pacific birds. I. Types of niche shifts. Proc. Natl. Acad. Sci. 69:529-536.

————. 1978. Niche shifts and the rediscovery of interspecific competition. Amer. Sci. 66:322-331.

DIAMOND, J. M., and R. M. MAY. 1977. Species turnover rates on islands; dependence on census interval. Science 197:266-270.

GRINNELL, J., and A. H. MILLER. 1944. The distribution of the birds of California. Pacific Coast Avifauna 27:1-608.

HOWELL, A. B. 1917. Birds of the islands off the coast of southern California. Pacific Coast Avifauna 12:1-127.

HUNT, G. L., JR., and M. W. HUNT. 1974. Trophic levels and turnover rates: the avifauna of Santa Barbara Island, California. Condor 76:363-369.

HUNT, G. L., JR., R. PITMAN, and H. L. JONES. 1980. Distribution and abundance of seabirds breeding on the California Channel Islands. Pp. 443-459 in D.M. Power, ed., The California Islands: proceedings of a multidisciplinary symposium. Santa Barbara Museum of Natural History, Santa Barbara, Calif.

JOHNSON, N. K. 1972. Origin and differentiation of the avifauna of the Channel Islands, California. Condor 74:295-315.

JONES, H. L. 1975. Studies of avian turnover, dispersal, and colonization of the California Channel Islands. Ph.D. thesis, University of California, Los Angeles, Calif.

JONES, H. L., and J. M. DIAMOND. 1976. Short-time-base studies of turnover in breeding birds of the California Channel Islands. Condor 76:526-549.

KIFF, L. F. 1980. Historical changes in resident populations of California Islands raptors. Pp. 651-673 in D.M. Power, ed., The California Islands: proceedings of a multidisciplinary symposium. Santa Barbara Museum of Natural History, Santa Barbara, Calif.

LYNCH, J. F., and N. K. JOHNSON. 1974. Turnover and equilibria in insular avifaunas, with special reference to the California Channel Islands. Condor 76:370-384.

PHILBRICK, R. N. 1972. The plants of Santa Barbara Island, California. Madroño 21:329-393.
————. 1980. Distribution and evolution of endemic plants of the California Islands. Pp.
    173-187 *in* D.M. Power, ed., The California Islands: proceedings of a multidisciplinary
    symposium. Santa Barbara Museum of Natural History, Santa Barbara, Calif.
POWER, D. M. 1972. Numbers of bird species on the California Islands. Evolution 26:451-463.
————. 1976. Avifauna richness on the California Channel Islands. Condor 78:394-398.
————. 1980. Evolution of land birds on the California Islands. Pp. 613-649 *in* D.M. Power,
    ed., The California Islands: proceedings of a multidisciplinary symposium. Santa
    Barbara Museum of Natural History, Santa Barbara, Calif.
REED, T. M. 1977. Island biogeographic theory and the breeding landbirds of Britain's offshore
    islands. Honors thesis, St. John's College, Cambridge University.
WENNER, A. M., and D. L. JOHNSON. 1980. Land vertebrates on the California Channel
    Islands: sweepstakes or bridges? Pp. 497-530 *in* D.M. Power, ed., The California
    Islands: proceedings of a multidisciplinary symposium. Santa Barbara Museum of
    History, Santa Barbara, Calif.
WILCOX, B. A. 1980. Species number, stability, and equilibrium status of reptile faunas on the
    California Islands. Pp. 551-564 *in* D.M. Power, ed., The California Islands: proceed-
    ings of a multidisciplinary symposium. Santa Barbara Museum of Natural History, Santa
    Barbara, Calif.
YEATON, R. I. 1974. An ecological analysis of chaparral and pine forest bird communities on
    Santa Cruz Island and mainland California. Ecology 55:959-973.

Evolution of Land Birds on
the California Islands

Dennis M. Power

Santa Barbara Museum of Natural History,
Santa Barbara, California 93105

INTRODUCTION

Knowledge of island plants and animals can contribute significantly to our understanding of speciation. On oceanic islands, isolation and new selective forces often lead to dramatic evolution. Adaptive radiation in Galapagos finches, for example, has become well known (Darwin 1845, Lack 1945, Bowman 1961). On near-shore, continental islands, genetic changes in populations are commonly not as great, being usually at the species level in sedentary forms and at the subspecies level in more mobile ones. This can be due to gene flow and to the fact that the physical and biotic differences, compared with those on the mainland, are usually less for fringing islands than for oceanic ones.

On an assemblage of oceanic islands, divergent populations on different islands may show similarities to each other, but their mainland ancestor may not be readily identifiable. With continental islands, a mainland form (usually an ancestor) often is identifiable and can be compared with the island populations (usually derived species or races). In such comparisons some interesting trends have been discovered. For example, Murphy (1938) found that 21 of 27 North American passerine birds breeding on islands have, on the average, larger bills than their nearest mainland relative. Grant (1965a, 1965b), summarizing size trends in island birds of North America, and in particular those of the Tres Marías Islands, Mexico, found that there is a strong tendency for island passerines to have a longer tarsus and bill than their mainland counterparts. However, island forms do not tend to have longer wings and tail. Grant believes that a longer bill is correlated with a greater range of food sizes and that the tarsus is longer because a greater variety of perches is used. He argued that these differences have arisen as a result of an absence or a reduction in the number of competing species, allowing those forms that are present to occupy wider niches and, in some cases, totally new habitats. In another case, Foster (1963) reported on the relative sizes of 12 species of land birds on the Queen Charlotte Islands, British Columbia. On the average, in most island populations the tarsus was larger; bills were longer in many island populations, as well. Wing and tail measurements did not tend to differ from mainland conspecifics in Foster's study.

The first noteworthy comparative analysis of birds on the California Island was by Ridgway (1877) and concerned only Guadalupe Island (Fig. 1). Ridgway (1877:60) wrote:

> The more prominent characteristics of these Guadalupe birds, as compared with the mainland forms, are (1) increased size of the bill and feet, (2) shorter wings and tail, and (3) darker colors; these variations are by no means uniform, however, in the several species, the differentiation being in some slight, while in others it amounts to almost generic distinctness.

More recently, Johnson (1972:313) wrote on the origin and differentiation of the avifauna of the Southern California Channel Islands, and stated:

> Of the approximately 41 species of land birds which breed on the Channel Islands, California, 13 (32%) are represented by 18 endemic subspecies. When compared with their relatives on the adjacent mainland, these endemic forms are characterized by darker

TABLE 1. Species of land birds that have a morphologically distinct population on Guadalupe Island.

A. Not occurring on other California Islands
   1. Common Caracara (*Polyborus plancus*)*
   2. Ruby-crowned Kinglet (*Regulus calendula*)
   3. Dark-eyed Junco (*Junco hyemalis*)
B. Occurring but not differentiated on other California Islands
   1. Sparrow Hawk (*Falco sparverius*)
   2. Common Flicker (*Colaptes auratus*)*
C. Differentiated on one or more other California Islands
   1. Bewick Wren (*Thryomanes bewickii*)*
   2. Rock Wren (*Salpinctes obsoletus*)
   3. House Finch (*Carpodacus mexicanus*)†
   4. Rufous-sided Towhee (*Pipilo erythrophthalmus*)*

*Extinct on Guadalupe Island (A.O.U. 1957).   †Extinct on San Benito Islands (Jehl 1971).

or grayer coloration, longer and/or heavier bills, and longer and/or heavier tarsi and toes.

The present analysis is of geographic variation in California Islands land birds. In order to supplement, rather than duplicate, Johnson's (1972) work on Channel Islands birds, I investigated only those species with morphologically distinct populations on Guadalupe Island. The purpose was to document the morphological evidence for evolution on Guadalupe and populations of the same species on other California Islands.

There are nine resident species with clearly recognizable endemic races on Guadalupe Island; three of these species do not occur on other islands, two species are also found on other islands but are not differentiated on any of them, and four species show some kind of morphological differentiation on one or more of the other islands (Table 1). Four of the Guadalupe subspecies—the Common Caracara, Common Flicker, Bewick Wren, and Rufous-sided Towhee—are now extinct (A.O.U. 1957). The endemic race of the House Finch on the San Benito Islands is also extinct (Jehl 1971).

Much of my analysis relies on published measurements that were made before statistical testing became commonplace, and well before multivariate similarity analysis came into vogue. However, with new data I gathered on the House Finch and Rock Wren, two species that are widespread throughout the California Islands, I have been able to do multivariate similarity analyses for island and mainland samples.

METHODS

The characters used in this study were wing length, tail length, bill length (and in some cases bill depth), tarsus length, and middle toe or hind toe length. For the Common Caracara, Ruby-crowned Kinglet, Dark-eyed Junco, Common Flicker, Bewick Wren, and Rufous-sided Towhee, character measurements were taken from as many sources as possible in the literature.

New data were gathered for the House Finch and Rock Wren. Using museum specimens, supplemented by some new collecting, locality samples were designated as in Figure 1. For the Rock Wren, mainland samples included only the adjacent southern California and northern Baja California area, whereas for the House Finch I included samples from farther north and south. Characters were measured with dial calipers to the nearest 0.05 mm. Bill length (BL) was measured from the anterior edge of the nostril to the tip of the bill. Bill depth (BD) was

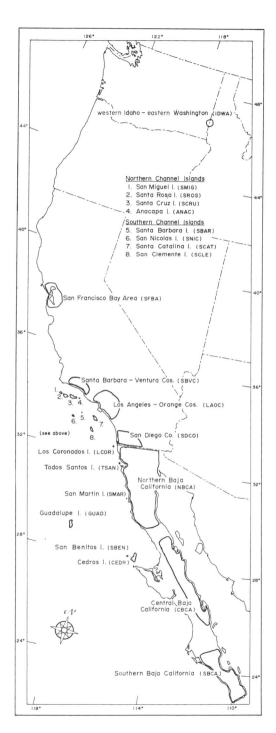

FIGURE 1. *Map of the California Islands, with locality codes and mainland sites that refer to the study of geographic variation in the House Finch. Most of the island sites and the mainland localities from Santa Barbara in the north to central Baja California in the south were also used for a study of geographic variation in the Rock Wren. For this species, locality designations differ as follows: SBCO = Santa Barbara Co.; LACO = Los Angeles Co.; and NATI = Natividad Island, located just south of Cedros Island off Punta Eugenia.*

measured at the base of the bill and is the distance from the lower edge of the lower mandible to the top of the upper mandible; on the Rock Wren, this measurement was taken at a line even with the back edge of the nostril, not at the base. Upper bill width (UBW) is the width of the upper mandible at its widest point near the base for the finch, and at a line even with the back edge of the nostril for the wren. Lower bill width (LBW) is the width of the lower mandible at its widest point near the base for the finch; this measurement was not taken for the wren. Wing primary length (WPL) was measured from the bend of the unflattened wing to the tip of the longest primary feather. Wing secondary length (WSL) was measured from the bend of the unflattened wing to the tip of the outermost secondary feather. Tail length (TL) was taken from the point of emergence of the two central rectrices to the tip of the longest rectrix. Tarsus length (TRL) was measured from the bend of the leg at the back of the tarsometatarsal-tibiotarsal joint to the prominent ridge on the inside of the leg at the point of attachment of the hind toe. Hind toe length (HTL) was taken from the distal end (not including the claw) to the groove formed at the base of the attachment of the other toes.

For the House Finch and Rock Wren data, within-sample statistics were calculated with Biomedical Computer Program BMDP2D (Dixon 1975). Similarity analysis was performed using canonical variates analysis (Cooley and Lohnes 1971) on which was superimposed a shortest connecting network (Prim 1958) of generalized ("Mahalanobis") distances (Blackith and Reyment 1971). Canonical variates plots also included 95 per cent confidence regions (Seal 1966).

RESULTS

Species That Have a Morphologically Distinct Population on Guadalupe Island But Do Not Occur on Other California Islands

Common Caracara *(Polyborus plancus)*

The caracara is the only land bird on Guadalupe Island that has an extensive distribution in South America. Although it has been on the island long enough to have evolved color differences (Brown and Amadon 1968), size and shape variation is slight at best. Measurements I have been able to glean from the literature are given in Table 2. The only consistent difference that emerges is a tendency for longer tails in the island population. (In Table 2 and the other tables that give character measurements it is best to compare values taken by a single author, otherwise slight differences in methods of measuring characters may be misinterpreted as suggesting geographic variation.)

According to Abbott (1933), the Guadalupe Caracara (*P. p. lutosus*) was last seen in December 1900 when a collector took nine of the 11 individuals he had observed. In the late 1800s, at least three other collectors took specimens, knowing that the population was becoming scarce because of habitat destruction by feral goats. This large, terrestrial falcon was even the victim of overt avarice. In one case, a goat hunter was reported to have captured four alive to sell; he could not get his price ($150 each) and they later died in captivity. The birds were easy marks for anyone with a rifle, and it was common for goat agents to shoot any that were seen (Bryant 1887).

Because there is some confusion in the literature about the scientific nomenclature of caracaras, it is worthwhile to sort out the taxonomy. The Guadalupe Caracara is referred to as *Caracara lutosus,* and the mainland form as *C. cheriway,* in the American Ornithologists' Union check-list of North American Birds (A.O.U. 1957); they are given as *Polyborus lutosus* and *P. cheriway* in the check-list of Mexican birds (Friedmann *et al.* 1950). Brown and Amadon (1968) retain the earlier genus name, *Polyborus,* and assign to it *P. lutosus* from Guadalupe, and *P. plancus* from central and southern Florida, southern Texas, and southern Arizona south to Tierra del Fuego. Brown and Amadon combined *P. plancus* with the form from northern

TABLE 2. Measurements (mm) of Common Caracara.

	Wing	Tail	Bill	Tarsus	Middle toe
A. Bryant (1887)					
Guadalupe Island ("*P. lutosus*")*					
Males, *n* = 10					
range =	390-418	257-285	32-33	84-92	50-56
mean =	407.1	266.5	32.7	88.6	53.3
B. Ridgway (1876a)					
Mainland: S. U.S., Mexico, N. South America ("*P. cheriway*")					
Males, *n* = 6					
range =	371-419	229-254	30-38	81-91	48-51
Females, *n* = 8					
range =	375-406	224-254	30-37	90-95	51-53
Guadalupe Island ("*P. lutosus*")					
Sexes combined, *n* = 16	16	15	16	16	
range =	381-417	267-296	32-34	89-95	46-53
mean =	398.3	277.6	32.8	91.7	49.5
C. Friedmann *et al.* (1950)					
Mainland: S. U.S. and Mexico ("*P. cheriway auduboni*")					
Males, *n* = 10					
range =	370-418	229-254	30-36.5	81-90.5	48-51
mean =	393.5	240.5	33.5	84.4	49.5
Females, *n* = 10					
range =	373.5-408	223.5-254	30-36	89-94	50.5-53.5
mean =	391.0	242.0	33.0	92.0	52.0
Guadalupe Island ("*P. lutosus*")					
Males, *n* = 6					
range =	381-402	260-279	32-33.5	84-92	45-53
	393.3	265.7	32.8	39.3	50.7
Females, *n* = 10					
range =	394-418	260-286	32-33	83-92	50-56
mean =	407.5	272.6	32.7	88.5	53.5

* Species names in quotation marks are those given by the author cited and are not the currently accepted names.

South America and Mexico (formerly *P. cheriway*), presumably because of the existence of intergrades from Brazil. Brown and Amadon, then, give the following distribution for the subspecies of *Polyborus plancus: auduboni* from North America south to western Panama, Cuba, and Isle of Pines; *pallidus* on the Tres Marías Islands; *cheriway* from eastern Panama and northern South America to Peru and the Amazon River; and *plancus* in southern South America from Peru to Tierra del Fuego and on the Falkland Islands. Thus, in the early descriptions and comparisons of Ridgway (1876a, 1877), "*P. cheriway*" is referable to *P. p. auduboni,* and "*P. tharus*" is referable to *P. p. cheriway.* Brown and Amadon list the Guadalupe Island form as a separate species but state (1968:736), "Now that *P. cheriway* is regarded as a race of *P. plancus*

TABLE 3. Measurements (mm) of Ruby-crowned Kinglet.

	Wing	Tail	Bill*	Tarsus	Middle toe
A. Ridgway (1877) — Sexes and *n* not given.					
Mainland ("*R. calendula*")					
range =	55.9-62.2	40.6-51.6	5.1-5.6	16.5-19.3	8.9
Guadalupe Island ("*R. obscurus*")					
range =	50.8-55.9	43.2-49.5	5.6-6.4	20.3	9.7-10.2
B. Bryant (1887)†					
Guadalupe Island only ("*R. obscurus*")					
Males, *n* = 10					
range =	53.0-56.5	40.0-46.0	6.0-7.5	18.0-20.0	10.0-11.0
mean =	54.9	42.9	6.7	19.6	10.3
Females, *n* = 3					
range =	51.0-52.0	38.5-40.5	6.0-6.5	19.0-19.5	10.0
mean =	51.3	39.7	6.2	19.2	10.0
C. Ridgway (1904)					
Mainland (*R. c. calendula*)					
Males, *n* = 10: from eastern U.S.					
range =	56.5-61.5	40.5-45.0	7.9-9.5	18.0-20.0	9.0-10.5
mean =	58.9	42.8	8.6	19	9.6
n = 10: from California					
mean =	59.8	45.2	8.4	18.8	9.3
Females, *n* = 10: from eastern U.S.					
range =	54.0-58.0	40.5-44.0	7.5-9.5	17.5-19.5	9.0-10.0
mean =	56.1	42.2	8.7	18.7	9.4
n = 9: from California					
mean =	56.7	42.7	8.1	18.7	9.2
Guadalupe Island (*R. c. obscurus*)					
Males, *n* = 4					
range =	53.5-56.0	41.0-43.5	10.0-10.5	19.5-20.0	9.0-10.0
mean =	54.6	42.2	10.1	19.8	9.5
Females, *n* = 1	50	39	10	20	9.5

* Bill measurements of Ridgway (1877) and Bryant (1887) are culmen length from the nostril, while those of Ridgway (1904) are of the exposed culmen; the latter are larger.
† Means calculated by D.M.P.

it would be no great extension to include *lutosus* also. The completely barred underparts are rather different and it is possible that this insular form had achieved specific status." I prefer to follow the lead of Mayr and Short (1970) and include *lutosus* as a subspecies of *plancus*.

Ruby-crowned Kinglet (*Regulus calendula*)

The Ruby-crowned Kinglet is a very small bird (length, 9.5 to 11.4 cm) found in conifer forests in Canada, Alaska, and the western U.S. Some populations are migratory and in winter they are found in woodlands and thickets from southern British Columbia south to the Gulf states and Guatemala. It is resident on Guadalupe Island and is restricted to the pines and cypress groves (Bryant 1887, Thayer and Bangs 1908). Ridgway (1877) considered "*R.*

obscurus" on Guadalupe Island to be the counterpart of "*R. calendula*" on the mainland. His comparison of measurements (Table 3, section A) suggested that the island form has a shorter wing and tail, and a larger bill, tarsus, and toe. He also stated that the island form is much darker. In Ridgway (1904), the status of the island form is as a subspecies of *R. calendula*, with the nominate race being listed from North America in general. Subsequently, two other subspecies came to be recognized (A.O.U. 1957). The mainland subspecies, for comparative purposes, is *R. c. cineraceus*, which breeds in western North America from south-central British Columbia through the western U.S. (A.O.U. 1957); it is not found in Baja California. The form on Guadalupe is designated *R. c. obscurus*. The data at hand (Table 3) suggest that the island form has shorter wings and tail, and larger bill, legs, and feet.

Dark-eyed Junco (*Junco hyemalis*)

The Dark-eyed Junco is a small (length, 12.5 to 15 cm) fringillid that breeds in conifer and mixed forests from southeastern coastal Alaska to Baja California and east through the Rocky Mountains (A.O.U. 1957). Most populations are migratory. The Guadalupe Island form (*J. h. insularis*) seems to have always been fairly abundant and is found predominantly in the cypress groves and pine woods (Thayer and Bangs 1908). It is the only insular member of the genus *Junco* and is nonmigratory (Miller 1941). *Junco hyemalis* includes very divergent groups of races which hybridize in zones of secondary contact (Mayr and Short 1970). Earlier references (*e.g.*, Miller 1941, A.O.U. 1957) considered *hyemalis, oreganus, caniceps, aikeni*, and *insularis* as separate species. Ridgway (1876b, 1877) compared the Guadalupe Island form to "*J. annectens*," which is now considered to be *J. hyemalis mearnsi* from Wyoming and parts of Montana and Idaho.

A comparison of measurements of the Guadalupe Island Junco with samples from various parts of the mainland shows that wing and tail are shorter and the bill longer in the island race (Table 4). Ridgway's (1876b) very small sample and Miller's (1941) much larger sample both indicate bills are thicker in the island race, as well. Although the data of Ridgway (1901) do not support this, I think it safe to assume Guadalupe Island Juncos have a heavier beak. Miller's (1941) data also show a tendency for tarsi to be longer in the island race. There is no difference among populations in middle toe length. Miller's paper provides data on hind toe length which show that this character is longer in the island race.

Miller's (1941) study is the most complete one we have on morphological variation within the genus *Junco*. He makes a number of relevant observations on color. *J. h. insularis*, he notes, has reduced sexual dimorphism (less than *J. h. mearnsi*), and differs in color from *J. h. townsendi*, its closest neighbor. *Insularis* also differs from *pinosus* in head and back color, and somewhat in side color. In regard to *insularis* Miller further states, "The climate and the affinity of the flora [of Guadalupe Island] to that of the closed-cone pine forest of the coast of California point to considerable similarity of the island habitat to that of *pinosus* in the Monterey district of central California." In both Ridgway (1901) and Miller (1941), *J. h. pinosus* tends most toward *J. h. insularis* in having a relatively short wing, but not in other characters. Miller also sees similarities among the paler forms (*insularis, pinosus, townsendi*, and *mearnsi*) and suggests that the fully black-headed juncos (*e.g., J. h. pontilis*) are a newer type. *Insularis* may therefore date back to an early period in the evolution of the "*oreganus*" group, retaining much of the ancestral coloration. Short wing and tail, and large bill and feet, may be specializations of insularity. This led Miller to conclude that the vagrants which established *insularis* probably came from a *pinosus* type, that the ancestral stock may have occurred as far south as San Diego during the Pleistocene, and that the establishment of *insularis* may have been pre-Pleistocene. It should also be added that Miller found no evidence of *insularis* interbreeding with other juncos. Only one record of another "*oreganus*" type is known for Guadalupe Island, and with its reduced wing and tail, *insularis* would not be likely to fly to the mainland.

TABLE 4. Measurements (mm) of Dark-eyed Junco.

	Wing	Tail	Bill length	Bill depth	Tarsus	Middle toe
A. Ridgway (1876b)						
Mainland: Rocky Mntns. ("*J. annectens*")						
1 Male	82.6	86.4	7.6	5.1	20.3	15.2
1 Female	76.2	71.1	7.6	5.1	20.3	14.0
Guadalupe Island ("*J. insularis*")						
Males, *n* = 4						
range =	68.6-72.4	63.5-66.0	8.9-9.7	6.4-6.9	20.3-21.6	14.0-15.2
mean* =	69.9	65.0	9.1	6.6	21.3	14.2
Females, *n* = 5						
range =	63.5-67.3	58.4-62.2	8.9-9.7	6.4	20.3-21.6	14.0-15.2
mean* =	65.5	60.7	9.1	—	20.8	14.5
B. Bryant (1887)						
Guadalupe Island only ("*J. insularis*")						
Males, *n* = 10						
range =	65.0-71.0	57.0-64.0	8.5-10.0	6.0-7.0	19.0-20.0	14.0-16.0
mean =	68.8	60.3	9.4	6.6	19.7	15.1
Females, *n* = 3						
range =	62.0-65.0	54.0-56.0	8.5-9.0	6.0-7.0	19.0-20.0	14.5-15.0
mean =	63.7	55.0	8.8	6.3	19.7	14.8
C. Ridgway (1901)						
Mainland: S. Oregon to N. Baja California ("*J. oreganus thurberi*")						
Males, *n* = 8						
range =	74.7-79.3	63.0-68.1	10.2-11.7	5.8-6.4	19.3-20.3	13.2-14.5
mean =	78.0	65.3	10.7	6.1	20.1	14.0
Females, *n* = 3						
range =	71.6-74.7	60.5-65.0	10.4-10.9	6.1	19.8-20.6	13.2-13.7
mean =	72.9	62.2	10.7	—	20.3	13.5
Mainland: S. coast range of California ("*J. oreganus pinosus*")						
Males, *n* = 5						
range =	69.1-73.7	58.4-64.8	10.2-11.4	6.9	19.8-20.3	14.0-15.2
mean =	70.9	61.2	10.9	—	20.3(?)	14.5
Females, *n* = 5						
range =	66.6-70.9	58.7-60.7	10.2-11.4	6.6	19.1-20.3	12.7-13.7
mean =	68.8	59.7	10.7	—	19.8	13.2
Mainland: Sierra San Pedro Mártir ("*J. oreganus townsendi*")						
Males, *n* = 6						
range =	75.4-81.8	63.8-68.6	10.7-11.4	6.6-6.9	20.1-21.3	13.5-14.7
mean =	78.5	66.8	11.2	6.7	20.6	14.2
Females, *n* = 5						
range =	72.1-81.0	63.5-65.8	10.7-11.9	6.4-6.9	20.1-20.8	12.7-14.0
mean =	75.2	64.5	10.9	6.6	20.6	13.5

TABLE 4. (Cont.)

	Wing	Tail	Bill length	Bill depth	Tarsus	Middle toe
Guadalupe Island ("*J. insularis*")						
Males, *n* = 3						
range =	67.8-70.0	58.2-59.2	12.7-13.2	6.6-7.1	20.8-21.1	14.5-14.7
mean =	68.6	58.7	13.0	6.9	20.8(?)	14.6
Females, *n* = 2						
range =	63.5-64.5	—	12.7	6.6	20.6-20.8	14.2-14.5
mean =	64.0	—	—	—	20.6(?)	14.4
D. Miller (1941)						
Mainland: Tahoe area, Sierra Nevada ("*J. oreganus thurberi*")						
Males, *n* =86	86	84	81	95	90	
mean = 76.81	68.82	8.04	5.59	19.64	11.29	
s.d. = 1.64	1.99	0.29	0.26	0.57	0.41	
Females, *n* = 48	42	42	43	49	48	
mean = 72.59	65.34	7.82	5.64	19.39	11.31	
s.d. = 1.85	1.80	0.35	0.28	0.64	0.42	
Mainland: Central coastal California ("*J. o. pinosus*")						
Males *n* = 62	62	58	58	67	64	
mean = 72.05	64.03	8.13	5.67	19.76	11.41	
s.d. = 1.50	2.27	0.29	0.27	0.55	0.48	
Females, *n* = 40	41	36	32	41	41	
mean = 69.20	61.26	8.07	5.76	19.62	11.27	
s.d. = 2.03	2.15	0.29	0.25	0.62	0.43	
Mainland: Sierra Juarez, N. Baja California ("*J. o. pontilis*")						
Males, *n* =16	16	14	14	16	16	
range = 75.0-81.2	66.6-73.8	7.4-8.6	5.8-6.6	19.0-20.5	10.8-11.8	
mean = 78.48	70.01	7.93	6.12	19.91	11.24	
Females, *n* = 12	11	7	7	12	12	
range = 71.6-76.0	61.3-68.7	7.3-8.2	5.8-6.1	18.8-20.8	10.5-11.5	
mean = 73.93	66.58	7.70	5.97	19.51	11.02	
Mainland: Sierra San Pedro Mártir, N. Baja California ("*J. o. townsendi*")						
Males, *n* =70	66	70	57	70	70	
mean = 79.31	71.20	7.94	6.07	20.10	11.49	
s.d. = 2.16	2.43	0.34	0.25	0.63	0.39	
Females, *n* = 55	52	52	47	55	52	
mean = 74.68	67.90	7.95	6.08	19.87	11.23	
s.d. = 1.81	1.95	0.31	0.30	0.58	0.35	
Guadalupe Island: ("*J. insularis*")						
Males, *n* =84	85	94	95	98	96	
mean = 69.30	62.65	9.30	6.59	20.20	11.54	
s.d. = 1.70	2.34	0.37	0.31	0.62	0.42	
Females, *n* = 25	22	28	29	29	28	
mean= 65.70	59.27	9.15	6.39	20.06	11.43	
s.d. = 1.82	2.09	0.42	0.28	0.60	0.46	

*Means by D.M.P.

TABLE 5. Measurements (mm) of Sparrow Hawk.

	Wing	Tail	Bill Length	Bill Depth	Tarsus*	Middle toe*
A. Bond (1943)						
Mainland: W. North America (*F. s. sparverius*)						
Males, *n* = 54	7	45	45	45 M + 43 F	20 M + 26 F
range =	181-200	116-125	13.1-15.7	5.6-7.5	38-44	21-26
mean =	187.79	119.38	13.94	6.46	41.11	23.78
s.d. =	4.24	—	0.57	0.37	1.37	1.04
Females, *n* = 44	7	37	38			
range =	188-206	116-131	13.0-15.3	5.9-7.4		
mean =	196.43	122.14	14.47	6.58		
s.d. =	4.87	—	0.60	0.38		
Mainland: S. Baja California (*F. s. peninsularis*)					9M+ 7F	2M+ 5F
Males, *n* = 9	1	7	7	38-43	22-26
range =	164-175	—	13.6-15.0	6.3-7.0	40.31	23.86
mean =	169.22	114	14.43	6.70	1.50	1.26
s.d. =	4.41	—	0.51	0.30		
Females, *n* = 8	3	7	6			
range =	166-182	102-113	13.2-16.2	6.3-7.1		
mean =	175.75	107.67	14.46	6.70		
s.d. =	5.51	—	1.01	0.30		
Mainland: S.W. U.S. (*F. s. sparverius* x *F. s. peninsularis*)						
Males, *n* = 19	3	14	15	19 M + 13 F	8 M + 8 F
range =	164-192	112-114	13.4-15.2	5.6-7.5	36-43	23-26
mean =	182.37	112.67	14.09	6.57	40.66	24.31
s.d. =	8.13	—	0.50	0.52	1.46	0.88
Females, *n* = 13	5	13	12			
range =	176-195	110-120	13.9-15.7	6.0-7.8		
mean =	187.62	116.60	14.62	6.79		
s.d. =	5.47	—	0.59	0.50		
Guadalupe Island: (*F. s. guadalupensis*)					5 M + 7 F	4 M + 5 F
Males, *n* = 6	1	5	5	40-44	23-26
range =	180-196	—	13.3-14.3	5.8-6.6	41.58	24.11
mean =	189.33	121	13.74	6.20	1.52	0.78
s.d. =	6.63	—	0.42	0.38		
Females, *n* = 7	5	7	7			
range =	193-202	116-129	13.3-14.9	5.9-6.6		
mean =	196.71	120.60	14.33	6.17		
s.d. =	3.61	—	0.51	0.23		

* Sexes combined for these characters.

Species Differentiated on Guadalupe Island
But Not on Other California Islands

Sparrow Hawk (*Falco sparverius*)

The Sparrow Hawk is a small falcon with a wingspread of about 45 to 60 cm and is found throughout most of North and South America (A.O.U. 1957). The extent of its morphological variation has not resulted in the description of very many subspecies, at least in North America. The nominate race occurs over most of the U.S. and Canada, and presumably breeds on most of the California Islands. Another race is found in the southeastern U.S. and a third occurs in a limited distribution in southern Baja California. Bond (1943) studied variation in the species and named a race on Guadalupe Island, based on size and color differences. Studies other than Bond's have not proved useful in gaining an idea of morphological differentiation on Guadalupe Island.

A comparison of measurements shows that Sparrow Hawks on Guadalupe Island have longer wings and tail, a shorter bill, longer legs, and probably larger feet (Table 5). Bond (1943) notes that the overall size of *F. s. guadalupensis* is equal to *F. s. sparverius* from central British Columbia, but is appreciably larger than *sparverius* in northwestern Baja California and the southern half of California. It is much larger than *F. s. peninsularis* from southern Baja California. The only color difference noted is that *guadalupensis* has a paler collar than do birds from other areas.

Common Flicker (*Colaptes auratus*)

The Common Flicker is an abundant woodpecker of open country near large trees. In North America, there are three morphologically divergent subspecies groups (Mayr and Short 1970): the "Yellowshafted Flicker" (*auratus*), distributed approximately from central Alaska through central and eastern Canada and across the eastern half of the U.S.; the "Red-shafted Flicker" (*cafer*), occurring in southwestern Alaska, through extreme western Canada, the western half of the U.S., and into Guatemala; and the "Gilded Flicker" (*chrysoides*), a common resident of the giant cactus region of Baja California, southern Arizona, and northwestern Mexico. Hybridization occurs among these forms.

The Guadalupe Island population (*C. auratus rufipileus*) was resident (it is now extinct) and is the only recognized island differentiate. Early in the 1900s, only about 40 individuals were seen (confined to the cypress woods) and, at that time, the population was considered "doomed to a speedy extinction" (Thayer and Bangs 1908). It has not been reported since (A.O.U. 1957). Flickers are also reported to breed on San Nicolas, Santa Cruz, and Santa Catalina Islands, these birds being assigned to the western race *C. auratus collaris* (A.O.U. 1957). The Gilded form is similar to the Red-shafted Flicker, differing primarily in having lighter underparts and yellow, instead of red-orange, on the undersurface of the wings and tail. It also has shorter wings, tail, bill, and tarsus than the Red-shafted form (Ridgway 1914).

The Guadalupe Island population is closest to the Red-shafted Flicker in plumage color; character measurements are therefore compared for these two types (Table 6). With regard to wing length, the Guadalupe Island population is smaller. In tail length, the Guadalupe form averages smaller than the northwest coastal race, but is about the same as those elsewhere in the west. In bill length measurements, the Guadalupe form is about the same as the northwest coast populations, but larger than those from elsewhere in the west. In tarsus length, the Guadalupe birds tend to be smaller than those from the mainland. In toe length, they are smaller than those from the northwest coast, and about the same as those from elsewhere in the west. Differences between island and mainland flickers are not entirely clear-cut, but if a summarizing statement had to be made one would say that Guadalupe Island flickers have shorter wings and *tend to*

TABLE 6. Measurements (mm) of Common Flicker.

	Wing	Tail	Bill length	Tarsus	Toe*
A. Ridgway (1877)					
Mainland (*"C. mexicanus"*)					
range =	169-178	140-152	29.2-31.8	30.5	21.6
Guadalupe Island (*"C. rufipileus"*)					
range =	150-159	121-135	34.3-40.6	27.9	23.4
B. Bryant (1887)					
Mainland (*"C. cafer"*)					
Females, *n* = 10					
range =	—	—	29.0-32.5	—	—
mean =	—	—	30.50	—	—
Guadalupe Island (*"C. rufipileus"*)					
Males, *n* = 10					
range =	145-152	120-129	30.0-36.5	—	—
mean =	147.5	124.7	33.7	—	—
Females, *n* = 10					
range =	141-154	117-129	29-36	—	—
mean =	146.6	122.8	32.5	—	—
C. Ridgway (1914)					
Mainland: W. U.S., S.W. British Columbia, N. Mexico (*"C. cafer collaris"*)					
Males, *n* = 46					
range =	156-174	101-121	33.5-40.0	27.0-32.0	20.5-24.0
mean =	165.8	112.6	37.9	29.8	22.4
Females, *n* = 36					
range =	152-173	99.5-120.0	34.0-41.5	27.0-31.5	20.0-23.0
mean =	163.2	109.8	36.9	28.7	21.8
Mainland: N.W. coast from N. California to S. Alaska (*"C. cafer staturatior"*)					
Males, *n* = 10					
range =	164.5-177.5	113.0-124.0	37.0-42.5	29.0-31.0	22.5-25.0
mean =	169.9	118.7	39.8	30.0	23.9
Females, *n* = 10					
range =	163.5-171.0	110.0-123.5	36.0-40.0	26.0-30.5	21.0-24.0
mean =	167.1	117.0	37.7	28.7	22.7
Guadalupe Island (*"C. cafer rufipileus"*)					
Males, *n* = 6					
range =	149-152	104-113	37.0-41.5	26.5-28.0	21.0-23.0
mean =	150.0	110.0	38.9	27.3	22.2
Females, *n* = 7					
range =	148.5-158.0	102.5-114.0	37.0-43.0	26.5-29.0	20.5-23.0
mean =	152.5	110.4	39.0	28.0	21.7

*Middle toe for Bryant (1887); outer anterior toe for other authors.

have shorter tails, longer bills, and shorter legs. Some color differences have also been noted. In island birds, for example, the top of the head is more reddish, or brighter, and the black undersurface of the tail is broader (Bryant 1887, Ridgway 1914).

Species Differentiated on Guadalupe Island and on One or More Other California Islands

Bewick's Wren *(Thryomanes bewickii)*

The Bewick's Wren is a fairly common insectivorous species found throughout much of the U.S. It favors thickets, underbrush, chaparral, and similar habitat. Among the wrens, it is average in size (length, 12.7 to 14 cm). Two subspecies are described exclusively from mainland Mexico (Miller *et al.* 1957), and 17 other subspecies occur elsewhere in North America (A.O.U. 1957), of which six occur on the California Islands or adjacent mainland. These are: *correctus* in southwestern California; *charienturus* in northwestern Baja California; *nesophilus* on Santa Rosa, Santa Cruz, and Anacapa Islands, and probably on Santa Barbara and San Nicolas Islands, as well; *catalinae* on Santa Catalina Island; *leucophrys* on San Clemente Island; *cerroensis* in coastal central-western Baja California and on Cedros Island; and *brevicauda,* formerly resident on Guadalupe Island and now extinct. In 1886, Bryant (1887) collected only seven specimens from the Guadalupe population and, in his words, " . . . fearing the complete extermination of a species so restricted in distribution, I refrained from taking more specimens." In 1892, Streator and Anthony, knowing how rare the species had become, collected a pair (Anthony 1901). By 1906 the race was extinct (Thayer and Bangs 1908). Although some size and shape differences have been recorded among the six subspecies, color differences were most often recorded in the original descriptions dating from the late 1800s and early 1900s. These color characteristics do not seem very reliable, however (*e.g.,* see Swarth 1916 regarding *catalinae,* and Miller 1951 regarding *nesophilus*).

Measurements of Bewick's Wrens are given in Table 7. Statistics from Oberholser (1898) and Ridgway (1904) show that the Guadalupe Island birds tend to have shorter wings and tails, longer bills, and shorter tarsi than mainland birds. Sample sizes for Guadalupe Island are very small. Cedros Island specimens do not seem to differ from those on the mainland, although Huey's (1942) data suggest that the Cedros Island race may have slightly shorter wings and tail than populations from mid-Baja California. San Clemente Island birds have a shorter tail than southern California mainland birds, according to the data of Swarth (1916); the data of Oberholser and Ridgway do not bear this out. Data from these two authors do, however, suggest San Clemente Island Bewick's Wrens have slightly longer bills—a difference that, unfortunately, is not duplicated by Swarth's data. For Santa Catalina Island, the data from Swarth do not suggest any mensural differences between island and mainland birds. A breakdown of mainland and island measurements within *T. b. charienturus* in Ridgway (1904) does suggest some differences. Four Santa Catalina Island males, compared with 10 mainland wrens, averaged 1.0 mm shorter in wing length, 1.3 mm shorter in tail length, and 0.9 mm longer in bill length. One female from Santa Catalina Island, compared with 12 females from the mainland, was 3.2 mm shorter in wing length, 3.2 mm shorter in tail length, and 0.7 mm longer in bill length. Finally, the Santa Cruz and Santa Rosa Islands populations appear to have shorter tails than those on the mainland.

For Bewick's Wren, there are specific island differences but no general trends in variation. Guadalupe Island birds do seem different on the basis of having shorter wings and tails and longer bills. The only consistent variation that is suggested for the other islands is a slight tendency for some populations to have short tails. Beyond these differences, island wrens seem very much like those on the mainland.

TABLE 7. Measurements (mm) of Bewick's Wren.

	Wing	Tail	Bill length	Tarsus	Middle toe
A. Oberholser (1898)					
S.W. California, N.W. Baja California, Santa Catalina Island (*"T. charienturus"*)					
Males, *n* = 14					
range =	50.0-55.0	47.5-54.5	13.5-14.5	18.0-19.5	15.0-16.0
mean =	52.5	52.0	14.0	19.0	15.5
Females, *n* = 9					
range =	48.5-52.0	49.5-53.0	12.5-14.0	18.0-19.0	14.0-16.0
mean =	50.5	50.8	13.4	18.4	15.2
Santa Cruz and Santa Rosa Islands (*"T. nesophilus"*)					
Males, *n* = 5					
range =	50.5-53.5	47.0-51.0	13.5-14.5	18.5-19.5	15.0-15.6
mean =	51.9	49.1	14.2	18.8	16.0
Females, *n* = 1	49.0	47.5	13.5	19.0	16.0
San Clemente Island (*"T. leucophrys"*)					
Males, *n* = 9					
range =	52.5-56.5	49.5-55.0	14.5-16.0	19.0-19.5	14.5-16.5
mean =	53.7	52.1	15.1	19.3	15.7
Females, *n* = 7					
range =	48.0-54.5	46.5-53.0	14.0-15.5	19.0-20.5	15.0-17.0
mean =	51.7	48.7	14.7	19.5	15.7
Cedros Island (*"T. cerroensis"*)					
Males, *n* = 1	51.0	52.0	13.0	18.5	14.5
Females, *n* = 2					
range =	49.0-51.0	47.5-50.5	12.5-13.0	17.5-18.0	14.5-15.0
mean =	50.0	49.0	12.8	17.8	14.8
Guadalupe Island (*"Thyothorus brevicaudus"*)					
Males, *n* = 1	50.0	42.0	16.0	17.0	16.5
Females, *n* = 1	49.0	44.0	—	18.0	15.5
B. Ridgway (1904)					
S. coast California, N.W. Baja California, Santa Catalina Island (*"T. b. charienturus"*)					
Males, *n* = 14					
range =	51.0-55.0	50.0-55.0	13.0-15.0	18.0-20.0	12.0-13.0
mean =	52.7	52.8	14.0	19.0	12.4
Females, *n* = 13					
range =	46.5-52.0	46.0-53.0	12.0-14.5	18.0-19.0	11.5-13.0
mean =	49.9	50.0	13.4	18.5	12.1
Santa Cruz and Santa Rosa Islands (*T. b. nesophilus*)					
Males, *n* = 5					
range =	51.5-53.5	46.5-51.5	14.5-15.5	19.0-19.5	11.5-12.5
mean =	52.5	48.9	15.0	19.3	12.2
Females, *n* = 2					
range =	50.0-52.0	48.0-49.0	14.5	19.5-20.0	11.5-12.5
mean =	51.0	48.5	—	19.7	12.0

TABLE 7. (Cont.)

	Wing	Tail	Bill length	Tarsus	Middle toe
San Clemente Island (*T. b. leucophrys*)					
Males, *n* = 6					
range =	52.0-55.5	51.5-54.0	14.0-16.0	18.5-20.0	12.5-13.0
mean =	53.3	52.5	15.3	19.3	12.7
Females, *n* = 5					
range =	49.0-54.5	46.0-54.0	13.5-16.0	18.5-20.5	12.0-13.5
mean =	51.7	48.9	15.0	19.6	12.5
Cedros Island (*T. b. cerroensis*)					
Males, *n* = 1	51.0	52.0	—	19.0	12.0
Females, *n* = 2					
range =	48.0-51.0	47.0-50.0	12.5-13.0	18.0	12.0
mean =	49.5	48.5	12.7	—	—
Guadalupe Island ("*T. brevicaudus*")					
Males, *n* = 2					
range =	48.0-48.5	42.0-44.5	16.0	17.5-18.0	12.0-12.5
mean =	48.2	43.2	—	17.7	12.2
Sex undetermined, *n* = 2					
range =	46.0-46.5	41.0-43.0	17.0	18.0-18.5	11.5-12.0
mean =	46.2	42.0	—	18.2	11.7

C. Swarth (1916)

	Wing	Tail	Bill length	Tarsus	Middle toe
Mainland: Los Angeles and Riverside Cos. (*T. b. charienturus*)					
Males, *n* = 10					
range =	50.5-55.5	50.2-56.0	14.0-15.5	18.0-19.5	10.5-12.0
mean =	52.4	53.6	14.9	18.7	11.7
Santa Catalina Island (*T. b. catalinae*)					
Males, *n* = 7					
range =	52.0-55.0	52.0-56.5	14.5-16.0	18.0-20.0	12.0-13.5
mean =	53.2	54.2	15.2	19.5	12.8
Santa Cruz Island (*T. b. nesophilus*)					
Males, *n* = 10					
range =	51.0-55.5	48.0-56.0	14.0-15.2	18.2-19.8	11.0-13.0
mean =	52.8	51.7	14.7	19.1	11.9
San Clemente Island (*T. b. leucophrys*)					
Males, *n* = 8					
range =	50.0-53.8	46.5-52.5	14.0-15.5	18.5-20.0	12.0-13.0
mean =	52.1	49.4	14.7	19.2	12.3

D. Huey (1942)

	Wing	Tail	Bill length	Tarsus	Middle toe
Mainland: Mid-Baja California ("*T. b. atricauda*")					
Males, *n* = 5					
range =	50.1-52.2	50.5-53.2	13.4-13.9	16.1-17.8	14.0-16.2
mean =	51.0	52.1	13.7	17.1	14.7

TABLE 7. (Cont.)

	Wing	Tail	Bill length	Tarsus	Middle toe
Females, n = 3					
range =	47.1-52.2	46.0-53.2	12.5-13.3	16.6-17.4	14.9-15.3
mean =	49.2	49.0	12.8	17.0	15.0
Cedros Island and adjacent Baja California coast (*T. b. cerroensis*)					
Males, n =	3	2	2	3	3
range =	50.3-50.7	49.4-49.5	13.0	17.7-18.0	14.8-15.3
mean =	50.5	49.4	—	17.8	15.0
Females, n =	6	5	5	6	6
range =	45.7-48.8	44.7-51.5	11.6-13.0	16.3-18.0	14.1-15.1
mean =	47.9	48.9	12.5	17.3	14.5

Rufous-sided Towhee *(Pipilo erythrophthalmus)*

The Rufous-sided Towhee is a large (length, 19.0 to 20.3 cm) fringillid that is common throughout most of North America in brush, heavy undergrowth, and margins of woods. Seven subspecies have been described exclusively from mainland Mexico (Miller *et al.* 1957), and 16 other subspecies are recognized elsewhere (A.O.U. 1957), four of which are on the California Islands or adjacent mainland. The race *megalonyx* is resident in southwestern California, including Santa Cruz Island, and northwestern Baja California to about 32°N, and is considered "casual" on San Miguel Island; *clementae* is resident on Santa Rosa, Santa Catalina, and San Clemente Islands; *umbraticola* is resident in northwestern Baja California between 32° and 30°N; and *consobrinus* was formerly resident on Guadalupe Island. Bryant (1887) collected at least 12 specimens in 1886 from Guadalupe Island, but collectors in 1892 (Anthony 1901) and 1906 (Thayer and Bangs 1908) did not find the bird, nor has it been seen since.

Measurements of towhees are given in Table 8. The Guadalupe Island race has shorter wings and tail than birds on the mainland. There seems to be a tendency to have smaller legs and feet, as well. The bill is about the same as in mainland birds, but if the smaller wing, tail, legs, and feet indicate a smaller overall body size, then the bill is proportionately longer. Birds from Santa Cruz, Santa Rosa, and San Clemente Islands do not differ appreciably from nearby mainland birds, with the exception that the towhees from San Clemente tend to have longer tarsi. Color differences have been used to separate the island and mainland races. Miller (1951) noted that Santa Rosa Island towhees resemble those on Santa Catalina and San Clemente Islands (*clementae*), but, on geographic grounds, should be more like those on Santa Cruz Island (*megalonyx*).

Rock Wren *(Salpinctes obsoletus)*

For this species and the House Finch (to follow) there is a departure from the previous method of analysis. Rather than rely on statistics in the literature, I measured characters and calculated new statistics for all the specimens I could find from the islands and adjacent mainland. In addition, canonical variates analysis was employed to assess the overall similarity among island and mainland populations.

The Rock Wren is an average-sized (length, 12.7 to 15.8 cm) insectivore that is locally distributed throughout much of western North America into southern Mexico. It favors rocky barrens. One subspecies, *obsoletus,* covers most of the species' range, including all of the islands except San Benito and Guadalupe (A.O.U. 1957). The race *tenuirostris* is limited to the San Benito Islands, and *guadeloupensis* is restricted to Guadalupe Island. Two other subspecies are described from the southern portion of the range in Mexico (Miller *et al.* 1957).

TABLE 8. Measurements (mm) of Rufous-sided Towhee.

	Wing	Tail	Bill length	Bill depth	Tarsus	Middle toe
A. Ridgway (1901)						
Mainland: California other than San Diego Co. (*"P. maculatus megalonyx"*)						
Males, *n* = 14						
mean = 87.4		97.5	13.7	10.9	27.9	19.8
Females, *n* = 9						
mean = 82.0		92.7	13.7	10.4	27.2	18.8
Mainland: S. coast California into Baja California (*"P. maculatus atratus"*)						
Males, *n* = 11						
range = 81.5-90.2		94.5-102.1	13.0-15.0	9.9-10.9	26.4-29.2	18.5-20.3
mean = 86.1		97.5	13.7	10.4	28.2	19.7
Females, *n* = 1						
83.3		—	13.0	9.9	26.7	17.8
Santa Cruz Island (*"P. maculatus clementae"*)						
Males, *n* = 4						
mean = 81.0		91.4	14.7	—	27.4	19.1
Females, *n* = 4						
mean = 78.4		91.2	14.5	—	27.7	19.1
Santa Rosa Island (*"P. maculatus clementae"*)						
Males, *n* = 1						
81.0		88.4	14.7	—	—	19.1
Females, *n* = 2						
mean = 80.3		89.4	13.7	—	25.9	19.3
San Clemente Island (*"P. maculatus clementae"*)						
Males, *n* = 6						
mean = 86.1		100.1	14.7	10.2	29.0	20.0
Females, *n* = 3						
mean = 79.3		90.2	14.2	9.9	29.2	19.8
Guadalupe Island (*"P. consobrinus"*)						
Males, *n* = 3						
range = 76.2-80.8		79.8-86.6	14.0-14.5	—	25.9-28.2	17.8-18.8
mean = 78.7		83.6	14.2	—	27.2	18.3
Females, *n* = 2						
range = 69.9-73.2		73.2-75.4	13.2-13.7	—	24.4-25.9	16.5-17.5
mean = 71.6		74.2	13.5	—	25.2	17.0

Means, samples sizes, and standard deviations are given in Appendix Tables 1 through 3 for measurements of the bill, wing and tail, and leg and foot. The Guadalupe Island population is characterized by having shorter wings and tail and longer bill than any other population. Birds from the San Benito Islands have bills that are, on the average, intermediate in length between those on Guadalupe and those occurring elsewhere. Males from Santa Rosa and Los Coronados Islands have short wings and tails, compared with birds from the mainland and from most island sites, as well. Males from Cedros Island tend to have short tails. Females from Santa Catalina also tend to have short wings and tails.

The best way to compare overall similarity among populations is by multivariate analysis.

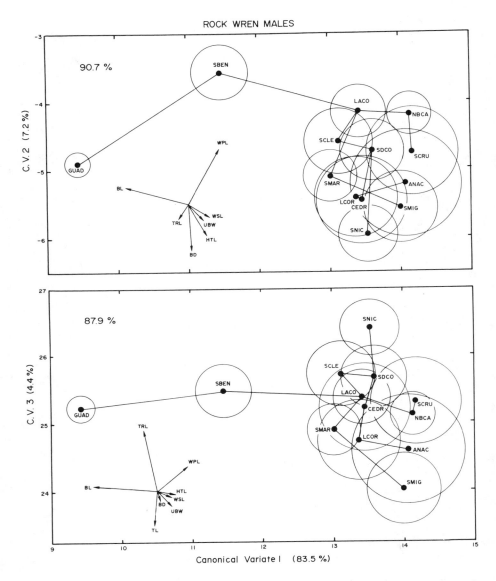

FIGURE 2. *Canonical variates diagram for Rock Wren males: axes 1 and 2 (upper) and axes 1 and 3 (lower). The three axes explain a total of 95.1 per cent of variation. To help visualize the positions of locality samples in a three-dimensional space, imagine the upper figure is a view down on a box and the lower figure is a view from the side in which locality samples are positioned relative to their phenetic distance. Locality samples are plotted by the position of the multivariate mean, around which is drawn a 95 per cent confidence circle. The vectors are labeled according to characters (see Methods) and indicate the contribution of characters in distinguishing among samples. Each vector is scaled so that its length is proportionate to the pooled within-groups standard deviation for that character.*

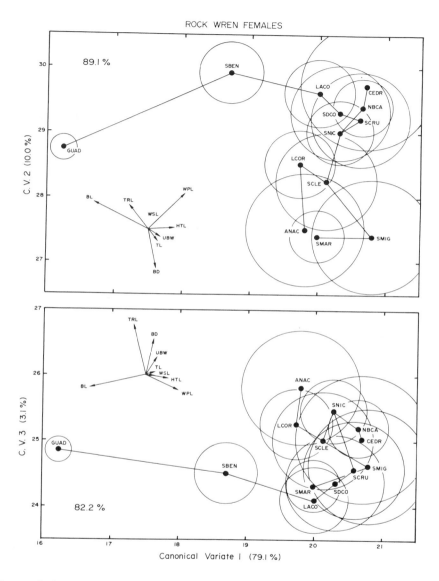

FIGURE 3. *Canonical variates diagram for Rock Wren females. The three axes explain a total of 92.2 per cent of the variation. See Figure 2 for further explanation.*

Canonical variates diagrams show the relative positions of locality samples in character hyperspaces—in the case of the Rock Wren with two, two-dimensional views of the first three canonical axes for males (Fig. 2) and females (Fig. 3). The analysis was carried out only for populations with sample sizes greater than five for males and greater than three for females. (For males, sample sizes ranged from six to 114, with a median of 18; for females, the range was four to 102 with a median of 13—see appendix tables for sample sizes.) The diagrams show the clear separation of Guadalupe Island Rock Wrens from all other populations, with bill length being the greatest contributor to this difference. San Benito Islands Rock Wrens are intermediate; the morphologically closest population is that from Los Angeles County, rather than any other island sample. With males, San Nicolas and San Miguel populations differ from one another on the basis of tarsus length; this pattern is not repeated with females, however. On the mainland, Los Angeles and San Diego County birds are highly similar. With the exception of the foregoing relationships, there is no clear-cut trend toward a pattern of phenetic variation. Instead, there seems to be highly localized variation with little concordance between males and females. One explanation for this is that high variation within populations, coupled with the small sample sizes in the analysis, may swamp any subtle trends among the islands and between the islands and the mainland. Another possibility is that there is random variation through time, so that collecting on different islands in widely spaced years has uncovered no trends; *i.e.*, temporal variation is swamping geographic variation.

House Finch (*Carpodacus mexicanus*)

The House Finch is a ubiquitous fringillid, about average in size (length, 12.7 to 14.6 cm), found throughout western North America and Mexico. Its habitat includes towns, ranches, urban areas, open woods, coastal scrub, canyons, and deserts. From an initial introduction near New York City in the early 1940s, the species has now become well established in the eastern states. Eight subspecies are recognized from mainland Mexico (Miller *et al.* 1957), and three others occur elsewhere in North America (A.O.U. 1957). Three additional races are restricted to one or more of the California Islands. The most widespread subspecies is *frontalis*, which occurs in Canada, the U.S., northwestern mainland Mexico, and the northern half of Baja California. This is also the subspecies assigned to populations on San Miguel, Santa Rosa, Santa Cruz, Anacapa, Todos Santos, San Martín, and Cedros Islands. The name *clementis* is assigned to populations from San Nicolas, Santa Barbara, Santa Catalina, San Clemente, and Los Coronados Islands. The San Benito Islands population (now extinct) is *mcgregori*, and the Guadalupe Island population is *amplus*.

Measurements of House Finches are given in Appendix Tables 4, 5, and 6. The Guadalupe Island population is clearly distinct in having larger wings and tail, a longer and heavier beak, and larger legs and feet. San Benito Islands birds are intermediate in this regard. When compared with those from the mainland, birds from other islands tend to have slightly smaller wings and tails, longer, thicker bills, and larger legs. Populations from the Washington-Idaho area are very similar to those from the southern California mainland. Birds from central and southern Baja California, however, have shorter wings and tails.

In general, the Guadalupe Island House Finch is a larger bird. It is not known, therefore, if this and other island populations have proportionately larger beaks, wings, tails, legs, and feet, or if variation in these characters is simply a direct function of overall size. One measure of size is body weight, the cube root of which can be used to correct variation in linear characters for the effect of size. Not all locality samples had weight data, but enough did so that an idea of size-independent character variation could be assessed (Table 9). Considering bill size first, it is apparent from the ratios that Guadalupe Island House Finches have a proportionately large bill. It is interesting to note that bill size for birds on other islands is no different than what would be expected in an overall larger House Finch. Thus, the trend for large bills on islands (other than

TABLE 9. Ratios of character* means to cube root of mean body weight for House Finches.

Locality	BL	BD	UBW	LBW	WPL	WSL	TL	TRL	HTL
A. Males									
Santa Barbara/Ventura Cos.	3.12	3.20	2.82	3.01	28.93	21.14	22.58	6.21	2.63
N. Baja California	3.04	3.09	2.73	2.92	28.36	20.76	22.07	6.06	2.52
Central Baja California	3.20	3.23	2.89	3.04	28.30	21.02	22.24	6.21	2.62
S. Baja California	3.20	3.10	2.76	2.95	27.53	21.69	21.75	6.05	2.52
San Miguel Island	3.04	2.99	2.70	2.87	27.32	20.31	21.40	5.98	2.50
Santa Rosa Island	3.03	3.05	2.70	2.89	27.42	20.26	21.43	6.07	2.52
Santa Cruz Island	3.02	3.14	2.72	2.93	27.71	20.36	21.46	6.11	2.93
San Nicolas Island	3.05	3.16	2.75	2.95	27.63	20.48	21.38	6.12	2.55
Guadalupe Island	3.35	3.75	3.05	3.36	27.35	20.43	21.38	6.31	2.69
B. Females									
Santa Barbara/Ventura Cos.	3.13	3.12	2.79	2.99	27.67	20.70	21.51	6.14	2.58
N. Baja California	3.03	3.10	2.75	2.95	27.45	20.32	21.43	6.11	2.53
Central Baja California	3.22	3.06	2.82	3.00	27.11	20.35	21.23	6.09	2.57
San Miguel Island	2.95	3.04	2.68	2.85	26.21	19.60	20.36	5.96	2.47
Santa Rosa Island	3.02	2.98	2.69	2.86	26.35	19.72	20.59	6.02	2.46
San Nicolas Island	3.09	3.12	2.76	2.95	26.51	20.06	20.44	6.11	2.59
Guadalupe Island	3.31	3.62	2.96	3.23	26.12	19.66	20.33	6.16	2.64

*Character codes are explained in Methods.

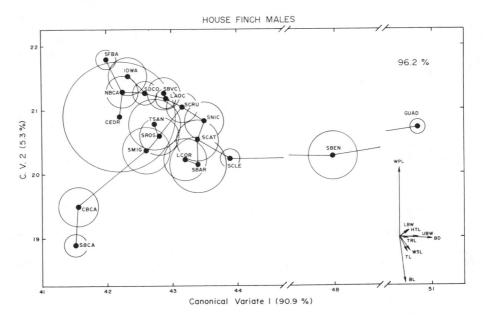

FIGURE 4. *Canonical variates diagram for House Finch males. Axes 1 and 2 explain a total of 96.2 per cent of the variation. See Figure 2 for further explanation.*

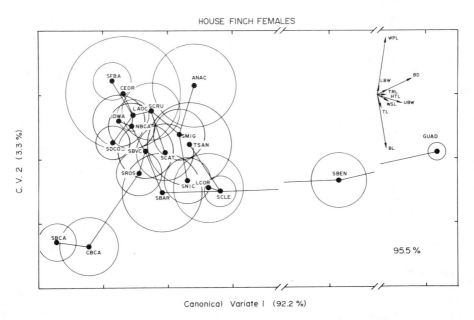

FIGURE 5. *Canonical variates diagram for House Finch females. Axes 1 and 2 explain a total of 95.5 per cent of the variation. See Figure 2 for further explanation.*

on Guadalupe and probably the San Benito Islands, as well) seems no more than a function of larger body size. Wing and tail lengths, on the other hand, are proportionately smaller in all island populations. Guadalupe Island finches are no different than finches from other islands in this regard. For tarsus and hind toe length, there is no difference in ratios between island and mainland birds; variation in these characters is simply a function of body size.

The canonical variates analyses for males (Fig. 4) and females (Fig. 5) show patterns of variation that are much easier to interpret than was the case for Rock Wrens. There is a geographical logic to the pattern of morphological variation and the patterns are similar for both sexes. This is probably due to the fundamentally different evolutionary histories of the two species and, in part, to the larger sample sizes for House Finches. There were 1,604 males in locality samples that ranged in size from five to 283 (median = 45), and 738 females in samples that ranged from five to 175 (median = 21). As with Rock Wrens, the Guadalupe Island birds are clearly set off from the others, with San Benito Islands birds occupying an intermediate position. In this case, the greatest separation is due to an increase in bill thickness. Populations from central and southern Baja California are also distinct; these populations are part of the race *ruberrimus* which also occurs across the Gulf of California in Sonora, Sinaloa, and Chihuahua; they need not be discussed further here. Nearest in appearance to the extreme island types is the population from San Clemente Island, followed by birds from Santa Barbara, San Nicolas, and Los Coronados Islands—all members of the race *clementis*. Santa Catalina Island males tend to align with this group but females do not, suggesting that Catalina birds are intermediate between *clementis* and Northern Channel Islands phenotypes. Birds from Santa Rosa, San Miguel, and Todos Santos Islands are intermediate between those from the mainland and those on the Southern Channel Islands. Santa Cruz birds are even more like those on the mainland, and the Cedros Island population is totally within the range of variation of mainland populations. It is clear that assigning island and west coast populations to the subspecies *clementis* or *frontalis* is an oversimplification and that we are dealing with a situation of almost clinal variation on which the subspecific designations are imposed.

Putting together the phenetic picture obtained through canonical variates analysis—with knowledge of the predominant north, northwest, and west winds in the area—allows a hypothetical recreation of the evolutionary history of this species on the California Islands (Fig. 6). As I have discussed earlier (Power 1979), for nonmigratory species such as the House Finch, islands seem to be the catalyst for race and species formation. Once free from the effects of widespread and abundant mainland populations, there is rapid evolution that, presumably, could have taken place within the last 10,000 to 20,000 years. This process is due not to actual geographic distance between populations, but to a combination of unique ecological characteristics on the islands, the isolation imposed by water barriers, and interference to dispersal posed by winds, possibly enhanced by small population size. There was probably over-water colonization of the Northern Channel Islands, followed by dispersal to the Southern Channel Islands and marked evolution *in situ* (see also Johnson 1972). Limited immigration from the mainland to the Northern Channel Islands and to Santa Catalina Island may continue to the present day. Whether colonization of Los Coronados Islands was from the Southern Channel Islands or from the nearby mainland remains problematical. Separate colonizations and parallel evolution, however, have probably taken place on the islands off Baja California, where the most extreme island phenotypes are found on Guadalupe and San Benito Islands.

DISCUSSION

Various studies (cited in the Introduction to this paper) have reported that natural selection in land birds on islands has tended more often than not to produce birds with longer or heavier bills, longer or heavier legs and feet, and, in some cases, shorter wings and tails. It is useful,

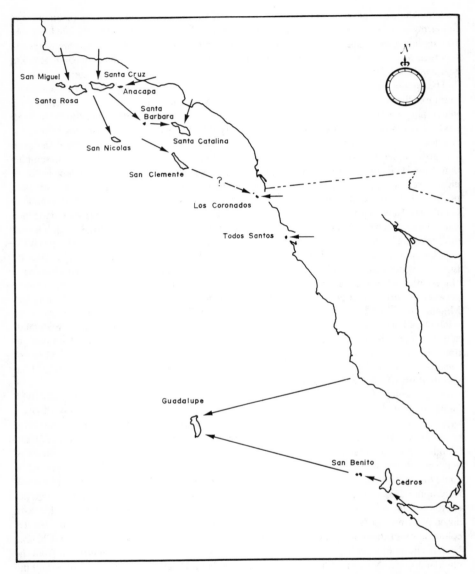

FIGURE 6. *Hypothetical pattern of colonization and evolution in California Islands House Finches. Predominant winds along the coast of southern and Baja California are from the northwest, north, and west. These would promote the distribution of birds from the Santa Barbara coastline to the Northern Channel Islands, and from there to the Southern Channel Islands. Colonization from the mainland to most of the islands off Baja California is believed to have taken place separately, with parallel evolution on these islands, rather than colonization from the more northern islands. See text for further explanation.*

therefore, to discuss variation in the nine species of land birds treated here in relation to these general trends. Also of interest is whether or not populations from the near-shore islands are intermediate between the mainland phenotypes and the most extreme island phenotypes found on Guadalupe Island. The following discussion relates to the summary of results in Table 10.

Wing and tail feathers make up the propulsion and maneuvering system for flight in birds. Wing primary length is a function of the length of the wing, wing secondary length is a function of the width of the extended wing, and tail length is a function of the size of the tail. These characters, therefore, are related to the surface area of the flight feathers, and, if form relates to function as we suppose, variation in these characters will indicate something about variation in the flying abilities and the demands for flight. This is not discounted by the fact that the mass of the pectoral muscles, and even the microstructure (such as density of mitochondria), are also related to the powers of flight. In Guadalupe Island populations, wings and/or tails are larger in the two falcons—the terrestrial Common Caracara and the aerial Sparrow Hawk— and are smaller in all of the smaller, passerine species (Table 10). This takes into account the fact that absolute wing and tail measurements are larger for the House Finch, but, when corrected for body weight, are smaller in proportion to overall body size.

The difference between the falcons and the passerines in the pattern of flight feather variation may relate to diet and foraging behavior. The falcons, being more predatory than the other species, may spend more time aloft in the windy island environment and require greater flying ability, or may have to fly greater distances in search of food. It may well be, however, that an increase in flight feathers is simply an indication of greater body size in these birds. It is somewhat easier to imagine selection for smaller wings in the passerine birds. There may be selection against birds prone to taking long flights because of the risk of being blown to sea. A reduction in the powers of flight is often seen in birds and insects that colonize an island with few predators. In ground feeding birds, true flightlessness has sometimes evolved (Carlquist 1974).

All of the passerine species on Guadalupe Island have larger bills than their mainland counterparts, or, in the case of the towhee, a proportionately larger bill. No difference is found for the caracara, but the Sparrow Hawk has a smaller bill. The larger bills in the passerine species may allow a greater range of food sizes to be taken in the absence of competing species (as Grant, 1965, and others have suggested), or it may indicate an increase in body size, which may also be related to a broader niche in a habitat with relatively few competitors (Grant 1968). A large bill may also evolve in response to dietary changes; larger and harder seeds and insects may have to be handled. Selection for seed size and insect body size may also be a function of the risk of being blown off the island and out to sea. On San Benito Islands, the Rock Wren and House Finch have proportionately larger bills. However, there is no tendency for proportionately large bills in the passerine birds that I have examined on any of the other California Islands. House Finches on most of the islands have larger bills than those on the mainland. However, as was pointed out previously, this is directly related to an increase in overall size; bills are not larger in proportion to body weight.

Legs and feet are larger in Guadalupe Island populations of the Ruby-crowned Kinglet, Dark-eyed Junco, Sparrow Hawk, and House Finch. There is no indication, however, that this is not in relation to overall size. An increase in leg and foot measurements, therefore, may not be related to increased foraging on the ground or to selection for the use of larger perches.

The existence of forms on San Benito Islands that are nearly intermediate in phenotype between conspecifics on Guadalupe Island and on the mainland is an interesting problem. The Sparrow Hawk is a strong flyer and it is not surprising that the San Benito population is like that on the adjacent mainland. However, two passerines have phenetically intermediate populations

TABLE 10. Summary of results.

	Common Caracara	Ruby-crowned Kinglet	Dark-eyed Junco	Sparrow Hawk	Common Flicker	Bewick Wren	Rock Wren	House Finch	Rufous-sided Towhee
1. Larger (L) or smaller (S) wing and/or tail on Guadalupe Island	L	S	S	L	S	S	S	L[2]	S
2. Larger (L) or smaller (S) wing and/or tail on other California Islands	—[1]	—	—	no	no	some S	some S	S[2]	no
3. Larger (L) or smaller (S) bill on Guadalupe Island	no	L	L	S	L	L	L	L[3]	no[3]
4. Larger (L) or smaller (S) bill on other California Islands	—	—	—	no	no	no	some L	L[4]	no
5. Larger (L) or smaller (S) leg and/or foot on Guadalupe Island	no	L	L	L	S(?)	S(?)	no	L[4]	S
6. Larger (L) or smaller (S) leg and/or foot on other California Islands	—	—	—	no	no	no	no	L[4]	some L
7. Presence of intermediate form on San Benito Islands	—	—	—	no	—	—	yes	yes	—
8. Intermediate forms on other California Islands	—	—	—	no	no	no	no	yes	no
9. Evolution in another direction on other California Islands	—	—	—	no	no	(?)	yes(?)	no	yes
10. Probable relict (R) or new evolution (N) on the islands	N	N	R	N	N	N	N	N	N

[1] "—" = not applicable; no comparison or statement possible. 　[4] Not larger in proportion to overall body size.

[2] Actually smaller in proportion to overall body size.

[3] Actually larger in proportion to overall body size. Possibly longer in the case of the towhee.

on San Benito. It is possible that San Benito Islands may have been the jumping-off point for colonizations to Guadalupe. Selection for an extreme island phenotype may take place on San Benito, but, because of its relative nearness to the mainland, the evolution of extreme island morphs may be thwarted by gene flow from the mainland. Another hypothesis is that San Benito is the site of hybridization between Guadalupe and mainland phenotypes. Although the distance between Guadalupe and San Benito is relatively great, the predominant west and northwest winds in the area could favor dispersal from Guadalupe to San Benito, but certainly not the other way around (see Power 1979 for more on winds).

As for intermediate forms on other California Islands, only in the House Finch has there been evolution in the same phenotypic direction as found on Guadalupe Island. All the evidence suggests that this is parallel evolution. On geographic grounds alone it seems highly unlikely that the California Islands phenotype on the Southern Channel Islands, for example, could have given rise first to the San Benito population and then to the Guadalupe population, or that the Southern Channel Islands are the site of hybridization between Guadalupe/San Benito populations and mainland birds. Relative to the flying powers of House Finches, the distances between the islands are simply too great. In the Rock Wren and Rufous-sided Towhee, there is some indication of variation which is not like that of conspecific Guadalupe Island populations.

The question of whether or not island differentiates are relicts of more widespread forms from earlier times or the result of new evolution away from the adjacent mainland phenotype has not been investigated in any systematic way. This is a very difficult problem to get at under any circumstances. If similarity between an island population and a population other than on the adjacent mainland is an indication of relictual status, then none of these species, except possibly the junco, seem to be relicts. Miller (1941) has suggested that the Dark-eyed Junco on Guadalupe Island may be derived from ancestors of the population that now occurs near Monterey, California, rather than the population in northern Baja California.

Up to this point, my main concern has been with the species on islands. I would now like to turn briefly to the islands themselves and look at relative degrees of endemicity. The number of land bird species and the number of endemic subspecies breeding on the California Islands are given in Table 11. For Guadalupe Island, the proportion of the total avifauna represented by endemics is very high—nearly 70 per cent. Endemicity in the range of 40 to 45 per cent is found for San Miguel, Santa Rosa, Anacapa, and San Clemente Islands. In absolute numbers of endemics, Santa Cruz and Santa Catalina Islands are also high. The high proportion of endemics on Guadalupe Island is expected in view of its relatively great distance from the mainland and the fact that predominant ocean winds do not favor dispersal from the mainland to the island. The moderate proportion of endemics on many of the other California Islands is perhaps surprising when considering the mobility of birds. However, these results do underscore the importance of the California Islands in fostering genetic diversity in bird species.

A final note stems from the results I obtained for the House Finch, which do not support the strict use of subspecies for the Channel Islands populations. The subspecific designations of earlier studies are useful in attempting to grasp something of the variation in island birds. However, the results of multivariate analysis in the House Finch show that, for island populations off Southern California, variation is clinal, with phenetic variation occurring in rather gradual steps from one island to the next. This is similar to some patterns we see on the mainland in which there are no barriers to dispersal among adjacent populations. This indicates that each island population is not a closed, independently evolving system. Instead, depending on the degree of vagility of the species in question, there is gene flow among island populations, a situation that would tend to smooth out extreme island specialization resulting from selection or genetic drift. On San Benito and Guadalupe Islands, however, the races of the House Finch

TABLE 11. Endemic subspecies of land birds on the California Islands.

Island	Total number of species*	Number of endemics†	Per cent endemics
San Miguel	10	4	40
Santa Rosa	22	9	41
Santa Cruz	32	10	31
Anacapa	16	7	44
Santa Barbara	13	4	31
San Nicolas	9	2	22
Santa Catalina	28	9	32
San Clemente	23	10	43
Los Coronados	12	3	25
Todos Santos	13	2	15
San Martín	4	—	—
San Geronimo	2	—	—
Cedros	11	—	—
Natividad	5	—	—
San Benito	7	2	29
Guadalupe	13	9	69

* Modified from Power (1972).
† From Johnson (1972, table 1) and A.O.U. (1957). "Endemics" are taxonomically recognized subspecies on islands that are not the same subspecies on the mainland.

and Rock Wren are clearly distinguishable on the basis of mensural differences, and in these cases the subspecies do relate to fully differentiated populations. The Guadalupe Island forms of all nine species considered here are also distinguishable on the basis of color and/or mensural differences, a fact that bears witness to the evolutionary effect on land birds of more extreme isolation from the parent population and natural selection in a novel environment.

SUMMARY

Variation in morphology is compared for the Common Caracara, Sparrow Hawk, Common Flicker, Bewick Wren, Rock Wren, Ruby-crowned Kinglet, Rufous-sided Towhee, House Finch, and Dark-eyed Junco on the California Islands. All of these species have, or had, morphologically distinct populations on Guadalupe Island; the Guadalupe populations of the caracara, flicker, Bewick Wren, and towhee are now extinct, as is the San Benito Islands House Finch. All of the island populations are derived from species on the mainland.

The caracara, kinglet, and junco show phenetic divergence on Guadalupe Island but do not occur on other California Islands. In the caracara, there is a tendency for longer tails in the Guadalupe Island population, compared with populations on the Mexican and southern U.S. mainland. The Ruby-crowned Kinglet on Guadalupe has shorter wings and tail and larger bill and hind limbs than mainland counterparts. The Dark-eyed Juncos on Guadalupe have shorter wings and tails, larger beaks, and slightly longer tarsi than juncos of the same species from the nearby mainland.

The Sparrow Hawk and flicker are differentiated on Guadalupe Island and occur, but are not differentiated, on other California Islands. The Sparrow Hawk has longer wings and tail, a shorter bill, longer legs, and probably larger feet on Guadalupe than on other islands or on the nearby mainland. The Common Flicker on Guadalupe—closest to the "red-shafted" form elsewhere—tends to have a shorter tail, longer bill, and shorter legs, although there is much overlap among samples.

Two wrens, the towhee, and the finch are differentiated on Guadalupe and on one or more other California Islands. The Bewick Wren on Guadalupe tends to have shorter wings and tail, longer bill, and shorter tarsi than elsewhere. On other islands, there are specific differences (*e.g.*, shorter wings and tail and longer bill on Santa Catalina Island in one data set), but no clear trends of variation emerge, except for short tails in a few island populations. Rufous-sided Towhees on Guadalupe have shorter wings and tail and smaller hind limbs than nearby mainland towhees, perhaps indicating an overall smaller body size. Bill length does not differ in absolute measurement but, relative to body size, may be greater in the Guadalupe Island form. Except for a tendency for San Clemente Island towhees to have longer tarsi, birds from other islands do not seem to differ from those on the mainland in mensural characters. For the Rock Wren, the Guadalupe Island population is characterized by having shorter wings and tails and longer bills. Birds from the San Benito Islands have bills that are of intermediate length between those of populations on Guadalupe and those of populations elsewhere. On other islands, there are no clear trends toward phenetic variation and males and females do not vary in parallel (*e.g.*, males from Santa Rosa and Los Coronados Islands have short wings and tails, but females do not). House Finches show more clinal variation than any other species. Guadalupe Island House Finches are larger in every character and have proportionately (relative to cube root of body weight) larger bills. Birds from other islands tend to have slightly smaller wings and tails, larger bills, and larger legs. Relative to overall size, wing and tail measurements are smaller in island populations; other characters vary in accordance with a pattern of increasing body size on other islands.

A multivariate (canonical variates) analysis of Rock Wren and House Finch samples showed that in both species the most extreme island phenotype is on Guadalupe Island, with intermediate phenotypes on San Benito Islands. Variation is in a rather random pattern for the Rock Wren on other islands. For the House Finch, populations on San Clemente, San Nicolas, Santa Barbara, Los Coronados, and Santa Catalina Islands tend toward the extreme island phenotype. Populations on San Miguel, Santa Rosa, Santa Cruz, and Todos Santos are intermediate between those on the foregoing islands and populations on the mainland.

The possible adaptive significance of variation in island birds is discussed relative to diet and the advantages and disadvantages to flight in an island environment. Much of the variation in the characters may relate only to variation in one parameter—body size. Intermediate phenotypes exist on San Benito Islands for the Rock Wren and House Finch. Only for the House Finch do intermediate types also exist on other islands. The only relictual population may be the Dark-eyed Junco on Guadalupe Island, which closely resembles the population now in the region of Monterey, California. Island populations of other species were probably newly evolved from types similar to those on the nearby mainland.

On Guadalupe Island, nearly 70 per cent of the total land bird avifauna is represented by endemic races. Endemicity ranges from 40 to 45 per cent on San Miguel, Santa Rosa, Anacapa, and San Clemente Islands. Numbers of endemic subspecies are relatively high for Santa Cruz and Santa Catalina Islands.

ACKNOWLEDGMENTS

This research was supported by a grant from the Systematic Biology Program of the National Science Foundation.

642   EVOLUTION IN LAND BIRDS

REFERENCES

ABBOTT, C. G. 1933. Closing history of the Guadalupe Caracara. Condor 35:10-14.

AMERICAN ORNITHOLOGISTS' UNION. 1957. Check-list of North American birds. American Ornithologists' Union (Lord Baltimore Press), Baltimore, Md.

ANTHONY, A. W. 1901. The Guadalupe Wren. Condor 3:73.

BLACKITH, R. E., and R. A. REYMENT. 1971. Multivariate morphometrics. Academic Press, New York, N.Y.

BOND, R. M. 1943. Variation in western Sparrow Hawks. Condor 45:168-185.

BOWMAN, R. I. 1961. Morphological differentiation and adaptation in the Galapagos Finches. University of California Press, Berkeley and Los Angeles, Calif.

BROWN, L., and D. AMADON. 1968. Eagles, hawks and falcons of the world. Vol. 2. McGraw-Hill, New York, N.Y.

BRYANT, W. E. 1887. Additions to the ornithology of Guadalupe Island. Bull. California Acad. Sci. 2:269-318.

CARLQUIST, S. 1974. Island biology. Columbia University Press, New York, N.Y.

COOLEY, W. W., and P. R. Lohnes. 1971. Multivariate data analysis. John Wiley & Sons, New York, N.Y.

DARWIN, C. 1845. Journal of researches into the natural history and geology of the countries visited during the voyage of H.M.S. *Beagle* round the world, under the command of Capt. Fitz Roy, R.N. 2nd rev. ed. John Murray, London.

DIXON, W. J. 1975. BMDP biomedical computer programs. University of California Press, Berkeley, Calif.

FOSTER, J. B. 1963. The evolution of the native land mammals of the Queen Charlotte Islands and the problem of insularity. Ph.D. thesis, University of British Columbia, Vancouver, B.C., Canada.

FRIEDMANN, H., L. GRISCOM, and R. T. MOORE. 1950. Distributional check-list of the birds of Mexico. Pt. 1. Pacific Coast Avifauna 29.

GRANT, P. R. 1965a. The adaptive significance of some size trends in island birds. Evolution 19:355-367.

――――. 1965b. A systematic study of the terrestrial birds of the Tres Marias Islands, Mexico. Postilla 90.

――――. 1968. Bill size, body size, and the ecological adaptations of bird species to competitive situations on islands. Syst. Zool. 17:319-333.

HUEY, L. M. 1942. Two new wrens and a new jay from Lower California, Mexico. Trans. San Diego Soc. Nat. Hist. 9:427-434.

JEHL, J. R. 1971. The status of *Carpodacus mcgregori*. Condor 73:375-376.

JOHNSON, N. K. 1972. Origin and differentiation of the avifauna of the Channel Islands, California. Condor 74:295-315.

LACK, D. 1945. The Galapagos Finches (Geospizinae): a study in variation. Occas. Papers California Acad. Sci. 21.

MAYR, E., and L. L. SHORT. 1970. Species taxa of North American birds. Publs. Nuttall Ornith. Club 9, Cambridge, Mass.

MILLER, A. H. 1941. Speciation in the avian genus Junco. Univ. California Publs. Zool. 44:173-434.

――――. 1951. A comparison of the avifaunas of Santa Cruz and Santa Rosa Islands, California. Condor 53:117-123.

MILLER, A. H., H. FRIEDMANN, L. GRISCOM, and R. T. MOORE. 1957. Distributional check-list of the birds of Mexico. Pt. II. Pacific Coast Avifauna 33.

MURPHY, R. C. 1938. The need of insular exploration as illustrated by birds. Science 88:533-539.

OBERHOLSER, H. C. 1898. A revision of the wrens of the genus *Thryomanes* Sclater. Proc. U.S. Natl. Mus. 21:421-450.

POWER, D. M. 1972. Numbers of bird species on the California Islands. Evolution 26:451-463.

————. 1979. Evolution in peripheral isolated populations: *Carpodacus* finches on the California Islands. Evolution 33:834-847.

PRIM, R. C. 1957. Shortest connection networks and some generalizations. Bell Syst. Tech. J. 36:1389-1401.

RIDGWAY, R. 1876a. Studies of the American Falconidae. Monograph of the Polybori. U.S. Geol. and Geogr. Surv. Terr. Bull. Ser. 2. Vol. 1(6):451-473.

————. 1876b. Ornithology of Guadeloupe Island, based on notes and collections made by Dr. Edward Palmer. Bull. U.S. Geol. and Geogr. Surv. Terr. 2:183-195.

————. 1877. The birds of Guadalupe Island, discussed with reference to the present genesis of species. Bull. Nuttall Ornith. Club 2:58-66.

————. 1901. The birds of North and Middle America. Bull. U.S. Natl. Mus. 50, pt. 1.

————. 1904. The birds of North and Middle America. Bull. U.S. Natl. Mus. 50, pt. 3.

————. 1914. The birds of North and Middle America. Bull. U.S. Natl. Mus. 50, pt. 6.

SEAL, H. L. 1966. Multivariate statistical analysis for biologists. Methuen, London.

SWARTH, H. S. 1916. The Pacific coast races of the Bewick Wrens. Proc. California Acad. Sci. Ser. 4, 6:53-85.

THAYER, J. E., and O. Bangs. 1908. The present state of the ornis of Guadeloupe Island. Condor 10:101-106.

Appendix Table 1. Rock Wrens: statistics for bill measurements—mean (mm), sample size (*n*), standard deviation.

Locality*	Sex	Bill length	Bill depth	Upper bill width
A. Mainland				
SBCO	M	13.05 (1) —	3.55 (1) —	3.80 (1) —
	F	14.25 (2) —	3.32 (2) —	4.42 (2) —
LACO	M	13.91 (24) 0.720	3.61 (24) 0.221	4.16 (24) 0.235
	F	14.08 (14) 0.628	3.47 (14) 0.181	4.24 (14) 0.186
SDCO	M	13.71 (17) 0.867	3.62 (18) 0.132	4.19 (18) 0.212
	F	13.25 (6) 0.940	3.47 (7) 0.107	4.15 (7) 0.196
NBCA	M	13.61 (35) 0.599	3.59 (35) 0.176	4.21 (37) 0.237
	F	13.66 (18) 0.717	3.68 (21) 0.200	4.19 (20) 0.291
B. Islands				
SMIG	M	13.37 (14) 0.682	3.69 (14) 0.268	4.33 (14) 0.204
	F	12.57 (5) 0.780	3.62 (5) 0.160	4.24 (5) 0.139
SROS	M	13.00 (2) —	3.40 (2) —	3.82 (2) —
	F	—	—	—
SCRU	M	13.66 (8) 0.679	3.64 (8) 0.171	4.43 (6) 0.202
	F	13.41 (7) 0.284	3.49 (7) 0.210	4.32 (7) 0.076
ANAC	M	13.92 (6) 1.031	3.84 (6) 0.193	4.39 (6) 0.341
	F	13.39 (4) 0.206	3.84 (5) 0.198	4.43 (5) 0.271
SBAR	M	13.78 (4) 1.150	3.68 (3) 0.247	4.17 (4) 0.202
	F	13.67 (2) —	3.62 (2) —	4.35 (2) —
SNIC	M	14.09 (21) 0.822	3.80 (22) 0.261	4.34 (22) 0.354
	F	13.70 (16) 0.677	3.66 (15) 0.186	4.28 (16) 0.517
SCAT	M	14.35 (2) —	3.55 (2) —	4.57 (2) —
	F	13.80 (1) —	4.00 (1) —	4.05 (1) —
SCLE	M	14.03 (15) 0.533	3.58 (15) 0.268	4.21 (16) 0.248
	F	13.06 (7) 0.678	3.59 (7) 0.304	4.19 (7) 0.248
LCOR	M	13.80 (10) 0.749	3.72 (11) 0.280	4.45 (11) 0.242
	F	13.94 (12) 0.648	3.66 (13) 0.234	4.55 (12) 0.244
TSAN	M	—	—	—
	F	13.17 (2) —	3.40 (1) —	4.30 (2) —
SBEN	M	15.25 (22) 0.905	3.49 (21) 0.193	4.16 (23) 0.239
	F	14.89 (16) 1.160	3.50 (17) 0.202	4.32 (17) 0.218
CEDR	M	14.01 (8) 0.974	3.78 (8) 0.187	4.30 (9) 0.187
	F	13.95 (4) 0.618	3.65 (4) 0.135	4.34 (4) 0.347
GUAD	M	15.99 (112) 0.765	3.72 (111) 0.208	4.20 (113) 0.231
	F	15.67 (101) 0.945	3.61 (99) 0.199	4.17 (101) 0.260
SMAR	M	14.10 (24) 0.916	3.75 (28) 0.202	4.24 (27) 0.337
	F	13.29 (21) 0.970	3.69 (23) 0.194	4.13 (24) 0.268
NATI	M	—	—	—
	F	12.78 (3) 0.511	3.48 (3) 0.029	4.12 (3) 0.104

*See Figure 1 for explanation of locality codes.

Appendix Table 2. Rock Wrens: statistics for feather measurements—mean (mm), sample size (n), standard deviation.

Locality	Sex	Wing primary length	Wing secondary length	Tail length
A. Mainland				
SBCO	M	68.40 (1) —	58.25 (1) —	51.00 (1) —
	F	68.65 (2) —	58.42 (2) —	52.62 (2) —
LACO	M	70.63 (24) 1.996	59.51 (24) 1.167	53.86 (23) 2.013
	F	68.95 (14) 1.871	57.65 (14) 1.492	52.32 (14) 1.979
SDCO	M	70.05 (18) 1.456	58.71 (18) 1.267	52.19 (18) 2.020
	F	68.59 (7) 1.028	57.57 (7) 1.148	51.64 (6) 1.737
NBCA	M	71.00 (37) 2.099	59.99 (37) 1.589	53.43 (35) 2.614
	F	69.67 (21) 2.444	58.86 (21) 2.166	52.33 (21) 1.623
B. Islands				
SMIG	M	68.76 (14) 2.215	58.56 (14) 1.739	52.78 (14) 4.614
	F	67.01 (4) 2.700	56.21 (4) 1.517	51.76 (5) 2.289
SROS	M	64.20 (2) —	56.07 (2) —	50.45 (2) —
	F	—	—	—
SCRU	M	70.82 (9) 2.145	59.81 (9) 1.615	53.30 (9) 3.247
	F	68.70 (6) 1.954	58.15 (7) 1.798	52.62 (7) 1.304
ANAC	M	70.80 (6) 1.905	59.70 (6) 1.335	53.16 (5) 1.684
	F	67.19 (4) 1.353	55.24 (4) 0.788	49.83 (3) 0.407
SBAR	M	69.70 (4) 1.756	59.69 (4) 0.712	53.09 (4) 1.112
	F	68.70 (2) —	59.82 (2) —	53.63 (2) —
SNIC	M	70.24 (22) 0.354	59.75 (22) 1.969	52.21 (21) 1.990
	F	68.17 (16) 2.078	57.89 (16) 1.739	51.99 (16) 1.106
SCAT	M	69.97 (2) —	58.80 (2) —	53.20 (2) —
	F	63.35 (1) —	55.50 (1) —	46.50 (1) —
SCLE	M	69.75 (16) 1.704	58.76 (16) 1.585	52.20 (14) 1.882
	F	66.73 (7) 1.796	57.04 (7) 1.175	50.59 (7) 1.382
LCOR	M	68.75 (11) 1.986	58.20 (11) 1.277	50.89 (11) 2.632
	F	67.23 (13) 2.557	56.91 (13) 1.907	49.70 (13) 3.439
TSAN	M	—	—	—
	F	67.75 (2) —	56.50 (2) —	49.92 (2) —
SBEN	M	69.56 (22) 1.808	58.52 (22) 1.768	52.20 (22) 1.836
	F	67.68 (16) 1.419	57.41 (15) 1.406	50.28 (17) 1.768
CEDR	M	69.66 (9) 1.800	58.42 (9) 1.097	51.56 (9) 1.994
	F	69.86 (4) 1.074	59.17 (4) 0.487	51.75 (4) 1.373
GUAD	M	66.36 (111) 1.867	56.41 (110) 1.658	50.17 (112) 2.125
	F	64.50 (102) 1.592	54.88 (102) 1.442	48.54 (101) 2.103
SMAR	M	69.44 (28) 1.929	58.72 (28) 1.844	52.97 (27) 2.060
	F	66.25 (24) 1.240	56.50 (23) 1.175	50.19 (23) 1.814
NATI	M	—	—	—
	F	68.05 (3) 0.850	58.78 (3) 1.338	51.25 (3) 1.500

Appendix Table 3. Rock Wrens: statistics for leg measurements and weight—mean (mm or g), sample size (*n*), standard deviation.

Locality	Sex	Tarsus length	Hind toe length	Weight
A. Mainland	M	20.05 (1) —	9.20 (1) —	—
	F	20.75 (2) —	9.13 (2) —	—
LACO	M	20.58 (23) 0.730	8.96 (24) 0.454	—
	F	20.04 (14) 0.664	8.94 (14) 0.399	—
SDCO	M	20.71 (18) 0.804	9.22 (18) 0.283	—
	F	20.21 (7) 0.811	8.84 (7) 0.523	—
NBCA	M	20.31 (36) 0.644	9.10 (37) 0.428	16.47 (20) 0.744
	F	20.57 (21) 0.650	8.98 (21) 0.478	16.62 (11) 2.023
B. Islands				
SMIG	M	19.90 (14) 0.887	9.31 (14) 0.403	18.35 (11) 1.224
	F	19.62 (5) 0.737	8.73 (5) 0.266	18.58 (5) 1.632
SROS	M	20.62 (2) —	8.45 (2) —	—
	F	—	—	—
SCRU	M	20.64 (9) 0.610	9.11 (9) 0.732	—
	F	20.23 (7) 0.719	8.98 (7) 0.530	17.50 (1) —
ANAC	M	20.08 (6) 0.572	9.37 (6) 0.572	17.60 (1) —
	F	20.15 (5) 1.226	9.06 (4) 0.633	17.20 (1) —
SBAR	M	20.06 (4) 0.654	9.35 (4) 0.303	15.90 (1) —
	F	19.85 (2) 0.654	8.97 (2) —	16.30 (1) —
SNIC	M	21.43 (22) 0.924	9.58 (22) 0.495	16.43 (3) 0.603
	F	20.64 (16) 0.610	9.26 (16) 0.599	16.32 (6) 0.954
SCAT	M	21.07 (2) —	9.57 (2) —	—
	F	19.80 (1) —	8.45 (1) —	—
SCLE	M	20.79 (16) 0.711	9.19 (16) 0.562	—
	F	20.27 (6) 0.923	8.98 (7) 0.520	—
LCOR	M	20.16 (11) 0.931	9.07 (11) 0.489	—
	F	20.18 (13) 0.680	9.06 (13) 0.397	—
TSAN	M	—	—	—
	F	20.02 (2) 0.106	8.57 (2) 0.106	—
SBEN	M	20.44 (23) 0.773	8.95 (23) 0.442	16.15 (4) 0.733
	F	20.37 (17) 0.518	8.98 (17) 0.377	17.90 (2) —
CEDR	M	20.46 (9) 0.653	9.29 (9) 0.394	—
	F	20.50 (4) 0.667	9.21 (4) 0.679	—
GUAD	M	20.44 (113) 0.643	8.69 (113) 0.429	14.95 (6) 1.122
	F	20.24 (100) 0.662	8.56 (102) 0.395	16.35 (6) 1.941
SMAR	M	20.40 (28) 0.553	9.10 (28) 0.450	16.80 (8) 1.268
	F	19.37 (24) 0.664	8.80 (24) 0.387	16.18 (10) 1.009
NATI	M	20.80 (2) —	9.37 (2) —	—
	F	—	—	—

Appendix Table 4. House Finches: statistics for bill characters: mean (mm), sample size (n), standard deviation.

Locality	Sex	Bill length	Bill depth	Upper bill width	Lower bill width
A. Mainland					
IDWA	M	8.29 (43) 0.291	8.25 (44) 0.294	7.44 (45) 0.239	8.00 (45) 0.335
	F	8.30 (24) 0.343	8.31 (23) 0.326	7.39 (24) 0.230	8.04 (24) 0.288
SFBA	M	7.99 (186) 0.345	8.34 (175) 0.331	7.43 (186) 0.238	7.97 (192) 0.274
	F	8.01 (48) 0.319	8.35 (45) 0.344	7.42 (48) 0.227	7.95 (47) 0.302
SBVC	M	8.35 (67) 0.329	8.57 (62) 0.333	7.56 (67) 0.268	8.06 (67) 0.288
	F	8.43 (20) 0.493	8.38 (19) 0.284	7.53 (20) 0.218	8.07 (20) 0.315
LAOC	M	8.33 (148) 0.322	8.58 (143) 0.372	7.54 (149) 0.239	8.09 (148) 0.308
	F	8.21 (66) 0.357	8.42 (65) 0.358	7.49 (67) 0.228	7.98 (67) 0.297
SDCO	M	8.29 (122) 0.344	8.41 (115) 0.306	7.52 (123) 0.220	8.05 (122) 0.274
	F	8.26 (54) 0.285	8.31 (53) 0.332	7.44 (54) 0.215	7.93 (53) 0.250
NBCA	M	8.26 (58) 0.317	8.39 (56) 0.286	7.42 (59) 0.235	7.93 (50) 0.296
	F	8.23 (28) 0.376	8.42 (26) 0.364	7.48 (29) 0.236	8.01 (29) 0.296
CBCA	M	8.34 (45) 0.348	8.39 (44) 0.307	7.52 (45) 0.228	7.92 (44) 0.266
	F	8.54 (19) 0.264	8.11 (18) 0.292	7.48 (19) 0.227	7.95 (17) 0.182
SBCA	M	8.51 (140) 0.359	8.25 (131) 0.327	7.36 (140) 0.214	7.85 (139) 0.273
	F	8.42 (42) 0.362	8.08 (42) 0.319	7.32 (44) 0.278	7.78 (43) 0.255
B. Islands					
SMIG	M	8.51 (28) 0.347	8.37 (28) 0.465	7.56 (28) 0.253	8.01 (28) 0.262
	F	8.37 (24) 0.377	8.64 (24) 0.263	7.62 (24) 0.193	8.10 (24) 0.295
SROS	M	8.45 (44) 0.419	8.50 (44) 0.364	7.53 (44) 0.245	8.07 (43) 0.267
	F	8.46 (29) 0.341	8.35 (28) 0.288	7.53 (29) 0.246	8.01 (29) 0.337
SCRU	M	8.39 (67) 0.398	8.72 (66) 0.274	7.56 (68) 0.235	8.14 (67) 0.308
	F	8.28 (18) 0.244	8.59 (18) 0.329	7.44 (20) 0.253	8.05 (20) 0.322
ANAC	M	7.90 (2) —	8.65 (1) —	7.65 (2) —	8.02 (2) —
	F	8.23 (8) 0.228	8.74 (7) 0.195	7.65 (9) 0.170	8.14 (9) 0.317
SBAR	M	8.82 (19) 0.299	8.63 (17) 0.329	7.69 (19) 0.202	8.21 (19) 0.277
	F	8.67 (9) 0.415	8.46 (9) 0.511	7.65 (10) 0.162	8.14 (8) 0.155
SNIC	M	8.48 (45) 0.366	8.81 (38) 0.332	7.65 (44) 0.257	8.22 (44) 0.292
	F	8.56 (30) 0.295	8.64 (28) 0.348	7.64 (30) 0.167	8.18 (29) 0.343
SCAT	M	8.67 (36) 0.339	8.75 (30) 0.335	7.60 (36) 0.252	8.19 (36) 0.280
	F	8.55 (20) 0.308	8.67 (18) 0.301	7.50 (20) 0.241	8.17 (18) 0.298
SCLE	M	8.88 (169) 0.337	8.86 (168) 0.349	7.79 (173) 0.225	8.37 (169) 0.265
	F	8.87 (66) 0.352	8.75 (63) 0.319	7.77 (65) 0.241	8.33 (65) 0.294
LCOR	M	8.67 (35) 0.382	8.68 (31) 0.296	7.63 (35) 0.281	8.25 (35) 0.303
	F	8.82 (13) 0.386	8.60 (12) 0.427	7.81 (12) 0.165	8.35 (13) 0.319
TSAN	M	8.52 (24) 0.321	8.39 (23) 0.304	7.55 (23) 0.192	8.02 (23) 0.269
	F	8.62 (9) 0.414	8.48 (9) 0.422	7.61 (9) 0.154	8.20 (9) 0.311
CEDR	M	8.27 (5) 0.309	8.60 (5) 0.355	7.39 (5) 0.246	7.72 (5) 0.160
	F	8.16 (5) 0.643	8.42 (5) 0.309	7.28 (5) 0.220	7.63 (5) 0.303
SBEN	M	9.78 (27) 0.566	10.38 (24) 0.574	8.59 (27) 0.395	8.98 (26) 0.454
	F	9.86 (21) 0.408	10.54 (18) 0.491	8.55 (21) 0.434	8.91 (20) 0.391
GUAD	M	9.97 (283) 0.564	11.14 (277) 0.601	9.06 (283) 0.337	9.99 (282) 0.449
	F	10.05 (174) 0.512	10.99 (169) 0.619	8.99 (175) 0.324	9.81 (173) 0.463

Appendix Table 5. House Finches: statistics for feather characters: mean (mm), sample size (*n*), standard deviation.

Locality	Sex	Wing primary length	Wing secondary length	Tail length
A. Mainland				
IDWA	M	77.99 (45) 1.515	57.03 (45) 1.111	61.13 (45) 1.817
	F	75.20 (24) 1.467	55.93 (24) 1.090	58.98 (24) 1.534
SFBA	M	77.03 (181) 1.754	55.87 (179) 1.348	59.22 (184) 1.978
	F	74.64 (48) 1.774	54.86 (48) 1.649	56.80 (48) 1.839
SBVC	M	77.46 (67) 1.758	56.61 (67) 1.512	60.45 (67) 1.983
	F	74.58 (20) 1.839	55.78 (20) 1.360	57.97 (20) 2.127
LAOC	M	77.37 (147) 1.802	57.00 (146) 1.293	60.55 (145) 1.941
	F	74.73 (64) 1.630	55.34 (66) 1.593	58.22 (67) 1.818
SDCO	M	77.38 (119) 1.828	56.75 (122) 1.450	60.51 (121) 2.003
	F	74.11 (54) 1.862	54.89 (55) 1.420	57.93 (55) 2.312
NBCA	M	77.09 (58) 1.796	56.42 (58) 1.633	59.99 (59) 2.227
	F	74.51 (28) 1.883	55.19 (28) 1.585	58.21 (28) 2.188
CBCA	M	73.74 (45) 1.603	54.78 (45) 1.429	57.96 (45) 1.824
	F	71.92 (19) 1.553	53.98 (19) 1.313	56.32 (19) 1.920
SBCA	M	73.28 (140) 1.799	54.75 (139) 1.541	57.90 (139) 2.224
	F	71.51 (42) 1.849	53.77 (42) 1.311	56.24 (43) 1.822
B. Islands				
SMIG	M	76.37 (27) 1.633	56.78 (27) 1.508	59.84 (28) 2.155
	F	74.42 (24) 1.695	55.66 (24) 1.508	57.82 (24) 1.639
SROS	M	76.49 (43) 1.736	56.50 (44) 1.496	59.76 (44) 1.931
	F	73.75 (30) 1.607	55.21 (30) 1.114	57.62 (30) 1.964
SCRU	M	77.03 (68) 1.817	56.61 (68) 1.398	59.67 (67) 2.044
	F	74.58 (20) 1.635	55.31 (20) 1.157	57.41 (20) 1.856
ANAC	M	78.75 (2) —	58.05 (2) —	59.97 (2) —
	F	75.54 (8) 1.374	56.24 (8) 1.086	58.29 (8) 1.443
SBAR	M	76.94 (18) 1.940	57.47 (18) 1.373	59.39 (18) 2.083
	F	74.31 (9) 1.312	55.80 (10) 1.476	57.27 (10) 1.722
SNIC	M	76.93 (45) 1.712	57.03 (45) 1.394	59.52 (45) 1.567
	F	73.49 (30) 1.670	55.62 (30) 1.093	56.65 (30) 1.824
SCAT	M	77.22 (36) 1.880	57.29 (36) 1.650	60.02 (35) 2.397
	F	74.33 (20) 1.882	55.15 (20) 0.973	57.76 (19) 2.558
SCLE	M	77.09 (168) 1.733	56.95 (168) 1.476	59.74 (172) 1.966
	F	74.77 (64) 1.610	56.12 (65) 1.450	57.97 (65) 1.862
LCOR	M	75.97 (34) 2.031	56.45 (34) 1.182	57.96 (33) 2.117
	F	74.16 (12) 2.349	55.01 (13) 1.264	56.41 (12) 2.346
TSAN	M	76.90 (24) 2.133	56.64 (24) 1.828	59.44 (24) 2.705
	F	75.33 (9) 1.218	56.32 (9) 1.045	57.44 (8) 1.678
CEDR	M	76.56 (5) 2.472	56.03 (5) 0.727	59.34 (5) 2.909
	F	75.39 (5) 1.458	56.39 (5) 1.059	57.97 (5) 2.168
SBEN	M	79.68 (24) 1.966	58.64 (22) 1.490	61.19 (26) 1.920
	F	77.78 (20) 1.864	57.72 (20) 1.414	59.90 (20) 2.360
GUAD	M	81.33 (268) 1.929	60.75 (264) 1.395	63.58 (273) 2.062
	F	79.24 (171) 1.971	59.63 (170) 1.349	61.68 (173) 2.241

Appendix Table 6. House Finches: statistics for hind limb characters and weight: mean (mm or g), sample size (*n*), and standard deviation.

Locality	Sex	Tarsus length	Hind toe length	Weight
A. Mainland				
IDWA	M	16.49 (45) 0.479	7.00 (44) 0.249	—
	F	16.35 (24) 0.537	6.81 (24) 0.247	—
SFBA	M	16.35 (186) 0.577	6.84 (187) 0.295	—
	F	16.32 (48) 0.525	6.87 (48) 0.304	—
SBVC	M	16.63 (67) 0.587	7.03 (67) 0.304	19.19 (26) 2.107
	F	16.54 (20) 0.586	6.95 (20) 0.356	19.58 (6) 1.685
LAOC	M	16.67 (148) 0.581	6.99 (149) 0.333	—
	F	16.45 (67) 0.624	6.90 (67) 0.291	—
SDCO	M	16.57 (123) 0.563	6.95 (123) 0.323	20.70 (1) —
	F	16.31 (55) 0.753	6.90 (55) 0.323	—
NBCA	M	16.47 (57) 0.583	6.86 (57) 0.259	20.08 (25) 1.658
	F	16.58 (29) 0.544	6.87 (29) 0.325	20.03 (11) 2.974
CBCA	M	16.19 (45) 0.590	6.82 (45) 0.321	17.70 (13) 1.542
	F	16.15 (19) 0.632	6.81 (19) 0.285	18.67 (3) 2.663
SBCA	M	16.11 (140) 0.626	6.70 (140) 0.309	18.87 (3) —
	F	15.92 (44) 0.473	6.71 (44) 0.214	—
B. Islands				
SMIG	M	16.72 (28) 0.672	6.99 (28) 0.337	21.85 (24) 1.811
	F	16.93 (23) 0.287	7.02 (24) 0.394	22.89 (24) 1.893
SROS	M	16.94 (44) 0.530	7.02 (44) 0.310	21.70 (37) 1.156
	F	16.84 (30) 0.604	6.88 (30) 0.366	21.93 (28) 1.830
SCRU	M	16.99 (66) 0.579	7.02 (68) 0.320	21.49 (61) 1.045
	F	16.86 (20) 0.621	6.91 (20) 0.389	20.80 (2) —
ANAC	M	17.30 (2) —	7.10 (2) —	—
	F	16.98 (9) 0.560	7.09 (9) 0.440	—
SBAR	M	17.04 (19) 0.532	7.03 (19) 0.359	—
	F	16.62 (10) 0.611	6.84 (10) 0.368	—
SNIC	M	17.01 (45) 0.540	7.11 (45) 0.430	21.58 (27) 1.327
	F	16.93 (30) 0.584	7.17 (30) 0.273	21.30 (22) 1.649
SCAT	M	16.92 (36) 0.664	6.94 (36) 0.276	—
	F	17.02 (20) 0.622	6.80 (20) 0.349	—
SCLE	M	17.15 (171) 0.489	7.02 (172) 0.317	—
	F	16.99 (66) 0.539	7.07 (66) 0.314	—
LCOR	M	17.03 (35) 0.522	7.09 (66) 0.242	—
	F	17.08 (13) 0.515	7.13 (13) 0.292	—
TSAN	M	17.06 (24) 0.653	7.10 (24) 0.303	20.70 (2) 1.414
	F	17.11 (9) 0.679	7.11 (9) 0.286	21.45 (2) 0.354
CEDR	M	16.23 (5) 0.342	6.74 (5) 0.455	—
	F	16.48 (5) 0.869	6.91 (5) 0.175	—
SBEN	M	17.78 (27) 0.639	7.57 (27) 0.365	—
	F	17.96 (21) 0.613	7.56 (21) 0.320	—
GUAD	M	18.76 (283) 0.562	8.01 (283) 0.317	26.29 (14) 1.248
	F	18.68 (175) 0.578	8.02 (175) 0.319	27.92 (6) 3.592

Historical Changes in Resident Populations of California Islands Raptors

Lloyd F. Kiff

Western Foundation of Vertebrate Zoology,
1100 Glendon Ave., Los Angeles, California 90024

INTRODUCTION

The California Islands have been the scene of repeated avian extinctions (Jones and Diamond 1976), but no group of species has experienced more dramatic population changes in this century than the large birds of prey. The islands formerly supported resident populations of the Bald Eagle (*Haliaeetus leucocephalus*), Osprey (*Pandion haliaetus*), and Peregrine Falcon (*Falco peregrinus*), but all are now extinct.

This paper summarizes the existing data on historical changes in the status of these three raptors on the California Islands and evaluates the relative importance of known mortality factors in causing their disappearance as breeding residents. The raptor populations discussed here are those formerly resident on the California Channel Islands (San Clemente, Santa Catalina, Santa Barbara, San Nicolas, Anacapa, Santa Cruz, Santa Rosa, and San Miguel) and Los Coronados Islands, off the coast of northwestern Baja California about 40 km SW of San Diego, California.

METHODS

This study is an outgrowth of a larger project undertaken to establish an inventory of museum egg sets of all species collected on these islands. For the present report, I attempted to compile all available data for Bald Eagles, Ospreys, and Peregrine Falcons on the islands prior to 1965 from the following sources.

(1) Data accompanying museum egg sets. Forty-three of the principal egg collections in North America were examined personally, or for me by their staff members, for island egg sets of Bald Eagles, Ospreys, and Peregrine Falcons (Appendix 1). Specific set collection data will be presented elsewhere (Kiff in prep.). Although I have probably accounted for the great majority of egg sets collected on the California Islands by ornithologists and oologists, some sets, especially those taken as curiosities by casual visitors to the islands, have doubtless not come to my attention.

(2) Specimen labels on study skins and skeletons of the three raptors in the major California bird collections. No attempt was made to locate such specimens in other collections; I suspect that few others exist.

(3) The unpublished field notes or manuscripts of 40 persons, mostly collectors, who visited the California Islands prior to 1965 (Appendix 2).

(4) Interviews with long-time residents of the larger Channel Islands and with visitors to all of the islands.

(5) Published accounts of the birds of the California Islands. The principal sources of detailed information are Willett (1912, 1933), Howell (1917), Johnson (1972), Power (1972), Jones (1975), and Jehl (1977).

Because many of these data sources are anecdotal in nature, collectively they yield only a fragmentary picture of the extinct raptor populations, particularly of their former sizes and the causes of their disappearance.

RESULTS
Bald Eagle
Distribution and status

Bald Eagles nested at one time or another on all of the Channel Islands and on Los Coronados Islands. The resident population was apparently nonmigratory, but was augmented in some winters by an increment of birds from northern populations (Grinnell and Miller 1944).

Bald Eagles were reported from San Miguel Island as early as the spring of 1886 (Streator 1888), and a party led by George Willett (1910) found them to be common there during June. J. R. Pemberton and Dudley S. DeGroot visited the island on 31 March 1927 and saw three adult eagles and two inactive nests on the northwest side. On the following day, they took a set of eggs (WFVZ 2002) from a nest on the southwest side of the island (DeGroot field notes). Herbert Lester, then the caretaker of the island, told Lowell Sumner and Richard Bond in April, 1939 that two pairs of eagles nested regularly on San Miguel in addition to a pair on nearby Prince Island (Sumner unpubl. ms.).

The Pemberton-DeGroot party counted ten eagles and found three nests, two containing small young, during their visit to Santa Rosa Island between 2 and 4 April 1927 (Pemberton 1928). Because ornithological coverage of Santa Rosa was so meager during the years when eagles occurred there, it is likely that more than three pairs were usually resident on that large island. Most California Islands eagle nests were located on rocky cliffs and exposed pinnacles, but all of those seen on Santa Rosa Island by Pemberton were situated in trees in sheltered canyons (Pemberton 1928). He believed that the strong winds characteristic of Santa Rosa prevented the eagles from building their nests in more exposed sites. However, later visitors to Santa Rosa found some eagle nests on sea cliffs there (E. N. Harrison, pers. comm.; WFVZ 22562).

Santa Cruz Island regularly supported at least five resident pairs of Bald Eagles, and a steady procession of egg collectors and other visitors to the island frequently commented on the species' abundance there. Judging from the data slips accompanying egg sets, traditional nest sites were located at Pelican Bay, San Pedro Point, Blue Banks, Valley Anchorage, China Bay (Chinese Harbor), Potato Bay (Potato Harbor), and Middle Grounds, although not all were necessarily occupied by eagles every year. Almost all Santa Cruz Island eagle nests were in niches and potholes on exposed sea cliffs, but the Pelican Bay birds regularly nested in pine trees (Howell and van Rossem 1911, Canterbury field notes for 1919, Sheldon field notes for 1927-1928).

In some years, nearby Anacapa Island had three pairs of nesting eagles (Willett 1910, Burt 1911, DeGroot field notes for 1927), but two pairs were more usual in the 1930s (E. N. Harrison, pers. comm.). Sumner (unpubl. ms.) stated that on 16 April 1939 the species was "almost constantly in sight on Anacapa, two adults and four immatures having been seen over the highest peak at once." Burt (1911) thought the eagles nesting on Anacapa Island were required to transport their principal nesting materials, large sticks, from Santa Cruz Island because of the virtual lack of trees on Anacapa. However, later visitors to Anacapa (Sumner unpubl. ms., Quigley field notes for 1949) found an active eagle nest actually situated in a sizeable Island Oak (*Quercus tomentella*).

Howell (1917) thought it probable that Santa Barbara Island, because of its small size, supported only a single pair of Bald Eagles. Although an actual nest was never described, eagles were reported from Santa Barbara Island during the usual breeding season by Grinnell (1897), Willett (1912), Wright and Snyder (1913), and DeGroot (field notes for 1927).

Bald Eagles were evidently abundant on Santa Catalina Island in the nineteenth century. Cooper (1870), recounting a visit that he made to the island in the early 1860s, wrote that "I have seen more than thirty of these eagles in young plumage, soaring about the north end of

Catalina Island on the 9th of July, and their nests were numerous among the inaccessible cliffs of that island.'' At the turn of the century, several visitors to the island, including Zahn (1895), Grinnell (1898), Richardson (1908), and Snyder (1909), commented on seeing eagles and, usually, their nests on Santa Catalina. A. J. van Rossem (field notes) found four probably active eagle nests on 18 February 1921 while rowing along the shoreline from the town of Avalon. He concluded that the nests occurred at intervals of about two miles of coastline, indicating the apparent large size of the eagle population on the island at that time.

Few specific details are available concerning the status of Bald Eagles on San Nicolas Island, although Howell (1917) stated that eagles were reportedly abundant there, probably based on information supplied to him by C. B. Linton, one of the few early visitors to San Nicolas. Although Loye Miller (unpubl. ms.) did not encounter eagles on San Nicolas during his visit between 7 and 18 July 1938, Rett (1947) investigated a recently active eagle nest there on 23 September 1945.

Most visitors to San Clemente Island found eagles to be common there (Grinnell 1897, Linton 1908, Howell 1917), and a minimum of three nests were active in late February, 1923 (egg sets at WFVZ). Presumably, other nesting pairs existed in the more poorly investigated sections of the island.

Bald Eagles were surprisingly scarce on Los Coronados Islands. The only evidence suggesting that the species ever nested there at all was provided by Grinnell and Daggett (1903), who saw one on South Coronado Island on 6 and 7 August 1902 and wrote that ''We were told that a pair had a nest there.'' Howell (1917) did not record the species during several visits to Los Coronados between 1910 and 1917. Stephens (1921) saw an immature over North Coronado Island on 5 March 1921, but it was evidently a transient. If the species had nested there at that time, this would surely have been known to the egg collectors, who visited the islands almost annually.

In summary, the highest numbers of active Bald Eagle nests reported (or inferred from the available data) during a single year for the various California Islands are as follows: San Miguel (including Prince Island), 3; Santa Rosa, 3; Santa Cruz, 5; Anacapa, 3; Santa Barbara, 1; Santa Catalina, 4; San Nicolas, 1; San Clemente, 3; Los Coronados, 1—for a total of 24 nests. Because of incomplete coverage by observers of the larger islands, including Santa Rosa, Santa Cruz, Santa Catalina, and San Clemente, these figures are undoubtedly low; the actual maximum number of Bald Eagles that nested concurrently on the California Islands within historical times was surely much higher.

Food habits

Of the three raptors discussed here, Bald Eagles were by far the most catholic in their food preferences. They reportedly fed on a variety of fish, birds, and mammals, including a high percentage of carrion.

Grinnell (1897) saw the species feeding on dead fish washed up on the beach at San Clemente Island, and he contended that the eagles there did not rob Ospreys of their food as frequently as had been popularly supposed. Burt (1911) found half-eaten fish in an Anacapa Island eagle nest that contained young two to three days old. Other than DeGroot's (field notes) observation of ''some large sea bass'' in a Santa Rosa Island eagle nest, there are no specific reports on the size and species of fish utilized by Bald Eagles on the California Islands.

The nest examined by DeGroot on Santa Rosa also contained a Surf Scoter (*Melanitta perspicillata*), a raven (*Corvus corax*), and the feet of several gulls (*Larus* sp.) (DeGroot field notes). Sumner (unpubl. ms.) looked into an eagle nest on Prince Island on 18 April 1939 that contained the remains of two young pelicans (*Pelecanus occidentalis*), a guillemot (*Cepphus* sp.), and the wing of a California Gull (*Larus californicus*). On San Nicolas Island, a resident told Rett (1947) that he had found the wing of a gull and some large black wings, possibly those of a cormorant (*Phalacrocorax* sp.) or raven, in an eagle nest that he had visited in the summer of 1945.

Many writers mentioned that Bald Eagles ate sheep and lambs on the islands where these domestic animals had been introduced. Although there seems to have been a prevalent belief that eagles took living lambs (*e.g.*, Burt 1911, Dawson 1923, Sheldon field notes for 1927-1928), I have been unable to find a firsthand account of such predation on the California Islands. On the other hand, certain residents of the islands told visiting ornithologists that they thought that eagles ate only sheep and lambs that had died from other causes. The ranch foreman on San Clemente Island, Charles Howland, had lived there for 15 years when A. B. Howell, D. R. Dickey, and L. M. Huey visited in 1915. He stated that he had seen an eagle carrying a lamb only once during his tenure on the island, and that the animal had died of natural causes (Howell 1917). Sumner (unpubl. ms.) was told by Herbert Lester, the caretaker on San Miguel Island, that eagles did not take living sheep there, and the residents of Santa Cruz Island made similar statements to E. N. Harrison (pers. comm.) during his visits to that island in the 1930s.

Several egg collectors mentioned finding sheep carcasses in the immediate vicinity of eagle nests or actually incorporated into the substructure of nests (Linton 1908, Carpenter field notes for 1922, Bancroft field notes for 1923, Dawson 1923, Sheldon field notes for 1927-1928). A nest investigated by Bancroft on San Clemente Island on 24 February 1923 contained the carcasses of seven sheep (data slip for WFVZ 10084).

Bald Eagles probably also fed regularly on carcasses of the native Island Fox (*Urocyon littoralis*) on those islands where it occurs. Rett (1947) found the hind leg of a fox in a San Nicolas Island eagle nest, and D. R. Dickey discovered the entire desiccated carcass of a fox stuck in the wall of a nest on San Clemente Island in 1915 (Howell 1917).

Period of decline

Willett (1912) and Howell (1917) regarded the Bald Eagle as a common resident of the Channel Islands. By the early 1920s, Dawson (1923) felt that the species was still fairly common there, although he noted that the population had been greatly reduced by human persecution. He predicted, "Unless the Bald Eagle is actually protected, not alone from lawless marauders in motor boats, but from the vengeance of the sheepmen . . . its days are numbered." In a revision of his 1912 work, Willett (1933) amended his earlier assessment of the eagle's status on the islands to "fairly common." Nevertheless, Grinnell and Miller (1944) described the Channel Islands as being one of the two "breeding metropolises" of the Bald Eagles still remaining in California, the other being in the northeastern sector of the state. This was the last general reference on California birds in which the Bald Eagle was considered to be extant as a breeding form on the California Islands.

It is not possible to specify the year of the eagle's disappearance from most of the islands because of the paucity of recorded observations for several decades. The latest report of nesting eagles cannot be considered a meaningful estimate of when the species vanished. For example, an apparently active eagle nest examined on San Clemente Island on 26 March 1927 by the DeGroot-Pemberton party (DeGroot field notes) represents the latest record of the species that I have been able to locate for the island, but virtually no observations were reported for San Clemente birds between 1927 and recent years. Similarly, the latest record of nesting eagles for San Miguel Island was April, 1939, but no further bird observations were reported from there until the 1960s. By then, the Bald Eagle had vanished from the island.

Extinction of the Bald Eagle on Santa Barbara Island evidently occurred between 27 March 1927, when the species was noted there by the DeGroot-Pemberton party (DeGroot field notes), and 1939, when it was not found by L. Sumner and R. Bond in April (Sumner unpubl. ms.), or by a biological survey party from the Los Angeles County Museum of Natural History between 27 and 30 May (J. C. von Bloeker, Jr. *in litt.*). The island is so small that these visitors could

FIGURE 1. *Bald Eagle chick in 1949 Anacapa Island nest. Photo by Raymond J. Quigley.*

scarcely have missed eagles, had they been present.

At least one pair of eagles nested on San Nicolas Island in 1945 (Rett 1947), but a party from the University of California at Los Angeles did not record the species during field work between 9 and 13 January 1959 (Collias field notes). Townsend (1968) did not see any eagles during his long stay on San Nicolas Island between 2 May 1962 and 1 January 1964.

Bald Eagles nested on Anacapa Island as late as May, 1949 when Raymond Quigley, Telford Work, and Harold Hill investigated a nest containing a nestling three or four days old (Quigley field notes). The photographs made of the nest and chick (Fig. 1) may be the latest certain documentation of a Bald Eagle nesting attempt on the California Islands. When he visited Anacapa again on 27 May 1962, Quigley (field notes) did not see any Bald Eagles, and Banks (1966) found none during his visits to the island in 1963, 1964, and 1965.

On the remaining Channel Islands—Santa Catalina, Santa Cruz, and Santa Rosa—the Bald Eagle probably survived as a resident until the late 1950s, although a gradual decline in their numbers had evidently been occurring prior to that time. Referring to the Santa Catalina Island population, Howell (1917) wrote, "A number are killed here annually by tourists and sheep-herders, until they are now not quite so abundant," and van Rossem (field notes for 1921) noted that the Santa Catalina Island eagles were seeking more remote nesting sites as the popularity of the island increased. Nevertheless, A. Douglas Propst (pers. comm.) informed me that he noticed Bald Eagles on Santa Catalina for several years after he became a resident there in 1953, and he estimated that the resident eagle population vanished from the island completely in the late 1950s.

Similarly, long-time residents of Santa Cruz Island think that Bald Eagles were last seen there in about 1958 (Lyndal Laughrin, pers. comm.), although it is not known whether the birds were still attempting to nest then. Bill Wallace, ranch foreman on Santa Rosa Island, stated that the foreman who preceded him persecuted eagles in various ways on the island during the 1950s (pers. comm. to H. L. Jones). Wallace believes that these activities ceased in about 1958 when no more eagles could be found on the island.

With the extirpation of the Bald Eagle from these three large islands, the once thriving Channel Islands breeding population became totally extinct. Although some authors have stated that the extinction of Bald Eagles occurred at virtually the same time on the southern California mainland as on the Channel Islands (Diamond 1969, Lynch and Johnson 1974), the species essentially vanished as a breeding form on the adjacent mainland long before it disappeared from the islands.

Henshaw (1876) reported that Bald Eagles were abundant on the southern California mainland in the 1870s, but they barely persisted there past the turn of the century. I am aware of only seven southern California mainland nest localities used by Bald Eagles since 1900: (1) La Jolla Canyon, Ventura County (van Rossem field notes for 1922; egg set purportedly taken by O. W. Howard in 1921 not located by me); (2) Zuma Canyon, Los Angeles County (set of two eggs taken by W. L. Chambers on 13 March 1897, now WFVZ 65873; nesting continued until much later, according to E. N. Harrison, pers. comm.); (3) Malibu Canyon, Los Angeles County (Willett 1933; also set of two eggs taken by D. S. DeGroot on 21 March 1931, now WFVZ 58517); (4) Little Tecate Mountain (= "Lookout Mountain"), San Diego County (fresh egg taken by A. O. and Adan Treganza on 8 March 1936, now WFVZ 55005); (5) near the Sweetwater Reservoir, San Diego County, where a pair had a nest on top of a smokestack in an abandoned brick factory during the early part of the century (J. B. Dixon *in litt.*); (6) Rincon Creek, near Carpinteria, Santa Barbara County until the late 1930s (W. Abbott, pers. comm.); and (7) Dos Pueblos Ranch, Santa Barbara County. According to W. Abbott (pers. comm.), this nest was active until the early 1950s. It was photographed by L. T. Stevens on 8 February 1954 when it may still have been in use. No eggs are known to have been collected from Santa Barbara County mainland nest sites.

Causes of decline

Reported historical causes of Bald Eagle mortality on the California Islands include shooting, egg collecting, nest destruction, nest disturbance leading to desertion, removal of young from nests, trapping, and poisoning. Shooting, particularly by sheepherders but also by visitors to the islands, was probably the most important of these factors (Howell 1917, Dawson 1923). A single shooting incident could have accounted for the disappearance of eagles from the smaller islands (*e.g.*, Los Coronados and Santa Barbara), where only a single pair may have constituted the entire breeding population. On the larger islands, eagle populations seem to have been remarkably resilient, despite intensive persecution. On a visit to San Miguel Island between 27 and 29 December 1930, A. J. van Rossem (field notes) saw the wings of twenty or more Bald Eagles nailed to the wall of a barn by the caretaker of the island, who claimed that he had shot or poisoned all of the birds during the past year. Nevertheless, van Rossem reported that he saw

TABLE 1. Number of Bald Eagle egg sets collected on the Channel Islands and Los Coronados.

Island	Number of egg sets
San Clemente	15
San Nicolas	1*
Santa Catalina	10
Santa Barbara	0
Anacapa	15
Santa Cruz	35
Santa Rosa	5
San Miguel	2
Los Coronados	0
Total	82

* Not confirmed.

the "usual number" of live eagles on the island at the time of his visit. Some of the dead birds, as well as the living ones seen by van Rossem, could have been wintering individuals from northern populations. In April, 1939, L. Sumner and R. Bond encountered a more benevolent caretaker, Herbert Lester, and a healthy breeding population of Bald Eagles on San Miguel Island (Sumner unpubl. ms.).

George Breninger (1904) collected two sets of eggs (FMNH 481 and 15785) and at least two adult birds on San Clemente Island in February, 1903. His colorful account of eagle behavior at the nest, if true, indicates that the birds allowed close approach by Breninger and an assistant and may have engaged in actual nest defense. Such behavior, if typical, and the conspicuous nature of their nests would have contributed to the vulnerability of eagles to shooting.

Other birds were taken by museum collectors, but the number appears to be comparatively insignificant. My data sources yielded evidence of only six Bald Eagle study skins or skeletons from the California Islands, including those of Breninger, although a few others were no doubt collected.

At least 82 sets of Bald Eagle eggs were collected on the Channel Islands between 1875 and 1949. The total number of sets taken on each island is given in Table 1. In addition, at least one set was reportedly collected by C. B. Linton on San Nicolas Island (Willett 1912), but I could not locate it.

There appears to be no record of a replacement clutch being laid by a Bald Eagle on the California Islands after the loss of its eggs. Several veteran oologists with whom I have discussed this matter, as well as Dawson (1923), agreed that the former California Bald Eagles did not replace eggs that were collected, apparently differing in this respect from the Florida population (Bent 1937). Therefore, each set of eggs that was collected presumably cancelled the reproductive output of a given pair of eagles for an entire year.

Egg collecting probably had a negligible impact on eagle populations on most islands, since it occurred sporadically and usually involved only a single pair of birds in a given year. However, intense collecting pressure on Anacapa and Santa Cruz Islands between 1916 and 1922 may have temporarily reduced the resident eagle populations there, since at least 30 sets of eggs were taken from the two islands during that period. In his field notes covering a visit to Santa Cruz Island in 1920, van Rossem wrote, "All known nests on the island were robbed by a party of egg-hunters from Ventura (accounts of fishermen and islanders varied from seven to nine sets). These people are evidently making a yearly clean-up of eagles on all the northern group of islands, as I have reliable information of seven sets taken last year." That an actual

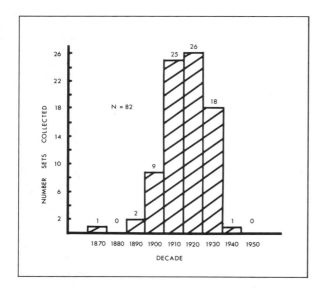

FIGURE 2. *Number of Bald Eagle egg sets collected on the California Islands per decade.*

decline in the eagle population occurred is suggested by Ross (1926), who reported, during a visit to Santa Cruz Island between 29 March and 1 April, being "impressed by the abundance of Ravens, and the scarcity of Bald Eagles."

Yet eagles were found nesting at nearly all of their traditional sites on Anacapa and Santa Cruz Islands in later years, according to the notes of collectors and others who visited the islands. During the 1930s, at least 14 more egg sets were taken (10 on Santa Cruz and 4 on Anacapa), but other nests successfully fledged young (E. N. Harrison, pers. comm., Sumner unpubl. ms.). Possibly, the eagle populations on Santa Cruz and Anacapa Islands were augmented by individuals hatched on other islands (*e.g.*, nearby Santa Rosa), where the birds were subjected to less harassment.

Collecting of Bald Eagle eggs on the Channel Islands was most intense between approximately 1915 and 1936 (Fig. 2); only a single set is known to have been taken after 1939. Although egg collecting probably contributed to short-term declines in eagle populations on some islands, it cannot account for the extirpation of the species from any island. Even where collectors were most active (*i.e.*, Anacapa and Santa Cruz Islands), nesting eagles were still present in significant numbers well after egg collecting had ceased.

Other forms of Bald Eagle mortality on the California Islands are more poorly documented, but some may have taken a considerable toll. Dawson (1923) reported that sheepherders destroyed nests on some islands, as well as routinely shot eagles. Even in the 1950s, the Santa Rosa Island population was still suffering from several forms of rancher-induced persecution, including destruction of nests and capturing of young, in addition to shooting (H. L. Jones, pers. comm.). A pair of eagles on San Clemente Island deserted their nest, which contained two eggs, after Donald Dickey left a camera set up beside it (Howell field notes for 1915).

Aside from Rett's (1947) report of an active eagle nest on San Nicolas Island in 1945, virtually nothing is known of Bald Eagles on the California Islands during the 1940s, a period when San Miguel, San Nicolas, and San Clemente Islands were under the jurisdiction of the United States Navy. The impact of wartime activities on eagles and other conspicuous animals on the islands is now a matter of conjecture, but it may have been severe. There are no post-war records of Bald Eagles from any of these islands, but field work on each of them was too inadequate in the late 1940s and 1950s to confirm the disappearance of the species.

Poisoning programs were administered at one time or another on nearly all of the Channel Islands, mostly to control populations of introduced mammals. Such activities reportedly resulted in Bald Eagle deaths from primary or secondary poisoning on San Miguel Island (van Rossem field notes for 1930) and Santa Rosa and Santa Cruz Islands (E. N. Harrison, pers. comm.). However, the extent of these programs, the types of poisons used, and the actual incidence of eagle deaths from this source escaped documentation.

No environmental poison has had a more profound impact on avian populations than DDT. This pesticide was first used widely in the United States in 1947, and DDT-related residues were detected in the sediments of the Santa Barbara basin in about 1952 (Hom *et al.* 1974). Levels of DDT-type compounds have been unusually high in the southern California marine ecosystem, primarily as the result of the effluent from a DDT manufacturing company in Los Angeles (Burnett 1971). Numerous studies have shown that low dietary levels of p,p'DDE, the principal metabolite of DDT, are the primary, and perhaps sole, cause of eggshell thinning in populations of bird-eating and fish-eating wild birds (Cooke 1973, Stickel 1975, Peakall 1975).

At the time DDT was introduced in California, Bald Eagles still nested on at least Anacapa, Santa Cruz, Santa Rosa, and Santa Catalina Islands, although probably in lower numbers than previously because of the combined factors already discussed. For example, R. Quigley, H. Hill, and T. Work found only one active Bald Eagle nest on Anacapa Island in 1949 (Quigley field notes), whereas the island had traditionally supported two or three pairs of nesting eagles (Banks 1966). By 1960, resident Bald Eagles were completely extinct on all of the Channel Islands. A causal relationship between the disappearance of eagles and the introduction of DDT into the southern California marine ecosystem is suggested by the following points.

(1) Significant eggshell thinning has occurred in Bald Eagle eggs from most other parts of its range, and some eggs contained DDE residues of the same magnitude as those that produced shell thinning in experimental species (Anderson and Hickey 1972, Wiemeyer *et al.* 1972).

(2) Channel Islands populations of two piscivorous species, the Brown Pelican (*Pelecanus occidentalis*) and Double-crested Cormorant (*Phalacrocorax auritus*), have suffered severe eggshell thinning and population declines that were attributed to the effects of DDE (Risebrough *et al.* 1971, Gress *et al.* 1973, Anderson *et al.* 1975).

(3) Bald Eagles vanished at about the same time—in the late 1950s—from several of the larger islands, suggesting that a single factor was responsible.

(4) The timing of the extinction is compatible with the expected life span of this long-lived species. If DDE did affect eagle reproductive success on the Channel Islands by the early 1950s, adults may have occupied nesting sites for several years without reproducing successfully, leaving the sites vacant upon their deaths.

Osprey
Distribution and status
The Osprey occurred as a breeding resident only on the southernmost Channel Islands, specifically, San Clemente, Santa Catalina, and San Nicolas (Howell 1917). The nesting population was migratory (Howell 1917, Grinnell and Miller 1944) and occasional individuals seen in winter were probably transients from more northern populations.

Howell (1917) thought that it was doubtful that Ospreys nested on Los Coronados Islands, but an apparently authentic set of two eggs was taken there on 10 May 1897 by H. McConville for the noted oologist R. Magoon Barnes and is now in the collection of the American Museum of Natural History (AMNH 7074).

The largest nesting population of Ospreys off the California coast appears to have been located on San Clemente Island. On visits to that island during the spring of 1897, Grinnell (1897) found Ospreys "quite abundant about the south end of the islands, and there was hardly a rocky promontory or pinnacle which was not used as a nesting site. The nests were either on pillars of rock standing directly in the surf, or on over-hanging ledges close above the water." During February, 1903, Breninger (1904) saw additional Osprey nests at the north end of the island, although he did not specify their number or status. C. B. Linton (1908) investigated 12 to 14 Osprey nests on the southeastern coast of San Clemente in early April, 1907, probably the same colony mentioned earlier by Grinnell. On a data slip accompanying a set of eggs (WFVZ 32401) he took on 4 April, Linton stated that he found a total of 20 Osprey nests on San Clemente Island in 1907, the largest number mentioned by an observer for any of the islands in a single year.

Ospreys were also common on Santa Catalina Island, although I have encountered no specific estimates of their former numbers there. Howell (1917) noted that on Santa Catalina "every detached rock of any height has its resident pair."

Ospreys were "tolerably common" and presumably nesting on San Nicolas Island in May, 1897 (Grinnell 1897). A single egg was taken from an Osprey nest on that island in 1901 by Blanche Trask (MVZ 4236). A statement by Howell (1917) that C. B. Linton found the species "plentiful" on San Nicolas Island is ambiguous, since the accompanying citation refers to the latter author's 1908 paper on the birds of San Clemente Island, which includes no mention of San Nicolas observations. However, at least three sets of Osprey eggs (MCZ 8695 and 8696, WFVZ 97065), including one set taken by Linton, were collected on San Nicolas Island in 1909.

Period of decline

Willett (1912) stated that the Osprey was common on the Channel Islands, but Howell (1917) categorized the species as a "fairly common breeder on some of the islands." By the early 1920s its status had been reduced to: "breeds sparingly upon the Santa Barbara Islands" (Dawson 1923). A decade later, Willett (1933) reported that the species occurred on San Clemente Island in much reduced numbers, was seldom seen on Santa Catalina Island, and that its status on San Nicolas Island was unknown to him. He presented no evidence that the Osprey still actually nested on the Channel Islands, and it is possible that the species ceased to breed there by 1930.

The last documented nesting of the Osprey on the Channel Islands was on 26 March 1927 when a party consisting of D. S. DeGroot, J. R. Pemberton, H. W. Carriger, and O. W. Howard collected two sets of eggs (WFVZ 59971; other set in collection of James B. Dixon, Escondido, California) from a colony of six nests located on rocky pinnacles off the south end of San Clemente Island. DeGroot (field notes) commented on the fact that few active nests were found there, compared with the colony's much larger size when Howard had collected eggs there in 1905.

As in the case of the Bald Eagle, Ospreys survived on the Channel Islands long after they had vanished as a breeding species on the adjacent southern California mainland. Cooper (1887) found the species "common along the coast of Ventura County in the early 1870s," but Willett (1912) concluded that the species had been nearly exterminated along the mainland since then.

The species appears never to have been common as a breeding resident on the mainland within recent time, and I am aware of only three specific Osprey nesting records for the southern California mainland. Cooper (1870) described the attempts of a pair to build a nest on the main-top platform of an old boat anchored in San Diego Bay. Despite efforts to discourage them, the birds persisted in carrying nesting material to the boat until its resident became exasperated and shot one of the pair, thus ending the nesting attempt. Willett (1912) cited an

Osprey nesting record of unknown outcome by E. Davis near Laguna Beach, Orange County on 5 March 1895. A "set" of four eggs was taken singly from a nest on top of a light beacon in San Diego Bay by a boat captain for A. M. Ingersoll on 11, 14, 18, and 21 April 1912 (WFVZ 71019). This was apparently the last known nesting attempt by Ospreys on the southern California mainland.

Farther south along the Pacific coast of Baja California, a similar decline in the populations of nesting Ospreys occurred on many islands and along the mainland coast between about 1910 and the mid-1940s (Kenyon 1947). Kenyon felt that the disappearance of Ospreys was more marked in the northernmost Baja California localities, and his data suggest that the most precipitous declines occurred there after the mid-1920s.

Causes of decline

Shooting of Ospreys was repeatedly mentioned by early writers as the most significant cause of mortality. In discussing the status of the species in southern California, Willett (1912) stated, "Many have been shot by gunners and most of those remaining have taken refuge on the islands." Howell (1917) noted that Ospreys were not as abundant as they had been formerly on Santa Catalina Island, "owing to the depredations of the tourists." DeGroot (field notes) speculated that the decline in the number of Ospreys noted by his party on San Clemente in 1927 might have been due to shooting of the birds by fishermen, who regarded them as competitors, or merely as attractive targets.

In attempting to find a cause for the apparent reduction of Ospreys along the coast of Baja California and its adjacent islands, Kenyon (1947) concluded that shooting by commercial fishermen, mostly Americans, was the most devastating form of human persecution suffered by the species there, although he also noted that Mexican fishermen occasionally ate both Osprey eggs and young.

On San Clemente and Santa Catalina Islands, as well as further south along the coast of Baja California, Ospreys built their large conspicuous nests on offshore pinnacles of rock that were easily approached by boats. As Kenyon (1947) pointed out, the birds were vulnerable to shooting and other harassment throughout their long incubation and nestling periods, which together amount to about 12 weeks.

I have records of 19 sets of Osprey eggs taken by collectors on the Channel Islands between 1893 and 1927 (12 on San Clemente, four on San Nicolas, and three on Santa Catalina). Although these activities were temporarily detrimental to the island Ospreys, egg collecting cannot account for their extinction. It affected relatively few pairs of birds and had essentially ceased before the period of precipitous decline in the Osprey populations. Only three sets of eggs are known to have been taken after 1909. Furthermore, although Ospreys raise only a single brood per season, they generally replace lost first clutches (Bent 1937). A factor that may have reduced the potential oological toll on Channel Islands Ospreys was the ready availability of their eggs from Eastern collectors who lived in areas where the species was more accessible and abundant.

While the combined effects of all forms of human persecution of Channel Islands Ospreys may have been sufficient to extirpate them, the concomitant decline in the Osprey population along the Pacific coast of Baja California (Kenyon 1947) suggests that some major environmental change may have affected the species throughout the region. Although there appear to be no available data concerning the food habits of Channel Islands Ospreys, the birds were presumably almost exclusively piscivorous there, like other North American Osprey populations (Bent 1937). It is possible that some deleterious change in the food supply of Pacific coast Ospreys occurred during the 1920s to 1930s that contributed to their extinction. Without specific data on the fish species eaten by Ospreys here, however, this is a matter of speculation.

Peregrine Falcon

Distribution and status

The Peregrine Falcon was a common permanent resident on the Channel Islands and Los Coronados Islands (Willett 1912, Howell 1917), although specific breeding records are lacking from some islands. Migrants and wintering birds from more northern populations also occurred on the islands (Grinnell and Miller 1944).

Compared with Bald Eagles and Ospreys, both peregrines and their nests are much less conspicuous to casual observers. From his studies of the Aleutian Islands population, White (1975) concluded that "unless specifically searching for Peregrines, the types of faunal studies that are generally carried out reveal only a minor percentage of the total Peregrines present." Thus, historical estimates of the number of peregrines on the California Islands were almost certainly too low, except on the smallest islands. Furthermore, the lack of reported observations of the species by island visitors is *not* conclusive evidence of its absence (see Hunt and Hunt 1974, Jones and Diamond 1976).

The Peregrine Falcon was most abundant on Los Coronados Islands, and the former density of breeding pairs there may have been the highest ever recorded for the race *Falco peregrinus anatum*. At least three pairs nested regularly on Los Coronados (Howell 1917), but in some, perhaps many, years the number was higher. Wright (1909) found three pairs on South and Middle Coronados Islands on 22 June 1908, and earlier in the same year Osburn (1909) saw apparently the same birds on South Island, plus an additional two pairs on North Island. L. M. Huey (*in* Howell field notes for 1913) saw 11 peregrines on North Island alone on 30 May 1913, despite the fact that this island is only "1 mile long, 0.12 miles wide, and 467 feet high" (Jehl 1977).

Banks (1969) was told by Lewis Wayne Walker that in about 1932 there were two or three pairs of peregrines on North Island, one on Middle Island, and four or five on South Island. Because these estimates are much higher than those of other observers for the same period, and because they were made over 30 years after Walker's visit to Los Coronados, they may be unrealistic. In about 1945, Walker reportedly thought that there were only four active peregrine sites on Los Coronados—two on North Island and two on South Island (Zuk unpubl. ms.).

Although an actual nest was never reported from San Clemente Island, peregrines were presumably resident there. The earliest report of the species from the island was that of Mearns (1907), who, with A. W. Anthony, recorded it there between 22 and 29 August 1894. Grinnell (1897) apparently did not find peregrines on two trips to San Clemente totaling 18 days in 1897. However, as previously pointed out, this does not rule out the presence of the species on San Clemente, considering the relatively large size of the island and the limitations of a single observer. Breninger (1904) saw a pair of peregrines on San Clemente in February, 1903 and collected the male. Linton (1908) found pairs at two different sites during his four visits to San Clemente Island in 1907. He stated that at least one pair bred on the island during that year, but gave no further details. Howell (1917) and his party saw a pair of peregrines repeatedly on San Clemente during late March and early April, 1915, but did not succeed in locating a suspected nest site.

On Santa Catalina Island, Willett (1912) took a set of four eggs (WFVZ 23185) at Long Point on 8 April 1904, and a set of three eggs (WFVZ 63151) was collected on 5 May 1905 from another site on the island by O. W. Howard. Howell (1917) stated that he had seen several peregrines on the northwest part of Santa Catalina, and the species was also reported during the breeding seasons of 1920 by A. J. van Rossem (field notes) and 1938 by R. Arnold (field notes).

Of all the California Islands, it is least certain that Peregrine Falcons nested on San Nicolas. Loye Miller (unpubl. ms.) found the bodies of a pair of peregrines discarded on the beach at San Nicolas Island on 7 July 1938. The birds appeared to have been shot some months earlier, and their wings and feet had been cut off. Miller assumed that they had been nesting in the vicinity. Rett (1947) saw two Peregrine Falcons fly over the north shore of San Nicolas Island, heading southward, on 14 March 1945. I am aware of no other specific reports of peregrines from the island.

Cooper (1870) wrote that on Santa Barbara Island in May, 1863, a pair of peregrines "which probably were still feeding their young swept boldly around my head, when I must have been fully half a mile from the nest, and I shot the female, a very fine specimen." On 1 May 1908, Howell (1917) flushed a pair "from the cliff on the seaward side of Santa Barbara Island, where they undoubtedly had a nest of young." The DeGroot-Pemberton party visited the island on 27 March 1927 and "this species was seen by all members of the field party" (DeGroot field notes), although the number of birds involved was not mentioned.

Lowell Sumner and Richard Bond did not record peregrines during their short visit to Santa Barbara Island in April, 1939 (Sumner unpubl. ms.). However, a biological survey party from the Los Angeles County Museum of Natural History observed a pair of peregrines daily between 27 and 30 May of the same year as they flew about in the vicinity of Sutil Islet, a rocky pinnacle just off the main island (J. C. von Bloeker, Jr. *in litt.*). The birds appeared to be defending an active nest site. Since Hunt and Hunt (1974) concluded from Sumner's observations, or lack of them, that the Peregrine Falcon was extinct on Santa Barbara Island by 1939, this is a clear example of the difficulties involved in assessing the significance of "non-sightings" of peregrines.

Nesting peregrines were found on Anacapa Island by Willett (1910), Burt (1911), and probably by Wright and Snyder (1913) in 1912. The DeGroot-Pemberton party visited the island on 28 March 1927 and flushed peregrines from both the landward and seaward sides of the island (DeGroot field notes). R. Bond (*in* Thelander 1977) thought that three pairs of Peregrine Falcons nested on Anacapa in 1935 and that three sets of eggs were taken there that year. I have been unable to locate the egg sets, however. Bond also visited active peregrine nests on Anacapa in 1934 and 1939 (Sumner unpubl. ms.). From a boat off the west end of Anacapa Island on 18 March 1941, J. C. von Bloeker, Jr. (*in litt.*) watched a peregrine stoop repeatedly on a feral housecat that rose on its hind legs each time to meet the attack. Finally, the falcon struck the cat a blow on the head that knocked it off a cliff and into the sea many feet below. Presumably the peregrine was engaging in nest defense, rather than attempting to take the cat as prey.

Peregrine Falcons were common on Santa Cruz Island, although few actual nest sites were reported. O. W. Howard took a set of three eggs there on 5 April 1906 (Willett 1912), and Linton (1908) made observations on peregrines on various parts of the island in 1907. M. C. Badger (field notes) found an active nest on 4 March 1918, and he and R. Canterbury (field notes) independently recorded what seemed to be nesting birds in 1919. R. Bond (*in* Thelander 1977) located two peregrine nests with "fair accessibility" on Santa Cruz in 1935. Nests were also found during the 1930s by several egg collectors, including E. N. Harrison (pers. comm.), L. T. Stevens (field notes), and M. C. Badger (field notes), but no eggs were taken during this period, to my knowledge.

The DeGroot-Pemberton party located three pairs of Peregrine Falcons, two of them far inland in canyons, on Santa Rosa Island between 2 and 4 April 1927 (Pemberton 1928). Although their apparent nest sites were located, none contained eggs at that date. Pemberton and DeGroot returned to Santa Rosa Island on 22 April of the following year and collected a set of three eggs from one of the sites (WFVZ 58685).

The only definite nesting records of peregrines for San Miguel Island were those of the DeGroot-Pemberton party, which spent 31 March to 2 April 1927 on the island (DeGroot field notes). They did not find peregrines until their second day on the island, despite the fact that the group consisted of four seasoned field ornithologists: DeGroot, Pemberton, Carriger, and Howard. On 1 April, Pemberton found a female on an apparent nest in a pothole on the northwest side of the island. The site proved to be inaccessible, even with a rope. Another nest was found later in the day on the southwest end of the island in a large pothole 300 feet down a huge cliff. Although the female sat tightly on the nest, DeGroot found that the scrape was empty when he climbed down to it; apparently eggs were about to be laid.

In summary, the highest numbers of Peregrine Falcon nests reported (or inferred from the available data) during a single year for the California Islands are as follows: Los Coronados, 5 (or up to 9 if the report of L. W. Walker *in* Banks 1969 is accepted); San Clemente, 1 (probably 2); Santa Catalina, 2; San Nicolas, 1?; Santa Barbara, 1; Anacapa, 3; Santa Cruz, 2; Santa Rosa, 3; and San Miguel, 2—for a total of at least 20 nests.

Food habits

Peregrines evidently fed exclusively on avian prey on the California Islands and there are reports of at least 22 species of birds being taken. Howell (1917) concluded that California Islands peregrines were most common in the vicinity of colonies of small pelagic birds, a view consistent with the data presented in the previous section. On Los Coronados Islands, such species included primarily Leach's Storm Petrels (*Oceanodroma leucorhoa*), Black Storm Petrels (*Oceanodroma melania*), Xantus' Murrelets (*Endomychura hypoleuca*), Cassin's Auklets (*Ptychoramphus aleuticus*), and even Rhinoceros Auklets (*Cerorhinca monocerata*) (Howell 1910, 1917). Grinnell and Daggett (1903) found the remains of gulls (probably *Larus occidentalis*) on Los Coronados for which they thought peregrines were accountable. Cassin's Auklets were also taken by peregrines on the Channel Islands, according to Breninger (1904) and Bond (1946). Bond also observed peregrines taking nestling Double-crested Cormorants (*Phalacrocorax auritus*), a Black Oystercatcher (*Haematopus bachmani*), and a Pigeon Guillemot (*Cepphus columba*) on the Channel Islands.

Peregrines must have had a considerable impact on both the resident and migratory birds occurring on the California Islands. Huey (field notes for 1924) made an informal examination of avian remains in a peregrine nest site on Los Coronados Islands that contained four well-developed young. He found evidence of the following species: Storm Petrels (probably both Leach's and Black), Mourning Dove (*Zenaida macroura*), Ash-throated Flycatcher (*Myiarchus cinerascens*), an *Empidonax* flycatcher, Swainson's Thrush (*Catharus ustulatus*), Hermit Thrush (*Catharus guttatus*), Orange-crowned Warbler (*Vermivora celata*), Western Tanager (*Piranga ludoviciana*), House Finch (*Carpodacus mexicanus*), and Fox Sparrow (*Passerella iliaca*). In addition, the nest contained at least 42 pairs of wings of Xantus' Murrelets. On a nearby trail, Huey's companion, A. J. van Rossem, found a Western Flycatcher (*Empidonax difficilis*) and a Black-throated Gray Warbler (*Dendroica nigrescens*) that had apparently been killed by the peregrines.

Elsewhere, DeGroot (field notes for 1927) saw peregrines feeding on Horned Larks (*Eremophila alpestris)* on Santa Rosa Island, and Linton (1908) observed them taking a Red Phalarope (*Phalaropus fulicarius*) and Black Turnstones (*Arenaria melanocephala*) on Santa Cruz Island.

Period of decline

Up until the 1940s, virtually all authorities considered the peregrine to be at least fairly common on the California Islands and on the adjacent mainland (Willett 1912, 1933, Howell 1917, Dawson 1923, Grinnell and Miller 1944). Based on data presented by Bond (1946), as well as on his unpublished notes, Herman et al. (1970) concluded that approximately 100 peregrine eyries were producing young annually during the mid-1940s in California, including the Channel Islands. There was no indication that a population decline was then in progress.

In the two decades following 1945, a catastrophic decline occurred in California peregrine populations (Herman *et al.* 1970). A survey of historical sites conducted in the breeding season of 1970 indicated that the mainland breeding population was reduced at least 95 per cent from the numbers that nested in California in the mid-1940s (Herman 1971). Furthermore, Herman *et al.* (1970) felt that nests along the southern California coast, including those on the offshore islands, suffered the earliest reduction. Although they had no on-site data, they suspected that the Channel Islands peregrine population was extirpated by 1955. The more detailed, albeit fragmentary, data that I have gathered support this conclusion. On an island-by-island basis, the last reliable report of probable resident peregrine occurrence, and the earliest subsequent survey on which the species was not recorded, are as follows.

Los Coronados. —E. N. Harrison (pers. comm.) located four active nests on these islands on 30 April 1940 (two on South Island, one on Big Middle Island, and one on North Island). He felt that other active nests may have been overlooked. D. Brimm (pers. comm.) found single nesting pairs of peregrines on South and North Islands in 1948. When T. Cade visited the islands in 1954, he found no peregrines present (Herman *et al.* 1970).

San Clemente. —No reports of peregrines subsequent to 27 March 1915 (Howell field notes) are known to me.

Santa Catalina. —The latest report was by R. Arnold, who saw peregrines chasing Bald Eagles and also being chased by ravens on 15 April 1938.

San Nicolas. —Rett (1947) saw two peregrines on 14 March 1945. A party from the University of California at Los Angeles did not find the species between 9 and 13 January 1959 (Collias field notes).

Santa Barbara. —Apparently, nesting peregrines were noted between 27 and 30 May 1939 (J. C. von Bloeker, Jr. *in litt.*), but none recorded during a rabbit destruction program administered on the island between 1953 and 1957 (Sumner unpubl. ms.).

Anacapa. —An adult that was probably nesting was seen on 21 May 1949, but none was found on 27 May 1962 by R. Quigley (pers. comm.), or by subsequent visitors (*e.g.*, Banks 1966). The latest certain nesting was documented by Sumner (unpubl. ms.) on 16 April 1939.

Santa Rosa. —No observations of peregrines were reported after 1927 (Pemberton 1928).

Santa Cruz. —R. Bond (*in* Thelander 1977) found two nests in April, 1935, and M. C. Badger and L. T. Stevens saw an apparently resident pair on 7 March 1937 (Badger field notes). Peregrines were not encountered by A. Miller (field notes) during March, 1950.

San Miguel. —The latest pre-1965 sighting was by L. Sumner (unpubl. ms.), who saw a single adult flying along the coast of the island in mid-April, 1939.

In summary, peregrines survived until at least 1937 on seven islands. There is no evidence that they were gone from any island prior to 1950. The last reported sighting of a probable breeding adult was on 21 May 1949 on Anacapa Island.

Causes of decline

Documented causes of peregrine mortality on the California Islands include shooting, skin collecting, egg collecting, and removal of young from nests. Additional possible causes of the peregrine's disappearance from the islands include the effects of DDE and changes in the food supply.

Probably few peregrines were shot on the California Islands, at least compared with the destruction of the larger, more conspicuous, and slower-flying Bald Eagles and Ospreys. There is only one actual report of wantonly shot peregrines, the pair found by L. Miller on San Nicolas Island on 7 July 1938 (Miller unpubl. ms.).

At least 14 museum specimens (all study skins) of peregrines were collected on the islands: 11 from Los Coronados, and one each from San Clemente, Santa Barbara, and Santa Catalina. The latest of these were taken in 1924. Eight of the Los Coronados Islands birds were juveniles of less than a year, seven of them collected by L. Huey from two nests in May, 1917 and May, 1924.

As with study skins, most egg sets of peregrines from the California Islands were collected on Los Coronados. At least 14 egg sets were taken there between 1898 and 1940. I know of only four sets definitely collected on the Channel Islands: two on Santa Catalina, one on Santa Rosa, and one on Santa Cruz. Bond (*in* Thelander 1977) believed that three sets of eggs were collected on Anacapa Island in 1935 by an unnamed collector, but I have been unable to locate these sets in any collection.

Based on my conversations with several old-time egg collectors, I have concluded that sets of peregrine eggs were taken on the California Islands in such limited numbers for the following reasons: (1) peregrine eggs, unlike those of Bald Eagles, could be readily obtained from mainland nest sites; (2) with the exception of Los Coronados Islands (Howell 1917), peregrine eyries on the California Islands were usually very difficult to reach, and probably few collectors had either the equipment or the persistence to gain access to them; and (3) most oologists visited the islands specifically to collect eggs of waterbirds, Bald Eagles, and/or endemic passerines.

Peregrines usually replace lost clutches on the California mainland (Thelander 1977) and, presumably, also did so on the California Islands. Two sets of eggs were taken on Los Coronados Islands in 1920, 1921, and 1931, and in each instance the second set was believed by the collectors to be a replacement clutch. Most of the other sets taken by egg collectors were probably actually replaced by the birds, with net productivity being little affected by the collecting activities.

Although removal of young peregrines from nests for falconry purposes has posed a significant threat to the depleted mainland California peregrine populations in recent years (Herman *et al*. 1970), it is unlikely that many birds were lost for such reasons from the former California Islands population. Thelander (pers. comm.) informed me that young were taken from an Anacapa Island peregrine nest by falconers in the 1940s, and another juvenile from a Santa Rosa Island nest in 1942, but no other instances of this kind have come to my attention. Perhaps some of the same factors that minimized the effects that egg collecting had on California Islands peregrines also operated to reduce the toll by falconers.

In summary, the available data indicate that neither the chronology nor magnitude of shooting, skin collecting, egg collecting, or removal of young from nests can be considered factors of any significance in the disappearance of the Peregrine Falcon from the California Islands.

The events suggesting a causal relationship between the appearance of DDT in the southern California marine ecosystem and the extirpation of the Bald Eagle from the California Islands serve equally well, or better, to explain the disappearance of the Peregrine Falcon from the same islands. In fact, it was the precipitous decline of the peregrine in England that led to the discovery of the deleterious effect of DDT on populations of bird-eating and fish-eating birds (Ratcliffe 1967); DDE-induced eggshell thinning in peregrines now appears to be a nearly universal phenomenon (Peakall and Kiff 1979).

Hickey and Anderson (1968) showed that all California mainland peregrine eggshells collected after 1947 were significantly thinner than those taken before World War II. Peakall (1974) demonstrated the presence of DDE in California peregrine eggs as early as 1948 in concentrations sufficient to account for the observed shell thinning. Reproductive failures of the type that have come to be known as the "DDT syndrome," including egg breakage, reduced clutch size, and behavioral abnormalities, are known to have occurred in the late 1940s or early 1950s at most peregrine nest sites on the portion of the mainland nearest the California Islands (Thelander *et al*. in prep.). The pattern of decline observed in peregrine populations on the California mainland is apparently related to worldwide patterns of DDE contamination of prey species; peregrines in marine environments, where DDE levels are highest, are the quickest to disappear and the slowest to recover (Herman *et al.* 1970, Thelander 1977). In short, the effects of DDE on peregrine reproduction are almost certainly the primary and, perhaps, the only factor responsible for the extirpation of the species on the California Islands.

Peregrines, like most higher trophic level species, are particularly vulnerable to changes in their food supply. In addition to causing reproductive failure, DDT and other environmental contaminants can cause a reduction in the bird populations upon which peregrines subsist. Although historical data are largely unsatisfactory for making rigorous quantitative estimates of changes in seabird populations on the California mainland, there has clearly been an overall reduction in their size and diversity since the turn of the century (Hunt *et al.* 1980). Nelson and Myres (1976) related a decline in the resident peregrine population on Langara Island, British Columbia to nest failures caused by DDE in their usual prey item, Ancient Murrelets (*Synthliboramphus antiquus*). They stated that, in a year, a family of peregrines (two adults and four young) will kill about 1,000 murrelets. Although California Islands peregrines had a more varied diet, it is doubtful that the southern California marine ecosystem now provides a sufficient food base to support the number of peregrines that occurred there historically, especially on Los Coronados Islands.

DISCUSSION

Since the publication of Diamond's (1969) paper on avian turnover rates, there has been much interest in the interaction of immigrations and extinctions on the Channel Islands. The three species of raptors treated here have figured prominently in these discussions since they account for a large proportion of the extinctions recognized by Diamond (*op. cit.*). Lynch and Johnson (1974) pointed out that since most or all of these extinctions were probably caused by human activities, their inclusion in the calculation of island turnover rates yields artificially high figures. Jones and Diamond (1976) argued that the net effect of the elimination of the large raptors from the islands and the southern California mainland pool was to reduce actual turnover rates in the long run since these species turn over more rapidly than most other groups in the island avifauna.

Whatever the case, the Channel Islands appear to be a rather poor arena for examining turnover characteristics of the large raptors. From the data presented earlier, it seems highly probable that man was directly responsible for the extirpation of the Bald Eagle and Peregrine Falcon from the California Islands. This may also have been the case with the Osprey, but the available data are too nebulous to be certain. It is difficult to see the relevance to natural turnover rates of calculations based, in large part, upon man-induced extinctions.

Various authors, including Hunt and Hunt (1974) and Jones and Diamond (1976), have stated that predatory birds tend to experience more rapid turnover on islands than species at lower trophic levels, primarily because of their relatively lower population sizes. If so, this contrasts sharply with mainland raptor populations, which are remarkable among birds for their stability over long periods of time in environments free from human interference. Newton (1976) cited numerous examples of such stability based on long-term studies of populations of fourteen falconiforms, and he listed seven such studies of peregrine populations. For example, Ratcliffe (1972) noted that out of 49 peregrine eyries known to falconers in England between the 16th and 19th centuries, 42 were still occupied by 1930. Bald Eagles are also notorious for their long-term occupancy of nest sites, and several egg collectors, including D. R. Dickey, M. C. Badger, and Sidney Peyton, commented in their field notes or on egg data slips about the extreme age of some of the nests from which they collected eggs.

Jones and Diamond (1976) stated that the extirpation of the Bald Eagle and Osprey on the southern California mainland had the effect of lowering expected turnover rates, since it eliminated the most important potential source of immigrants for the recolonization of the islands following extinctions. While this is true, the islands themselves served as a potential source of colonizers for the unsaturated mainland during much of this century, yet there is little or no evidence that such immigration took place.

If the adverse effects of DDE were the ultimate cause of the extirpation of the peregrine and Bald Eagle from the California Islands, then it is possible that the reduction of residue levels in the local marine environment that has occurred since 1972 (Anderson et al. 1975) will permit the re-establishment of these species on the islands. Recolonization of the peregrine may occur without human intervention, since the nearby mainland population appears to be slowly recovering (Thelander 1977, D. Harlow, pers. comm.). The nearest breeding population of Bald Eagles, however, is presently in northeastern California, and it is probable that man will have to aid their reintroduction to the islands. The successful re-establishment and maintenance of populations of these two species on the Channel Islands would provide still further evidence implicating DDE in their local extinctions.

SUMMARY

The California Channel Islands and Los Coronados Islands formerly supported resident populations of Bald Eagles, Ospreys, and Peregrine Falcons. Data on the former status of these species on the islands were obtained from museum egg and study skin collections, field notes and unpublished manuscripts of visitors to the islands, interviews with island residents and visitors, and the published literature.

Bald Eagles once nested on all the islands. They became gradually more scarce from man-induced factors, including shooting, nest disturbance, and poisoning, finally becoming extinct in the late 1950s, possibly from the effects of DDE. The islands supported a minimum of 24 pairs of Bald Eagles within the present century, a decrease from the 1800s. Both Bald Eagles and Ospreys were essentially extirpated on the adjacent mainland by the turn of the century.

Ospreys, which nested only on the southernmost Channel Islands, vanished by about 1930 from unknown causes. A similar decline occurred about the same time along the coast of northern Baja California. Ospreys were most common on San Clemente Island, where at least one colony contained over 20 pairs.

Peregrine Falcons were apparently resident on all the islands. The population became extinct between the mid-1940s and early 1950s, and a severe decline in the California mainland population occurred during the same period. Evidence suggesting that DDE caused the extirpation of the peregrine and the Bald Eagle on the California Islands includes the correlation between the extinctions and the introduction of DDT, the simultaneous nature of the extinctions on all the islands, DDE-caused breeding failures in both species elsewhere in their ranges, unusually high local DDE residue levels, and well-documented DDE-caused breeding failures in certain seabirds resident on the islands. No other significant mortality factor is known for the island peregrines. At least 20 pairs of peregrines may have been resident on the California Islands.

The California Islands are ill-suited for examining turnover rates of large raptors because of man's persistent interference with the birds and their environment. Elsewhere, however, raptors are distinguished by the extreme constancy of their populations in stable environments; a natural extinction on the islands of any of the three species treated here has not been convincingly documented. If formerly high DDE residue levels in local food chains resulted in the extirpation of the peregrine and the Bald Eagles on the California Islands, then the southern California marine ecosystem may now be "clean" enough to permit the re-establishment of resident populations of these species.

ACKNOWLEDGMENTS

This study was made possible by Ed N. Harrison and the Western Foundation of Vertebrate Zoology. Julie Kiff, Dana Gardner, Michael Morrison, Sam Sumida, and Ray Quigley aided in preparation of the manuscript and in many other ways. I received gratifying cooperation in providing me with data or allowing me access to their collections from the curatorial staffs of the collections listed in Appendix 1. Ed N. Harrison, Lyndal Laughrin, A. Douglas Propst, Ray Quigley, Carl Thelander, and Jack von Bloeker, Jr. provided valuable unpublished data. I am especially grateful to H. Lee Jones for generously sharing unpublished data and original ideas on Channel Islands birds and to Robert Risebrough for suggesting this project and offering wise counsel.

REFERENCES

ANDERSON, D. W., and J. J. HICKEY. 1972. Eggshell changes in certain North American birds. Pp. 514-540 *in* K. H. Voous, ed., Proc. XVth Int. Ornithol. Congr. E. J. Brill, Leiden.

ANDERSON, D. W., J. R. JEHL, JR., R. W. RISEBROUGH, L. A. WOODS, JR., L. R. DEWEESE, and W. G. EDGECOMB. 1975. Brown Pelicans: improved reproduction off the southern California coast. Science 190:806-808.

BANKS, R. C. 1966. Terrestrial vertebrates of Anacapa Island. Trans. San Diego Soc. Nat. Hist. 14:175-188.

BANKS, R. M. 1969. The Peregrine Falcon in Baja California and the Gulf of California. Pp. 81-91 *in* J. J. Hickey, ed., Peregrine Falcon populations. University of Wisconsin Press, Madison, Wisc.

BENT, A. C. 1937. Life histories of North American birds of prey. Pt. 1. U.S. Natl. Mus. Bull. 167.

BOND, R. M. 1946. The peregrine population of western North America. Condor 48:101-116.

BRENINGER, G. F. 1904. San Clemente Island and its birds. Auk 21:218-223.

BURNETT, R. 1971. DDT residues: distribution of concentrations in *Emerita analoga* (Stimpson) along coastal California. Science 174:606-608.

BURT, H. C. 1911. An early spring trip to Anacapa Island. Condor 13:164-167.

COOKE, A. S. 1973. Shell thinning in avian eggs by environmental pollutants. Environ. Pollut. 4:85-152.

COOPER, J. G. 1870. Geological survey of California. Ornithology, Vol. 1. Land Birds. Edited by S. F. Baird from the manuscript and notes of J. G. Cooper. California State Legislature, Sacramento, Calif.

_____. 1887. Additions to the birds of Ventura County, California. Auk 4:85-94.

DAWSON, W. L. 1923. The birds of California. Vol. 4. South Moulton Co., San Diego, Calif.

DIAMOND, J. M. 1969. Avifaunal equilibrium and species turnover rates on the Channel Islands of California. Proc. Natl. Acad. Sci. 64:57-63.

GRESS, F. G., R. W. RISEBROUGH, D. W. ANDERSON, L. F. KIFF, and J. R. JEHL, JR. 1973. Reproductive failures of Double-crested Cormorants in southern California and Baja California. Wilson Bull. 88:197-208.

GRINNELL, J. 1897. Report on the birds recorded during a visit to the islands of Santa Barbara, San Nicolas and San Clemente, in the spring of 1897. Pasadena Acad. Sci. 1:1-25.

_____. 1898. Land birds observed in mid-winter on Santa Catalina Island, California. Condor 15:233-236.

GRINNELL, J., and F. S. DAGGETT. 1903. An ornithological visit to Los Coronados Island, Lower California. Auk 20:27-37.

GRINNELL, J., and A. H. MILLER. 1944. The distribution of the birds of California. Pacific Coast Avifauna 27.

HENSHAW, H. W. 1876. Report on the ornithology of the portions of California visited during the field-season of 1875 by H. W. Henshaw. *In* G. M. Wheeler, Annual report of the geographic survey west of the 100th meridian. Appendix JJ. Washington, D.C.

HERMAN, S. G. 1971. The Peregrine Falcon decline in California. Pt. 2. The breeding status in 1970. Amer. Birds 25:818-820.

HERMAN, S. G., M. N. KIRVEN, and R. W. RISEBROUGH. 1970. The Peregrine Falcon decline in California. Audubon Field Notes 24:609-613.

HICKEY, J. J., and D. W. ANDERSON. 1968. Chlorinated hydrocarbons and eggshell changes in raptorial and fish-eating birds. Science 162:271-273.

HOM, W., R. W. RISEBROUGH, A. SOUTAR, and D. R. YOUNG. 1974. Deposition of DDE and polychlorinated biphenyls in dated sediments of the Santa Barbara basin. Science 184:1197-1199.

HOWELL, A. B. 1910. Notes from Los Coronados Islands. Condor 12:184-187.

―――. 1917. Birds of the islands off the coast of southern California. Pacific Coast Avifauna 12.

HOWELL, A. B., and A. J. VAN ROSSEM. 1911. Further notes from Santa Cruz Island. Condor 13:208-210.

HUNT, G. L., JR., and M. W. HUNT. 1974. Trophic levels and turnover rates: the avifauna of Santa Barbara Island, California. Condor 76:363-369.

HUNT, G. L., JR., R. L. PITMAN, and H. L. JONES. 1980. Distribution and abundance of seabirds breeding on the California Channel Islands. Pp. 443-459 *in* D.M. Power, ed., The California Islands: proceedings of a multidisciplinary symposium. Santa Barbara Museum of Natural History, Santa Barbara, Calif.

JEHL, J. R., JR. 1977. An annotated list of birds of Islas Los Coronados, Baja California, and adjacent waters. Western Birds 8:91-101.

JOHNSON, N. K. 1972. Origin and differentiation of the avifauna of the Channel Islands, California. Condor 74:295-315.

JONES, H. L. 1975. Studies of avian turnover, dispersal and colonization of the California Channel Islands. Ph.D. thesis, University of California, Los Angeles, Calif.

JONES, H. L., and J. M. DIAMOND. 1976. Short-time-base studies of turnover in breeding bird populations of the California Channel Islands. Condor 78:526-549.

KENYON, K. W. 1947. Breeding populations of the Osprey in Lower California. Condor 49:152-158.

LINTON, C. B. 1908. Notes from San Clemente Island. Condor 10:82-86.

LYNCH, J. F., and N. K. JOHNSON. 1974. Turnover and equilibria in insular avifaunas, with special reference to the California Channel Islands. Condor 76:370-384.

MEARNS, E. A. 1907. Mammals of the Mexican boundary of the United States. U.S. Natl. Mus. Bull. 56.

NELSON, R. W., and M. T. MYRES. 1976. Declines in populations of Peregrine Falcons and their seabird prey at Langara Island, British Columbia. Condor 78:281-293.

NEWTON, I. 1976. Population limitation in diurnal raptors. Canadian Field-Natur. 90:274-300.

OSBURN, P. I. 1909. Notes on the birds of Los Coronados Islands, Lower California. Condor 11:134-138.

PEAKALL, D. B. 1974. DDE: its presence in peregrine eggs in 1948. Science 183:673-674.

―――. 1975. Physiological effects of chlorinated hydrocarbons on avian species. Pp. 343-360 *in* R. Haque and V. H. Freed, eds., Environmental dynamics of pesticides. Plenum, New York, N.Y.

PEAKALL, D. B., and L. F. KIFF. 1979. Eggshell thinning and DDE residue levels in the Peregrine Falcon: a global perspective. Ibis 121:200-204.

PEMBERTON, J. R. 1928. Additions to the known avifauna of the Santa Barbara Islands. Condor 30:144-148.

POWER, D. M. 1972. Numbers of bird species on the California Islands. Evolution 26:451-463.

RATCLIFFE, D. A. 1967. Decrease in eggshell weight in certain birds of prey. Nature 215:208-210.

————. 1972. The peregrine population of Great Britain in 1971. Bird Study 19:117-156.

————. 1973. Studies of the recent breeding success of the peregrine (*Falco peregrinus*). J. Reproduction and Fertility (Suppl.) 19:377-389.

RETT, E. Z. 1947. A report on the birds of San Nicolas Island. Condor 49:165-168.

RICHARDSON, C. H., JR. 1908. Spring notes from Santa Catalina Island. Condor 10:65-68.

RISEBROUGH, R. W., F. C. SIBLEY, and M. N. KIRVEN. 1971. Reproductive failure of the Brown Pelican on Anacapa Island in 1969. Amer. Birds 25:8-9.

ROSS, R. C. 1926. A spring trip to Santa Cruz Island. Condor 28:240-241.

SNYDER, G. K. 1909. Dusky Warbler haunts. Oologist 26:188.

STEPHENS, F. S. 1921. Early spring notes on birds of Coronados Islands, Mexico. Condor 23:96-97.

STICKEL, W. H. 1975. Some effects of pollutants in terrestrial ecosystems. Pp. 25-74 *in* A. D. McIntyre and C. F. Mills, eds., Ecological toxicology research. Plenum, New York, N.Y.

STREATOR, C. P. 1888. Notes on the birds of the Santa Barbara Islands. Ornithologist and Oologist 13:52-54.

THELANDER, C. B. 1977. The breeding status of Peregrine Falcons in California. M.A. thesis, California State University, San Jose, Calif.

TOWNSEND, W. C. 1968. Birds observed on San Nicolas Island, California. Condor 70:266-268.

WHITE, C. M. 1975. Studies on Peregrine Falcons in the Aleutian Islands. Pp. 33-50 *in* J. R. Murphy and C. M. White, eds., Population studies of raptors. Raptor research rep. 3. Raptor Research Foundation, Vermillion, S. Dakota.

WIEMEYER, S. N., B. M. MULHERN, F. M. LIGAS, R. J. HENSEL, J. E. MATHISEN, F. C. ROBARDS, and S. POSTUPALSKY. 1972. Residues of organochlorine pesticides, polychlorinated biphenyls, and mercury in Bald Eagle eggs and changes in shell thickness—1969 and 1970. Pest. Monit. J. 6:50-55.

WILLETT, G. 1910. A summer trip to the northern Santa Barbara Islands. Condor 12:170-174.

————. 1912. Birds of the Pacific slope of southern California. Pacific Coast Avifauna 7.

————. 1933. A revised list of the birds of southwestern California. Pacific Coast Avifauna 21.

WRIGHT, H. W. 1909. An ornithological trip to Los Coronados Islands, Mexico. Condor 11:96-100.

WRIGHT, H. W., and G. K. SNYDER. 1913. Birds observed in the summer of 1912 among the Santa Barbara Islands. Condor 15:86-92.

ZAHN, O. J. 1895. The Mexican raven on Catalina Island. Avifauna 1:24-25.

APPENDIX 1

The following collections were examined for egg sets of Bald Eagles, Ospreys, and Peregrine Falcons from the California Islands (abbreviations are those used in the text):

Western Foundation of Vertebrate Zoology, Los Angeles, Calif. (WFVZ)
Museum of Vertebrate Zoology, University of California, Berkeley, Calif. (MVZ)
California Academy of Sciences, San Francisco, Calif. (CAS)
Field Museum of Natural History, Chicago, Ill. (FMNH)
American Museum of Natural History, New York, N.Y. (AMNH)
Museum of Comparative Zoology, Harvard University, Cambridge, Mass. (MCZ)
Santa Barbara Museum of Natural History, Santa Barbara, Calif.
San Bernardino County Museum of Natural History, Redlands, Calif.
San Diego Natural History Museum, San Diego, Calif.
Denver Museum of Natural History, Denver, Colo.
Puget Sound Museum of Natural History, University of Puget Sound, Tacoma, Wash.
Royal Ontario Museum, Toronto, Ontario, Canada
Carnegie Museum of Natural History, Pittsburgh, Penn.
Peabody Museum of Natural History, Yale University, New Haven, Conn.
Los Angeles County Museum of Natural History, Los Angeles, Calif.
United States National Museum, Washington, D.C.
Museum of Zoology, University of Michigan, Ann Arbor, Mich.
Florida State Museum, University of Florida, Gainesville, Fla.
Delaware Museum of Natural History, Greenville, Del.
British Museum (Natural History), Tring, Hertfordshire, England
James B. Dixon private collection, Escondido, Calif.
Nelson D. Hoy private collection, Media, Penn.
Zoology Museum, Clemson University, Clemson, South Carolina
Rob and Bessie Welder Wildlife Foundation, Sinton, Texas
Life Sciences Museum, Brigham Young University, Provo, Utah
Museum of Zoology, Louisiana State University, Baton Rouge, La.
Cleveland Museum of Natural History, Cleveland, Ohio
Chicago Academy of Sciences, Chicago, Ill.
Thomas Burke Memorial Washington State Museum, University of Washington, Seattle, Wash.
Reading Public Museum and Art Gallery, Reading, Penn.
University of Arkansas, Fayetteville, Ark.
Strecker Museum, Baylor University, Waco, Texas
Charleston Museum, Charleston, South Carolina
University of Massachusetts, Amherst, Mass.
Milwaukee Public Museum, Milwaukee, Wisc.
Ohio State University, Columbus, Ohio
National Museum of Canada, Ottawa, Ontario, Canada
Philadelphia Academy of Natural Sciences, Philadelphia, Penn.
Putnam Museum, Davenport, Iowa
Buffalo Museum of Science, Buffalo, N.Y.
Cowan Vertebrate Museum, University of British Columbia, Vancouver, B.C., Canada
El Paso Centennial Museum, University of Texas at El Paso, El Paso, Texas
State Museum, University of Nebraska, Lincoln, Neb.

APPENDIX 2

Unpublished field notes or manuscripts of the following visitors to the California Islands were examined for data on Bald Eagles, Ospreys, and Peregrine Falcons (all are housed in the archives of the Western Foundation of Vertebrate Zoology): A. W. Anthony, J. S. Appleton, R. Arnold, M. C. Badger, G. Bancroft, Sr., R. Canterbury, B. P. Carpenter, N. K. Carpenter, H. W. Carriger, W. L. Chambers, D. S. DeGroot, D. R. Dickey, H. A. Edwards, C. L. Field, P. H. Field, E. N. Harrison, O. W. Howard, A. B. Howell, L. R. Howsley, L. M. Huey, A. Jay, L. Miller, E. Paquette, J. R. Pemberton, L. G. Peyton, S. B. Peyton, W. M. Pierce, R. J. Quigley, C. O. Reis, J. S. Rowley, W. J. Sheffler, L. T. Stevens, F. Truesdale, A. J. van Rossem, G. Willett, and L. Zuk.

In addition, Dr. H. L. Jones allowed me to examine copies of unpublished field notes of J. B. Dixon, N. C. Collias, A. H. Miller, and H. H. Sheldon, as well as two unpublished manuscripts by E. L. Sumner, Jr.

Breeding Biology of the
Santa Cruz Island Scrub Jay

Jonathan L. Atwood[1]

Department of Biology, California State University,
Long Beach, California 90840

INTRODUCTION

The Santa Cruz Island Scrub Jay, *Aphelocoma coerulescens insularis,* is a genetically isolated population limited in its geographic distribution to Santa Cruz Island, Santa Barbara County, California. This insular form is characterized by rather pronounced morphological differentiation from mainland populations of the same species; its uniqueness was quickly recognized by early observers, who described the jay as "the most interesting bird on the island" (Howell and van Rossem 1911) and "the most sharply differentiated of any of the island species" (Swarth 1918). Yet in spite of this early interest in the Santa Cruz Island Scrub Jay, remarkably little has been published concerning the details of its biology. Most of the recent references to *A. c. insularis* in the literature deal with its morphological characteristics (Pitelka 1951) or possible evolutionary history (Johnson 1972); Yeaton's (1974) ecological analysis of island and mainland bird communities included a cursory examination of the Santa Cruz Island Scrub Jay's foraging niche. Prior to the present study, however, no long-term, detailed field observations of the population had been made. This paper summarizes available data concerning the breeding biology of *A. c. insularis* and provides comparisons of this information with known mainland Scrub Jay populations. The results of an ongoing study of social interactions in the Santa Cruz Island Scrub Jay will be presented elsewhere (Atwood in prep.); brief analyses of the population's vocalizations, feeding ecology, and morphological characteristics are included in Atwood (1978, 1979).

The Santa Cruz Island Scrub Jay was initially described as a distinct species, *Aphelocoma insularis,* on the basis of strong morphological contrasts between the insular population and mainland Scrub Jay races (Henshaw 1886). More recently, the A.O.U. Check-list Committee (1957) considered the Santa Cruz Island Scrub Jay to be a well-marked subspecies of *A. coerulescens.* The question of what constitutes a biologically distinct species is frequently difficult to deal with and, in particular, the lack of sympatry of *A. c. insularis* with any mainland subspecies prevents any natural testing of isolating mechanisms. Pitelka (1951) concluded that "in the absence of natural or experimental proof of intersterility, specific segregation of the Santa Cruz Island form from its mainland relatives would seem to me to distort the facts of relationship which nomenclature attempts to convey."

Pitelka (1951) recognized eighteen subspecies of Scrub Jay which were divided into four major groupings. Numerically, the largest of these is the *"californica"* group, consisting of ten subspecies distributed in Oregon, California, and Baja California. *A. c. insularis* is clearly affiliated with the *"californica"* group (Pitelka 1951).

To appreciate the unique characteristics of the Santa Cruz Island Scrub Jay, it is necessary to briefly evaluate its history as an insular population. Henshaw's (1886) early postulation that vagrant Scrub Jays had become established on Santa Cruz Island probably represents the opinion held by most ornithologists at the turn of the century. Dawson (1920) later stated that

---

[1] Present address: Department of Biology, University of California, Los Angeles, California 90024.

since the wings of *A. c. insularis* are "too short and weak to permit of its attempting a sheer flight of twenty-five miles," the colonization of Santa Cruz Island "must have been assisted either by storm, or by drifting wreckage used as a refuge, or by human agency . . . or migration occurred at a time when the channel which separates the island from the mainland was much narrower than at present." The improbability of Scrub Jays successfully colonizing Santa Cruz Island via a direct over-water flight of at least eighteen miles (29 km) has been further suggested by more recent data. The low degree of vagility in *A. coerulescens* is evident in the failure of *A. c. insularis* to colonize the apparently suitable habitat of nearby Santa Rosa Island (Miller 1951). Also, recent intensive field work on the avifauna of the Channel Islands has failed to provide records of "vagrant" Scrub Jays from any of the islands (Jones 1975), and the species is unrecorded from Los Coronados Islands, located only eight miles (13 km) from the Mexican mainland (Jehl 1977). Similarly, Johnson (1972) considered the single individual of the species recorded for the Farallon Islands to have arrived probably via "accidental transport to the island, perhaps by ship." Pitelka (1951) described the movements of *A. coerulescens* as rarely involving any but relatively short flights and suggested that this characteristic is associated, at least in part, with a relatively weak humerus present in the species.

Based on the poor colonizing potential of *A. coerulescens,* as well as on early suggestions of possible land bridges between Santa Cruz Island and the mainland, Johnson (1972) concluded that the ancestors of *A. c. insularis* colonized overland "during the peninsular stage of the northern group of islands in the Pleistocene." More recent evidence, however, suggests the absence of such a land connection since at least early to mid-Pleistocene times (Vedder and Howell 1980, Wenner and Johnson 1980). The possibility of Scrub Jays arriving on the island by over-water colonization is increased by Wenner and Johnson's (1980) hypothesis that glacial lowering of the sea level between 70,000 and 10,000 years ago substantially reduced the width of the channel separating the mainland from the offshore land mass.

Regardless of how Scrub Jays reached Santa Cruz Island, the population's morphological divergence from mainland forms indicates an extensive period of genetic isolation (Johnson 1972). A detailed morphogical comparison of *A. c. insularis* with mainland subspecies has been provided by Pitelka (1951).

DESCRIPTION OF STUDY AREA AND METHODS

Santa Cruz Island, located approximately eighteen miles (29 km) from the nearest mainland point, is the largest and most topographically diverse of the Channel Islands. The climate is typically Mediterranean and is similar to that of the adjacent southern California mainland (Yeaton 1974). For the period 1904-72, mean annual rainfall on Santa Cruz Island was 20 inches (50.8 cm) and the mean annual temperature was 60°F (15.6°C) (Laughrin 1977). During the period of this study, rainfall patterns included approximately average conditions during the winter of 1974-75, drought conditions during the winters of 1975-76 and 1976-77, and greater than average precipitation during the winter of 1977-78.

The majority of my data were obtained within an approximately 500-acre area located in the central valley immediately west of the Stanton Ranch headquarters. This area includes typical examples of *A. c. insularis* breeding habitat—specifically, coast live oak woodland and chaparral occurring on both northern and southern slope exposures. Additionally, limited areas of marginal or unsuitable Scrub Jay breeding habitat are present, such as heavily grazed grassland, open *Baccharis* thickets, and groves of introduced *Eucalyptus* trees.

Within the principal study area, scrub oak (*Quercus dumosa*) was the dominant plant species of the chaparral, occurring on both north- and south-facing slopes. Other important plant species included California lilac (*Ceanothus megacarpus* and *C. arboreus*), chamise (*Adeno-stoma fasciculatum*), lemonadeberry (*Rhus integrifolia*), Catalina cherry (*Prunus lyonii*), toyon (*Heteromeles arbutifolia*), and mountain mahogany (*Cercocarpus betuloides*). Coast live oak (*Quercus agrifolia*) was present in deep canyons on both northern and southern slope exposures. The dense, arborescent, north-facing slope chaparral was nearly continuous in its overall distribution, while chaparral occurring on south-facing slopes was patchy in distribution, being restricted to gullies and shallowly sloped alluvial deposits.

Limited observations of Santa Cruz Island Scrub Jays were made in the insular pine forest located near the head of Christi Canyon. The dominant plant species in this habitat was Bishop pine (*Pinus muricata*); a dense understory composed of toyon, manzanita (*Arctostaphylos* sp.), summer-holly (*Comarostaphylis diversifolia*), and various oak species was usually present.

Santa Cruz Island was visited on a total of 129 days between November 1974 and November 1977. Observations were made during the following months: January (17 days), February (4), March (21), April (15), May (24), June (11), July (8), August (8), September (8), October (5), and November (8). Approximately 600 hours of field work were accomplished during these visits.

A total of 248 individual Santa Cruz Island Scrub Jays were marked with unique color band combinations between January 1975 and November 1977. This figure includes an estimated 80 to 90 per cent of the jay population within the principal study area. Captured birds were aged according to the criteria described by Pitelka (1945); in most cases, sex determination was possible only on the basis of behavioral and vocal characteristics.

To supplement field data on clutch size, nesting chronology, and nest placement, information was obtained from the Western Foundation of Vertebrate Zoology (WFVZ) oological collections. Additionally, L. Kiff (pers. comm.) provided information on similar data housed at the Santa Barbara Museum of Natural History, the San Bernardino County Museum of Natural History, the Museum of Vertebrate Zoology (University of California, Berkeley), the California Academy of Sciences, and the private collection of Nelson D. Hoy.

RESULTS AND DISCUSSION
Social Organization

Although details concerning social interactions in the Santa Cruz Island Scrub Jay will be presented elsewhere (Atwood in prep.), in general, *A. c. insularis* appears to be permanently monogamous in mating, with breeding pairs defending approximately four-acre territories throughout the year. No indication of cooperative breeding, such as has been described in the Florida Scrub Jay, *A. c. coerulescens* (Woolfenden 1975), was observed.

Chronology of Nesting

The primary references in the literature concerning the breeding schedule of the Santa Cruz Island Scrub Jay present variable dates for the peak of the nesting season. Willett (1912) claimed that the nesting season is in April and May, while Dawson (1923) stated that "the Santa Cruz Jay nests early. The last week in March is the height of the season." The extreme published dates for fresh eggs of *A. c. insularis* are 10 March (Dawson 1923) and 7 June (Willett 1912).

The following analysis of nesting chronology in the Santa Cruz Island Scrub Jay is based on the present study, as well as on the data of various egg collectors and ornithologists from 1897-1947 (Beck 1899, L. Kiff, pers. comm.). Two potential sources of error are immediately apparent. The pooled data may be biased by year-to-year variation in the onset of breeding, particularly since nearly 50 per cent of the nests for which specific collection data on the stage of incubation are available were taken during only three years (1906, 1916, and 1927). Annual differences in the initiation of breeding, correlated primarily with climatic variations, have been described for a number of bird species (Van Tyne and Berger 1959), including at least one corvid, the Piñon Jay (*Gymnorhinus cyanocephalus*) (Ligon 1971). In fact, the presence of "severe drought" conditions was suggested early as having a possible influence on the breeding of the Santa Cruz Island Scrub Jay (Mailliard 1899). Ritter (1972) suggested that in *A. c. superciliosa* the timing of egg laying was correlated with ambient temperature. However, based on a considerably greater sample size, Woolfenden (1974) stated that in *A. c. coerulescens* "variation in weather seems to have little effect on the breeding schedule. . . . Drought and warm winter temperatures broke long-term records during the field work, but I observed no changes in the timing of the laying of first clutches." In the absence of evidence to the contrary, I have assumed that, like the Florida Scrub Jay, the chronology of nesting for the Santa Cruz Island Scrub Jay is little affected by annual climatic variations and that the available data for the period 1897-1977 can therefore be combined for analysis.

A second potential source of error relates to the large number of ornithologists whose data have been incorporated into this analysis. Terms describing the stage of incubation undoubtedly vary in usage from one worker to another. Therefore, several arbitrary decisions have been made in determining for each clutch an approximate date for the initiation of incubation. Clutches designated "fresh" have been plotted on the date on which they were found. Based on an estimated incubation period of eighteen days (Woolfenden 1974, Ritter 1972), clutches described as "started," "begun," "⅓," or "commenced" have been plotted an arbitrary six days earlier than the date on which they were actually collected. Similarly, dates for the initiation of incubation for clutches termed "advanced," "½," "¾," "well begun," "well incubated," or "far along" have been defined arbitrarily as being 10 days prior to the actual date of collection. Based on an approximate 21-day nestling stage (Ritter 1972), nests containing young were defined as having begun incubation 30 days prior to the date on which they were actually located (except where more accurate adjustments were possible due to specific information on the age of the nestlings present). These data are presented in Figure 1.

An analysis of nesting chronology in the Santa Cruz Island Scrub Jay indicates that 91 per cent of the recorded incubation initiation dates fall between 15 March and 23 April. Furthermore, 60 per cent of the dates occur during the 15-day period between 19 March and 2 April; excluding the relatively uncertain dates extrapolated from nestlings of unknown age, 51 per cent of the total nest starts still fall between 19 March and 2 April. Figure 1 indicates an apparent peak in egg laying in early March; however, since these data points are composed almost entirely of dates extrapolated from nestlings of unknown age, I suspect that the early March peak in egg laying has no real significance.

The peak of nesting by the Santa Cruz Island Scrub Jay appears to occur during the last two weeks of March. Actually, the period of maximum nesting activity may average slightly earlier than indicated; undoubtedly some of the clutches recorded as "fresh" could have been described as "started," in which case there would have been additional backward projections for the date of incubation initiation. A more extensive computer analysis of Scrub Jay egg data indicates that *A. c. insularis* lays about eleven days earlier, on the average, than the adjacent mainland population (L. Kiff, pers. comm.); the significance of this difference is not yet clear.

I have been unable to obtain any evidence, either from my field study or from the available literature, that the Santa Cruz Island Scrub Jay regularly produces more than a single brood per season. Woolfenden (1974) reported only a single instance of a true second brood attempt from a large sample of Florida Scrub Jay nesting records. The smaller sample of Ritter (1972) included one instance of a true second brood in *A. c. superciliosa*. As with other Scrub Jay populations, *A. c. insularis* rapidly produces replacement clutches following nesting failures. Dawson (1923) mentioned that "in two cases we noted complete sets of five thirteen days after the first had been taken. The quick recovery was the more remarkable in one instance, because the first set had been near hatching." This rapid replacement rate is comparable to that which has been described for the Florida Scrub Jay (Woolfenden 1974) and *A. c. superciliosa* (Ritter

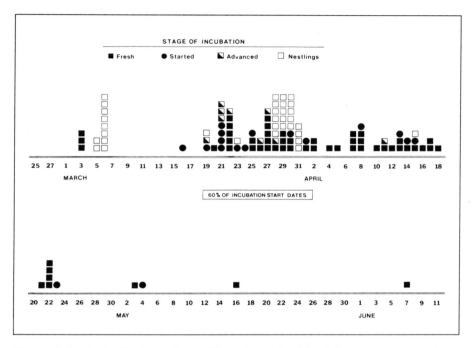

FIGURE 1. *Incubation initiation dates of Santa Cruz Island Scrub Jay nests. Clutches desig-nated "fresh" have been plotted on the date when located; others have been projected backwards according to the stage of incubation (see text). Data for the period 1897-1977 are presented.*

1972). While 7 June is the latest date on which eggs have actually been seen, the observation of "adults feeding at least one well-grown fledgling" on 6 September (Pitelka 1950) probably indicates a nest which would have held eggs during late June or, possibly, early July. Such late dates for active nests probably represent renesting efforts.

As has been suggested for the Florida Scrub Jay (Woolfenden 1974), the timing of breeding in *A. c. insularis* appears to be closely correlated with the annual cycles of the local oak species. Although considered evergreen (Munz 1970), scrub oaks drop most of their leaves during January and February and then rapidly replace them with new foliage during mid-February and March. Leaf replacement in coast live oak is much more gradual; the species never appears largely devoid of leaves as does scrub oak in late winter. Both species flower mainly in March and April and acorns are present from August through November.

An observed increase in arthropods during March and April appears closely linked to the period of flowering and new foliage production in the chaparral plant species, as well as to the increase in ambient temperatures. The increased abundance of arthropods as a food resource is probably the primary factor influencing the breeding schedule of *A. c. insularis*. Similar correlations between the timing of spring production of flowers and new foliage, the period of maximum invertebrate abundance, and the peak of breeding in the Florida Scrub Jay have been suggested by Woolfenden (1974).

Woolfenden (1974) also commented that "if more Scrub Jays bred earlier, desertion of nests would increase because of exposure due to spring leaf fall." This may be true for the Santa Cruz Island Scrub Jay as well. Between late February and early March, much of the island chaparral, including the frequently dominant scrub oak, is decidedly lacking in dense foliage and suitably concealed Scrub Jay nest sites remain scarce until new foliage has been produced. The earliest recorded Santa Cruz Island Scrub Jay clutches are three on 3 March (L. Kiff, pers. comm.). The only one of these for which data concerning nest placement were available was located in the more truly evergreen coast live oak. Similarly, Woolfenden (1974) found that most of the unusually early nests of *A. c. coerulescens* were located in true evergreens rather than in those species subject to pronounced spring leaf fall.

Courtship Behavior

The only form of courtship behavior which I observed in the Santa Cruz Island Scrub Jay was courtship feeding, which was seen on 25 March 1975, 27 April 1975, 5 March 1977, 6 March 1977 (two instances involving different pairs), and 20 March 1977. Three of these cases involved pairs known to have been mated during at least the previous breeding season. I have never definitely observed the formation of a new pair, which may include additional courtship displays. Courtship feeding in *A. c. insularis* appears similar to that which has been described for *A. c. woodhouseii* (Hardy 1961), *A. c. superciliosa* (Ritter 1972), and *A. c. coerulescens* (G.E. Woolfenden, pers. comm.). Courtship feeding away from the nest reportedly is rare in the congeneric Mexican Jay (*Aphelocoma ultramarina*) (Brown 1963).

During courtship feeding, the female jay normally received food from the male without the use of vocalizations or pronounced postural displays. Occasionally I observed the female solicit courtship feeding by crouching slightly in front of the male while making nibbling or probing motions toward his bill. Whether food was actually passed from the male to the female was difficult to discern during most of these contacts. In one instance, the female dropped a small item which she had received from the male and did not retrieve it.

On 25 March 1975, I observed a prolonged example of courtship feeding which continued for approximately 90 minutes. During this period, the female followed the male as he foraged within an area of approximately 12 m radius and gave frequent short, wheezy, begging calls. These were repeated as frequently as every 5 seconds. The female maintained her head, tail, and body in the normal jay perching posture while giving this call, except that the vocalization was usually accompanied by rapid fluttering of her slightly drooped wings. Hardy (1961) stated that in *A. c. woodhouseii* courtship feeding during the nest building period involves "little display by either member of a pair. The feeding is accomplished quickly, with little or no fluttering of the wings by the female. Usually no vocalizations are given but occasionally a suppressed begging call is uttered by both birds or by the female."

Courtship feeding begins prior to egg laying and continues through incubation in both *A. c. californica* (Verbeek 1973) and *A. c. superciliosa* (Ritter 1972). At least two of my observations of courtship feeding away from the nest in the Santa Cruz Island Scrub Jay involved pairs which were known to be engaged in the process of nest construction; the stage of breeding in the remaining cases was unknown. The functions of courtship feeding in the Corvidae have been discussed by Hardy (1961), Brown (1963), and Goodwin (1976). In general, the behavior appears to solidify the pair bond and prepare the male for his future role in feeding the incubating and brooding female, as well as the nestlings.

Nest Construction

Santa Cruz Island Scrub Jays build a typical corvid nest—an open, bulky structure composed of coarse outer sticks and a firm lining of finer twigs and rootlets. The outer structure is usually approximately 30 cm in diameter and 15 cm high. However, these dimensions vary greatly according to the supportive characteristics of the site selected; one nest built in the relatively flexible portions of a *Baccharis* thicket was 45 cm at its greatest diameter. Of the nests which I observed, most of the sticks used in the outer shell were from oaks, although I also identified manzanita, mountain mahogany, chamise, *Baccharis,* and California lilac twigs in various nests. The outer shells of two nests which were dismantled contained 242 and 184 sticks or twigs. The lining cup of most *A. c. insularis* nests is approximately 10 cm in diameter and 7 cm deep; rootlets from a variety of plant species are used, with grasses sometimes being incorporated. Dawson (1923) reported that horsehair rarely was found in the nest lining of the Santa Cruz Island Scrub Jay. As has been found in the Florida Scrub Jay (Woolfenden 1974) and *A. c. superciliosa* (Ritter 1972), *A. c. insularis* does not use foreign materials or mud in the nest lining as do Blue Jays (*Cyanocitta cristata*) (Hardy 1961).

The actual nest building process in the Santa Cruz Island Scrub Jay appears to be similar to that which has been described in *A. c. coerulescens* (Woolfenden 1974), *A. c. superciliosa* (Ritter 1972), and *A. c. woodhouseii* (Hardy 1961) in that both members of a pair participate in the activity. During limited observations of actual nest building, I only saw nesting materials being broken from nearby trees and bushes, rather than being collected from the ground. Twigs which were dropped while flying to the nest site were not retrieved. Woolfenden (1974) reported similar observations for *A. c. coerulescens.* However, according to Ritter (1972) and Hardy (1961), *A. c. superciliosa* and *A. c. woodhouseii* regularly gathered nest building materials from the ground. I encountered no instances of *A. c. insularis* re-using old nests or the materials from old nests. On 30 April 1976, a male Santa Cruz Island Scrub Jay was observed vigorously pulling at several sticks in the outer shell of an old nest located in his territory, but no material was actually removed. Since this individual was clearly agitated by my presence, I suspect that his behavior at the old nest merely represented a displacement response.

Each of the five nests that I observed which were in the process of construction was carried to completion with no indication of incomplete or false nest building as has been described in the Blue Jay (Hardy 1961) and which was previously suggested for *A. c. insularis* (Howell 1917). Woolfenden (1974) stated that Florida Scrub Jays do not make incomplete nests, but Ritter (1972) found that "all pairs of Scrub Jays (*A. c. superciliosa*) observed prior to their building of a complete nest exhibited false nest-building."

Nest Placement

Santa Cruz Island Scrub Jays generally nest in dense bushes and trees where numerous twigs and small branches provide suitable support and concealment. Most nests are placed in terminal branches. In plant species such as mule fat (*Baccharis viminea*) and willow (*Salix* sp.), which lack an abundance of stiff, divergent twigs, nests usually are supported by major branches or by the trunk. All nests are remarkably well concealed and normally are visible only from below.

Santa Cruz Island Scrub Jay nests frequently persist for several years before disintegrating; of the 89 nests located between 1974 and 1977, 21 were found during the year in which they had been constructed and 68 had been built in previous years. The following list presents the number of Santa Cruz Island Scrub Jay nests that have been recorded in each of twelve plant species. The sample size of 172 nests includes those located during the present study, as well as 83 which were found during the period 1897-1947 (L. Kiff, pers. comm.):

Scrub oak (*Quercus dumosa*)—61, including 5 mixed with poison oak (*Toxicodendron diversilobum*) and one each with lemonadeberry (*Rhus integrifolia*), California sagebrush (*Artemesia californica*), and chamise (*Adenostoma fasciculatum*); coast live oak (*Quercus agrifolia*)—32; "oak" (*Quercus* spp., undoubtedly including mainly *Q. dumosa* and *Q. agrifolia*)—28; Catalina cherry (*Prunus lyonii*)—14; Catalina ironwood (*Lyonothamnus floribundus*)—12; lemonadeberry—7, including one mixed with poison

TABLE 1. Nest site preferences of Santa Cruz Island Scrub Jays in two habitats.

Plant species	Chaparral (southern slope exposure)		Chaparral (northern slope exposure)	
	% dominance	% of nests ($n=46$)	% dominance	% of nests ($n=36$)
Quercus dumosa	75	62	51	53
Quercus agrifolia	2	4	27	31
Adenostoma fasciculatum	1	-	8	-
Ceanothus megacarpus	7	2	-	-
Arctostaphylos insularis	-	-	4	3
Cercocarpus betuloides	2	-	3	3
Rhus integrifolia	3	11	1	5
Heteromeles arbutifolia	3	7	2	-
Prunus lyonii	3	7	1	5
Ceanothus arboreus	-	-	1	-
Salix sp.	1	7	-	-
Totals	97	100	98	100

oak; mule fat (*Baccharis viminea*)—5; willow (*Salix* sp.)—4; island manzanita (*Arctostaphylos insularis*)—3; toyon (*Heteromeles arbutifolia*)—3; California lilac (*Ceanothus insularis*)—1; mountain mahogany (*Cercocarpus betuloides*)—1; Bishop pine (*Pinus muricata*)—1.

Table 1 compares the percentage of nests which I found in given plant species with the dominance of those species in the study area; data are provided for the chaparral habitats occurring on both northern and southern slope exposures. The vegetation analysis of each habitat was based on ten randomly selected 25-m transects; the distance along the transect line covered by each plant species was measured and these values were used in calculating the percentage of the total area of woody vegetation occupied by each plant species in the habitat.

On both northern and southern slope exposures, scrub oak was clearly dominant; coast live oak occurred frequently on the northern slope exposures and in the adjacent canyon bottoms. Within the principal study area, Santa Cruz Island Scrub Jays nest primarily in these two oak species. The fact that relatively large numbers of nests were placed in the less frequently occurring lemonadeberry, toyon, Catalina cherry, and willow may indicate that these species are somewhat preferred as nest sites when available. However, in at least the cases of nests built in toyon and willow, these data are probably biased by the nesting preferences of particular pairs of jays. That is, all three nests found in toyon were present in a small, unusually thick stand of this species and are presumed to have been constructed by one pair of jays. Similarly, two of the three nests found in willow were present in a single tree and are known to have been built by a single pair of jays during successive years. Earlier authors have noted the tendency of *A. c. insularis* to nest within a relatively limited area during successive breeding seasons (Dawson 1923).

Few data are available for the nesting preferences of Santa Cruz Island Scrub Jays in the vicinity of the insular pine forests. Although earlier references state that nests are sometimes placed in the pines (Howell and van Rossem 1911, Dawson 1923), I know of only one specific nest which has been recorded in *Pinus*. The only nests which I was able to locate in the pine forest habitat were built in the chaparral understory; most of the pines do not seem to have

numerous small, stiff, divergent branches which are necessary for nest support and concealment.

Nest placement for the Santa Cruz Island Scrub Jay has been stated as varying in height from
1.8 to 9.2 m (Blake 1887). Based on estimates made to the nearest 0.5 m, I have recorded nest
heights ranging from 1.0 to 18.0 m. For the 89 nests located during the present study, the mean
height was 4.0 m and the mode 2.5 m. Including data from 82 additional nests located between
1897 and 1947 (L. Kiff, pers. comm.), the mean for the total sample of 171 nests was 4.3 m and
the mode 2.5 m.

Variation in the vegetation structure of different pairs' territories affected the height of nest
placement. Nests found in dense thickets of *Baccharis* were at a mean height of 1.2 m ($n = 5$);
suitable nesting sites in this vegetation type were available from ground level to approximately
1.3 m. In the south-facing slope chaparral, where the dense shrub layer extended from ground
level to approximately 6.0 m, mean height for nest placement was 3.2 m ($n = 45$). Within the
more arborescent, north-facing slope chaparral and the frequently associated coast live oak
woodland, nests were at a mean height of 5.2 m ($n = 36$); in this habitat, suitable nesting sites
were available from approximately 2.5 to 12.0 m.

Clutch Size

In addition to the present field study, data on clutch size for *A. c. insularis* were obtained
from specimens housed at the WFVZ and from Beck (1899), Mailliard (1899), Howell and van
Rossem (1911), and Kiff (pers. comm.). The mean clutch size for the total sample ($n = 121$) is
3.71 (*s.d.* $= 0.70$). Dawson (1923) reported that the Santa Cruz Island Scrub Jay lays "three or
four, rarely five" eggs. From the overall sample, 7 nests held two eggs, 31 nests contained three
eggs, 73 nests held four eggs, and 10 nests held five eggs. Of the nine active nests I observed in
which egg laying progressed to completion, three nests contained three eggs and six nests held
four eggs. I have included in this analysis clutch size values based on 10 nests that contained
nestlings when found; exclusion of these values resulted in no statistically significant difference
in mean clutch size. The fact that some early collectors of *A.c. insularis* eggs routinely selected
only larger clutches (L. Kiff, pers. comm.) suggests that the true mean clutch size may be
smaller than indicated by the collection data.

Table 2 presents clutch size data obtained primarily from the WFVZ oological collections
for the following Scrub Jay populations: *A. c. superciliosa* (including data from Ritter 1972),
woodhouseii, oocleptica, obscura, immanis, californica, coerulescens (including data from
Woolfenden 1974), *cactophila, hypoleuca* (including data from Bancroft 1930 and Bryant
1899), and *insularis*. The mean clutch size of the Santa Cruz Island Scrub Jay is significantly
smaller than the mean clutch sizes of both coastal southern California mainland subspecies
(*californica* and *obscura*), as well as the more geographically distant populations of *superciliosa, woodhouseii, oocleptica,* and *immanis*. The Santa Cruz Island Scrub Jay is most
similar in clutch size to the Florida Scrub Jay; these populations also resemble each other in the
absence of six-egg clutches, which have been found in *superciliosa, woodhouseii, oocleptica,
obscura, californica,* and *immanis*. Although the sample sizes are small, the two subspecies of
Scrub Jay restricted to Baja California (*hypoleuca* and *cactophila*) have mean clutch sizes
which are significantly smaller than those of any more northerly Scrub Jay populations for
which adequate data were available.

In its reduction of clutch size, the Santa Cruz Island Scrub Jay appears to fit the model of a
K-selected population as described by MacArthur and Wilson (1967) and Pianka (1970). Based
on Cody's (1966) study of clutch size, MacArthur and Wilson (1967) summarized that "on the
seasonal temperate mainland where r-selection is often more important, clutch size should be
larger and feeding efficiency somewhat less. On the other hand, the effect should be reduced on

TABLE 2. Clutch size data for ten subspecific populations of *Aphelocoma coerulescens*.

Subspecies	Clutch size					Sample size	Mean	Standard deviation	95% confidence interval	Range	Mode
	2	3	4	5	6						
hypoleuca	11	9	-	-	-	20	2.45	0.51	2.68-2.22	2-3	2
cactophila	7	7	1	-	-	15	2.60	0.63	2.94-2.26	2-4	2/3
coerulescens	6	66	81	3	-	156	3.52	0.60	3.62-3.42	2-5	4
insularis	7	31	73	10	-	121	3.71	0.70	3.84-3.58	2-5	4
obscura	1	28	88	46	3	166	4.13	0.73	4.24-4.02	2-6	4
californica	-	19	93	50	14	176	4.34	0.77	4.46-4.22	3-6	4
oocleptica	-	7	127	88	16	238	4.47	0.67	4.56-4.38	3-6	4
superciliosa	-	4	18	31	3	56	4.59	0.71	4.78-4.40	3-6	5
woodhouseii	-	2	17	30	10	59	4.81	0.75	5.01-4.61	3-6	5
immanis	-	-	4	14	2	20	4.90	0.55	5.15-4.65	4-6	5

TABLE 3. Survival data for Santa Cruz Island Scrub Jays.

Banding date	Months after banding												
	0	1	2	3	4	5	6	7	8	9	10	11	12
Jan 1975	3*	3	3	3	1	1	1	1	1	1	1	1	1
Mar 1975	9	9	9	9	9	9	9	8	8	8	8	8	8
Apr 1975	14	14	14	14	14	14	14	14	14	14	14	14	14
Jun 1975	45	34	34	33	33	33	33	33	31	31	29	29	29
Aug 1975	8	7	5	5	5	5	4	4	4	4	4	4	4
Sep 1975	5	5	5	5	5	5	5	5	5	5	5	5	5
Jan 1976	26	20	20	20	20	18	18	16	16	14	14	14	14
Mar 1976	12	11	11	11	11	11	11	9	8	8	8	8	8
May 1976	8	6	6	5	5	5	5	5	5	5	5	4	4
Totals	130	109	107	105	103	101	100	95	92	90	88	87	87

* Numbers indicate minimum number of surviving jays at monthly time intervals.

offshore temperate islands, which enjoy a generally milder, less fluctuating climate." During the initial period of colonization and subsequent expansion by the ancestors of *A. c. insularis,* *r*-selection presumably was operative (MacArthur and Wilson 1967); however, the population's present-day saturation of the insular environment (Atwood in prep.) suggests that *K*-selection is now more important. While additional data concerning the relative climatic stabilities of island and mainland environments are essential for a conclusive analysis, the phenomenon of reduced clutch size in the Santa Cruz Island Scrub Jay is similar to that reported from a variety of other temperate, insular bird populations subject to *K*-selection (Cody 1966).

Reproductive Success and Survival

Although the data on reproductive success are very limited, it appears that nest predation, particularly egg loss, may be high in the Santa Cruz Island Scrub Jay. Of six nests containing eggs which were located during the study period, none successfully reached the nestling stage. Also, nine recently constructed nests located between 1 and 16 May 1976 were empty when found and were not used subsequently; it seems unlikely that all of these broods had successfully fledged prior to these relatively early dates of nest discovery. I suspect that at least several, if not most, of these clutches had been taken by predators. Three additional nests contained young when initially located; all of these successfully produced fledglings.

Potential nest predators are extremely few on Santa Cruz Island, being limited to two species of snake (Blue Racer, *Coluber constrictor,* and Gopher Snake, *Pituophis melanoleucus*), Western Spotted Skunk (*Spilogale gracilis*), Island Fox (*Urocyon littoralis*), Common Raven (*Corvus corax*), and *A. c. insularis* itself. Within my principal study area, snake populations appeared to be quite low; during three years of field work, I encountered only three small Gopher Snakes and one Blue Racer. Similarly, Spotted Skunks have been rare on Santa Cruz Island for at least the past ten years (Laughrin 1977). I never observed a Common Raven engaged in any activity which might be interpreted as searching for the well-concealed nests of small passerines. Therefore, I suspect that most nest predation in *A. c. insularis* results from Island Foxes and, possibly, other Santa Cruz Island Scrub Jays. Additional data concerning the extent and source of nest predation in *A. c. insularis* are currently being sought.

Beyond the fledgling stage, Santa Cruz Island Scrub Jays appear to be relatively long-lived with low adult mortality rates. Table 3 presents survival data for 130 jays that were banded between January 1975 and May 1976; no individuals less than eight months old are included in the sample. From this total sample, 87 individuals (67 per cent) were known to have been alive twelve months following their initial captures. The real survival rate of *A. c. insularis* undoubtedly is much higher. To compensate for unknown dispersal, as well as for birds which were attracted to the trapping station from territories distant from my principal study area, I have chosen to use for the initial population figure only those birds which were present two months following the date of their initial capture. These 107 individuals represent more accurately the resident population which could reasonably be expected to be re-encountered in the study area. On the basis of this análysis, Santa Cruz Island Scrub Jays have an annual survival rate of 81 per cent. Woolfenden (1974) found similarly high values in the Florida Scrub Jay (yearlings, 88 per cent; breeding adults at least two years of age, 80 per cent).

Based on a mortality rate of 19 per cent per year, the average life expectancy of a Santa Cruz Island Scrub Jay which survives the relatively dangerous early months of its fledgling existence (Woolfenden 1974) is 4.8 years.

SUMMARY

In its basic aspects of reproduction, the Santa Cruz Island Scrub Jay appears to resemble western mainland Scrub Jay populations. The peak of the breeding season for *A. c. insularis* falls during the last two weeks of March. No true second brood attempts were encountered; late nesting records most likely involve replacement clutches.

Observed courtship behavior in the Santa Cruz Island Scrub Jay was limited to courtship feeding, which appeared similar in form and function to that which has been described for *A. c. superciliosa, A. c. woodhouseii,* and *A. c. coerulescens. A. c. insularis* constructs a typical corvid nest, with both members of the pair participating in the building activity. I observed no indication of false nest building such as has been described in *A. c. superciliosa.* Nests were placed in a wide variety of chaparral and oak woodland plant species, with scrub oak and coast live oak being the most frequently used. Recorded nest heights ranged from 1.0 to 18.0 m, with a mean value of 4.3 m and a mode of 2.5 m.

Mean clutch size for the Santa Cruz Island Scrub Jay is 3.71. Since both adjacent coastal mainland subspecies lay significantly larger clutches, the island population appears to fit MacArthur and Wilson's (1967) hypothesis that well-established, temperate insular forms are more subject to K-selection than their more r-selected mainland relatives.

Preliminary data suggest that nest predation, especially egg loss, may be high in *A. c. insularis.* Beyond the nest and early fledgling stages, however, Santa Cruz Island Scrub Jays have very low mortality (19 per cent per year); this figure closely resembles that which has been reported in the Florida Scrub Jay.

ACKNOWLEDGMENTS

Many individuals and groups contributed to various phases of this study. Special thanks are due to Dr. Charles T. Collins, who provided invaluable assistance and enthusiastic support both in the field and during preparation of the final manuscript. Drs. Glen E. Woolfenden, Stuart L. Warter, and Dennis M. Power also contributed important insights and assistance. Lloyd F. Kiff kindly provided data which have proven very useful in portions of this analysis. It is a pleasure to express my deep thankfulness to these colleagues and friends.

I wish to thank Dr. Carey Stanton and Henry Duffield of the Santa Cruz Island Company for their hospitality during the field aspects of this research. Also, this study would have been impossible without the superb cooperation of Dr. Lyndal L. Laughrin and Marla Daily of the University of California Santa Cruz Island Reserve.

Special gratitude is due to my wife, Judy, for her patient love, encouragement, and assistance throughout the study. Also, my parents and a multitude of friends were constant sources of help and support.

Financial assistance was partially provided by the American Museum of Natural History Frank M. Chapman Memorial Fund, the El Dorado Audubon Society, the Pasadena Audubon Society, and William R. Atwood.

REFERENCES

AMERICAN ORNITHOLOGISTS' UNION. 1957. Check-list of North American birds. American Ornithologists' Union (Lord Baltimore Press), Baltimore, Md.
ATWOOD, J. L. 1978. The breeding biology of the Santa Cruz Island Scrub Jay, *Aphelocoma coerulescens insularis.* M.A thesis, California State University, Long Beach, Calif.
————. 1979. Body weights of the Santa Cruz Island Scrub Jay. North American Bird-Bander 4:148-153.
BANCROFT, G. 1930. The breeding birds of central Lower California. Condor 32:20-49.
BECK, R. H. 1899. Nesting of the Santa Cruz Jay. Bull. Cooper Ornith. Club 1:6.
BLAKE, E. W. 1887. Summer birds of Santa Cruz Island, California. Auk 4:328-330.
BROWN, J. L. 1963. Social organization and behavior of the Mexican Jay. Condor 65:126-153.

BRYANT, W. E. 1889. Descriptions of the nest and eggs of some Lower California birds. Proc. California Acad. Sci., 2nd ser., 2:20-24.

CODY, M. L. 1966. A general theory of clutch size. Evolution 20:174-184.

DAWSON, W. L. 1920. The case of the Santa Cruz Island Jay, *Aphelocoma insularis* Hensh. J. Mus. Comp. Oology 1:26-29.

———. 1923. The birds of California, v. I. South Moulton Co., San Diego, Calif.

GOODWIN, D. 1976. Crows of the world. Cornell University Press, Ithaca, N.Y.

HARDY, J. W. 1961. Studies in behavior and phylogeny of certain New World jays (Garrulinae). Univ. Kansas Sci. Bull. 42:13-149.

HENSHAW, H. W. 1886. Description of a new jay from California. Auk 3:452-453.

HOWELL, A. B. 1917. Birds of the islands off the coast of southern California. Pacific Coast Avifauna 12:1-127.

HOWELL, A. B., and A. J. VAN ROSSEM. 1911. Further notes from Santa Cruz Island. Condor 13:208-210.

JEHL, J. R., JR. 1977. An annotated list of birds of Islas Los Coronados, Baja California, and adjacent waters. Western Birds 8:91-101.

JOHNSON, N. K. 1972. Origin and differentiation of the avifauna of the Channel Islands, California. Condor 74:295-315.

JONES, H. L. 1975. Studies of avian turnover, dispersal and colonization of the California Channel Islands. Ph.D. thesis, University of California, Los Angeles, Calif.

LAUGHRIN, L. L. 1977. The Island Fox: a field study of its behavior and ecology. Ph.D. thesis, University of California, Santa Barbara, Calif.

LIGON, J. D. 1971. Late summer-autumnal breeding in the Piñon Jay in New Mexico. Condor 73:147-153.

MACARTHUR, R. H., and E. O. WILSON. 1967. The theory of island biogeography. Princeton University Press, Princeton, N.J.

MAILLIARD, J. 1899. Spring notes on the birds of Santa Cruz Island, Cal., April 1898. Bull. Cooper Ornith. Club 1:41-45.

MILLER, A. H. 1951. A comparison of the avifaunas of Santa Cruz and Santa Rosa Islands, California. Condor 53:117-123.

MUNZ, P. A. 1970. A California flora. University of California Press, Berkeley, Calif.

PIANKA, E. R. 1970. On *r*- and *K*-selection. Amer. Natur. 104:592-597.

PITELKA, F. A. 1945. Pterylography, molt, and age determination of American jays of the genus *Aphelocoma*. Condor 47:229-260.

———. 1950. Additions to the avifaunal record of Santa Cruz Island, California. Condor 52:43-46.

———. 1951. Speciation and ecologic distribution in American jays of the genus *Aphelocoma*. Univ. California Publ. Zool. 50:195-464.

RITTER, L. V. 1972. The breeding biology of Scrub Jays. M.A. thesis, California State University, Chico, Calif.

SWARTH, H. S. 1918. The Pacific coast jays of the genus *Aphelocoma*. Univ. California Publ. Zool. 17:405-422.

VAN TYNE, J., and A. J. BERGER. 1959. Fundamentals of ornithology. John Wiley & Sons, New York, N.Y.

VEDDER, J. G., and D. G. HOWELL. 1980. Topographic evolution of the southern California borderland during late Cenozoic time. Pp. 7-31 *in* D. M. Power, ed., The California Islands: proceedings of a multidisciplinary symposium. Santa Barbara Museum of Natural History, Santa Barbara, Calif.

VERBEEK, N. A. M. 1973. The exploitation system of the Yellow-billed Magpie. Univ. California Publ. Zool. 99:1-58.

WENNER, A. M., and D. L. JOHNSON. 1980. Land vertebrates on the California Channel Islands: sweepstakes or bridges? Pp. 497-530 *in* D. M. Power, ed., The California Islands: proceedings of a multidisciplinary symposium. Santa Barbara Museum of History, Santa Barbara, Calif.

WILLETT, G. 1912. Birds of the Pacific coast of southern California. Pacific Coast Avifauna 21:1-204.

WOOLFENDEN, G. E. 1974. Nesting and survival in a population of Florida Scrub Jays. Living Bird 12:25-49.

————. 1975. Florida Scrub Jay helpers at the nest. Auk 92:1-15.

YEATON, R. I. 1974. An ecological analysis of chaparral and pine forest bird communities on Santa Cruz Island and mainland California. Ecology 55:959-973.

Analysis of Avifaunal and Bat Remains from Midden Sites on San Miguel Island

Daniel A. Guthrie

Joint Science Department, Claremont Colleges,
Claremont, California 91711

INTRODUCTION

Remains of birds were recovered from four sites on San Miguel Island excavated by Charles Rozaire for the Los Angeles County Museum of Natural History between 1964 and 1968. This paper reports on the information this excavated material provides on the past avifauna of San Miguel Island, as well as on the role of birds in the subsistence of the aboriginal inhabitants. Preliminary ages, based on artifacts and on information provided by Charles Rozaire, are also reported here. I also describe material from a cave deposit that includes bones referable to *Desmodus stocki,* an extinct species of vampire bat.

The four San Miguel Island deposits are:

SMI 1.—A large village site located on the bluffs overlooking Cuyler Harbor on the north coast of San Miguel. This site was subdivided on a grid and 68 random squares were excavated. Artifacts date occupation of this site from 4770 B.P. to no later than 1400 B.P.

SMI 525.—This excavation consisted of a 5 x 10-ft (1.5 x 3.0 m) test pit sunk along the face of a cliff where several midden and soil layers were exposed on the northwest shore of San Miguel. This site was occupied from 2000 to 400 B.P., with the major period of occupation from 2000 to 1200 B.P.

SMI 261.—This site is a cave at the base of a cliff near Bay Point on the northeast side of San Miguel. The whole interior of the cave was excavated and a trench dug perpendicular to the cave entrance, extending outward about 50 ft (15.2 m). Artifacts indicate that this site and 261A were occupied from 3150 B.P. to no later than 980 B.P.

SMI 261A.—Material from this locality is from a trench along the floor of a vertical fissure in the cliff near SMI 261. At its base, the fissure is about 5 ft (1.5 m) wide.

METHODS

All sites were excavated in 5-ft (1.5 m) squares, 6 inches (15.3 cm) at a time, and sieved with a quarter-inch (6.4 mm) mesh screen. Avian remains were identified with the aid of collections from the University of California at Los Angeles, the Los Angeles County Museum of Natural History, and the Joint Science Department of the Claremont Colleges. Minimum numbers of individuals (MNI) were calculated per level of excavation by summing the frequencies of the most commonly occurring unique skeletal element of each age class for each species. MNI values are biased upward, in that their calculation assumes no vertical scattering of faunal remains as might have occurred due to digging by pot hunters.

Skeletal completeness values (CSI) were calculated using the formula of Thomas (1971) where, for each species:

$$CSI = \frac{\text{number of bones found x 100}}{\text{MNI x estimated number of identifiable elements}}$$

The estimated number of identifiable elements for small birds, where vertebrae and phalanges are lost by sieving, was taken as 25. This is an overestimate for individual species of passerines and for this reason a CSI value is given for passerines as a group. For larger species, where

TABLE 1. Bird remains from SMI 1 (number of bones/MNI).

| Species | Depth in inches | | | | | | Totals | CSI |
	0-6	6-12	12-18	18-24	24-30	30-36		
Common Loon	-	-	-	4/1	1/1	-	5/2	5.0
Arctic Loon	-	-	-	1/1	3/1	-	4/2	4.0
Eared Grebe	-	-	-	1/1	-	-	1/1	4.0
Short-tailed Albatross	-	1/1	5/1	-	-	-	6/2	6.0
Northern Fulmar	-	-	1/1	-	-	-	1/1	4.0
Brown Pelican	-	1/1	1/1	-	-	-	2/2	2.0
Brandt's Cormorant	1/1	16/3	33/4	24/3	1/1	1/1	76/13	11.7
Pelagic Cormorant	-	4/1	4/2	1/1	-	-	9/4	9.0
Double-crested Cormorant	-	1/1	1/1	-	-	-	2/2	2.0
Snow Goose	-	-	3/1	-	-	-	3/1	6.0
Chendytes sp.	-	8/3	13/3	19/3	3/2	-	43/11	7.8
Surf Scoter	-	1/1	-	-	-	-	1/1	4.0
Heerman's Gull	-	-	1/1	-	-	-	1/1	4.0
Common Murre	-	-	1/1	-	-	-	1/1	4.0
Pigeon Guillemot	-	1/1	-	-	-	-	1/1	4.0
Cassin's Auklet	-	-	-	1/1	-	-	1/1	4.0
Rhinoceros Auklet	-	-	2/1	-	1/1	-	3/2	6.0
Tufted Puffin	-	-	1/1	-	-	-	1/1	4.0
Raven	-	1/1	-	-	1/1	12/1	14/3	18.6

vertebrae and phalanges were not lost in screening, the number of identifiable elements per species was taken as 50 (see Ziegler 1973).

Evidence of human use was noted, including butcher marks, burning, and working of bone. The degree of breakage of skeletal elements was also noted. Finally, the number of each skeletal element recovered for each species was recorded, as were the horizontal and vertical distributions of bones at each site.

RESULTS
Agencies of Accumulation

Material at SMI 1 and SMI 525 (Tables 1 and 2) was, in all probability, brought there by humans or agencies associated with them, such as domestic dogs (a single dog bone was found at SMI 261). Both sites seem far from caves or suitable den sites for the only carnivore on the island, the Island Fox (*Urocyon littoralis*). Although there is evidence of human occupation, much of the material at SMI 261 and 261A (Tables 3 and 4) was collected by owls. Barn Owl (*Tyto alba*) remains are numerous at these sites; their distribution at the mouth of the cave at SMI 261, rather than in its interior, corresponds to the distribution of bones of small mammals and small birds. Petrels and murrelets are a major component of the prey of Barn Owls on other islands off the west coast of California (see Banks 1965, Bennett 1928). Given the high percentage of small prey species at SMI 261 and SMI 261A, and their virtual absence at SMI 525 and SMI 1 (Table 5), it seems likely that nearly all the passerines, murrelets, small auklets, and petrels, as well as some shorebirds and small grebes, at SMI 261 and SMI 261A were brought in by owls. The high CSI values for these species and low figures for bone breakage

TABLE 2. Bird remains from SMI 525 (number of bones/MNI).

Species	Depth in inches												Totals	CSI
	0-12	12-24	24-36	36-48	48-60	60-72	72-84	84-96	96-108	108-120	120-132	132-140		
Red-throated Loon	-	-	-	-	1/1	-	-	-	-	-	-	-	1/1	2.0
Short-tailed Albatross	-	-	-	2/1	1/1	1/1	2/1	-	-	-	2/1	-	8/5	3.2
Sooty Shearwater	-	-	-	-	-	-	-	-	-	-	8/2	-	8/2	16.0
Brown Pelican	-	-	-	3/1	-	-	4/1	1/1	-	1/1	-	-	9/4	4.5
Brandt's Cormorant	-	-	2/1	9/2	6/1	-	4/2	3/1	-	-	-	1/1	24/8	6.0
Pelagic Cormorant	-	-	-	-	-	-	1/1	-	-	1/1	-	-	2/2	4.0
Osprey	-	-	-	-	-	-	1/1	-	-	-	-	-	1/1	4.0
Western Gull	-	-	-	-	-	1/1	-	-	-	2/1	1/1	-	4/3	5.3
Cassin's Auklet	-	6/2	3/1	-	-	-	-	-	-	-	-	-	9/3	13.0
Tufted Puffin	-	-	-	-	-	-	-	1/1	-	-	-	-	1/1	4.0
Raven	-	-	-	-	-	-	-	1/1	-	-	-	-	1/1	4.0
Common Murre	-	-	-	-	-	-	1/1	-	1/1	-	-	-	2/2	4.0

TABLE 3. Bird remains from SMI 261 (number of bones/MNI).

Species	Depth in inches						Total	CSI
	0-12	12-24	24-36	36-48	48-60	60-72		
Common Loon	1/1	-	3/2	27/3	5/1	-	36/7	10.3
Arctic Loon	3/1	9/1	6/2	13/2	5/1	2/1	35/8	8.8
Red-throated Loon	-	1/1	-	-	1/1	-	2/2	2.0
Red-necked Grebe	1/1	-	-	-	-	-	1/1	4.0
Horned Grebe	-	1/1	-	1/1	-	-	2/2	4.0
Eared Grebe	12/2	10/4	26/5	20/5	4/1	-	72/17	16.9
Western Grebe	-	-	4/1	-	-	-	4/1	16.0
Short-tailed Albatross	8/2	3/2	14/3	13/3	2/1	-	40/11	7.2
Northern Fulmar	4/1	-	1/1	-	-	-	5/3	6.7
Sooty Shearwater	-	-	1/1	1/1	-	-	2/2	4.0
Manx Shearwater	7/2	2/2	2/1	1/1	19/3	7/2	38/11	13.8
Leach's Storm Petrel	5/2	3/1	7/3	1/1	-	-	16/7	9.1
Ashy Storm Petrel	-	1/1	3/1	3/1	-	-	7/3	9.3
Black Storm Petrel	1/1	1/1	-	-	-	-	2/2	4.0
Brown Pelican	4/2	1/1	-	-	-	-	5/3	3.3
Brandt's Cormorant	231/16	90/6	13/1	12/2	5/2	-	351/27	26.0
Pelagic Cormorant	91/13	30/8	5/1	1/1	-	-	127/23	11.1
Black Brant	1/1	-	-	1/1	-	-	2/2	4.0
Snow Goose	18/3	7/2	6/1	29/3	6/1	6/3	72/13	13.1
Chendytes sp.	1/1	8/2	10/2	23/4	7/2	2/1	51/12	8.5
Ross' Goose	-	1/1	-	-	-	-	1/1	4.0
Surf Scoter	-	-	2/1	-	-	-	2/1	8.0
White-winged Scoter	-	-	-	1/1	-	-	1/1	4.0
Northern Shoveller	1/1	-	-	-	-	-	1/1	4.0
California Condor	-	1/1	-	-	-	-	1/1	2.0
Red-tailed Hawk	-	-	1/1	2/1	-	1/1	4/3	5.3
Rough-legged Hawk	1/1	1/1	-	2/1	-	-	4/3	5.3
Kestrel	-	-	1/1	-	-	-	1/1	4.0
Sandhill Crane	1/1	-	-	-	-	-	1/1	2.0
Coot	-	-	-	2/1	-	-	2/1	8.0
Sanderling	-	-	-	1/1	-	-	1/1	4.0
Black-bellied Plover	-	1/1	-	-	-	-	1/1	4.0
Wandering Tattler	-	1/1	-	-	-	-	1/1	4.0
Willet	-	1/1	-	1/1	-	-	2/2	4.0
Red Phalarope	1/1	-	1/1	-	-	-	2/2	4.0
Northern Phalarope	-	-	1/1	-	-	-	1/1	4.0
Western Gull	1/1	-	4/1	5/1	-	-	10/3	6.7
California Gull	-	1/1	-	-	-	-	1/1	4.0
Bonaparte's Gull	-	-	-	1/1	-	-	1/1	4.0
Black-legged Kittiwake	1/1	2/1	2/1	3/2	-	-	8/5	6.4
Common Murre	-	1/1	-	2/1	-	-	3/2	6.0
Pigeon Guillemot	1/1	4/1	1/1	-	-	-	6/3	8.0
Xantus' Murrelet	23/8	21/8	44/9	29/6	6/3	-	123/34	14.7
Cassin's Auklet	42/8	56/9	77/12	68/10	15/3	1/1	259/43	24.1

TABLE 3. (Cont.)

Species	Depth in inches						Total	CSI
	0-12	12-24	24-36	36-48	48-60	60-72		
Rhinoceros Auklet	10/4	2/2	2/2	-	-	-	14/8	7.0
Barn Owl	-	2/1	5/2	8/3	20/4	7/2	42/12	14.0
Burrowing Owl	-	-	3/1	2/1	4/1	3/1	12/4	12.0
Short-eared Owl	1/1	-	1/1	-	-	-	2/2	8.0
Raven	3/1	-	3/1	-	2/1	-	8/3	10.6
Passerines	21/5	9/4	51/11	15/4	3/1	4/1	103/27	15.3
Western Meadowlark	-	-	3/1	2/1	3/1	2/1	10/4	-
Brewer's Blackbird	3/1	-	1/1	-	-	1/1	4/3	-
Zonotrichia sp.	-	2/2	4/2	-	-	-	6/4	-
Fox Sparrow	-	-	1/1	-	-	-	1/1	-

TABLE 4. Bird remains from SMI 261A (number of bones/MNI).

Species	Depth in inches							Total	CSI
	0-6	6-12	12-18	18-24	24-30	30-36	36-48		
Common Loon	-	2/1	-	1/1	-	-	-	3/2	3.0
Horned Grebe	-	-	-	1/1	-	-	-	1/1	4.0
Eared Grebe	4/1	3/1	5/2	1/1	-	-	-	13/5	10.4
Short-tailed Albatross	-	-	-	1/1	-	-	-	1/1	2.0
Manx Shearwater	-	-	-	1/1	-	-	-	1/1	4.0
Leach's Storm Petrel	1/1	3/1	1/1	-	-	-	-	5/3	6.3
Ashy Storm Petrel	1/1	2/1	2/1	1/1	-	-	-	6/4	6.0
Brandt's Cormorant	3/1	-	-	5/1	-	1/1	1/1	10/4	5.0
Snow Goose	-	-	-	-	-	1/1	-	1/1	2.0
Chendytes sp.	-	3/1	1/1	-	-	-	-	4/2	4.0
Red-tailed Hawk	2/1	1/1	-	-	-	-	-	3/2	7.0
Rough-legged Hawk	1/1	-	-	-	-	-	-	1/1	4.0
Swainson's Hawk	-	1/1	-	-	-	-	-	1/1	4.0
Western Gull	-	-	-	2/1	-	1/1	-	3/2	3.0
California Gull	-	-	1/1	-	-	-	-	1/1	4.0
Black-legged Kittiwake	1/1	-	-	-	-	-	-	1/1	4.0
Common Murre	1/1	-	-	-	-	-	-	1/1	4.0
Xantus' Murrelet	7/2	17/4	15/3	3/1	-	1/1	-	43/11	15.6
Cassin's Auklet	57/5	177/10	62/7	11/2	-	-	-	307/24	51.2
Rhinoceros Auklet	2/2	-	-	-	-	-	-	2/2	4.0
Barn Owl	-	3/1	2/1	-	-	-	-	5/2	10.0
Burrowing Owl	-	4/1	2/1	-	-	-	-	6/2	12.0
Raven	-	8/2	-	1/1	-	-	-	9/3	12.0
Passerines	3/4	80/18	13/5	20/4	-	-	-	120/31	15.5
Western Meadowlark	-	2/1	-	-	-	-	-	2/1	-
Zonotrichia sp.	2/2	6/5	-	1/1	-	-	-	9/8	-
Fox Sparrow	-	11/4	1/1	-	-	-	-	12/5	-

TABLE 5. Summary of owl and bird remains from San Miguel Island localities.

Species groups	Localities			
	1	525	261	261A
Small birds (MNI)	2	3	149	81
Large birds (MNI)	48	30	153	24
Barn Owl remains (MNI)	-	-	12	2

TABLE 6. Distribution of skeletal elements for common species for SMI 261 and 261A.

Species	Number of bones MNI	CSI	Number of complete bones/total number of bones							
			Humerus	Ulna	Femur	Tibia	Tarso-metatarsus	Coracoid	Pelvis	Sternum
Cassin's Auklet	566/67	33.79	79/110	79/101	41/44	51/66	41/41	42/43	25/29	13/25
Xantus' Murrelet	155/45	14.7	49/59	27/31	13/15	12/18	3/4*	12/12	4/4*	0/5
Passerines	223/58	15.4	30/34	12/17	10/12	9/16	6/6	0/0	3/3	0/3
Snow Goose	56/14	8.0	3/13	0/9	0/0	0/2	0/2	0/1	0/0	0/2
Brandt's Cormorant	361/31	23.3	1/52	2/42	17/22	2/37	15/30	40/47	2/9	0/6
Pelagic Cormorant	127/23	11.1	2/24	0/7	4/7	0/12	6/12	8/13	3/5	4/6
Short-tailed Albatross	41/12	6.8	0/5	0/2	1/6	1/5	1/4	-	-	-
Manx Shearwater	38/12	13.0	3/7	6/17	1/2	1/3	2/3	4/4	-	0/2
Arctic Loon	35/8	8.7	0/4	0/3	1/1	1/2	3/6	4/4	2/2	0/1
Eared Grebe	85/23	14.8	11/35	4/12	6/8	2/11	4/9	5/6	2/2	0/3
Chendytes sp.	55/14	15.7	1/2	-	8/10	0/2	2/3	0/0	1/4	1/3
Barn Owl	47/14	13.4	0/6	0/1	1/11	1/5	2/13	1/3	1/2	1/1

* Values may be low due to problems of identification.

TABLE 7. Breeding marine birds on San Miguel Island and their abundance in archaeological sites.

Species	Current status (in breeding pairs)	MNI from sites			
		SMI 261	261A	525	1
Cassin's Auklet	10,000-20,000	43	24	3	1
Brandt's Cormorant	1,300	27	4	8	13
Ashy Storm Petrel	200-400	3	4	-	-
Pigeon Guillemot	200-300	3	-	-	1
Western Gull	200	3	2	3	-
Pelagic Cormorant	150	23	-	2	4
Common Murre	100	2	1	2	1
Xantus' Murrelet	50	34	11	-	-
Double-crested Cormorant	15	-	-	-	2
Tufted Puffin	formerly small numbers	-	-	1	1
Brown Pelican	? none today	3	-	4	2
Chendytes sp.	? extinct	12	2	-	11
Manx Shearwater	? none today	11	1	-	-
Black Storm Petrel	? none today	2	-	-	-
Leach's Storm Petrel	? none today	7	3	-	-

(Table 6) also support this conclusion. Some of the large birds at SMI 261 and SMI 261A could have been brought in by foxes, as the caves provide good den sites.

Frequency of Recovery of Avian Species

All sea bird species currently breeding on San Miguel or its offshore islands were recovered from the sites (see Table 7). Among the small-sized species (believed accumulated by owls), the surface-nesting Xantus' Murrelet (*Endomychura hypoleuca*) is more abundant than the petrels and auklets that nest underground. Presumably, murrelets were easier prey for owls. Among the larger species believed to have been killed by man, there seems to have been a preference for Pelagic Cormorants (*Phalacrocorax pelagicus*). That this species and Pigeon Guillemots (*Cepphus columba*) breed on San Miguel proper, while all other breeding marine birds occur only on the small islands off the coast of San Miguel, may account for its abundance.

Species that winter on or near San Miguel—the loons, grebes, geese, and ducks—are also fairly abundant in the deposits, with the frequency of occurrence generally reflecting present or historic wintering numbers. Short-tailed Albatross (*Diomedia albatrus*) was a common offshore species before 1900 and Snow Geese (*Chen hyperborea*) wintered on the Channel Islands in large numbers before the 1930s (H.L. Jones, pers. comm.).

Despite the seasonal abundance of such migratory species as the Sooty Shearwater (*Puffinus griseus*) and phalaropes, bones of these species are rarely recovered. Remains of the Manx Shearwater (*Puffinus puffinus*) and Leach's Storm Petrel (*Oceanodroma leucorhoa*) are more frequently recovered than would be expected if these species had been only occasional visitors to San Miguel, as they are today. This suggests that these species once bred on San Miguel. Leach's Storm Petrel currently nests both to the north (Farallon Islands) and south (Mexico) of San Miguel, while Manx Shearwater breeds only to the south of the island today.

Although not all passerine bones have been identified, the absence of House Finch (*Car-

podacus mexicanus) remains in the collection supports Johnson's (1972) view that this species is a recent addition to the island avifauna.

Season of Human Occupation

The data reveal little about the seasonality of human occupation of the sites. Loons, geese, ducks, and albatross are species that are present only during the winter at San Miguel and are found at all sites. Summer use of the sites is more difficult to determine, as most breeding species on the island are also present on or near the island throughout the year.

Human Uses of Birds

Artifacts recovered from the sites include three awls made from the radii of Brandt's Cormorant (*Phalacrocorax penicillatus*), seven bone tubes fashioned from the ulni of geese, albatross, and a gull, a whistle made from the ulna of a Black-legged Kittiwake (*Rissa tridactyla*), and a scraper made from the ulna of an albatross or goose. Also recovered was a cache of feathers of Brandt's Cormorant.

Bones showing evidence of having been worked include a tibia and humerus of Brandt's Cormorant and an ulna of a Brown Pelican (*Pelecanus occidentalis*). Only a few bones of the Pelagic Cormorant (four bones), Brandt's Cormorant (two bones), and Barn Owl (one bone) show any evidence of burning. Thus, out of a total of 2,204 bones recovered, only 22 show definite evidence of working or burning.

Distribution of preserved elements, breakage patterns, and CSI values for the more common species from SMI 261 are presented in Table 6. All elements of the skeleton are present for such species as Cassin's Auklet (*Ptychoramphus aleutica*), Xantus' Murrelet, and passerine birds—species preyed upon by owls. Most of the bones of these species are unbroken. Although the numbers of different skeletal elements vary, these differences seem attributable to either the size of the bone (smaller bones being lost more readily in sieving) or to the fragility of individual bones. Thus, there are fewer femora and tarsometatarsi than humeri (due to size difference), and fewer pelvi than femora, and a higher percentage of whole femora than tibia (due to differences in fragility).

Among species usually believed to serve as food for humans, only remains of the Snow Goose are common. In this species, most of the bones are broken and, although a large number of wing bones were recovered, nearly all body and leg bones are absent. This suggests preparation of Snow Geese as food items by removal of the wings, which have little meat, and destruction or removal from the site of the remainder of the skeleton.

The pattern of skeletal preservation for cormorants is different than that found for Snow Geese; there is a higher degree of bone breakage among the larger bones, but less breakage of smaller bones. All elements of the skeleton are present, however, and the frequencies for the occurrence of each element are generally correlated with size or fragility. The presence of complete skeletons and the low frequency of butcher marks or burned bone suggest that cormorants were used for some purpose other than food. Although there are records of immature cormorants serving as food items (Howard 1929), there is little evidence that adult birds were taken for food on the California coast. Certainly, marine, fish-eating birds are not known for their palatability, at least by modern standards.

It seems likely that cormorants were killed for their feathers. Reports of the discovery of the "lost woman" of San Nicolas Island state that she was clothed "in a robe of bird's plumage, made of small squares neatly matched and sewed together" (Heizer 1973:23-24). The collection of breast feather patches from sea birds would result in some breakage of long bones, but not in the destruction of skeletal elements, as might result from cooking.

Remains of other fish-eating species (*e.g.*, albatrosses, shearwaters, loons, and larger alcids) are too fragmentary to show clearly the pattern of skeletal preservation. However, the few remains that have been recovered seem to follow the pattern for cormorants rather than for Snow Geese. The distribution of recovered skeletal elements for *Chendytes,* an extinct, flightless, diving duck, more nearly resembles that of cormorants than that of Snow Geese and may indicate that this species also served as a source of feathers rather than food. The pattern of skeletal preservation for the Eared Grebe (*Podiceps caspicus*), especially in the number of unbroken bones, is intermediate between that of species that were prey for owls and those believed killed for their feathers by man. Use of the Eared Grebe for its feathers is more likely, the greater number of unbroken elements possibly being due to the smaller size of this species.

Although the number of skeletal elements from SMI 525 and SMI 1 is too small to feel confident about applying the foregoing type of analysis, there seems to be no indication that any differences in type of skeletal preservation pattern exist among the four sites.

Almost all skeletal elements recovered are from adult birds. Partially developed bones were found only for the Raven (*Corvus corax*), Barn Owl, Manx Shearwater, and Western Grebe (*Aechmophorus occidentalis*). These bones from immature individuals are, however, at a stage of development which permitted flight. No bones of immature cormorants or pelicans were found. No eggshell fragments are preserved in this collection.

Horizontal and Vertical Distribution Patterns

Horizontal patterns of skeletal distribution are clear only at site SMI 261, where a large contiguous area was excavated. At this site, smaller-sized species of birds tend to be distributed across the mouth of the cave and along the cliff face near the cave entrance. This distribution correlates well with Barn Owl remains (Fig. 1). Larger birds, such as cormorants, are distributed more randomly over the site.

Remains from SMI 1 and SMI 525 are too fragmentary to allow differences in distribution by depth to be analyzed. However, *Chendytes* is absent from SMI 525, the youngest of the four sites. This may indicate that *Chendytes* died out before 2000 B.P. and that its inclusion in younger levels at other sites is due to post-depositional disturbance of these sites. Careful examination of undisturbed sites will be necessary to determine if this is the case. At site SMI 261, there is a significant increase in cormorant bones in the top 24 inches of the site; fewer remains of owls and their prey occur in this interval (Table 3). Rozaire (pers. comm.) indicates that the top 2 ft of this deposit represent the last 2,000 years and that during this period there occurred a shift in fishing techniques, as indicated by fishhook type. This and the shift to cormorants, species that nest primarily on the offshore rocks, may correlate with advances in seamanship. Earliest evidence for use of the plank canoe by Chumash Indians dates from about 1300 B.P. (Walker in press).

Comments on the Identification of Individual Species

While many species have bones which are easily identifiable by size and configuration, there are some groups in which the identification of individual bones is difficult, if not impossible. Therefore, a few comments on identification seem in order.

Howard (1929) described methods of identifying bones in some genera (*e.g., Buteo, Phalacrocorax*) where species are extremely similar. Through the use of the excellent comparative material available to me, I was able to identify nearly all specimens, exclusive of passerines, to species level. Details of skeletal differences in such groups as alcids and the genera *Buteo* and *Larus* will be published elsewhere. Two identifications are worth commenting on here as they could significantly affect species lists.

Examination of skeletal elements from alcids revealed that, except for the Xantus' Murrelet and Ancient Murrelet (*Synthliboramphus antiquus*), all species could be identified by config-

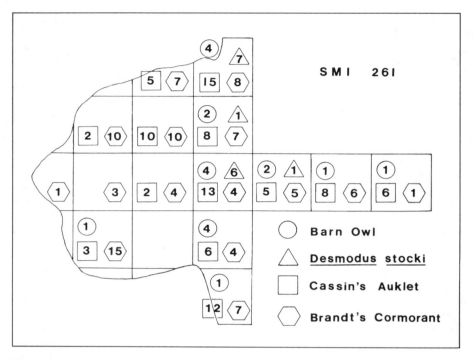

FIGURE 1. *Floor plan of SMI 261, excavated in 5-ft squares. Numbers represent MNI values for species indicated.*

urational differences. These two species are identical in skeletal form and vary only in size. Jehl and Bond (1975) noted this similarity, suggesting that these two species are clinally related on the west coast of North America, with larger individuals farther north.

Bones of this group from San Miguel Island seem slightly bimodal in distribution (Fig. 2), matching the size of modern Xantus' Murrelets and Ancient Murrelets (Table 8). I originally believed, therefore, that both species were represented in the collection. This combined sample, however, contains no more variation than is now found in a single species. It seems unlikely that two such closely related species could coexist on San Miguel. It is more likely that the sample represents a single species, with perhaps some sexual dimorphism (see Jehl and Bond 1975). If this interpretation is correct, the question of why the San Miguel bones are so much larger than modern Xantus' Murrelets from southern California arises. The recent specimens used in this comparison (Table 8) were obtained on southern California beaches in winter and, I believe, represent smaller individuals of more southerly populations of Xantus' Murrelet. Whether this interpretation is correct or not will have to await the collection of osteological material from nesting Xantus' Murrelets on San Miguel.

Bones referable to species of small petrels from San Miguel show a distinct bimodal distribution in size (Fig. 2). The two sizes correspond to measurements taken from recent material of the Ashy Storm Petrel (*Oceanodroma homochroa*) and Leach's Storm Petrel; the two populations are so identified. However, the recent material of Leach's Storm Petrel is from

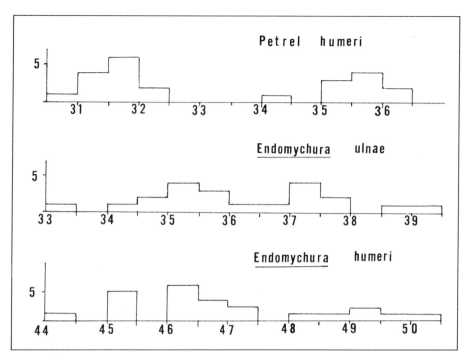

FIGURE 2. *Frequency histograms of maximum length measurements of murrelet and petrel wing bones from San Miguel Island.*

Guadalupe Island. The possibility of clinal variation in these species makes identification of bones tenuous until skeletal material from areas closer to San Miguel Island is obtained.

An Extinct Vampire Bat

Material from the cave deposit SMI 261 includes several bones referable to *Desmodus stocki*, an extinct species of vampire bat. The material (now deposited in the Department of Archaeology, Los Angeles County Museum of Natural History) consists of 12 humeri, five radii, and a partial scapula and is identical in both morphology and size to the type of material of *Desmodus stocki* from San Josecito Cave in Nuevo León, Mexico, described by Jones in 1958 (Table 9).

Distribution of material within the deposit shows that the occurrence of bones of small mammals, small birds, and *Desmodus* is correlated with the presence of the remains of the Barn Owl (*Tyto alba*); such a correlation is not found for the bones of birds such as cormorants, which are too large to serve as prey for owls. The usual prey of Barn Owls on the mainland are voles (*Microtus*), mice (*Peromyscus*), or gophers (*Thomomys*) (Evans and Emlen 1947). On islands, where these prey species are often absent, owls are known to prey on a much wider variety of organisms, including auklets and petrels (Bennett 1928, Banks 1965). Whether the presence of bat bones in the cave is due to owl predation or to use of the cave by living bats, the remains of at least eight individual *Desmodus* indicate a population of this species on the island in the past.

The exact age of the bat material is not known. Based on bead types, the deposit is considered

TABLE 8. Measurements (in mm) of murrelets from SMI 261 and SMI 261A.

Bone	Ancient Murrelet*			Xantus' Murrelet†			Material from 261 and 261A				
	n	Range	Mean	n	Range	Mean	n	Range	Mean (±s.e.)	S.D. (±s.e.)	C.V. (±s.e.)
Humerus	3	48.7-51.3	50.2	4	44.3-46.6	45.9	24	44.3-50.9	47.57±0.45	2.22±0.32	4.67±0.68
Ulna	3	37.8-39.7	38.9	3	33.6-35.4	34.8	18	34.2-39.1	36.38±0.35	1.47±0.25	4.04±0.67
Femur	3	24.7-26.0	25.4	4	21.0-23.2	22.4	11	22.3-26.1	24.90±0.38	1.27±0.27	5.09±1.09
Coracoid	3	22.3-23.6	23.1	4	20.2-21.8	21.1	13	20.5-24.0	22.35±0.33	1.17±0.23	5.24±1.03

*All Ancient Murrelets are from Del Monte, Monterey County, Calif. (sex unknown).
†All Xantus' Murrelets are females from San Pedro, Calif. (collected in winter).

TABLE 9. Measurements of the humeri of *Desmodus stocki* (in mm).

Measurement	Potter Creek Cave*			San Miguel Island			San Josecito Cave*		
	n	Range	Mean	n	Range	Mean	n	Range	Mean
Length	1	--	43.8	4	44.30-46.62	45.41	42	39.3-47.5	43.63
Proximal Width	2	6.75-6.8	6.77	5	6.50-6.98	6.80	47	5.8-6.8	6.27
Distal Width	5	6.5-7.1	6.95	4	6.95-7.25	7.08	52	6.4-7.3	6.78
Medial Width	7	2.5-2.8	2.67	12	2.50-2.95	2.72	56	2.0-2.9	2.52

*Measurements for Potter Creek and San Josecito Cave from Hutchison (1967).

no older than 3000 B.P. (C. King, pers. comm.), but beads are found only to a depth of about 54 inches (137 cm). The *Desmodus* material was recovered from depths ranging from 42 to 72 inches (107 to 183 cm). There are no noticeable differences in other parts of the fauna between depths of 40 and 72 inches (102 and 183 cm). The age of the material, then, is probably no younger than 2500 B.P. and no older than 5000 B.P.

Desmodus stocki, recently reviewed by Hutchison (1967), is known from Potter Creek Cave, Shasta County, California, and southern Florida, as well as from the type locality in Nuevo León, Mexico. All these localities are late Pleistocene and indicate a wide distribution for this species at that time. The San Miguel material is much more recent.

Living vampire bats are not migratory, but are adaptable species, occupying a wide variety of habitats. In Mexico, the preferred prey of vampires are horses, cows, and, in some places, domestic fowl (Dalquest 1955). The population of vampires on San Miguel Island was contemporary with man and might also have preyed on the sea mammals breeding there (Elephant Seal, California Sea Lion, and Harbor Seal), the numerous large sea birds (pelicans, cormorants, and gulls), or, at an earlier time, on the Pygmy Mammoths that inhabited the island.

SUMMARY

There is evidence that three species of birds not currently known to nest on San Miguel Island bred there within the last 2,000 years. These are the extinct genus *Chendytes* and the Manx Shearwater and Leach's Storm Petrel. Remains of House Finch are absent from the abundant passerine material from SMI 261, an indication that this species was absent from San Miguel before 500 B.P.

Snow Geese, and probably other granivorous anatids, were eaten by the prehistoric inhabitants of San Miguel. Most marine species of birds found in middens, however, appear to have been killed for their feathers rather than for food. An increase in the use of cormorants, beginning about 2000 B.P., may correlate with advances in boat building. A very small percentage of bird remains seems to have been used as artifacts. There is no evidence that young sea birds were harvested for food.

The analysis of bird remains from archaeological sites on San Miguel Island provides valuable information on the past avifauna of the island, as well as on the uses of birds by early human inhabitants. However, some of this information must be of a tentative nature because of the paucity of good osteological collections of recent birds and the need for large samples of skeletal material from the island.

The presence of the remains of at least eight individuals of *Desmodus* indicates a population of this extinct vampire bat once occurred on the island.

ACKNOWLEDGMENTS

The author wishes to thank C. E. Ray for critically reviewing the section on the vampire bat.

REFERENCES

BANKS, R. C. 1965. Some information from barn owl pellets. Auk 82:506.

BENNETT, P. 1928. An outlaw barn owl. Condor 30:320.

DALQUEST, W. W. 1955. Natural history of the vampire bat of eastern Mexico. Amer. Midl. Natur. 53:79-87.

EVANS, F. C., and J. T. EMLEN, JR. 1947. Ecological notes on the prey selected by a Barn Owl. Condor 49:3-9.

HEIZER, R. F., and A. B. ELSASSER. 1973. Original accounts of the lone woman of San Nicolas Island. Ballena Press, Ramona, Calif.

HOWARD, H. 1929. The avifauna of Emeryville Shellmount. Univ. California Publ. Zool. 32:301-387.

HUTCHISON, J. H. 1967. A Pleistocene vampire bat (*Desmodus stocki*) from Potter Creek Cave, Shasta County, California. Paleobios 3:1-6.

JEHL, J. R., and S. I. BOND. 1975. Morphological variation and species limits in murrelets of the genus *Endomychura*. Trans. San Diego Soc. Nat. Hist. 18:9-24.

JOHNSON, N. K. 1972. Origin and differentiation of the avifauna of the Channel Islands, California. Condor 74:295-315.

JONES, J. K. 1958. Pleistocene bats from San Josecito Cave, Nuevo León, Mexico. Univ. Kansas Publ. Mus. Nat. Hist. 9:389-396.

THOMAS, D. H. 1971. On distinguishing natural from cultural bone in archaeological sites. Amer. Antiquity 36:366-371.

WALKER, P. L. Diet, dental attrition and molar size of island and mainland Chumash (in press).

ZIEGLER, A. C. 1973. Inference from prehistoric faunal remains. Addison Wesley Module in Anthropology no. 43.

Archaeological Evidence for the Recent Extinction of Three Terrestrial Mammals on San Miguel Island

Phillip L. Walker

*Department of Anthropology, University of California,
Santa Barbara, California 93106*

INTRODUCTION

In this paper, evidence is presented concerning the recent extinction on San Miguel Island of western spotted skunks (*Spilogale gracilis*), ornate shrews (*Sorex ornatus*), and a large insular species of deer mouse (*Peromyscus nesodytes*). Skeletal remains from these species are present in a faunal collection made by Charles Rozaire during the excavation of two archaeological middens (4-SMI-261 and 4-SMI-261A) on the northeast coast of the island.

SMI-261 is a small coastal cave located east of Bay Point. The faunal remains from this site were obtained by excavating most of the cave's interior and a 5-ft (1.5 m) wide trench extending 15 ft (4.6 m) into the talus at the mouth of the cave (Fig. 1). The SMI-261A site is located at the bottom of a vertical fissure in the cliff, a few meters below SMI-261. Both sites were excavated in arbitrary 6-inch (15.2 cm) levels and all faunal remains retained by a quarter-inch screen were collected. These deposits contained disc-shaped beads made by grinding the wall portion of purple olive shells (*Olivella biplicata*). *Olivella* beads of this type are characteristic of Middle Period (*ca.* 400 B.C. to 300 A.D.) occupations of the Santa Barbara Channel mainland (Gibson 1975).

Stratigraphic profiles indicate that SMI-261 is composed of a complex series of well-defined, more or less horizontal, interbedded strata (C. Rozaire, pers. comm.). According to Rozaire, the SMI-261A midden is comparatively homogeneous and lacks the obvious stratification that characterizes SMI-261. It is evident from this dissimilarity in midden structure that differences exist in the depositional histories of the two sites.

Human skeletal remains were present in the sites and it is probable that both middens were disturbed prehistorically by intrusive burial pits. Apparently, additional mixing of deposits occurred due to recent digging by grave robbers. This is evidenced by the concentration of highly fragmented, completely disarticulated human skeletons on the surface and in the zero to 6-inch levels of SMI-261 and SMI-261A (Table 1).

SPECIES ACCOUNTS

Peromyscus nesodytes and *Peromyscus maniculatus* (Deer Mice)

The faunal collections from SMI-261 and SMI-261A contain numerous remains of *Peromyscus nesodytes* (Fig. 2), a large species of deer mouse previously reported only from late Pleistocene deposits on Santa Rosa Island (Wilson 1936, White 1966). *P. nesodytes* is larger than any modern *Peromyscus* from the United States (White 1966). The mean molar row length of the Santa Rosa Island specimen is 5.95 mm (Table 2). This value does not differ significantly from those of *P. nesodytes* from either SMI-261 ($x = 6.06, t = 1.21, P > 0.50$) or SMI-261A ($x = 5.75, t = 0.753, P > 0.50$). Mean mandibular molar row dimensions of the San Miguel Island *P. nesodytes* do differ significantly from those of *P. anyapahensis*, a small species of extinct deer mouse from late Pleistocene deposits on Anacapa Island ($t = 7.41, P < 0.05$).

In addition to *Peromyscus nesodytes*, the archaeological collections also contain bones of *Peromyscus maniculatus* that are, in most respects, comparable to *P. m. streatori*, the only

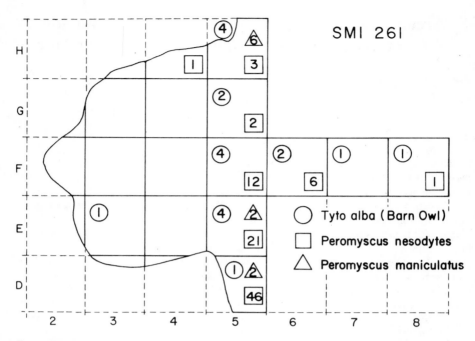

FIGURE 1. *Map of SMI-261 showing distribution of Barn Owl,* Peromyscus nesodytes, *and* Peromyscus maniculatus.

TABLE 1. Distribution of human skeletal remains in SMI-261 and SMI-261A.

Site number	Excavation unit	Surface	Levels in inches					
			0-6	6-12	12-18	12-36	18-24	24-30
SMI-261	—	5	—	—	—	—	—	—
"	D-5	1	—	—	—	—	—	—
"	E-3	—	—	—	1	1	—	—
"	F-5, 6, 7	—	—	—	—	—	—	—
"	G-4	—	—	1	—	—	—	1
"	H-5	—	—	—	—	—	1	—
SMI-261A	First room	2	8	—	—	—	—	—
"	Test pit #1	—	—	—	—	—	1	—

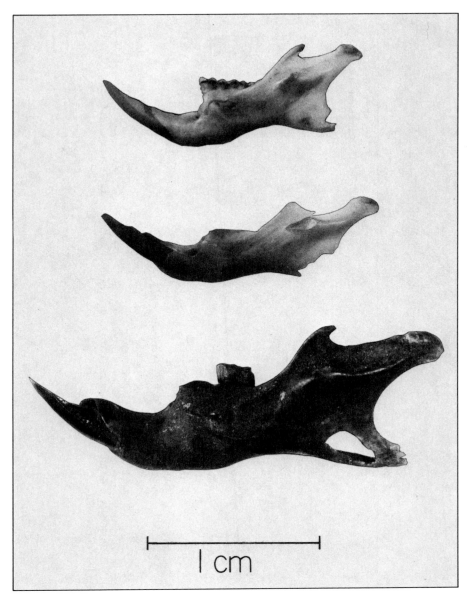

FIGURE 2. *Lateral view of hemimandibles of:* (**top**) Peromyscus nesodytes *from SMI-261A;* (**center**) Peromyscus maniculatus streatori; *and* (**bottom**) Peromyscus nesodytes *from San Miguel Island.*

TABLE 2. Dental dimensions of deer mice from the Northern Channel Islands.

Species	Origin of specimens	Dating	Alveolar length of mandibular molar row†			Mesiodistal width of mandibular incisors		
			n	X̄	S.D.	n	X̄	S.D.
Peromyscus maniculatus streatori	San Miguel Island: specimens were trapped at various localities	1939	12	3.88	0.20	12	0.57	0.07
Peromyscus maniculatus	San Miguel Island: SMI-261 & SMI-261A	Middle period (400 B.C.-300 A.D.?)	9	4.12	0.11	3	0.65	0.09
Peromyscus nesodytes	San Miguel Island: SMI-261 & SMI-261A	Middle period (400 B.C.-300 A.D.?)	20	6.00	0.17	10	0.95	0.06
*Peromyscus nesodytes**	Santa Rosa Island: deposits	Late Pleistocene	7	5.95	0.16	—	—	—
*Peromyscus anyapahensis**	Santa Rosa Island: deposits	Late Pleistocene	7	5.51	0.14	—	1.09	0.04

* Data from White (1966). White's measurements are estimated to the nearest 0.01 mm. All other measurements are estimated to the nearest 0.05 mm.

† Measurement as defined by White (1966).

endemic form of rodent previously reported from San Miguel Island (Nelson and Goldman 1931).

At least 99 *P. nesodytes* and 28 *P. maniculatus* individuals are represented in the collections from the archaeological sites. These figures are based on counts of the most frequently occurring unique (*i.e.,* from one side of the body) skeletal remains from each excavation unit. The deer mouse bones from SMI-261 and SMI-261A are well preserved and do not exhibit burning, cut marks, or other obvious evidence of processing by humans. *Peromyscus* bone is not evenly distributed in the archaeological middens. Instead, it tends to be concentrated at only a few levels of each excavation unit (Table 3). Levels containing high densities of deer mouse bone were probably produced during periods when the SMI-261 cave was not occupied by humans and was therefore available as a roosting place for owls. In this site there is a negative association between deer mouse remains and artifacts. Although shell artifacts occurred in 32 of the 6-inch levels excavated at SMI-261, only two of these artifact-bearing levels also contained deer mouse bone. The role of owls in the deposition of *Peromyscus* at SMI-261 is also indicated by the presence of barn owl (*Tyto alba*) remains in units that also contained deer mouse bone and by the presence of high densities of *Peromyscus* bone at the lateral margin of the cave's mouth near potential owl roosts (Fig. 1 and Table 3). Even though owl remains occur in SMI-261A (Guthrie 1980), these predators may not be responsible for all of the *Peromyscus* in the deposit. Both ends of the SMI-261A fissure are blocked and the site could have functioned as a natural trap during part of its depositional history (C. Rozaire, pers. comm.).

Fusion of Long-bone Epiphyses

Differences exist between the *P. nesodytes* and *P. maniculatus* samples with respect to epiphyseal fusion. Eight per cent of the *P. nesodytes* femora from the archaeological collections have completely fused proximal and distal epiphyses (Table 3). The *P. maniculatus* material, in contrast, contains many more femora with completed epiphyseal union (40 per cent). In *P. nesodytes* 18 per cent, and in *P. maniculatus* 5 per cent of the femora recovered from the archaeological sites belonged to young individuals lacking any fused epiphyses. Differences in age structure of the two species cannot be inferred from these data since the bones of relatively small immature *P. maniculatus* pass through quarter-inch mesh screen and are lost at a higher rate than are the bones of larger immature *P. nesodytes*. Additional biases may have been introduced by the disproportionate preservation and recovery of denser, relatively resistant adult bones.

Coronoid Process Morphology

A significant difference in mandibular morphology exists between the *P. maniculatus* preserved in the archaeological middens and modern *P. maniculatus streatori* trapped on San Miguel Island. The coronoid processes of *P. maniculatus* jaws from SMI-261 and SMI-261A are relatively small and have little or no posterior recurve. *P. m. streatori* collected on the island during the 1930s contrast with these specimens by frequently exhibiting prominent, markedly recurved coronoid processes (Fig. 3). Seven of the 11 *P. maniculatus* hemimandibles from SMI-261 were determined to have intact coronoid processes after careful examination with a dissecting microscope. The absence of recurved coronoid processes in the archaeological collection is not, therefore, explained by low preservation rates of processes with recurved morphology.

Modifications in coronoid process shape have been produced in laboratory rats by feeding them experimental diets of contrasting consistencies (Whiteley, Kendrick, and Matthews 1966). Rats fed a diet of hard food items that required vigorous mastication developed prominent coronoid processes that extended to the level of, or superior to, the zygomatic arches. Animals fed the same food after it had been ground to a fine powder and mixed with water developed comparatively short coronoid processes that never extended to the level of the

TABLE 3. *Peromyscus* remains (SMI-261 and SMI-261A).

Species	Bone	Grid	0-6"	6-12"	12-18"	18-24"	24-30"	30-36"	36-42"	42-48"	48-54"	54-60"	60-66"	66-72"
SMI-261														
P. maniculatus	R.Mandible	D-5	1											
"	L Femur	D-5	1						2					
"	R.Tibia	D-5	1						1					
"	L.Mandible	E-5						1						
"	R.Mandible	E-5	1											
"	L.Femur	E-5						2						
"	R.Femur	E-5						2						
"	L.Tibia	E-5						2						
"	R.Tibia	E-5						2						
"	R.Mandible	G-5						1						
"	L.Femur	H-4							1					
"	L.Mandible	H-5						5						
"	R.Mandible	H-5						2						
"	L.Femur	H-5						2						
"	R.Femur	H-5						6						
"	L.Tibia	H-5						3						
"	R.Tibia	H-5						5						
"	L.Pelvis	H-5						3						
P. nesodytes	L.Mandible	D-5	8											
"	R Mandible	D-5	10											
"	R.Maxilla	D-5	1											
"	L.Femur	D-5	46											
"	R.Femur	D-5	45											
"	L.Humerus	D-5	5											
"	R.Humerus	D-5	4											
"	L.Radius	D-5	1											
"	R.Ulna	D-5	1											

	Part	Grid							
"	L.Pelvis	D-5	8						
"	R.Pelvis	D-5	17						
"	Sacrum	D-5	2						
"	L.Mandible	E-5				2			
"	R.Mandible	E-5				2			
"	R.Maxilla	E-5					3		
"	L.Femur	E-5				10	11		
"	R.Femur	E-5				8	5		
"	R.Pelvis	E-5				1	2		
"	Sacrum	E-5					2		
"	L.Mandible	F-5						1	2
"	R.Mandible	F-5						5	2
"	L.Tibia	F-5						5	4
"	R.Tibia	F-5						2	7
"	L.Pelvis	F-5			5			2	4
"	R.Pelvis	F-5			1				2
"	L.Femur	F-6						1	
"	R.Femur	F-6						3	
"	L.Tibia	F-6						1	
"	R.Tibia	F-6						1	
"	R.Humerus	F-6					1		
"	L.Pelvis	F-6					1		
"	R.Pelvis	F-6					1		
"	L.Pelvis	F-8		1					
"	L.Mandible	G-5				1			
"	R.Mandible	G-5				1			
"	L.Maxilla	G-5				1			
"	R.Maxilla	G-5				1			
"	L.Femur	G-5				2			
"	L.Humerus	G-5				1			
"	R.Pelvis	G-5				2			

TABLE 3. (Cont.)

Species	Bone	Grid	0-6"	6-12"	12-18"	18-24"	24-30"	30-36"	36-42"	42-48"	48-54"	54-60"	60-66"	66-72"
"	R.Femur	H-4					1							
"	L.Femur	H-5									1			
"	R.Fem	H-5									3			
"	L.Tibia	H-5									1			
"	R.Tibia	H-5									2			
SMI-261A														
P. maniculatus	L.Mandible	TP1		18	1									
"	R.Mandible	TP1		12										
"	L.Femur	TP1		12										
"	R.Femur	TP1		6										
"	L.Tibia	TP1		19										
"	R.Tibia	TP1		16										
"	L.Pelvis	TP1		1	2									
"	R.Pelvis	TP1		2										
P. nesodytes	L.Mandible	TP1		1	5			10						
"	R.Mandible	TP1		1	5	4		5						
"	R.Maxilla	TP1				2		2						
"	R.Femur	TP1		2		1								
"	L.Tibia	TP1		1				5						
"	R.Tibia	TP1		3				7						
"	L.Humerus	TP1		2		2		3						
"	R.Humerus	TP1		2		7		1						
"	L.Ulna	TP1				7								
"	R.Ulna	TP1				2								
"	L.Pelvis	TP1		4		10		9						
"	R.Pelvis	TP1		4		6		14						
"	Sacrum	TP1		1				4						

Abbreviations: L. = left; R. = right; TP1 = Test pit 1.

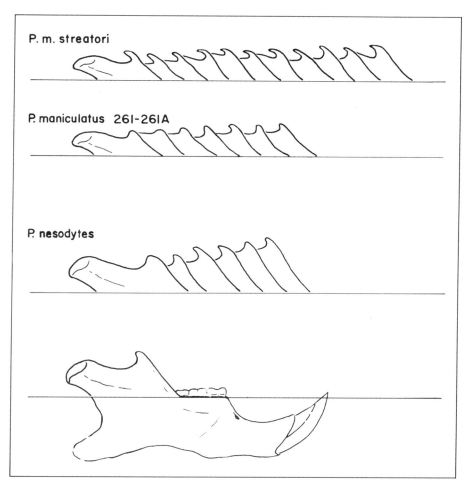

FIGURE 3. *Lateral view of coronoid processes of* Peromyscus *from San Miguel Island. The upper three figures show series of processes arranged from lowest to highest —mandibles are oriented parallel to the superior edge of the alveolus (see bottom figure).*

zygomatic arch. These experiments suggest the possibility that the morphological differences observed in the jaws of deer mice from San Miguel Island are the result of dietary rather than genetic factors.

Habitat Preferences

P. m. streatori is morphologically (Nelson and Goldman 1931) and biochemically (Gill 1976) distinct from other Channel Island races of *Peromyscus*. Presumably, this subspecies of deer mouse has been isolated on San Miguel Island for a considerable period of time. From data on post-Pleistocene sea-level changes and bathymetric readings of the San Miguel passage, it can be inferred that San Miguel Island has existed as a discrete geographical unit for about ten thousand years (Orr 1967). Recent landscape evolution on the island has been characterized by

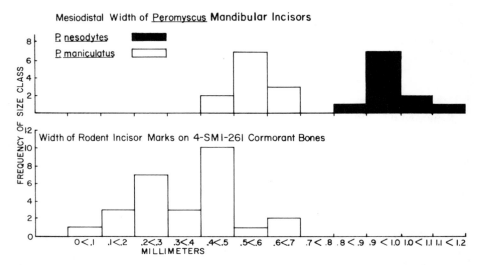

FIGURE 4. *Illustration comparing width of rodent incisor marks on bird bones and mesiodistal diameters of* Peromyscus *mandibular incisors.*

overgrazing and large-scale wind and water erosion. This modern episode of catastrophic vegetation stripping began when sheep overgrazed the island during a severe drought in the 1860s (Johnson 1972, 1980). The extinction of *P. nesodytes* may have resulted from the loss of habitat associated with this recent transformation of much of the island into defoliated sand dunes. The occurrence of *P. nesodytes* and *P. maniculatus* in the same archaeological sites is circumstantial evidence that these species lived on the island contemporaneously. It cannot be assumed that both species occupied coastal habitats in the vicinity of the archaeological sites since *Peromyscus* bones could have been transported from the interior of the island by owls. Occupancy of the SMI-261 cave by deer mice is indicated by incisor marks on gnawed bird bones from this deposit. Polyvinyl alcohol surface replicas (Walker 1976, Walker and Long 1977) were used to examine these bones microscopically. Many of the grooves on the gnawed bones have diameters that fall within the range of variation of *P. maniculatus* incisor widths (Fig. 4). The inference that prehistoric *P. maniculatus* occupied coastal habitats in the vicinity of SMI-261 is consistent with reports that modern *P. m. streatori* occur at highest densities in coastal areas (Gill 1976, D. Johnson, pers. comm.).

Sorex ornatus (Ornate Shrew)

A damaged *Sorex* cranium is present in the faunal remains from SMI-261A (Test pit 1, 6 to 12-inch level). The only shrew previously reported from the Channel Islands is a single specimen discovered on Santa Catalina Island in 1941 and originally described by von Bloeker (1941) as a new species, *Sorex willetti*. Von Bloeker (1967) subsequently demoted the specimen to subspecific status (*i.e., Sorex ornatus willetti*). *S. o. willetti* differs from mainland races in its slightly larger size, longer cranium, and darker pelage (von Bloeker 1967). Comparisons of cranial measurements of the *S. o. willetti* type specimen, *S. ornatus* specimens from mainland localities, and the SMI-261A cranium (Table 4) indicate that the SMI-261A specimen and the Santa Catalina Island shrew both have larger cranial dimensions than shrews from the mainland. It is possible that the SMI-261A specimen represents a race of San Miguel Island shrews.

TABLE 4. Cranial dimensions of *Sorex ornatus* from the Santa Barbara Channel area.

Species	Locality	n	Molar length		Interorbital breadth		Maxillary breadth	
			$\bar{X}$	S.D.	$\bar{X}$	S.D.	$\bar{X}$	S.D.
*Sorex ornatus willetti**	Santa Catalina Island	1	4.00		3.40		4.30	
Sorex ornatus cf. *willetti*	San Miguel Island	1	3.80		3.50		4.80	
*Sorex ornatus**	Mainland	5	3.71	0.17	3.07	0.21	3.90	0.51

*Los Angeles County Museum of Natural History (LACM) specimens.

An alternative explanation is that the SMI-261A *Sorex* was captured on the mainland by a raptorial bird that subsequently roosted at the island site. This possibility is suggested by the presence of barn owl remains in the excavation unit containing the shrew cranium (Guthrie 1980) and by reports of mainland rodent species in owl pellets discovered in a cave on one of Los Coronados Islands, situated approximately eight miles (13 km) from the mainland (Banks 1965). Arguing against transportation by owls is the relatively great distance, 30 miles (48 km), between the Santa Barbara mainland and San Miguel Island.

Spilogale gracilis (Western Spotted Skunk)

Test pit 1 at SMI-261A contained a fragmentary cranium (6 to 12-inch level) and a complete right femur (zero to 6-inch level) from *Spilogale gracilis*. Western spotted skunks do not inhabit the island at present and have not previously been reported from either archaeological or paleontological contexts on San Miguel Island. The only other record of skunks on San Miguel Island is in the unpublished field notes of C. D. Voy, who visited the island sometime around 1893 (Johnson 1972). Voy reported that a small species of skunk was caught in a trap some years prior to his visit.

Cranial dimensions of the San Miguel Island specimen are small compared with those of *S. gracilis amphialus* from the other Channel Islands (Table 5). For most dimensions, the San Miguel Island spotted skunk falls outside the range of variation of the female Santa Cruz Island and Santa Rosa Island spotted skunks measured by van Gelder (1959). If this specimen is not a recently extinct endemic form, its relatively small dimensions suggest affinities with *S. g. phenax* on the mainland rather than with the larger *S. g. amphialus* subspecies from the Channel Islands.

Large abscesses perforate the frontal sinuses of the San Miguel Island spotted skunk cranium. Lesions of this sort result from infection by metastrongylid sinus worms of the genus *Skrjabingylus* (Hill 1939, Duncan 1976). Similar frontal sinus abscesses are present on almost all the available prehistoric and recent *S. g. amphialus* crania from the Channel Islands (Walker and Collins in prep.).

The western spotted skunk femur from SMI-261A has a maximum length of 43.5 mm. This dimension is close to the mean length of 14 right femora I recovered from a dry cistern on Santa Cruz Island ($\overline{X}$ = 43.07, $S.D.$ = 2.74, range = 38.21-47.79 mm).

HUMANS AS DISPERSAL AGENTS

American Indians may have had an important role in transporting animals to the Channel Islands. The historic Chumash Indians living in the Santa Barbara Channel area possessed a specialized maritime economy that involved the trade of natural resources and manufactured goods among villages on the Northern Channel Islands and on the mainland (King 1971, Hudson, Timbrook, and Rempe 1978). Descriptions of historic Chumash canoe trips suggest numerous occasions for the inadvertent dispersal of small animals across the channel: "When going to sea to trade, they make ready all that they will need. Four men begin by going to the place where *tomol* (plank canoe) is stored, situated in much tule and removing the boat. They keep it there shaded and in water so that the tarring does not get soft and the boards will not shrink if they should get dry" (informant cited *in* Hudson, Timbrook, and Rempe 1978:131). Ornate shrews inhabit coastal and inland marshes (Hall and Kelson 1959) and could have boarded canoes stored in these habitats. Contrary to popular belief, shrews are capable of fasting (Hamilton 1930) and could easily survive the half-day canoe trip across the channel (Hudson, Timbrook, and Rempe 1978).

Beached canoes would have been attractive to deer mice as nesting places and sources of food. Indians living on the Santa Barbara mainland traded seeds, acorns, and chia to people on

TABLE 5. Cranial dimensions of western spotted skunks (*Spilogale gracilis*) from the Northern Channel Islands and Los Angeles County.

Cranial dimension*	Origin of specimen	Sex	n	Measurement or mean	S.D.
Interorbital breadth	San Miguel Island: SMI-261	U	1	13.90	—
	Santa Rosa Island†	M	20	16.53	0.87
		F	8	15.19	0.50
	Santa Cruz Island	M	4	16.34	0.79
		F	2	15.51	0.08
	Los Angeles Co.†	M	7	15.68	0.45
		F	8	13.69	0.68
Postorbital breadth	San Miguel Island: SMI-261	U	1	15.20‡	—
	Santa Rosa Island†	M	20	16.60	0.76
		F	7	15.89	0.63
	Santa Cruz Island	M	4	15.94	0.69
		F	2	15.60	0.04
	Los Angeles Co.†	M	7	16.11	0.63
		F	8	14.69	1.01
Palatal length	San Miguel Island: SMI-261	U	1	19.70	—
	Santa Rosa Island†	M	22	21.66	0.83
		F	8	19.81	0.62
	Santa Cruz Island	M	4	20.67	0.70
		F	2	20.05	0.56
	Los Angeles Co.†	M	7	21.32	0.45
		F	8	18.88	0.37
Height of cranium	San Miguel Island: SMI-261	U	1	15.50	—
	Santa Rosa Island†	M	21	18.27	0.60
		F	7	17.18	0.35
	Santa Cruz Island	M	4	17.36	0.41
		F	2	17.60	0.52
	Los Angeles Co.†	M	6	17.42	0.69
		F	7	16.69	0.72
Length of molar row	San Miguel Island: SMI-261	U	1	16.90	—
	Santa Rosa Island†	M	22	18.59	0.49
		F	8	17.63	0.47
	Santa Cruz Island	M	4	18.12	0.52
		F	2	17.58	0.31
	Los Angeles Co.†	M	7	18.61	0.38
		F	8	17.06	0.66

Abbreviations: U = unknown; M = male; F = female.
† Measurements were made according to the definitions of van Gelder (1959).
* Data from van Gelder (1959).
‡ Measurement estimated.

the islands in exchange for items such as fish, shell beads, and abalone shell (King 1971, Hudson, Timbrook, and Rempe 1978). Considering the nesting and feeding opportunities provided by the plant foods traded to the islands, it is probable that *Peromyscus* occasionally crossed the Santa Barbara Channel secreted in baskets of cargo.

CONCLUSIONS

The substantial quantity of *P. nesodytes* bone in the SMI-261 and SMI-261A middens is convincing evidence that this species survived on San Miguel Island at least until approxi mately 2,000 years ago. Deer mice have been trapped extensively on the island during the past few years and there is little doubt that *P. nesodytes* is extinct. It is conceivable that the extinction of *P. nesodytes* was caused by changes American Indians produced in San Miguel Island's floral and/or faunal communities. It is more likely, however, that *P. nesodytes* became extinct due to recent, large-scale habitat destruction caused by wind erosion, water erosion, and overgrazing (Johnson 1980).

The evidence for the presence of *Sorex* and *Spilogale* populations on the island is equivocal. In the absence of additional specimens, it remains possible that the *Sorex* and *Spilogale* bones from SMI-261A represent isolated individuals that reached San Miguel Island with the aid of humans, or by some other means.

REFERENCES

BANKS, R. C. 1965. Some information from barn owl pellets. Auk 82:506.

DUNCAN, N. 1976. Theoretical aspects concerning transmission of the parasite *Skrjabingylus nasicola* (Leukart 1842) to stoats and weasels, with a review of the literature. Mammal Rev. 6:63-74.

GIBSON, R. O. 1975. The beads of Humaliwo. J. California Anthro. 2:110-119.

GILL, A. E. 1976. Genetic divergence of insular populations of deer mice. Biochem. Genetics 14:835-848.

GUTHRIE, D. 1980. Analysis of avifaunal and bat remains from midden sites on San Miguel Island. Pp. 689-702 *in* D. M. Power, ed., The California Islands: proceedings of a multidisciplinary symposium. Santa Barbara Museum of Natural History, Santa Barbara, Calif.

HALL, E. R., and K. R. KELSON. 1959. The mammals of North America, v. 1. Ronald Press, New York, N.Y.

HAMILTON, W. J. 1930. The food of the *Soricidae*. J. Mammal. 11:26-39.

HILL, W. C. 1939. The nematode *Skrjabingylus chitwoodorum* n. sp. from the skunk. J. Parasitol. 25:475-478.

HUDSON, T., J. TIMBROOK, and M. REMPE. 1978. Tomol: Chumash watercraft as described in the ethnographic notes of John P. Harrington. Ballena Press Anthropol. Papers, 9.

JOHNSON, D. 1972. Landscape evolution on San Miguel Island, California. Ph.D. thesis, University of Kansas, Lawrence, Kan.

———. 1980. Episodic vegetation stripping, soil erosion, and landscape modification in prehistoric and recent historic time, San Miguel Island, California. Pp. 103-121 *in* D. M. Power, ed., The California Islands: proceedings of a multidisciplinary symposium. Santa Barbara Museum of Natural History, Santa Barbara, Calif.

KING, C. 1971. Chumash inter-village economic exchange. Indian Historian 4:31-43. San Francisco, Calif.

NELSON, E. W., and E. A. GOLDMAN. 1931. Mammalogy—six new white-footed mice (*Peromyscus maniculatus* group) from islands off the Pacific coast. J. Washington Acad. Sci. 21:530-535.

ORR, P. C. 1967. Geochronology of Santa Rosa Island, California. Pp. 317-325 *in* R. N. Philbrick, ed., Proceedings of the symposium on the biology of the California Islands. Santa Barbara Botanic Garden, Santa Barbara, Calif.

VAN GELDER, R. G. 1959. A taxonomic revision of the spotted skunks (genus *Spilogale*). Bull. Amer. Mus. Nat. Hist. 117:233-392.

VON BLOEKER, J. C., JR. 1941. A new shrew from Santa Catalina Island, California. Bull. So. California Acad. Sci. 40:163-164.

————. 1967. The land mammals of the Southern California Islands. Pp. 245-263 *in* R. N. Philbrick, ed., Proceedings of the symposium on the biology of the California Islands. Santa Barbara Botanic Garden, Santa Barbara, Calif.

WALKER, P. L. 1976. Wear striations on the incisors of *Ceropithecid* monkeys as an index of diet and habitat preference. Amer. J. Phys. Anthro. 45:299-308.

————. 1978. A quantitative analysis of dental attrition rates in the Santa Barbara Channel area. Amer. J. Phys. Anthro. 48:101-106.

WALKER, P. L., and J. C. LONG. 1977. An experimental study of the morphological characteristics of tool marks. Amer. Antiquity 42:605-616.

WHITE, J. A. 1966. A new *Peromyscus* from the late Pleistocene of Anacapa Island, California, with notes on variation in *Peromyscus nesodytes*. Los Angeles Co. Mus. Contrib. Sci. 96.

WHITELEY, A. T., G. S. KENDRICK, and J. L. MATTHEWS. 1966. The effects of function on osseous and muscle tissue in the craniofacial area of the rat. Angle Orthod. 36:13-17.

WILSON, R. W. 1936. A new Pleistocene deer-mouse from Santa Rosa Island, California. J. Mammal. 17:408-410.

Evolutionary Genetics of California Islands *Peromyscus*

Ayesha E. Gill[1]

Department of Biology, University of California, Los Angeles, California 90024

INTRODUCTION

Population genetics is at a point where its model building must be re-examined. Many of the parameters important in models are extremely hard to measure in practice, and debates on interpretations of these models have not led to clarity. It is clear that a large body of data is necessary to progress beyond the stalemate of present-day, established schools of thought.

Very little is known about the actual process of speciation, but we do know that the old axiom that evolution is merely a change in gene frequencies is not necessarily true. Some changes are homeostatic, while others are of evolutionary significance, but they can occur initially without a great deal of measurable genetic change. We must re-examine the first steps in speciation. We do not know the relative importance of morphological, biochemical, or chromosomal variation during the beginning stages of speciation. Detailed studies of specific cases are necessary to cope with the complexity of this problem, and generalizations will not be apparent until a large enough data base exists to compare the patterns in different situations.

All evolutionary change depends upon the presence of genetic variability in populations, for it is on this pool of variability that selection acts in the evolutionary process. A major concern of population genetics is the measurement of this genetic variation. We need to know what levels of variability exist in natural populations and need to gain some idea of quantitative changes in gene frequencies and genetic variability as populations evolve.

Holistic studies using a diversity of methods are important to an understanding of the variation found in natural populations (Berry and Peters 1976, Pizzimenti 1976, Shvarts 1977). If one considers only a single type of variation, the impression obtained of divergence between groups or rates of change may be quite different from that arising from a comparative analysis of different types of variation. For example, divergence between populations in electrophoretically detectable genic variation is not necessarily reflected in the levels of morphological or karyotypic variations (Lewontin 1974, Selander *et al.* 1974, Turner 1974, Nixon and Taylor 1977). Selection may operate in different ways at each of these levels.

In this evolutionary study of the Deer Mouse, *Peromyscus maniculatus,* I compare morphological and genic divergence of populations on the Channel Islands and of their closest mainland relatives. The Channel Islands are easily accessible and offer a rich opportunity for in-depth study of natural populations. Precisely because they are not divorced from the mainstream of evolution on the mainland and generally do not exhibit the strikingly aberrant forms found on oceanic islands, they may be of greater value than either mainland or oceanic species in clarifying general evolutionary processes. The time for quick and easy studies of natural populations is past, and it is time now for detailed studies on a larger scale. Continental slope islands are particularly important to general evolutionary studies because the plants and animals they support have the potential to interact with and influence the course of evolution of mainland species.

Morphological traits examined in this study include measures of overall body size, skull

---

[1] Present address: Department of Biology, University of Nevada, Reno, Nevada 89557.

TABLE 1. Areas and distances of Channel Islands.*

Island	Area (km²)	Distance to mainland (km)	Distance to nearest island (km)
Santa Cruz	249.0	30	7
Santa Rosa	217.0	44	5
Santa Catalina	194.0	32	34
San Clemente	145.0	79	34
San Nicolas	58.0	98	45
San Miguel	37.0	42	5
Anacapa	2.9	20	7
Santa Barbara	2.6	61	39

* Adapted from Tables 1 and 2 of the Introduction to Philbrick (1967).

anatomy, and weights of some organs. The latter traits, although far more variable than other anatomical or "hard" traits, are useful as indicators of differential adaptations at the physiological level. I have carried out factor and discriminant analyses of the subspecies of Deer Mice on the basis of these morphological characters, utilizing computer programs for multivariate analysis. In addition, I have analyzed 30 protein systems by means of horizontal starch gel electrophoresis and have calculated measures of genic variability and genetic divergence based on the electrophoretic analysis. The composite analysis of morphogenetic variability at the morphological and biochemical levels is directed to questions of (1) the comparative rates of anatomical and genic divergence among the insular populations and (2) the amounts of gene flow and the population sizes necessary to maintain the observed levels of variability. As will be seen, the analysis brings new insights into the amount of genetic variability that can be maintained in island populations and into the differing levels of heterozygosity in the various types of structural genes studied. The patterns of heterozygosity suggest different selection pressures on these various classes of structural genes.

   P. maniculatus is an ideal subject for this study, for it is a highly variable and widespread species which occurs in a diversity of habitats and eats a variety of foods (Blair 1968). Furthermore, it is easily trapped and will breed in the laboratory. It is the only small mammal to have evolved endemic subspecies on all eight of the California Channel Islands (Hall and Kelson 1959, von Bloeker 1967). These islands vary in size and distance from the mainland and from their nearest island neighbors (Table 1), and, due to tectonic emergence and eustatic sea-level fluctuations, have been isolated for varying periods of time since their establishment in the late Pliocene (Thorne 1969, Vedder and Howell 1980). The subspecies of *P. maniculatus* on the eight Channel Islands, as given by Hall and Kelson (1959), are: *anacapae* von Bloeker (Anacapa), *santacruzae* Nelson and Goldman (Santa Cruz), *sanctaerosae* von Bloeker (Santa Rosa), *streatori* Nelson and Goldman (San Miguel), *exterus* Nelson and Goldman (San Nicolas), *elusus* Nelson and Goldman (Santa Barbara), *catalinae* Elliott (Santa Catalina), and *clementis* Mearns (San Clemente). The closest mainland relative is *P. maniculatus gambelii* Baird, which ranges from Baja California to Washington.

MATERIALS AND METHODS

   Deer Mice belonging to different nominal subspecies of *Peromyscus maniculatus* were live-trapped from populations on the eight Channel Islands and from California mainland sites in Ventura, Riverside, San Bernardino, and Inyo Counties. All the island mice and those from Ventura County were transported live to the laboratory, where they were weighed and measured. They were maintained for at least a week under standard laboratory conditions and were subsequently bred or processed for electrophoresis. The other mainland mice were live-trapped by other researchers for their own studies and later made available to me. For these samples, data on body measurements at the time of capture are lacking. A list of the samples taken at each site detailing the site, subspecies, abbreviations for subspecies, dates of capture, and number captured follows:

Santa Cruz Island, *santacruzae* (CRU), July 1975, 123.

Middle Anacapa Island, *anacapae* (ANA), July 1976, 25.

Santa Catalina Island, *catalinae* (CAT), Nov. 1975 and March 1976, 17.

Santa Barbara Island, *elusus* (ELU), Nov. 1976, 34.

San Miguel Island, *streatori* (STR), May 1975 and Sep. 1976, 140.

Santa Rosa Island, *sanctaerosae* (ROS), Feb., Apr., and May 1976 and May 1977, 70.

San Nicolas Island, *exterus* (EXT), Apr. 1975 and May 1976, 25.

San Clemente Island, *clementis* (CLE), Jan. and Apr. 1975 and Apr. 1976, 57.

Pt. Mugu and Camarillo, Ventura County, *gambelii* (GAM, MUG), Mar., Apr., and May 1976 and Apr. 1977, 19.

Riverside, Riverside County, *gambelii* (GAM, RIV), received July 1977 and Feb. 1978, 35.

Black Mountain, Riverside County, *gambelii* (GAM, BKM), received Feb. 1978, 10.

Heart Bar Campground, San Bernardino County, *gambelii* (GAM, HTB), received Feb. 1978, 16.

Owens Valley, Inyo County, *sonoriensis* (OWV), received Feb. 1977, 10.

Many of the females live-trapped in the field were pregnant and their offspring (approximately 300 individuals) were born in the laboratory. Crosses were set up within and between subspecies in the laboratory, as well. The data thus obtained from known relatives were used to establish the genetic basis of all electrophoretic variants reported in this study; only those variants that represent allozymes at a genetic locus are included in the analysis. Litters were reared in the laboratory until they reached maturity and only adults were used in the morphological and electrophoretic analyses. Pelage type was used to determine age classes in field-caught Deer Mice.

There are two developmental molts in *Peromyscus maniculatus*: (1) the post-juvenal molt from the gray juvenal pelage to the browner, subadult pelage, which occurs within an age range of 4 to 12 weeks (Layne 1968), and (2) the post-subadult molt to the adult pelage, which begins at an average age of 16 weeks and is usually completed by 21 weeks (based on data from *P. m. gambelii*, McCabe and Blanchard 1950). Only animals that had completed the post-subadult molt to the adult pelage were used in this study. Growth rate in body dimensions becomes essentially zero by eight weeks of age in *P. maniculatus* (Layne 1968), so that the field-caught animals compared in this study can be assumed to have reached their full adult growth. Both eruption of molars and sexual maturity occur at an early age in *P. maniculatus* and are not suitable characters for determining adult status in this study. We have observed in our laboratory-reared animals that all three molars have already erupted in mice with juvenal pelage; incisors erupt at a mean age of 5.7 days (Layne 1968) and become yellowish while the animals are still juveniles. Sexual maturity has been reported to be as early as seven weeks in females and nine in males (McCabe and Blanchard 1950). This finding is consistent with results in my laboratory where 2½-month-old sibs have produced litters. Since the gestation period is 23 to 24 days (Layne 1968), this is evidence of sexual maturity at seven to eight weeks of age in both sexes.

I used starch gel electrophoresis to detect protein variation in blood, liver, and kidney

TABLE 2. External measurements of body size in nine subspecies of *Peromyscus maniculatus.* *

Subspecies†	n	Body weight (g)		Lengths (mm)							
				Body		Tail		Foot		Ear	
		Mean	S.D.	Mean	S.D.	Mean	S.D.	Mean	S.D.	Mean	S.D.
CRU	134	26.0	4.0	87.8	6.2	80.1	5.1	19.5	1.1	17.0	1.3
ANA	25	25.8	2.8	85.2	3.7	81.2	3.0	19.7	0.6	16.7	1.0
CAT	15	21.8	2.5	88.7	4.8	77.5	4.7	20.1	1.2	20.0	0.9
ELU	24	24.6	3.2	89.7	3.3	68.7	3.2	16.8	0.8	19.5	0.6
STR	132	23.9	4.6	88.5	4.7	70.4	4.9	18.2	1.5	19.0	1.5
ROS	65	23.8	4.0	88.1	7.5	70.8	4.5	19.4	0.7	17.2	1.1
EXT	20	21.5	4.2	84.0	5.6	72.5	2.6	18.9	0.7	17.8	0.9
CLE	54	19.7	2.6	83.6	4.9	67.8	4.6	19.0	0.9	17.8	1.2
Island total	469	23.9	4.4	87.4	5.8	73.8	6.8	18.9	1.3	17.9	1.6
GAM	14	19.5	3.3	79.4	7.6	65.3	3.8	18.1	0.8	15.9	1.1
Grand total	483	23.8	4.4	87.2	6.0	73.5	6.9	18.9	1.3	17.9	1.6

* Samples include pregnant females.

† Samples are from these islands: CRU = Santa Cruz, ANA = Anacapa, CAT = Santa Catalina, ELU = Santa Barbara, STR = San Miguel, ROS = Santa Rosa, EXT = San Nicolas, and CLE = San Clemente; and these mainland sites: GAM = Pt. Mugu and Camarillo.

samples. The experimental procedures employed were essentially those described by Yang in the appendix to the paper by Selander *et al.* (1971). Animals were weighed just before they were sacrificed. The blood samples were prepared, and plasma and hemolysate extracts run immediately. The kidneys and liver were then dissected, homogenized, and centrifuged in preparation for immediate electrophoretic runs, or the whole animal was kept frozen at −76°C and the tissues prepared later. The organs were weighed before extracts were prepared.

After tissues had been dissected for electrophoresis, the skull and flat skin of each animal were prepared as museum specimens. These specimens are housed at the University of Nevada at Reno. Specimens of mice born both in the field and in the laboratory were prepared. The following 12 measurements were taken on each skull with dial calipers accurate to 0.1 mm: (1) greatest skull length, (2) nasal length, (3) nasal breadth (greatest distance across nasal bone), (4) zygomatic breadth (greatest distance across zygomatic arches), (5) interorbital constriction, (6) palatal length, (7) mastoidal breadth (greatest distance across mastoidal bones), (8) maxillary breadth, (9) length of upper toothrow, (10) length of lower toothrow, (11) rostral depth (least vertical distance from top of skull to anterior border of toothrow), and (12) mandible length. All the raw data from skull measurements were transformed into logarithms in the computer analyses. These transformations improve comparisons of the subspecies samples, since growth-related characters generally vary proportionally rather than arithmetically.

MORPHOLOGICAL VARIATION

Three different sets of morphological characters are analyzed here: (1) the external characters of body size measured for all animals caught in the field, (2) organ and body weights for both field-born and laboratory-born mice, and (3) skull indices for field and laboratory mice. The means and standard deviations of the size characters—body weight, body plus head length, and lengths of tail, hind foot, and ear—are given in Table 2, with data arranged in order of generally decreasing body size. As is typical of size relationships in small mammals, the mainland subspecies, *P. m. gambelii*, is smaller than any of the island subspecies. Among the island mice, San Clemente Island mice are smallest. There is great variation in size among the mice on the different islands and this inter-island variation is highly significant ($P < 0.001$ by analysis of variance) for each of the five measurements. Analyses of variance show the differences between average island measurements of body size and average mainland measurements to be highly significant ($P < 0.001$) for every trait except foot length, for which the difference is not as great, but is still significant ($P < 0.05$). When males and females were analyzed separately, it was found that males of different subspecies differ in foot length, but females do not. There was no sexual dimorphism in body size except for foot length ($P < 0.01$, analysis of variance), males having larger feet. The lack of sexual differences in body weight usually found in this species was no doubt due to the fact that many females caught in the field were pregnant.

San Clemente Island mice are the smallest insular mice not only in general body size but in relative organ weights, as well (Table 3). Their characteristically small size persists in their laboratory-born progeny (Table 4). Santa Barbara Island mice (ELU, Table 3) also have small kidneys and livers. The body and relative organ weights are significantly different among the island populations ($P < 0.001$, analyses of variance) for all four variables, suggesting differences in physiological adaptations among the insular populations. Morpho-physiological indices are very responsive to environmental changes and their high variability between populations reflects development under different environmental conditions and not random fluctuations (Shvarts 1975). This comparison of organ weights, although approximate because it does not deal with seasonal variation, clearly shows that, even when the island mice are maintained in a uniform environment and their progeny develop in a uniform environment, differences between San Clemente Island mice and others remain. This suggests that genetic changes have occurred (Tables 3 and 4), distinguishing San Clemente Island mice from the other island forms in organ size. Mainland mice have relatively heavier kidneys and hearts than island mice ($P < 0.01$, analyses of variance), but there is no significant difference in relative liver weights. Sexual dimorphism in kidney weights was observed in field-caught animals, but the differences were relaxed in laboratory-born animals. The animals on which the data in Tables 3 and 4 were based did not include any pregnant females, and a highly significant sexual dimorphism in body weight was found ($P < 0.001$, analyses of variance) in both field- and laboratory-born animals (the mean weight ± standard deviation for field-caught males is 24.7 ± 6.6 g, and for females 22.8 ± 7.8 g; laboratory males weigh 22.7 ± 3.6 g, females weigh 19.5 ± 3.1 g).

The relative liver weights of laboratory-born Deer Mice—which live in a uniform environment, unlike their parents born on the islands or mainland—were much lower (42.0 ± 6.4 mg/g) than those of island (49.7 ± 11.8 mg/g) or mainland mice (46.6 ± 6.8 mg/g). The liver is important in regulation and metabolism (*e.g.*, in controlling blood sugar levels, the interconversion of various nutrients, and detoxification of injurious chemical compounds). The larger liver weights of field-born mice may be due to such factors as greater storage of glycogen or a heavier workload on this organ in natural habitats, which have a variety both in type of food (including, probably, some toxic compounds in the plants they eat) and in its availability. Not only did liver weights decline in the laboratory-born progeny but the coefficients of variation were also greatly decreased for progeny of all insular mice (calculated from S.D./mean, Tables 3 and 4). The greatest change in relative liver weights occurred between Santa Rosa and Anacapa Island mice and their progeny. Despite the fact that relative organ weights reflect greater sensitivity to environmental factors than the other morphological measures used in this

TABLE 3. Body and organ weights of field-caught *Peromyscus maniculatus.**

Subspecies†	n	Body weight (g)		Relative weights (mg/g)					
				Liver		Kidneys		Heart	
		Mean	S.D.	Mean	S.D.	Mean	S.D.	Mean	S.D.
CRU	82	25.5	4.7	50.0	8.8	10.8	2.1	4.6	1.1
ANA	18	23.4	3.2	57.2	10.0	11.8	1.0	4.5	0.9
CAT	12	22.2	3.9	48.2	16.1	11.1	1.7	4.9	0.8
ELU	24	26.8	3.5	41.9	5.8	9.6	1.3	4.2	0.7
STR	111	23.6	5.0	53.2	9.8	10.6	1.7	4.1	0.7
ROS	65	23.6	3.8	51.6	16.2	10.7	1.5	4.9	1.1
EXT	20	23.3	3.1	50.1	11.4	10.0	1.4	4.6	1.0
CLE	43	22.8	4.1	38.7	5.4	9.2	1.6	3.8	0.7
Island total	375	24.1	3.7	49.7	11.8	10.5	1.8	4.4	1.0
GAM(M)	15	19.7	2.9	47.0	7.6	11.5	2.0	5.2	1.0
GAM(R)	5	20.4	3.1	45.3	4.2	12.0	2.1	4.6	0.4
Mainland total	20	19.9	2.9	46.6	6.8	11.7	1.9	5.0	0.9
Grand total	395	23.8	4.5	49.5	11.6	10.5	1.8	4.4	1.0

* Samples do not include any pregnant females.
† Subspecies abbreviations for the island mice are identified in Table 2. GAM(M) are from Pt. Mugu and Camarillo, GAM(R) from Riverside.

TABLE 4. Body and organ weights of laboratory-born *Peromyscus maniculatus.**

Subspecies†	n	Body weight (g)		Relative weights (mg/g)					
				Liver		Kidneys		Heart	
		Mean	S.D.	Mean	S.D.	Mean	S.D.	Mean	S.D.
CRU	19	21.4	4.3	43.4	5.0	13.3	2.8	4.8	0.9
ANA	20	22.5	4.1	43.5	4.4	9.4	1.3	3.7	1.1
CAT	3	23.5	4.4	49.6	4.3	11.7	2.2	4.8	1.1
STR	85	21.6	3.3	43.1	6.4	10.7	2.3	4.1	0.9
ROS	24	20.5	4.4	38.1	5.9	9.9	2.0	4.4	1.0
EXT	16	20.5	2.4	44.1	7.3	9.9	1.5	4.1	0.9
CLE	21	18.7	2.9	35.9	3.3	8.8	1.1	3.0	0.6
GAM(M)	5	19.5	2.7	39.4	6.8	10.7	2.4	5.1	0.4
GAM(R)	12	20.1	4.3	44.1	7.5	12.7	2.2	5.3	0.7
Total	214	21.1	3.7	42.0	6.4	10.6	2.4	4.1	1.0

* No laboratory ELU were available.
† Subspecies identification given in Tables 2 and 3.

TABLE 5. Representative skull indices of field-caught *Peromyscus maniculatus*.

Subspecies*	n	Total length (mm)		Zygomatic breadth (mm)		Rostral depth (mm)	
		Mean	S.D.	Mean	S.D.	Mean	S.D.
CRU	60	26.22	.82	13.56	.48	6.04	.30
ANA	17	25.86	.61	13.65	.34	5.96	.18
CAT	12	25.40	.69	13.47	.31	5.67	.30
ELU	23	25.42	.41	13.38	.18	5.87	.18
STR	65	25.27	.66	13.14	.35	5.86	.30
ROS	43	25.51	.70	13.39	.36	5.96	.24
EXT	18	25.66	.81	13.15	.50	5.71	.32
CLE	34	24.74	.57	13.01	.46	5.78	.23
GAM(M)	14	24.09	.71	12.89	.31	5.67	.20
GAM(R)	6	24.55	.62	12.91	.32	5.85	.25
Total	292	25.44	.88	13.29	.45	5.88	.29

* Subspecies identification given in Tables 2 and 3.

study, significant differences among the progeny of island and mainland mice still remained.

Skull measurements are particularly useful for comparative purposes, both among living groups and for fossil specimens. Analyses of skull indices revealed significant differences among the island populations and between island and mainland populations in all 12 variables measured. As with the other morphological measurements, the island mice are larger than the mainland mice in skull indices. Representative data on three of the skull indices measured on field-caught mice, which give an idea of the volume of the skull, are presented in Table 5. Variation among island populations is highly significant for all three variables ($P < 0.001$, analyses of variance), San Clemente mice having the smallest skulls and Santa Cruz Island mice the largest. The island mice have significantly longer ($P < 0.001$), wider ($P < 0.001$), and deeper skulls ($P < 0.009$) than the mainland mice. A sample of 122 laboratory progeny of these mice were also measured; they were found to differ significantly, depending on island of origin, displaying differences similar to those found between island and mainland progenitors. There was no sexual dimorphism found in these skull indices.

In terms of morphological, morpho-physiological, and anatomical variability as measured by body size, organ weights, and skull indices, respectively, the insular populations of Deer Mice are distinct from one another and from the mainland populations. They are larger than the mainland populations, but vary greatly in size among themselves.

Multivariate Analysis of Morphological Data

Morphological data were analyzed by factor analysis, using BMDP4M (Dixon and Brown 1977) to determine correlations of the variables and common factors. Analysis of the skull measurements of 409 field-caught and laboratory-born Deer Mice revealed that the total length of the skull was the variable that correlated most highly with all other skull indices, its squared multiple correlation being 0.805. Skull length had the highest unrotated factor loading (0.911) for the largest principal component. Two factors of notably different character accounted for 61 per cent of the variance in skull indices, the other factors being minor. The first factor alone, for which the variables of zygomatic breadth and mandible length had the highest loadings after rotation of the factors, accounted for 50.2 per cent of the variance. Rostral depth and palatal and skull lengths also had relatively high loadings for this factor. Only two variables, the lengths of the lower and upper toothrows, had high loadings on the second factor, which accounted for an additional 10.6 per cent of the variance in skull variables. It is, of course, obvious that selection would lead to correlation of the lengths of the toothrows, although they are no doubt under separate genetic control.

Variance in body measurements of 316 field-caught mice was also assessed using factor analysis, and three factors were found to account for 73 per cent of the variance. Body and organ weights had high loadings for factor 1, which accounted for 49 per cent of the variance. Only tail and foot lengths were important in factor 2, and ear length in factor 3, the latter two factors each contributing about 10 per cent of the variance.

The measurements that contribute most to the factors accounting for the largest part of the variance are not necessarily the measurements that are most important in discriminating between groups. A stepwise discriminant analysis (BMDP7M, Dixon and Brown 1977) was used to determine if the *P. maniculatus* subspecies were separable on the basis of the morphological variables described. Using a subset of 219 animals for which the entire battery of 22 measurements was available showed a high percentage of correct subspecific classification (85 per cent) based on 17 of these variables. The remaining five variables did not improve the discrimination. Tail and ear lengths were the variables first in importance to discrimination, followed by three skull indices of minor importance in the factor analyses. The finding that almost all the variables entered into the discrimination shows that the differentiation of subspecies is not due to change in one or a few major variables but to distinct changes in many variables, each contributing in its own way to the discrimination of the groups. A large number (eight) of canonical variables were needed to discriminate between the subspecies; none of these variables had particularly large eigenvalues.

In discriminating between two groups, a canonical variable is that combination of the original variables that maximizes the distance between groups. For a larger number of groups, discrimination between them can be visualized in the following way for three variables: each group is represented by a point in three-dimensional space which corresponds to the values of the three measurements (*e.g.,* mean skull length, rostral depth, and palatal length). As an example, if these points form a football-shaped cluster, the first canonical variable would lie along the long axis and would be some combination of the original variables. Its eigenvalue would be proportional to its length through the cluster of points. The second canonical variable, a different combination of the measurements, would be perpendicular to the first, and its eigenvalue would be proportional to its length. In this football-shaped example, the second and third canonical variables would have equal eigenvalues which would be smaller than the eigenvalue of the first canonical variable. In the discrimination of the nine subspecies in the present study, the eigenvalues of the first three canonical variables, which accounted for 74 per cent of the total dispersion, were 2.977, 1.934, and 1.063, respectively. The canonical variables consisted largely of contrasts between skull length and other skull indices: canonical variable 1 consisted of a contrast of skull length and mastoidal breadth with palatal length, and canonical variable 2 contrasted skull length and zygomatic breadth with mandible length and maxillary breadth. Thus, in Figure 1, where the subspecies are graphed in units of the first two canonical variables, it can be seen that the mice from Anacapa and Santa Cruz Islands have relatively longer skulls and greater mastoidal breadth than palatal length, the reverse holding true for the mice from San Clemente Island and the mainland *gambelii* subspecies. Discrimination between the other insular populations occurs along canonical variable 2. In this case, skull length and zygomatic breadth are relatively greater than mandible length and maxillary breadth

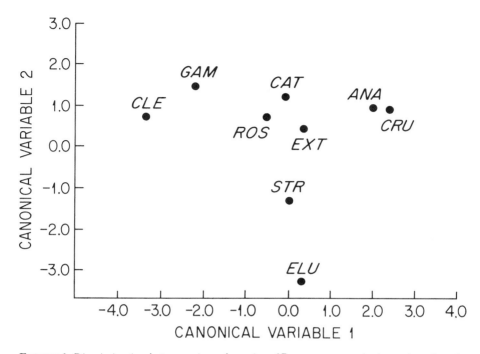

FIGURE 1. *Discrimination between nine subspecies of* Peromyscus maniculatus, *based on the first two of eight canonical variables. The means of the subspecies are shown. The coefficients of the original variables that contributed most heavily to the canonical variables are: for canonical variable 1, 31.6 skull length, 37.7 mastoidal breadth, and* −40.2 palatal length; *and, for canonical variable 2, 45.5 skull length, 45.5 zygomatic breadth,* −31.5 mandible length, *and* −26.1 maxillary breadth.

for mice from Santa Catalina, Santa Rosa, and San Nicolas Islands, compared with those from San Miguel and Santa Barbara Islands.

The majority of misclassifications between the nine subspecies in the stepwise discrimination involved mice from San Miguel (subspecies STR), Santa Rosa (ROS), and San Nicolas (EXT) Islands. I therefore removed those three subspecies from the analysis and compared the remaining five island and one mainland subspecies (reducing the sample size to 116). Using 12 of the 22 variables, the discrimination improved to 98 per cent correct classification. One of the *P. m. clementis* mice was statistically misclassified as *gambelii,* and one of the *santacruzae* mice as *catalinae;* the other 114 mice were correctly classified to subspecies. Not only was the discrimination almost completely accurate, but the "jackknifed" classification was also high—97 per cent. The P7M program uses the "jackknife" (Mosteller and Tukey 1977) to cross-validate classifications. This procedure gives a good indication of the reliability of classification for additional data—so it can be seen from the highly accurate jackknifed classification that morphological variables provide a reliable basis for classification of these subspecies. The relationships between morphological variables that are important in the discrimination of subspecies can be gauged from the canonical variables generated in the analysis. Five canonical variables were generated to discriminate between these six subspecies, the first variable consisting of a contrast of tail length and mastoidal breadth with palatal length, and the second canonical variable a contrast of foot and palatal lengths with lengths of mandible and ear. It is clear that six of the subspecies are now so divergent in skull and body measurements that they can be accurately distinguished on this morphological basis. Discrimination is not as sharp between the populations of Deer Mice on San Nicolas, San Miguel, and Santa Rosa Islands, but even for this subset (sample size 103) a separate discriminant analysis showed 82 per cent correct classification. The canonical variables, again, involved contrasts of skull indices.

GENIC VARIATION

Horizontal starch gel electrophoresis was used to obtain measures of genic variation among the *P. maniculatus* subspecies. This method allows the detection of proteins of different net charge and mobility in an electric field (Hubby and Lewontin 1966, Harris 1966). Since the proteins are the initial gene products, we can infer that there is variation in the alleles controlling proteins of different mobility. Comparisons of known relatives were used to establish the electrophoretic variants as allozymes of genetic loci. The method provides a lower limit estimate of genetic variability because it can only distinguish proteins of different net charge.

Protein Systems

Thirty loci were analyzed; 23 of these were found to be polymorphic within or between subspecies. Ten subspecies were compared: the eight insular subspecies (labeled as ANA, CRU, ROS, STR, EXT, ELU, CAT, and CLE) and two California mainland subspecies (*P. m. gambelii*, represented by four mainland populations [MUG, RIV, BKM, and HTB; see Materials and Methods section for identification], and *P. m. sonoriensis*, represented by one mainland population [OWV]). *P. m. gambelii* is considered the closest mainland relative of the island mice (Hall and Kelson 1959) and *sonoriensis* is a neighboring subspecies included for comparison. The thirty loci analyzed are a good representation of the three groups of proteins: (I) glucose-metabolizing enzymes, (II) other enzymes, and (III) nonenzymatic proteins.

Glucose-metabolizing Enzymes

The polymorphic systems include two enzymes found in the kidneys, 6-phosphogluconate dehydrogenase (6-Pgd) and a lactic dehydrogenase (Ldh-1), which is polymorphic only in *P. m. sonoriensis*. Polymorphic systems found in the liver are α-glycerophosphate dehydrogenase (αGpd), a malate hydrogenase that is Nadp-dependent (Mdh-3), and three phosphoglucomutases (Pgm-1, Pgm-3, and Pgm-4). Another phosphoglucomutase (Pgm-2) is variable, but cannot be clearly interpreted. The monomorphic glucose-metabolizing enzymes are two malate dehydrogenases (Mdh-1 anodal and Mdh-2 cathodal) in liver and a lactic dehydrogenase (Ldh-1) in kidney.

Other Enzymes

Ten polymorphic nonglucose-metabolizing enzymes are found in liver. These are sorbitol dehydrogenase (Sdh), two peptidases (Pept-1 and Pept-2), an indophenol oxidase (Ipo-1) that is polymorphic only in the Santa Barbara Island mice, two glutamic oxaloacetic transaminases (Got-1 and Got-2) which are polymorphic only in the Santa Rosa Island population, and four esterases in liver and hemolysate that are not included because their separation and genetic basis are not yet clarified. The monomorphic Group II enzymes are leucine amino peptidase (Lap) in plasma, alcohol dehydrogenase (Adh) in liver, and an indophenol oxidase (Ipo-2) in liver.

Nonenzymatic Proteins

Hemoglobin (Hb) from hemolysate is polymorphic only in *P. m. sonoriensis* and serves to differentiate *sonoriensis* from *gambelii* (L. Snyder, pers. comm.) and the insular subspecies.

Genetic control of the hemoglobin loci in mainland *P. maniculatus* is described by Snyder (1978a and 1978b). There are two variable general proteins (Gp-1 and Gp-2) also found in hemolysate. Three polymorphic proteins are found in plasma, transferrin (Trf) and two general proteins (Gp-3 and Gp-4). There is only one monomorphic protein, albumin (Alb), found in plasma.

Subspecific Variation in Allozymes

Allelic frequencies for the 23 variable loci found in *P. maniculatus* are given in Table 6. Frequencies are given for eight insular populations, each representing a different subspecies, and for five mainland populations, four of *gambelii* subspecies (MUG, RIV, BKM, and HTB) and one of *sonoriensis* (OWV). The number of alleles sampled for each population was not constant because animals were trapped over an extended period and all the systems were not perfected at the same time. For the majority of loci analyzed, the number of alleles sampled (two per individual) was as follows: ANA 48, CRU 164, ROS 120, STR 190, EXT 46, ELU 50, CAT 30, CLE 102, MUG 32, RIV 66, OWV 20, BKM 20, and HTB 32. The smallest sample sizes were obtained for the esterases in most cases, for which the minimum numbers of alleles sampled in the given population were: ANA 14, ROS 34, STR 86, EXT 22, CAT 14, MUG 10, RIV 24, BKM 18, and HTB 24. The minimum numbers of alleles sampled in the remaining populations were: CRU 60 for Mdh-3, ELU 16 for Pgm, CLE 58 for Mdh-3, and OWV 14 for Pept.

For all but two loci, the populations differ only in the frequencies of alleles, and, if an allele has reached fixation, it is the same allele in all populations (Table 6). The two exceptions to this are the Got-1 and Trf loci, for which different alleles have reached fixation in the San Clemente Island population than in other populations. The Got-1 locus is highly variable, only the Anacapa and San Clemente populations being monomorphic for it. The Got-1 allele found in the Anacapa Island mice is also common in neighboring Santa Cruz Island mice, in the Santa Barbara and San Miguel Island populations, and in the mainland *sonoriensis* population (OWV). The Got-1 allele that is fixed in the San Clemente Island population is common on Santa Catalina Island. All four *P. m. gambelii* populations and the populations on Santa Rosa and San Nicolas Islands have extremely similar frequencies at this locus, suggesting selection may be maintaining the alleles close to a ratio of 0.57 to 0.43. The analysis of the Got-1 system reported here differs from that given for an earlier sample from four of the islands (Gill 1976) because a different buffer system is used here. I found that I obtained far better results using lithium hydroxide buffers—LiOH AB gel buffer and LiOH A, pH 8.1 tray buffer (buffer system 2 *in* Selander *et al.* 1971)—than the previously employed continuous triscitrate II, TC pH 8.0 gel and tray buffer system (system 5 *in* Selander *et al.* 1971). The dimeric nature of the Got-1 system is clear in LiOH, the three bands of the heterozygote being sharp and distinct. The TC pH 8.0 buffer is still used for the cathodal system, Got-2, since better results are obtained.

Only three populations are monomorphic for Trf. The same allele has reached fixation in the Anacapa and San Nicolas mice and a different allele is fixed in the San Clemente Island population. Again, the San Clemente Island allele is common in the Santa Catalina Island population. The allele fixed in the Anacapa and San Nicolas Island populations is common in the remaining Northern Channel Island populations.

There are five glucose-metabolizing enzymes for which the same allele is common in all populations; it has reached fixation in most. These are Ldh-1 (for which only *P. m. sonoriensis* has a rare alternate allele), α-Gpd, Mdh-3, Pgm-1, and Pgm-3. In contrast, both 6-Pgd and Pgm-4 are highly variable, showing no particular pattern of variation.

For most of the enzymes not involved with glucose metabolism (Group II), the same pattern of common alleles is found in the populations. The island populations are monomorphic for Sdh and Pept-2, with the same allele common on the mainland. All populations but one are

TABLE 6. Allele frequencies at 23 variable loci in *Peromyscus maniculatus* subspecies.

Loci and alleles	Island								Mainland				
	ANA*	CRU	ROS	STR	EXT	ELU	CAT	CLE	MUG	RIV	OWV	BKM	HTB
Group I. Glucose-metabolizing enzymes.													
Ldh-1													
a†											0.10		
b	1.00	1.00	1.00	1.00	1.00	1.00	1.00	1.00	1.00	1.00	0.90	1.00	1.00
α-Gpd													
a	1.00	1.00	1.00	0.61	1.00	1.00	1.00	1.00	0.89	1.00	0.75	1.00	1.00
b				0.39							0.15		
c									0.11		0.10		
Mdh-3													
a			0.01								0.10		
b	0.94	0.98	0.96	1.00	1.00	1.00	0.90	0.97	0.90	1.00	0.90	1.00	0.81
c	0.06	0.02	0.03				0.10	0.03	0.10				0.19
6-Pgd													
a	0.47	0.74	0.67	0.36	0.39	0.10	0.10		0.22	0.19		0.20	0.50
b	0.53	0.26	0.33	0.64	0.61	0.80	0.15	0.60	0.56	0.56	0.80	0.80	0.50
c						0.10	0.75	0.40	0.22	0.08	0.10		
d										0.17	0.10		
Pgm-1													
a		0.30		0.05						0.07			
b	1.00	0.70	0.98	0.95	1.00	1.00	1.00	1.00	1.00	0.89	1.00	0.95	0.97
c			0.02							0.04		0.05	0.03
Pgm-3													
a	1.00	1.00	1.00	1.00	1.00	1.00	0.77	1.00	0.93	1.00	1.00	1.00	0.93
b							0.23		0.07				0.07
Pgm-4													
a	0.39	0.09	0.27	0.11	0.33	0.50	0.13	0.40	0.31	0.54	0.50	0.15	0.37
b	0.22	0.89	0.35	0.59	0.13		0.80	0.11	0.31	0.09	0.20	0.25	0.25
c	0.39	0.02	0.38	0.30	0.54	0.50	0.07	0.49	0.38	0.37	0.30	0.60	0.38
Group II. Other enzymes.													
Sdh													
a											0.10		
b											0.30	0.20	0.06
c	1.00	1.00	1.00	1.00	1.00	1.00	1.00	1.00	1.00	1.00	0.60	0.80	0.94

Locus	Allele	1	2	3	4	5	6	7	8	9	10	11
Pept-1	a	1.00	1.00	0.06	1.00	1.00	1.00	0.94	0.05	0.71	0.90	1.00
	b			0.94				0.06	0.95	0.29	0.10	
	c											
Pept-2	a	1.00	1.00	1.00	1.00	1.00	0.79	0.11	0.05	0.15	0.10	1.00
	b						0.21	0.89	0.95	0.85	0.90	
Ipo-1	a	1.00	1.00	1.00	1.00	1.00	0.08	1.00	1.00	1.00	1.00	1.00
	b						0.92					
Got-1	a	1.00	0.19	0.54	0.37	0.57	1.00	0.87	0.59	0.20	0.55	0.59
	b		0.81	0.46	0.63	0.43		0.13	0.41	0.80	0.45	0.41
Got-2	a	1.00	1.00	0.98	1.00	1.00	1.00	1.00	1.00	1.00	1.00	1.00
	b			0.02								
Es-2	a	0.07	0.01	1.00	0.15	1.00	1.00	0.03	1.00	1.00	1.00	1.00
	b	0.93	0.99		0.85			0.97				
Es-3	a	0.86	1.00	1.00	1.00	1.00	1.00	0.92	0.75	0.17	1.00	1.00
	b	0.14						0.08	0.25	0.83		
	c											
Es-5	a	0.50	0.03	0.73	0.84			0.64	0.19	0.23	0.25	0.37
	b	0.50	0.59	0.06	0.16	0.27		0.36	0.16	0.23	0.50	0.17
	c		0.38	0.21		0.73			0.65	0.54	0.25	0.46
	d											
	e											
Es-6	a	0.30	0.82	0.55	0.91	0.08	0.39	0.56	0.17	0.23	0.15	0.12
	b	0.50	0.18	0.45	0.09	0.46	0.35	0.11	0.10	0.09	0.30	0.46
	c	0.20				0.29	0.26	0.22	0.50	0.64	0.30	0.29
	d							0.11	0.23	0.04	0.25	0.13
	e					0.17						

Group III. Nonenzymatic proteins.

Locus	Allele	1	2	3	4	5	6	7	8	9	10	11
Hb	a	1.00	1.00	1.00	1.00	1.00	1.00	1.00	1.00	0.25	1.00	1.00
	b									0.75		

TABLE 6. (Cont.).

Loci and alleles		Island								Mainland				
		ANA*	CRU	ROS	STR	EXT	ELU	CAT	CLE	MUG	RIV	OWV	BKM	HTB
Trf	a	1.00								0.38	0.68	0.25	0.05	0.03
	b		0.99	0.88	0.80	1.00	0.24	0.05		0.62	0.32	0.75	0.40	0.59
	c		0.01	0.12	0.20		0.76	0.95	1.00				0.55	0.38
GP-1	a	1.00	1.00	1.00	0.05		1.00		0.01	1.00	1.00			
	b				0.95	1.00		1.00	0.99			1.00	1.00	1.00
GP-2	a	0.13			0.03	0.03								
	b	0.87	0.90	1.00	0.93	0.97	1.00	1.00	1.00	0.86	0.89	1.00	0.95	1.00
	c		0.10		0.04					0.14	0.11		0.05	
GP-3	a									0.03	0.08			
	b	1.00	1.00	1.00	0.98	1.00	1.00	0.95	1.00	0.90	0.80	1.00	1.00	1.00
	c				0.02			0.05		0.07	0.12			
GP-4	a										0.05	0.15	0.56	
	b	1.00	1.00	1.00	1.00	1.00	1.00	1.00	1.00	1.00	0.90	0.85	0.33	0.93
	c										0.05		0.11	0.07

* Samples are from these islands: ANA = Anacapa, CRU = Santa Cruz, ROS = Santa Rosa, STR = San Miguel, EXT = San Nicolas, ELU = Santa Barbara, CAT = Santa Catalina, CLE = San Clemente. Mainland *gambelii* are from MUG = Pt. Mugu and Camarillo, RIV = Riverside, BKM = Black Mountain, HTB = Heart Bar Campground, and *sonoriensis* is from OWV = Owens Valley.
† Alleles are listed in order of increasing mobility; *a* is the slowest.

monomorphic for Ipo-1 and Got-2, and in the polymorphic populations the second allele is rare. Mainland populations are monomorphic for Es-3, with the same allele common throughout the island populations; for both Pept-1 and Es-3, one allele is common throughout all populations and fixed in most of them. Only Got-1 (already described), Es-5, and Es-6 show more variability. Both esterase loci have a larger number of detected alleles; no single allele is common throughout the populations sampled.

With the exception of Trf, there is little variability in the nonenzymatic proteins. The inheritance of Trf is consistent with a one-locus, codominant allelic system, as described by Rasmussen and Koehn (1966) for *P. maniculatus*. In this study, in addition to the two common alleles, a rarer, slow allele was found paired with the intermediate allele in a heterozygote from Black Mountain, and with the fast allele in a heterozygote from Heart Bar Campground, both mice of the *gambelii* subspecies. Hemoglobin is variant only in *P. m. sonoriensis*, as mentioned earlier. In all the insular subspecies and *gambelii*, it exhibits the usual two-banded electrophoretic pattern. For each of the general proteins, one allele is common in all populations and has reached fixation in most. The only exception to this is the variation for Gp-4 in the Black Mountain population (BKM) of *gambelii*, where a usually rare allele has reached high frequency. Among the insular populations, that on San Miguel Island (STR) has the most variable general proteins.

The likelihood ratio (Wilks' λ) was used to test for equilibrium at all loci. All of the populations are in Hardy-Weinberg equilibrium for transferrin and Got-1, except the San Miguel Island population, which has an excess of heterozygotes for Got-1. The only other loci for which there is an excess of heterozygotes in some insular populations are Pgm-4 and Es-6. At the other esterase loci there is an excess of homozygotes in some of the populations, both island and mainland. All the populations are in equilibrium for the remaining loci, with the following exceptions at which there is an excess of homozygotes: 6-Pgd in some island and mainland populations, GP-3 and Pept-2 in RIV, Sdh in MUG and BKM, α-Gpd in STR, and Pept-1 in ROS. This deficiency of heterozygotes, occurring mostly in the mainland populations, suggests that those populations are subdivided.

Measures of Genic Variability

Measures of genic variability based on the electrophoretic data for the 30 protein systems analyzed are given in Table 7. Three measures of variability are calculated for each of the different kinds of loci and for the total of all loci, with island and mainland populations considered separately. The three measures are: the mean number of alleles per locus ($\bar{A}$), the fraction of loci polymorphic ($\bar{P}$), and the mean heterozygosity per locus per individual ($\bar{H}$). The criterion for polymorphism is that the most common allele does not exceed a frequency of 0.99. Heterozygosity per individual was determined for each locus by dividing the number of heterozygotes by the sample size; the unweighted mean over all loci, $\bar{H}$, was then calculated. The standard error of $\bar{H}$ over all loci is also given in Table 7.

What is immediately impressive about the data in Table 7 are the high levels of polymorphism apparent in the mainland populations. Forty-three per cent of the loci in mainland populations are polymorphic, as compared, for example, with 23 per cent for *Peromyscus polionotus*, 29 per cent for *Mus musculus musculus*, and 29 per cent for *Homo sapiens* (Lewontin 1974). As Selander (1975) notes, it was evident early in electrophoretic work that some proteins are more likely to be polymorphic than others. The particular protein systems included in a study will therefore influence the levels of variability. For example, the addition of four new systems in this study and the exclusion of two used in a previous study (Gill 1976) resulted in a change of some measures of variability, although the overall pattern remained the same. In this study, all three groups of loci in mainland populations have the same level of

TABLE 7. Genic variation in island and mainland populations of *Peromyscus maniculatus*: mean number of alleles per locus ($\bar{A}$), fraction of loci polymorphic ($\bar{P}$), and mean heterozygosity per locus per individual ($\bar{H}$).

Population	Group I loci			Group II loci			Group III loci			All loci			
	$\bar{A}$	$\bar{P}^*$	$\bar{H}$	$\bar{A}$	$\bar{P}$	$\bar{H}$	$\bar{A}$	$\bar{P}$	$\bar{H}$	$\bar{A}$	$\bar{P}$	$\bar{H}$	±S.E.
Island populations													
ANA†	1.40	.30	.065	1.38	.31	.083	1.14	.14	.007	1.33	.27	.059	.028
CRU	1.50	.40	.070	1.38	.31	.073	1.29	.29	.030	1.40	.33	.062	.022
ROS	1.60	.40	.073	1.46	.38	.106	1.14	.14	.035	1.43	.33	.079	.039
STR	1.50	.40	.138	1.23	.23	.081	1.71	.57	.082	1.43	.37	.100	.032
EXT	1.30	.20	.056	1.46	.31	.070	1.14	.14	.008	1.33	.23	.051	.025
ELU	1.30	.20	.100	1.31	.23	.079	1.14	.14	.052	1.27	.20	.080	.041
CAT	1.60	.40	.046	1.31	.31	.066	1.29	.29	.015	1.40	.33	.048	.016
CLE	1.40	.40	.072	1.46	.31	.051	1.14	.14	.004	1.37	.27	.047	.030
Island averages	1.45	.34	.078	1.37	.30	.076	1.25	.23	.029	1.37	.29	.066	
Mainland populations													
MUG	1.70	.50	.100	1.62	.38	.081	1.57	.43	.076	1.63	.43	.086	.031
RIV	1.70	.30	.079	1.69	.46	.049	1.88	.57	.093	1.73	.43	.069	.030
OWV	1.80	.50	.077	1.85	.54	.167	1.43	.43	.086	1.73	.50	.118	.040
BKM	1.40	.30	.040	1.62	.46	.086	1.71	.43	.102	1.57	.40	.074	.027
HTB	1.60	.50	.046	1.54	.31	.080	1.43	.29	.071	1.53	.37	.067	.028
Mainland averages	1.64	.42	.068	1.66	.43	.093	1.60	.43	.086	1.64	.43	.083	

* Criterion for polymorphism is 0.01.
† Abbreviations for populations are explained in Table 6.

polymorphism, whereas in many studies a greater variability has been found in Group II compared with Group I enzymes (for example in *Drosophila*, Gillespie and Kojima 1968). The mean number of alleles per locus is also similar for all three groups of loci in mainland populations—about 1.64 alleles per locus.

Heterozygosities are relatively high for all loci in mainland populations: 0.068 for Group I, 0.093 for Group II, and 0.086 for Group III loci, with an overall mean of $\bar{H} = 0.083$. These measures can be compared with an average heterozygosity of 0.039 for mammals (25 taxa), calculated from the literature by Powell (1975), or 0.054 for rodents (26 taxa), calculated by Selander (1975).

Not only is variability high on the mainland, but a great deal of variation is maintained in the California insular populations, which have unusually high levels of variability compared with other insular populations surveyed (Gill 1976). However, the reduction in variability that is found in the insular populations is not uniform. With the exception of *P. m. streatori*, in all island populations the reduction of variability in nonenzymatic proteins of Group III is far greater than the reduction in variability of enzymes, especially in terms of mean individual heterozygosity, $\bar{H}$. This dramatic decrease in variability of the nonenzymatic proteins, compared with enzymes, strongly suggests different selection pressures on these different groups of loci. Mean heterozygosity for glucose-metabolizing enzymes is actually higher in the island populations than on the mainland (0.078 compared with 0.068) but there is a wide range of Group I heterozygosities among the island populations (0.046 to 0.138) and among the mainland populations (0.040 to 0.100). The *P. m. streatori* population on San Miguel Island again exhibits a pattern of variation different from the other insular populations. It has the exceptionally high heterozygosity of 0.138 for glucose-metabolizing loci. For most of the island populations the highest heterozygosities are found for Group II enzymes, followed by Group I glucose-metabolizing enzymes, with much reduced heterozygosities in Group III nonenzymatic proteins. An explanation of the higher variability of Group II loci was offered by Kojima *et al.* (1970), who reasoned that enzymes with a variety of substrates that may vary in concentration are likely to be more variable than enzymes (such as Group I enzymes) with a single, fairly constant substrate. Only *P. m. elusus* on Santa Barbara Island and *clementis* on San Clemente Island, like *streatori*, are more highly heterozygous for Group I than Group II enzymes. *P. m. streatori* is also exceptional both in its pattern of variability and in being the most variable of the island populations.

Gene flow between the islands would, of course, affect the patterns of genic variability. To gain some insight into present possible levels of gene flow, we have set up crosses in the laboratory to study the interfertility of the subspecies. Although this investigation is not complete, certain trends are noticeable in the data from 103 crosses already analyzed. All subspecies have bred successfully in the laboratory; however, no offspring have been produced by *P. m. streatori* females, although 25 crosses were set up with males from other islands and 9 with *streatori* males. *P. m. streatori* males, on the other hand, have mated successfully with females from many of the other subspecies. These results suggest that gene flow between the mice on San Miguel Island and the other islands is possible through migrant *streatori* males entering other populations, but the results are not informative as to the possibility of gene flow due to the matings of female *streatori*. San Clemente Island females have bred successfully only with *catalinae* males and their own subspecies in the laboratory, although 24 crosses were set up with other subspecies. *P. m. streatori* and *clementis* females differ in this respect from females of the other subspecies that have been adequately tested in the laboratory (*anacapae*, *catalinae*, *exterus*, and *gambelii*), all of which have mated with males from several other subspecies and produced offspring.

TABLE 8. Ecological parameters for the eight Channel Islands.*

Island	Elevation (ft)	Number† of native plants	Number‡ of native mammals	Number of endemic plants	Trapping success (per cent)
Anacapa	930	70	1	0	32
Santa Cruz	2,470	420	10	7	36
Santa Rosa	1,560	340	4	3	41
San Miguel	830	190	2	0	51
San Nicolas	910	120	4	2	8
Santa Barbara	635	40	1	1	23
Santa Catalina	2,125	392	9	3	8
San Clemente	1,965	235	7	11	18

* Island areas and distances to mainland and nearest neighbor are given in Table 1. Trapping success is from this study. All other data, except where specified, are adapted from Johnson *et al.* (1968).

† Includes species, subspecies, and varieties. Anacapa data from Raven (1967).

‡ Includes recent (living) native land mammals. Data from von Bloeker (1967).

The islands differ in a number of ecological factors and it would be of value to know if the pattern of genetic variability observed was related in some discernible manner to ecological variants. To investigate this question, a canonical correlation analysis was done to relate the following two data sets compiled for each of the eight islands: (1) measures of genetic variability—the mean individual heterozygosities, $\bar{H}_I$, $\bar{H}_{II}$, and $\bar{H}_{III}$, for the three types of loci calculated for each population (Table 7); and (2) ecological measures—the area, distance to the mainland, and distance to the nearest island (Table 1), and elevation, number of native plant species, number of recent native land mammal species, number of endemic plants, and per cent trapping success (Table 8). Trapping success is based on field work done in this study and is a rough measure of population density. The other data in Table 8 are adapted from papers given at an earlier symposium on the California Islands (von Bloeker 1967, Raven 1967) and from a paper by Johnson *et al.* (1968). The canonical analysis was done with logarithms of distances and areas and square roots of frequencies. The program (BMDP6M, Dixon and Brown 1977) also calculates the correlations between variables; the results showed that many of the ecological parameters are highly correlated. Correlations between island area and elevation and the numbers of native plants and mammals ranged from 0.83 to 0.93. The number of endemic plant species is also well correlated with elevation (0.77). There is a strong correlation between trapping success and distance to the nearest island (0.90). As far as the genetic parameters are concerned, heterozygosities of Group I and Group III loci are highly correlated (0.9); their correlations with Group II heterozygosities are low (0.23 with $\bar{H}_I$ and 0.42 with $\bar{H}_{III}$). Because of the high correlations between some of the ecological parameters, only a few of these parameters are needed to check for dependency between the genetic and ecological sets of variables. Island area, distance to the mainland, and distance to the nearest island were chosen since these parameters are of basic significance and are not highly correlated with each other; all the other ecological parameters correlated with one of these three parameters. No significant relationship was found between the heterozygosities and the ecological parameters.

Each of the heterozygosities was regressed on the three ecological parameters (BMDP2R, Dixon and Brown 1977). The analysis suggested that distance to the nearest island may be a

TABLE 9. Genetic distance (above diagonal) and standard error (below diagonal) between populations of *Peromyscus maniculatus*.*

	Island								Mainland				
	ANA	CRU	ROS	STR	EXT	ELU	CAT	CLE	MUG	RIV	HTB	BKM	OWV
Island													
ANA		.033	.035	.046	.034	.045	.096	.100	.045	.028	.029	.057	.052
CRU	.033		.027	.021	.045	.071	.071	.099	.050	.056	.045	.072	.075
ROS	.034	.030		.023	.028	.054	.058	.066	.027	.037	.030	.058	.060
STR	.040	.027	.028		.042	.079	.049	.083	.039	.062	.047	.080	.079
EXT	.034	.043	.031	.038		.047	.070	.053	.044	.024	.028	.046	.065
ELU	.039	.049	.043	.052	.040		.084	.045	.042	.036	.037	.038	.029
CAT	.058	.049	.045	.041	.049	.054		.040	.040	.064	.051	.077	.077
CLE	.059	.059	.048	.054	.043	.039	.037		.035	.041	.039	.043	.063
Mainland													
MUG	.039	.041	.030	.037	.039	.038	.037	.034		.025	.017	.040	.040
RIV	.031	.044	.036	.046	.029	.035	.047	.037	.029		.015	.029	.038
HTB	.031	.039	.032	.040	.031	.036	.042	.037	.024	.022		.028	.042
BKM	.044	.050	.045	.053	.040	.036	.052	.038	.037	.032	.031		.038
OWV	.042	.051	.045	.052	.047	.031	.052	.046	.037	.036	.038	.036	

*Abbreviations for populations are explained in Table 6.

helpful variable in predicting heterozygosities for Group II loci. Distance to the nearest island is the best predictor of $\bar{H}_{\text{II}}$. The regression coefficients of the island distance parameters are remarkably similar for each of the three dependent variables: 0.027 in the case of $\bar{H}_{\text{I}}$, 0.024 for $\bar{H}_{\text{II}}$, and 0.026 for $\bar{H}_{\text{III}}$. Even if not a significant effect, there seems to be a consistent relationship between the heterozygosities and the distance to the nearest island. As mentioned before, distance to the nearest island is highly correlated with trapping success, which is a rough measure of population density, and it may well be that heterozygosity actually depends on population size.

Genetic Distance Between Populations

Genetic distance, D, which is a measure of the accumulated number of gene differences per locus between populations (Nei 1971, 1972), was used as an overall measure of genetic divergence between the populations sampled in this study. $D = -\log_e I$, where I is the normalized identity of genes between two populations, X and Y, with respect to all loci. $I = J_{XY}/\sqrt{J_X J_Y}$ where J_{XY} is the arithmetic mean of the probability of identity of a gene from X and a gene from Y, the probability being $\Sigma x_i y_i$ for a locus i, calculated for all loci including monomorphic loci; and J_X and J_Y are the arithmetic means of the probabilities of identity for randomly chosen genes within $X(\Sigma x_i^2)$ and within Y (Σy_i^2), respectively. Genetic distances between pairs of all island and mainland populations are given in Table 9, with the standard errors of D. The standard error of genetic distance, S_D, is calculated according to Nei's (1971) formula: $S_D = [(1 - I)/I n_s]_{1/2}$ where I is the normalized identity of genes and n_s is the number of proteins. The standard error depends only on I, and for closely related populations, for which I is large, standard errors are also large, as can be seen in Table 9. An inordinately large number of loci would have to be included to reduce the standard errors noticeably.

Genetic distances between subspecies of *P. maniculatus* and mainland populations of *P. m.*

gambelii are small, as is expected of such closely related groups. Nei (1976), using published electrophoretic data on gene frequencies, estimated D for a variety of organisms at various levels of differentiation: for local races of rodents, D lies between zero and 0.058; for subspecies of rodents, D lies between 0.004 and 0.262. In Table 9, all pairwise comparisons are between subspecies, except for comparisons among MUG, RIV, HTB, and BKM, which are all populations of *P. m. gambelii.* The smallest genetic distances occur between the pairs MUG-HTB and RIV-HTB (0.017 and 0.015, respectively). Distances between subspecies range from 0.021 to 0.100.

The striking feature of the genetic distances in this study is their consistency with the distribution and known history of the islands. The smallest genetic distances between island subspecies are found between the populations on Santa Cruz, Santa Rosa, and San Miguel Islands—three neighboring islands in the Northern Channel Island group which are thought to have been temporarily interconnected about 20,000 years ago. The populations on Anacapa, the fourth island in the Northern Channel Island group, and San Nicolas Island are genetically closer to these three islands than they are to any of the other islands. The remaining three Southern Channel Island populations are more distinct genetically from the other island populations, just as the islands themselves have been isolated for a longer period of time than have the northern islands. The San Clemente Island population is at the greatest genetic distance from other populations; Santa Catalina Island mice are similarly distinct.

The genetic distance of island subspecies from the closest mainland subspecies, *P. m. gambelii,* or even from *sonoriensis,* is relatively small—smaller than some of the genetic distances found between certain of the Southern and Northern Channel Island populations. As was stated earlier, the populations differ for the most part in the frequencies of alleles, rather than in the presence or absence of alleles. Furthermore, all populations, insular as well as mainland, have a high degree of variability (Table 7) within the populations, which tends to produce smaller genetic distances.

Sarich (1977) has suggested that there are two sets of proteins, one changing ten times as rapidly as the other, and that the fast group contributes the bulk of the measured genetic distance during the first five to six million years of divergence. The rapidly evolving proteins include the plasma proteins, nonspecific esterases, and certain enzymes not involved in complex metabolic pathways (*i.e.,* many Group II and III loci). His suggestion is supported by the evidence in this study, for the loci contributing most to genetic distances are Trf, Got-1, Es-5, Es-6, and Pgm-4. Sarich also proposes a test for neutral alleles, arguing that if the alleles sampled are neutral, higher heterozygosity values would be expected for more rapidly evolving loci. The exceptionally low heterozygosity values found for Group III loci in all insular populations except *P. m. streatori* clearly do not fit the neutral allele hypothesis. There seem to be selective forces on these islands whose actions result specifically in reduced variability of nonenzymatic proteins.

DISCUSSION AND CONCLUSIONS

The populations of Deer Mice inhabiting the Channel Islands have undergone significant morphological divergence from mainland populations and among themselves. This morphological divergence has not been accompanied by a comparable rate of genic divergence—genetic distances between insular and mainland subspecies remain relatively small. The factor that underlies this disparity is no doubt the high level of genetic variability maintained in insular populations. In the island populations, selection can act on a large available store of genetic variability, as measured by levels of polymorphism and individual heterozygosity.

To allow a direct comparison of morphological divergence between islands with genic divergence, as measured by genetic distance (Table 9), I have compiled a table of inter-island distances based on skull measurements (Table 10). These are the distances in canonical units

Table 10. Distance between island subspecies of *Peromyscus maniculatus* based on skull measurements.*

	CRU	ROS	STR	EXT	ELU	CAT	CLE
ANA†	0.44	2.58	3.02	1.68	4.57	2.05	5.35
CRU		3.02	3.30	2.09	4.72	2.49	5.78
ROS			2.13	1.03	4.08	0.83	2.77
STR				1.78	1.97	2.66	3.61
EXT					3.69	1.02	3.77
ELU						4.62	5.40
CAT							3.38

* Distances are given in units of the canonical variables depicted in Figure 1.
† Abbreviations for populations are explained in Table 6.

between the subspecies' means depicted in Figure 1, in which the axes are the first two canonical variables discriminating the subspecies. Only the island populations are included here because comparable data were not available for most of the mainland populations. A significant positive correlation, $r = 0.380$ ($P = 0.05$), was found between elements of the genetic data (genetic distance, Table 9) and elements of the morphological data (skull distance, Table 10) for all pairwise comparisons between islands ($n = 28$). None of the correlations for individual islands (which involve only the seven possible comparisons with each of the other islands) was significant, but the correlations were relatively high for Santa Cruz, Anacapa, and San Clemente Islands (0.661, 0.483, and 0.454, respectively). The relationship between Santa Barbara Island and the other islands is surprising in that it has the only population for which there is a negative correlation between genetic and morphological distances (-0.382). These correlations for individual islands give an idea of trends, but there are too few comparisons possible (seven) to establish significance. In general, there is a significant correlation between genetic and morphological distances between islands, although the rate of morphological divergence has been much greater than the rate of genic divergence.

Highly significant changes have occurred in body size, the island mice all being larger than the mainland mice, but size varies significantly between islands. San Clemente Island mice are the most distinct in all morphological traits. Significant differences in organ weights—differences which are maintained among the progeny of island mice reared in a uniform environment—suggest the existence of differential physiological adaptations in the island subspecies. Comparison of skull indices clearly shows the distinctness of the island populations and the increase in their average size over mainland populations.

The *P. maniculatus* subspecies can be distinguished on the basis of skull indices and body size variables and it is important to note that this discrimination is based on distinct changes in many different variables, rather than a few major ones. It is likely that many different genes are involved in the traits that distinguish the subspecies. *P. maniculatus* is known for marked geographic variation in morphological characters, as documented especially in the work of Dice (*e.g.*, 1940, 1941). Blair (1950) has suggested that the wide distribution and variation in morphological traits and in ecological preferences shown by *P. maniculatus* leads to an increase in its genetic variability and may favor the survival of the species and increase its opportunities for speciation.

Genetic variability is unusually high for both mainland and island subspecies in this study, compared with other mammals, but it is not maintained at the same level in the insular populations for all types of genetic loci. There is evidence for selection acting to reduce variability in nonenzymatic proteins in the insular habitat, while variability remains high in loci coding for glucose-metabolizing and other enzymes. There are also differences in the pattern of variability among insular populations, *P. m. streatori* on San Miguel Island being exceptional for its high levels of heterozygosity for nonenzymatic proteins and glucose-metabolizing enzymes. No correlation could be found between any of the major ecological parameters characterizing the islands and the levels of genic heterozygosity found. There is, however, a consistent relationship between the heterozygosities of the three groups of loci (I, glucose-metabolizing enzymes; II, other enzymes; and III, nonenzymatic proteins) and the distance to the nearest island, a parameter that has a high correlation with trapping success, which is, in turn, a rough measure of population density.

The genetic distances (based on Nei's measure, 1971, 1972) calculated from the electrophoretic data are relatively small because, for most of the variable loci, the populations differ in the frequencies of alleles rather than in the kinds of alleles. The pattern of variation in the magnitude of genetic distance is entirely consistent with the spatial distribution and known history of the islands. Furthermore, it agrees extremely well with the morphological differentiation of the subspecies. Just as *P. m. clementis* is morphologically the most distinct subspecies, it is also genetically the most distant from other insular subspecies and displays relative behavioral isolation in mating. Although most of the subspecies are well differentiated morphologically, with almost 100 per cent correct classification possible, there is some overlap between samples from San Miguel, Santa Rosa, and San Nicolas Islands. Genetic distances between these insular populations are also relatively small; this is especially true for the two Northern Channel Island populations on San Miguel and Santa Rosa.

The morphological and genic data indicate possible routes of gene flow among the islands in the past. The greatest amount of gene flow apparently occurred between the three westernmost Northern Channel Islands, probably during their period of interconnection. The mice on Anacapa Island most closely resemble their neighbors on Santa Cruz Island, apparently having less gene exchange with the other two Northern Channel Islands. It is likely that rafting or transportation by humans contributed both to the exchange of genes of Santa Rosa and San Miguel Deer Mice with San Nicolas mice and to gene flow between San Clemente and Santa Catalina Island mice. This pattern of gene flow seems consistent with the fact that there is a cold ocean current flowing south past San Miguel and Santa Rosa Islands toward San Nicolas Island and a warm current that goes north past San Clemente and Santa Catalina Islands. The distinct morphological differences that have evolved in the insular populations, distinguishing them, indicate a fair amount of isolation and argue against much gene flow at the present time. Even if there is some individual movement of Deer Mice between islands, these individuals would have to participate in breeding to contribute to the gene pool. There is some evidence from laboratory breeding studies of differential breeding behavior among females of different subspecies to support the idea of behavioral blocks to gene exchange.

The high levels of genic variability maintained in the insular populations have not undergone periods of serious diminution. The founders apparently carried fairly large stores of genetic variability and the populations seem not to have suffered severe reductions in size. Based on the data summarized in Table 9, there is no evidence for large random fluctuations in gene frequencies from one island to the next, as might occur with small population sizes and genetic bottlenecks. On the contrary, the patterns of gene frequencies are consistent with the distribution and history of the islands. That the high levels of variability are maintained by a sufficiently large population, rather than by gene flow between islands, is indicated by the highly significant anatomical and external morphological differences that have developed between insular populations.

ACKNOWLEDGMENTS

I would like to thank the many persons who made it possible for me to carry out my work on the Channel Islands by granting access to the islands and providing needed facilities, especially C. Stanton of Santa Cruz Island, L. Laughrin of the University of California at Santa Barbara Field Station on Santa Cruz Island, and J. Larson on San Clemente Island. Permission was kindly granted by the U.S. Department of the Navy and by the Channel Islands National Monument, National Parks Service, for work on some of the islands. Transportation to Santa Catalina Island was provided by the University of Southern California and use of the field station there is also greatly appreciated. I wish to thank P. Collins and W. Abbott of the Santa Barbara Museum of Natural History for trapping mice on Santa Rosa Island for me. The Island Packers Co. and J. Farrell were generous in providing transportation to some of the islands. I am especially grateful to a number of people who on occasion helped me trap on the islands, namely, J. Larson, K. Richkind, M. Richkind, M. Gordon, R. Byles, P. Auvenshine, and R. Hiemstra. I also wish to thank K. Richkind, K. Nagy, T. Chandler, and especially L. Snyder for Deer Mice they trapped on the mainland and gave to me. My appreciation goes to P. Auvenshine and K. Brown for technical assistance. This research was supported by the U.S. Public Health Service, National Institutes of Health grant GM22228.

REFERENCES

BERRY, R. J., and J. PETERS. 1976. Genes, survival and adjustment in an island population of the House Mouse. Pp. 23-48 *in* S. Karlin and E. Nevo, eds., Population genetics and ecology. Academic Press, New York, N.Y.

BLAIR, W. F. 1950. Ecological factors in speciation of *Peromyscus*. Evolution 4:253-275.

————. 1968. Introduction. Pp. 1-5 *in* J. A. King, ed., Biology of *Peromyscus* (Rodentia). Amer. Soc. Mammal. Spec. Publ. 2.

DICE, L. R. 1940. Speciation in *Peromyscus*. Amer. Natur. 74:289-298.

————. 1941. Variation in the Deer-Mouse, *Peromyscus maniculatus,* in parts of Oregon, California, and Baja California. Contrib. Lab. Vert. Genet. 18:1-11.

DIXON, W. J., and M. B. BROWN, eds. 1977. Biomedical computer programs P-Series. University of California Press, Los Angeles, Calif.

GILL, A. E. 1976. Genetic divergence of insular populations of Deer Mice. Biochem. Genet. 14:835-848.

GILLESPIE, J. H., and K. KOJIMA. 1968. The degree of polymorphism in enzymes involved in energy production compared to that in nonspecific enzymes in two *Drosophila ananassae* populations. Proc. Natl. Acad. Sci. 61:582-585.

HALL, E. R., and K. R. KELSON. 1959. The mammals of North America, v. II. Ronald Press, New York, N.Y.

HARRIS, H. 1966. Enzyme polymorphism in man. Proc. Roy. Soc. London B 164:298-310.

HUBBY, J. L., and R. C. LEWONTIN. 1966. A molecular approach to the study of genic heterozygosity in natural populations. I. The number of alleles at different loci in *Drosophila pseudoobscura*. Genetics 54:577-594.

JOHNSON, M. P., L. G. MASON, and P. H. RAVEN. 1968. Ecological parameters and plant species diversity. Amer. Natur. 102:297-306.

KOJIMA, K., J. GILLESPIE, and Y. N. TOBARI. 1970. A profile of *Drosophila* species enzymes assayed by electrophoresis. I. Number of alleles, heterozygosities, and linkage disequilibrium in glucose-metabolizing systems and some other enzymes. Biochem. Genet. 4:627-637.

LAYNE, J. N. 1968. Ontogeny. Pp. 148-253 *in* J. A. King, ed., Biology of *Peromyscus* (Rodentia). Amer. Soc. Mammal. Spec. Publ. 2.

LEWONTIN, R. C. 1974. The genetic basis of evolutionary change. Columbia University Press, New York, N.Y.

MCCABE, T. T., and B. D. BLANCHARD. 1950. Three species of *Peromyscus*. Rood Associates, Santa Barbara, Calif.

MOSTELLER, F., and J. W. TUKEY. 1977. Data analysis and regression. Addison-Wesley, Reading, Mass.

NEI, M. 1971. Interspecific gene differences and evolutionary time estimated from electrophoretic data on protein identity. Amer. Natur. 105:385-398.

————. 1972. Genetic distance between populations. Amer. Natur. 106:283-292.

————. 1976. Mathematical models of speciation and genetic distance. Pp. 723-765 *in* S. Karlin and E. Nevo, eds., Population genetics and ecology. Academic Press, New York, N.Y.

NIXON, S. E., and R. J. TAYLOR. 1977. Large genetic distances associated with little morphological variation in *Polycelis coronata* and *Dugesia tigrina* (Planaria). Syst. Zool. 26:152-164.

PHILBRICK, R. N., ed. 1967. Proceedings of the symposium on the biology of the California Islands. Santa Barbara Botanic Garden, Santa Barbara, Calif.

PIZZIMENTI, J. J. 1976. Genetic divergence and morphological convergence in the Prairie Dogs, *Cynomys gunnisoni* and *Cynomys leucurus*. II. Genetic analyses. Evolution 30:367-379.

POWELL, J. R. 1975. Protein variation in natural populations of animals. Evol. Biol. 8:79-119.

RASMUSSEN, D. I., and R. K. KOEHN. 1966. Serum transferrin polymorphism in the Deer Mouse. Genetics 54:1353-1357.

RAVEN, P. H. 1967. The floristics of the California Islands. Pp. 57-67 *in* R. N. Philbrick, ed., Proceedings of the symposium on the biology of the California Islands. Santa Barbara Botanic Garden, Santa Barbara, Calif.

SARICH, V. M. 1977. Rates, sample sizes, and the neutrality hypothesis for electrophoresis in evolutionary studies. Nature 265:24-28.

SELANDER, R. K. 1975. Genic variation in natural populations. Pp. 21-45 *in* F. J. Ayala, ed., Molecular evolution. Sinauer Associates, Sunderland, Mass.

SELANDER, R. K., D. W. KAUFMAN, R. J. BAKER, and S. L. WILLIAMS. 1974. Genic and chromosomal differentiation in Pocket Gophers of the *Geomys bursarius* group. Evolution 28:557-564.

SELANDER, R. K., M. H. SMITH, S. Y. YANG, W. E. JOHNSON, and J. B. GENTRY. 1971. Biochemical polymorphism and systematics in the genus *Peromyscus*. I. Variation in the Old-field Mouse (*Peromyscus polionotus*). Stud. Genetics 6:49-90.

SHVARTS, S. S. 1975. Morpho-physiological characteristics as indices of population processes. Pp. 129-152 *in* F. B. Golley, K. Petrusewicz, and L. Ryszkowski, eds., Small mammals: their productivity and population dynamics. Cambridge University Press, Cambridge.

————. 1977. The evolutionary ecology of animals. (Translated from Russian by A. E. Gill, ed.) Consultants Bureau, New York, N.Y.

SNYDER, L. R. G. 1978a. Genetics of hemoglobin in the Deer Mouse, *Peromyscus maniculatus*. I. Multiple α- and β-globin structural loci. Genetics 89:511-530.

————. 1978b. Genetics of hemoglobin in the Deer Mouse, *Peromyscus maniculatus*. II. Multiple alleles at regulatory loci. Genetics 89:531-550.

THORNE, R. F. 1969. The California Islands. Ann. Missouri Bot. Gard. 56:391-408.

TURNER, B. J. 1974. Genetic divergence of Death Valley pupfish species: biochemical versus morphological evidence. Evolution 28:281-294.

VEDDER, J. G., and D. G. HOWELL. 1980. Topographic evolution of the southern California borderland during late Cenozoic time. Pp. 7-31 *in* D. M. Power, ed., The California Islands: proceedings of a multidisciplinary symposium. Santa Barbara Museum of Natural History, Santa Barbara, Calif.

VON BLOEKER, J. C., JR. 1967. The land mammals of the Southern California Islands. Pp. 254-263 *in* R. N. Philbrick, ed., Proceedings of the symposium on the biology of the California Islands. Santa Barbara Botanic Garden, Santa Barbara, Calif.

Populations and Status of the Island Fox

Lyndal Laughrin

*Santa Cruz Island Reserve, University of California,
Santa Barbara, California 93106*

INTRODUCTION

The six largest of southern California's Channel Islands support populations of a diminutive relative of the Gray Fox (*Urocyon cinereoargenteus*) known as the Island Fox (*U. littoralis*). Each of these islands is considered to contain its own endemic subspecies: *U. l. littoralis* on San Miguel Island, *U. l. santarosae* on Santa Rosa Island, *U. l. santacruzae* on Santa Cruz Island, *U. l. dickeyi* on San Nicolas Island, *U. l. catalinae* on Santa Catalina Island, and *U. l. clementae* on San Clemente Island. The inter-island taxonomic affinities of this species and the degree of relationship to the mainland Gray Fox are not well understood. Discussions, though partially speculative, of the Island Fox's evolutionary history, systematics, and zoogeographical relationships can be found in Merriam (1903), Grinnell and Linsdale (1930), Grinnell *et al.* (1937), Stock (1943), von Bloeker (1967), Savage (1967), Orr (1968), Remington (1971), and Johnson (1975). Natural history observations can be found in Grinnell *et al.* (1937) and Laughrin (1973, 1977).

Prior to my studies, the only indications of the status of any of these fox populations had been derived from casual observations, some of which were reported in the literature (Grinnell *et al.* 1937). Dr. C. Stanton (pers. comm.) of the Santa Cruz Island Company, whose family first came to the island in 1937, stated that he remembered years when foxes were seldom seen. Company records show that, prior to Prohibition in 1918, foxes were so abundant that ranch hands were employed to kill them because they were destroying the grapes in the vineyards. H. H. Sheldon (unpubl. ms.) found foxes to be plentiful during 1928 on Santa Cruz Island; he trapped 155 of them over the course of that year. Sheldon also stated that "Mr. Fred Caire [then owner of the island] . . . had noticed a scarcity of foxes at certain periods during the forty years he [had] been at the island." During the 1950s, a mammal collecting group from the Museum of Vertebrate Zoology at the University of California, Berkeley observed only two or three individuals during a two-week visit to Santa Cruz Island (Bills 1969). Fluctuations in numbers have also been noted for Santa Rosa Island (A. Vail, pers. comm.) and Santa Catalina (Grinnell *et al.* 1937, D. Propst, pers. comm.). Comparable observations for the other Island Fox populations are unknown.

In 1971, because of the low abundance of the Santa Catalina Island Fox population and the geographical restrictions of all the island populations, the Island Fox was classified by the Fish and Game Commission as a rare species, according to the California Endangered Species Act of 1970. This classification and the lack of prior information on this species led me to begin studies of its natural history. This report is an attempt to provide information on the status of the six populations; as such, it focuses on abundance, distribution, and age structure. Other investigations are concerned with food habits, behavior, and home range movements.

METHODS

Abundance and population structure data for the six Island Fox populations were obtained by live-trapping methods. Accessibility, logistics, and facilities permitted more intensive investigation of the Santa Cruz Island population, though all of the other islands were visited at least once.

Quantitative estimates of fox abundance for different habitats, years, and islands were

TABLE 1. Population data of California Island Foxes.

	San Miguel	Santa Rosa	Santa Cruz	San Nicolas	Santa Catalina	San Clemente	Gray Fox	Red Fox
Number of trap periods	45	120	1310	165	126	384		
Total captures	18	43	543	29	2	150		
Total individuals	18	34	307	29	2	103		
					55*			
Trap efficiency (%)	43	50	67	27	3	52		
					11*			
Number fox/mi²	7	11	20.4	3	0.8	11	4†	0.8-1.4‡

* Propst (1975).   † Lord (1961).   ‡ Sargeant (1972).

desirable, so a procedure providing comparative indices was necessary. A live-trapping modification of the methods used with Gray Foxes in the southeastern U.S. (Wood 1959a, 1959b) was the basis of my trapping technique. Two sizes of National collapsible wire mesh traps were used: 8″ x 8″ x 18″ and 6″ x 6″ x 14″. The traps were placed in a line along roads or trails at 0.2-mile (0.32 km) intervals and were baited and set, then checked the following morning. Traplines were run for three nights and usually contained thirty traps. The techniques and bait used were the same for all of the islands.

Captured foxes were examined for ectoparasites, pelage condition, eye condition, general health, and age. Ages of the animals were determined by examining the degree of wear of the first upper molars (Wood 1959a). Though this method was developed for Gray Foxes, it also worked well for Island Foxes. On all of the islands, only one litter per pair is produced each year, at about the same time each year, so that differential tooth wear between separate age classes is distinct enough to distinguish ages up to five years. After this period of time, wear is usually to the gum level; age classes beyond five years, therefore, were combined for analysis. For convenience, one-year intervals were arbitrarily established beginning with May 1 (approximately the normal time of birth) and ending April 30. After examination, the foxes were tagged with numbered ear tags and released.

Traplines were placed in different habitat types on the various islands, as follows: coastal sage scrub and grassland-iceplant associations on San Miguel; grassland, coastal sage scrub, and some woodland scrub on Santa Rosa; chaparral and woodland on Santa Cruz; grassland and coastal dunes on San Nicolas; coastal sage scrub, woodland, chaparral, and riparian habitat on Santa Catalina; and grassland and coastal sage scrub on San Clemente. These habitats represent the majority of the important and widespread types available on all of the islands, except that on Santa Cruz trapping was not done in coastal sage scrub, grasslands, or pine forests. The Santa Cruz traplines were placed in the same location each year because sightings and scat frequency indicated it as a possible area of high density. Further studies will compare other habitat types on Santa Cruz Island.

Two abundance indices were used to compare the status of the island populations. One was trapping efficiency, which is the ratio of the number of captured foxes to the number of *available* trap periods (not *total* trap periods). The number of available trap periods is the total of trap periods minus the number of traps not available to capture foxes. Traps were sometimes not available for the following reasons: malfunctions, capture of other animals (e.g., birds, juvenile pigs, feral cats), disturbance of the trap, or removal of the bait by other animals. The second index was devised to estimate densities of the various island populations within the

TABLE 2. Population data of San Nicolas and Santa Catalina Island Foxes.

	San Nicolas Island			Santa Catalina Island		
	1971	1974	1977	1972	1975*	1977
Trap periods	40	52	75	60	597	66
Captures	24	2	3	2	55	0
Individuals	24	2	3	2	55	0
Efficiency (%)	72	4	4.7	6	11	0
Fox/mi^2	7	1.3	0.3	0.3	2	0

*Propst (1975).

habitats sampled. Because a grid trap layout was not used, a width factor (0.5 mi, 0.8 km), based upon other studies of recapture distance and home range data (Laughrin 1977), was multiplied by the trapline length to yield an estimate of the true area sampled. The number of individual foxes captured along the line during the three-day session was then divided by the estimated area to give a density estimate. Not all of the island habitats were sampled, nor were the extents of these habitats determined. Sampling was not done over most of each island's area. Thus, only a crude estimate of each island's total fox population is available.

RESULTS AND DISCUSSION

Island Fox populations are distributed over most of the area of the islands on which they occur, though the abundance varies by habitat type (Laughrin 1977). Estimates of the abundance of each Island Fox population are given in Table 1 and are for the habitat types sampled on each island (see Methods). The data for San Miguel Island are from one trapping session in 1971. Data for Santa Rosa are from one session in 1972. Data for Santa Cruz are from seven sessions from 1973 to 1977; the abundance estimates are means. Data for San Nicolas are from three sessions from 1971 to 1977; the abundance estimates for this island also are means. Similarly, data for Santa Catalina are from three sessions from 1972 to 1977, while those for San Clemente are from four sessions in 1972. Also included are data from a study by Propst (1975) on Santa Catalina. For comparative purposes, estimates of densities for midwestern U.S. Gray Foxes (Lord 1961) and Red Foxes (*Vulpes vulpes*) (Sargeant 1972) are given.

The results in Table 1 show that, generally, Island Fox populations exist at higher densities than fox populations on the mainland. They also show that there is a considerable difference in abundance for different islands. Part of this can be accounted for by habitat differences. The higher estimate for the Santa Cruz Island population is, in large part, due to having trapped in a richer vegetative area of woodland-chaparral—a habitat type quite abundant on Santa Cruz. Areas of greater food productivity and availability can support denser populations (Laughrin 1977).

There is also a discrepancy between estimates for islands of similar habitat types, however. Foxes on San Miguel, Santa Rosa, San Nicolas, and San Clemente Islands were trapped in essentially similar vegetation, but were much less abundant on San Nicolas. This same discrepancy is evident in comparisons between populations on Santa Cruz and Santa Catalina, with Santa Catalina having far fewer foxes.

Because of the low estimates of density on San Nicolas and Santa Catalina Islands, repeat visits were made to gather more information. Data for these comparisons are found in Table 2. While San Nicolas initially showed a population level comparable to similar situations on other islands, data from later visits indicated a decline in abundance. The population on Santa

TABLE 3. Trapping results for population data of Santa Cruz Island Foxes.

	3/73	10/73	5/74	2/75	2/76	9/76	9/77
Trap periods	180	80	75	144	115	150	75
Captures	100	49	35	87	41	63	41
Individuals	53	36	28	45	28	37	32
Trap efficiency (%)	71	66	65	76	49	64	78
Number fox/mi²	25.4	21.2	16.4	22.2	15.2	18.2	23.8

Catalina appears to have been, and remained, at a rather low level. Propst's (1975) study indicated a slightly greater abundance, or the possibility of an increase, but this was not substantiated in 1977. Other signs of fox activity, such as scat, tracks, trails, and casual sightings by me and other island personnel, were also very limited for these two islands. Qualitative observations of the vegetation in habitats on these islands did not offer any clues for causes of low numbers of foxes. On San Nicolas Island there was an alarming trend of an increase in abundance and dispersal of feral cats. Feral cats have also been trapped on Santa Catalina, but there is no information regarding the extent of their distribution or relationship to fox population levels. San Clemente has a large number of feral cats, but apparently there has been little adverse effect on the fox population (R. Wilson, pers. comm.). I suspect, however, that the fox population would be higher in the absence of the cats.

Table 3 gives Santa Cruz Island abundance estimates for the years 1973 to 1977. There have been some minor fluctuations during this period, especially considering the uncontrollable parameters involved in live-trapping techniques, but, overall, there are indications of relative stability.

The results of age structure analysis indicated a high proportion of older animals in the Island Fox populations. The ratio of juveniles (first-year animals) to adults for Santa Cruz Island was 0.19, while the mean ratio for all the islands was 0.26. Juvenile to adult ratios for Red Foxes are 1.06 to 7.5 (Petrides 1950, Schofield 1958, Phillips 1970) and for Gray Foxes are 1.08 to 1.63 (Petrides 1950, Layne 1958, Wood 1959a, Lord 1961). Thus, first-year animals represent a smaller proportion in island populations and, presumably, there are lower mortality rates among the older age classes of Island Foxes.

SUMMARY

Investigations of Island Foxes, utilizing live-trapping techniques, during the period 1971 to 1977 have shown that the populations on Santa Cruz, Santa Rosa, San Miguel, and San Clemente Islands have maintained themselves at high densities relative both to the populations on Santa Catalina and San Nicolas Islands and to the populations of the closely related mainland Gray Fox. Reasons for the decline and low densities of two of the Island Fox populations remain speculative. An analysis of the age structures of the populations shows there to be a high percentage of old individuals, in contrast to mainland fox populations.

ACKNOWLEDGMENTS

I wish to thank M. M. Erickson for her support and encouragement. For equipment, facilities, and hospitality, the support of the following persons and organizations is greatly appreciated: Commanding Officers of the U.S. Navy's Pacific Missile Range, Pt. Mugu, and San Clemente Island Facility; Al Vail of Vail and Vickers Company; and D. Propst of the Santa Catalina Island Conservancy. I would also like to thank the following personnel of the California Department of Fish and Game: H. Leach, Nongame Wildlife Supervisor, for support and programming aspects of the study, and Lt. H. Hoover, formerly skipper of the patrol boat *Yellowtail*, Warden J. Voorhies, and Game Manager R. Fordice, for assistance in the field. I want to especially thank Dr. C. Stanton and H. Duffield of the Santa Cruz Island Company for their encouragement, support, and interest. Financial support for this study was provided by the California Department of Fish and Game and by the Department of Biological Sciences and the Santa Cruz Island Reserve, University of California, Santa Barbara.

REFERENCES

BILLS, A. R. 1969. A study of the distribution and morphology of the mice of Santa Cruz Island: an example of divergence. M.A. thesis, University of California, Santa Barbara, Calif.

GRINNELL, J., J. DIXON, and J. LINSDALE. 1937. Fur-bearing mammals of California. University of California Press, Berkeley, Calif.

GRINNELL, J., and J. LINSDALE. 1930. Two new foxes from the Southern California Islands. Proc. Biol. Soc. Washington 43:153-156.

JOHNSON, D. L. 1975. New evidence on the origin of the fox, *Urocyon littoralis clementae*, and feral goats on San Clemente Island, California. J. Mammal. 56:925-928.

LAUGHRIN, L. 1973. California Island Fox survey. California Dept. Fish and Game, Wildl. Mgmt. Branch Admin. Rep. 73-3.

———. 1977. The Island Fox: a field study of its behavior and ecology. Ph.D. thesis, University of California, Santa Barbara, Calif.

LAYNE, J. N. 1958. Reproductive characteristics of the Gray Fox in southern Illinois. J. Wildl. Mgmt. 22:157-163.

LORD, R. K., JR. 1961. A population study of the Gray Fox. Amer. Midl. Natur. 66:87-110.

MERRIAM, C. H. 1903. New mammals from the United States. Proc. Biol. Soc. Washington 16:74-75.

ORR, P. C. 1968. Prehistory of Santa Rosa Island. Santa Barbara Museum of Natural History, Santa Barbara, Calif.

PETRIDES, G. A. 1950. The determination of sex and age ratios in fur animals. Amer. Midl. Natur. 43:355-382.

PHILLIPS, R. L. 1970. Age ratios of Iowa foxes. J. Wildl. Mgmt. 34:52-56.

PROPST, B. 1975. A population survey of the Santa Catalina Island Fox. California Dept. Fish and Game, Nongame Wildl. Investigations, Project W-54-R-8, Job I-1.10, final report.

REMINGTON, C. L. 1971. Natural history and evolutionary genetics of the California Channel Islands. Discovery 7:3-18.

SARGEANT, A. B. 1972. Red Fox spatial characteristics in relation to waterfowl predation. J. Wildl. Mgmt. 36:225-236.

SAVAGE, J. M. 1967. Discussion of the significance of distribution patterns. P. 265 *in* R. N. Philbrick, ed., Proceedings of the symposium on the biology of the California Islands. Santa Barbara Botanic Garden, Santa Barbara, Calif.

SCHOFIELD, R. D. 1958. Litter size and age ratios of Michigan Red Foxes. J. Wildl. Mgmt. 22:313-315.

STOCK, C. 1943. Foxes and elephants of the Channel Islands. Los Angeles Co. Mus. Quart. 3:6-9.

VON BLOEKER, J. C., JR. 1967. The land mammals of the Southern California Islands. Pp. 245-263 *in* R. N. Philbrick, ed., Proceedings of the symposium on the biology of the California Islands. Santa Barbara Botanic Garden, Santa Barbara, Calif.

WOOD, J. E. 1959a. Age structure and productivity of a Gray Fox population. J. Mammal. 39:74-86.

———. 1959b. Relative estimates of fox population levels. J. Wildl. Mgmt. 23:53-63.

Distribution of Bats of the California Channel Islands

Patricia E. Brown

Department of Biology, University of California,
Los Angeles, California 90024

INTRODUCTION

The power of flight has preadapted bats for island colonization. This accounts for their disproportionately high representation in the terrestrial mammalian fauna of the California Islands. Of the eighteen species of native mammals found on the islands (excluding man and marine mammals), eleven, or 61 per cent, are bats. Some bat species are better dispersers than others, but not only must a bat be capable of crossing the water barrier, it must find suitable food and habitat upon its arrival. Bats have voracious appetites and may consume up to 25 per cent of their body weight in insects daily. Some are specific in their food requirements, while others are generalists and opportunists, snatching up any insect within a certain size class. Needless to say, generalists are better island colonizers since the specialist may not find its favorite food item present on the island. Bats with specific roost preferences, such as trees or rock crevices, may find a barren sandy island a difficult place on which to live and reproduce. In this paper, I will attempt to summarize what is known about the distribution of bats on the islands and provide new data resulting from my own field work.

DISTRIBUTION AND SPECIES ACCOUNTS

Figure 1 summarizes the known distribution of bats on the California Islands. It is not surprising that 82 per cent of the species should occur on Santa Cruz Island, the largest and most ecologically diverse of the group. Santa Catalina is second with 45 per cent of the known species, while larger Santa Rosa has but a single species. The distribution of the bat records may also reflect the amount of time spent by mammalogists in pursuit of specimens—the more accessible islands have been more thoroughly sampled. Due to bats' nocturnal activity and secretive diurnal retreats, bat collectors in the past have had to rely on the shotgun technique or random discovery of day roosts. Mist-netting over water sources has been employed in this survey, yielding valuable species data with a minimum of disturbance to the bats. Unfortunately, only Santa Catalina and Santa Cruz Islands have been sampled using this technique. On Santa Cruz, the netting of *Lasionycteris noctivagans* established a range extension as well as a new record for the islands. Less than half (36 per cent) of the bat species found on the Channel Islands are known to breed there (*Myotis californicus* and *M. yumanensis, Plecotus townsendii,* and *Antrozous pallidus*), with the remaining seven bat species represented by only a few specimens, often captured during migratory periods. In discussing the species found on the islands, I will begin with the most common.

California Myotis (*Myotis californicus caurinus*)

Myotis californicus is the most widespread of the bats, occurring on the five largest islands (Santa Rosa, Santa Cruz, Santa Catalina, San Nicolas, and San Clemente). Reports of small, dark bats flying over Santa Barbara, Anacapa, and San Miguel are probably attributable to this species as well. They can be identified by their small size, dark, dull brown pelage, and very tiny feet. They roost in crevices which are often in manmade structures such as barns. I have found California myotis (including lactating females in June) under the roof supports in the horse barn at the Stanton Ranch and in the attic of the chapel on Santa Cruz Island, and have mist-netted several more over both the stream and swimming pool by the ranch. A maternity

BATS OF THE CALIFORNIA CHANNEL ISLANDS

	Antrozous pallidus	Myotis evotis	Myotis thysanodes	Myotis californicus	Myotis yumanensis	Eptesicus fuscus	Plecotus townsendii	Lasiurus cinereus	Lasionycteris noctivagans	Tadarida brasiliensis
	Pallid bat	Big-eared Myotis	Fringed Myotis	California Myotis	Yuma Myotis	Big Brown bat	Lump-nosed bat	Hoary bat	Silver-haired bat	Free-tailed bat
San Miguel				?						
Santa Rosa				O						
Santa Cruz	XO	O		XO		O	XO	X	X	O
Anacapa										
Santa Barbara								X		
Santa Catalina	O	O		XO	XO		O			
San Nicolas				O			O			
San Clemente			O	O			O			O

X Present Study
O Past Records

FIGURE 1. *Records of occurrence of bats on the California Channel Islands.*

roost of approximately fifty bats uses the attic of the bunkhouse at Christi Ranch on the west end of Santa Cruz. Traces of small guano adhering to the stucco walls of the ranch buildings are probably attributable to night-roosting California myotis. Fresh guano, deposited around the chapel on Santa Cruz during a cold February evening, suggests that these bats may be active even during winter nights.

On Santa Catalina Island, I found 20 of these bats under the roof peak of a wooden building at Gallagher's Camp on August 17, 1976. They also roost under the tarpaper on the sides of old frame buildings at Camp Cactus on Santa Catalina, and can be seen flying after dark in the barn at Middle Ranch. They feed on a variety of small aerial insects. This wide food tolerance may have preadapted them for island colonization. It is expected that mist-netting will yield records of this bat from San Miguel, if not from all of the islands. Existing museum specimens include 43 from Santa Cruz Island (Prisoners Harbor, Frys Harbor, and the Stanton Ranch); five from Santa Rosa (taken near the ranch buildings at Beecher's Bay); seven from Santa Catalina (White's Landing, Avalon, and Middle Ranch); five from San Clemente; and one from San Nicolas (von Bloeker 1967).

Big-eared Myotis (*Myotis evotis*)

This small, yellowish-brown bat is easily distinguished from other *Myotis* by its relatively large, black, pointed ears that extend 7 to 10 mm beyond the base when laid forward. On the mainland, this bat inhabits wooded areas and is more common farther north or at higher elevations in the south (Barbour and Davis 1969). It is not surprising that the three records for *Myotis evotis* are from the most densely vegetated islands. One male was taken from a crevice in a building at Prisoners Harbor on Santa Cruz Island, while another was procured by von Bloeker from the rafters of the winery in Cañada del Medio. A third bat was taken from under a corrugated iron roof at White's Landing on Santa Catalina (von Bloeker 1967). Little is known of the movements or habits of these bats.

Fringed Myotis (*Myotis thysanodes*)

Like the long-eared myotis, not much is known of the movements of this bat in California, except that it is found only in summer roosts and is assumed to be migratory. It has a wide but irregular distribution, being locally common in the southwestern deserts, where it often forms large roosts in caves, although in California it is usually found roosting alone in buildings. This small bat can be distinguished from other *Myotis* by the fringe of short, stiff hairs along the posterior border of the interfemoral membrane. An adult female was hand-netted by von Bloeker (1967) outside the buildings at Wilson's Cove on San Clemente Island in 1943. This is the only record for the islands.

Yuma Myotis (*Myotis yumanensis*)

Von Bloeker (1967) predicted that the Yuma myotis would eventually be discovered on the California Islands. In fact, Bancroft had already collected a male in Avalon on Santa Catalina on August 1, 1893 (Los Angeles County Museum of Natural History [LACM]). In the past three years, I have banded 163 *Myotis yumanensis* on Santa Catalina, with a recapture rate of 10 per cent. In the late spring, pregnant females can be found roosting under the tarpaper at Camp Cactus. A large night roost is present in the deserted army bunker above Ben Weston beach. Late in the evening, the barn at Middle Ranch is often alive with bats swooping and darting after insects.

This bat is slightly larger than *Myotis californicus,* but its feet are more than twice as large. On the mainland, it has a wide geographical and ecological range, but always roosts near fresh water, even in desert situations. In parts of California it apparently hybridizes with *Myotis lucifugus* and the two are easily confused. *M. lucifugus* could also occur on the Northern Channel Islands, as could the small-footed myotis (*Myotis leibii*) or the long-legged myotis (*Myotis volans*).

Lump-nosed Bat (*Plecotus townsendii*)

This light brown bat is readily identified by the extremely long ears which may equal almost half its body length. When the bat is torpid, these ears are tightly curled and resemble a ram's horns. There are two lumps on either side of and above each nostril to further distinguish it. This species is recorded from four islands: Santa Catalina (two from Middle Ranch, one from Johnson Harbor, and three from White's Landing); Santa Cruz (two from Christi Ranch and 246 from Prisoners Harbor); San Clemente (one); and San Nicolas (one).

Lump-nosed bats forage late in the evening and often can be seen hovering as they glean insects from vegetation. They are locally common on the mainland, the females sometimes forming maternity roosts of about a hundred individuals, while the males roost singly. They are very susceptible to disturbance and will abandon a roost that is too frequently visited by people. On the mainland they change roosts, but on islands these possibilities are limited. When *Plecotus* was first discovered roosting in the second story of the old building at Prisoners Harbor on Santa Cruz Island, the colony was estimated at 300, mostly females. Within the next eight days, 111 bats were collected from this colony (von Bloeker 1967). In 1948, Pearson estimated the roost to contain 200 bats, including young (Pearson *et al.* 1952)—or 315 acres/lump-nosed bat on the island. He, in turn, collected more bats. In 1964, more bat specimens were removed from the island by collectors from the University of California at Santa Barbara. In 1974, I observed four *Plecotus* roosting at the roof peak in the brick building at Prisoners Harbor, then mist-netted another male over the stream and released him. Since then, on subsequent visits I have not observed any *Plecotus townsendii*. They perhaps have moved to a less accessible roost. It is hoped that the population density has not dropped too low for recovery.

Big Brown Bat (*Eptesicus fuscus*)

The big brown bat resembles a large *Myotis* with a more rounded muzzle. It is common on the mainland and has a wide geographical distribution. It feeds on a variety of insects, but appears to prefer beetles, and regularly roosts in buildings. Von Bloeker (1967) discovered a torpid *Eptesicus* in December 1943 in the attic of the old building at Prisoners Harbor. This is the only record for the California Islands. Mainland populations of these bats are sedentary and do not often move between roosts. Possibly the twenty miles of ocean has been an effective barrier against island colonization, although if any did arrive they could probably become established on the larger islands.

Pallid Bat (*Antrozous pallidus pacificus*)

This long-eared, large-eyed, golden-brown bat is larger than the big brown bat. The pallid bat is a social animal, with an array of audible communication sounds (Brown 1976), and forms large roosts in ranch buildings in grassland habitats on the mainland. It forages on the ground for large, ground-dwelling arthropods such as Jerusalem crickets (*Stenopelmatus fuscus*). Since these insects are common in the grassland areas of Santa Cruz Island, it is not surprising that pallid bats have established a breeding colony there.

Between spring and fall 1978, individual pallid bats were radiotelemetered in order to determine their roost sites and foraging areas. Pallid bats spend the day in the barns and the old winery building at the Stanton Ranch. Within an hour after sunset, they begin to fly low over the adjacent pastures in search of prey. After one to two hours of foraging, they return to a central night roost in the barn for the remainder of the night, often departing for a brief predawn feeding bout before returning to their diurnal retreat. I have banded 240 of these bats on Santa Cruz Island over the past four years, with a 25 per cent recapture rate. This population appears to be resident on the island since none of the bats banded here turn up in mainland roosts, nor do any of the more than one thousand banded pallid bats from the mainland ever appear in the island colony. The bats are not present in the ranch buildings during the winter months and probably hibernate in rock crevices. Possibly because of their isolation from the mainland population, the island pallid bats are developing a distinct dialect in their communication sounds ("directives"). The desert subspecies of the pallid bat, *Antrozous pallidus pallidus,* also communicates with a dialect distinct from the coastal subspecies *pacificus* (Brown 1973).

One specimen of pallid bat was collected on Santa Catalina Island roosting under the eaves of a house. This was in addition to the 127 specimens collected on Santa Cruz (von Bloeker 1967).

Silver-haired Bat (*Lasionycteris noctivagans*)

This bat has black, silver-tipped fur and short, round ears and is common in northern forests, where it roosts in trees. Since its normal range begins two hundred miles to the north, its appearance in a mist net on June 14, 1974 over the stream in Cañada del Medio on Santa Cruz Island was unexpected (the specimen is a male—LACM #46231). *Lasionycteris* is a migratory bat and this specimen may possibly have wandered off course during spring migration. Two other specimens have recently been taken at Agua Caliente Spring in San Diego County (T. McDonnell, pers. comm.). Other vagrants of this species may be expected.

Hoary Bat (*Lasiurus cinereus*)

Like its relative, the silver-haired bat, the silver and gray hoary bat is solitary and undertakes long migrations of over a thousand miles in the spring and fall. Hoary bats roost in trees and Tenaza (1966) has taken them in the three trees on the Farallon Islands. He noted that in August and September sometimes as many as 21 per day pass through in migratory waves. The hoary bat has colonized both the Hawaiian and Galapagos Islands. Hoary bats are widespread, occurring in all fifty states, although they are most abundant in the southwestern U.S. With the coniferous forests on Santa Cruz and Santa Rosa, it is possible that suitable habitat exists for this species. They are certainly capable of making the over-water flight. Two sightings have been made of this bat and one specimen has been collected (Santa Barbara Museum of Natural History [SBMNH]). In the spring of 1974, Dr. Carey Stanton found a hoary bat lying in the dust near the ranch buildings on Santa Cruz Island. Fearing that it was rabid, he killed the animal, which was later identified by Dr. Lyndal Laughrin. The bat was sent to Public Health for rabies testing (the results were negative), but unfortunately the specimen was lost. On September 25, 1978, I mist-netted a solitary male over the stream in Cañada del Medio on Santa Cruz.

At noon on October 11, 1974, Dr. H. Lee Jones and fifteen ornithologists located a hoary bat on the ground in the ice plants (*Mesembryanthemum*) on Santa Barbara Island. Several pictures were taken before the animal was aroused and flew away, landing again in some ice plants. It is possible that more hoary bats will be found on the island, especially during times of migration.

Red Bat (*Lasiurus borealis*)

This smaller version of the hoary bat is distinguished by its coppery red fur, which covers most of the wing and tail membranes. The red bat is more common to the north and east, with only occasional records from southern California. Like the hoary and silver-haired bats, it is migratory and solitary, usually roosting in trees. A single male was mist-netted over the swimming pool at the Stanton Ranch on September 23, 1978 (specimen in SBMNH). This was during a period when warm Santa Ana winds were blowing off the mainland. The single male hoary bat mentioned earlier and four free-tailed bats were also collected during this time, possibly having been blown off course during their fall migrations.

Free-tailed Bat (*Tadarida brasiliensis*)

The free-tailed bat is so named because half of its tail extends beyond the interfemoral membrane. It has broad, rounded ears and long, narrow wings. This enables rapid flight over long distances during nightly foraging. In Texas, they have been known to fly over fifty miles between their day roosts and feeding areas, often ascending to 10,000 feet before they spread out to feed (Davis *et al.* 1962). They undertake long, seasonal migrations often of more than a thousand miles over the Gulf of Mexico to winter in southern Mexico. All this should certainly preadapt them for over-water dispersal and island colonization. The surprising thing is that they have not colonized the California Islands. Only ten records exist for the islands. A single female was captured at the Marine Corps Training Center on San Clemente Island in 1943. I mist-netted a single male over the stream in Cañada del Medio on Santa Cruz Island on September 22, 1978. Four mummified and one live free-tailed bat were found by von Bloeker (1967) on Santa Cruz Island in a pallid bat roost. On September 28, 1978, I discovered three additional males in the same barn on the Stanton Ranch. Free-tailed bats are commonly associated with pallid bats in mainland roosts. They are fairly common in the California coastal ranges, where they form large colonies in buildings. Their appearance on the islands is therefore to be anticipated, as is that of other members of their family (Molossidae), such as the mastiff bat (*Eumops perotis*).

SUMMARY

The power of flight has preadapted bats for island colonization. Bats compose 61 per cent of the mammalian species found on the California Islands. It is likely that this number will be increased with modern collecting techniques such as mist-netting. Since von Bloeker's summary in 1967, four bat species—*Myotis yumanensis, Lasionycteris noctivagans,* and *Lasiurus cinereus* and *L. borealis*—have been added to the faunal list. The known distribution of bats on the California Islands is summarized in this paper.

ACKNOWLEDGMENTS

I am indebted to Dr. Carey Stanton for his permission and encouragement to study the bats on Santa Cruz Island, and to Dr. Lyndal Laughrin for his help and patience during my stay at the field station there. I would also like to thank Mr. A. Douglas Propst, President of the Santa Catalina Island Conservancy, for allowing me to study the bats around Middle Ranch and for providing transportation and living quarters; and Drs. Timothy Brown, Alan Grinnell, John Moss, and H. Lee Jones, and Mr. Roald Roverud, Ms. Nancy Meyers, and Ms. Cathy Brown for their assistance in the field and with other aspects of this study.

REFERENCES

BARBOUR, R. W., and W. H. DAVIS. 1969. Bats of America. University of Kentucky Press, Lexington, Kent.

BROWN, P. E. 1973. Vocal communication and the development of hearing in the pallid bat, *Antrozous pallidus*. Ph.D. thesis, University of California, Los Angeles, Calif.

_____. 1976. Vocal communication in the pallid bat, *Antrozous pallidus*. Zeit. Tierpsychol. 47:34-54.

DAVIS, R. B., C. F. HERREID, II, and H. L. SHORT. 1962. Mexican free-tailed bats in Texas. Ecol. Monogrs. 32:311-346.

PEARSON, O. P., M. R. KOFORD, and A. K. PEARSON. 1952. Reproduction of the lump-nosed bat (*Corynorhinus rafinesquii*) in California. J. Mammal. 33:273-320.

TENAZA, R. R. 1966. Migration of hoary bats on South Farallon Island, California. J. Mammal. 47:533-535.

VON BLOEKER, J. C., JR. 1967. The land mammals of the Southern California Islands. Pp. 245-264 *in* R. N. Philbrick, ed., Proceedings of the symposium on the biology of the California Islands. Santa Barbara Botanic Garden, Santa Barbara, Calif.

Summary

Dennis M. Power

*Santa Barbara Museum of Natural History,
Santa Barbara, California 93105*

It is interesting to compare the works in this symposium with the research of the past. Progress can be measured by the fact that there are new means of gathering and analyzing data and that, with these tools, new information continues to be obtained on the geology, biology, and anthropology of the islands. New ideas and theories also are being tested, such as the dynamic equilibrium model and related concepts in the theory of island biogeography. In this section, I want to examine some of the new facts that are being gathered, some of the established theories being analyzed, and some of the more recent models being tested. I will also deal in a very general way with multidisciplinary comparisons of marine faunas, species diversity, evolution, and with the direct and indirect impact of man on the islands.

Multivariate Statistics

Among the new research tools that have become widely available in the last ten years are computers and multivariate data analysis. "Cluster analysis" is used by Littler in assessing the biogeography of macrophytes and macroinvertebrates of the rocky intertidal zone, by Seapy and Littler in examining the biogeography of macroinvertebrates, by Murray, Littler, and Abbott for the biogeography of marine algae, by Kanter for the biogeography of invertebrate communities in mussel beds, and by Ebeling, Larson, and Alevizon to describe kelp-bed fish assemblages. "Canonical variates analysis" (also called "multiple discriminant functions analysis") is used by Kanter to examine the importance of certain abiotic ecological factors for island and mainland mussel communities, by Haldorson to examine morphological similarities among populations of surfperches, by Bezy, Gorman, Adest, and Kim to analyze scalation patterns and divergence in the Island Night Lizard, by Power to describe phenetic variation in island and mainland populations of House Finches and Rock Wrens, and by Gill to analyze skull variation in island and mainland Deer Mice (*Peromyscus*). "Factor analysis" is used by Ebeling, Larson, and Alevizon to examine habitat variables for kelp-bed fishes and by Gill to assess morphological variation in Deer Mice. "Principal components analysis" is also employed by Haldorson in his study of gene flow to and from Santa Cruz Island populations of surfperches.

Multivariate data analysis is often used to seek patterns that might not otherwise be discerned and to *generate*, rather than *test*, hypotheses. A causal pathway may be inferred in a descriptive multivariate analysis, but is often not tested. This situation should not detract from the utility of these methods, just as models that are often so simplified as to not reflect a specific ecosystem still have a place in pointing the way toward greater understanding.

Biochemical Systematics

Electrophoretic analysis of tissue proteins has also become an important analytical method in recent years. Starch gel electrophoresis is used by Busath to investigate genetic variation between island and mainland populations and between beach and non beach "races" of an amphipod on Santa Cruz Island. Haldorson uses starch gel electrophoresis to determine that Channel Island populations of surfperches were genetically isolated from mainland populations of the same species. In Yanev's electrophoretic survey of salamanders of the genus *Batrachoseps*, genetic distances are used to derive divergence times of sibling species. Bezy *et al.*

also use electrophoretic analysis to derive genetic distances and to hypothesize divergence times among populations of the Island Night Lizard and their mainland relatives. Finally, Gill analyzes 30 protein systems to examine genic heterozygosity and distance among populations of the Deer Mouse.

The Distribution and Biology of Species

Continuing research on a number of fronts has brought new information on the distribution and biology of species. Lindberg, Roth, Kellogg, and Hubbs, for example, give descriptions of fossil invertebrate species from Guadalupe Island and find that faunal components in the late Pleistocene indicate that ocean temperatures averaged 2 to 3°C warmer than present. Recent species from the Californian Province dominate the assemblage now, a change characterized by the extinction of Panamanian elements. In an appendix to the foregoing paper, Durham describes a new fossil species from Guadalupe Island.

Considering extant forms, Wicksten provides new knowledge on the distribution of crab species in the Southern California Bight, especially in relation to substrate characteristics. T. Brown confirms the existence of a Garter Snake population on Santa Catalina Island, and P. Brown reports on the distribution of bats on the Channel Islands, including new records of several species.

Hunt, Pitman, and Jones compare past and present distributions of sea birds on the Channel Islands. They find, for example, that Common Murres and Tufted Puffins once nested on the islands but no longer do so. The numbers of Brown Pelicans, cormorant species, and Cassin's Auklets have decreased, while numbers of Xantus' Murrelets have increased. Many of these changes may be linked with the activities of man. Studies of the breeding biology of certain sea birds have also revealed some new twists. Wingfield, Martin, Hunt, Hunt, and Farner find that homosexual (female-female) pairs of Western Gulls occur on Santa Barbara Island with a frequency of seven to thirteen per cent of clutches. This may be related to a skewed sex ratio in favor of females, or may be a result of abnormal hormonal cycles. Hand reports that in a colony of Western Gulls on Bird Rock, Santa Catalina Island, the population is not shrinking but the number of young birds fledged is significantly lower than that of a decade ago; increased nesting density may be causing higher rates of chick mortality. Le Boeuf and Bonnell examine changes in pinniped populations since the time of Bartholomew's review at the 1965 symposium (Philbrick 1967). The Northern Fur Seal, Northern Elephant Seal, California Sea Lion, Harbor Seal, and Guadalupe Fur Seal are all increasing their numbers.

Records of bird and mammal faunas from the recent past have been uncovered in Indian middens. Guthrie determines that three species of sea birds not currently known to nest on San Miguel Island probably bred there within the last 2,000 years—the extinct, eider-like genus *Chendytes,* Manx Shearwater, and Leach's Storm Petrel. Over 50 species of marine and land birds have been identified from one midden site alone. An extinct species of vampire bat was also recorded. Walker examines mammal remains from middens on San Miguel Island. There is a substantial number of bones of a large form of Deer Mouse which went extinct roughly 2,000 years ago, possibly due to large-scale habitat destruction caused by wind erosion, water erosion, and overgrazing by elephants. There is also evidence for the presence of a shrew and a spotted skunk, species which do not now occur on San Miguel.

Land Bridges

As more information comes to light, old concepts often give way to new. One case for the California Islands concerns inter-island and island-mainland connections. Vedder and Howell summarize geological and paleontological information on the period covered by the late Miocene (five to six million years ago) to the Recent to describe, in general terms, the key events that created the present seafloor topography of the southern California borderland.

Because of intervening deep water, it is unlikely that San Clemente or Santa Cruz-Santa Catalina Ridges formed pathways over which terrestrial biota could move. There appears to be no evidence for the widely-held idea of a Pleistocene land bridge from the Santa Monica Mountains to the Northern Channel Islands platform (see papers in Philbrick 1967). Junger and Johnson provide geological evidence for the absence of a Pleistocene land bridge between Anacapa Island and the mainland. They report that sub-bottom seismic reflection profiles across the narrow eastern end of the Santa Barbara Channel force them to conclude that at no time during the Quaternary was the water depth between the island and the mainland less than 100 m. Wenner and Johnson call attention to the lack of geologic evidence for a Pleistocene land bridge and explain vertebrate distribution on the Northern Channel Islands in this new light. They note that the land vertebrate fauna is depauperate and not at all representative of the mainland, or of what would be expected if a direct land connection had existed. As an alternate theory, they interpret biological and anthropological evidence to suggest a combination of "sweepstakes" dispersal by rafting and both conscious and unintentional transport by Indians in plank canoes. One interesting case is the Dwarf Mammoth, which, based on information about modern elephants, is now believed to have been a capable swimmer. At a time of lowered sea levels in the Pleistocene, ancestors of the Dwarf Mammoth would have had to cross only a relatively short, 6-km stretch of water between the mainland and the eastern end of Anacapa Island.

Dynamic Equilibrium Theory

MacArthur and Wilson (1963, 1967) were the first to develop the idea that the diversity or richness (numbers) of species on islands results from a dynamic balance between the rate of addition of new species through immigration and the rate of loss through extinction. These rates are affected by the physical characteristics of an island, such as size and distance from a source of colonizing species. Wilcox explains why some reptile faunas on the California Islands are above or below the predicted equilibrium number of species. The higher latitude Channel Islands are subsaturated, presumably due to climatic instability associated with Pleistocene glacial advances and retreats. Islands with recent land bridges to the mainland are regarded as supersaturated. The reptile fauna on the San Benito Islands appears to be in balanced equilibrium.

Diamond and Jones also address the issue that species composition on an island will vary through time, even though the number of species may remain roughly constant. On the Channel Islands, average annual turnover of breeding land birds is one to six per cent of the avifauna per year. It is also pointed out that turnover studies are not accurate unless based on data gathered in several consecutive years; there is a decline in "apparent turnover" with increasing census interval.

Density Compensation

Theoretically, if a fauna on an island is depauperate, the species that do exist there can use part of the resources that might otherwise have gone to the missing species. The existing species may therefore occur in greater numbers than on the mainland. The phenomenon of species in an impoverished community compensating in abundance for absent species was termed "density compensation" by MacArthur, Diamond, and Karr (1972). In this regard, Laughrin finds that densities of the Island Fox on Santa Cruz Island are greater than densities of Gray and Red Foxes on the mainland. An analysis of age structure also indicates a higher proportion of older animals in Island Fox populations. Diamond and Jones note that species of land birds that reach the islands and successfully establish breeding populations may increase their abundance or broaden their ecological niches by using resources that, on the mainland, would have been pre-empted by competitors. Philbrick also reports that some island plant species seem superabundant in comparison with mainland relatives.

Vicariance

With the widespread acceptance of plate tectonics and continental drift, it became apparent that the explanation of biotic distribution and subsequent evolution now fell into two classes—dispersal and vicariance (*e.g.*, see Platnick and Nelson 1978). Dispersal models explain disjunction in distribution by dispersal across pre-existing barriers, such as Wenner and Johnson discuss for the recent distribution of land vertebrates on the Northern Channel Islands. Vicariance models explain disjunction by the appearance of barriers fragmenting the ranges of ancestral species. Yanev relies on the vicariance approach to hypothesize possible divergences of lineages of *Batrochoseps* salamanders. The lineages are superimposed on maps showing a time-series of reconstructions of the geologic, botanic, and climatic history of California.

Faunal Components

Cool waters in the California Current System run south along the coast of California. Veering from the east-west trending coastline at about Point Conception, the current eventually begins a counterclockwise loop, called the Southern California Eddy, which runs in a northerly and northwesterly direction and brings warmer water along the coast. The currents become more complex as they strike the submarine ridges and platforms on which the Channel Islands are situated. There is also considerable variation in direction and intensity of the currents, brought on by changes in the seasons and weather. Seapy and Littler give a general description of the current system, and maps are provided in Kanter's paper. These currents affect the dispersal of marine organisms from one island to the next. Temperature differences lead to the survival of more northern species in the cool waters of the northern and outermost islands and favor the survival of more southerly species in the warmer waters of the islands to the south and nearer to shore.

To begin the section dealing with the marine realm, Owen reviews the existence of eddies, transport, and the ecological effects of the California Current System. The Southern California Eddy owes its character, and perhaps its existence, to the islands and banks off southern California. It is seasonal, occurring only from July through January. The presence and absence of eddies and countercurrents have an important impact on enrichment of the ecosystem— nutrient concentrations, phytoplankton production, zooplankton, nekton stocks, and most marine communities.

Littler finds some relationship to the predicted faunal-components patterns in his data on macrophyte and macroinvertebrate cover in the rocky intertidal zone. His analysis of similarity between various island and mainland sites shows a clustering of (1) warm-water sites of Santa Catalina and San Clemente Islands; (2) cold-water sites of San Miguel and San Nicolas Islands; and (3) mixtures of cold- and warm-water sites, such as Santa Barbara and Santa Cruz Islands. It is also shown, however, that these relations are affected by other factors, such as the degree of site disturbance.

Seapy and Littler record macroinvertebrates in the rocky intertidal zone and observe that the percentages represented by northern and southern species are essentially in agreement with the hypothesis of inter-island affinities based on hydrographic conditions. Santa Catalina and San Clemente Islands—two of the Southern Channel Islands—had the highest percentage of southern species, followed by Anacapa and Santa Barbara Islands. Northern species exceeded southern ones on the more northerly islands of San Miguel, Santa Rosa, and Santa Cruz and on outlying San Nicolas Island. Similarity analysis supports this by linking San Miguel Island, San Nicolas Island, and Cayucos Point on the mainland—all sites subject to the cold California Current. Rocky intertidal faunas are also similar on Santa Catalina and San Clemente Islands—sites which are in the path of the warm Southern California Eddy.

Murray, Littler, and Abbott look at range end-points of marine algae and show that Point

Conception is an important biogeographical boundary, especially for species with a more southerly distribution. Similarity analysis linkage groups are: (1) Anacapa, San Clemente, and Santa Catalina Islands; (2) Santa Barbara and Santa Cruz Islands; and (3) San Miguel, San Nicolas, and Santa Rosa Islands. They conclude that these clusters exist because of sea temperatures and the current system in the Southern California Bight.

Kanter examines marine invertebrates associated with mussel beds. His similarity analysis shows the following clusters: (1) Corona del Mar and San Diego on the southern mainland; (2) San Miguel, Santa Rosa, Santa Cruz, and San Nicolas Islands (most of the Northern Channel Islands); (3) Government Point near Point Conception on the northern mainland; and (4) Goleta Point, a northern mainland site with southern exposure. For these special intertidal communities, Kanter suggests it is not so much temperature regimes that are accounting for salient similarities, but the sea currents that carry planktonic larvae. There are also site-specific patterns—most notably due to quantities of tar, amount and size of sediment, and amount of detritus—the latter two factors relating to the number of microhabitats within the mussel community.

On the other hand, interlocality differences in kelp-bed fish density, diversity, and composition in the Santa Barbara Channel reflect differences in habitat structure, rather than variations in the oceanographic regime. Ebeling, Larson, and Alevizon examine fish at a site on the north side of Santa Cruz Island which receives relatively warm water from the Southern California Eddy system. Island reefs in the Santa Barbara Channel are in clearer water and are steeper, deeper, and physically much more diverse than nearby mainland reefs. The composition of kelp-bed fish faunas is primarily dependent on these physical conditions.

Sea birds, because of their vagility, might not be expected to demonstrate the overlap of northern and southern faunas that is evident in some other classes of organisms. However, Hunt, Pitman, and Jones report that, of the thirteen species of sea birds known to breed or to have bred on the California Channel Islands, five reach their southern breeding limits and three reach their northern limits within the Channel Islands. All of the northern species have their greatest numbers on San Miguel Island, while southern species occur almost entirely on Santa Barbara and Anacapa Islands.

Gill, in her study of genic similarities of populations of Deer Mice, suggests that there may be gene flow from populations on San Miguel and Santa Rosa Islands to that on San Nicolas Island. Transport of mice could have been by rafting (carried along by the southward-flowing California Current) or by Indian canoes.

Species Diversity and Richness
The diversity of species on the California Islands, relative to that on the mainland, is low for terrestrial plants and animals but high for elements of the marine biota. Littler finds greater average biomass, numbers of taxa, richness, evenness, and diversity for the island rocky intertidal biota than for the mainland sites. Island sites also have greater cover and density of macroinvertebrates, but no island-mainland differences in these two attributes are found for macrophytes. Kanter finds that island invertebrate communities in mussel beds contain more species than do most of those on the mainland, which appears related, in part, to human disturbance of mainland sites and to other site-specific factors. For example, richness increases with physical heterogeneity as measured by the quantity of coarse fraction material and sediment size, but decreases with an increase in amounts of detritus and tar from natural seeps. Straughan and Hadley observe that the island sandy beach macrofaunas follow trends of increasing abundance of species with increasing stability of the habitat (*e.g.*, finer sediments and more sheltered conditions). Ebeling, Larson, and Alevizon find that island kelp beds favor higher fish density and diversity than do similar mainland habitats.

On the other hand, Wilcox reports that reptile faunas of the California Islands have fewer species than those on the mainland, and Diamond and Jones note that there are fewer land bird species on the islands. Wenner and Johnson discuss why the land vertebrate faunas of the island should be depauperate—colonization was by sweepstakes dispersal and Indian transport, not land bridges.

Evolution

The California Islands have always been a natural laboratory for the study of evolution. The first naturalists on the islands were concerned with taxonomy and the description of variation in populations. Evolutionary biologists today continue to describe new variation but they also are interested in its adaptive significance. For plants, Philbrick discusses the range of endemic taxa on the islands, Guadalupe and San Clemente emerging as islands that have a high proportion of endemic plants. Power finds high edemicity for land birds on these two islands, as well. Philbrick also describes some general trends he has found in the evolution of island plants: a tendency for pinkish flowers; a tendency for grayish foliage; a relatively large habit of growth, leaves, or fruits (Carlquist's [1974] "gigantisms"); a genetically determined prostrate form; and hybridization.

Hochberg describes the characteristic of larger leaves in a number of island chaparral species; the adaptive significance of this trait is not yet known. Young documents hybridization between two species of *Rhus* in an ecotone between chaparral and coastal sage scrub on Cedros Island. Davis describes hybridization in *Malacothrix* and suggests such interbreeding may have played a role in the evolution of species of this plant genus. Vivrette examines the association between certain coastal plant species and salt gradients in the soil and provides evidence that, instead of the plants having adjusted to natural degrees of salinity in the soil, the salt gradients are due to species-specific rates of salt recycling.

Busath examines genic differences in island and mainland populations of an amphipod and identifies beach and non-beach "races" on Santa Cruz Island. Haldorson finds genetic variation in two species of surfperches, a result that shows even species regarded as highly vagile may be genetically differentiated in island waters. This parallels the situation in birds—discussed by Power and by Diamond and Jones—in that even potentially mobile species may come to differ from mainland populations through natural selection or genetic drift if actual dispersal rates are low.

Divergence times of species can be inferred from genetic distance data. Yanev examines *Batrachoseps* salamanders and hypothesizes that the island form of *B. pacificus* diverged from the mainland form about four million years ago, that certain semispecies within *pacificus* diverged from one another about eight to ten million years ago, and that the sibling species *pacificus, attenuatus,* and *nigriventris* diverged between twenty and thirty-five million years ago. Bezy places divergence times for populations of the Island Night Lizard at about one million years ago, while divergence between the island species and the nearest mainland relative is put at about ten to fifteen million years ago. Bezy also reports that data on genetic distance, scalation, color pattern, and body size all suggest a consistent order to the relationship among populations of this lizard: Santa Barbara—San Clemente—San Nicolas, a pattern which correlates with distance from the mainland but not with island area, elevation, latitude, plant species number, or lizard species number.

Power examines morphological variation in certain species of land birds on the California Islands. Seventy per cent of the total resident avifauna on distant Guadalupe Island are endemic races; on many of the Channel Islands, endemicity ranges from 40 to 45 per cent of the breeding land bird fauna. Some species, such as the House Finch, show rather gradual morphological variation along the islands, culminating with the most extreme island phenotype on Guadalupe. Others, such as the Rock Wren, may also show extreme differentiation on Guadalupe but vary hardly at all, or in a less regular pattern, on other California Islands. Several island bird populations show larger body size and, in some cases, proportionately larger bills and shorter flight feathers, presumably as an adaptation to island conditions.

A more specialized case of evolution concerns one of the most clearly marked races of birds on the Channel Islands—the Santa Cruz Island Scrub Jay. Atwood examines the breeding biology of this form. In most respects, it is like its mainland counterpart; however, mean clutch size is lower in the island jay than in the adjacent coastal mainland subspecies. This suggests that the island population is at or near carrying capacity on Santa Cruz and that natural selection is tending to favor greater efficiency in raising a few young that are likely to survive, rather than a high reproductive output, as is common in an expanding population or in one subject to less climatic stability.

Gill examines genic and morphological variation among island and mainland populations of Deer Mice (*Peromyscus*). Morphologic divergence has been much greater than genic divergence. The island mice are all larger than mainland mice. San Clemente Island mice are the most distinct in all traits—genic and morphological—a situation which matches Power's data for certain land birds and Philbrick's records of high endemicity in plants. Populations of mice from the Northern Channel Islands are the most similar to one another; however, there is also a somewhat surprising relatively high similarity between mice on San Nicolas Island and those on Santa Rosa and San Miguel Islands. Among the Southern Channel Islands, San Clemente and Santa Catalina populations are similar. In general, there seems to be little gene flow between populations. Observations in the laboratory suggest that behavioral mechanisms may enhance reproductive isolation among island populations. There is also a high level of genetic variability in island populations, suggesting that they have not undergone serious diminution or a genetic bottleneck. High levels of variability are taken by Gill to indicate large populations, not gene flow between the islands.

Aboriginal Man

Interactions between humans and the biota of the islands have gone on for thousands of years. Indian villages are known from most of the islands, the most notable exception being Guadalupe. The plank canoe was a unique mode of transportation among Indians of southwestern California, making possible colonization and trade between islands.

How long ago were people on the islands? To answer this question, charcoal from a fire area believed to be a hearth was subjected by Berger to a radiocarbon assay. He found no measurable radiocarbon activity, which indicates an age of greater than 40,000 years. If this date is correct, it represents a new record for early man on the islands—earlier than many have suspected man was even in the New World. The site appears to be in conjunction with a Dwarf Mammoth kill and may be one of the oldest early man sites in the Americas.

Working with evidence of more recent human occupation, Glassow notes that, because of isolation, the number of intact Indian sites on the islands is especially high, in stark contrast to the coastal mainland strip. In a survey of recent archaeological sites, Glassow finds that individual sites may contain episodes of midden occupation distributed intermittently through the course of 3,000 years. Depth or size of a site turns out to be an unreliable indicator of the length of occupation of a site. Some sites on Santa Cruz show no change of constituents through 2,000 to 3,000 years, while others, such as those on the south coast, do show change. Guthrie's analysis of bird remains in a midden site on San Miguel Island has turned up evidence that Snow Geese and other granivorous ducks and geese were eaten by the Indians. Most marine species represented in middens (*e.g.*, cormorants) appear to have been killed for their feathers rather than for food. Whistles and tools, such as awls, tubes, and scrapers, are made from sea bird limb bones. Guthrie's sites vary in age from 2800 B.C. to A.D. 1500.

Recent Landscape Changes

Early voyagers from Europe visited the islands, and whaling and trade in seal oil and furs were booming in the 1800s. Purposely-introduced exotic species, or domestic stock that returned to a wild state, have had a severe impact on the landscape of many of the islands. The history of people on the islands indicates both harmony and flagrant abuse, with the most recent trend being a greater appreciation of the unique character of the islands and the fragility of their plant and animal communities.

Johnson examines the history and geography of San Miguel Island. He shows that, since the mid-1800s, drought, overgrazing by domestic stock, and cultivation have led to vegetation stripping, sand dune encroachment, and wind erosion. Dramatic landscape changes may pre-date man, however, for it is suspected by Johnson that prehistoric fires and overgrazing by elephants led to episodes of erosion on San Miguel Island during the Pleistocene.

Minnich maps vegetation of Santa Cruz and Santa Catalina Islands. Some of the most interesting aspects of the island vegetation are the arborescent appearance of chaparral shrubs, open configuration of stands, relative unimportance of woody vegetation, and widespread extent of grassland. Rather than being due to a cool, equable climate, Minnich believes these characteristics are attributable to long-term overgrazing by feral sheep and goats. Grazing also reduces the natural fire regime by removing flammable brushland fuels. It is surmised that without feral animals (and given occasional fires) prehistoric island vegetation would have resembled that on coastal southern California mountains today. Brumbaugh reports that on Santa Cruz Island coastal sage is especially reduced, while pines and chaparral woodland suffered slow attrition due to the introduction of sheep in the mid-19th century. Upland erosion and adjacent valley bottom deposits correlate with changes in vegetation. Also on Santa Cruz, Hobbs notes that the northern populations of pines and shrubs have been reduced and are not regenerating because of grazing by feral sheep. Coblentz examines a similar problem—goats on Santa Catalina Island. In addition to overbrowsing, goats adversely affect vegetation by preventing a buildup of a mulch layer, which normally retains soil moisture, slows erosion, keeps soil temperature low, and provides nutrients.

Conservation

The case of feral animals having a severe impact on island vegetation bears an obvious message concerning conservation of the unique ecosystems on the California Islands. It is reassuring to have Brumbaugh note that there is evidence for a reversal of vegetation loss and erosion with the removal of sheep from parts of Santa Cruz Island. Coblentz also notes that there has been a resurgence of plant growth where goats have been removed from areas of Santa Catalina Island.

In the rocky intertidal zone, Littler's data suggest that human disturbance of certain mainland sites has caused declines of species; only species which were already rare have disappeared completely. Kanter observes that, near natural oil seeps, there are increased tar deposits which lead to a decrease in invertebrate species diversity in mussel communities. This observation suggests the kinds of problems that may occur due to oil pollution.

The populations of a number of sea birds nesting in the Southern California Bight have changed in recent decades. Hunt, Pitman, and Jones note that the major declines in the Brown Pelican and two cormorant species seem to have been caused by human disturbance of nesting grounds and the ingestion of chlorinated hydrocarbons. Increases in numbers of Xantus' Murrelets and Cassin's Auklets on Santa Barbara Island seem influenced by the removal of feral cats in recent years and the extinction of a natural predator, the Peregrine Falcon. These authors note that the impact of man on island sea birds includes harvesting by Indians, predation due to feral cats and rats, vegetation destruction and erosion caused by feral goats and sheep, disturbance by egg and specimen collectors, use of the islands as military practice targets, chemical pollution of the sea, and greater recreational use of the channel.

Kiff gives a historical account of certain birds of prey on the Channel Islands. The Bald Eagle once nested on all the Southern California Islands, including Los Coronados. Their populations declined because of shooting, nest disturbance, and poisoning. The Bald Eagle and the Peregrine Falcon finally became extinct locally in the mid-1900s, owing to effects of the pesticide derivative DDE in the food chain. This is suggested by the fact that extirpation is correlated with the introduction and widespread use of DDT, the simultaneous extinction of these species on all the islands, DDE-caused breeding failures of both species elsewhere in their ranges, unusually high DDE levels in the channel, and DDE-caused breeding failures of certain resident sea birds. The Osprey vanished about 1930 from unknown causes. Protection of the fauna and the natural "cleansing" of the marine ecosystem may permit re-establishment of these species.

Several pinniped species were near extinction in the late 1800s and early 1900s. They are now under federal protection. Le Boeuf and Bonnell describe the recent increase in abundance and distribution of seals and sea lions on the California Islands. Since 1965, Northern Fur Seals have established a strong population on San Miguel Island. The Northern Elephant Seal is showing a very good recovery from the brink of extinction—60,000 individuals were recorded in 1977. There are nearly twice as many California Sea Lions (80,000 to 125,000) and three times as many Harbor Seals (2,000) as estimated in 1965. The Guadalupe Fur Seal is continuing a much slower recovery—the entire world's population numbers less than 2,000.

A new form seems destined for the endangered species list. T. Brown suggests the endemic race of garter snake on Santa Catalina Island be accorded special status because of its restricted distribution and the transient and fragile nature of its habitat.

Support of Research

There has been significant private support of research on the California Islands over the years, and institutions have also made important financial and in-kind contributions. It should be noted that the federal government has been directly responsible for assisting a vast array of research projects on the California Islands. Eight of the 43 studies in this volume were substantially financed by the Bureau of Land Management in its effort to gather baseline data on the Southern California Bight: Littler on the ecology of the rocky intertidal biota; Seapy and Littler on the biogeography of rocky intertidal macroinvertebrates; Murray, Littler, and Abbott on the biogeography of marine algae; Wicksten on the biogeography of benthic decapods; Kanter on the biogeography of mussel communities; Straughan and Hadley on the ecology of sandy beaches; Hunt, Pitman, and Jones on the distribution of sea birds; and Le Boeuf and Bonnell on the abundance and distribution of seals and sea lions.

Two projects were directly administered by government agencies: Vedder and Howell, who wrote on the geology of the southern California borderland, are with the U.S. Geological Survey, and Owen, who wrote on ocean currents, is with the National Marine Fisheries Service. In addition, the data for Junger and Johnson's paper on land bridges were from U.S. Geological Survey cruises.

The National Science Foundation directly supported the research of Berger on early man, of Glassow on archaeology, of Ebeling, Larson, and Alevizon on fish ecology, of Wingfield on gull ecology, of Le Boeuf and Bonnell on pinnipeds, and of Power on evolution in birds. The National Institutes of Health provided research grants for the work by Wilcox on biogeography of reptiles and by Gill on the evolution of *Peromyscus*. Berger's study was also aided by the U.S. Navy, and additional funding for the work of Ebeling, Larson, and Alevizon was furnished by the National Oceanic and Atmospheric Administration.

REFERENCES

CARLQUIST, S. 1974. Island biology. Columbia University Press, New York, N.Y.

MACARTHUR, R. H., and E. O. WILSON. 1963. An equilibrium theory of insular zoogeography. Evolution 17:373-387.

———. 1967. Island biogeography. Princeton University Press, Princeton, N.J.

MACARTHUR, R. H., J. M. DIAMOND, and J. R. KARR. 1972. Density compensation in island faunas. Ecology 53:330-342.

PLATNICK, N. I., and G. NELSON. 1978. A method of analysis for historical biogeography. Syst. Zool. 17:1-16.

Index to Common and Scientific Names